ANNUAL REVIEW OF PHYSIOLOGY

ANNUAL REVIEW OF PHYSIOLOGY

VOLUME 53, 1991

JOSEPH F. HOFFMAN, *Editor*
Yale University School of Medicine

PAUL De WEER, *Associate Editor*
University of Pennsylvania School of Medicine

ANNUAL REVIEW INC. 4139 EL CAMINO WAY, P.O. Box 10139 PALO ALTO, CALIFORNIA 94303-0897

ANNUAL REVIEWS INC.
Palo Alto, California, USA

International Standard Serial Number: 0066–4278
International Standard Book Number: 0–8243–0353-9
Library of Congress Catalog Card Number: 39-15404

♾ The paper used in this publication meets the minimum requirements of American National Standard for Information Sciences—Permanence of Paper for Printed Library Materials, ANSI Z39.48-1984.

Typesetting by Kachina Typesetting Inc., Tempe, Arizona; John Olson, President
Typesetting Coordinator, Janis Hoffman

PRINTED AND BOUND IN THE UNITED STATES OF AMERICA

PREFACE

Because prefaces are generally perceived as containing descriptive if not obligatory information relative to the content and/or production of the volume that follows, they are usually considered non-essential reading if not, indeed, otiose. Even so, prefaces to the *Annual Review of Physiology* series, have been written to provide not just policy and operational procedures for the contained chapters, but also to comment directly or indirectly on the status of physiology as seen by the Editorial Committee. The Editorial Committee makes a real effort to avoid operating in isolation and is constantly seeking advice and input from colleagues not only in our own fields, but in areas that either currently relate or could influence or evolve into future directions and/or developments in physiology. Sometimes the surfeit of available options makes the choices of subjects for inclusion difficult, but in any one volume, which perforce is limited, the evident heterogeneous structure tends to fall within the scope defined by the current themes and special topics that characterize each volume.

The current volume is no exception, nor is the content of its preface. The special topic section of the current volume surveys microtubule-based motors emphasizing important and emerging aspects of non-muscle motility. The two themes that are interspersed among the Review's traditional sectional subjects focus on the intracellular roles of magnesium and the effects of growth factors on function. Note that these are indexed in the Table of Contents within the listings of the traditional sections. The Editorial Committee hopes that, in fact, all of the chapters will be interesting and stimulating to readers of the *Annual Review of Physiology*.

Joseph F. Hoffman
Editor

Annual Review of Physiology
Volume 53, 1991

CONTENTS

OTHER REVIEWS OF INTEREST TO PHYSIOLOGISTS

From the *Annual Review of Biochemistry*, Volume 60 (1991):

Model Systems for the Study of Seven-Transmembrane-Segment Receptors, R. J. Lefkowitz

Cell Adhesion Molecules: Implications for a Molecular Histology, G. M. Edelman and K. L. Crossin

Activation of Oxygen, T. Traylor

Regulation of Phosphoinositide-Specific Phospholipase C, S. G. Rhee

The Enzymology of Protein Translocation Across Escherichia coli *Membranes,* W. T. Wickner, A. J. M. Driessen, and F.-U. Hartl

Ligand-Gated Ion Channels, A. Karlin

Structure and Function of Hexose Transport, M. Silverman

From the *Annual Review of Medicine*, Volume 42 (1991):

Weight Homeostasis, G. A. Bray

Pathophysiology of Hashimoto's Thyroiditis and Hypothyroidism, B. Rapoport

Cell-Mediated Immunity in Glomerular Disease, B. H. Rovin and G. F. Schreiner

Unusual Forms of Insulin Resistance, S. I. Taylor, D. Accil, A. Cama, E. Imano, H. Kadowaki, and T. Kadowaki

From the *Annual Review of Neuroscience*, Volume 14 (1991):

Molecular Approaches to Hereditary Diseases of the Nervous System: Huntington's Disease as a Paradigm, N. S. Wexler, E. A. Rose, and D. E. Housman

Higher Order Motor Control, A. P. Georgopoulos

Modulation of Neural Networks for Behavior, R. M. Harris-Warrick, E. Marder

Molecular Biology of Serotonin Receptors, D. Julius

From the *Annual Review of Pharmacology & Toxicology*, Volume 31 (1991):

Functional Architecture of the Nicotinic Acetylcholine Receptor: From Electric Organ to Brain, J.-L. Galzi, F. Revah, A. Bessis, and J.-P. Changeux

Mechanism of Action of Nerve Growth Factor, A. Levi and S. Alemà

Neuroendocrine Pharmacology of Serotonergic (5-HT) Neurons, L. D. Van de Kar

ANNUAL REVIEWS INC. is a nonprofit scientific publisher established to promote the advancement of the sciences. Beginning in 1932 with the *Annual Review of Biochemistry*, the Company has pursued as its principal function the publication of high quality, reasonably priced *Annual Review* volumes. The volumes are organized by Editors and Editorial Committees who invite qualified authors to contribute critical articles reviewing significant developments within each major discipline. The Editor-in-Chief invites those interested in serving as future Editorial Committee members to communicate directly with him. Annual Reviews Inc. is administered by a Board of Directors, whose members serve without compensation.

ANNUAL REVIEWS OF
Anthropology
Astronomy and Astrophysics
Biochemistry
Biophysics and Biophysical Chemistry
Cell Biology
Computer Science
Earth and Planetary Sciences
Ecology and Systematics
Energy
Entomology
Fluid Mechanics
Genetics
Immunology
Materials Science
Medicine
Microbiology
Neuroscience
Nuclear and Particle Science
Nutrition
Pharmacology and Toxicology
Physical Chemistry
Physiology
Phytopathology
Plant Physiology and Plant Molecular Biology
Psychology
Public Health
Sociology

SPECIAL PUBLICATIONS

Excitement and Fascination of Science, Vols. 1, 2, and 3

Intelligence and Affectivity, by Jean Piaget

A detachable order form/envelope is bound into the back of this volume.

Annu. Rev. Physiol. 1991. 53:1–16

EXCITATION-CONTRACTION COUPLING AND THE MECHANISM OF MUSCLE CONTRACTION

Setsuro Ebashi

National Institute for Physiological Sciences, Okazaki 444, Japan

KEY WORDS: Ca^{2+} antagonist-binding protein as voltage sensor, ryanodine-binding protein as Ca release channel, Ca-induced Ca release, troponin as Ca^{2+} receptor, connectin

INTRODUCTION

Muscle contraction including excitation-contraction coupling (E-C coupling) was one of the most fascinating subjects of biological sciences in the 1950s and 1960s. Numerous articles were published and attracted much attention, even from those who were not involved in muscle research.

Today scientists in many fields seem to feel that the essential part of muscle physiology has been clarified. As will be described later, however, my impression is rather the opposite. Muscle research has just reached a new starting line.

In 1976 I wrote an article for the *Annual Review of Physiology* titled E-C Coupling and promised the reader that fundamental progress would be made very soon. Although I was a little too hasty, recent remarkable progress based on new means, including a molecular genetic approach, has rekindled my optimism.

The subjects to be dealt with here will be confined in principle to the events of skeletal muscle, where we can see the most simplified features of contraction. Although I have been working on smooth muscle for some fifteen years, I will not refer to this attractive muscle because my opinion about its contractile mechanism is quite at variance with the current concept held by the majority of scientists.

0066-4278/91/0315-0001$02.00

While writing this article, which is concerned primarily with skeletal muscle physiology, I feel myself something of a stranger in this field. The words of an outsider, such as I am, are usually scoffed at, but they may be occasionally amusing to the reader because the lack of the depth of his knowledge makes him so bold that he tends to focus on his favorite subjects and to depict them in a caricature-like manner, paying no attention to other eminent achievements that others might think far more worthy. I hope that this article will somehow prove enjoyable to the reader, even if not profitable at all.

HISTORICAL OVERVIEW OF E-C COUPLING RESEARCH

From Galvani to Ca^{2+}

The discovery by Galvani (1791) (32) might have led to the research of E-C coupling, but his successors instead focused on electricity, not on muscle contraction. In the studies on biological electricity, movement of muscle induced by electrical stimulation was an unnecessary disturbance. Consequently, the nerve became a more favorable tissue for research, and the new field of nerve physiology opened. Electrophysiology was often employed as a synonym for nerve physiology.

It should be noted, however, that illuminating discoveries from the viewpoint of general physiology were made using muscle as experimental material. For instance, Bernstein (1902) (2) found the dependence of membrane potential on the potassium gradient across the muscle membrane, and Overton (1902) (71) noticed the requirement of sodium (and lithium) for excitability.

It was Hill (1949) (39) who brought a new phase to the relationship between electrical activity and contraction. He examined the time course of contraction with some mathematical consideration and concluded that a substance diffusing from the surface membrane could not reach the interior part of a muscle cell within the latent time, i.e. the time from the electrical stimulation to onset of the active state of contraction. Hill's comment, being critical rather than encouraging, became a counterattack to Heilbrunn's proposal (see below), which was made with undeniable ardor but lacked quantitative analysis.

Although his comment was not favorable to the Ca^{2+} concept, Hill was perhaps the first person who consciously distinguished between the events at the surface membrane and subsequent processes inside the cell. This thought corresponds to today's most popular concept of biological science, transmembrane signaling or signal transduction.

In the meantime, it became clear that only the electric current across the surface membrane, not the current running inside the muscle cell along its longitudinal axis, could induce the contraction (58). In this way, people gradually became aware of a new genre of physiology, excitation-contraction coupling, the term given by Sandow in 1952 (76).

Since E-C coupling is, in a sense, a matter how to deal with Ca^{2+}, it may not be unreasonable at this point to make a brief survey of how Ca^{2+} became recognized as the intracellular trigger (the historical work of Ringer (74) will not be referred to here because it is not directly connected with the current Ca^{2+} concept).

Prior to the proposal of Heilbrunn that Ca^{2+} must be the physiologic factor inducing muscle contraction (1940) (36), there were a few reports that indicated the importance of Ca^{2+} in the movement of protozoa (e.g. 6). Even in muscle, we can find notable work of Chambers & Hale (1932) (5) and of Keil & Sichel (1936) (52), the latter especially full of suggestive findings. None of them, however, stated that Ca^{2+} must be the physiologic factor. Heilbrunn's proposal was supported by the more persuasive findings of Kamada & Kinosita (1943) (51) and Heilbrunn & Wiercinski (1947) (37).

In spite of these, Ca^{2+} was not widely recognized until the work of Weber and that of Ebashi carried out around 1959 (10, 11, 89, cf. 16), which unequivocally showed that Ca^{2+} exerted its effect directly on the contractile proteins; the latter demonstrated that only a few μM Ca^{2+} were enough for nearly full activation, even 0.2 μM being definitely effective. Thus the first recognition of Ca^{2+} on the molecular level was made in muscle research, and Ca^{2+} in this sense was confined to muscle until the discovery of Ca^{2+} dependence of brain phosphodiesterase in 1970 (50).

The question arises then of why Ca^{2+} had been disregarded for so long after Heilbrunn's proposal, in spite of his strong assertion and supporting data. One explanation was that Heilbrunn's claim was overshadowed by the discovery of the actomyosin-ATP system by A. Szent-Györgyi and his colleagues (cf. 80), the first success in reproducing an important physiologic function in vitro. The fact that this remarkable system apparently did not require Ca^{2+} furthered the disbelief in Heilbrunn's hypothesis by some people, especially those on biochemical side. Another explanation might be the view of Hill (39) whose proposal was so clear and elegant that many physiologists might have thought that the contraction could not be induced by a simple chemical substance, but rather through a more sophisticated process of a physical nature such as crystallization.

Recognition of the T-system (T-tubule, transverse tubule) as the device transferring various factors from the outer medium into the interior of the cell (19, 44) confirmed the suggestions from anatomical (73) and physiologic (42) viewpoints and eventually answered the question raised by Hill (39) and allowed scientists to make a reasonable compromise with the Ca concept.

As emphasized in another article (16), the development of the Ca^{2+} concept was indebted to studies on the relaxing factor contained in a simple extract of muscle (4, 53, 59, 61). In view of the findings that the factor was the sarcoplasmic reticulum (SR) itself in its fragmented state (18) and that it showed a strong and rapid Ca-binding activity that was able to remove Ca from the actomyosin system (11), it was not difficult to depict the scheme for E-C coupling (12) that was not essentially different from that known today (e.g. 14). In this scheme the step that was not backed by experimental evidence was that of Ca release from SR induced by the depolarization of the T-system. Subsequent discovery of troponin (17, cf. 13, 16) as the sole Ca receptor site for contraction further simplified the situation.

Search for a Ca Release Mechanism

In 1968 Endo et al (23, 24) and Ford & Podolsky (28, 29) reported that Ca release from the SR was facilitated by Ca^{2+} itself. It was plausible that this interesting regenerative process, Ca-induced Ca release (CICR), could be the mechanism involved in E-C coupling. Endo, however, presented various pieces of evidence against its physiologic significance (20, 21). This was correct, but recently affairs concerning CICR have taken a dramatic turn, as will be described in a later section.

In the early 1970s Chandler & his colleagues (7, 77) demonstrated the voltage-dependent charge movement at the T-system membrane. They thought that this charge movement was directly involved in the process to open the Ca^{2+} channel located at the foot of the terminal cisternae (called cistern hereafter) of SR; their idea was well illustrated in a model (see Figure 11 in 7). The nature of the charge transfer coincided well with various properties of E-C coupling, e.g. inactivation of E-C coupling simultaneously abolished the charge movement. Recent gains reached through biochemical and molecular genetic approaches (see below) are expected to shed new light on this attractive idea.

Reference must also be made to the Ca^{2+} release from SR by depolarization (depolarization was induced by changing the ionic composition in the medium surrounding skinned fibers) noted by Endo's group (22). Since it was later shown that the ionic composition in the cistern is essentially the same as that in the myoplasm except for Ca^{2+} (79), there seems no ionic basis for electrical disturbances at the SR membrane and, therefore, the depolarization hypothesis does not hold in its original form. As we have seen in the case of CICR (see below), however, we cannot deny the possibility that an unrevealed mechanism hidden behind this finding may have a significant role in the Ca release process.

FRONTIERS IN E-C COUPLING RESEARCH

Ca^{2+} Antagonist-Binding Protein as a Voltage Sensor

As stated above, E-C coupling is the process by which the depolarization at the T-system induces the release of Ca from the cistern of SR. Thus E-C coupling is the oldest and still up-to-date subject of signal transduction across the membrane. For better understanding it may be convenient to divide this process into two steps. First, the depolarization is transduced into a different type of signal; this transduction system resides in the T-system membrane. Second, the transduced signal is transferred to the interior system that is dedicated to Ca release; the system is composed of a foot region (30) and a part localized in the cistern membrane.

The developments in the studies of Ca^{2+} antagonists have revealed that an enormous amount of L-type Ca^{2+} channel or, strictly speaking, Ca^{2+} antagonist-binding protein [dihydroxypyridine (DHP) derivatives were the most useful tool in this research; the DHP-binding protein, or DHP receptor used hereafter] exists in the T-system membrane (3, 8, 27). The whole primary structure of DHP-binding protein of a molecular mass of about 170 kd, which is responsible for the first step, i.e. the process of transduction of electrical signal, has been deduced from its complementary DNA (cDNA) by Numa & his colleagues; it has a feature common to that of the Na^{+} channel (84). The structure of the cardiac DHP-binding protein has also been determined (see below) and has a high homology with the skeletal one (65).

The postulation that the DHP-binding protein is the voltage transducer, or the voltage sensor, has been substantiated using a dysgenic mouse that genetically lacks the DHP receptor (82); cultured myotubes of the mouse restored E-C coupling by introducing the corresponding cDNA. It is worthy of note that the restoration of E-C coupling was also achieved by introducing cardiac DHP-receptor's cDNA (83). Interestingly and rather unexpectedly, the mode of coupling thus induced was very much like that of cardiac muscle, e.g. quick rise of Ca^{2+} current and abolition of the coupling in the absence of Ca^{2+}.

The step of transduction is complicated by its intricate nature, inactivation, i.e. the prolonged depolarization abolishes this transducing step and a fairly long time for recovery is required following repolarization (cf. p. 297 in 14). The process of inactivation in skeletal muscle is controlled by Ca^{2+} in a complex manner:

1. The twitch is not affected even by the complete removal of Ca^{2} from the outer medium under normal conditions, i.e. Ca^{2+} in the outer medium has no direct effect on E-C coupling.

2. The inactivation upon depolarization, however, is markedly facilitated by the removal of Ca^{2+}, e.g. the fall of sustained contracture induced by high K^{+} solution is intensely quickened by the removal of Ca^{2+} from the outer medium.
3. The effect of Ca antagonists is essentially the same as that of the removal of Ca^{2+}.

Under physiologic conditions, E-C coupling in skeletal muscle is not liable to inactivation; the L-type Ca^{2+} channel has the least tendency to inactivate among various types of voltage-dependent Ca^{2+} channels. This does not mean, however, that inactivation is not significant in muscle research. On the contrary, this phenomenon can be utilized as an important clue, as exemplified by the aforementioned work of Chandler & his colleagues (7).

While no attention was paid to T-system proteins other than DHP-binding proteins in this section (cf. 84), it is possible that they have supporting roles, especially in steric arrangement of DHP- and ryanodine-binding proteins.

Ryanodine-binding Protein: Ca Release and CICR

Ryanodine has been known to cause irreversible contracture of skeletal muscle and repression of cardiac contractility. Fleischer & his colleagues (26) showed that ryanodine firmly bound to the open state of Ca release channels thus making this drug a useful tool for isolating Ca release channel. The conditions for ryanodine binding were very similar to those for CICR, which suggested that the proteins for both processes were closely related. Indeed, isolated ryanodine-binding protein embedded in the lipid bilayer membrane showed all the properties of both the Ca channel and CICR (46–48, 60). Surprisingly, electron microscopic structure of ryanodine-binding protein is identical with the foot protein (30, 48, 75). Its primary structure was subsequently determined by Numa's group (81) also. It was a single protein of a molecular mass about 565 kd, composed of the foot region and the Ca release channel part.

Although Endo's disbelief in the physiologic role of CICR is reasonable (see above), the CICR channel thus appears to be identical with the channel utilized in the physiologic process (see below).

Furthermore, CICR now seems to be the mechanism common to the endoplasmic reticulum of almost all kinds of tissues (e.g. 57). Since the events occurring in non-muscle cells are not as fast, it is quite possible that CICR has a physiologic significance in intracellular mobilization of Ca^{2+} of these tissues.

In view of these new facts, it is necessary to expand on the properties of CICR.

First a little pharmacology of CICR (cf. 14; 20, 21): enhancers, i.e. Ca^{2+}

(this is CICR itself), caffeine, ATP, adenine [much weaker activity than ATP with substantial affinity for the site comparable to ATP, so it can be utilized as an antagonist of ATP and also as a tool to detect CICR under physiologic conditions (49)] and its derivatives, and halothane (see below), facilitate the opening of the ryanodine receptor. Repressors, i.e. Mg^{2+}, procaine, ruthenium red, and so on prevent its opening.

CICR seems to have crucial role in the pathogenesis of malignant hyperthermia, for which halothane is often the cause (21, 25). Those who suffer from this disease have been genetically determined to have increased inclination for CICR. Dantrolene, the remedy for the disease, also depresses CICR at body temperature, but not at lower temperature; its mechanism is complicated (cf. 21).

In skeletal muscle, E-C coupling is exclusively carried out by the system represented by the DHP- and ryanodine-binding proteins. Ca^{2+} release by inositol-1,4,5 trisphosphate, IP_3, does not participate in the physiologic process (87). Perhaps the situation in cardiac muscle is not greatly different from that in skeletal muscle. CICR, not physiologically functioning in skeletal muscle, may also not play a substantial role in cardiac muscle (21). In smooth muscle, however, CICR appears to be utilized as an intracellular Ca^{2+} mobilization system (cf 21) together with the IP_3 system.

Brief Comments on E-C Coupling Proteins

To summarize, depolarization is transduced by the DHP-binding protein into a signal of a different nature, which is then transmitted to the ryanodine-binding protein, composed of the foot part and the Ca^{2+} release channel. It is possible that this signal is a conformational change of the DHP-binding protein, the change which subsequently affects the foot region of ryanodine-binding protein to open the Ca^{2+} release channel.

The time course of E-C coupling is fairly fast, comparable to that of contractile processes that are controlled by the troponin system, a derepression-type device (13, 16). Since the derepression-type regulation is suitable for rapid processes, it is conceivable that E-C coupling is also operated by a derepression-type mechanism, i.e. the DHP-binding protein exerts an inhibitory effect on the foot in the resting state, and its conformational change resulting from depolarization removes this inhibition and causes Ca^{2+} release. This mechanism is in accord with the postulation by Chandler & his colleagues (7).

The spatial arrangement of these two proteins has been schematically depicted by Numa & his associates (see Figure 6 in 81). We cannot deny that an additional protein(s) might be involved as a modulator (see above), but it is very attractive to assume that this remarkable function, E-C coupling, is principally carried out by the two proteins.

At this point we are aware of two puzzling facts. First, the matter concerning DHP-binding protein: Ca antagonists were first recognized in the research on cardiac and smooth muscles, and there is no doubt that they block the entry of Ca^{2+} in these muscles. The DHP-binding protein in the T-system of skeletal muscle is a Ca^{2+} channel protein. It does not function as the Ca^{2+} channel, however, but as the voltage sensor, although Ca^{2+} may pass through it on depolarization. The dyad and subsurface cistern in cardiac muscle may perform a similar function to the triad of skeletal muscle. This means that the DHP-binding protein of cardiac muscle has a dual function; some molecules simply act as the Ca channel, but others act as the voltage sensor if they are confronted by the foot protein.

The other enigma is that the channel for CICR, which has no role in the physiologic process of skeletal muscle, but is a good target of drugs, now appears to be identical with the physiologic Ca^{2+}-release channel; there still remains a possibility that the two are different proteins, but they are, at any rate, closely related to each other. Thus we meet another case where one protein has a dual function. This may sound unusual, but in pharmacology similar phenomena have been noticed.

Some physiologic receptors are stimulated by drugs, e.g. baroreceptor in heart ventricle muscle by veratrine. Since it is not likely that such an agent as veratrine exists in the blood stream as a humoral agent, the drug action may have no physiologic meaning. It was natural to suppose that the receptor protein for such a drug must be different from that for a physiologic function. In view of the dual function of the ryanodine receptor, however, it is now conceivable that both receptors, physiologic and pharmacological, may reside in the same molecule.

Then the question is whether the two processes, CICR and physiologic Ca^{2+} release, are independent of each other, and utilize different parts of the protein, or are inseparably related and use the same molecular structure. This question has general significance in unraveling the secret of how the proteins are constructed as a physiologic device.

In this connection, there are several receptors on which drugs (including chemical transmitters) show marked pharmacological effects, but the physiologic roles of the receptors have not been identified. One such example is the acetylcholine receptor in the vascular system. Since there is no cholinergic nerve and acetylcholine-containing tissue adjacent to the vascular system, it is not likely that acetylcholine can reach it because of the abundance of cholinesterase in the blood. Hence, there is little possibility that acetylcholine affects the vascular system under physiologic conditions. This is puzzling, but in view of the dual function, physiologic and pharmacological, of the ryanodine-binding protein, we must consider that another function involved in a physiologic phenomenon may be present in this receptor.

Addendum

Ca^{2+} is taken up by the whole surface of the SR during relaxation. Then the rate of Ca^{2+} return to the cistern is a limiting factor in recycling of contraction. This rate in frog skeletal muscle now appears to be faster than once reported, i.e. 1.1 sec for half recovery at room temperature (78). It was noted that this time constant coincided with the off-rate of Ca^{2+} from parvalbumin (78), a strong Ca^{2+}-binding protein of undefined function abundantly present in amphibian and fish skeletal muscle (72). It is possible that parvalbumin in these muscles intervenes between the troponin and the SR on the path of Ca^{2+} back to the SR. In this connection Gillis (33) has proposed that parvalbumin facilitates the removal of Ca^{2+} from troponin by reducing the myoplasmic Ca^{2+} concentration, thus increasing the rate of relaxation after twitch and brief tetanus (cf. 33, 79).

The decisive role of troponin C as the sole Ca^{2+} receptor protein was established on the basis of various experiments with isolated contractile protein systems (cf. 70), but there was no comparable work done with a fiber model such as glycerinated muscle fibers. This left room for the assertion that Ca^{2+} also might exert an effect on contractility through a route other than troponin. Recently, Ohtsuki & his colleagues (66) succeeded in removing troponin C perfectly from a glycerinated muscle fiber using cyclohexanediaminetetraacetic acid (CDTA) and found that the fiber thus treated completely lost its contractility, which then could fully be restored by the addition of troponin C. This procedure also removed the myosin light chain 2 to a considerable extent, but troponin C by itself was enough to restore the original contractility; this may indicate that the light chain has a little, if any, role in the contractile machinery.

ELEMENTAL AND VITAL PHYSIOLOGY OF MUSCLE

Some Facets of Sliding Mechanism

1954 was a memorable year for muscle science because the proposal of the sliding mechanism was made by A. F. Huxley & Niedergerke (41) as well as by H. E. Huxley & Hanson (45). This ingenious idea was further substantiated and fully established mainly by the efforts of both Huxleys; two papers published late in the 1950s (40, 43) were particularly impressive and crucial. Since then, efforts of muscle scientists have concentrated on the precise mechanism of sliding.

Remarkable progress in muscle research has recently been made in utilizing the optical microscope, the most classical and useful instrument in the biological sciences. The long term effort of Oosawa's group to see the movement of a single actin filament is now realized using the filament labeled with fluorescent phalloidine (92). This technique combined with the method of binding myosin, or its subfragment, to a glass surface coated with nitrocellulose (56), or hydrophobic substance (34), has brought in a new era in muscle research.

One of the rewards was the clear answer to whether or not the entire structure of the myosin molecule, composed of a shaft (L-meromyosin), a hinge (subfragment-2), and two heads (subfragment-1, or S-1), is required for sliding.

As first shown by Spudich's group, glass surface-bound S-1, the intramolecular movement of which must be intensely restricted, can dislocate an actin filament with a speed comparable to that of myosin (half the velocity of the latter) (85, 35). Furthermore, a new technique developed by Yanagida's group (55) has shown that the interaction of glass surface-bound S-1 molecules and a single actin filament can produce a force almost the same as that of intact myosin (35). Thus it is now clear that S-1, the single head, can exhibit almost full activity in sliding and force generation.

Another result is interesting but puzzling. It was thought that the formation of a transient but definite binding between one myosin head and one actin molecule, the cross-bridge formation, was the elemental reaction of muscle contraction, which thereby resulted in the breakdown of one ATP. Yanagida & his colleagues, however, showed that under specified conditions actin filaments in myofibrils slid a distance about 60 nm per ATP (91). Essentially the same phenomenon, i.e. sliding more than 100 nm per ATP, was also observed using glass surface-bound myosin (35). On the other hand Spudich's group (86) showed that the sliding distance with heavy meromyosin (HMM, composed of a hinge and two heads) was about 8 nm, which was compatible with the classical concept. The most marked difference in experimental conditions between the two groups was the temperature, 22°C for the former and 30°C for the latter. Since myosin once isolated is very heat labile, it is hoped that the two groups will repeat their experiments using the same (preferably a lower) temperature.

Stoichiometry is one of the most fundamental concepts in chemistry, but it may not be an a priori principle if the matter concerns a process where the conversion of the form of energy is involved. This is particularly so when ATP is the source of energy, the amount of energy released from which being only around 10 kT, not much different from that of thermal agitation. In this connection the stoichiometry in the transport ATPase also might be a subject for reconsideration [e.g. a very high ratio of Ca to ATP in Ca transport of SR was reported (9)].

Another enigma is that no rotational movement of the myosin head of a frequency expected from the time course of sliding has been found (cf. 67). Recently a very rapid rotational motion on a ten microsecond scale during isometric contraction, the rate of which is almost the same as that in the relaxed state, has been noticed (1). The implication of this finding may be profound, but so far no clear explanation has been given.

Thus the situation is exciting but perplexing, and this may not be the time to conclude what is right and what is wrong. Most likely something important is still missing.

Physiology of Resting Muscle

It is well known that if the intact fiber is stretched beyond a certain length, so-called passive tension develops, which has considerable size and can exceed maximum active tension. The origin of this tension had long been an enigma to physiologists. The fact that the Natori's fiber, or mechanically skinned fiber (68), showed essentially the same properties as intact fibers upon stretching (69), excluded the sarcolemma from the list of candidates responsible for the passive tension.

Maruyama became deeply interested in this phenomenon and eventually found that a gigantic protein with an elastic nature was responsible; he named it connectin (63) and Wang confirmed this result and termed the protein titin (88). Connectin has an affinity for myosin, connecting a myosin filament to an adjacent Z-band (cf. 62). The molecular mass of α-connectin, perhaps the native form, is about 3,000 kd (54). It does not contain a helical structure, but does have considerable amounts of β-sheet and β-turn.

An elegant study involving the removal of actin filament from a skinned fiber by gelsolin has visualized a connectin filament in the sarcomere and provided conclusive evidence that connectin is entirely responsible for the tension developed by resting muscle (31).

If a muscle contracts in the body, its movement is constrained by antagonistic muscles, which are more or less in the resting state. Thus the mechanical property of resting muscle is an important factor in body movement.

It has also been shown that actin filaments, which have lost their way back because of overstretching in the resting state, can regain their original position upon activation (38). This means that the role of connectin is not confined to the resting state, but is also involved in the dynamic movement of muscle as an indispensable supporting player. Hence the study on connectin should be a new subject of exercise physiology.

Since the physicochemical studies of such a gigantic molecule are a new subject of protein chemistry, and knowledge of the physiology of resting muscle is still in an immature stage, collaboration between physiologists and biochemists or biophysicists is essential. This may open a new field in muscle physiology.

In addition to the physiologic aspects mentioned above, we must emphasize the extremely protease-sensitive nature of connectin (cf. 62). In various muscle diseases, connectin may be the first myoplasmic protein to be affected by proteolysis. This consideration is particularly important in elucidating the pathogenesis of progressive muscular dystrophy.

Connectin is classified as one of the cytoskeleton proteins. It is localized in the myoplasm and retains an ordered arrangement of myofilaments so that contractile processes can be carried out without fail, but it has no contact with the protein group beneath the plasma membrane. I would like to propose the term endo- and exocytoskeleton by the analogy of endo- and exoskeleton. The endocytoskeleton is represented by connectin. α-Actinin, a Z-band protein (64), initially discovered as a superprecipitation-promoting factor (15), belongs to the category of the endocytoskeleton in skeletal and cardiac muscle, but to that of the exocytoskeleton in smooth muscle and non-muscle tissues in which this protein lies under the surface membrane (when we found α-actinin, I was totally fascinated with it because I thought it the third contractile protein following myosin and actin; its identification as a mere Z-band protein was thus a deep disappointment to me).

CONCLUDING REMARKS

Muscle contraction is based on the interaction of two proteins, myosin and actin, in the presence of ATP. This interaction is a subtle device for chemomechanical energy conversion. Its mechanism remains as fascinating a topic as ever.

Now it appears that the interaction of two kinds of Ca^{2+} channel proteins, i.e. DHP- and ryanodine-binding proteins, is the key step in E-C coupling. This interaction involves a different mode of energy conversion from the above, and the essential feature of this conversion remains to be solved.

The discovery of an endocytoskeleton protein, connectin, which is responsible not only for the elasticity of resting muscle, but also for appropriate positioning of myofilaments in a vital state of muscle, seems to have opened a new aspect of muscle research.

As a whole, muscle is still a very attractive subject. Perhaps we are at the beginning of a renewed and prosperous age in muscle science.

Literature Cited

1. Barnett, V. A., Thomas D. D. 1989. Microsecond rotational motion of spin-labeled myosin heads during isometric muscle contraction. *Biophys. J.* 56:517–23
2. Bernstein, J. 1902. Untersuchungen zur Thermodynamik der bioelektrischen Ströme. *Pflügers Arch.* 92:521–67
3. Borsotto, M., Barhanin, J., Norman, R. I., Lazdunski, M. 1984. Purification of the dihydropyridine receptor of the voltage-dependent Ca^{2+} channel from skeletal muscle transverse tubules. *Biochem. Biophys. Res. Commun.* 122:1357–66
4. Bozler, E. 1951. Mechanism of relaxation in extracted muscle fibers. *Am. J. Physiol.* 167:276–83
5. Chambers, R., Hale, H. P. 1932. The formation of ice in protoplasm. *Proc. R. Soc. London Ser. B* 110:336–53
6. Chambers, R., Reznikoff, P. 1926. Mi-

crurgical studies in cell physiology. I. The action of the chlorides of Na, K, Ca and Mg on the protoplasm of *Amoeba proteus*. *J. Gen. Physiol.* 8:369–401

7. Chandler, W. K., Rakowski, F. R., Schneider, M. F. 1976. Effects of glycerol treatment and maintained depolarization on charge movement in skeletal muscle. *J. Physiol.* 254:285–316
8. Curtis, B. M., Catterall, W. A. 1984. Purification of the calcium antagonist receptor of the voltage-sensitive calcium channel from skeletal muscle transverse tubules. *Biochemistry* 23:2113–18
9. Ebashi, F., Yamanouchi, I. 1964. Calcium accumulation and adenosinetriphosphatase of the relaxing factor. *J. Biochem.* 55:504–9
10. Ebashi, S. 1960. Calcium binding and relaxation in the actomyosin system. *J. Biochem.* 48:150–51
11. Ebashi, S. 1961. Calcium binding activity of vesicular relaxing factor. *J. Biochem.* 50:236–44
12. Ebashi, S. 1961. The role of "relaxing factor" in contraction-relaxation cycle of muscle. *Progr. Theor. Phys.* 17:35–40
13. Ebashi, S. 1974. Regulatory mechanism of muscle contraction with special reference to the Ca-troponin-tropomyosin system. In *Essays in Biochemistry*, Vol. 10, ed. P. N. Campbell, F. Dickens, pp. 1–36. London: Academic
14. Ebashi, S. 1976. Excitation-contraction coupling. *Annu. Rev. Physiol.* 38:293–313
15. Ebashi, S., Ebashi, F., Maruyama, K. 1964. A new protein factor promoting contraction of actomyosin. *Nature* 203: 645–46
16. Ebashi, S., Endo, M. 1968. Ca ion and muscle contraction. *Progr. Biophys. Mol. Biol.* 18:123–83
17. Ebashi, S., Kodama, K. 1965. A new protein factor promoting aggregation of tropomyosin. *J. Biochem.* 58:188–90
18. Ebashi, S., Lipmann, F. 1962. Adenosine triphosphate-linked concentration of calcium ions in a particulate fraction of rabbit muscle. *J. Cell Biol.* 14:389–400
19. Endo, M. 1964. Entry of a dye into the sarcotublar system of muscle. *Nature* 202:1115–16
20. Endo, M. 1977. Calcium release from the sarcoplasmic reticulum. *Physiol. Rev.* 57:71–108
21. Endo, M. 1985. Calcium release from sarcoplasmic reticulum. *Curr. Top. Membr. Trans.* 25:181–230
22. Endo, M., Nakajima, Y. 1973. Release of calcium induced by "depolarisation" of the sarcoplasmic reticulum membrane. *Nature New Biol.* 246:216–18
23. Endo, M., Tanaka, M., Ebashi, S. 1968. Release of calcium from sarcoplasmic reticulum in skinned fibers of the frog. *Proc. Intern. Congr. Physiol. Sci.* 24th. 7:126
24. Endo, M., Tanaka, M., Ogawa, Y. 1970. Calcium induced release of calcium from the sarcoplasmic reticulum of skinned skeletal muscle fibres. *Nature* 228:34–36
25. Endo, M., Yagi, S., Ishizuka, T., Horiuchi, K., Koga, Y., Amaha, K. 1983. Changes in the Ca-induced Ca release mechanism in the sarcoplasmic reticulum of the muscle from a patient with malignant hyperthermia. *Biomed. Res.* 4:83–92
26. Fleischer, S., Ogunbunmi, E. A., Dixon, M. C., Fleer, E. A. M. 1985. Localization of Ca^{2+} release channels with ryanodine in junctional terminal cisternae of sarcoplasmic reticulum of fast skeletal muscle. *Proc. Natl. Acad. Sci. USA* 82:7256–59
27. Flockerzi, V., Oeken, H.-J., Hofmann, F. 1986. Purification of a functional receptor for calcium-channel blockers from rabbit skeletal-muscle microsomes. *Eur. J. Biochem.* 161:217–24
28. Ford, L. E., Podolsky, R. J. 1968. Activation mechanisms of skinned muscle fibers. *Proc. Intern. Congr. Physiol. Sci.* 24th 7:139
29. Ford, L. E., Podolsky, R. J. 1970. Regenerative calcium release within muscle cells. *Science* 167:58–59
30. Franzini-Armstrong, C. 1970. Studies of the triad. I. Structure of the junction in frog twitch fibers. *J. Cell Biol.* 47:488–99
31. Funatsu, T., Higuchi, H., Ishiwata, S. 1990. Elastic filaments in skeletal muscle revealed by selective removal of their filaments with plasma gelsolin. *J. Cell Biol.* 110:53–62
32. Galvani, L. 1791. *De viribus electricitatis in motu musculari commentarius. De Bononiensi Scientiarum et Artium Instituto atque Academia Commentarii* 7:363–418, English version 1953, transl. R. M. Green, Cambridge, Mass: Elizabeth Licht
33. Gillis, J. M., Thomason, D., Lefèvre, L., Kretsinger, R. H. 1982. Parvalbumins and muscle relaxation: a computer simulation study. *J. Muscle Res. Cell Motil.* 3:377–98
34. Harada, Y., Noguchi, A., Kishino, A., Yanagida, T. 1987. Sliding movement of single actin filaments on one-headed myosin filaments. *Nature* 326:805–8

35. Harada, Y., Sakurada, K., Aoki, T., Thomas, D. D., Yanagida, T. 1990. Mechanochemical coupling in actomyosin energy transduction. *J. Mol. Biol.* In press
36. Heilbrunn, L. V. 1940. The action of calcium on muscle protoplasm. *Physiol. Zool.* 13:88–94
37. Heilbrunn, L. V., Wiercinski, F. J. 1947. The action of various cations on muscle protoplasm. *J. Cell. Comp. Physiol.* 29:15–32
38. Higuchi, H., Yoshioka, T., Maruyama, K. 1988. Positioning of actin filaments and tension generation in skinned muscle fibres released after stretch beyond overlap of the actin and myosin filaments. *J. Muscle Res. Cell Motil.* 9:491–98
39. Hill, A. V. 1949. The abrupt transition from rest to activity in muscle. *Proc. R. Soc. London Ser. B* 136:399–420
40. Huxley, A. F. 1957. Muscle structure and theories of contraction. *Prog. Biophys. Biophys. Chem.* 7:255–318
41. Huxley, A. F., Niedergerke, R. 1954. Interference microscopy of living muscle fibres. *Nature* 173:971–73
42. Huxley, A. F., Taylor, R. E. 1958. Local activation of striated muscle fibres. *J. Physiol.* 144:426–41
43. Huxley, H. E. 1957. The double array of filaments in cross-striated muscle. *J. Biophys. Biochem. Cytol.* 3:631–48
44. Huxley, H. E. 1964. Evidence for continuity between the central elements of the triads and extracellular space in frog sartorius muscle. *Nature* 202:1067–71
45. Huxley, H. E., Hanson, J. 1954. Changes in the cross-striations of muscle during contraction and stretch and their structural interpretation. *Nature* 173: 973–76
46. Hymel, L., Inui, M., Fleischer, S., Schindler, H. 1988. Purified ryanodine receptor of skeletal muscle sarcoplasmic reticulum forms Ca^{2+}-activated oligomeric Ca^{2+} channels in planar bilayers. *Proc. Natl. Acad. Sci. USA* 85:441–45
47. Imagawa, T., Smith, J. S., Coronado, R., Campbell, K. P. 1987. Purified ryanodine receptor from skeletal muscle sarcoplasmic reticulum is the Ca^{2+}-permeable pore of the calcium release channel. *J. Biol. Chem.* 262:16636–43
48. Inui, M., Saito, A., Fleischer, S. 1987. Purification of the ryanodine receptor and identity with feet structures of junctional terminal cisternae of sarcoplasmic reticulum from fast skeletal muscle. *J. Biol. Chem.* 262:1740–47
49. Ishizuka, T., Iijima, T., Endo, M. 1983. Effect of adenine on twitch and other contractile responses of single fibers of amphibian fast skeletal muscle. *Proc. Jpn Acad.* 59B:97–100
50. Kakiuchi, S., Yamazaki, R. 1970. Stimulation of the activity of cyclic 3', 5'-nucleotide phosphodiesterase by calcium ion. *Proc. Jpn Acad.* 46B:387–92
51. Kamada, T., Kinosita, H. 1943. Disturbances initiated from naked surface of muscle protoplasm. *Jpn. J. Zool.* 10: 469–93
52. Keil, E. M., Sichel, E. J. M. 1936. The injection of aqueous solutions, including acetylcholine, into the isolated muscle fiber. *Biol. Bull.* 71:402
53. Kielley, W. W., Meyerhof, O. 1948. Studies on adenosinetriphosphatase of muscle. II. A new magnesium-activated adenosinetriphosphatase. *J. Biol. Chem.* 176:591–601
54. Kimura, S., Maruyama, K. 1989. Isolation of α-connectin, an elastic protein, from rabbit skeletal muscle. *J. Biochem.* 106:952–54
55. Kishino, A., Yanagida, T. 1988. Micromanipulation of a single actin filament by glass needles under a fluorescence microscope. *Nature* 334:74–76
56. Kron, S. J., Spudich, J. A. 1986. Fluorescent actin filaments move on myosin fixed to a glass surface. *Proc. Natl. Acad. Sci. USA* 83:6272–76
57. Kuba, K. 1980. Release of calcium ions linked to the activation of potassium conductance in a caffeine-treated sympathetic neurone. *J. Physiol.* 298:251–69
58. Kuffler, S. W. 1947. The relation of electric potential changes to contracture in skeletal muscle. *J. Neurophysiol.* 9:367–77
59. Kumagai, H., Ebashi, S., Takeda, F. 1955. Essential relaxing factor in muscle other than myokinase and creatine phosphokinase. *Nature* 176:166–68
60. Lai, F. A., Erickson, H. P., Rousseau, E., Liu, Q.-Y., Meissner, G. 1988. Purification and reconstitution of the calcium release channel from skeletal muscle. *Nature* 331:315–19
61. Marsh, B. B. 1951. A factor modifying muscle fibre synaeresis. *Nature* 167: 1065–66
62. Maruyama, K. 1986. Connectin, an elastic filamentous protein of striated muscle. *Int. Rev. Cytol.* 104:81–114
63. Maruyama, K., Nonomura, Y., Natori, R. 1976. New elastic protein from muscle. *Nature* 262:58–60

64. Masaki, T., Endo, M., Ebashi, S. 1967. Localization of 6S component of α-actinin at Z-band. *J. Biochem.* 62:630–32
65. Mikami, A., Imoto, K., Tanabe T., Mori, Y., Takashima, H., Narumiya, S., Numa, S. 1987. Primary structure and functional expression of the cardiac dihydropyridine-sensitive calcium channel. *Nature* 340:230–33
66. Morimoto, S., Fujiwara, T., Ohtsuki, I. 1988. Restoration of Ca^{2+}-activated tension of CDTA-treated single skeletal muscle fibers by troponin *C. J. Biochem.* 104:873–74
67. Nagano H., Yanagida, T. 1984. Predominant attached state of myosin cross-bridges during isometric contraction and relaxation at low ionic strength. *J. Mol. Biol.* 177:769–85
68. Natori, R. 1954. The role of myofibrils, sarcoplasma and sarcolemma in muscle contraction. *Jikeikai Med. J.* 1:18–28
69. Natori, R. 1954. Viscoelastic properties and contraction responses of myofibrils. *Jikeikai Med. J.* 1:72–79
70. Ohtsuki, I., Maruyama, K., Ebashi, S. 1986. Regulatory and cytoskeletal proteins of vertebrate skeletal muscle. *Adv. Protein Chem.* 38:1–67
71. Overton, E. 1902. Beiträge zur allgemeinen Muskel und Nervenphysiologie. II. Ueber die Unentbehrlichkeit von Natrium (oder Lithium-) Ionen für den Contractionsact des Muskels. *Pflügers Arch.* 92:346–86
72. Pechere, J.-F., Capany, J.-P., Ryden, L. 1971. The primary structure of the major parvalbumin from hake muscle. Isolation and general properties of the protein. *Eur. J. Biochem.* 23:421–28
73. Porter, K. R., Palade, G. E. 1957. Studies on the endoplasmic reticulum. III. Its form and distribution in striated muscle cells. *J. Biophys. Biochem. Cytol.* 3: 269–300
74. Ringer, S. 1883. A further contribution regarding the influence of the different constituents of the blood on the contraction of the heart. *J. Physiol.* 4:29–42
75. Saito, A., Inui, M., Radermacher, M., Frank, J., Fleischer, S. 1988. Ultrastructure of the calcium release channel of sarcoplasmic reticulum. *J. Cell Biol.* 107:211–19
76. Sandow, A. 1952. Excitation-contraction coupling in muscular response. *Yale J. Biol. Med.* 25:176–201
77. Schneider, M. F., Chandler, W. K. 1973. Voltage-dependent charge movement in skeletal muscle: a possible step in excitation-contraction coupling. *Nature* 242:224–46
78. Somlyo, A. V., McClellan, G., Gonzalez-Serratos, H., Somlyo, A. P. 1985. Electron probe X-ray microanalysis of post-tetanic Ca^{2+} and Mg^{2+} movements across the sarcoplasmic reticulum in situ. *J. Biol. Chem.* 260:6801–7
79. Somlyo, A. V., Shuman, H., Somlyo, A. P. 1977. Elemental distribution in striated muscle and the effects of hypertonicity. Electron probe analysis of cryo sections. *J. Cell Biol.* 74:828–57
80. Szent-Györgyi, A. 1951. *Chemistry of muscular contraction,* 2nd ed. New York: Academic. 162 pp.
81. Takeshima, H., Nishimura, S., Matsumoto, T., Ishida, H., Kangawa, K., Minamino, N., Matsuo, H., Ueda, M., Hanaoka, M., Hirose, T., Numa, S. 1989. Primary structure and expression from complementary DNA of skeletal muscle ryanodine receptor. *Nature* 339:439–45
82. Tanabe, T., Beam, K. G., Powell, J. A., Numa, S. 1988. Restoration of excitation-contraction coupling and slow calcium current in dysgenic muscle by dihydropyridine receptor complementary DNA. *Nature* 336:134–39
83. Tanabe, T., Mikami, A., Numa, S., Beam, K. G. 1990. Cardiac-type excitation-contraction coupling in dysgenic skeletal muscle injected with cardiac dihydropyridine receptor cDNA. *Nature* 344:451–53
84. Tanabe, T., Takeshima, H., Mikami, A., Flockerzi, V., Takahashi, H., Kangawa, K., Kojima, M., Matsuo, H., Hirose, T., Numa, S. 1987. Primary structure of the receptor for calcium channel blockers from skeletal muscle. *Nature* 328:313–18
85. Toyoshima, Y. Y., Kron, S. J., McNally, E. M., Niebling, K. R., Toyoshima, C., Spudich, J. A. 1987. Myosin subfragment-1 is sufficient to move actin filaments in vitro. *Nature* 328:536–39
86. Toyoshima, Y. Y., Kron, S. J., Spudich, J. A. 1990. The myosin step size: Measurement of the unit displacement per ATP hydrolysed in an in vitro assay. *Proc. Natl. Acad. Sci. USA.* In press
87. Walker, J. W., Somlyo, A. V., Goldman, Y. E., Somlyo, A. P., Trentham, D. R. 1987. Kinetics of smooth and skeletal muscle activation by laser pulse photolysis of caged inositol 1,4,5-trisphosphate. *Nature* 327:249–52
88. Wang, K., McClure, J., Tu, A. 1979.

Titin: Major myofibrillar components of striated muscle. *Proc. Natl. Acad. Sci. USA* 76:3698–702
89. Weber, A. 1959. On the role of calcium in the activity of adenosine 5'-triphosphate hydrolysis by actomyosin. *J. Biol. Chem.* 234:2764–69
90. Deleted in proof
91. Yanagida, T., Arata, T., Oosawa, F. 1985. Sliding distance of actin filament induced by a myosin cross-bridge during one ATP hydrolysis cycle. *Nature* 316:336–69
92. Yanagida, T., Nakase, M., Nishiyama, K., Oosawa, F. 1984. Direct observation of single F-actin filaments in the presence of myosin. *Nature* 307:58–60

Annu. Rev. Physiol. 1991. 53:17–35

THYROID HORMONE REGULATION OF GENE EXPRESSION

Gregory A. Brent, David D. Moore[1], P. Reed Larsen

Thyroid Division and Howard Hughes Medical Institute Laboratory, Brigham and Women's Hospital, Department of Medicine, Harvard Medical School, Boston, Massachusetts 02115
and

KEY WORDS: thyroid hormone receptor, rat growth hormone, thyroid hormone response element, C erbA

THYROID HORMONE RECEPTOR

Virtually all of the physiologic effects of thyroid hormone are thought to be initiated by the binding of 3,5,3'-triiodothyronine (T3) to DNA-binding proteins termed T3 receptors (T3R). Either positive or negative effects on gene transcription can be generated by the hormone/receptor/DNA complex, depending on the gene and target tissue. Proteins capable of conferring thyroid hormone responsiveness are now known to be coded for by two cellular homologues of the viral oncogene v-erbA, one of two oncogenes carried by the avian erythroblastosis virus (28, 32, 58, 71).

The most global physiologic effect of thyroid hormone is stimulation of oxygen consumption, which appears to be the consequence of the additive effects of small changes in the levels of numerous rate-limiting enzymes. One of the most carefully studied thyroid hormone responsive proteins is rat growth hormone (rGH). In the rat, unlike the human, normal growth hormone synthesis rates require the presence of thyroid hormone. Samuels et al recently reviewed the biological studies of this protein, which indicate that the

[1]Department of Molecular Biology, Massachusetts General Hospital, Department of Genetics, Harvard Medical School, Boston, Massachusetts 02114

0066–4278/91/0315–0017$02.00

initial effect of T3 interaction is to stimulate the transcription of the growth hormone gene (56). Whether later events also include stabilization of rGH message and to what extent this might contribute to the overall increment in rGH mRNA remains a matter of some controversy (16, 63, 72). Nonetheless, this experimental paradigm has been used to great advantage in the exploration of how the interaction of thyroid hormone with its receptor can influence gene transcription.

In all vertebrates examined to date, two genes code for different, but highly homologous, thyroid hormone receptor proteins denoted T3Rα and T3Rβ. These two genes are members of a nuclear hormone receptor superfamily that includes many receptors for circulating hormones or ligands, including steroids and retinoic acid (18), as well as numerous other putative receptors for unknown ligands. It was recently suggested that some of these receptors may bind ligands that are biosynthetically related to steroids and retinoids, which include several terpenoid hormones whose function is less well understood (43). While there are many different members of this nuclear hormone receptor superfamily, they have two common structural features. One is a cysteine rich portion of the protein, which by analogy with the DNA-binding transcription factor TFIIIa is thought to coordinate with zinc atoms to form two loops or fingers that specify the DNA sequences to which the protein is bound (18, 39, 67). The second is a ligand-binding domain that confers the specificity for a given hormone. Within these essential components, considerable variations are found with respect to molecular size, the numbers of receptors per cell, the requirement of ligand binding for nuclear localization, and the interaction with other cytosolic or nuclear proteins. The complexity of the specificity of action of this receptor family is demonstrated by the fact that multiple receptor types may recognize a single DNA-binding site (21, 42, 68). In this review we focus on the thyroid hormone receptor/DNA interaction and emphasize the unique aspects of this ligand-dependent enhancer protein.

Physiologic Analysis of the T3 Receptor

The thyroid hormone receptors were first identified by their capacity to bind T3 with extremely high affinity ($K_a = 1 \times 10^9 - 10^{10}$) in vivo and in vitro (50, 56). Thyroxine (T4) is also specifically bound to the receptors, but with an affinity that is an order of magnitude lower. Since intranuclear T4 concentrations are lower than those of T3, virtually all thyroid hormone specifically bound to the T3R proteins is T3, and its intranuclear concentration determines the thyroid status of the cell. Until the cloning of the cDNA for thyroid hormone receptor, most physiologic and biochemical studies of T3R were based on the capacity of ^{125}I T3 to bind specifically to the receptor. Using this property, it was shown that the T3R protein is exclusively nuclear, binds tightly to chromatin in the presence or absence of the hormone, and may be associated with the linker DNA regions (52, 56, 62). Photoaffinity studies combined with results of partial purification of the receptor by conventional techniques suggested that two forms of the receptor were present, a 57- and a 47-kd protein (26). A major characteristic of thyroid hormone receptors, which facilitated the recognition of their physiologic role, is the limited and relatively constant number of molecules in each nucleus. This is a specific property of each tissue with the number varying from 6 to 8,000 sites per nucleus in rat pituitary and brown fat, 4,000 in liver, and 2,000 in cerebral cortex. Most of the latter sites are found in neuronal nuclei (33). Only a few hundred receptors per nucleus are present in human peripheral blood mononuclear cells and even fewer in the spleen or testes. The latter deficiency presumably explains the inability of these tissues to increase their O_2 consumption in response to thyroid hormone (1). On the other hand, the brain is similarly unresponsive even though the number of receptors is comparable to those in liver and kidney. This raises the possibility that there may be other reasons for the absence of a metabolic response to thyroid hormone. One explanation, the expression in the central nervous system (CNS) of a non-T3-binding splicing variant of one of the two receptor proteins (31), is discussed below.

In euthyroid rats approximately half of the nuclear receptor sites in most tissues are occupied by T3 (50). Thyroid hormone receptor number in a given tissue changes very little during most physiologic perturbations unlike the situation for many hormonal receptors, particularly those located at the cell surface. Not only do wide swings in thyroid status cause less than 20% variations in nuclear ^{125}I T3 binding (51, 61), but in the rat, even the most severe stresses such as starvation do not cause more than a 50% fall in receptor binding (17). Since T3R number remains relatively constant, it appears that the thyroid hormone status is determined by the availability of T3 to the T3R. In this connection it is of interest that while affinity of receptor for various T3 analogues varies, occupancy of the ligand-binding domain by any iodothyronine or similar ligand will initiate a thyromimetic effect. To date no analogue has been found to act as an antagonist.

Cloning of T3 Receptor and Subtypes

The discovery that two separate genes code for T3Rs was a major surprise (Figure 1). Multiple retinoic acid receptor genes have now been identified, but there are only single genes for the receptors for estrogen, glucocorticoid, mineralocorticoids, and androgens. The product of one of the genes, termed the T3Rα, was first identified in a chick liver cDNA library (58) and later in rat brain (65). The human homologue is a 408 amino acid protein (kd 47,000), which is coded for by a gene on human chromosome 17. The TRα gene shares the highest homology with the v-erb-A protein, although the latter

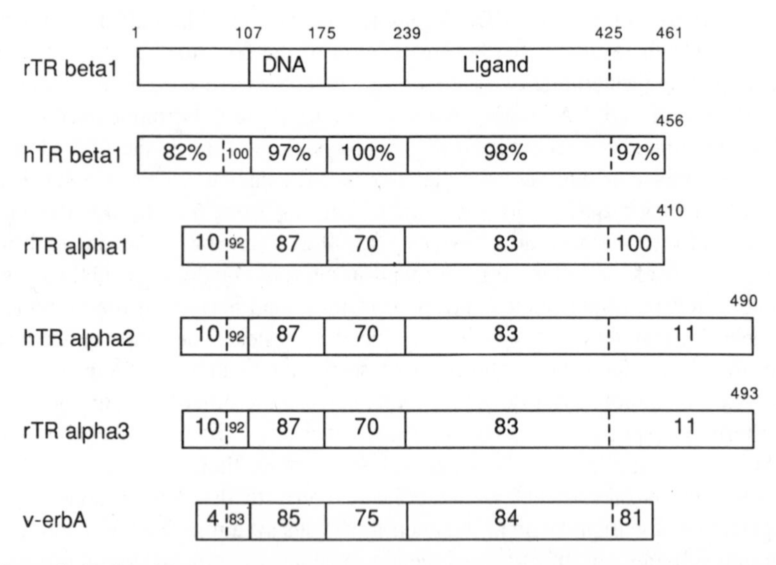

Figure 1 Deduced amino acid length based on cDNA for the various subtypes of rat (r) and human (h) thyroid hormone receptors (T3R) and the v-erbA oncogene. Putative DNA- and ligand-binding domains are shown. The % amino acid similarity with the ratT3Rβ1 is shown for the domains of each receptor type.

contains the viral gag sequences as well as important differences in the ligand-binding domain, which result in the inability of this protein to bind T3 (see Figure 1). The second receptor protein, T3Rβ, was initially isolated from a human placental cDNA library (71). This protein contains 456 amino acids (approximately 57,000 kd) with considerable homology to T3Rα and the v-erb A-related protein (Figure 1). All rat (47) and human (54) tissues studied express both receptor types, although the relative levels of expression can vary substantially. In vitro translated products of these cDNAs bind T3 with high affinity, bind to DNA containing appropriate thyroid hormone response elements (T3REs), and transfer the capacity to respond to T3 in transient transfection systems (28, 32, 45, 64).

The complexity of the T3R family is substantially complicated by the fact that several splicing variants of T3Rα have been identified. In addition to the fully functioning protein, termed α1, two non-T3-binding T3Rα mRNAs, α2 and α3, have been identified (Figure 1). The latter two code for a protein identical to the T3Rα1 up to amino acid 370, but diverge after that point. It was initially reported that hT3Rα2 could bind T3 (2, 48), while rT3Rα2 could not (38, 41). Subsequent studies have shown that neither the rat nor human T3Rα2, nor α3 variants, can bind ligand (37, 38, 60). The rat T3Rα2 is coded for by a 2.6 kb mRNA (as opposed to 5.5 kb for T3Rα1) and is highly expressed in the CNS, but is also found to a varying extent in rat heart, testes, kidney, brown fat, and skeletal muscle (24, 40, 47). An additional T3Rα related non-T3-binding protein, rev-erbAα, has been described (38a). The rat rev-erbAα and erbAα2 genes overlap in a 269 base pair exon, with their coding strands oriented opposite to each other.

The T3Rβ gene also encodes more than one protein product. In the rat, activation of an additional, tissue-specific promoter is thought to lead to expression of a variant of the T3Rβ receptor, T3Rβ2, which is found only in the rat pituitary (25). In this variant, an entirely different 147 amino acid exon replaces the 94 amino acid amino terminal portion of the β1 T3R. The β2 variant binds to DNA and functions as well as T3Rβ1 in a transient transfection system to confer a thyroid hormone response (25).

Given the relatively constant number of nuclear T3-binding proteins discussed earlier, it is surprising to find considerable thyroid-status related variations in expression of the two T3R genes in the rat. In general, the T3Rβ1 mRNA, like the nuclear T3-binding activity, is not affected by thyroid status, whereas in most tissues or cells, T3 decreases T3Rα1 and T3Rα2 mRNAs (24, 40). In the rat pituitary, however, the T3Rβ2 mRNA is reduced by T3, whereas the β1 mRNA is markedly increased (24). Another example of a dissociation between T3R mRNA expression and receptor protein is found during differentiation of chick erythroid cells (3). At least six closely related c-erbA proteins were identified in chick embryonic cells. The molecular weights for these products are consistent with initiation of translation at internal start sites within the cT3Rα mRNA. Furthermore, while cT3Rα mRNA expression remained relatively constant during early development, a three to fivefold increase in cT3Rα protein was observed. These results emphasize the limited understanding we have concerning the control of T3R formation, especially at the post-transcriptional level.

A number of structural and functional analyses of the T3Rα and β have led to the conclusion that a functional T3R must contain an intact DNA- and ligand-binding domain (64). The amino terminus can vary considerably or can be completely eliminated without loss of function (G. Brent, D. Moore, P. Larsen, unpublished results). As described in more detail below, receptor variants that contain an intact DNA-binding domain, but cannot bind T3, have the potential to act as dominant negative mutations. These include v-erbA (12, 58) and rat (31) and human (37) T3Rα2. It is not known whether the T3Rα3 variant could subserve the same role. Recently, an interesting series of mutations have been described within the ligand-binding domain that can block the transcriptional activation function of the T3Rβ receptor without affecting either DNA or T3 binding (49). As would be expected, such proteins can inhibit the action of the rT3Rβ1 receptor in a transient expression experiment.

RAT GROWTH HORMONE PROMOTER ELEMENTS THAT CONFER RESPONSE TO T3 RECEPTOR

Identification of the T3 Receptor-Binding Site

The localization of the rGH promoter T3 receptor-binding site was dependent on the production of purified T3 receptor. Utilizing a partially purified T3 receptor preparation from hypothyroid rat liver and methylation interference footprinting, we were able to identify a footprint in the area −188 to −172 upstream of the mRNA start site (TSS) (Figure 2) (30). The region immediately downstream of the site (−171 to −165), which did not show methylation protection contact sites, interacts with T3R by alternative approaches and is required for full functional induction by T3 (5, 7). Inspection of this expanded site reveals two imperfect direct hexamer repeats with four of six bases in common and an inverted hexamer that forms an imperfect palindrome with the second direct repeat (Figure 2). For convenience we have labeled these three domains A, B, and C. Recent reports suggest that additional factors may be required for optimal T3R binding to DNA (8, 46) as well as for the previously described interactions with cell-specific factors (74). Further purification of the T3 receptor has resulted in the identification of additional sites in the rGH promoter that bind T3 receptor (36). Despite the apparent ability of these additional sites to bind receptor in vitro, the consensus is that the primary region of the rGH promoter responsible for functional T3 induction is in the region −209 to −166 relative to the TSS (14, 56). The potential importance of an additional site contributing to the T3 response of rGH, however, is suggested by a recent report identifying a high affinity T3R-binding site in the third intron of the rGH gene (59). When inserted into an appropriate promoter context, this binding site functions as an efficient T3 response element, but its level of involvement in the T3 response of the native rGH gene remains unclear.

The functional analysis of the rGH promoter sequences involved in T3 induction has relied on transient transfections in rat pituitary tumor cells, which contain functional T3Rs, and transient cotransfections with T3R ex-

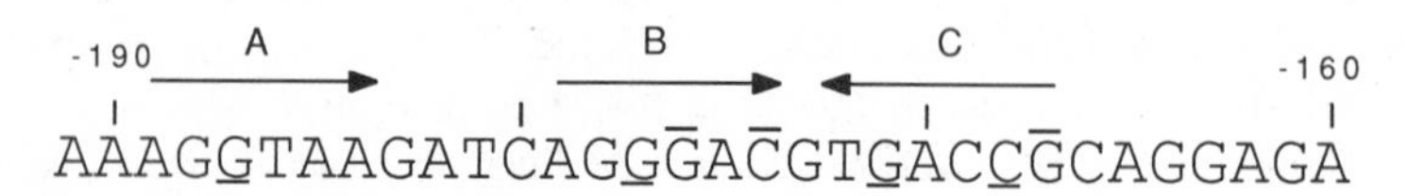

Figure 2 Sequence of the rat growth hormone promoter −191 to −160 with *horizontal arrows* designating thyroid hormone receptor hexamer-binding half-sites (see text and reference 5). *Horizontal lines* indicate G residues protected in a methylation interference-binding assay (reference 30).

pression vectors in a variety of non-pituitary cells, which lack functional endogenous T3 receptors (COS-7, JEG-3, CV1). Initial studies utilized progressive 5' deletions of the rGH promoter and demonstrated that promoter constructs that included bases to −237 preserved the full levels of T3 induction (34, 35). A further deletion to −183 dramatically reduced T3 induction, and a deletion to −137 completely eliminated a T3 response. These results correlated well with the methylation interference footprint, since a deletion at −183 removes the upstream hexamer half-site and a deletion at −137 deletes the entire site.

A more detailed functional analysis involved the insertion of double-stranded synthetic oligonucleotides containing portions of the rGH T3 receptor-binding site upstream of the truncated and T3-unresponsive 137 nucleotide rGH promoter. A fragment containing the wild-type sequence −200 to −157 conferred T3 induction in transient transfection studies, and deletion of the proposed T3 response element (T3RE) eliminated this response (7).

Mutational Analysis of the T3 Response Element

Based on 5' and 3' deletion studies, an oligonucleotide −190 to −164 was identified that was the minimal element required to confer full T3 induction on the rGH promoter truncated at position −137 (5). In the context of this oligonucleotide, G residues in the various T3 receptor-binding domains specifically identified as contact sites in the methylation interference footprint were mutated and were required for T3 induction. These results confirmed the importance of the A and B repeats. Similarly, the importance of the C repeat was confirmed with the appropriate mutations.

Several mutations that resulted in an increase in T3 induction were also created. These included two point mutations in the B domain (base −176 G to T, base −174 C to A) that created a perfect repeat of the A domain and a single mutation in the C domain (base −167 C to A), thus making it a perfect palindrome of the A domain. Both mutant response elements show significantly increased induction by T3, and the combination of the B and C up-mutations results in a greater than additive T3 response. These results are consistent with the report by Glass et al (20), which showed that a synthetic 16 base pair palindromic sequence that was based on five base pairs of the wild-type sequence from the C domain, TGACC, conferred a high level of T3 induction. Using the background of the C domain up-mutation, down-mutations were made in each of the three domains and demonstrated that each site is required for a full respose to T3. In the presence of either up-mutation, however, two half-sites were sufficient for induction by T3 (5, 7). Results similar to those obtained in the context of the homologous rGH promoter were also found with the same elements upstream of the heterologous herpes virus thymidine kinase (TK) promoter.

Based on this mutational analysis, we have proposed a consensus T3 receptor-binding half-site, AGGT C/A A, which is similar to that described for the estrogen receptor (Figure 3) (5). At least two half-sites are required for a T3 response. The T3R presumably binds as a dimer, as has been shown for the glucocorticoid and progesterone receptors (66), as well as T3R-retinoic acid receptor heterodimers (22). Inspection of a variety of T3R-binding sites from T3-regulated genes reveals that each contains two or more copies with a greater than four of six base pair match for this hexamer (Figure 4). The promoter for the rat α myosin heavy chain gene contains a T3 response element with an arrangement of three hexamers similar to that found in the rGH promoter. In contrast, the T3RE in the promoter for bovine growth hormone (bGH) (6) seems to be a direct repeat of two hexamers. The T3RE from the Moloney murine leukemia virus (59) appears to consist of a direct repeat of two hexamers. It is noteworthy that the two T3REs, which confer a negative response to T3, rat TSH α, and β subunits (7a, 8a), contain closely spaced direct repeats of the hexameric consensus.

MECHANISMS OF REGULATION OF GENE EXPRESSION BY T3 RECEPTOR

While it is clear that the hormone/receptor/DNA complex directly affects transcription of nearby genes, the precise mechanisms that underly this process are still mysterious. Nonetheless, it is possible to relate at least some of the structural aspects of this complex to its various functions.

Repression of Transcription by the ApoT3R

As described above, the T3 receptor, like other members of the nuclear hormone receptor superfamily, can be divided into three parts: amino-terminal, DNA-binding, and T3-binding. With regard to function, however, the T3 receptors show a remarkable divergence from other members of the receptor family in that they appear to be bound to DNA in the absence as well as the presence of ligand. The steroid receptors do not seem to share this property. In the extreme case, the glucocorticoid receptor is held in an inactive complex in the cytoplasm in the absence of hormone (10, 73). In contrast, it has been known for many years that T3 receptors are found bound to chromatin in the absence of ligand (50, 62).

Two distinct lines of evidence have been used to show that the hormone-free receptor proteins (aporeceptors) can bind to T3REs. In one type of experiment, it was shown that the apoT3R can act directly to repress the activity of several different T3RE-containing promoters (4, 12, 23, 59). In

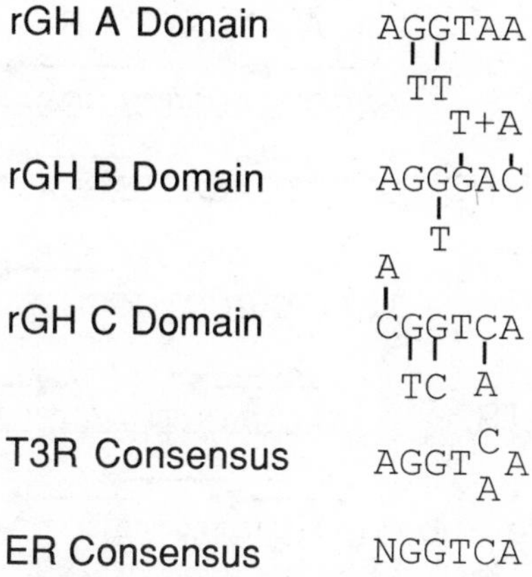

```
rGH A Domain      AGGTAA
                   ||
                   TT
                     T+A
                     | |
rGH B Domain      AGGGAC
                     |
                     T
                  A
                  |
rGH C Domain      CGGTCA
                   || |
                   TC A
                       C
T3R Consensus     AGGT  A
                       A

ER Consensus      NGGTCA
```

Figure 3 Summary of point mutations in the various domains of the rat growth hormone promoter thyroid hormone receptor-binding site based on a functional analysis in transient transfection assays (reference 5). Mutations that increased T3 induction are shown above the sequence, and mutations that decreased response are shown below the sequence. A consensus T3 receptor-(T3R) binding half-site sequence is shown compared to the consensus-binding half-site for the estrogen receptor (ER).

such experiments, the repressive effect is dependent on the presence of both the apoT3R (in *trans*) and the T3RE (in *cis*). In addition, a strong correlation is observed in different test plasmids between the strength of the repressive effect and the strength of the expression with the addition of hormone (4). Together these results argue strongly that the negative effect is an inherent function of the T3 receptor itself.

Although the magnitude of the negative effect of the apoT3R is somewhat less than the magnitude of the inductive effect, its potential physiologic relevance is supported by an additional series of experiments in which the effect of endogenous T3 receptors present in pituitary cell lines was examined with transfected wild-type or mutant versions of the rGH promoter (4). In these studies, mutations that inactivated the T3RE increased basal (−T3) expression, while a mutation that strengthened the element decreased basal expression. Thus the negative effect of the apoT3R can be observed with the endogenous receptors and is not seen as a consequence of the overexpression usually associated with the cotransfection approach.

Direct measurement of the effect of the hormone on functional affinity of the T3R for a T3RE was achieved by correlating the levels of induction and repression in cotransfections over a wide range of receptor levels (Figure 5). The receptor dose was altered from a low ineffective level to a high saturating level. Surprisingly, the level of receptor generating half-maximal induction in the presence of T3 was indistinguishable from that causing half-maximal

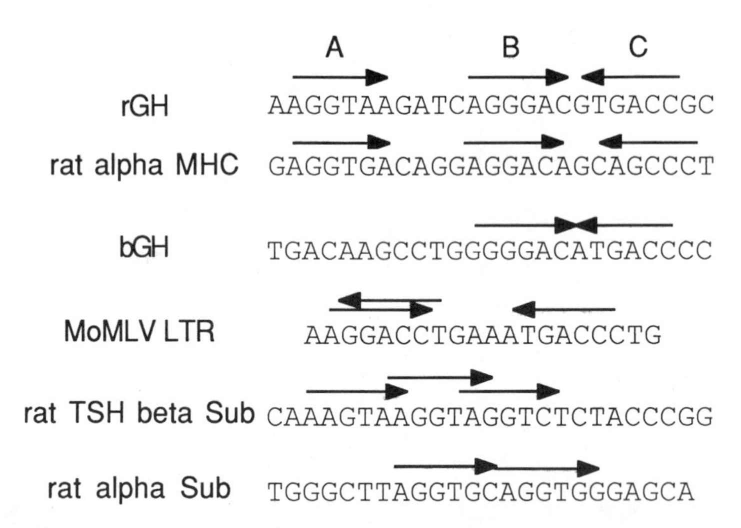

Figure 4 The thyroid hormone receptor-binding half-sites based on the consensus (Figure 3) are shown for promoters from rat growth hormone (rGH) (−190 to −166), rat α myosin heavy chain (−131 to −157, opposite strand shown), bovine growth hormone (bGH) (−187 to −163), Moloney murine leukemia virus (MoMLV LTR) (332 to 351), rat β TSH (19 to 43), and rat α subunit (−74 to −51), all shown to be induced by T3 (References 5, 6, 7a, 8a, 28, 59).

repression in its absence. This equivalence of apparent affinity in vivo is in agreement with in vitro binding results obtained using a relatively crude preparation of receptor (36), and it strongly supports the possibility that the negative effect of the aporeceptor is physiologically important. Furthermore, binding of receptor to a DNA fragment in an oligonucleotide-binding assay or gel retardation assay does not require ligand.

As described above, T3REs are constructed by combining two or more copies of sequences related to a consensus hexamer, AGGTCA, that is also recognized by other members of the nuclear receptor superfamily. In particular, the wild-type rGH T3RE and synthetic derivatives of it also function as response elements for the retinoic acid receptors (67, 68). Thus the demonstration of the DNA binding ability of the apoT3R led directly to the prediction that this function should interfere with the ability of the (RAR) to induce expression via such elements. This prediction was quickly verified: in combined cotransfections the expression of apoT3R can strongly decrease the level of retinoic acid receptor (RAR) + retinoic acid (RA)-induced expression. Since the effect of the apoT3R is also seen in the absence of RA, as would be expected (4, 23), the RAR does retain an overall inductive effect. In contrast, the apoRAR does not show direct negative effects on expression in either the presence or absence of T3.

These results strongly suggest that the hypothyroid state with an increased

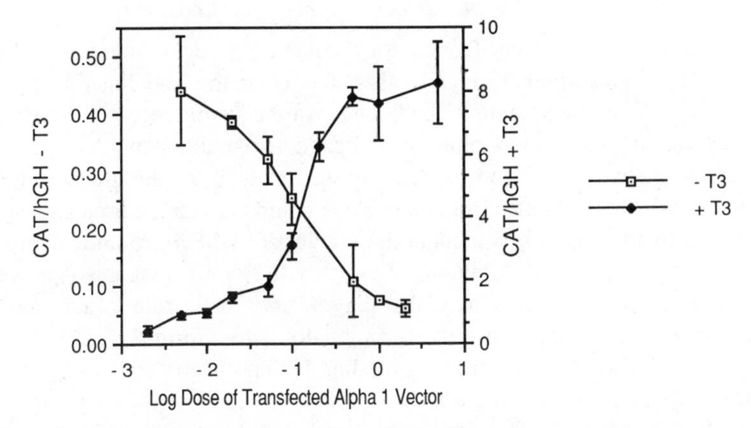

Figure 5 The mean (± SEM) expression (CAT/hGH) of a reporter plasmid containing a palindromic T3 response element transfected in CV-1 cells with *(solid diamonds)* and without *(open squares)* 10^{-8} M T3. A vector expressing the mouse $\alpha 1$ T3R is cotransfected in increasing amounts (reference 4).

level of apoT3R could cause developmental aberrations in an indirect fashion, by interfering with the important activities of the RARs. Moreover, the strong similarity of DNA-binding specificity determining regions is not limited to the T3Rs and RARs (44). Recent results suggest that vitamin D response elements may also overlap with T3RE/RAREs, and there is also some similarity between T3RE/RAREs and the binding sites recognized by the vitamin D receptor (15), estrogen receptor (5, 21), and perhaps a number of other receptors. It is an intriguing possibility that the apparently unique ability of the T3 receptor to interact with its response element in the absence of hormone may allow it to influence the expression of a great variety of genes not ordinarily thought of as T3 responsive.

Finally, the negative regulatory effect of the apoT3R suggests a novel interpretation for the mechanism of action of the viral oncogene v-erbA (12, 59). In addition to other alterations relative to its c-erbA$\alpha 1$ homologue, the v-erbA protein has a number of amino acid sequence changes in the carboxy-terminal domain. As a consequence of these changes, the viral protein does not bind T3. By analogy with the results described above, one would expect that such a protein, if overexpressed, could prevent the wild-type T3R from binding to T3REs. Particularly if the v-erbA protein retained the negative effect of the apoT3R, this could strongly decrease expression of genes expressed in the presence of normal levels of the hormone. Direct evidence that the viral product has such a repressive effect has been obtained in cotransfection experiments (12, 59). Further analysis will be needed to determine how this repressive effect is associated with loss of growth control.

Hormone-Dependent Activation of Gene Expression

By comparison to the other ligands for the nuclear receptor superfamily, the role of T3 seems simpler. In all cases it is clear that the function of the receptor is altered by binding of the ligand. For the steroid receptor, however, the activation that follows binding of ligand is a multi-step process. This activation pathway has been particularly well studied for the glucocorticoid receptor, which dissociates from an inactive complex with the protein HSP90 when the ligand binds. It is thought that the loss of HSP90 from the complex frees the receptor for DNA binding. Results with steroid antagonists, however, suggest that the ligands may also play a more direct role in altering the structure of the complex to a transcriptionally active form.

Removal of an inhibitor of DNA binding is unnecessary for the T3R, and recent studies show that there is no evidence of a T3R-HSP90 interaction (11). It seems likely, therefore, that the hormone plays a direct role in alteration of the transcriptional regulatory properties of the receptor. In this model the primary function of the binding of T3 would be to change the accessibility of various portions of the ligand-binding domain to the transcriptional apparatus. One might imagine, for example, that T3 binding could expose an amphipathic alpha helix, or some other simple transcriptional activation domain.

Hormone-Dependent Repression of Gene Expression

The ability of the apoT3R to bind to T3REs has important consequences for models of T3-dependent repression of expression. In the most popular models, which have gained support from studies of negative regulation of several different genes by glucocorticoids, the addition of ligand causes the receptor to bind and displace some other powerful activation factor. A net negative effect is observed because the hormone-bound receptor is either less active than the displaced factor, or is otherwise prevented from acting as an activator.

A slightly different model has been proposed to explain the negatively acting T3REs that have been found close to the mRNA start of both the genes encoding the specific beta and the common alpha subunits of TSH (thyroid stimulating hormone, thyrotropin) (7a, 8a, 9). In these cases it has been thought that simple steric hindrance by the hormone-bound T3R inhibits assembly of the basic transcription initiation complex. Clearly, if the apoT3R could bind these T3REs, the simplest version of this model would be ruled out.

Among a number of possible explanations for the resolution of this problem, two classes of models deserve some discussion. The first is simply that the mode of interaction of the T3R with nT3REs (negative T3 response elements) is different from the interaction with positively acting T3REs. In particular, it is possible that these elements are simply not bound by the aporeceptor, but are by the T3-bound receptor. As noted above, this possibility may be supported by the apparently different arrangement of receptor-binding hexamers in such nT3REs (5). A more complicated version of this model suggests that the conformation of the T3-bound receptor/nT3RE complex is different from the complex with the positive element. In such a situation, the binding of the hormone might not lead to activation of this receptor. This latter version predicts that such receptor-binding sites could behave as hormone-dependent negative elements even if they were moved away from their normal position.

The second model is a more complex version of the steric model in which the hindrance only occurs when T3 is present. In this case, one might imagine that the DNA-bound apoT3R, with no exposed activation domains, would not interact strongly with the transcription apparatus and would have little or no negative effect. In contrast, the binding of the ligand would expose the activation domains, which could strongly interact with the transcription machinery. If the receptor site were in an unfavorable position, such as those of the TSH genes, this could result in an unproductive complex and and inhibition of expression. This model predicts that the nT3REs in these genes would become positive elements if they were moved upstream, away from their sterically interfering position.

Action of Receptor Subtypes in the T3 Response

As described in detail above, the T3 receptor family shows surprising diversity at both the protein and DNA level. There are at least five forms of the T3 receptor that have been deduced from an analysis of cDNAs. The $\alpha1$, $\beta1$, and $\beta2$ forms bind T3 and show the transcriptional regulatory functions expected for T3 receptors. One simple explanation for the existence of these different forms, that they bind to different T3REs, was quickly ruled out by the demonstration that all three forms were able to activate expression from a single T3RE sequence (25, 32). In general, this is in agreement with the high conservation of the DNA-binding domains of the two T3R genes. The α forms of both the human and rat receptors, however, do show several differences from the β forms in a short segment of the second zinc finger termed the D box (13, 67). This segment has been associated with determining the specificity of interactions of receptors with response elements that differ by arrangement of hexameric binding sites rather than by sequence of the hexamers. As would be expected from functionally significant differences, these changes are strongly conserved among the different α and β genes from different species. Thus it seems possible that the two forms could show different affinities for more complex elements. In support of this possibility is the report (64) that the $\alpha1$ form induces the rGH T3RE more strongly than the $\beta1$ form in cotransfections. We have also consistently observed this phenomenon.

Of the two forms that do not bind T3, the $\alpha2$ form has been investigated in more detail. In combined cotransfections with either the $\alpha1$ or $\beta1$ receptors, this protein shows a remarkable ability to repress T3-induced expression (31). Thus at least the c-erbAα gene encodes products with opposing functions. It is interesting that the existence of multiple spliced forms is becoming a relatively common observation for transcription factor genes. The analysis of the T3R α proteins provided the first demonstration of distinct functions for such alternate products.

The mechanism of the $\alpha2$ inhibition is not yet clear. A priori, one might suspect that $\alpha2$ could either block response directly, by binding to the T3RE as an inactive complex, or indirectly, by forming inactive heterodimers or higher order oligomers with the functional receptors.

What is the function of the repression of expression conferred by the $\alpha2$ (and presumably the $\alpha3$) form? One suggestion arises from the fact that the $\alpha2$ form is particularly abundant in the brain, a tissue that does not respond to T3 with such classical responses as increase in O_2 utilization. Thus the $\alpha2$ form may direct the T3 response away from the genes ordinarily induced to a new group of genes, as yet uncharacterized. It is particularly important to determine whether or not the $\alpha2$ and/or $\alpha3$ forms respond to a distinct, novel ligand.

An even more complex issue concerning the multiple forms of T3 receptors is the possibility of heterodimeric or higher order heterooligomeric forms. One might imagine that a particular T3RE could preferentially interact with a putative $\alpha1:\beta1$ heterodimer, rather than either of the homodimeric forms. Direct support for the existence of such forms comes from studies of the effect of expressing mutant receptors lacking amino-terminal and DNA-binding domains (4, 19). It is thought that the members of the nuclear hormone receptor superfamily act as dimers and that the dimerization functions lie in the ligand-binding domains. By analogy with a variety of studies of bacterial repressor proteins deficient in DNA binding, but able to dimerize, one would expect the free ligand-binding domains to act as dominant negative repressors of receptor function. It has been observed that the ligand-binding domains of either the α or β forms of the receptors act to inhibit function of the endogenous receptors in pituitary cell lines (4, 19). Since such cells are presumed to contain functional α and β receptor forms, this strongly suggests that each ligand-binding domain can form inactive complexes with both types of receptor.

Remarkably, there is some evidence that there are naturally occurring versions of the dominant negative ligand-binding domain constructs generated by various manipulations of receptor expression vectors (3). These shorter forms of the endogenous receptor have been identified in chick cells using antibodies. It is thought that they arise by initiation at internal AUGs in the receptor open reading frame; such smaller products are often seen when T3 receptors are synthesized by in vitro translation. The abundance of the smaller forms is not high, however, and their relevance to in vivo function is not clear.

The many possibilities for complex interactions between and among the various T3 receptor forms are even further clouded by considerations of the other receptors that could interact with T3REs. The potential physiologic relevance of this daunting additional complication has recently received strong support from a description of heterodimers of T3Rα1 and RARα1 (22). This report includes not only biochemical results supporting the existence of such forms, but also in vivo cotransfection results, which suggest that they show distinct biological effects at different T3REs. Clearly, substantial analysis will be needed to sort out which of the great number of possible heteromeric forms actually exist and how they function.

Mutant Receptor Function in Generalized Thyroid Hormone Resistance

A group of patients were first identified by Refetoff et al (53) with normal or elevated serum thyroid hormone concentrations, but with clinical evidence of thyroid hormone deficiency. A considerable spectrum of clinical manifestations of deficient thyroid hormone action exists in this condition, termed generalized thyroid hormone resistance (GTHR), which can include mental retardation, delayed growth, reduced heart rate, and delayed Achilles tendon reflex time. All cases have been congenital with the exception of one reported case of acquired thyroid hormone resistance (29).

A variety of methods have been utilized to investigate the underlying defect that leads to the syndrome of GTHR. Family studies have shown an underlying genetic defect that is transmitted in an autosomal dominant and, in some cases, a recessive fashion. The clinical manifestations are quite similar within a kindred, but vary considerably between kindreds. This observation points to a spectrum of underlying genetic defects that may lead to the phenotype of GTHR. Defects in a number of steps in thyroid hormone action, including intracellular or intranuclear transport of thyroid hormone, T3 receptor mutations, or production of T3 receptor antagonists may be responsible for a variety of GTHR defects.

The availability of the human clones for the α and β T3 receptor has stimulated the investigation of potential abnormalities at the genetic level in patients with GTHR. It was initially shown through the use of restriction fragment polymorphisms (RFLP) that there was linkage in one kindred between the β type T3 receptor gene and the gene for GTHR (69). Recently, two reports have identified point mutations in the ligand-binding domain of the β T3 receptor gene, which appear to be responsible for thyroid hormone resistance (55, 70). In vitro translation of one of the identified mutations resulted in a product that was not capable of binding thyroid hormone (55). The presence of a presumably normal α T3 receptor gene in these individuals with a β gene mutation suggests that the mutated gene products may be acting as receptor antagonists. The identified βT3R gene mutations lie in the area of the ligand-binding domain affected by alternative splicing in the T3Rα2. This area has also been associated with defects in the binding of T3 (27). These findings suggest a physiologic relevance to the previously described studies of receptor subtypes and mutants that function as T3R antagonists. The further characterization of genetic defects associated with GTHR and the correlation of these defects with the variety of observed phenotypes should significantly extend our understanding of the function of the various T3Rs.

Literature Cited

1. Barker, S. B., Klitgaard, H. M. 1952. Metabolism of tissues excised from thyroxine injected rats. *Am. J. Physiol.* 170:81–86
2. Benbrook, D., Pfahl, M. 1987. A novel thyroid hormone receptor encoded by a cDNA clone from a human testis library. *Science* 238:788–91
3. Bigler, J., Eisenman, R. N. 1988. c-erbA encodes multiple proteins in chick erythroid cells. *Mol. Cell. Biol.* 8:4155–61
4. Brent, G. A., Dunn, M. K., Harney, J. W., Gulick, T., Larsen, P. R., Moore, D. D. 1989. Thyroid hormone aporeceptor represses T3-inducible promoters and blocks activity of the retinoic acid receptor. *New Biolog.* 1:329–36
5. Brent, G. A., Harney, J. W., Chen, Y., Warne, R. L., Moore, D. D., Larsen, P. R. 1989. Mutations of the rat growth hormone promoter which increase and decrease response to thyroid hormone define a consensus thyroid hormone response element. *Mol. Endocrinol.* 3:1996–2004
6. Brent, G. A., Harney, J. W., Moore, D. D., Larsen, P. R. 1988. Multihormonal regulation of the human, rat, and bovine growth hormone promoters: differential effects of 3',5'-cyclic adenosine monophosphate, thyroid hormone, and glucocorticoids. *Mol. Endocrinol.* 2:792–98
7. Brent, G. A., Larsen, P. R., Harney, J. W., Koenig, R. J., Moore, D. D. 1989. Functional characterization of the rat growth hormone promoter elements required for induction by thyroid hormone with and without a co-transfected β type thyroid hormone receptor. *J. Biol. Chem.* 264:178–82

7a. Burnside, J., Darling, D. S., Carr, F. E., Chin, W. W. 1989. Thyroid hormone regulation of the rat glycoprotein hormone α-subunit gene promoter activity. *J. Biol. Chem.* 264:6886–91

8. Burnside, J., Darling, D. S., Chin, W. W. 1990. A nuclear factor which enhances binding of thyroid hormone receptors to thyroid hormone response elements. *J. Biol. Chem.* 265:2500–4

8a. Carr, F. E., Burnside, J., Chin, W. W. 1989. Thyroid hormones regulate rat thyrotropin β gene promoter activity expressed in GH3 cells. *Mol. Endocrinol.* 3:709–16

9. Chatterjee, V. K. K., Lee, J. K., Rentoumis, A., Jameson, J. L. 1989. Negative regulation of the thyroid-stimulating hormone α gene by thyroid hormone: receptor interaction adjacent to the TATA box. *Proc. Natl. Acad. Sci. USA* 86:9114–18
10. Dalman, F. C., Bresnick, E. H., Patel, P. D., Perdew, G. H., Watson, S. J., et al. 1989. Direct evidence that the glucocorticoid receptor binds to hsp90 at or near the termination of receptor translation *in vitro*. *J. Biol. Chem.* 264:19815–21
11. Dalman, F. C., Koenig, R. J., Perdew, G. H., Massa, E., Pratt, W. B. 1990. In contrast to the glucocorticoid receptor, the thyroid hormone receptor is translated in the DNA binding state and is not

associated with hsp90. *J. Biol. Chem.* 265:3615–18

12. Damm, K., Thompson, C. C., Evans, R. M. 1989. Protein encoded by v-erbA functions as a thyroid-hormone receptor antagonist. *Nature* 339:593–97
13. Danielsen, M., Hinck, L., Ringold, G. M. 1989. Two amino acids within the knuckle of the first zinc finger specify DNA response element activation by the glucocorticoid receptor. *Cell* 57:1131–38
14. DeGroot, L. J., Sakurai, A., Macchia, E. 1989. The molecular basis of thyroid hormone action. *J. Endocrinol. Invest.* 12:843–61
15. DeMay, M. B., Gerardi, J. M., DeLuca, H. F., Kronenberg, H. M. 1990. DNA sequences in the rat osteocalcin gene that bind the 1,25-dihydroxyvitamin D3 receptor and confer responsiveness to 1,25-dihydroxyvitamin D3. *Proc. Natl. Acad. Sci. USA* 87:369–73
16. Diamond, D. J., Goodman, H. M. 1985. Regulation of growth hormone messenger RNA synthesis by dexamethasone and triiodothyronine. *J. Mol. Biol.* 181:41–62
17. Dillmann, W. H., Schwartz, H. L., Oppenheimer, J. H. 1978. Selective alterations in hepatic enzyme response after reduction of nuclear triiodothyronine receptor sites by partial hepatectomy and starvation. *Biochem. Biophys. Res. Comm.* 80:259–66
18. Evans, R. M. 1988. The steroid and thyroid hormone receptor superfamily. *Science* 240:889–95
19. Forman, B. M., Yang, C.-R., Au, M., Casanova, J., Ghysdael, J., Samuels, H. H. 1989. A domain containing leucine-zipper-like motifs mediate novel *in vivo* interactions between thyroid hormone and retinoic acid receptors. *Mol. Endocrinol.* 3:1610–26
20. Glass, C. K., Franco, R., Weinberger, C., Albert, V. R., Evans, R. M., Rosenfeld, M. G. 1987. A c-erb-A binding site in rat growth hormone gene mediates *trans*-activation by thyroid hormone. *Nature* 329:738–41
21. Glass, C. K., Holloway, J. M., Devary, O. V., Rosenfeld, M. G. 1988. The thyroid hormone receptor binds with opposite transcriptional effects to a common sequence motif in thyroid hormone and estrogen response elements. *Cell* 54:313–23
22. Glass, C. K., Lipkin, S. M., Devary, O. V., Rosenfeld, M. G. 1989. Positive and negative regulation of gene transcription by a retinoic acid-thyroid hormone receptor heterodimer. *Cell* 59:697–708
23. Graupner, G., Wills, K. N., Tzukerman, M., Zhang, X., Pfahl, M. 1989. Dual regulatory role for thyroid-hormone receptors allows control of retinoic-acid receptor activity. *Nature* 340:653–56
24. Hodin, R. A., Lazar, M. A., Chin, W. W. 1990. Differential and tissue-specific regulation of the multiple rat c-erbA messenger RNA species by thyroid hormone. *J. Clin. Invest.* 85:101–5
25. Hodin, R. A., Lazar, M. A., Wintman, B. I., Darling, D. S., Koenig, R. J., et al. 1989. Identification of a thyroid hormone receptor that is pituitary-specific. *Science* 244:76–79
26. Horowitz, Z., Sahnoun, H., Pascual, A., Casanova, J., Samuels, H. H. 1988. Analysis of photoaffinity label derivatives to probe thyroid hormone receptor in human fibroblasts, GH_1 cells and soluble receptor preparations. *J. Biol. Chem.* 263:6636–42
27. Horowitz, Z. D., Yang, C., Forman, B. M., Casanova, J., Samuels, H. H. 1989. Characterization of the domain structure of chick c-erbA by deletion mutation: in vitro translation and cell transfection studies. *Mol. Endocrinol.* 3:148–56
28. Izumo, S., Mahdavi, V. 1988. Thyroid hormone receptor α isoforms generated by alternative splicing differentially activate myosin HC gene transcription. *Nature* 334:539–42
29. Kaplan, M. M., Swartz, S. L., Larsen, P. R. 1981. Partial peripheral resistance to thyroid hormone. *Am. J. Med.* 70:1115–21
30. Koenig, R. J., Brent, G. A., Warne, R. L., Larsen, P. R., Moore, D. D. 1987. Thyroid hormone receptor binds to a site in the rat growth hormone promoter required for induction by thyroid hormone. *Proc. Natl. Acad. Sci. USA* 84:5670–74
31. Koenig, R. J., Lazar, M. A., Hodin, R. A., Brent, G. A., Larsen, P. R., et al. 1989. Inhibition of thyroid hormone action by a non-hormone binding c-erbA protein generated by alternative mRNA splicing. *Nature* 337:659–61
32. Koenig, R. J., Warne, R. L., Brent, G. A., Harney, J. W., Larsen, P. R., Moore, D. D. 1988. Isolation of a cDNA clone encoding a biologically active thyroid hormone receptor. *Proc. Natl. Acad. Sci. USA* 85:5031–35
33. Kolodny, J. M., Larsen, P. R., Silva, J. E. 1985. *In vitro* 3,5,3'-triiodothyronine binding to rat cerebrocortical neuronal and glial nuclei suggest the presence of

binding sites unavailable *in vivo*. *Endocrinology* 116:2019–28
34. Larsen, P. R., Harney, J. W., Moore, D. D., 1986. Sequences required for cell-specific thyroid hormone regulation of rat growth hormone promoter activity. *J. Biol. Chem.* 261:4373–76
35. Larsen, P. R., Harney, J. W., Moore, D. D. 1986. Repression mediates cell-type-specific expression of the rat growth hormone gene. *Proc. Natl. Acad. Sci. USA* 83:8283–87
36. Lavin, T. N., Baxter, J. D., Horita, S. 1988. The thyroid hormone receptor binds to multiple domains of the rat growth hormone 5'-flanking sequence. *J. Biol. Chem.* 263:9418–26
37. Lazar, M. A., Hodin, R. A., Chin, W. W. 1989. Human carboxyl-terminal variant of α-type c-erbA inhibits trans-activation by thyroid hormone receptors without binding thyroid hormone. *Proc. Natl. Acad. Sci. USA* 86:7771–74
38. Lazar, M. A., Hodin, R. A., Darling, D. S., Chinn, W. W. 1988. Identification of a rat c-erbAα-related protein which binds deoxyribonucleic acid but does not bind thyroid hormone. *Mol. Endocrinology* 2:893–901
38a. Lazar, M. A., Hodin, R. A., Darling, D. S., Chin, W. W. 1989. A novel member of the thyroid/steroid hormone receptor family is encoded by the opposite strand of the rat c-erbAα transcriptional unit. *Mol. Cell. Biol.* 9:1128–36
39. Miller, J., McLachlan, A. D., Klug, A. 1985. Repetitive zinc-binding domains in the protein transcription factor IIIA form *Xenopus* oocytes. *EMBO J.* 4:1609–14
40. Mitsuhashi, T., Nikodem, V. M. 1989. Regulation of expression of the alternative mRNAs of the rat α-thyroid hormone receptor gene. *J. Biol. Chem.* 264:8900–4
41. Mitsuhashi, T., Tennyson, G. E., Nikodem, V. M. 1988. Alternative splicing generates messages encoding rat c-erbA proteins that do not bind thyroid hormone. *Proc. Natl. Acad. Sci. USA* 85:5804–8
42. Moore, D. D. 1989. Promiscuous behavior in the steroid hormone receptor superfamily. *Trends Neurosci.* 12:165–68
43. Moore, D. D. 1990. Diversity and unity in the nuclear hormone receptors: a terpenoid receptor superfamily. *New Biolog.* 2:100–105
44. Morrison, N. A., Shine, J., Fragonas, J.-C., Verkest, V., McMenemy, M. L., Eisman, J. A. 1989. 1,25-dihydroxyvitamin D-responsive element and glucocorticoid repression in the osteocalcin gene. *Science* 246:1158–61
45. Munoz, A., Hoppner, W., Sap, J., Brady, G., Nordstrom, K., et al. 1990. The chicken c-erbA α-product induces expression of thyroid hormone-responsive genes in 3,5,3'-triiodothyronine receptor-deficient rat hepatoma cells. *Mol. Endocrinol.* 4:312–20
46. Murray, M. B., Towle, H. C. 1989. Identification of nuclear factors that enhance binding of the thyroid hormone receptor to a thyroid hormone response element. *Mol. Endocrinol.* 3: 1434–42
47. Murray, M. B., Zilz, N. D., McCreary, N. L., MacDonald, M. J., Towle, H. C. 1988. Isolation and characterization of rat cDNA clones for two distinct thyroid hormone receptors. *J. Biol. Chem.* 263:12770–77
48. Nakai, A., Seino, S., Sakurai, A., Szilak, I., Bell, G. I., DeGroot, L. J. 1988. Characterization of a thyroid hormone receptor expressed in human kidney and other tissues. *Proc. Natl. Acad. Sci. USA* 85:2781–85
49. ODonnell, A. L., Koenig, R. J. 1990. Mutational analysis identifies a new functional domain of the thyroid hormone receptor. *Mol. Endocrinol.* 4:715–20
50. Oppenheimer, J. H., Schwartz, H. L., Mariash, C. N., Kinlaw, W. B., Wong, N. C. W., Freake, H. C. 1987. Advances in our understanding of thyroid hormone action at the cellular level. *Endocrine Rev.* 8:288–308
51. Oppenheimer, J. H., Schwartz, H. L., Surks, M. I. 1975. Nuclear binding capacity appears to limit the hepatic response to 1-triiodothyronine (T3). *Endocrinol. Res. Comm.* 2:309–25
52. Perlman, A. J., Stanley, F., Samuels, H. H. 1982. Thyroid hormone nuclear receptor: evidence for multimeric organization in chromatin. *J. Biol. Chem.* 257:930–38
53. Refetoff, S., DeWind, L. T., DeGroot, L. J. 1967. Familial syndrome combining deafmutism, stippled epiphyses, goiter, and abnormally high PBI: possible target organ refractoriness to thyroid hormone. *J. Clin. Endocrinol. Metab.* 27:279–94
54. Sakurai, A., Nakai, A., DeGroot, L. J. 1989. Expression of three forms of thyroid hormone receptor in human tissues. *Mol. Endocrinol.* 3:392–99
55. Sakurai, A., Takeda, K., Ain, K., Ceccarelli, P., Nakai, A., et al. 1989. Generalized resistance to thyroid hor-

mone associated with a mutation in the ligand-binding domain of the human thyroid hormone receptor β. *Proc. Natl. Acad. Sci. USA* 86:8977–81
56. Samuels, H. H., Forman, B. M., Horowitz, A. D., Ye, Z. S. 1988. Regulation of gene expression by thyroid hormone. *J. Clin. Invest.* 81:957–67
57. Sap, J., de Magistris, L., Stunnenberg, H., Vennstrom, B. 1990. A major thyroid hormone response element in the third intron of the rat growth hormone gene. *EMBO J.* 9:887–96
58. Sap, J., Munoz, A., Damm, K., Goldberg, Y., Ghysdael, J., et al. 1986. The c-erb-A protein is a high-affinity receptor for thyroid hormone. *Nature* 324:635–40
59. Sap, J., Munoz, A., Schmitt, J., Stunnenberg, H., Vennstrom, B. 1989. Repression of transcription mediated at a thyroid hormone response element by the v-erb-A oncogene product. *Nature* 340:242–44
60. Schueler, P. A., Schwartz, H. L., Strait, K. A., Mariash, C. N., Oppenheimer, J. H. 1990. Binding of 3,5,3'-triiodothyronine (T3) and its analogs to the *in vitro* translational products of c-erbA protooncogenes: differences in the affinity of the α- and β-forms for the acetic acid analog and failure of the human testis and kidney α-2 products to bind T3. *Mol. Endocrinol.* 4:227–34
61. Silva, J. E., Larsen, P. R. 1978. Contributions of plasma triiodothyronine and local thyroxine monodeiodonation to triiodothyronine and nuclear triiodothyronine receptor saturation in pituitary, liver and kidney of hypothroid rats. Further evidence relating saturation of pituitary nuclear triiodothyronine receptors and the acute inhibition of thyroid-stimulating hormone release. *J. Clin. Invest.* 61:1247–59
62. Spindler, B. J., MacLeod, K. M., Ring, J., Baxter, J. D. 1975. Thyroid hormone receptors. Binding characteristics and lack of hormonal dependency for nuclear localization. *J. Biol. Chem.* 250:4113–19
63. Spindler, S. R., Mellon, S. H., Baxter, J. D. 1982. Growth hormone gene transcription is regulated by thyroid hormone and glucocorticoid hormones in cultured rat pituitary cells. *J. Biol. Chem.* 257:11627–32
64. Thompson, C. C., Evans, R. M. 1989. *Trans*-activation by thyroid hormone receptors: functional parallels with steroid hormone receptors. *Proc. Natl. Acad. Sci. USA* 86:3494–98
65. Thompson, C. C., Weinberger, C., Lebo, R., Evans, R. M. 1987. Identification of a novel thyroid hormone receptor expressed in the mammalian central nervous system. *Science* 237:1610–14
66. Tsai, S. Y., Carlstedt-Duke, J., Weigel, J. L., Dahlman, K., Gustafsson, J. A., et al. 1988. Molecular interactions of steroid hormone receptor with its enhancer element: evidence for receptor dimer formation. *Cell* 55:361–69
67. Umesono, K., Evans, R. M. 1989. Determinants of target gene specificity for steroid/thyroid hormone receptors. *Cell* 57:1139–46
68. Umesono, K., Giguere, V., Glass, C. K., Rosenfeld, M. G., Evans, R. M. 1988. Retinoic acid and thyroid hormone induce gene expression through a common responsive element. *Nature* 336:262–64
69. Usala, S. J., Bale, A. E., Gesundheit, N., Gesundheit, C., Weinberger, R. W., et al. 1988. Tight linkage between the syndrome of generalized thyroid hormone resistance and the human c-erbAβ gene. *Mol. Endocrinol.* 2:1217–20
70. Usala, S. J., Tennyson, G. E., Bale, A. E., Lash, R. W., Gesundheit, N., et al. 1990. A base mutation of the c-erbAβ thyroid hormone receptor in a kindred with generalized thyroid hormone resistance. *J. Clin. Invest.* 85:93–100
71. Weinberger, C., Thompson, C. C., Ong, E. S., Lebo, R., Gruol, D. J., et al. 1986. The c-erb-A gene encodes a thyroid hormone receptor. *Nature* 324:641–46
72. Yaffe, B. M., Samuels, H. H. 1984. Hormonal regulation of the growth hormone gene. *J. Biol. Chem.* 259:6284–91
73. Yamamoto, K. R., Godowski, P. J., Picard, D. 1988. Ligand regulated nonspecific inactivation of receptor function. A versatile mechanism for signal transduction. *Cold Springs Harbor Symp. Quant. Biol.* 53:803–11
74. Ye, Z. S., Samuels, H. H. 1987. Cell- and sequence-specific binding of nuclear proteins to 5'-flanking DNA of the rat growth hormone gene. *J. Biol. Chem.* 262:6313–17

Annu. Rev. Physiol. 1991. 53:37–57

RECEPTOR-G PROTEIN SIGNALING IN YEAST

Kendall J. Blumer[1] and Jeremy Thorner[2]

[1]Department of Cell Biology and Physiology, Washington University School of Medicine, St. Louis, Missouri 63110

[2]Division of Biochemistry and Molecular Biology, Department of Molecular and Cell Biology, University of California, Berkeley, California 94720

KEY WORDS: receptor, G protein, phosphorylation, endocytosis, farnesylation, myristoylation, desensitization, cell cycle, gene regulation

---

INTRODUCTION

In this review we discuss the components and regulation of a G protein-linked signaling pathway in the yeast *Saccharomyces cerevisiae*. Studies of signal transduction in yeast permit rigorous genetic, physiological, and biochemical criteria to be applied for understanding receptor and G protein action. The study of receptor-G protein signaling in the yeast system can reveal novel principles and unique insights not accessible by studies of G protein-linked signaling systems in vertebrates.

Here we review evidence that the oligopeptide mating pheromones of yeast act via a G protein-linked signal transduction pathway. Emphasized are the striking similarities in mechanism and regulation of receptor-G protein signaling between yeast and higher eukaryotes. We include newly emerging evidence that suggests mechanisms previously unidentified in other organisms regulate the G protein-mediated signaling pathway of yeast. There still are certain gaps in our current knowledge of the yeast G protein-linked signaling pathway. For this reason, we suggest plausible hypotheses to explain these uncertainties that can be scrutinized by further investigation.

We have omitted detailed discussions of the general physiology and genetic regulation of yeast mating and the processing and secretion of oligopeptide

0066-4278/91/0315-0037$02.00

mating pheromones. These topics have been the subject of recent reviews (23, 35, 44, 45). Excellent reviews are also available concerning the general biochemistry and cell biology of vertebrate signal-transducing G proteins (33, 36, 84, 100), posttranslational modification of GTP-binding proteins (102), and phosphorylation and desensitization of mammalian G protein-coupled receptors (3, 95, 96). Reviews of receptor-G protein signaling in another lower eukaryote, *Dictyostelium discoideum*, are also of general interest (25, 31, 48).

PHYSIOLOGICAL ROLE OF OLIGOPEPTIDE MATING PHEROMONES OF *SACCHAROMYCES CEREVISIAE*

Yeast can exist stably in either of two haploid cell types, **a** and α, that can conjugate to yield **a**/α diploid cells. Mating is initiated when haploid cells of one type are exposed to the oligopeptide mating pheromone secreted by haploid cells of the opposite type. Mating pheromones produced by **a** and α cells (**a**-factor and α-factor, respectively) trigger in their target cells identical sets of physiological responses that are preparatory for mating, including transient arrest in the G1 phase of the cell cycle (42, 91, 92), changes in gene transcription (27, 38, 41, 60, 81, 98, 104), and alterations of cellular architecture (29, 65, 71, 90, 103). The **a**/α diploid cells produced by mating neither secrete nor respond to mating pheromones.

MATING PHEROMONES ACT THROUGH A G PROTEIN-LINKED SIGNALING SYSTEM

The components and regulators of the mating pheromone signaling network were initially identified through the isolation and characterization of mutations that affect signal transduction in any of three distinct ways. Positive elements that are required for signaling were identified because their loss results in an unresponsive (or sterile) phenotype when pheromone is present (43, 68). Negative elements that hold the response network in check when pheromone is absent were uncovered because their loss results in constitutive signaling (26, 34, 47, 73). Additional elements that control the activity of the response pathway have been identified because their loss affects the apparent sensitivity and/or duration of the cellular response to pheromones (16, 17, 97). These three classes of phenotypic effects also provide the in vivo physiological basis for determining epistasis relationships among the various components involved in the signaling process.

The Pheromone Receptors

Among the positive elements needed for cellular response are the cell-surface receptors specific for binding each of the peptide mating pheromones. The receptor specific for α-factor is encoded by the *STE2* gene (which is expressed only in **a** cells) (79); the receptor specific for **a**-factor is encoded by the *STE3* gene (which is expressed only in α cells) (79). Mutant **a** cells defective in the *STE2* gene are unable to respond to α-factor (43, 68), and temperature-sensitive *ste2* mutants display thermosensitive binding of α-factor in vitro (50). Similarly, *ste3* mutations specifically eliminate cellular response to **a**-factor (68). The *STE2* and *STE3* genes (13, 37, 79) encode proteins predicted by hydropathy analysis to contain seven highly hydrophobic, potentially α-helical (presumably membrane-spanning) segments and a hydrophilic C-terminal domain rich in serine, threonine, and charged residues. This topological motif, with certain variations, is common to members of a large superfamily of cell-surface receptors (28, 53, 58, 61, 70, 82, 83; see also 46 for a recent review), which includes the β-adrenergic receptor (28) and rhodopsin (82). Receptors of this class in vertebrates signal by being coupled to intracellular guanine nucleotide-binding proteins (G proteins) consisting of α, β, and γ subunits (36, 100).

Direct evidence that the *STE2* and *STE3* products function as the pheromone receptors has been obtained. Affinity labeling procedures (8) have shown that the *STE2* gene product exhibits the principle hallmark of a receptor; it binds its cognate ligand, α-factor, specifically and with high affinity. The *STE2* product seems to be the sole protein responsible for ligand recognition because the α-factor binding sites exhibited by *Xenopus* oocytes injected with synthetic *STE2* mRNA (109) display an equilibrium binding constant similar to that exhibited by receptors found on yeast **a** cells (51). Correspondingly, *S. cerevisiae* **a** *ste2* mutants expressing the *STE2* gene of a distantly related yeast species (*Saccharomyces kluyveri)* are able to respond to the distinct form of pheromone secreted by *S. kluyveri* α cells (69). A similar kind of result indicates that the *STE3* gene encodes the **a**-factor receptor. When **a** cells express the *STE3* gene from a heterologous promoter, the cells display an autocrine response to their own secreted **a**-factor, which results in growth arrest (2). Autocrine arrest also occurs when α cells are forced to express the *STE2* gene (80).

Studies of the post-translational modification of the *STE2* and *STE3* products support their deduced topologies. *STE2* protein contains six potential sites for the addition of N-linked oligosaccharide chains (two Asn-X-Thr and four Asn-X-Ser sequences; X = any amino acid) (13, 79); three sites occur in the putative N-terminal extracellular domain, two in the potential extracellular loops, and one in the presumed C-terminal intracellular domain. Inhibition of protein glycosylation (8) reduces the apparent mass of the *STE2* product by ~6 kd, equivalent to the mass of 2–3 N-linked core oligosaccharide units. Because a proteolytic fragment comprising the C-terminal 70% of the *STE2* polypeptide lacks oligosaccharide moieties (8), the N-terminal 30% contains the sites for glycosylation. Because Asn-X-Thr seems to be the preferred target for N-linked glycosylation in yeast (74) and because both of the Asn-X-Thr sites reside within the first 50 N-terminal residues of the *STE2* protein, it seems likely that this hydrophilic N-terminal domain is disposed on the extracellular face of the plasma membrane. The C-terminal portion of *STE2* polypeptide was shown to be phosphorylated on serine and threonine residues (9, 89), and thus it is likely that the C-terminal hydrophilic tail is exposed to the cytosol. In order to join an extracellular N-terminal region with an intracellular C-terminal domain, the *STE2* polypeptide must thread through the plane of the lipid bilayer an odd number (probably seven) of times.

A similar conclusion has been reached for the topology of the *STE3* gene product. The *STE3* product contains five potential glycosylation sites (37, 79): one located in the second putative transmembrane segment; one in the third putative intracellular loop; and three in C-terminal domain. If the *STE3* protein possesses a topology like that predicted for the *STE2* molecule, all of these potential glycosylation sites would be inaccessible to the glycosylation enzymes in the lumen of the endoplasmic reticulum. Indeed, inhibition of protein glycosylation fails to affect the apparent mass of the *STE3* protein, which suggests that the **a**-factor receptor is not modified by N-linked oligosaccharide (19).

G Protein Subunits

Two yeast genes, *GPA1 (SCG1)* and *GPA2*, that encode proteins of 472 and 449 residues, respectively, which are ~45% identical to vertebrate G_α subunits, were isolated by using vertebrate $G_{i\alpha 2}$ and $G_{o\alpha}$ cDNA clones as probes to screen a yeast genomic library under low stringency conditions (75, 76). Completely conserved in these yeast G_α homologues are the signature sequences believed to mediate binding of the guanine ring and hydrolysis of GTP (24). The physiological function of the *GPA2* product is unresolved. This gene product probably plays no role in pheromone response because *gpa2* deletion mutants respond normally to mating pheromones and engage in conjugation (76).

By contrast, genetic evidence strongly argues that *GPA1* encodes a critical, negatively-acting component of the pheromone response pathway. First, the *GPA1* gene is expressed only in the two haploid cell types (26, 73), whereas the *GPA2* gene is expressed in all three cell types (76). Second, when haploid cells lack a functional *GPA1* gene product, the cells undergo G1 arrest and display constitutively the constellation of other responses normally elicited by the peptide mating factors (26, 73). This property enables *gpa1* null mutants to bypass the requirement for pheromone receptors in order to conjugate (47, 73). Third, as predicted, if the *GPA1* product has a specific role in the pheromone response pathway, certain *gpa1* alleles allow growth but cause sterility in both **a** and α cells (34, 64), presumably because coupling of G protein to the receptors is defective.

Homologues of the β and γ subunits of vertebrate G proteins have also been found in yeast and are directly implicated in the yeast pheromone response pathway. The *STE4* gene encodes a 432-residue protein that (excluding a unique region inserted near its C-terminus) is 43% identical to the β_1 and β_2 subunits of bovine transducin (106). The *STE18* gene encodes a hydrophilic, 110-amino acid protein that (if nonhomologous blocks present near its N- and C-termini are excluded from the comparison) is 32% identical to the γ_1 subunit of transducin (106). The deduced product of the *STE18* gene terminates in the sequence Cys-AAX (A = aliphatic amino acid; X = any amino acid), a sequence motif that occurs at the C-terminus of γ_1 transducin, as well as in *ras* proteins and fungal peptides (including **a**-factor) (1, 40, 93, 102). The Cys residue within this motif is the site for farnesylation of the proteins (1, 40, 93, 102). This polyisoprenylation is required for the membrane association and biological activity of the *STE18* protein (30).

Several observations indicate a direct involvement of these G_β and G_γ homologues in the pheromone response pathway. First, consistent with a role in mating, the *STE4* and *STE18* genes are expressed only in haploid cells (106). Second, deletion of either the *STE4* or the *STE18* gene causes sterility and prevents haploid cells of either type from responding to mating pheromones (106). Third, either *ste4* or *ste18* mutations relieve the growth arrest caused by *gpa1* null mutations (78, 106). Fourth, certain mutant alleles of the *STE4* gene (*STE4*^{Hp1}) elicit a constitutive response because they appear to encode β subunits that are defective in the ability to associate with G_α and are therefore no longer under pheromonal control (6). Fifth, even in the absence of added pheromone, overproduction of the normal *STE4* gene product stimulates the response pathway in otherwise wild-type haploid cells (21, 86, 105).

MECHANISM OF SIGNALING

Receptor-G Protein Coupling

Because the mating pheromone receptors and G proteins of yeast appear analogous to their vertebrate counterparts, the mechanism of signal transduction is likely to be similar. Pheromone-occupied receptors presumably function by coupling with and activating their cognate G proteins thereby causing the α subunit to release GDP and bind GTP (Figure 1). Subsequent dissociation of the G protein heterotrimer into a free α subunit and a free $\beta\gamma$ complex leads to a response.

Support for this model of pheromonal signaling comes from studies of functional coupling between the α-factor receptor and its cognate G protein in vitro (10). Kinetic and equilibrium binding methods employing yeast mem-

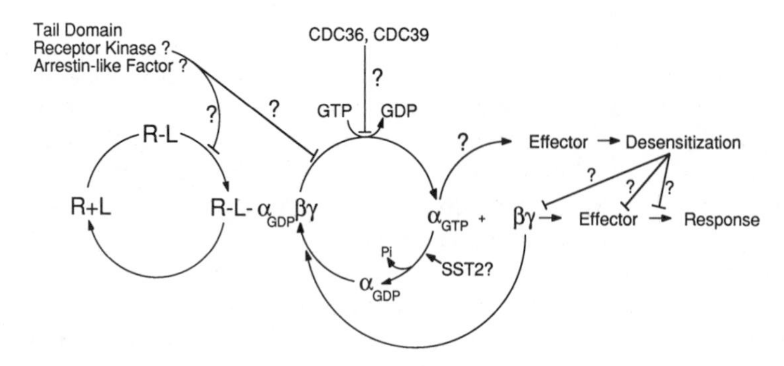

Figure 1 Response-desensitization network of the G protein-linked signal transduction pathway that mediates response to oligopeptide mating pheromones of the yeast *Saccharomyces cerevisiae*. The mechanism and regulation of pheromonal signaling in yeast has been inferred from genetic identification of signaling and regulatory components, biochemical tests of their modes of action, and the physiological effects elicited by changes in the structure or expression levels of relevant gene products. *R*, pheromone receptor; *L*, pheromone ligand; α, *GPA1* gene product; β, *STE4* gene product; γ, *STE18* gene product. Other components of the network are discussed in the text.

brane fractions showed that receptor-binding affinity is decreased seven to tenfold in the presence of GTP-γS, a diagnostic feature of many G protein-coupled receptors (36). Analysis of membranes derived from appropriate mutants indicated that guanine nucleotide-dependent modulation of receptor-binding affinity requires normal forms of the *GPA1*, *STE4*, and *STE18* gene products. In addition to establishing a functional link between the α-factor receptor and the G protein subunits, these findings indicate that all three G protein subunits are essential for receptor coupling.

Because yeast cells apparently respond to only a limited number of extracellular stimuli, it could be argued that pheromone receptor-G protein interaction is not very specific. In the absence of its cognate G protein, however, the α-factor receptor fails to be coupled detectably in vitro with any other yeast G proteins, including the *GPA2* product (10). Likewise, G proteins in the pheromone response network apparently do not simply interact with any receptor that is capable of coupling with G proteins. β-adrenergic receptors expressed in yeast are capable of binding agonists, but they are incapable of triggering a cellular response unless the cells also express mammalian $G_{s\alpha}$ (and lack *GPA1* protein) (56). Furthermore, expression of various mammalian G_α subunits in *gpa1* mutants suppresses growth arrest, but results in sterility, which suggests that the mammalian G_α subunits can interact with the yeast $\beta\gamma$ complex to prevent activation of the pheromone response pathway, but cannot productively associate with yeast pheromone receptors (54). Therefore, interaction between the pheromone receptors and G proteins of yeast exhibits a high degree of specificity.

Role of Individual G Protein Subunits in Receptor Coupling

The behavior of yeast cells expressing heterologous G_α subunits indicates that *GPA1* protein is a primary determinant of receptor-coupling specificity. Expression of mammalian G_α subunits in yeast blocks the G1 arrest of *gpa1* mutants (26, 54) and even prevents normal $GPA1^+$ haploids from responding to pheromone (54), which indicates that mammalian G_α subunits can associate efficiently with the effector-stimulating *STE4* and *STE18* products. Because both *GPA1* and *gpa1* cells expressing mammalian G_α fail to respond to mating pheromones (26, 54, 56), however, productive receptor coupling apparently does not occur. Construction of an appropriate chimera between yeast *GPA1* and mammalian $G_{s\alpha}$, however, does allow cells expressing β_2-adrenergic receptor to respond to agonists, even when *GPA1* product is present (K. King, R. Lefkowitz, personal communication). As expected from previous work on transducin α subunit (15, 39), it is the C-terminal region of mammalian $G_{s\alpha}$ that is required for recognition of β-adrenergic receptors in yeast, whereas the amino terminal domain of yeast *GPA1* permits efficient association with yeast G_β and G_γ.

Although the β and γ subunits of the yeast G protein appear to be essential for receptor coupling (10), their precise role in this process is uncertain. Because the *STE18* product is membrane-associated due to its farnesyl moiety (30), one possible role for the $\beta\gamma$ complex may be simply to anchor the α subunit to the membrane. Cell fractionation studies (10) indicate, however, that in the absence of the γ subunit, or in the presence of a β subunit that apparently is defective in its interaction with G_α, the *GPA1* product remains membrane-bound. Indeed, the N-terminus of the *GPA1* protein appears to be myristoylated (J. Reid, K. Matsumoto, personal communication). Hence it seems unlikely that $\beta\gamma$ complexes have an essential membrane-anchoring function. Perhaps $\beta\gamma$ subunits contact pheromone receptors and/or induce a conformational change in the *GPA1* product that promotes its coupling to the receptors.

Receptor Domains Involved in G Protein Coupling

Because the **a**-factor and α-factor receptors utilize the same G protein subunits to activate the response pathway, the domains of the two receptors involved in G protein coupling should have some common feature. Little direct experimental evidence is available to pinpoint those parts of the pheromone receptors that specifically mediate G protein coupling.

Similar to the well-studied G protein-coupled receptors of vertebrates (32, 57, 62, 99), one region of the pheromone receptors potentially involved in G protein coupling is the third putative cytoplasmic loop. In the pheromone receptors, the predicted third loops differ somewhat in size (*STE2* = 13 residues; *STE3* = 22 residues) and lack discernable homology. There are, however, similarities between these loops. First, there is a cluster of basic

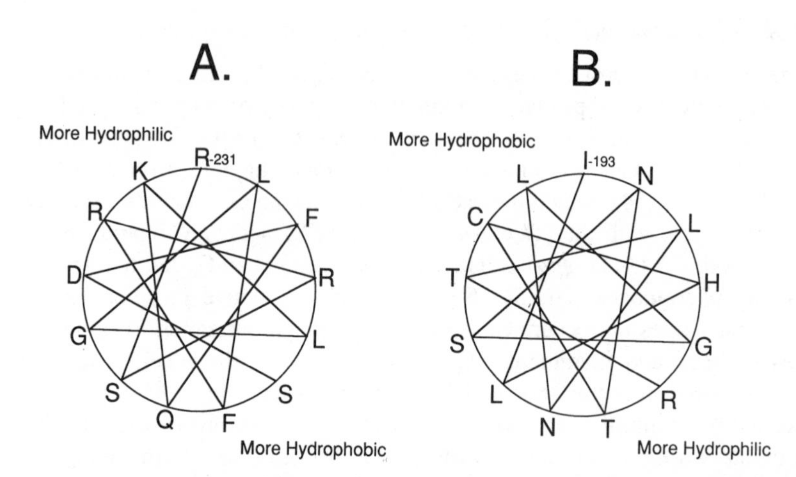

Figure 2 Helical projections of amino acid sequences in the carboxyl-proximal portions of the third putative cytoplasmic loops of the yeast pheromone receptors. *(A)* α-factor receptor (*STE2* gene product); *(B)* **a**-factor receptor (*STE3* gene product). Loop regions are presumed to form α-helical conformations with a periodicity of 3.6 amino acid residues per turn. The amino-proximal residue *(top of each projection)* is numbered according to the deduced amino acid sequences of the receptors (79). The carboxyl-proximal residue immediately precedes the sixth putative membrane-spanning segment of each receptor. Indicated are the faces of the helices having a more hydrophobic or a more hydrophilic character.

residues located within the amino-proximal part of each loop. Second, if the carboxyl-proximal portions of the loops are arranged in an α helix, each helix has a distinct amphipathic character (Figure 2). The segments of the third loops required for G protein coupling to rhodopsin and to β-adrenergic receptor likewise have the potential to form amphipathic helices (32, 62, 99).

Another region of the pheromone receptors potentially involved in G protein coupling [again suggested by studies of vertebrate G protein-coupled receptors (87, 99)] is the membrane-proximal portion of the C-terminal cytoplasmic tail. This region of the two pheromone receptors appears to differ in its involvement in G protein coupling. Truncation of the α-factor receptor at residue 296 removes the entire C terminal domain; yet cells expressing this truncated receptor still bind α-factor and conjugate (89). In contrast, cells expressing forms of the **a**-factor receptor truncated to the same extent are sterile (N. Davis, G. Sprague, personal communication). Forms of the **a**-factor receptor that retain the membrane-proximal portion of the C-terminal domain are, however, functional signal transducers. Although the membrane-proximal segment of the C-terminal tail of the **a**-factor receptor merely could be essential for protein folding, membrane insertion, or receptor stability, this domain may be required for G protein coupling.

Models of G Protein Action in Pheromone Response

Current models of G protein action, formulated from studies of mammalian G protein-based signaling systems, posit that dissociation of G_α from $G_{\beta\gamma}$ frees these entities to modulate their targets (36). Genetic approaches have been used in yeast to distinguish among several possible mechanisms for G protein action in pheromonal signaling.

The β and γ subunits encoded by the *STE4* and *STE18* genes appear to function together as positive regulators of the pheromonal signaling network. A constitutive response is provoked in cells by loss of the *GPA1* gene product (26, 73), but only if functional *STE4* and *STE18* products are present (78, 106). A constitutive signal is also elicited when the wild-type *STE4* product is overexpressed (21, 86, 105), thus indicating that in normal cells the level of the β subunit is limiting. Overexpression of the *STE4* product in *ste18* null mutants does not elicit a constitutive signal (21, 86, 105), which supports the view that the *STE4* and *STE18* products act as a $\beta\gamma$ complex.

As suggested from studies of mammalian G proteins, several potential modes for G protein action in pheromonal signaling have been considered. In the first model, based on the mechanism by which stimulatory G proteins trigger responses to light or to catecholamines, G_α-GTP functions as a positive regulatory element that activates the effector enzyme, and the $\beta\gamma$ complex is inhibitory (36, 100). This model is inconsistent with genetic data demonstrating that *GPA1* product acts negatively to repress the pheromonal response network and that the *STE4* and *STE18* products are required for response.

According to a second model, proposed for inhibitory G proteins of vertebrates, G_α-GTP would act as a negative regulator by inhibiting the effector enzyme (adenylate cyclase, in mammals) by a direct, but unknown, mechanism (101), and the reduction of an effector signal would cause G1 arrest and the other responses. Again, this is an untenable model for the action of yeast G proteins involved in pheromone response because it predicts that loss of *GPA1* should lead to an unresponsive cell. Most *gpa1* mutants display the opposite effect, namely constitutive response (26, 73).

There is, however, another mode of action proposed for inhibitory G proteins in vertebrates. Activation of $G_{i\alpha}$ is proposed to release $\beta\gamma$ subunits, that, by associating with free $G_{s\alpha}$ subunits, block the stimulatory effects of $G_{s\alpha}$ on the effector, adenylate cyclase (36). In yeast, this model requires that a response be produced upon pheromonal stimulation (or upon deletion of *GPA1*) because $\beta\gamma$ subunits are released that, in turn, sequester a different G_α subunit whose role it is to stimulate an effector that generates a growth-promoting signal. Although this model is consistent with all of the genetic data, it predicts that mutation of the gene encoding the postulated second class of G_α subunit would have the same effect as loss of *GPA1*, namely a constitutive response. Such a gene has not yet been identified on the basis of sequence homology, or the predicted mutant phenotype.

If the *GPA1* gene encodes the sole species of G_α subunit involved in pheromone response, then the genetic and biochemical data suggest a straightforward, but unprecedented, model for G protein action. Pheromone-bound receptors catalyze the exchange of GTP for GDP bound to the *GPA1* product. GTP binding causes the G_α subunit to dissociate from the $\beta\gamma$ complex. Free $\beta\gamma$ subunits, in turn, directly modulate the downstream effector of the pathway (Figure 1). There is some evidence, albeit controversial, that $G_{\beta\gamma}$ subunits of vertebrates can directly or indirectly activate retinal phospholipase A_2 (49) and K^+ channels of atrial cardiomyocytes (55, 63, 66; for a countervailing view see 20).

Yeast G Proteins Trigger the Pheromone Response Pathway Via an Unknown Effector

Although a number of genes required for cellular response to mating pheromone have been identified, none appears to encode a homologue of a well-characterized effector enzyme (44), such as adenylate cyclase, that is known to be regulated by G protein subunits in vertebrate cells. In yeast, an essential role for adenylate cyclase in pheromone response seems unlikely because cells carrying multiple mutations that cripple the cAMP synthesis and response machinery nonetheless respond to mating pheromones (W. Courchesne, M. Hasson, J. Thorner, unpublished observations) and are capable of mating (14).

Certain genetic findings suggest that the effector regulated by the yeast $\beta\gamma$ complex may be membrane-bound. Mutations in the *SGP2* gene (also called *RAM1, DPR1,* or *STE16*) inhibit the constitutive signal produced in cells lacking a functional *GPA1* gene (77), and also cause **a** cells to produce a biologically inactive form of **a**-factor (see 35 for a review). These two effects are apparently related owing to the lack of farnesylation of both **a**-factor (1, 93) and the G_γ subunit (30) in *sgp2* mutants. Thus in the absence of this modification, the hydrophilic G_γ subunit, which is complexed with G_β, may interact less efficiently with the membrane, or with a membrane-bound effector. This putative membrane-associated effector remains to be found.

REGULATION OF RECEPTOR-G PROTEIN SIGNALING

Regulatory mechanisms that control steps early in the pheromone signaling pathway have been inferred primarily by determining whether cellular recovery from pheromone-induced cell-cycle arrest is affected by changes in the structure or expression level of the receptors, the G protein subunits, or other elements. Complementary biochemical assays for modulation of G protein or effector enzyme activity in vitro are currently unavailable.

The C-Terminal Domains of the Pheromone Receptors Control Desensitization and Internalization

Evidence that the receptors themselves regulate cellular response to pheromones comes from the behavior of cells expressing various truncated forms of the α-factor and **a**-factor receptors (59, 89, N. Davis, G. F. Sprague, personal communication). Progressive removal of portions of the hydrophilic C-terminal domain of the α-factor receptor causes cells to become defective in adaptation, as manifest by an increase (3 to 25-fold) in apparent sensitivity to pheromone-induced growth arrest, as determined by a bioassay (halo test) that primarily measures the efficiency of cellular recovery, or adaptation, after pheromone-induced cell cycle arrest. Complete removal of the 134-residue C-terminal tail of the α-factor receptor causes cells to become exquisitely sensitive ($>$100-fold more sensitive than wild-type cells) to pheromone action. Similarly, cells expressing truncated forms of the **a**-factor receptor are also defective in recovery from growth arrest (N. Davis, G. F. Sprague, personal communication).

One potential role of the C-terminal domain in the desensitization process is suggested by studies of ligand-induced endocytosis of the α-factor receptor (18, 52, 59, 89). As indicated by the kinetics of endocytosis determined for the series of truncated receptors, the severity of the desensitization defect as measured by the halo assay somewhat parallels the severity of the defect in the rate and extent of receptor endocytosis. Partial truncations of the C-terminal domain of the α-factor receptor can cause significant ($\sim$ 10 to 20-fold) defects in desensitization, yet display only slight effects on the kinetics of endocytosis (59, 89). On the other hand, α-factor receptor completely lacking its C-terminal domain is dramatically defective in desensitization ($\sim$ 100-fold) and correspondingly is completely defective in endocytosis (89). Nonetheless, an obligatory connection between receptor desensitization and ligand-induced endocytosis seems unlikely because new receptors are synthesized and expressed on the surface of desensitized cells, even though the cells are refractory to pheromone action (52).

Studies of receptor phosphorylation (9, 89) suggest a second possible means by which the C-terminal segment of a pheromone receptor regulates desensitization. Ligand binding triggers rapid (within five min) hyperphosphorylation (up to threefold) at multiple sites located throughout the C-terminal domain of the α-factor receptor. Although hyperphosphorylation could simply reflect an increased accessibility of the C-terminal tail resulting from the conformational changes induced by agonist binding to the receptor, the elevated phosphorylation could also be the signal recognized by cellular factors that, for example, bind to the receptor and prevent coupling of receptor-G protein complexes. Both rhodopsin (94) and β-adrenergic receptor (12) become hyperphosphorylated on their C-terminal tails upon activation of the receptors. A cellular uncoupling factor, called arrestin (S antigen or 48 K protein), has been identified that binds to phosphorylated rhodopsin and prevents coupling to its G protein, transducin (107, 108). An arrestin-like factor also appears to be responsible for preventing coupling of the phosphorlated β-adrenergic receptor and G_s (4, 5, 12).

Although progressive removal of potential phosphorylation sites by C-terminal truncation of the α-factor receptor correlates with increasing defects in desensitization, the significance of receptor phosphorylation in the process of desensitization must be viewed with some caution. First, the apparent increase in stoichiometry of phosphorylation that occurs upon agonist binding is modest (9, 89). Second, the vacant and agonist-bound receptors appear to be phosphorylated at the same sites, as judged by peptide mapping (89); only the level of phosphorylation at these sites seems to change upon pheromone binding. Finally, no in vitro assays have been developed to test whether receptor phosphorylation in yeast actually affects G protein coupling, or whether the C-terminal domain specifically promotes uncoupling.

If an arrestin-like mechanism for receptor-promoted desensitization exists in yeast, and if receptor molecules function independently of one another, then *STE2* C-terminal truncation mutations should be dominant because truncated receptors should be immune to arrestin action, even when full-length receptors are present. *STE2* truncation mutations, however, are largely recessive to the wild-type genes. Compared with wild-type cells, cells expressing both full-length and truncated receptors are only slightly more sensitive to pheromone action (59, 89). This finding need not exclude the arrestin model because, as suggested by the fact that dimers of the α-factor receptor are observed under some conditions of membrane solubilization (8), full-length receptors could interact with truncated receptors and promote arrestin binding to the complex. If the receptors do function independently, full-length receptors could promote desensitization by an alternative mechanism, even in the presence of truncated receptors. For example, intact receptors could facilitate reformation of inactive G protein $\alpha\beta\gamma$ heterotrimers, even if the truncated receptors cannot.

The Level and Activity of GPA1 Protein Controls Cellular Desensitization

The level of expression of the *GPA1* product affects cellular response, as predicted by the subunit dissociation model for G protein action. Expression of *GPA1 (SCG1)* from multicopy plasmids promotes cellular recovery (26), and reduced expression of *GPA1* (by repressing transcription of *GPA1* fused to the *GAL1* promoter) provokes a cellular response (73). Cells that overexpress wild-type *GPA1* are able to become desensitized in the presence of high levels of α-factor that are sufficient to cause nearly permanent growth arrest in cells expressing normal levels of the G_α subunit (21). Similarly, overexpression of *GPA1* suppresses the constitutive signal that is generated by overexpression of the *STE4* product (21, 86, 105). A simple interpretation of these findings is that *GPA1* protein promotes desensitization by sequestering $\beta\gamma$ subunits encoded by the *STE4* and *STE18* genes.

GPA1 protein appears to promote desensitization in another way, based on the phenotype of cells expressing an altered G_α subunit (*GPA1*$^{Val\text{-}50}$) (72) that, by analogy with mutations causing constitutively activated *ras* proteins, has been proposed to be defective in GTP hydrolysis. Relative to wild-type cells, *GPA1*$^{Val\text{-}50}$ mutants are initially supersensitive to low doses of pheromone, yet at higher doses of mating factor they display an enhanced recovery ability. When cells are scored on the basis of initial sensitivity, the *GPA1*$^{Val\text{-}50}$ mutation is found to be recessive to the wild-type *GPA1* allele. The recessive phenotype of *GPA1*$^{Val\text{-}50}$ mutants can be interpreted according to the $\beta\gamma$ sequestration model. The *GPA1*$^{Val\text{-}50}$ mutation promotes a signal at low doses of pheromone because the lifetime of G_α-GTP is long enough so that the critical threshold level of free $\beta\gamma$ subunits can accumulate and activate the response machinery. If wild-type *GPA1* product is also present, however, the free $\beta\gamma$ subunits can be sequestered because the normal *GPA1* protein is capable of hydrolyzing GTP to GDP more efficiently than the *GPA1*$^{Val\text{-}50}$ form.

If the *GPA1*$^{Val\text{-}50}$ mutation simply affects GTP hydrolysis by the G_α subunit, it should also be recessive when scored for its ability to adapt to high levels of α-factor. It is, however, dominant (72). To account for the enhanced recovery ability of GPA1$^{Val\text{-}50}$ mutants even in the presence of wild-type *GPA1* product, it has been proposed that the *GPA1*$^{Val\text{-}50}$ protein promotes desensitization because it has an enhanced ability to act as a positive regulatory element that interacts with a component other than the $\beta\gamma$ complex (72). *GPA1*$^{Val\text{-}50}$ protein (and, perhaps to a lesser extent, wild-type *GPA1* product as well) could modulate an effector involved in recovery (rather than the effector involved in pheromone response). Alternatively, *GPA1* could negatively regulate the same effector that is positively regulated by the $\beta\gamma$ complex (Figure 1).

One caveat should be raised concerning the *GPA1*$^{Val\text{-}50}$ mutation. The analogous substitution (Gly-49→Val) in vertebrate $G_{s\alpha}$ (11), rather than causing a defect in GTP hydrolysis, is believed to weaken GTP binding: in membranes of S49 *cyc*$^-$ cells expressing this mutant $G_{s\alpha}$ subunit, β-adrenergic receptor agonists, GTP-γS, and AlF_4^- only weakly stimulate adenylyl cyclase. Thus the *GPA1*$^{Val\text{-}50}$ substitution could influence more than one biochemical activity of the *GPA1* product. Resolving these uncertainties will require knowledge of the ratio of associated and dissociated G protein subunits, the state of the bound guanine nucleotide under various physiological and genetic circumstances, and the identification of the putative target(s) of the *GPA1* product that might be involved in the recovery process.

CDC36 and CDC39 Gene Products May Negatively Regulate G Protein Activity

Recent genetic analysis has provided the first indication that, in the absence of mating pheromone, G protein activity is repressed by the *CDC36* and *CDC39* gene products. Under nonpermissive conditions, temperature-sensitive, *cdc36* and *cdc39* mutants express pheromone-responsive genes in the absence of pheromone and permit cells lacking receptors to conjugate (67, 85). This constitutive activation of the pheromone response pathway does not occur if cells also lack the β and γ subunits encoded by the *STE4* and *STE18* genes, or if *GPA1* is overproduced, which implies that the *CDC36* and *CDC39* products act at the level of the G protein (Figure 1).

Potential functional roles for the *CDC36* and *CDC39* gene products are not immediately suggested by their deduced amino acid sequences. *CDC36* encodes a 21-kd protein that is 26% identical to the C-terminal portion of the *CDC4* gene product (88), a yeast protein that controls the cell cycle in an unknown way. The *CDC36* product also shares 22% identity with an amino-terminal segment of the *ets* oncogene of avian erythroblastosis virus E26 (88); the function of the *ets* oncoprotein is unknown. *CDC39* encodes a 230-kd protein that displays no significant homology with protein sequences in the current database (S. Reed, personal communication).

The property of a certain *gpa1 (scg1) cdc39* double mutant suggests one way that G protein activity might be silenced by the *CDC39* product in the absence of pheromone (85). A truncation mutation *(scg1-ctt1)* that removes the 5 carboxyl-terminal residues of the G_α subunit permits cell growth, but prevents pheromone response (possibly because GDP binding occurs more tightly, or because coupling to receptor is defective, but association with $\beta\gamma$ is not) (64). When the *scg1-ctt* allele is present, *cdc39* mutations do not trigger a constitutive response at the non-permissive temperature (85). Because the C-terminal region of mammalian G_α subunits is thought to promote receptor coupling and trigger the release of GDP, the *CDC39* product might also interact with this region of the G_α subunit. In normal cells, *CDC39* product might function by stabilizing G_α-GDP, thereby maintaining the quiescent $G_{\alpha\beta\gamma}$ complex.

In contrast, the role of the *CDC36* product is less certain because the *scg1-ctt1* mutation fails to suppress a *cdc36* mutation (85). This finding suggests, however, that the *CDC36* product functions as a putative negative regulator of G protein function (or synthesis) in a manner that is distinct from *CDC39* (85).

Also it should be noted that the *CDC36* and *CDC39* gene products must regulate cellular processes other than the mating response pathway because **a**/α diploid cells homozygous for *cdc36* and *cdc39* mutations arrest growth at the restrictive temperature. Furthermore, even in haploid cells, the pheromone response pathway is not constitutively induced, but cell growth is still arrested when *cdc36* or *cdc39* mutants are grown on non-fermentable carbon sources and then shifted to the restrictive temperature (67).

SST2 Encodes a Key Regulator of the Recovery Process

A key, but enigmatic, regulator of cellular desensitization to mating pheromone is encoded by the *SST2* gene. Mutants lacking *SST2* function are sensitive to very low doses of mating pheromone and are defective in recovery from pheromone-induced cell cycle arrest (16, 17). A specific role for the *SST2* product in pheromonal regulation is further suggested because *SST2* expression, which is restricted to haploid cells, is induced at least 50-fold in pheromone-treated cells (22, 27).

Rather than preventing the production of an initial signal or degrading a key second messenger in the response pathway, *SST2* protein apparently promotes desensitization by negatively regulating the response network after it becomes activated. This conclusion is drawn from the observation that overexpression of *SST2* prior to challenging cells with mating pheromone does not significantly blunt initial responsiveness, but does increase the rate of subsequent desensitization (89; W. Courchesne, J. Thorner, unpublished results).

Like *CDC36* and *CDC39*, the biochemical function of the *SST2* product is elusive. The deduced product of the *SST2* gene (22, 27) is a hydrophilic, 698-residue protein, rich in serine and threonine residues, which displays no striking similarity with other yeast or mammalian proteins that could suggest its potential function.

It seems unlikely that the *SST2* protein could interact with the C-terminal domain of the pheromone receptor and prevent G protein coupling, a mode of action proposed for retinal arrestin, because the effects of receptor tail truncation and the absence of a functional *SST2* protein are additive (59, 89), and because overexpression of *SST2* suppresses the desensitization defect of cells expressing tailless α-factor receptors (89). Other observations indicate that the pheromone receptors may not be the obligatory target of the *SST2* product. *SST2* function can promote recovery of *STE4*$^{\text{Hp1}}$ mutants (7), in which a constitutive arrest signal can be generated in the absence of the α-factor receptor. These observations suggest that the *SST2* protein may act by inactivating another component of the response pathway, perhaps a G protein subunit (Figure 1).

CONCLUSIONS AND FUTURE PROSPECTS

Biologists studying cellular regulation by transmembrane signaling pathways have two major goals. One is to identify the components of the signal transduction networks and the other is to understand the regulatory mechanisms that control the signaling pathways. Our current understanding of receptor-G protein signaling in yeast is summarized in Figure 1. To date, studies of mating pheromone signal transduction indicate that the receptors and G proteins in yeast function mechanistically in much the same way as their counterparts in vertebrate organisms. One unexpected concept that is strongly supported by findings in yeast is that $\beta\gamma$ subunits probably modulate the downstream effector, an idea that in mammalian systems remains controversial. A critical, open question in this work is the identity of the yeast effector and second messenger. Defining the effector in yeast regulated by $\beta\gamma$ subunits may eventually help clarify the mechanism by which $\beta\gamma$ subunits function in vertebrates.

Just emerging from studies of pheromonal signaling is the possibility that a single type of yeast G_α subunit negatively regulates cellular responsiveness in two discrete ways: in its GDP-bound form, G_α may sequester $\beta\gamma$ subunits, while in the GTP-bound form, it may act as a positive regulator of a desensitization pathway. Unraveling this putative desensitization network will be of particular interest.

Another long-standing puzzle is the function of the *SST2* product in controlling cellular desensitization. This yeast gene may define a heretofore unrecognized regulator of G protein-linked signaling systems. Although G protein subunits have been proposed as the targets of *SST2* action (89), there is no compelling genetic data for or against this model (7, 72). This issue may be one where biochemical, rather than genetic, approaches in yeast may provide an answer.

In conclusion, we find it remarkable that G protein-coupled receptor signaling systems evolved in simple eukaryotes like yeast and slime mold (25, 31, 48), and that these cells have elaborated an array of regulatory mechanisms that control transmembrane signaling even at its earliest steps. We speculate that the physiological advantage of this complex regulatory network in yeast is twofold. First, because yeast cells are nonmotile, desensitization mechanisms might ensure that cells can recover from growth arrest if conjugation is unsuccessful. Second, in the event of successful mating, desensitization mechanisms might facilitate re-entry of diploids into the mitotic cell cycle.

Literature Cited

1. Anderegg, R. J., Betz, R., Carr, S. A., Crabb, J. W., Düntze, W. 1988. Structure of *Saccharomyces cerevisiae* mating hormone **a**-factor: identification of S-farnesyl cysteine as a structural component. *J. Biol. Chem.* 263:18236–40
2. Bender, A., Sprague, G. F. Jr. 1986. Yeast peptide pheromones, **a**-factor and alpha-factor, activate a common response mechanism in their target cells. *Cell* 47:929–37
3. Benovic, J. L., Bouvier, M., Caron, M., Lefkowitz, R. J. 1988. Regulation of adenylyl cyclase-coupled beta-adrenergic receptors. *Annu. Rev. Cell. Biol.* 4:405–28
4. Benovic, J. L., Kühn, H., Weyand, I., Codina, J., Caron, M., Lefkowitz, R. J. 1987. Functional desensitization of the isolated β-adrenergic receptor by the β-adrenergic receptor kinase: potential role of an analog of the retinal protein arres-

tin (48-kDa protein). *Proc. Natl. Acad. Sci. USA* 84:8879–82

5. Benovic, J. L., Strasser, R. H., Caron, M. G., Lefkowitz, R. J. 1986. β-adrenergic receptor kinase: identification of a novel protein kinase that phosphorylates the agonist-occupied form of the receptor. *Proc. Natl. Acad. Sci. USA* 83:2797–2801
6. Blinder, D., Bouvier, S., Jenness, D. D. 1989. Constitutive mutants in the yeast pheromone response: ordered function of the gene products. *Cell* 56:479–86
7. Blinder, D., Jenness, D. D. 1989. Regulation of postreceptor signaling in the pheromone response pathway of *Saccharomyces cerevisiae*. *Mol. Cell. Biol.* 9:3720–26
8. Blumer, K. J., Reneke, J. E., Thorner, J. 1988. The *STE2* gene product is the ligand binding component of the α-factor receptor of *Saccharomyces cerevisiae*. *J. Biol. Chem.* 263:10836–42
9. Blumer, K. J., Reneke, J. E., Courchesne, W. E., Thorner, J. 1988. Functional domains of a peptide hormone receptor: the α-factor receptor (*STE2* gene product) of *Saccharomyces cerevisiae*. *Cold Spring Harbor Symp. Quant. Biol.* 53:591–603
10. Blumer, K. J., Thorner, J. 1990. β and γ subunits of a yeast guanine nucleotide-binding protein are not essential for membrane association of the α subunit but are required for receptor coupling. *Proc. Natl. Acad. Sci. USA* 87:4363–67
11. Bourne, H. R., Masters, S. B., Miller, R. T., Sullivan, K. A., Heideman, W. 1988. Mutations probe structure and function of G-protein α chains. *Cold Spring Harbor Symp. Quant. Biol.* 53:221–28
12. Bouvier, M., Hausdorff, W. P., De Blasi, A., O'Dowd, B. F., Kobilka, B. K., et al. 1988. Removal of phosphorylation sites from the β_2-adrenergic receptor delays onset of agonist-promoted desensitization. *Nature* 333:370–73
13. Burkholder, A. C., Hartwell, L. H. 1985. The yeast α-factor receptor: structural properties deduced from the sequence of the *STE2* gene. *Nucleic Acids Res.* 13:8463–75
14. Cameron, S., Levin, L., Zoller, M., Wigler, M. 1988. cAMP-independent control of sporulation, glycogen metabolism, and heat shock resistance in *S. cerevisiae*. *Cell* 53:555–66
15. Cerione, R. A., Kroll, S., Rajaram, R., Unson, C., Goldsmith, P., Spiegel, A. M. 1988. An antibody directed against the carboxyl-terminal decapeptide of the alpha subunit of the retinal GTP-binding protein, transducin. Effects on transducin function. *J. Biol. Chem.* 263:9345–52
16. Chan, R. K., Otte, C. A. 1982. Isolation and genetic analysis of *Saccharomyces cerevisiae* mutants supersensitive to G1 arrest by **a**-factor and α-factor pheromones. *Mol. Cell. Biol.* 2:11–20
17. Chan, R. K., Otte, C. A. 1982. Physiological characterization of *Saccharomyces cerevisiae* mutants supersensitive to G1 arrest by **a**-factor and α-factor pheromones. *Mol. Cell Biol.* 2:21–29
18. Chvatchko, Y., Howald, I., Reizman, H. 1986. Two yeast mutants defective in endocytosis are defective in pheromone response. *Cell* 46:355–64
19. Clark, K. L., Davis, N. G., Wiest, D. K., Hwang-Shun, J.-J., Sprague, G. F. Jr. 1988. Response of yeast α cells to **a**-factor pheromone: topology of the receptor and identification of a component of the response pathway. *Cold Spring Harbor Symp. Quant. Biol.* 53:611–20
20. Codina, J., Yatani, A., Grenet, D., Brown, A. M., Birnbaumer, L. 1987. The α subunit of the GTP binding protein G_k opens atrial potassium channels. *Science* 236:442–45
21. Cole, G. M., Stone, D. E., Reed, S. I. 1990. Stoichiometry of G protein subunits affects the *Saccharomyces cerevisiae* mating pheromone signal transduction pathway. *Mol. Cell. Biol.* 10:510–17
22. Courchesne, W. E., Thorner, J. 1986. Control of pheromone response in *Saccharomyces cerevisiae:* isolation of the *SST2* gene. *Yeast* 2: S74
23. Cross, F., Hartwell, L. H., Jackson, C., Konopka J. B. 1988. Conjugation in *Saccharomyces cerevisiae*. *Annu. Rev. Cell Biol.* 4:429–57
24. Dever, T. E., Glynias, M. J., Merrick, W. C. 1987. GTP-binding domain: three consensus sequence elements with distinct spacing. *Proc. Natl. Acad. Sci. USA* 84:1814–18
25. Devreotes, P. 1989. *Dictyostelium discoideum:* a model system for cell-cell interactions in development. *Science* 245:1054–58
26. Dietzel, C., Kurjan, J. 1987. The yeast *SCG1* gene: a G_α-like protein implicated with the α- and **a**-factor response pathway. *Cell* 50:1001–10
27. Dietzel, C., Kurjan, J. 1987. Pheromonal regulation and sequence of the *Saccharomyces cerevisiae SST2* gene: a model for desensitization to pheromone. *Mol. Cell. Biol.* 7:4169–77
28. Dixon, R. A. F., Kobilka, B. K., Stra-

der, D. J., Benovic, J. L., Dohlman, H. G., et al. 1986. Cloning of the gene and cDNA for mammalian β-adrenergic receptor and homology with rhodopsin. *Nature* 321:75–79
29. Fehrenbacher, G., Perry, K., Thorner, J. 1978. Cell-cell recognition in *S. cerevisiae:* regulation of mating specific adhesion. *J. Bacteriol.* 134:893–901
30. Finegold, A. A., Schafer, W. R., Rine, J., Whiteway, M., Tamanoi, F. 1990. Trimeric G proteins and *ras* protein share a common mechanism for membrane association. *Science* 249:165–69
31. Firtel, R. A., van Haastert, P. J., Kimmel, A. R., Devreotes, P. N. 1989. G protein linked signal transduction pathways in development: *Dictyostelium* as an experimental system. *Cell* 58:235–39
32. Franke, R. R., Sakman, T. P., Oprian, D. D., Khorana, H. G. 1988. A single amino acid substitution in rhodopsin (lysine 248→leucine) prevents activation of transduction. *J. Biol. Chem.* 263:2119–22
33. Freissmuth, M., Casey, P. J., Gilman, A. G. 1989. G proteins control diverse pathways of transmembrane signaling. *FASEB J.* 3:2125–31
34. Fujimura, H.-A. 1989. The yeast G-protein homolog is involved in the mating pheromone signal transduction pathway. *Mol. Cell. Biol.* 9:152–58
35. Fuller, R. S., Sterne, R. E., Thorner, J. 1988. Enzymes required for yeast prohormone processing. *Annu. Rev. Physiol.* 50:345–62
36. Gilman, A. 1987. G proteins: transducers of receptor generated signals. *Annu. Rev. Biochem.* 56:615–49
37. Hagen, D., McCaffrey, G., Sprague, G. F. Jr. 1986. Evidence the yeast *STE3* gene encodes a receptor for the peptide pheromone **a**-factor: gene sequence and implications for the structure of the presumed receptor. *Proc. Natl. Acad. Sci. USA* 83:1418–22
38. Hagen, D. C., Sprague, G. F. Jr. 1984. Induction of the yeast α-specific *STE3* gene by the peptide pheromone **a**-factor. *J. Mol. Biol.* 178:835–52
39. Hamm, H. E., Deretic, D., Arendt, A., Hargrave, P. A., Koenig, B., Hofmann, K. P. 1988. Site of G protein binding to rhodopsin mapped with synthetic peptides from the alpha subunit. *Science* 241:832–35
40. Hancock, J. F., Magee, A. I., Childs, J. E., Marshall, C. J. 1989. All *ras* proteins are polyisoprenylated but only some are palmitoylated. *Cell* 57:1167–77
41. Hartig, A., Holly, J., Saari, G., MacKay, V. L. 1986. Multiple regulation of *STE2*, a mating-type specific gene of *Saccharomyces cerevisiae*. *Mol. Cell. Biol.* 6:2106–14
42. Hartwell, L. 1973. Synchronization of haploid yeast cells cycles, a prelude to conjugation. *Exp. Cell Res.* 76:111–17
43. Hartwell, L. 1980. Mutants of *Saccharomyces cerevisiae* unresponsive to cell division control by polypeptide mating hormone. *J. Cell Biol.* 85:811–22
44. Herskowitz, I. 1988. Life cycle of the budding yeast *Saccharomyces cerevisiae*. *Microbiol. Rev.* 52:536–53
45. Herskowitz, I. 1989. A regulatory hierarchy for cell specialization in yeast. *Nature* 342:749–57
46. Jackson, T. R. 1990. Cell surface receptors for nucleosides, nucleotides, amino acids, and amine neurotransmitters. *Curr. Opin. Cell Biol.* 2:167–73
47. Jahng, K.-Y., Ferguson, J., Reed, S. I. 1988. Mutations in a gene encoding the α subunit of a *Saccharomyces cerevisiae* G protein implicate a role in mating pheromone signaling. *Mol. Cell. Biol.* 8:2484–93
48. Janssens, P. M., van Haastert, P. J. 1987. Molecular basis of transmembrane signal transduction in *Dictyostelium discoideum*. *Microbiol. Rev.* 51:396–418
49. Jelsema, C. L., Axelrod, J. 1987. Stimulation of phospholipase A_2 activity in bovine rod outer segments by the $\beta\gamma$ subunits of transducin and its inhibition by the α subunit. *Proc. Natl. Acad. Sci. USA* 84:3623–27
50. Jenness, D. D., Burkholder, A. C., Hartwell, L. H. 1983. Binding of α-factor pheromone to yeast **a** cells: chemical and genetic evidence for an α-factor receptor. *Cell* 35:521–29
51. Jenness, D. D., Burkholder, A. C., Hartwell, L. H. 1986. Binding of α-factor pheromone to *Saccharomyces cerevisiae* **a** cells: dissociation constant and number of binding sites. *Mol. Cell. Biol.* 6:318–20
52. Jenness, D. D., Spatrick, P. 1986. Down-regulation of the α-factor pheromone receptor in *S. cerevisiae*. *Cell* 46:345–53
53. Julius, D., MacDermott, A., Axel, R., Jessell, T. 1988. Molecular characterization of a functional cDNA encoding the serotonin lc receptor. *Science* 241:558–64
54. Kang, Y.-S., Kane, J., Kurjan, J., Stadel, J. M., Tipper, D. J. 1990. Effect of expression of mammalian G_α and hybrid mammalian-yeast G_α proteins on the yeast pheromone response signal

transduction pathway. *Mol. Cell Biol.* 10:2582–90
55. Kim, D., Lewis, D. L., Graziadei, L., Neer, E., Bar-Sagi, D., Clapham, D. 1989. G protein $\beta\gamma$-subunits activate the cardiac muscarinic K^+-channel via phospholipase A_2. *Nature* 337:557–60
56. King, K., Dohlman, H. G., Thorner, J., Caron, M. G., Lefkowitz, R. J. 1990. Control of mating signal transduction in yeast by a mammalian β_2-adrenergic receptor and G protein α subunit. *Science*. In press
57. Kobilka, B. K., Kobilka, T. S., Daniel, K., Regan, J. W., Caron, M. G., Lefkowitz, R. J. 1988. Chimeric α_2-,β_2-adrenergic receptors: delineation of domains involved in effector coupling and ligand binding specificity. *Science* 240:1310–16
58. Kobilka, B. K., Matsui, H., Kobilka, T. S., Yang-Feng, T. L., Francke, U., et al. 1987. Cloning, sequencing, and expression of the gene coding for the human platelet α_2-adrenergic receptor. *Science* 238:650–56
59. Konopka, J. B., Jenness, D. D., Hartwell, L. H. 1988. The C-terminus of the *Saccharomyces cerevisiae* α-pheromone receptor mediates an adaptive response to pheromone. *Cell* 54:609–20
60. Kronstad, J. W., Holly, J. A., MacKay, V. L. 1987. A yeast operator overlaps an upstream activation site. *Cell* 50:369–77
61. Kubo, T., Fukuda, K., Mikami, A., Maeda, A., Takahashi, H., et al. 1986. Cloning, sequencing and expression of complementary DNA encoding the muscarinic acetylcholine receptor. *Nature* 323:411–16
62. Kühn, H., Hargrave, P. 1981. Light-induced binding of guanosine triphosphatase to bovine photoreceptor membranes. Effect of limited proteolysis of the membranes. *Biochemistry* 20:2410–17
63. Kurachi, Y., Ito, H., Sugimoto, T., Shimizu, T., Miki, I., Ui, M. 1989. Arachidonic acid metabolites as intracellular modulators of the G protein-gated cardiac K^+ channel. *Nature* 337:555–57
64. Kurjan, J., Dietzel, C. 1988. Analysis of the role of *SCG1*, a G_α homolog and *SST2* in pheromone response and desensitization in yeast. *Cold Spring Harbor Symp. Quant. Biol.* 53:577–84
65. Lipke, P. N., Taylor, A., Ballou, C. E. 1976. Morphogenetic effects of α-factor on *Saccharomyces cerevisiae* **a** cells. *J. Bacteriol.* 127:610–18
66. Logothetis, D. E., Kurachi, Y., Galper, J., Neer, E. J., Clapham, D. E. 1987. The $\beta\gamma$ subunits of GTP-binding proteins activate the muscarinic K^+ channel in heart. *Nature* 325:321–26
67. Lopes, M., Ho, J.-Y., Reed, S. I. 1990. Mutations in cell division cycle genes *CDC36* and *CDC39* activate the *Saccharomyces cerevisiae* mating-pheromone response pathway. *Mol. Cell. Biol.* 10:2966–72
68. MacKay, V., Manney, T. R. 1974. Mutations affecting sexual conjugation and related processes in *Saccharomyces cerevisiae*. I. Isolation and phenotypic characterization of non-mating mutants. *Genetics* 76:255–71
69. Marsh, L., Herskowitz, I. 1988. *STE2* protein of *Saccharomyces kluyveri* is a member of the rhodopsin/β-adrenergic receptor family and is responsible for recognition of the peptide ligand α-factor. *Proc. Natl. Acad. Sci. USA* 85:3855–59
70. Masu, Y., Nakayama, K., Tamaki, H., Harada, Y., Kuno, M., Nakanishi, S. 1987. cDNA cloning of bovine substance-K receptor through oocyte expression system. *Nature* 329:836–38
71. McCaffrey, G., Clay, F. J., Kelsay, K., Sprague, G. F. Jr. 1987. Identification and regulation of a gene required for cell fusion during mating of the yeast *Saccharomyces cerevisiae*. *Mol. Cell. Biol.* 7:2680–90
72. Miyajima, I., Arai, K.-I., Matsumoto, K. 1989. *GPA1*$^{\text{Val-50}}$ mutation in the mating-factor signaling pathway in *Saccharomyces cerevisiae*. *Mol. Cell. Biol.* 9:2289–97
73. Miyajima, I., Nakafuku, M., Nakayama, N., Brenner, C., Miyajima, A., et al. 1987. *GPA1*, a haploid-specific essential gene, encodes a yeast homology of mammalian G protein which may be involved in mating factor signal transduction. *Cell* 50:1011–19
74. Moehle, C. M., Tizard, R., Lemmon, S. K., Smart , J., Jones, E. W. 1987. A protease of the lysosome-like vacuole of the yeast *Saccharomyces cerevisiae* is homologous to the subtilisin family of serine proteases. *Mol. Cell Biol.* 7:4390–99
75. Nakafuku, M., Itoh, H., Nakamura, S., Kaziro, Y. 1987. Occurrence in *Saccharomyces cerevisiae* of a gene homologous to the cDNA coding from the α subunit of mammalian G proteins. *Proc. Natl. Acad. Sci. USA* 84:2140–44
76. Nakafuku, M., Obara, K., Kaibuchi, K., Miyajima, I., Miyajima, A., et al. 1988. Isolation of a second G protein homologous gene *(GPA2)* from *Sac-*

charomyces cerevisiae. *Proc. Natl. Acad. Sci. USA* 85:1374–78

77. Nakayama, N., Arai, K., Matsumoto, K. 1988. Role of *SGP2*, a suppressor of a *gpa1* mutation, in the mating factor signaling pathway mediated by *GPA1* in *Saccharomyces cerevisiae*. *Mol. Cell. Biol.* 8:5410–16
78. Nakayama, N., Kaziro, Y., Arai, K., Matsumoto, K. 1988. Role of *STE* genes in the mating factor signaling pathway mediated by *GPA1* in *Saccharomyces cerevisiae*. *Mol. Cell Biol.* 8:3777–83
79. Nakayama, N., Miyajima, A., Arai, K. 1985. Nucleotide sequences of *STE2* and *STE3*, cell type-specific sterile genes from *Saccharomyces cerevisiae*. *EMBO J.* 4:2643–48
80. Nakayama, N., Miyajima, A., Arai, K. 1987. Common signal transduction system shared by *STE2* and *STE3*, cell type-specific genes from *Saccharomyces cerevisiae:* autocrine cell-cyle arrest results from forced expression of *STE2*. *EMBO J.* 4:2643–48
81. Nasmyth, K., Shore, D. 1987. Transcriptional regulation in the yeast life cycle. *Science* 237:1162–70
82. Nathans, J., Hogness, D. S. 1984. Isolation and nucleotide sequence of the gene encoding human rhodopsin. *Proc. Natl. Acad. Sci. USA* 81:4851–55
83. Nathans, J., Thomas, D., Hogness, D. S. 1986. Molecular genetics of human color vision: the genes encoding blue, green, and red pigments. *Science* 232:193–202
84. Neer, E. J., Clapham, D. E. 1988. Roles of G protein subunits in transmembrane signalling. *Nature* 333:129–34
85. Neiman, A. M., Chang, F., Komachi, K., Herskowitz, I. 1990. *CDC36* and *CDC39* are negative elements in the signal transduction pathway of yeast. *Cell Reg.* 1:391–401
86. Nomoto, S., Nakayama, N., Arai, K., Matsumoto, K. 1990. Regulation of the yeast pheromone response pathway by G protein subunits. *EMBO J.* 19:691–96
87. O'Dowd, B. F., Hnatowich, M., Regan, J. W., Leader, W. M., Caron, M. G., Lefkowitz, R. J. 1988. Site-directed mutagenesis of the cytoplasmic domains of the human β_2-adrenergic receptor. Localization of regions involved in G protein-receptor coupling. *J. Biol. Chem.* 263:15985–92
88. Peterson, T. A., Yochem, J., Byers, B., Nunn, M. F., Duesberg, P. H., et al. 1984. A relationship between the yeast cell cycle genes *CDC4* and *CDC36* and the *ets* sequence of oncogenic virus E26. *Nature* 309:556–59
89. Reneke, J. E., Blumer, K. J., Courchesne, W. E., Thorner, J. 1988. The carboxyl-terminal segment of the yeast α-factor receptor is a regulatory domain. *Cell* 55:221–34
90. Rose, M. D., Price, B. R., Fink, G. R. 1986. *Saccharomyces cerevisiae* nuclear fusion requires prior activation by alpha-factor. *Mol. Cell. Biol.* 6:3490–97
91. Samokhin, G. P., Lizlova, L. V., Bespalova, J. D., Titov, M. I., Smirnov, V. N. 1980. The effect of α-factor on the rate of cell-cycle initiation in *Saccharomyces cerevisiae:* α-factor modulates transition probability in yeast. *Exp. Cell Res.* 131:267–75
92. Samokhin, G. P., Minin, A. A., Bespalova, J. D., Titov, M. I., Smirnov, V. N. 1981. Independent action of α-factor and cycloheximide on the rate of cell-cycle initiation in *Saccharomyces cerevisiae*. *FEMS Microbiol. Lett.* 10:185–88
93. Schafer, W. R., Kim, R., Sterne, R., Thorner, J., Kim, S.-H., Rine, J. 1989. Genetic and pharmacological suppression of oncogenic mutations in *ras* gene of yeast and humans. *Science* 245:379–85
94. Shichi, H., Somers, R. L. 1978. Light dependent phosphorylation of rhodopsin: purification and properties of rhodopsin kinase. *J. Biol. Chem.* 253: 7040–46
95. Sibley, D. R., Lefkowitz, R. J. 1985. Molecular mechanisms of receptor desensitization using the β-adrenergic receptor-coupled adenylate cyclase system as a model. *Nature* 317:124–129
96. Sibley, D. R., Benovic, J. L., Caron, M. G., Lefkowitz, R. J. 1987. Regulation of transmembrane signaling by receptor phosphorylation. *Cell* 48:913–22
97. Sprague, G. F. Jr., Herskowitz, I. 1981. Control of yeast cell type by the mating type locus. I. Identification and control of expression of the **a**-specific gene. *BARI*. *J. Mol. Biol.* 153:305–21
98. Stetler, G. L., Thorner, J. 1984. Molecular cloning of hormone responsive genes from the yeast *Saccharomyces cerevisiae*. *Proc. Natl. Acad. Sci. USA* 81:1144–48
99. Strader, C. D., Sigal, I. S., Dixon, R. A. F. 1989. Structural basis for β-adrenergic receptor function. *FASEB J.* 3:1825–32
100. Stryer, L., Bourne, H. R. 1986. G proteins: a family of signal transducers. *Annu. Rev. Cell Biol.* 2:391–419

101. Toro, M. J., Montoya, E., Birnbaumer, L. 1987. Inhibitory regulation of adenylyl cyclase. Evidence inconsistent with $\beta\gamma$ complexes of G_i proteins mediating hormonal effects by interfering with activation of G_s. *Mol. Endocrinol.* 1:669–676
102. Towler, D. A., Gordon, J. I., Adams, S. P., Glaser, L. 1988. The biology and enzymology of eukaryotic protein acylation. *Annu. Rev. Biochem.* 57:69–99
103. Trueheart, J., Boeke, J. D., Fink, G. R. 1987. Two genes required for cell fusion during yeast conjugation: evidence for a pheromone-induced surface protein. *Mol. Cell. Biol.* 7:2316–28
104. Van Arsdell, S. W., Stetler, G. L., Thorner, J. 1987. The yeast repeated element sigma contains a hormone-inducible promoter. *Mol. Cell. Biol.* 7:749–59
105. Whiteway, M., Hougan, L., Thomas, D. Y. 1990. Overexpression of the *STE4* gene leads to mating response in haploid *Saccharomyces cerevisiae*. *Mol. Cell. Biol.* 10:217–22
106. Whiteway, M., Hougan, L., Dignard, D., Thomas, D. Y., Bell, L., et al. 1989. The *STE4* and *STE18* genes of yeast encode potential β and γ subunits of the mating factor-coupled G protein. *Cell* 56:467–77
107. Wilden, U., Hall, S. W., Kühn, H. 1986. Phosphodiesterase activation by photoexcited rhodopsin is quenched when rhodopsin is phosphorylated and binds the intrinsic 48-kDa protein of rod outer segments. *Proc. Natl. Acad. Sci. USA* 83:1174–78
108. Wilden, U., Kühn, H. 1982. Light-dependent phosphorylation of rhodopsin: Number of phosphorylation sites. *Biochemistry* 21:3014–22
109. Yu, L., Blumer, K. J., Davidson, N., Lester, H. A., Thorner, J. 1989. Functional expression of the yeast α-factor receptor in *Xenopus* oocytes. *J. Biol. Chem.* 264:20847–50

Annu. Rev. Physiol. 1991. 53:59–70

ADAPTATIONS TO HYPOXIA IN BIRDS: HOW TO FLY HIGH

Frank M. Faraci

Department of Internal Medicine, The Cardiovascular Center, University of Iowa College of Medicine, Iowa City, Iowa 52242

KEY WORDS: cerebral circulation, hypocapnia, gas exchange, hemoglobin

INTRODUCTION

Birds are generally more tolerant than mammals to hypoxia. For example, at an altitude of 6,100 m, house sparrows *(Passer domesticus)* are alert and active and exhibit normal behavior (74). In contrast, mice exposed to the same altitude are comatose (74). Bar-headed geese *(Anser indicus)* normally migrate over the Himalayan mountains and have been sighted flying over the summit of Mt. Everest (8848 m) (72, 73). These birds may begin their migration near sea level and reach altitudes near 9,000 m in less than one day, allowing essentially no time for acclimatization.

Active flight in birds requires more energy than any other form of exercise in vertebrates of similar size (6). It is known from studies of freely flying birds in wind tunnels that oxygen consumption may increase 15-fold during flapping flight (6). How do species such as bar-headed geese maintain adequate oxygen transport while performing such vigorous exercise during severe hypoxia?

In recent years, a number of studies have provided insight into physiologic mechanisms that appear to contribute to the exceptional tolerance of birds to hypoxia. This review will address adaptations in oxygen transport in birds including (*a*) gas exchange efficiency of the lung, (*b*) oxygen-binding affinity of hemoglobin, (*c*) regulation of cardiac output and regional oxygen delivery, (*d*) unique aspects of cerebral vascular regulation, and (*e*) adaptations at the level of individual tissues.

0066-4278/91/0315-0059$02.00

RESPIRATORY SYSTEM

In birds the crosscurrent arrangement of gas and blood flow makes the lung inherently more efficient than the alveolar lung of mammals (64, 67). When exposed to severe hypoxia, birds such as the Pekin duck *(Anas platyrhynchos)* and bar-headed goose respond with pronounced hyperventilation, which can decrease arterial P_{CO_2} to less than 10 mmHg (9, 26, 68, 69). The combination of the increase in ventilation and the efficiency of gas exchange in the lung reduces the oxygen partial pressure difference between the inspired gas and arterial blood, which is approximately 50 mmHg during normoxia (9, 26, 52, 69, 78). During severe hypoxia, the difference between inspired and arterial P_{O_2} is only a few mmHg, which indicates that the gas exchange parabronchi are exposed to essentially fresh inspired gas (9, 26, 69). Under these conditions ventilation is not a limitation for gas exchange, but diffusion becomes a potentially important limiting factor for movement of oxygen from the air to blood capillaries. The gas-blood barrier, however, is much thinner in birds, and the lung membrane diffusing capacity is much greater than in mammals of similar body mass (21, 54, 55).

Quantitative analysis of gas exchange in resting ducks has been performed in order to estimate the factors that may limit gas exchange during severe hypoxia and to compare performance of the avian and mammalian lungs (69). This analysis suggests that perfusion is the main limitation to gas exchange during severe hypoxia in birds. Although it is clear that cardiac output increases during hypoxia (23, 69), it is possible that maximal levels of cardiac output are reached, or that hypoxia has an inhibitory effect on cardiac performance, which limits the extent of cardiac output.

The quantitative analysis of Shams & Scheid (69) and measurements of arterial blood gases in a number of other studies (9, 26, 69) indicate that for a given inspired P_{O_2}, the arterial P_{O_2} will be higher in a bird than in a mammal. For example, at an inspired P_{O_2} of 49 mmHg (equivalent to approximately 8000 m), the greater arterial P_{O_2} in birds than in mammals is equivalent to a gain in altitude for the bird of about 1000 m (69). It is important to recall that, because of the steepness of the oxyhemoglobin dissociation curve during hypoxia, small differences in P_{O_2} can result in large differences in hemoglobin oxygen saturation and, therefore, large differences in arterial oxygen content.

Due to major technical limitations, very little is known about gas exchange during hypoxia in flying birds. Berger (3) observed an increase in oxygen extraction of the lung during hovering at 4000 m in the hummingbird *Colibri coruscans*. Additional limited data exist for running birds during moderate hypoxia. Running exercise produces an increase in arterial P_{O_2} from 31 to 37 mmHg in bar-headed geese breathing 7% O_2 (inspired P_{O_2} of 48 mmHg) (28). Because this change occurs along the steep portion of the oxyhemoglobin dissociation curve, the 6 mmHg increase in arterial P_{O_2} increased the oxygen content of arterial blood by 32% (28).

Quantitative analysis of the available data suggests that exercise increases the oxygen-diffusing capacity and the total conductance of oxygen in the lung (47). It should be noted that a number of assumptions are made in calculating oxygen-diffusing capacity and that the accuracy of the estimate of diffusing capacity is not certain, particularly during normoxia (11, 39, 69). The mechanisms that produce this apparent increase in gas exchange efficiency are unknown, but they may involve a decrease in inequality of ventilation-perfusion (39). Changes in oxygen-diffusing capacity are important because this variable is a major determinant of maximal oxygen uptake (11, 79).

In addition to reduced oxygen tension, gas exchange may be affected by the extreme cold at high altitude. For example, a flock of swans, probably Whooper swans *(Cygnus cygnus)*, were sighted flying at 8,200 m where the ambient temperature was −48°C (22). Extreme cold, in itself, increases efficiency of gas exchange in the avian lung by a mechanism that may involve a decrease in ventilatory shunt, or an increase in oxygen-diffusing capacity (2, 42).

BLOOD OXYGEN TRANSPORT

A major determinant of oxygen transfer from the lung to individual cells is the oxygen-binding property of hemoglobin. Species that are well-adapted to high altitude, such as the bar-headed goose and the Andean goose *(Cheophaga melatoptera)*, which may reside permanently at 6000 m, possess hemoglobin with a relatively high oxygen affinity (10, 36, 40, 63). The affinity of hemoglobin for oxygen can be expressed as the oxygen partial pressure at which hemoglobin is 50% saturated (P_{50}). The P_{50} value of the blood of the vulture *Gyps rueppellii*, which has been reported flying at approximately 11,300 m (50), and of *Aegypius monachus* is very low (16.4 mmHg and 21.3 mmHg, respectively) (77).

During severe hypoxia, the low P_{50} observed in birds that are adapted to high altitude is clearly an advantage for oxygen transport. For example, at arterial P_{O_2} levels of approximately 30 mmHg, blood of the bar-headed goose (P_{50} = 27.2 mmHg) carries two and one half times more oxygen than blood of the Pekin duck (P_{50} = 42.6 mmHg) (10, 26). As in birds, mammals, such as the vicuna *(Lama vicugna)*, that are adapted to life at high altitude have a very high hemoglobin oxygen affinity (P_{50} = 17.6) (45).

In addition to the intrinsic oxygen affinity characteristics of the hemoglobin molecule, additional factors that modulate the position of the oxyhemoglobin dissociation curve are also important during hypoxia. The marked decrease in arterial P_{CO_2} and increase in arterial pH that occur because of increased ventilation are advantageous because respiratory alkalosis decreases the P_{50}, thereby increasing the affinity for oxygen. Arterial pH may increase to 7.7 and 7.85 during severe, acute hypoxia in bar-headed geese and pigeons *(Columba livia)*, respectively (26, 52).

Body temperature also affects the position of the oxyhemoglobin dissociation curve. Body temperature of resting birds is relatively well-maintained during normoxia (1, 2, 12, 15), but decreases in hypoxic birds during cold exposure (1, 5). A decrease in blood temperature of a few degrees significantly increases the affinity of hemoglobin for oxygen (53, 65). It is not known whether flight at extreme altitude is associated with a change in body temperature.

In summary, the oxygen affinity characteristics of the hemoglobin molecule appear to be one of the most important factors enabling high altitude adapted species to transport an adequate supply of oxygen during severe hypoxia.

CARDIOVASCULAR SYSTEM

The cardiovascular system of birds appears to be well-adapted to provide the convective transport of oxygen. Birds have larger hearts and a larger stroke volume when compared with mammals of similar body mass (31, 37). Although the resting heart rate is lower, cardiac output is greater than that in mammals (31). The greater size of the avian heart suggests that it can produce large increases in cardiac output during hypoxia or exercise.

Cardiac output in birds increases during hypoxia at rest (23, 69) and, based on limited data, increases in cardiac output of six to sevenfold can occur during exercise (18, 34). To what extent cardiac output increases in flying birds during hypoxia is not known. Because inadequate lung perfusion may limit gas exchange during severe hypoxia (69), the level of maximal cardiac output may limit the altitude at which a bird can fly.

During hypoxia at rest in birds such as Pekin ducks, blood flow is distributed away from organs, such as nonrespiratory muscle, the gastrointestinal tract, and spleen, and toward organs that are critically dependent on oxygen, such as the heart and brain (27). A similar pattern of blood flow redistribution has been described during hypoxia in mammals (11, 59). Marked increases in blood flow to the adrenal gland have also been observed in birds (27). These changes in adrenal blood flow may support increased secretion of catecholamines in response to hypoxia.

In the bar-headed goose, which maintains a much higher arterial oxygen content during severe hypoxia than the Pekin duck (9, 26), a less marked redistribution of blood flow is seen, and regional oxygen delivery to tissue such as skeletal muscle is maintained at normoxic levels (27).

Relatively little is known about changes in blood flow to working skeletal muscle in exercising birds. In normoxic tufted ducks *(Aythya fuligula)*, swimming increases blood flow to exercising muscle and the heart, while blood flow to nonexercising muscle and portions of the digestive system decrease (17). Blood flow to the brain was not affected by exercise (17).

CEREBRAL CIRCULATION

In mammals a reduction in arterial P_{O_2} below approximately 50 mmHg produces dilatation of cerebral blood vessels and an increase in cerebral blood flow (24, 49). Increases in cerebral blood flow are of sufficient magnitude to maintain oxygen delivery to the brain at normal levels, despite the reduced arterial oxygen content, during isocapnic hypoxia (44, 49). Studies of the duck suggest that the cerebral circulation of birds is very sensitive to decreases in arterial P_{O_2} because cerebral blood flow begins to increase when arterial P_{O_2} falls below approximately 75 mmHg and can increase up to sixfold during severe hypoxia (32).

A major limiting factor for mammals in the tolerance of hypoxia relates to regulation of cerebral blood flow. Reductions in inspired P_{O_2} at high altitude produce hyperventilation, which lowers arterial P_{CO_2}. During normoxia in mammals, hypocapnia constricts cerebral blood vessels (24, 83). For example, reducing arterial P_{CO_2} to 10 mmHg in humans decreases cerebral blood flow by approximately 50% (Figure 1). This powerful constrictor effect of hypocapnia attenuates increases in cerebral blood flow caused by hypoxia. If the level of hypocapnia is severe enough, as occurs at the highest altitudes, potential increases in cerebral blood flow resulting from hypoxia can be totally abolished (20). Thus oxygen delivery to the brain during hypocapnic hypoxia in mammals is below levels seen during normoxia (56, 59).

What is the functional consequence of decreases in cerebral oxygen delivery during hypocapnic hypoxia? Recent studies by Hornbein et al (41) suggest that decreases in oxygen delivery to the brain during ascent to extreme altitudes in humans produce a variety of long-term neurological impairments. In humans with acute mountain sickness at altitudes of 3400–5400 m, inhalation of 3% CO_2 increased cerebral blood flow by about 25% (38). This improvement in oxygen delivery to the brain was associated with prompt relief of symptoms such as headache, nausea, and ataxia.

In contrast to mammals, reducing arterial P_{CO_2} during normoxia in several species of birds does not decrease cerebral blood flow (25, 35, 82). For example, decreases in arterial P_{CO_2} to less than 10 mmHg in conscious bar-headed geese does not alter cerebral blood flow (Figure 1). The mechanism that accounts for the reduced sensitivity of avian cerebral vessels to hypocapnia is not clear. Hypercapnia increases cerebral blood flow in the

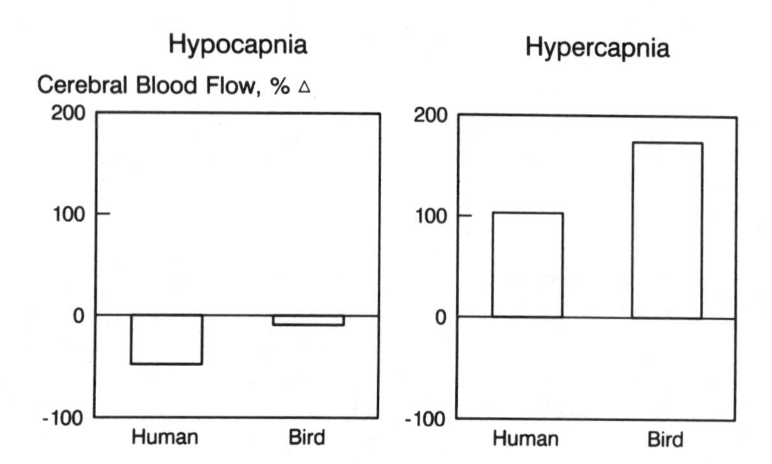

Figure 1 Changes in cerebral blood flow during severe hypocapnia and hypercapnia. Data represent the average change in cerebral blood flow during decreases in arterial P_{CO_2} to 10 mmHg in man (83) and less than 10 mmHg in geese (25). During hypercapnia, arterial P_{CO_2} was increased to 55 mmHg in geese (25). The change in blood flow in man is the predicted response based on the sensitivity of cerebral blood vessels in humans to the same increase in arterial P_{CO_2} (46, 60).

bar-headed goose (Figure 1) and other birds (35, 62), which indicates that cerebral blood vessels in birds are sensitive to changes in carbon dioxide. In fact, responses to increases in arterial P_{CO_2} tend to be greater in birds than in mammals (Figure 1) (35).

Because hypocapnia does not constrict cerebral vessels, marked increases in cerebral blood flow occur during severe hypoxia in birds in the presence of severe hypocapnia (26, 33). As a consequence, cerebral oxygen delivery is maintained at normal levels or may even increase during severe hypocapnic hypoxia (26).

The ability of birds to maintain oxygen delivery to the brain represents a unique regulatory mechanism that may contribute to the exceptional tolerance of some birds to extreme altitude. The lack of constriction of cerebral vessels during hypocapnia may also explain why birds are exceptionally tolerant of extreme hypocapnia and alkalosis during panting in response to thermal stress (19).

In contrast to these findings, a recent study of Muscovy ducks *(Carina moschata)* by Bickler et al (8) suggested that the cerebral circulation of birds does not exhibit unique regulatory mechanisms during hypocapnic hypoxia. This conclusion was based on data that suggested that cerebral blood flow decreased significantly during hypocapnia under normoxic or hypoxic conditions.

Bickler et al (8) measured cerebral blood volume (which was assumed to be an index of blood flow) using a reflectometric method in anesthetized ducks. Grubb et al (35) measured cerebral blood flow in unanesthetized birds, and their findings in ducks during changes in arterial P_{CO_2} have now been confirmed, by the microsphere method (25, 82), in two other species, including conscious bar-headed geese. In addition, the initial report of increases in cerebral blood flow during hypoxia and the ability of ducks to maintain oxygen delivery to the brain during hypocapnic hypoxia (33) were also confirmed in a later study of conscious ducks using microspheres (26). Thus methodological differences may account for these discrepant findings.

Based on measurements of brain redox balance during hypoxia and hypocapnia, Bickler et al (8) suggested that tolerance of brain tissue to hypoxia may be an important adaptation in those birds that tolerate severe hypoxia. These findings, however, differ from another study that examined changes in the redox state and cerebral tissue P_{O_2} in ducks and chickens during hypoxia (13). Biochemical evidence obtained in these two birds indicated that the duck, which is clearly more tolerant of hypoxia than the chicken, was not more resistant to cerebral tissue hypoxia. Tolerance of hypoxia in ducks appears to result from differences in cerebral vascular responses and better maintenance of brain P_{O_2} (13, 14).

Although the findings of all studies are not in agreement, the majority of the available evidence suggests that unique responses of the cerebral circulation to hypocapnia and hypoxia are present in birds. These findings do not exclude the possibility that biochemical adaptations in brain tissue are also present in some species.

Birds possess an extracranial network of arteries and veins located near the eye known as the rete opthalmicum. This structure functions as a site of countercurrent heat exchange, which is important in regulation of brain and eye temperature (48, 58). Bernstein et al (4, 7) have provided several lines of evidence that suggest that the rete may also function as a site of gas exchange where arterial blood passing through the rete exchanges oxygen with venous blood, which has a greater P_{O_2} than arterial blood after perfusing the highly vascular eye and upper airways. It has been proposed that arterial blood leaving the rete and flowing to the brain has a higher P_{O_2} than systemic arterial blood. Such a mechanism may provide enhanced oxygen delivery to the brain during hypoxia.

CELLULAR ADAPTATIONS

Additional adaptations that may benefit oxygen transport during hypoxia occur at the level of individual tissues. One such specialization involves the density of capillaries. In skeletal muscle, cardiac muscle, and in brain tissue, capillary density appears to be greater in birds than in mammals (29, 51, 57, 66, 71). Increases in capillary density decrease the distance for diffusion of oxygen and provide the potential for high rates of oxygen extraction. In addition, capillary density in skeletal muscle can increase in response to exercise or chronic hypoxia (17, 70).

Another adaptation that may influence the performance of muscle is the number or relative density of mitochondria and the activity of aerobic enzymes. The density of mitochondria in cardiac muscle of ducks appears to be greater than in mammals (75). The aerobic enzyme activity in pectoral muscle in flying species, such as the tufted duck, is high relative to other vertebrates (75). In addition, the activity of the oxidative enzyme citrate synthase is increased further by physical conditioning (16). Thus avian muscle has a high oxidative capacity that can support the high oxygen demand of flight.

A major determinant of oxygen transport at the cellular level in muscle is the intracellular concentration of myoglobin (81). Myoglobin has an extremely high affinity for oxygen. For example, the P_{50} for myoglobin in the pectoral muscle of the hummingbird *Melanotrochilus fuscus* is 2.5 mmHg (43). Myoglobin appears to play an important role in facilitating the diffusion of oxygen through the cell (81), and the majority of oxygen that is consumed in cardiac and red skeletal muscle is transported to mitochondria by myoglobin (81). Substantial levels of myoglobin are present in the heart and skeletal muscle of some birds (30, 43, 61, 76). This concentration of myoglobin is increased with physical conditioning (16).

CONCLUSIONS

It was once thought that humans could not reach the summit of Mt. Everest without supplemental oxygen. In recent years, a few individuals have accomplished this feat, but they do so with great difficulty and are at the limit of human performance (79, 80). In contrast, birds, in general, tolerate severe hypoxia very well, and some species perform the vigorous exercise of flight at this and even greater altitudes.

Recent studies have provided insight into a number of mechanisms that provide adequate transport of oxygen under such conditions. A major adaptation in birds is their ability to tolerate extreme hypocapnia. This ability appears to be related to unique aspects of regulation of the cerebral circulation and oxygen delivery to the brain. Other important adaptive mechanisms involve gas exchange efficiency of the lung, oxygen-binding properties of

Table 1 Physiological adaptations in birds to hypoxia

Adaptations
Respiratory
Cross-current lung
Marked ventilatory response to hypoxia
Thinness of blood-gas barrier
High lung-membrane diffusing capacity
Blood O_2 transport
High hemoglobin-oxygen affinity
Reduced P_{50} in response to marked respiratory alkalosis
Cerebral vascular
Minimal vasoconstrictor effect of hypocapnia
Marked vasodilatation during hypoxia
Maintenance of cerebral oxygen delivery
Cellular
High capillary density in muscle and brain

hemoglobin, enhanced cardiovascular performance, and cellular adaptations (Table 1).

Our understanding of these adaptations is restricted mostly to data obtained in resting birds. Available information on exercising birds was either obtained during normoxia or in moderately hypoxic birds performing running exercise. The challenge of understanding the physiology of freely flying birds at extreme altitudes is still to be met.

ACKNOWLEDGMENTS

The author thanks Drs. D. D. Heistad and M. R. Fedde for critical evaluation of the manuscript. The author was supported by National Institutes of Health grants HL-38901 and NS-24621 during preparation of this review.

Literature Cited

1. Barnas, G. M., Rautenberg, W. 1990. Shivering and cardiorespiratory responses during normocapnic hypoxia in the pigeon. *J. Appl. Physiol.* 68:84–87
2. Bech, C., Johansen, K., Brent, R., Nicol, S. 1985. Ventilatory and circulatory changes during cold exposure in the Pekin duck *Anas platyrhynchos*. *Respir. Physiol.* 57:103–12
3. Berger, M. 1978. Ventilation in the hummingbirds *Colibri coruscans* during altitude hovering. In *Respiratory Function in Birds, Adult and Embryonic*, ed. J. Piiper, pp. 85–88. Berlin: Springer-Verlag
4. Bernstein, M. H. 1989. Temperature and oxygen supply in the avian brain. In *Comparative Pulmonary Physiology*, ed. S. C. Wood, pp. 343–368. New York: Dekker
5. Bernstein, M. H. 1989. Body and brain temperatures in pigeons at simulated

high altitudes. In *Physiology of Cold Adaptation in Birds,* ed. C. Bech, R. E. Reinertsen, pp. 207–210. New York: Plenum

6. Bernstein, M. H. 1989. Respiration by birds at high altitude and in flight. See Ref. 5, pp. 197–206
7. Bernstein, M. H., Duran, H. L., Pinshow, B. 1984. Extrapulmonary gas exchange enhances brain oxygen in pigeons. *Science* 226:564–66
8. Bickler, P. E., Koh, S. O., Severinghaus, J. W. 1989. Effects of hypoxia and hypocapnia on brain redox balance in ducks. *Am. J. Physiol.* 257:R132–35
9. Black, C. P., Tenney, S. M. 1980. Oxygen transport during progressive hypoxia in high-altitude and sea level waterflow. *Respir. Physiol.* 39:217–39
10. Black, C. P., Tenney, S. M., Van Kroonenburg, M. 1978. Oxygen transport during progressive hypoxia in bar-headed geese *(Anser indicus)* acclimatized to sea level and 5600 meters. In *Respiratory Function in Birds, Adult and Embryonic,* ed. J. Piiper, pp. 79–83. Berlin: Springer-Verlag
11. Bouverot, P. 1985. *Adaptation to Altitude—Hypoxia in Vertebrates.* Berlin: Springer-Verlag
12. Brent, R., Pedersen, P. F., Bech, C., Johansen, K. 1985. Thermal balance in the European Coot *Fulica atra* exposed to temperatures from −28 to 40°C. *Ornis Scand.* 16:145–160
13. Bryan, R. M., Jones, D. R. 1980. Cerebral energy metabolism in diving and nondiving birds during hypoxia and apnoeic asphyxia. *J. Physiol.* 299:323–36
14. Bryan, R. M., Jones, D. R. 1980. Cerebral energy metabolism in mallard ducks during apneic asphyxia: the role of oxygen conservation. *Am. J. Physiol.* 239:R352–57
15. Bucher, T. L., Morgan, K. R. 1989. The effect of ambient temperature on the relationship between ventilation and metabolism in a small parrot *(Agapornis roseicollis). J. Comp. Physiol.* B159: 561–67
16. Butler, P. J., Turner, D. L. 1988. Effect of training on maximal oxygen uptake and aerobic capacity of locomotory muscles in tufted ducks, *Aythya fuligula. J. Physiol.* 401:347–59
17. Butler, P. J., Turner, D. L., Al-Wassia, A., Bevan, R. M. 1988. Regional distribution of blood flow during swimming in the tufted duck *(Aythya fuligula). J. Exp. Biol.* 135:461–72
18. Butler, P. J., West, N. H., Jones, D. R. 1977. Respiratory and cardiovascular responses of the pigeon to sustained, level flight in a wind tunnel. *J. Exp. Biol.* 71:7–26
19. Calder, W. A., Schmidt-Nielsen, K. 1968. Panting and blood carbon dioxide in birds. *Am. J. Physiol.* 215:477–82
20. Davies, D. G., Nolan, W. F., Sexton, J. A. 1986. Effect of hypocapnia on ventral medullary blood flow and pH during hypoxia in cats. *J. Appl. Physiol.* 61:87–90
21. Dubach, M. 1981. Quantitative analysis of the respiratory system of the house sparrow, budgerigar, and violet-eared hummingbird. *Respir. Physiol.* 46:43–60
22. Elkins, N. 1983. *Weather and Bird Behaviour,* Calton, England: Poyser
23. Faraci, F. M. 1986. Circulation during hypoxia in birds. *Comp. Biochem. Physiol.* 85A:613–20
24. Faraci, F. M. 1990. Cerebral circulation during hypoxia: Is a bird brain better? In *Hypoxia: The Adaptations,* ed. J. R. Sutton, G. Coates, J. E. Remmers, pp. 26–29. Philadelphia: Decker
25. Faraci, F. M., Fedde, M. R. 1986. Regional circulatory responses to hypocapnia and hypercapnia in bar-headed geese. *Am. J. Physiol.* 250:R499–R504
26. Faraci, F. M., Kilgore, D. L., Fedde, M. R. 1984. Oxygen delivery to the heart and brain during hypoxia: Pekin duck vs bar-headed goose. *Am. J. Physiol.* 247:R69–74
27. Faraci, F. M., Kilgore, D. L., Fedde, M. R. 1985. Blood flow distribution during hypocapnic hypoxia in Pekin ducks and bar-headed geese. *Respir. Physiol.* 61:21–30
28. Fedde, M. R., Orr, J. A., Shams, H., Scheid, P. 1989. Cardiopulmonary function in exercising bar-headed geese during normoxia and hypoxia. *Respir. Physiol.* 77:239–262
29. Folkow, B., Fuxe, K., Sonnenschein, R. R. 1966. Responses of skeletal musculature and its vasculature during "diving" in the duck: peculiarities of the adrenergic vasoconstrictor innervation. *Acta Physiol. Scand.* 67:327–42
30. Giardina, B., Corda, M., Pellegrini, M. G., Condo, S. G., Brunori, M. 1985. Functional properties of the hemoglobin system of two diving birds *(Podiceps nigricollis* and *Phalacrocorax carbo sinensis). Molec. Physiol.* 7:281–92
31. Grubb, B. 1983. Allometric relations of cardiovascular function in birds. *Am. J. Physiol.* 245:H567–72
32. Grubb, B., Colacino, J. M., Schmidt-Nielsen, K. 1978. Cerebral blood flow

in birds: effect of hypoxia. *Am. J. Physiol.* 234:H230–34
33. Grubb, B., Jones, J. H., Schmidt-Nielsen, K. 1979. Avian cerebral blood flow: influence of the Bohr effect on oxygen supply. *Am. J. Physiol.* 236: H744–49
34. Grubb, B., Jorgensen, D. D., Conner, M. 1983. Cardiovascular changes in the exercising emu. *J. Exp. Biol.* 104:193–201
35. Grubb, B., Mills, C. D., Colacino, J. M., Schmidt-Nielsen, K. 1977. Effect of arterial carbon dioxide on cerebral blood flow in ducks. *Am. J. Physiol.* 232:H596–H601
36. Hall, F. G., Dill, D. B., Barron, E. S. G. 1936. Comparative physiology in high altitudes. *J. Cell Comp. Physiol.* 8:301–13
37. Hartman, F. A. 1955. Heart weight in birds. *Condor* 57:221–38
38. Harvey, T. C., Raichle, M. E., Winterborn, M. H., Jensen, J., Lassen, N. A., et al. 1988. Effect of carbon dioxide in acute mountain sickness: a rediscovery. *Lancet* 8612:639–41
39. Hempleman S. C., Powell, F. L. 1986. Influence of pulmonary blood flow and O_2 flux on CO_2 in avian lungs. *Respir. Physiol.* 63:285–92
40. Hiebl, I., Braunitzer, G., Schneeganss, D. 1987. The primary structures of the major and minor hemoglobin-components of adult Andean goose *(Chloephaga melanoptera*, Anatidae): the mutation Leu-Ser in position 55 of the beta-chains. *Biol. Chem. Hoppe-Seyler* 368:1559–69
41. Hornbein, T. F., Townes, B. D., Schoene, R. B., Sutton, J. R., Houston, C. S. 1989. The cost to the central nervous system of climbing to extremely high altitude. *New Engl. J. Med.* 321:1714–19
42. Johansen, K., Bech, C. 1983. Heat conservation during cold exposure in birds (vasomotor and respiratory implications). *Polar Res.* 1:259–68
43. Johansen, K., Berger, M., Bicudo, J. E. P. W., Ruschi, A., De Almeida, P. J. 1987. Respiratory properties of blood and myoglobin in hummingbirds. *Physiol. Zool.* 60:269–78
44. Jones, M. D., Traystman, R. J., Simmons, M. A., Molteni, R. A. 1981. Effects of changes in arterial O_2 content on cerebral blood flow in the lamb. *Am. J. Physiol.* 240:H209–15
45. Jurgens, K. D., Pietschmann, M., Yamaguchi, K., Kleinschmidt, T. 1988. Oxygen binding properties, capillary densities and heart weights in high altitude camelids. *J. Comp. Physiol.* B 158:469–77
46. Kety, S. S., Schmidt, C. F. 1948. The effects of altered arterial tensions of carbon dioxide and oxygen on cerebral blood flow and cerebral oxygen consumption of normal young men. *J. Clin. Invest.* 27:484–92
47. Kiley, J. P., Faraci, F. M., Fedde, M. R. 1985. Gas exchange during exercise in hypoxic ducks. *Respir. Physiol.* 59:105–15
48. Kilgore, D. L., Boggs, D. F., Birchard, G. F. 1979. Role of the rete mirable ophthalmicum in maintaining the body-to-brain temperature differences in pigeons. *J. Comp. Physiol.* B129:119–22
49. Koehler, R. C., Traystman, R. J., Jones, M. D. 1986. Influence of reduced oxyhemoglobin affinity on cerebrovascular response to hypoxia. *Am. J. Physiol.* 251:H756–63
50. Laybourne, R. C. 1974. Collision between a vulture and an aircraft at an altitude of 37,000 feet. *Wilson Bull.* 86:461–62
51. Lierse, V. W. 1963. Die Kappillardichte im wirbeltiergehirn. *Acta Anat.* 54:1–31
52. Lutz, P. L., Schmidt-Nielsen, K. 1977. Effect of simulated altitude on blood gas transport in the pigeon. *Respir. Physiol.* 30:383–88
53. Maginniss, L. A. 1985. Blood oxygen transport in the house sparrow, *Passer domesticus*. *J. Comp. Physiol.* B155: 277–83
54. Maina, J. N., King, A. S. 1982. Morphometrics of the avian lung. 2. The wild mallard *(Anas platyrhynchos)* and graylag goose *(Anser anser)*. *Respir. Physiol.* 50:299–310
55. Maina, J. N., King, A. S. 1982. The thickness of the avian blood-gas barrier: qualitative and quantitative observations. *J. Anat.* 134:553–62
56. Manohar, M., Parks, C. M., Busch, M., Bisgard, G. E. 1984. Bovine regional brain blood flow during sojourn at a simulated altitude of 3,500 m. *Respir. Physiol.* 58:111–22
57. Mathieu-Costello, O. 1990. Histology of flight: Tissue and muscle gas exchange. In *Hypoxia: The Adaptations*, ed. J. R. Sutton, G. Coates, J. E. Remmers, pp. 13–19. Philadelphia: Decker
58. Midtgard, U. 1983. Scaling of the brain and the eye cooling system in birds: A morphometric analysis of the rete ophthalmicum. *J. Exp. Zool.* 225:197–207
59. Nesarajah, M. S., Matalon, S., Krasney, J. A., Farhi, L. E. 1983. Cardiac

output and regional oxygen transport in the acutely hypoxic conscious sheep. *Respir. Physiol.* 53:161–72
60. Olesen, J., Paulson, O. B., Lassen, N. A. 1971. Regional cerebral blood flow in man determined by the initial slope of the clearance of intra-arterially injected ^{133}Xe. *Stroke* 2:519–40
61. Pages, T., Planas, J. 1983. Muscle myoglobin and flying habits in birds. *Comp. Biochem. Physiol.* 74A:289–94
62. Pavlov, N. A., Krivchenko, A. I., Cherepivskaya, E. N., Zagvazdin, Y. S., Zayats, N. D. 1987. Reactivity of cerebral vessels in the pigeon. *J. Evol. Biochem. Physiol.* 23:447–51
63. Petschow, D., Wurdinger, I., Baumann, R., Duhm, J., Braunitzer, G., Bauer, C. 1977. Causes of high blood O_2 affinity of animals at high altitude. *J. Appl. Physiol.* 42:139–43
64. Piiper, J. 1989. Gas-exchange efficiency of fish gills and bird lungs. In *Physiological Functions in Special Environments*, ed. C. V. Paganelli, L. E. Farhi, pp. 159–171. New York: Springer-Verlag
65. Pinshow, B., Bernstein, M. H., Arad, Z. 1985. Effects of temperature and P_{CO_2} on O_2 affinity of pigeon blood: implications for brain O_2 supply. *Am. J. Physiol.* 249:R758–64
66. Rakusan, K., Ost'adal, B., Wachtlova, M. 1971. The influence of muscular work on the capillary density in the heart and skeletal muscle of pigeon *(Columbia livia). Can. J. Physiol. Pharmacol.* 49:167–70
67. Scheid, P. 1979. Mechanisms of gas exchange in bird lungs. *Rev. Physiol. Biochem. Pharmacol.* 86:137–86
68. Shams, H., Scheid, P. 1987. Respiration and blood gases in the duck exposed to normocapnic and hypercapnic hypoxia. *Respir. Physiol.* 67:1–12
69. Shams, H., Scheid, P. 1989. Efficiency of parabronchial gas exchange in deep hypoxia: measurements in the resting duck. *Respir. Physiol.* 77:135–46
70. Snyder, G. K., Byers, R. L., Kayar, S. R. 1984. Effects of hypoxia on tissue capillarity in geese. *Respir. Physiol.* 58:151–60
71. Stoeckenius, M. 1963. Die Kapillarisierung verschiedener Vogelgehirne. *Gegenbaurs Morphol. Jahrb.* 105:343–364
72. Swan, L. W. 1961. The ecology of the high Himalayas. *Sci. Am.* 205:68–78
73. Swan, L. W. 1970. Goose of the Himalayas. *Nat. Hist.* 79:68–75
74. Tucker, V. A. 1968. Respiratory physiology of house sparrows in relation to high altitude flight. *J. Exp. Biol.* 48:55–66
75. Turner, D. L., Butler, P. J. 1988. The aerobic capacity of locomotory muscles in the tufted duck. *J. Exp. Biol.* 135: 445–60
76. Weber, R. E., Hemmingsen, E. A., Johansen, K. 1974. Functional and biochemical studies of penguin myoglobin. *Comp. Biochem. Physiol.* 49B:197–214
77. Weber, R. E., Hiebel, I., Braunitzer, G. 1988. High altitude and hemoglobin functions in the vultures *Gyps rueppellii* and *Aegypius monachus. Biol. Chem. Hoppe-Seyler* 369:233–40
78. Weinstein, Y., Bernstein, M. H., Bickler, P. E., Gonzales, D. V., Samaniego, F. C., Escobedo, M. A. 1985. Blood respiratory properties in pigeons at high altitudes: effects of acclimation. *Am. J. Physiol.* 249:R765–75
79. West, J. B. 1989. Physiological responses to severe hypoxia in man. *Can. J. Physiol. Pharmacol.* 67:173–78
80. West, J. B., Hackett, P. H., Maret, K. H., Milledge, J. S., Peters, R. M., et al. 1983. Pulmonary gas exchange on the summit of Mount Everest. *J. Appl. Physiol.* 55:678–87
81. Wittenberg, B. A., Wittenberg, J. B. 1989. Transport of oxygen in muscle. *Annu. Rev. Physiol.* 51:857–78
82. Wolfenson, D., Frei, Y. F., Berman, A. 1982. Blood flow distribution during artificially induced respiratory hypocapnic alkalosis in the fowl. *Respir. Physiol.* 50:87–92
83. Wollman, H., Smith, T. C., Stephen, G. W., Colton, E. T., Gleaton, H. E. 1968. Effects of extremes of respiratory and metabolic alkalosis on cerebral blood flow in man. *J. Appl. Physiol.* 24:60–65

Annu. Rev. Physiol. 1991. 53:71–85

INTERACTIONS BETWEEN HYPOXIA AND HYPOTHERMIA

Stephen C. Wood

Oxygen Transport Program, Lovelace Medical Foundation, Albuquerque, New Mexico 87108

KEY WORDS: thermoregulation, hypoxia, behavior

INTRODUCTION

Hypoxia elicits a variety of compensatory responses in animals. Physiologic responses, including increased ventilation and cardiac output, increase O_2 supply. Hypoxia also elicits hypothermia, a response that decreases O_2 demand. Altered thermoregulatory behavior is involved in hypoxia-induced hypothermia in both poikilothermic and homeothermic vertebrates. This review discusses the interactions between hypoxia and thermoregulation. Some related stresses that induce hypothermia are also described.

All vertebrates have a brain region specialized for thermoregulation. The sensory and integrative circuits are similar for ectothermic and endothermic vertebrates (15). Most or all thermoregulatory functions can be interpreted by single or dual set point models (31, 4). The outputs of the thermoregulatory center, behavioral and physiologic, provide feedback control of core body temperature (T_b).

Ectotherms need behavioral mechanisms for T_b control. Physiologic mechanisms available to ectotherms are limited to color changes and autonomic control of cutaneous blood flow. Endotherms also use behavior for T_b control, but need physiologic mechanisms unavailable to ectotherms (shivering and non-shivering thermogenesis, sweating, panting, and so on) when ambient temperatures are outside of the thermoneutral zone. The distinction between ectotherms and endotherms is often blurred by examples of facultative en-

0066-4278/91/0315-0071$02.00

dothermy of ectotherms (e.g. brooding pythons, honey bee colonies, warm-muscled tunas) and facultative ectothermy of endotherms (e.g. torpor, hypoxic mammals).

Most ectotherms have a distinct thermal preference, detectable in thermal gradients. Pyrogens cause selection of a higher than normal T_b (behavioral fever) in fish, amphibians, and reptiles (40, 58). This response enhances survival via increased production of T cells and increased effectiveness of interferon, an antiviral agent. On the other hand, a number of factors induce selection of lower than normal T_b. The following sections review the mechanisms and importance of behavioral hypothermia as a stress response.

HYPOXIA AND THERMOREGULATION

Body temperature (T_b) has a marked effect on oxygen uptake ($\dot{V}_{O_2}$) of resting animals (42). For most animals, the temperature coefficient (Q_{10}) is ≈ 2.5, so resting $\dot{V}_{O_2}$ changes about 11% per°C change in T_b. Consequently, hyperthermia is deleterious for hypoxic animals. Conversely, hypothermia could be beneficial, particularly for O_2 sensitive organs, e.g. heart and brain. Indeed, most studies reviewed below show that hypothermia is a normal and adaptive response to hypoxia in both ectotherms and endotherms.

Physiologic Hypothermia

It is well established that heat loss occurs in hypoxic mammals from peripheral vasodilation (45, 24, 1, 50a). The recent finding of behavioral hypothermia in hypoxic mammals (see below) is significant because selection of a lower ambient temperature will accelerate the rate of heat loss. There is also decreased heat production in hypoxic mammals. This is due to redistribution of blood away from brown fat (69, 64).

Within a range of ambient temperatures (thermoneutral zone), homeotherms maintain T_b without supplementary heat production or sweat secretion. At ambient temperatures below thermoneutrality, T_b of homeotherms is maintained by thermogenic responses. Therefore, it is possible that hypothermia could interact with hypoxia by eliciting a thermogenic response. This could be deleterious because of the increasing O_2 demand of tissues involved in shivering and non-shivering thermogenesis. In hypoxic rats, however, the normal thermogenic response to reduced temperature is depressed (23). A reduced thermogenic response to cold also occurs in hypoxic and hypercapnic hamsters (44). Other evidence that the drop in T_b results from a change in central regulation includes a decrease impulse frequency of cold receptors during hypoxia (18) and a change in the set point of preoptic neurons during hypoxia (70). Thus, hypothermia during hypoxia can be interpreted by using the set point model (31) as a widening of the thermoneutral zone and downward shift of the threshold temperature for shivering thermogenesis.

In ectotherms, shivering and non-shivering thermogenesis does not occur during behavioral hypothermia. As with mammals, physiologic and behavioral mechanisms act in concert to lower T_b. In ectotherms hypothermia is primarily behavioral, but the rate of drop in T_b may be augmented by control of cutaneous blood flow. Under normoxic conditions, lizards cool more slowly than they heat, which indicates decreased peripheral blood flow during cooling. Hypoxia abolishes this difference in the iguana (35) thereby increasing the rate of cooling during hypoxia and shortening the time required for T_b to drop after hypoxic animals select a lower ambient temperature.

Behavioral Hypothermia

Most vertebrates, including mammals and birds, utilize behavior to regulate T_b in heterothermal environments. In nature or in laboratory thermal gradients, most species show definite thermal preferences. Many so-called cold-blooded animals, e.g. lizards, actually prefer a T_b of 35°C or higher.

An interaction between hypoxia and thermoregulation of ectotherms was predicted from models of O_2 transport (76). With venous admixture as a result of shunts, the arterial P_{O_2} of normoxic ectotherms lies near the shoulder of the oxygen dissociation curve rather than on the upper flat portion as in normoxic mammals. Lacking this normal reserve for hypoxia, ectotherms were predicted to select a lower T_b in an hypoxic environment. This hypothesis was confirmed in lizards (34) and other ectotherms (77). Behavioral hypothermia also occurs in water breathers including crayfish, amphibian larvae, and teleost fish (20, 8, 57).

Among animals how wide spread is this behavioral response to hypoxia? The answer is not yet known since only a few species of each vertebrate taxa and a few invertebrate species have been studied. We recently started a search for the simplest animal, beginning with a protozoan (48), to show this response. *Paramecium caudatum* were placed in an aquatic thermal gradient, exposed first to air, and then to nitrogen. The mean temperature selected by the paramecia during air exposure was, as previously shown by Mendelssohn (50), 26°C. During extreme hypoxia (P_{O_2} was not measured but assumed to be less than 1 torr), the selected temperature was significantly reduced to $\approx$ 16°C. This hypothermia was completely reversed when the gradient was returned to normoxia. These results can be incorporated into a model for temperature selection for paramecia based on the work of Hennessey et al (33). According to this model, temperature selection results from the following processes: (*a*) Heat at the selected temperature is tranduced by a mechanism that increases ion conductance of the body membrane, presumably by opening membrane ion channels; (*b*) ions flowing through channels cause depolarization if resting membrane voltage is less than −20 mV; (*c*) depolarization triggers opening of a voltage-dependent calcium channel in ciliary membranes, thus initiating an action potential; (*d*) the action potential (Ca influx) causes a change in the beat direction of the ciliary axoneme and backward swimming. Under severe hypoxia, we postulate that this sequence occurs at a lower temperature since the resting membrane potential at a given temperature will be decreased. *Paramecium caudatum* may provide a useful model for studies of mechanisms and significance of thermoregulation at the single-cell level.

Hypoxia-induced hypothermia for representative vertebrates is shown in Figures 1 and 2. In each case there is a distinct threshold for the behavioral

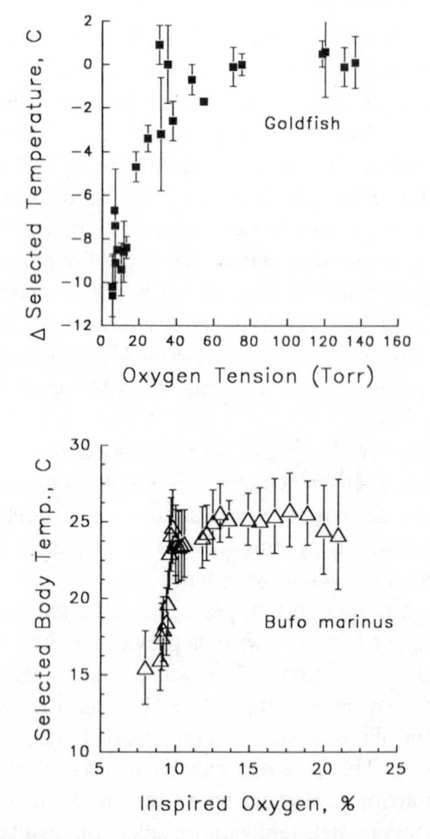

Figure 1 *Top:* Effect of inspired water P_{O_2} on temperature selection of goldfish and rainbow trout in a thermal gradient. Midpoint analysis indicates a breakpoint (hypoxic threshold) of about 35 torr for the goldfish. Data from (55). *Bottom:* Effect of inspired % oxygen on temperature selection of the toad, *Bufo marinus*. Data from S. C. Wood, unpublished.

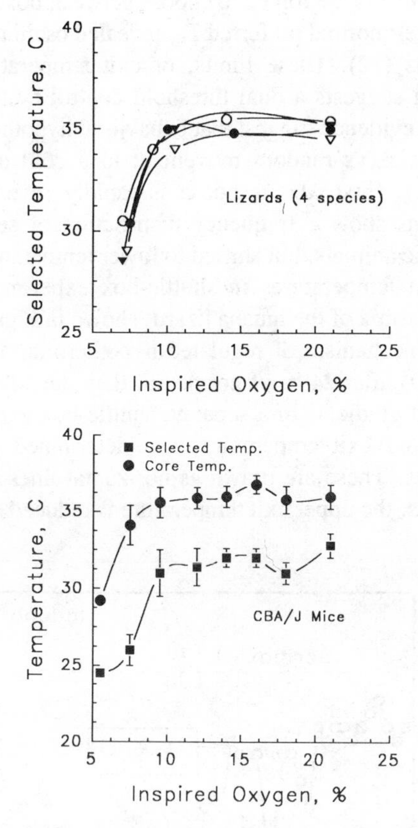

Figure 2 *Top:* Selected body temperature of four species of lizards during graded hypoxia. Data from (34). *Bottom:* Selected temperature and body temperature of mice during exposure to graded hypoxia. Data from C. Gordon, personal communication.

response to hypoxia. Behavioral hypothermia in hypoxic mammals is a recent finding that further blurs the distinction between ectotherms and homeotherms (7, 22, C. Gordon, personal communication). Data for mice (Figure 2) show a degree of behavioral hypothermia during hypoxia that closely parallels the pattern seen in ectotherms. The threshold for a behavioral response in both mice and lizards is at an inspired O_2 of ≈ 10%.

Mechanisms and Mediators

NEURAL MECHANISMS Behavioral thermoregulation of terrestrial ectotherms is modeled according to minimum and maximum temperatures based on the early work of Cowles & Bogert (13). Experiments with shuttle boxes, in which animals are forced to choose between boxes either too cold or too hot to allow their normal preferred T_b, revealed oscillations of T_b between reproducible limits (32). These limits, or exit temperatures, are normally distributed, which suggests a dual threshold control system (32, 4).

Several lines of evidence suggest that behavioral hypothermia is a regulated response to hypoxia (vs random movement to a cold area where animals become immobile). First, the response is rapidly reversible. Second, the hypoxic ectotherms show a frequency distribution of selected temperature similar to normoxic animals, but shifted to lower temperatures. Third, there is a resetting of exit temperatures in shuttle-box experiments (34, 35). The behavioral hypothermia of the iguana lizard, shown in Figure 3, illustrates the exit temperature mechanism of regulated hypothermia. When iguanas were exposed to 10% O_2 after 24 hr of normoxia, they quickly moved to the cold end of the thermal gradient. In a separate shuttle-box experiment, the upper (hot) and lower (cold) exit temperatures were determined under normoxic and hypoxic conditions. These are drawn as horizontal lines in Figure 3. Under hypoxic conditions, the upper exit temperature is reduced from ≈ 37 to 31°C.

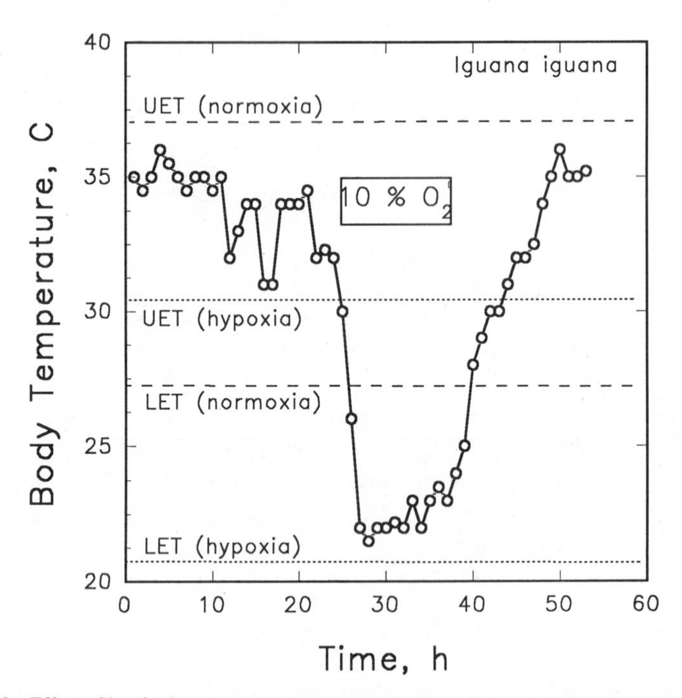

Figure 3 Effect of inspired oxygen on temperature selection of an iguana lizard in a 10 to 40°C thermal gradient. After 24 hr of normoxia, the chamber is filled with 10% O_2. UET and LET are upper and lower exit temperatures determined in a separate, shuttle-box experiment. Data from (34).

This exit temperature is now lower than the normal preferred T_b. Therefore, the iguanas exit the warm end of the thermal gradient the same as they would exit the hot shuttle box. The new selected T_b during hypoxia is ≈ 22°C, above the lower exit temperature during hypoxia. When normoxia is restored in the chamber, the selected T_b during hypoxia is below the lower exit temperature. Therefore, the animal exits the cold end of the chamber. Similar results were obtained with three other species of lizards (34).

ARGININE VASOPRESSIN AND VASOTOCIN Stimuli that elicit hypothermia are diverse, e.g. ethanol, urine, morphine, prostaglandins, histamine, hypoxia, dry air, anemia, pesticides, food deprivation, and heavy metals (27). There are also diverse pyrogens that, without crossing the blood brain barrier, also alter central thermoregulation (17). There are a host of potential mediators of hypothermia, including endogenous opioid peptides (39). For hypothermia induced by hypoxic hypoxia, anemic hypoxia, hypercapnia, and dry air, one mediator seems most likely, i.e. arginine vasopressin (AVP) (arginine vasotocin (AVT) in ectotherms). Although the evidence for involvement of AVP (or AVT), is convincing, this has yet to be proven.

Rationales for the AVP hypothesis are (*a*) *hypoxia:* Hypoxia stimulates the release of AVP in rats (73), in fetal sheep (67), and in human infants born after hypoxic distress (61). Hypoxic hypoxia in dogs caused a 250% increase in blood flow to the neurohypophysis and a concurrent rise in plasma AVP (74); (*b*) *thermoregulation:* AVP is an endogenous antipyretic peptide in mammals. Centrally administered AVP elicits hypothermia (53, 60). A vasotocin neurosecretory system has been identified in lizards (6); (*c*) *hypercapnia:* There is enhanced AVP release in response to hypercapnic acidosis in rats (72). Hypercapnia induces behavioral hypothermia in toads (59); (*d*) *dehydration:* Water deprivation is known to increase the release of AVP in response to increased extracellular tonicity and diminished plasma volume in mammals (71) and in amphibians (66). The toad, *Bufo marinus,* selects significantly lower T_bs when exposed to dry air (49); (*e*) *behavior:* AVT injections alter behavior in amphibians (reproductive behavior), and the altered behavior can be blocked by AVP antagonists (52).

Two approaches should be useful in testing the AVP/AVT hypothesis: (*a*) administering AVP and AVT antagonist to animals exposed to conditions known to elicit hypothermia; (*b*) using the Brattleboro rat, a strain that is genetically AVP deficient.

Physiologic Significance

Known effects of hypothermia that are pertinent to hypoxia are (*a*) a left shift of the oxyhemoglobin dissociation curve and improvement of O_2 loading in the lungs; (*b*) decreased V_{O_2} according to the Q_{10} effect; e.g. $\dot{V}_{O_2}$ would decrease ≈ 11% per°C; and (*c*) energetically costly responses to hypoxia e.g.

increased cardiac output and ventilation may be avoided. Known benefits of hypothermia in hypoxic animals encompass several categories.

SURVIVAL Neonatal mammals (50a) and anemic rabbits (26) have increased survival rates when they are hypothermic. Asphyxiated neonates treated by hypothermia have a mortality rate of 11.5% compared to 48% in 288 cases not using hypothermia (19). Mice exposed to 5% O_2 had increased survival times when T_b was reduced from 37 to 35°C and decreased survival when T_b was elevated to 40°C (3). Hypothermia also improves survival of rats following acute carbon monoxide poisoning (68). There is 100% survival of lizards allowed to cool during hypoxia vs 100% mortality of animals prevented from cooling down (34).

CONTROL OF BREATHING In reptiles and amphibians, lowering T_b markedly reduces the ventilatory response to hypoxia (25, 43). The arterial P_{O_2} needed to elicit a ventilatory response of turtles became progressively less as T_b was lowered (25). In spite of varying arterial P_{O_2} values at the hypoxic threshold, the arterial $[O_2]$ is relatively constant (25, 35). This is due to the effect of temperature on the position of the oxygen dissociation curve of blood. As shown in Figure 4, the reduction of selected T_b during hypoxia will reduce or abolish the ventilatory response and further conserve energy.

O_2 TRANSPORT The effect of hypothermia is predictable for $\dot{V}_{O_2}$ (Q_{10} effect) but not, a priori, for systemic O_2 transport (SOT), the product of cardiac output ($\dot{Q}$) × arterial O_2 content (CaO_2). Cardiac output may or may not decrease, depending on sympathetic reflexes or possible alterations in cardiac contractility. CaO_2 may or may not change depending on degree of hypoxia and left shift of the oxyhemoglobin dissociation curve (46). Both of the above will depend on changes in acid-base status due to metabolic, respiratory, or temperature effects.

Under normal conditions, $\dot{V}_{O_2}$ is a measure of metabolic demand and is not limited by SOT. However, if SOT decreases, $\dot{V}_{O_2}$ may fall below resting levels and become transport limited. This has been demonstrated in numerous studies of newborn and adult mammals (46) and recently confirmed in human infants and children (5). Newborn mammals are more susceptible to transport limited $\dot{V}_{O_2}$ because of limited cardiac reserve and limited ability to increase O_2 extraction because of high hemoglobin-O_2 affinity (47).

From the relationship that SOT = $\dot{Q} \times CaO_2$ and $\dot{V}_{O_2} = \dot{Q} \times (CaO_2 - C\bar{v}O_2)$, the equation may be derived (by combining these equations) that $\dot{V}_{O_2}$ = SOT × EO_2, where EO_2 is O_2 extraction $[(CaO_2 - C\bar{v}O_2)/CaO_2]$. There are three possible outcomes of the measurements of $\dot{V}_{O_2}$ and SOT in animals during hypothermia and hypoxia. First, if hypothermia reduces basal metabolic rate more than SOT, then EO_2 will decrease. This could be beneficial by

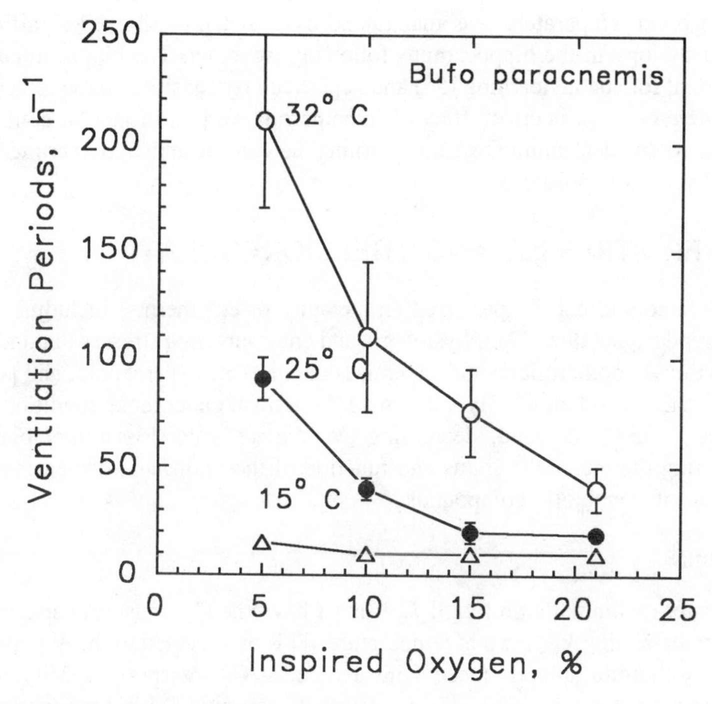

Figure 4 Effect of body temperature on the ventilatory response to hypoxia in the toad *Bufo paracnemius*. Data from Kruhøffer et al 1987 (43).

increasing venous and tissue P_{O_2}. Second, SOT and $\dot{V}_{O_2}$ could decrease by the same amount (same Q_{10}) with no net effect on EO_2. Third, SOT might decrease more than $\dot{V}_{O_2}$ with a potentially deleterious increase in EO_2.

BRAIN METABOLISM AND FUNCTION Hypoxia presents two problems for neuronal function: acidosis caused by lactic acid build up, and energy depletion resulting from lack of O_2. ^{31}P NMR spectroscopy has been used to study effects of hypercapnia (54), hypoxia (36), and hypothermia (38) in rodent models. The latter study showed that brain pH is increased during hypothermia as is phosphocreatine/P_i ratio and that both these changes were fully reversible upon rewarming. Hypothermia (27°C) has a protective effect on brain metabolism of hypoxic rats (11). This was attributed to the left shift of the oxyhemoglobin dissociation curve and the reduction in brain metabolic rate. Similar results with hypoxic-hypothermic rats also showed that hypothermia offers better cerebral protection than a dose of phenobarbital producing the same reduction of cerebral metabolic rate (30). Brain temperature of rats decreases spontaneously from 36 to 30–31°C during cerebral ischemia (10). This cooling of the brain prevented cell damage while animals whose brain temperature was maintained by heat lamps showed significant histopathology in the hippocampus following ischemia. The hippocampus is important for spatial learning (55) and is particularly sensitive to hypoxia (51, 2). Therefore a protective effect of hypothermia on brain function could be examined by determining spatial learning in control and hypothermic rats after hypoxia exposure.

OTHER STRESSES AND THERMOREGULATION

Many factors affect the preferred temperature of ectotherms, including season, gender, and diet (37). Physiologic and environmental stresses that induce behavioral hypothermia include anemia, dehydration, hypercapnia, and pesticides (references below). Hypothermia is beneficial under these conditions by reducing the O_2 demand, decreasing evaporative water loss (amphibians), protecting the metabolic status and function of the brain, and decreasing the toxicity of xenobiotic compounds.

Anemia

Whatever an animal's preferred T_b it must have the O_2 transport capacity to satisfy the resting $\dot{V}_{O_2}$ for that temperature. This premise led to the hypothesis that ectothermic animals faced with a reduced O_2 transport capacity, e.g. hematocrit reduction, would select a lower than normal T_b. In four species of lizards there was a rapid behavioral hypothermia of $\approx$ 8°C in response to hematocrit reduction and a return to normal T_b selection after spontaneous recovery of hematocrit (34). Similar results were obtained in an amphibian, *Bufo marinus* (75). In cross-sectional analysis, there was no correlation between selected T_b and hematocrit of toads. When hematocrit was lowered by removal of blood, however, all toads selected a significantly lower temperature. For example, a fall in hematocrit from 35 to 25% elicited the selection of a 4.9°C cooler T_b. This reduced $\dot{V}_{O_2}$ by $\approx$ 51%, assuming a Q_{10} of $\approx$ 2.5.

Hypercapnia

Physiologic thermoregulation of endotherms becomes impaired under hypercapnic as well as hypoxic conditions. In humans, hypercapnia reduces heat production and increases heat loss by augmenting sweating and inhibiting shivering (62). Little is known about behavioral thermoregulation of ectotherms or endotherms in response to hypercapnia. Exposure of *Bufo marinus* to 10% CO_2 elicits a significant behavioral reduction of selected T_b (59). This was not an effect of acidosis, however, since addition of 40% O_2 to the chamber air reversed the behavioral hypothermia without changing the pH. This severe hypercapnia is well outside the range of normally encountered CO_2 levels (in burrows). Exposure to 5% CO_2, a level that is encountered in burrows, has no effect on T_b selection (59). As reported for hamsters (44), there was an interaction between hypoxia and hypercapnia on thermoregulation in toads. Fifteen % O_2 and 5% CO_2 had no effect singly, but when combined they elicited behavioral hypothermia. More studies are needed to determine the mechanisms and significance of hypothermic responses to hypercapnia.

Dehydration

Lowering metabolic heat production to reduce water loss occurs in endotherms. For example, when drinking water is restricted, deer mice show a 25% reduction in metabolic rate and 47% decrease in evaporative water loss (12). Water deprivation in camels decreases metabolic rate by 77% (63). The mechanism of the decreased basal metabolic rate during dehydration of camels is inhibition of thyroid function (78).

In ectotherms, reducing heat gain from the environment should have a similar effect on water economy. Few studies, however, have investigated the relationship between dehydration and T_b in ectotherms. The lizard, *Anniella pulchra,* selects lower temperatures in a dry thermal gradient than in a moist one (9). In contrast, the desert iguana shows no effect of dehydration on upper and lower exit temperatures in a shuttle-box experiment. Salt loading, however, reduced upper and lower exit temperatures (21).

Amphibians are more prone to dehydration and experimental results are more consistent. Dehydration of *Chiromantis xerampelina* and *Phyllomedusa sauvagei* to 80–90% of their original weight caused them to select a lower T_b in a thermal gradient (65). These tree frogs are unique in that their skin is nearly impermeable to water. In most amphibians the skin is highly permeable to water, and T_b should have a major impact on water balance. Amphibians lose water at rates up to several hundred times that of most reptiles and waterproof frogs (66). Consequently, a reduction in T_b should be particularly beneficial to terrestrial amphibians in conserving water in arid environments. Selected T_b is significantly reduced in toads *(Bufo marinus)* exposed to dry air in a thermal gradient (49). This behavior occurs before there is significant dehydration, i.e. no change in plasma osmolality. The reduced T_b is not caused by increased evaporative cooling, but by movement of the animals to a colder temperature. This suggests a change in the thermoregulatory set point(s) since the evaporative cooling in dry air might, with no change in set point(s), elicit movement to the warm end of the chamber. The amount of water potentially saved by this response is considerable. The reduction of T_b from 24.3 to 15.7°C will reduce water loss by 41.3%. As discussed above, the factor mediating the behavioral response to dry air is unknown, but arginine vasotocin is hypothesized.

Toxic Chemicals and Metabolic Waste Products

Mammals exposed to toxic substances regulate T_b at a lower value. For example, nickel chloride affects both behavioral and autonomic control of T_b in rats (29). The resulting hypothermia reduces the toxicity of most zenobiotic compounds (27).

Exposure of fish to anoxia affects later T_b selection in a normoxic thermal gradient. Goldfish exposed to anoxia for 5 hr select a $T_b \approx 5°C$ lower than the corresponding normoxic controls (16). Ethanol, a by-product of anaerobic metabolism in goldfish, may mediate this response. When injected into the hypothalamic thermoregulatory center, ethanol elicits an 8°C reduction of selected T_b.

Nitrogenous excretory substances are not toxic at physiologic concentrations, but can become so in animals with renal failure. Prolonged uremia results in hypothermia (56, 41). Injection of urine or urea into experimental animals induces regulated hypothermia, which suggests the presence of an endogenous cryogen (41, 14). Mice become hypothermic when toxic levels of other nitrogenous waste products are injected (28).

SUMMARY AND CONCLUSIONS

Hypoxic animals have an impressive arsenal of defense mechanisms, many of which are common to other kind of stresses. Physiologic defense mechanisms, e.g. increasing cardiac output or ventilation, are effective but also energy demanding. An alternative to improving O_2 supply is reduction of O_2 demand. This is easily accomplished by ectothermic vertebrates by seeking a cooler environment and augmenting the rate of cooling by increased perfusion of the skin. More surprising is that endotherms respond to hypoxia in the same way. Unlike near drowning, where the hypothermia is forced (but still effective), the behavioral hypothermia appears to be regulated and analogous to fever. Much more work is needed in this formative area of research to establish mechanisms, functional significance, and pathways common to stresses other than hypoxia.

Literature Cited

1. Adolph, E. F. 1951. Tolerance to cold and anoxia in infant rats. *Am. J. Physiol.* 155:366–77
2. Aitken, P. G., Schiff, S. J. 1986. Selective neuronal vulnerability to hypoxia in vitro. *Neurosci. Lett.* 67:92–96
3. Artru, A. A., Michenfelder, J. D. 1981. Influence of hypothermia or hyperthermia alone or in combination with pentobarbital on phenytoin on survival time in hypoxic mice. *Anesth. Analg.* 60:867–70
4. Barber, B. J., Crawford, E. C. Jr. 1977. A stochastic dual-limit hypothesis for behavioral thermoregulation in lizards. *Physiol. Zool.* 50:53–60
5. Berman, W., Wood, S. C., Yabek, S., Dillon, T., Fripp, R., Burstein, R. 1987. Systemic oxygen transport in congenital heart diseases. *Circulation* 2: 360–68
6. Bons, N. 1983. Immunocytochemical identification of the mesotocin and vasotocin-producing systems in the brain

of temperate and desert lizard species and their modifications by cold exposure. *Gen. Comp. Endocrinol.* 52:56–66
7. Brauer, R. W., Johnson, E. D., Miller, C. G. 1986. Modification of temperature preference behavior by hypoxia and metabolic inhibitors. *Homeostasis and Thermal Stress, 6th Intl. Symp. Pharmacol. Thermoregulation,* ed. K. E. Cooper. pp. 27–29. Basel: Karger
8. Bryan, J. D., Hill, L. G., Niell, W. H. 1984. Interdependence of acute temperature preference and respiration in the plains minnow. *Trans. Am. Fish. Soc.* 113:557–62
9. Bury, R. B., Balgooyen, T. G. 1976. Temperature selectivity in the legless lizard, *Anniella pulchra. Copeia* 1976:152–55
10. Busto, R., Dietrich, W. D., Globus, M., Valdés, I., Scheinberg, P., Ginsberg, M. 1987. Small differences in intraischemic brain temperature critically determine the extent of ischemic neuronal injury. *J. Cereb. Blood Flow Metab.* 7:729–38
11. Carlsson, C. H. M., Siesjo, B. K. 1976. Protective effect of hypothermia in cerebral oxygen deficiency caused by arterial hypoxia. *Anesthesiology* 44:27–35
12. Chew, R. M. 1961. Water metabolism of desert vertebrates. *Biol. Rev.* 36:1–31
13. Cowles, R. B., Bogert, C. M. 1944. A preliminary study of the thermal requirements of desert reptiles. *Bull. Am. Mus. Nat. Hist.* 83:261–96
14. Cox, P. S., Rothenburg, B. A., Kluger, M. J. 1982. Characterization of an endogenous cryogen that appears in the urine. *Am. J. Physiol.* 243:R241–44
15. Crawshaw, L. I., Hammel, H. T. 1974. Behavioral regulation of internal temperature in the brown bullhead, *Ictalurus nebulosus. Comp. Biochem. Physiol.* 47A:51–60
16. Crawshaw, L. I., Wollmuth, L. P., O'Connor, C. S. 1989. Intracranial ethanol and ambient anoxia elicit selection of cooler water by goldfish. *Am. J. Physiol.* 256:R133–37
17. Dascombe, M. J. 1985. The pharmacology of fever. *Prog. Neurobiol.* 25:327–73
18. Dodt, E. 1956. Die Aktivitat der Thermorezeptoren-bei nichtthermischen Reizen bekannter thermoregulatorischer Wirkung. *Pflügers Arch.* 263:188–200
19. Dunn, J. M., Miller, J. A. 1969. Hypothermia combined with positive pressure ventilation in resuscitation of the asphyxiated neonate. *Am. J. Obstet. Gynecol.* 104:58
20. Dupré, R. K., Wood, S. C. 1988. Behavioral temperature regulation by aquatic ectotherms during hypoxia. *Can. J. Zool.* 66:2649–52
21. Dupré, R. K., Crawford, E. C. Jr. 1985. Behavioral thermoregulation during dehydration and osmotic loading of the desert iguana. *Physiol. Zool.* 58:357–63
22. Dupré, R. K., Owen, L. 1989. Behavioral thermoregulation by hypoxic rats. *FASEB J.* 3:A838 (Abst.)
23. Dupré, R. K., Romero, A., Wood, S. C. 1988. Thermoregulation and metabolism in hypoxic animals. In *Oxygen Transfer from Environment to Tissues,* ed. R. Fedde, N. Gonzales. pp. 347–351. New York: Plenum
24. Gellhorn, E., Janus, A. 1936. The influence of partial pressures of O_2 on body temperature. *Am. J. Physiol.* 116:327–29
25. Glass, M. L., Boutelier, R. G., Heisler, N. 1983. Ventilatory control of arterial P_{O_2} in the turtle, *Chrysemys picta bellii:* Effects of temperature and hypoxia. *J. Comp. Physiol.* 151:145–53
26. Gollan, F., Aono, M. 1973. The effect of temperature on sanguinous rabbits. *CryoBiology* 10:321–27
27. Gordon, C. J. 1988. Temperature regulation in laboratory mammals following acute toxic insult. *Toxicology* 53:161–78
28. Gordon, C. J. 1988. Thermoregulatory responses in mice following acute administration of principal nitrogenous excretory substances. *Pharmacol. Biochem. Behavior* 31:699–703
29. Gordon, C. J., Watkinson, W. P. 1989. Effect of nickel chloride on body temperature and behavioral thermoregulation in rats. *Fed. Proc.* 3:A701 (Abst.)
30. Hagerdal, M. W. F. A., Keykhah, M. M., et al. 1978. Protective effects of combinations of hypothermia and barbiturates in cerebral hypoxia in the rat. *Anesthesiology* 49:165–69
31. Hammel, H. T., Heller, H. C., Sharp, F. R. 1973. Probing the rostral brainstem of anesthetized, unanesthetized, and exercising dogs and of hibernating and euthermic ground squirrels. *Fed. Proc.* 32:1588–97
32. Heath, J. E. 1970. Behavioral regulation of body temperature in poikilotherms. *Physiologist* 13:399–410
33. Hennessey, T. M., Saimi, Y., Kung, C. 1983. A heat-induced depolarization of *Paramecium* and its relationship to thermal avoidance behavior. *J. Comp. Physiol.* 153:39–46
34. Hicks, J. W., Wood, S. C. 1985. Temperature regulation in lizards: effects of hypoxia. *Am. J. Physiol.* 248:R595–R600

35. Hicks, J. W., Wood, S. C. 1989. Oxygen homeostasis. In *Comparative Pulmonary Physiology: Current Concepts,* ed. S. C. Wood, pp. 311–42. New York: Dekker
36. Hitzig, B. M. 1989. Effects of hypoxia on brain cell acid-base and high-energy phosphate regulation by ^{31}P-NMR spectroscopy. In *Chemoreceptors and Reflexes in Breathing,* ed. S. Lahiri, R. E. Forster, R. O. Davies, A. I. Pack. pp. 255–66. New York: Oxford
37. Huey, R. B. 1982. Temperature, physiology, and ecology of reptiles. In *Biology of the Reptilia,* ed. C. Gans, F. H. Pough. pp. 25–92. New York: Academic
38. Johnson, D. C., Nishimura, M., Okunieff, P., Kazemi, H., Hitzig, B. M. Effects of hypothermia on rat brain pH_i and phosphate metabolite regulation by ^{31}P-NMR. *J. Appl. Physiol.* 67:2527–34
39. Kavaliers, M., Courtenay, S., Hirst, M. 1984. Opiates influence behavioral thermoregulation in the curly-tailed lizard, *Leiocephalus carinatus. Physiol. Behav.* 32:221–24
40. Kluger, M. J. 1979. Fever in ectotherms: evolutionary implications. *Am. Zool.* 19:295–304
41. Kluger, M. J., Turnbull, A. J., Cranston, W. I., Wing, A. J., Gross, M. P., Rothenburg, B. A. 1981. Endogenous cryogen excreted by the kidneys. *Am. J. Physiol.* 241:R271–76
42. Krogh, A. 1914. The quantitative relation between temperature and standard metabolism in animals. Int. Z. *Phys. Chem.* Biol. 1:491–508
43. Kruhøffer, M., Glass, M. L., Abe, A. S., Johansen, K. 1987. Control of breathing in an amphibian, *Bufo paracnemius:* effects of temperature and hypoxia. *Respir. Physiol.* 69:267–75
44. Kuhnen, G., Wloch, B., Wunnenberg, W. 1987. Effects of acute hypoxia and/or hypercapnia on body temperatures and cold induced thermogenesis in the golden hamster. *J. Therm. Biol.* 12:103–7
45. Lintzel, W. 1931. Uber die Wirkung der Luftverdunnung auf Tiere V Mitteilung Gaswechsel weisser Ratten. *Pflügers Arch.* 227:673–708
46. Lister, G. 1984. Oxygen transport in the intact hypoxic newborn lamb: acute effects of increasing P_{50}. *Ped. Res.* 18:172–77
47. Lister, G., Moreau, G., Moss, M., Talner, N. S. 1984. Effects of alterations of oxygen transport on the neonate. *Semin. Perinatol.* 8:192–204
48. Malvin, G. M., Wood, S. C. 1990. Behavioral hypothermia in the protozoan, *Paramecium caudatum. Physiologist.* In press
49. Malvin, G. M., Wood, S. C., Riedel, C. 1989. Behavioral hypothermia in dehydrated toads. *Fed. Proc.* 3:A234 (Abst.)
50. Mendelssohn, M. 1895. Uber den thermotropismus einzelliger Organismen. *Archiv* Gesamte Physiol. Menschen Tiere 60:1–27
50a. Miller, J. A., Miller, F. S. 1966. Interactions between hypothermia and hypoxia-hypercapnia in neonates. *Fed. Proc.* 25:1338–41
51. Misgeld, U., Frotscher, M. 1982. Dependence of the viability of neurons in hippocampal slices on oxygen supply. *Brain Res. Bull.* 8:993–1003
52. Moore, F. L., Miller, L. J. 1983. Arginine vasotocin induces sexual behavior on newts by acting on cells in the brain. *Peptides* 4:97–102
53. Naylor, A. M., Ruwe, W. D., Veale, W. L. 1986. Thermoregulatory actions of centrally admininstered vasopressin in the rat. *Neuropharm.* 25:787–94
54. Nishimura, M., Johnson, D. C., Hitzig, B. M., Okunieff, P., Kazemi, H. 1989. Effects of hypercapnia on brain pH_i and phosphate metabolite regulation by ^{31}P-NMR. *J. Appl. Physiol.* 66:2181–88
55. Olton, D. S., Becker, J. T., Handelmann, G. E. 1979. Hippocampus, space, and memory. *Behav. Brain Sci.* 2:313–65
56. Om, P., Hohenegger, M. 1980. Energy metabolism in acute uremic rats. *Nephron* 25:249–53
57. Rausch, R. N., Crawshaw, L. I. 1990. Effect of hypoxia on behavioral thermoregulation in the goldfish, *Carassius auratus. FASEB J.* 4:A551 (Abst.)
58. Reynolds, W. W., Casterlin, M. E. 1982. The pyrogenic response of nonmammalian vertebrates. In *Pyretics and Antipyretics,* ed. A. S. Milton, pp. 649–68. Berlin: Springer-Verlag
59. Riedel, C., Wood, S. C. 1988. Effects of hypercapnia and hypoxia on temperature selection of the toad, *Bufo marinus. Fed. Proc.* 2:A500 (Abst.)
60. Robinzon, B., Koike, T. I., Neldon, H. L., Kinzler, S. L., Hendry, I. R., el-Halawani, M. E. 1988. Physiological effects of arginine vasotocin and mesotocin in cockerels. *Brit. Poultry Sci.* 29:639–52
61. Ruth, V., Fyhrquist, F., Clemons, G., Raivio, K. O. 1988. Cord plasma vasopressin, erythropoietin, and hypoxanthine as indices of asphyxia at birth. *Ped. Res.* 24:490–94

62. Schaefer, K., Messier, A. A., Morgan, C., Baker, G. T. III. 1975. Effect of chronic hypercapnia on body temperature regulation. *J. Appl. Physiol.* 38: 900–6
63. Schmidt-Nielsen, K., Crawford, E. C., Newsome, A. E., Rawson, K. S., Hammel, H. T. 1967. Metabolism rate of camels: effect of body temperature and dehydration. *Am. J. Physiol.* 212:341–46
64. Schubring, C. 1986. Temperature regulation in healthy and resuscitated newborns immediately after birth. *J. Perinat. Med.* 14:27–33
65. Shoemaker, V. H., Baker, M. A., Loveridge, J. P. 1989. Effect of water balance on thermoregulation in waterproof frogs *(Chiromantis* and *Phyllomedusa). Physiol. Zool.* 62:133–46
66. Shoemaker, V. W., Nagy, K. A. 1977. Osmoregulation in amphibians and reptiles. *Annu. Rev. Physiol.* 39:449–71
67. Stegner, H., Leake, R. D., Palmer, S. M., Oakes, G., Fisher, D. A. 1984. The effect of hypoxia on neurohypophyseal hormone release in fetal and maternal sheep. *Ped. Res.* 18:188–91
68. Sutariya, B., Penney, D., Barnes, J., Helfman, C. 1989. Hypothermia protects brain function in acute carbon monoxide poisoning. *Vet. Hum. Toxicol:* 31/5:436–41
69. Szelenyi, Z., Donhoffer, S. 1968. The thermogenic function of brown adipose tissue and the response of body temperature to hypoxia and hypercapnia in the cold- and warm-adapted rat. *Acta Physiol. Acad. Sci. Hung.* 33:31–39
70. Tamaki, Y., Nakayama, T. 1987. Effects of air constituents on thermosensitivities of preoptic neurons: hypoxia versus hypercapnia. *Pflügers Arch.* 409:1–6
71. Wade, C. E., Keil, L. C., Ramsey, D. J. 1983. Role of volume and osmolality in the control of plasma vasopressin in dehydrated dogs. *Neuroendocrinology* 37:349–53
72. Walker, B. A. 1987. Cardiovascular effects of V1 vasopressinergic blockade during acute hypercapnia in conscious rats. *Am. J. Physiol.* 252:R127–33
73. Walker, B. A. 1986. Role of vasopressin in the cardiovascular response to hypoxia in the conscious rat. *Am. J. Physiol.* 251:H1316–23
74. Wilson, D. A., Hanley, D. F., Feldman, M. A., Traystman, R. J. 1987. Influence of chemoreceptors on neurohypophyseal blood flow during hypoxic hypoxia. *Circ. Res.* 61:94–101
75. Wood, S. C. 1990. Effect of hematocrit on behavioral thermoregulation of the toad, *Bufo marinus. Am. J. Physiol.* 27:R848–51
76. Wood, S. C. 1984. Cardiovascular shunts and oxygen transport in lower vertebrates. *Am. J. Physiol.* 247:R3–R14
77. Wood, S. C., Dupré, R. K., Hicks, J. W. 1985. Voluntary hypothermia in hypoxic animals. *Acta Physiol. Scand.* 124:46
78. Yagil, R., Etzion, Z., Ganani, J. 1978. Camel thyroid metabolism: effect of season and dehydration. *J. Appl. Physiol.* 45:540–44

Annu. Rev. Physiol. 1991. 53:87–105

INTERMITTENT BREATHING IN VERTEBRATES

W. K. Milsom

Department of Zoology, University of British Columbia, Vancouver, British Columbia, V6T 2A9, Canada

KEY WORDS: control of breathing, periodic breathing, breathing pattern regulation, respiratory physiology, ventilatory control

INTRODUCTION

The breathing patterns of most fish, birds, and mammals are continuous, while those of most air-breathing fish, amphibia, and reptiles are not. This latter group of animals exhibit one of two basic types of intermittent breathing: one where individual breaths are rather evenly spaced, or one where episodes of continuous breathing are separated by longer non-ventilatory periods (Figure 1). Although these breathing patterns can be quite labile, under resting conditions they are usually rhythmic. Under appropriate conditions (usually an elevation in metabolic rate and respiratory drive), these animals may breathe continuously. Conversely, intermittent breathing of these same two basic patterns appears in fish and mammals, under appropriate conditions (usually a reduction in metabolic rate and respiratory drive) (Figure 1). This review will focus on current ideas concerning the genesis and regulation of intermittent breathing. To begin with, the superficial similarities between the various breathing patterns illustrated in Figure 1[1] raise the

[1]Abbreviations in figure and text: T_I inspiratory interval; T_E, expiratory interval; T_{Tot}, duration of breath ($T_I + T_E$); T_{NVP}, non-ventilatory period or respiratory pause; V_T, tidal volume of breath; $\dot{V}_E$, minute ventilation; R, respiratory quotient; Pa_{O_2}, arterial oxygen tension; Pa_{CO_2}, arterial carbon dioxide tension.

0066-4278/91/0315-0087$02.00

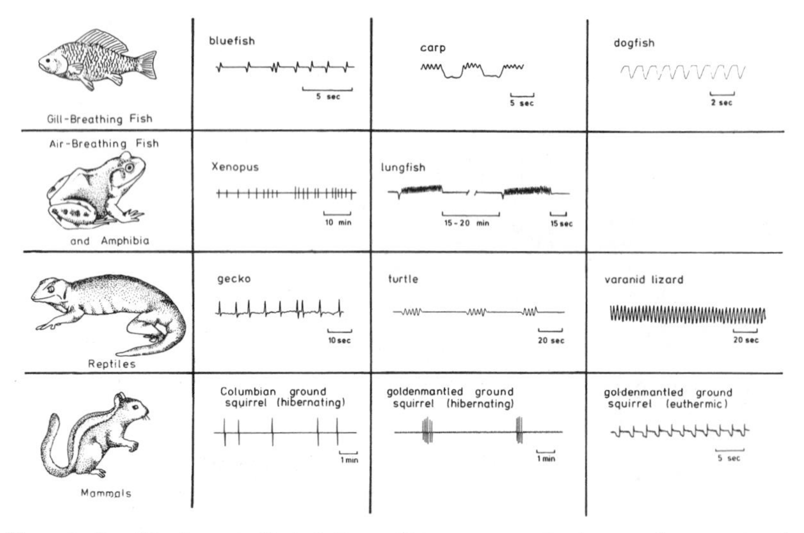

Figure 1 Breathing traces to illustrate the ventilatory patterns of various vertebrate species. See text for details.

question of whether all patterns in all vertebrates are manifestations of a common control system or whether they are simply analogous consequences of different control processes. The consequence of this question for our discussion is important since it determines the extent to which data from different vertebrate groups can be used to analyze the basic mechanisms underlying the control of intermittent breathing in the different groups.

INTERMITTENT VS CONTINUOUS BREATHING: MANIFESTATIONS OF A COMMON CONTROL SYSTEM?

In vertebrates that express a continuous breathing pattern under resting conditions (mammals, birds, and fishes), respiratory rhythm of a normal character persists following decerebration and decerebellation. Subsequent transection of the spino-medullary junction permanently abolishes respiratory rhythmic discharge of spinal motor nerves, but does not markedly affect the respiratory activity of the cranial nerves (4, 26, 27, 35, 64, 70, 72). Similar results have also been produced in vitro (2, 65, 66, 71, 74). Recordings from isolated brain stem spinal cord preparations from lampreys and neonatal rats reveal rhythmic discharges in cranial and spinal respiratory motorneurons.

Transections at the spino-medullary junctions in these preparations also abolish rhythmic respiratory discharge in spinal nerves without markedly affecting the rhythmic discharge of cranial nerves. Such preparations are devoid of all afferent sensory feedback except potentially from the central CO_2 chemoreceptors. The sum of this evidence is taken to indicate that there is a separate site of respiratory rhythmogenesis in the brain stem that functions independently of external input.

Using the technique of artificial, undirectional ventilation in fish and birds, several investigators have found that if they maintained normal values of arterial P_{CO_2} by removing CO_2 from venous blood at a rate equal to its rate of metabolic production, complete cessation of breathing occurred (15, 58, 61–63). Similar results have been obtained in mammals using an external membrane lung to condition the blood (60, 73). Such studies suggest that, in unanesthetized animals, respiratory rhythm is critically dependent on afferent respiratory stimuli. One interpretation of this data is that the respiratory neurons in the brain stem lack inherent automaticity (39, 60).

These two lines of research produce an apparent paradox; one line arguing convincingly for the presence of a central rhythm generator, the other arguing convincingly against it. The concept of a central rhythm generator, however, does not necessarily imply that the respiratory neurons of the brain stem can by themselves generate an effective respiratory output. They may operate at a sub-threshold level that requires some external stimulus to trigger respiratory events. In the cases mentioned above, a tonic respiratory input (such as elevated P_{CO_2}) is required to produce a phasic (rhythmic) respiratory output. It is the production of this rhythmic output by the central motor neurons, particularly in the in vitro preparations where no sensory afferent feedback other than a tonic input potentially arising from central CO_2 chemoreceptors is present, that is believed to reflect the additional input of a central rhythm generator (5, 13, 16, 36, 67, 68, 70).

Just as the presence of rhythmic ventilation has been used to argue for the presence of a central rhythm generator in fish, birds, and mammals, the intermittent nature of ventilation in amphibians and reptiles has been used to argue for its absence in these groups (70). This is further supported by observations that artificial ventilation sufficient to maintain blood gases and pH at normal levels will completely suppress spontaneous ventilation in these species also (37). But although pattern generation in amphibia and reptiles is more closely dependent on both peripheral receptor systems and higher centers than appears to be the case in fish, birds, and mammals, three lines of evidence argue that the basic mechanisms underlying central pattern generation are common to all groups. The first is that intermittent respiratory output can still be recorded from in vitro brain stem spinal cord preparations from amphibian tadpoles (A. Pack, R. Gallante, personal communication) and turtles (M. Douse, G. Mitchell, personal communication). The second is that in amphibians and reptiles, changes in respiratory drive primarily result in changes in tidal volume (V_T) and in the length of the interbreath interval or non-ventilatory period (T_{NVP}). The length of periods of inspiration and expiration change very little (46). This suggests that although peripheral inputs serve to regulate V_T and T_{NVP}, the timing of the respiratory events is under a separate (central) control. The third line of evidence comes from studies of hibernating mammals. During hibernation, mammals exhibit intermittent breathing patterns that closely resemble those seen in amphibians and reptiles, with the exception that the interbreath interval in mammals occurs at end-expiration, whereas in amphibians and reptiles it occurs at end-inspiration. All data collected to date, however, indicate that the control of the intermittent breathing patterns seen in hibernating animals is identical to that seen in lower vertebrates (46). It has been suggested that these similarities indicate that a common mechanism underlies the various intermittent breathing patterns seen under physiologic conditions in all air-breathing vertebrates. Furthermore, the conversion of continuous breathing to intermittent breathing in mammals entering hibernation suggests that both continuous and intermittent breathing are manifestations of a common control system (46). These conclusions are further supported by observations that many species of fish, which normally exhibit continuous ventilation, will switch to intermittent breathing under conditions of low metabolic rate in well-oxygenated water. Under these conditions, the control of this intermittent breathing pattern is again similar to that seen in other vertebrate groups (5, 33, 34, 41). These data further suggest that the basic mechanisms underlying the central nervous control of respiration are uniform throughout all vertebrate groups.

In summary, there is insufficient data at present to distinguish between three possible hypotheses regarding central rhythm generation. The first is that all vertebrates possess a central rhythm generator (either a pacemaker or a central neuronal network) that usually operates at sub-threshold levels, which require different levels of peripheral or higher central input to bring to threshold, and which may be manifested as continuous or intermittent motor outputs, depending on the overall level of respiratory drive. The second is that in all vertebrates, all aspects of respiratory pattern simply result from the integration of peripheral inputs. The third is that underlying control mechanisms are not common to all vertebrates and that central rhythm generators are present in animals that normally exhibit continuous breathing patterns (fish, birds, and mammals), but not those that breathe in an intermittent fashion (amphibia and reptiles). Based on recent evidence, the first of these hypotheses provides the most convincing and parsimonious explanation of the existing data.

PATTERNS OF INTERMITTENT BREATHING

Based on the breathing patterns illustrated in Figure 1, at least five different phases of the respiratory cycle can be defined (Figure 2). All vertebrates exhibit an active inspiratory phase (Phase 1, Figure 2). In most mammals this appears to be immediately followed by a post-inspiratory phase [Phase 3 (stage 1 expiration) Figure 2], during which inspiration is irreversibly terminated, inspiratory motor output declines, but still acts to brake the rate of deflation, and expiratory motor output is inhibited. This gives rise to the first breathing pattern illustrated at the bottom of Figure 2. If respiratory drive is high enough, inspiration may be followed by a second phase [Phase 4 (stage 2 expiration) Figure 2], during which active expiration occurs. This gives rise to the second breathing pattern illustrated in Figure 2. On the other hand, if

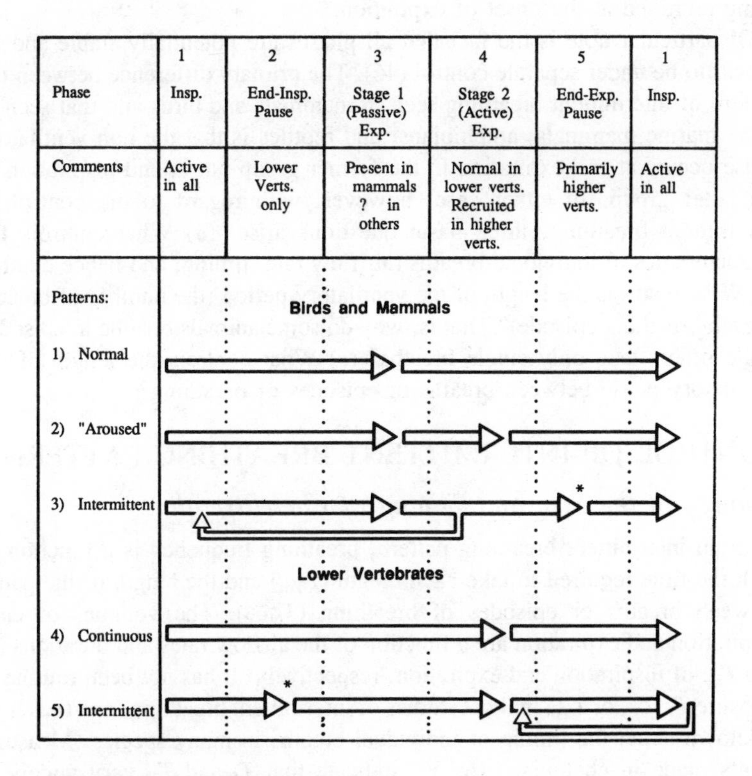

Figure 2 Phases of the ventilation cycle seen in various vertebrate groups. For the five breathing patterns listed in the lower part of the figure, the arrows link the successive phases of each cycle.

respiratory drive is sufficiently low, stage 1 expiration (Phase 3) may be followed by an end-expiratory phase, which is a true apneic pause preceding the next inspiration (Phase 5, Figure 2). In those species exhibiting episodic breathing patterns, this phase usually follows the last breath of an episode and gives rise to the third breathing pattern illustrated in Figure 2.

In the air-breathing fish, amphibia, reptiles, and some marine mammals (cetaceans), active inspiration is normally followed by an end-inspiratory pause (Phase 2, Figure 2). This is not a period of active breath holding, but rather a passive phase in which air is retained in the lungs by glottal trapping. In animals exhibiting episodic breathing patterns, this phase generally follows the last breath in an episode and gives rise to the fifth breathing pattern shown in Figure 2. It is not yet clear whether stage 1 expiration (Phase 3) is present in non-mammalian vertebrates or in marine mammals. In many of these animals, expiration is active (stage 2 expiration, Phase 4) with expiratory muscles being recruited at the onset of expiration.

Of particular note is the fact that all phases are potentially stable and all appear to be under separate control (46). The primary difference between the pattern of intermittent breathing seen in mammals and birds and that seen in some marine mammals, amphibians, and reptiles is that the non-ventilatory pause occurs at end-expiration in the former group but at end-inspiration in the latter group. In either case, however, with regard to the control of intermittent breathing, three basic questions arise. (*a*) What controls the characteristics of individual breaths (air flow rate, timing, and hence depth)? (*b*) What controls the length of the ventilatory period (the number of breaths in each breathing episode)? That is, why do some animals breathe in episodes while others take only single breaths? (*c*) What controls the length of the ventilatory pause between breaths or episodes of breathing?

CONTROL OF INTERMITTENT BREATHING PATTERNS

Control of the Size and Timing of Each Breath

With an intermittent breathing pattern, breathing frequency is a function of both the time required to take each breath (T_{Tot}) and the length of the pause between breaths or episodes of breathing (T_{NVP}). The volumes of each inspiration and expiration are a function of the airflow rates and durations (T_I and T_E) of inspiration and expiration, respectively. It has not been routine to measure T_I, T_E, or T_{Tot} in most studies of intermittent breathing, and thus little is known about the timing of individual breaths in many species. Measurements made in chelonians (6, 50) indicate that T_I and T_E vary widely in spontaneously breathing animals, but that mean values are little affected by increases in respiratory drive caused by inhalation of hypoxic or hypercapnic gas mixtures (6, 21, 50) (Figure 3*a*). The variations in T_I and T_E that occur

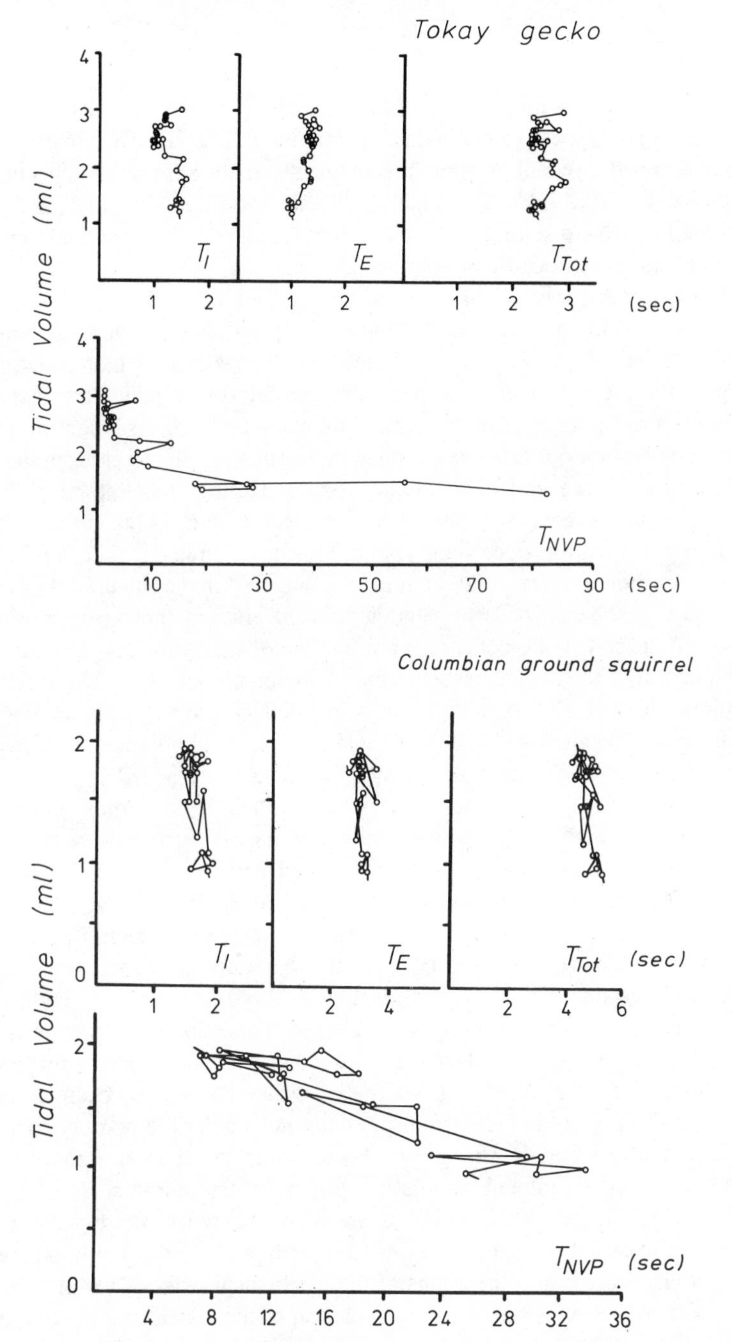

Figure 3 Tidal volume versus inspiratory interval (T_I), expiratory interval (T_E), total breath length (T_{Tot}) and length of the ventilatory pause (T_{NVP}) in a gecko (*a*) and a Columbian ground squirrel (*b*) during recovery from breathing 5% CO_2.

during normal breathing are inversely related to the rates of inspiration and expiration and appear to maintain tidal volume (V_T) relatively constant. This regulation is dependent on stretch receptor information from the lungs carried in the vagus nerve (50). The breath by breath variations seen in T_I and T_E in hibernating ground squirrels are much smaller, and they too are unaffected by changes in respiratory drive (Figure 3*b*).

Thus in both groups of animals, an increase in inspired CO_2 causes V_T to rise by increasing both inspiratory and expiratory flow rates without changing the mean values of T_I and T_E (Figure 3). The elevated motor output to inspiratory and expiratory muscles that is required to produce the increased flow rates must result from greater central excitation (or lesser central inhibition) of the motor output to the respiratory muscles. Such increases in inspired volume have been shown to elicit a Breuer-Hering, inspiratory-inhibitory reflex in all animals that have been studied to date. This reflex acts to terminate inspiration once lung volume reaches a time-dependent threshold level (12). For a greater tidal volume to be inspired in the same T_I, there must also be a change in the central integration of afferent input from the lungs involved in the volume-dependent termination of expiration and inspiration in conjunction with the increase in central motor output (10). The direct inhibitory effect of CO_2 on activity from pulmonary stretch receptors recorded in all vertebrate groups (31, 32) will also be of some importance in allowing a greater V_T before the central inhibitory threshold is reached.

These results suggest that T_{Tot} is determined by a central interaction between pulmonary afferent information and the respiratory drive caused by other stimuli. Regulation of T_{Tot} is associated with control of V_T rather than control of breathing frequency. Breathing frequency is now primarily a function of T_{NVP}. This causes a breathing pattern in which T_{Tot} remains relatively constant and V_T and T_{NVP} are the major controlled variables associated with responses to increased respiratory drive.

The extent to which changes in V_T and T_{NVP} are employed to adjust ventilation to match respiratory drive varies with the nature of the respiratory stimulus. In both reptiles and hibernating ground squirrels, changes in the concentration of O_2 and CO_2 in inspired air and changes in body temperature predominantly result in changes in T_{NVP}, while in reptiles, activity brings about changes in minute ventilation primarily through increases in tidal volume (7, 14, 21, 28, 52). For the western painted turtle and the Tokay gecko, at least, these results are consistent with predictions of optimal breathing patterns based on calculations of the mechanical work of ventilation (45, 77, 78). The work of breathing is a function of the elastic and flow-resistive forces that must be overcome to move air in and out of the lungs. Increasing tidal volume is extremely expensive energetically on the one hand, but tidal volume must always be sufficient to overcome the anatomical dead space of the respiratory system on the other hand. For a constant level of total ventilation, as breathing frequency increases, the work done to overcome elastic forces decreases, while that done to overcome flow resistive forces increases. In all animals, as a consequence of these opposing trends, for each level of pulmonary ventilation there is an optimum combination of V_T and instantaneous breathing frequency ($60/T_{Tot}$) that minimizes the mechanical work of breathing (45, 53, 77, 78). For animals where continuous breathing is not required to meet metabolic demands, the results suggest that it would be mechanically most efficient to intersperse these optimal breaths with ventilatory pauses. Furthermore, in response to increases in respiratory drive, it would be most efficient to increase minute ventilation by shortening these pauses, taking more breaths at this optimum combination of V_T and instantaneous breathing frequency. The resting breathing patterns and ventilatory responses of the western painted turtle and the Tokay gecko are totally consistent with such predictions. Bilateral vagotomy in both species drastically alters the breathing pattern, by producing an elevation in V_T, prolonging breath duration, and greatly increasing the mechanical cost of ventilation. This suggests that the intermittent breathing patterns seen in these species may represent adaptive strategies that are under vagal control and that serve to minimize the cost of breathing (45, 77, 78). Given that the oxidative cost of ventilation may comprise from 10 to 35% of the resting metabolic rate of these animals, such strategies could be of tremendous importance (37). Although this hypothesis is attractive, far more work is required to determine whether such correlations exist for the great variety of animals exhibiting these patterns.

Control of the Ventilatory Period

There has been little research to date into the mechanisms that underlie the two distinctive intermittent breathing patterns. Surprisingly, there is also very little known about what controls the number of breaths in each episode of breathing in those species exhibiting the episodic breathing pattern.

SINGLE BREATH VS EPISODIC BREATHING Naifeh et al, working on alligators (*Alligator mississippiensis*) and caimans (*Caiman sclerops*), demonstrated that both mild anesthesia (chloroform or pentobarbital) and brain stem section could convert the episodic breathing pattern normally seen in these animals into a single breath pattern (54, 55). The typical breath groups disappeared early during induction into anesthesia (54) while brain stem transection, similar to midcollicular decerebration in mammals, reduced the number of breaths in each breathing episode. Vagotomy, which reduces the number of breaths in each breathing episode in both crocodilians and turtles (50, 54, 55), did not reduce the number of breaths per episode further following midcollicular decerebration. Transection through the medulla just in front of the eminence covering the nucleus laminaris reduced the number of breaths in each breathing episode to a single breath (55).

Mild anesthesia will also convert episodic breathing to single breath breathing in the turtle (*Chrysemys picta*) and hibernating golden-mantled ground squirrel (*Spermophilus lateralis*), and increasing the inspired CO_2 concentration of these animals under this condition results in an increase in the number of single breaths by shortening T_{NVP} (C. Webb, W. Milsom, unpublished). Similar results have also been obtained in the hibernating ground squirrel by lowering body temperature to below 6 to 7°C (25, 52). As body temperature is reduced below this threshold, episodic breathing is slowly replaced by single breath breathing (Figure 4). Once animals are breathing with single breaths, increasing minute ventilation by adding CO_2 to the inspired air leads to an increase in the frequency of single breaths (C. Webb, W. Milsom, unpublished).

Recently, Juch & Ballintijn (33) recorded from neurons in the dorsal mesencephalic tegmentum of carp; fish that also exhibit an episodic breathing pattern. They describe a pool of neurons that appear to initiate each episode of breathing, but that will not sustain continuous respiration. Discharge by the neurons appears to overcome a time-dependent threshold and initiate an episode of breathing. Some factor or factors other than cessation of firing in these neurons is instrumental in terminating the episode of breathing. During light anesthesia these neurons lose their respiratory rhythmic firing pattern, and episodic breathing is replaced by a stable, single breath pattern. Brain

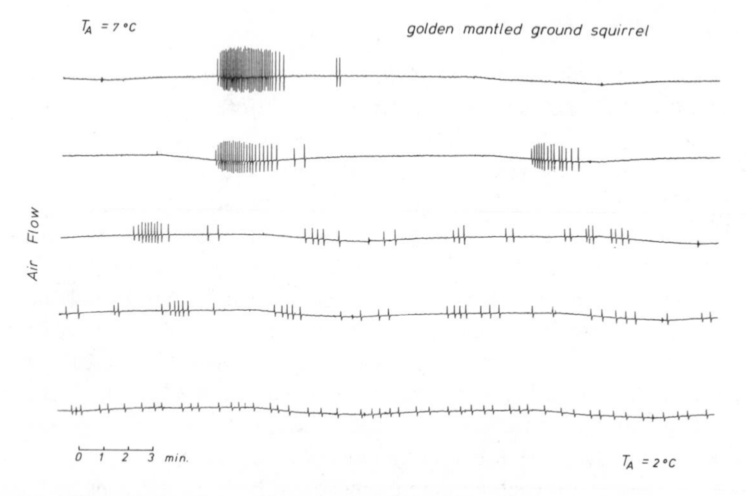

Figure 4 Effects of changing ambient temperature from 7 to 2°C on the breathing pattern of a golden-mantled ground squirrel. Traces are separated by roughly 30 min intervals.

stem transection at the rostral border of the medulla also results in a single breath pattern.

One hypothesis, consistent with these data, is that the episodic form of intermittent breathing seen in many species is generated by an input from higher (supramedullary) brain stem structures acting on the medullary respiratory neurons. Transection of the brain stem above the medulla, or cooling, or anesthetizing these higher brain stem structures, removes their influence and produces a single breath pattern. Once a single breath pattern has been produced, these animals respond to respiratory stimuli in the same manner as those species that normally breathe with single breaths. Vagal afferent input appears to be instrumental in producing episodic breathing in those species that exhibit this pattern, and it appears to exert this influence via the supramedullary structures. The specific brain stem sites involved in producing the episodic breathing pattern, the exact nature of the species differences in central integration that give rise to the two distinct patterns, and the functional significance of these differences remain to be discovered.

NUMBER OF BREATHS PER EPISODE In those animals that exhibit episodic breathing, it has already been noted that vagotomy acts to reduce the number of breaths in each breathing episode. It has also been shown that increasing the resting lung volume (V_{LR}) of turtles *(Chrysemys picta)*, which breathe episodically, acted to increase the number of breaths in each episode as well as to prolong the periods of breath holding between episodes (48) (Figure 5). These changes barely offset one another and thus overall breathing frequency remained unchanged as did tidal volume and minute ventilation (Figure 5). The data suggest that the increase in lung gas stores associated with increasing V_{LR} permitted longer periods of breath holding, but required a greater number of breaths in each breathing episode to replenish the enhanced gas store with a relatively smaller V_T (48). These changes in T_{NVP} and the number of breaths per episode, however, were largely the consequence of the changes in lung volume, per se, and not a direct consequence of the changes in gas stores. These data support the suggestion that the afferent information from pulmonary stretch receptors, carried in the vagus nerve, strongly influences the length of a breathing episode.

Changes in lung volume not withstanding, changes in lung and/or blood gases also significantly effect the number of breaths per episode of breathing in these species. It has been shown in a variety of chelonians that hypoxia, paradoxically, reduces the number of breaths in each episode of breathing while hypercapnia increases the number (18–20, 48, 50), although both gas mixtures increase ventilation overall (Figure 5). The mechanism underlying the differing effects of these gases on the length of the ventilatory period remains unclear. Furthermore in the golden-mantled ground squirrel (*Sper-*

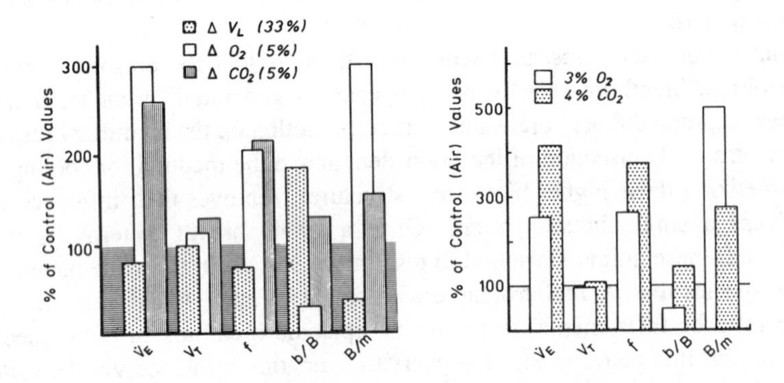

Figure 5 The % change in minute ventilation ($\dot{V}_E$), tidal volume (V_T), breathing frequency (f), number of breaths in each breathing episode (b/B), and the number of breathing episodes per unit time (B/m) in a turtle (*left*) and hibernating golden-mantled ground squirrel (*right*) under various conditions, compared to breathing air at resting lung volume. The turtles were given 5% CO_2 or 5% O_2 to breathe or their resting lung volume was increased by 33%. The squirrels were given 4% CO_2 or 3% O_2 to breathe.

mophilus lateralis), which also breaths episodically during hibernation, hypoxia decreases and hypercapnia increases the number of breaths in each episode of breathing (47, 52) (Figure 5).

It would thus appear that input from both mechanoreceptors in the lungs and arterial and central chemoreceptors are instrumental in determining the length of the ventilatory period in species that breath episodically, the significance of this control, however, remains unclear since not all respiratory stimuli (i.e. hypoxia) increase the length of the ventilatory period, and it is the length of the non-ventilatory period or ventilatory pause that is primarily instrumental in determining breathing frequency.

Control of the Ventilatory Pause

As indicated above, numerous studies have now shown that T_{Tot} does not change significantly with increasing respiratory drive, but that the breathing frequency in intermittent breathing is primarily a function of the length of the ventilatory pause (T_{NVP}) (Figure 3). Although it seems that fluctuations in lung and/or blood gas composition should be instrumental in determining the length of this pause, their role remains unclear.

The time course of changes in lung and blood gases during the ventilatory pause have been described for several species of amphibians, reptiles, and hibernating mammals (1, 8, 9, 11, 40–43, 44, 75). In all studies, lung P_{O_2} fell during the ventilatory pause at a highly variable rate while P_{CO_2} increased, but always at a slower rate such that the respiratory quotient for the lung (R) declined progressively as the ventilatory pause was extended. This decline in

R stemmed in part from non-pulmonary CO_2 elimination in some reptiles as well as from CO_2 storage in blood and tissues (1, 11). The levels of P_{O_2} and P_{CO_2} at which breathing stopped and at which breathing started again were unpredictable, however, and varied greatly from one ventilatory pause to another. Because there are persistent gradients between alveolar gas and pulmonary venous blood, and because there is central shunting of blood within the incompletely divided ventricle of amphibians and reptiles, large tension differences for both O_2 and CO_2 develop between alveolar gas and systemic arterial blood. Just as was found in the case of lung gas tensions, however, no clear correlation could be seen between the arterial P_{O_2}, P_{CO_2}, and pH levels at which animals were stimulated to start and stop breathing.

Despite this absence of clear-cut blood gas thresholds for the onset and termination of breathing, changes in both Pa_{O_2} and Pa_{CO_2} do affect T_{NVP} (8, 9, 19, 40, 47, 69). Paradoxically, although the responses to changes in Pa_{O_2} are usually small and only elicited by substantial falls in inspired O_2 concentration (<10%) (Figure 6) (70), hyperoxia has been shown to depress ventilation by increasing T_{NVP} slightly in all species that have been studied (18, 20, 21). Changes in Pa_{CO_2}, on the other hand, appear to stimulate ventilation strongly in all but a few species of reptiles. For instance, in chelonians and crocodilians, inhalation of 4 to 5% CO_2 at 20 to 25°C, results in a three to tenfold increase in ventilation owing to increases in both V_T and breathing frequency. The latter changes result from two to fourfold decreases in T_{NVP} (6, 20, 22, 50) (Figures 6). Inhalation of CO_2 in snakes and lizards, however, does not produce such uniform results. Although low levels of inspired CO_2 invariably increase minute ventilation, higher levels of inspired CO_2 (>3%) may further excite [*Coluber, Drymarchon, Varanus* (23, 57)] or depress ventilation [*Crotaphytus, Lacerta, Acrochordus, Natrix* (21, 24, 56, 76)] because of further decreases or increases in T_{NVP}. The reasons for such disparate results remain unclear.

Given the relationship that exists between T_{NVP} and levels of inspired O_2 or CO_2 in different species, it is hard to draw any firm conclusions about the relative roles of changes in blood gases in determining the length of the ventilatory pause. It is clear that broad oscillations of P_{O_2} and, to a lesser extent, P_{CO_2} occur in lungs, blood, and presumably tissues with accompanying pH fluctuations in body fluids. These fluctuations are greater in species with episodic breathing patterns caused by the longer periods of breath holding but are, nonetheless, ubiquitous to all species.

Mechanoreceptor information arising from the lungs has also been shown to play a role in determining the length of T_{NVP}. As mentioned earlier, increasing the resting lung volume of the turtle, *Chrysemys picta,* resulted in increases in T_{NVP}. Similar effects of changes in V_{LR} on T_{NVP} have also been reported for the Atlantic loggerhead turtle, *Caretta caretta* (29, 49), as well as

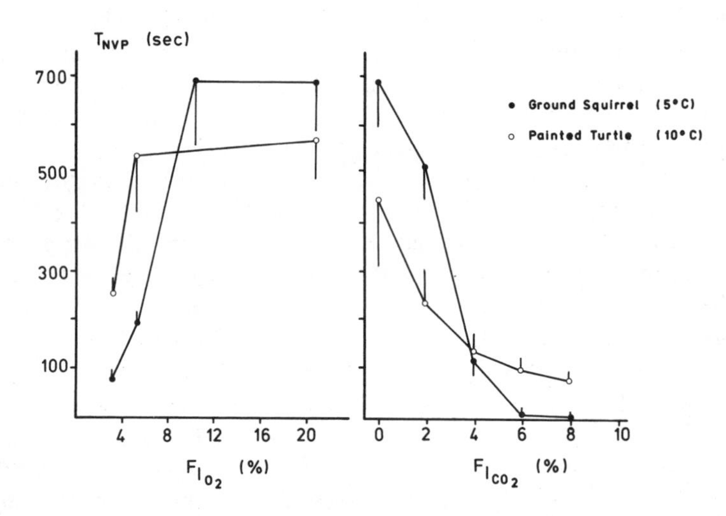

Figure 6 The relationship between the changes in the length of the ventilatory pause (T_{NVP}) and levels of inspired O_2 ($F_{I_{O_2}}$) and CO_2 ($F_{I_{CO_2}}$) in the turtle, *Chrysemys picta* and the hibernating ground squirrel, *Spermophilus lateralis*. (from 19; C. Webb, W. Milsom, unpublished).

for birds (3) and mammals (17). A consequence of the progressive decline in respiratory quotient in the lungs of many reptile species during breath holding resulting from CO_2 storage and/or CO_2 excretion via extrapulmonary routes (1, 11) is that lung volume will decline during breath holding as a function of the end-inspiratory lung volume and the rate and extent of oxygen consumption. Since this fall in lung volume should stimulate ventilation, it has been suggested that this could provide a correlation between breathing frequency and metabolic rate, independent of chemical stimuli (30). Despite these correlations, however, there is still a high degree of variability in the breath hold lengths measured at any given resting lung volume (1, 11, 49).

Arousal state is another factor that can have a profound effect on the length of the ventilatory pause. Thus the presence or absence of predators affects the frequency of air breathing in air-breathing fish (38). Changes in central arousal state affect the length of the ventilatory pause in hibernating squirrels and may mimic changes in sleep state, which are known to initiate intermittent breathing in humans (47, 51, 59).

Finally, it was recently shown that episodic breathing persists in reptiles on unidirectional ventilation (with gas containing some CO_2) despite the fact that both lung gas and blood gas compositions remain constant (M. Douse, G. Mitchell, unpublished). Since the breathing episodes have no effect on arterial blood gases under these conditions, these data suggest that on and off thresholds for initiating and terminating breathing episodes, in terms of blood gas concentrations, do not exist as such.

Thus the reported relationship between lung volume, lung gas stores, blood gas composition, and metabolic rate, along with the lack of a clear correlation between T_{NVP} and any single variable, suggest that T_{NVP} is most likely controlled by an interaction between several variables, including input from the peripheral and central chemoreceptors, pulmonary mechanoreceptors, and the level of central excitation of the animal. At present, however, there is insufficient data to define the mechanism for initiating and terminating the non-ventilatory period in such terms.

SUMMARY

The respiratory control system of animals exhibiting intermittent breathing patterns allows significant fluctuations in all respiratory variables. The extent of these fluctuations can be quite large, particularly in those species with episodic breathing patterns. In these animals, blood gases and pH seem to be regulated within a homeostatic range. Pattern generation in these animals would seem, therefore, to be less dependent on a central rhythm generator and more closely dependent on inputs from peripheral receptor systems and higher brain stem centers. The evidence does suggest, however, that the medulla is the important region for central nervous system coordination of ventilation in these animals just as it is in rhythmic breathers.

Peripheral input from mechanoreceptors associated with the lungs and chemoreceptors associated with the lungs and/or arterial blood appear important in regulating (*a*) the tidal volume of each breath, (*b*) the length of the ventilatory period, and (*c*) the length of the ventilatory pause. One of the more important conclusions that can be drawn from the data is that all three variables appear to be under separate control. The relative roles of the various receptor groups in the control of each respiratory variable remain unclear. Given the intermittent nature of the breathing, broad oscillations occur in the P_{O_2}, and to a lesser extent, P_{CO_2} in lungs, blood, and presumably tissues, with accompanying pH fluctuations in body fluids.

Although the functional significance of the two distinct ventilatory patterns seen in these animals remains unclear, the fact that the episodic breathing pattern can be converted to a single breath pattern experimentally, suggests that both patterns are manifestations of a common underlying control system. The data suggest that the episodic breathing pattern arises from a single breath pattern as a consequence of vagally modulated input from supramedullary centers in the brain.

The similarities between the data collected from all vertebrates is striking. These similarities suggest that a common mechanism may underlie the various intermittent breathing patterns seen under physiologic conditions in all vertebrates. The conversion of continuous breathing to intermittent breathing in some fish in normoxic or hyperoxic water, as well as in squirrels entering hibernation, further suggests that both continuous and intermittent breathing are manifestations of a common control system. Although it is still too early to do more than speculate, the possibility exists that intermittent breathing may be the consequence of a reduced metabolic rate (the one factor ectotherms and hibernating and sleeping endotherms have in common) such that animals no longer need to breath continuously to meet metabolic demands. Under these conditions, the patterns of intermittent breathing that appear may represent adaptive strategies that, in part, serve to minimize the cost of ventilation. What little data have been collected to date are consistent with such a unifying hypothesis.

Given the information presented above, it seems clear that an understanding of the central coordination of intermittent ventilation is essential, not only for describing the evolution of breathing patterns, but also for understanding the control mechanisms that produce continuous, rhythmic ventilation. This area, however, remains one about which surprisingly little is known, but in which great potential for progress exists.

Acknowledgments

I am grateful to my graduate students for their contributions to the work presented here. Financial support was provided by the National Science and Engineering Research Council of Canada.

Literature Cited

1. Ackerman, R. A., White, F. N. 1979. Cyclic carbon dioxide exchange in the turtle *Pseudemys scripta*. *Physiol. Zool.* 52:378–89
2. Adrian, E. D., Buytendijk, F. J. J. 1931. Potential changes in the isolated brain stem of goldfish. *J. Physiol.* 71:121–35
3. Ballam, G. O., Clanton, T. L., Kunz, A. L. 1982. Ventilatory phase duration in the chicken, role of mechanical and CO_2 feedback. *J. Appl. Physiol.* 53:1378–85
4. Ballintijn, C. M. 1982. Neural control of respiration in fishes and mammals. In *Exogenous and Endogenous Influences on Metabolic and Neural Control*, ed. A. S. F. Addink, N. Spronk, pp. 127–40. New York: Pergamon
5. Ballintijn, C. M. 1988. Evolution of central nervous control of ventilation in vertebrates. In *The Neurobiology of the Cardio-Respiratory System*, ed. E. W. Taylor, pp. 3–27. Manchester: Manchester Univ. Press
6. Benchetrit, G., Dejours, P. 1980. Ventilatory carbon dioxide drive in the tortoise *Testudo horsefeldii*. *J. Exp. Biol.* 87:229–36
7. Bennett, A. F. 1973. Ventilation in two species of lizards during rest and activity. *Comp. Biochem. Physiol.* 46A:653–72
8. Boutilier, R. G., Shelton, G. 1986. Gas exchange, storage and transport in voluntarily diving *Xenopus laevis*. *J. Exp. Biol.* 126:133–55
9. Boutilier, R. G., Shelton, G. 1986. Respiratory properties of blood from voluntarily and forcibly submerged *Xenopus laevis*. *J. Exp. Biol.* 121:285–300
10. Bradley, G. W., Von Euler, C., Marttila, I., Roos, B. 1975. A model of the central and reflex inhibition of inspiration in the cat. *Biol. Cybern.* 19:105–16
11. Burggren, W. W., Shelton, G. 1979.

Gas exchange and transport during intermittent breathing in chelonian reptiles. *J. Exp. Biol.* 82:75–92
12. Clark, F. J., Von Euler, C. 1972. On the regulation of rate and depth of breathing. *J. Physiol.* 222:267–95
13. Davey, N. J., Seller, T. J. 1987. Brain mechanisms for respiratory control. In *Bird Respiration*, ed. T. Seller, pp. 169–88. Boca Raton, Fla: CRC
14. Dmiel, R. 1972. Effect of activity and temperature on metabolism and water loss in snakes. *Am. J. Physiol.* 223:510–16
15. Fedde, M. R., Peterson, D. F. 1970. Intrapulmonary receptor response to changes in airway-gas composition in *Gallus domesticus*. *J. Physiol.* 209:609–25
16. Feldman, J. L., Smith, J. C., McCrimmon, D. R., Ellenberger, H. H., Speck, D. F. 1988. Generation of repiratory pattern in mammals. In *Neural Control of Rythmic Movements in Vertebrates*, ed. A. Cohen, pp. 73–100. New York: Wiley
17. Finkler, J., Iscoe, S. 1984. Control of breathing at elevated lung volumes in anesthetized cats. *J. Appl. Physiol.* 56:839–44
18. Frankel, H. M., Spitzer, A., Blaine, J., Schoener, E. P. 1969. Respiratory response of turtles *(Pseudemys scripta)* to changes in arterial blood gas composition. *Comp. Biochem. Physiol.* 31:535–46
19. Glass, M. L., Boutilier, R. G., Heisler, N. 1983. Ventilatory control of arterial PO_2 in the turtle *Chrysemys picta bellii:* effects of temperature and hypoxia. *J. Comp. Physiol.* 151:145–53
20. Glass, M. L., Burggren, W. W., Johansen, K. 1978. Ventilation in an aquatic and a terrestrial chelonian reptile. *J. Exp. Biol.* 72:165–79
21. Glass, M. L., Johansen, K. 1976. Control of breathing in *Acrochordus javanicus,* an aquatic snake. *Physiol. Zool.* 49:328–40
22. Glass, M. L., Johansen, K. 1979. Periodic breathing in the crocodile, *Crocodylus niloticus:* consequences for the gas exchange ratio and control of breathing. *J. Exp. Biol.* 208:319–26
23. Glass, M. L., Wood, S. C. 1983. Gas exchange and control of breathing in reptiles. *Physiol. Rev.* 63:232–60
24. Gratz, R. K. 1979. Ventilatory response of the diamond back water snake, *Natrix rhombifera,* to hypoxia, hypercapnia and increased oxygen demand. *J. Comp. Physiol.* 129:105–10
25. Hammel, H. T., Dawson, T. J., Abrams, R. M., Andersen, H. T. 1968. Total calorimetric measurements on *Citellus lateralis* in hibernation. *Physiol. Zool.* 41:341–57
26. Hukuhara, T. 1976. Functional organization of brain stem respiratory neurons and its afferences. In *Respiratory Centers and Afferent Systems,* ed. B. Duran, pp. 41–53. Paris: INSERM
27. Hukuhara, T., Okada, H. 1956. On automaticity of the respiratory centers of the catfish and crucian carp. *Jpn. J. Physiol.* 6:313–20
28. Jackson, D. C., Palmer, S. E., Meadow, W. L. 1974. The effect of temperature and carbon dioxide breathing on ventilation and acid-base status of turtles. *Respir. Physiol.* 20:131–46
29. Jacobs, W. 1939. Die Lunge der Seeschildkrote *Caretta caretta* (L) als Schwebeorgan. *Z. Vgl. Physiol.* 27:1–28
30. Johansen, K. 1970. Air breathing in fishes. In: *Fish Physiology IV,* ed. W. S. Hoar, D. J. Randall, pp. 361–411. London: Academic
31. Jones, D. R., Milsom, W. K. 1979. Functional characteristics of slowly adapting pulmonary stretch receptors in the turtle (*Chrysemys picta*). *J. Physiol.* 291:37–49
32. Jones, D. R., Milsom, W. K. 1982. Peripheral receptors affecting breathing and cardiovascular function in nonmammalian vertebrates. *J. Exp. Biol.* 100:59–91
33. Juch, P. J. W., Ballintijn, C. M. 1983. Tegmental neurons controlling medullary respiratory centre activity in the carp. *Respir. Physiol.* 51:95–107
34. Juch, P. J. W., Luiten, P. G. M. 1981. Anatomy of respiratory rhythmic systems in brainstem and cerebellum. *Brain Res.* 230:51–64
35. Kawasaki, R. 1979. Breathing rhythmgeneration in the adult lamprey, *Entosphenus japonicus*. *Jpn. J. Physiol.* 29:327–38
36. Kawasaki, R. 1984. Breathing rhythmgeneration mechanism in the adult lamprey, *Lampetra japonica*. *Jpn. J. Physiol.* 34:319–35
37. Kinney, T. L., White, F. N. 1977. Oxidative cost of ventilation in a turtle, *Pseudemys floridana*. *Respir. Physiol.* 31:327–32
38. Krammer, D. L. 1988. The behavioral ecology of air breathing by aquatic animals. *Can. J. Zool.* 66:89–94
39. Kunz, A. L. 1987. Peripheral mechanisms in the control of breathing. See Ref. 13, pp. 129–67
40. Lenfant, C., Johansen, K., Peterson, J. A., Schmidt-Nielsen, K. 1970. Respiration in the fresh water turtle *Chelys fimbriata*. *Respir. Physiol.* 8:261–75

41. Lomholt, J. P., Johansen, K. 1979. Hypoxia acclimation in carp—how it effects O_2 uptake, ventilation, and O_2 extraction from water. *Physiol. Zool.* 52:38–49
42. Lumsden, T. 1924. Chelonian respiration (tortoise). *J. Physiol.* 58:259–66
43. Malan, A. 1977. Blood acid-base state at a variable temperature: a graphical presentation. *Respir. Physiol.* 31:259–75
44. Malan, A., Arens, H., Walchter, A. 1973. Pulmonary respiration and acid-base state in hibernating marmots and hamsters. *Respir. Physiol.* 17:45–61
45. Milsom, W. K. 1984. The interrelationship between pulmonary mechanics and the spontaneous breathing pattern in the Tokay lizard, *Gekko gecko. J. Exp. Biol.* 113:203–14
46. Milsom, W. K. 1988. Control of arrhythmic breathing in aerial breathers. *Can. J. Zool.* 66:99–108
47. Milsom, W. K. 1990. Control of breathing during hibernation. In *Lung Biology in Health and Disease. Strategies of Physiological Adaptation,* ed. C. Lenfant, S. C. Wood, R. E. Weber, New York: Dekker
48. Milsom, W. K., Chan, P. 1986. The relationship between lung volume, respiratory drive and breathing pattern in the turtle, *Chrysemys picta. J. Exp. Biol.* 120:233–47
49. Milsom, W. K., Johansen, K. 1975. The effect of buoyancy induced lung volume changes on respiratory frequency in a chelonian *(Caretta caretta). J. Comp. Physiol.* 98:157–60
50. Milsom, W. K., Jones, D. R. 1980. The role of vagal afferent information and hypercapnia in control of the breathing pattern in chelonia. *J. Exp. Biol.* 87:53–63
51. Milsom, W. K., Krilowicz, B., Grahn, D., Radeke, C., Heller, H. C. 1989. Is periodic breathing "arousal-state" dependent? *Soc. Neurosci. Abst.* 15:244
52. Milsom, W. K., McArthur, M. D., Webb, C. L. 1986. Control of breathing in hibernating ground squirrels. In: *Living in the Cold: Physiological and Biochemical Adaptations,* ed. H. C. Heller, X. J. Mussachia L. C. H. Wang, pp. 467–75. New York: Elsevier
53. Milsom, W. K., Vitalis, T. Z. 1984. Pulmonary mechanisms and the work of breathing in the lizard *Gekko gecko. J. Exp. Biol.* 113:187–202
54. Naifeh, K. H., Huggins, S. E., Hoff, H. E. 1971. Study of the control of crocodilian respiration by anaesthetic dissection. *Respir. Physiol.* 12:251–60
55. Naifeh, K. H., Huggins, S. E., Hoff, H. E. 1971. Effects of brain stem section on respiratory patterns of crocodilian reptiles. *Respir. Physiol.* 13:186–97
56. Nielsen, B. 1961. On the regulation of the respiration in reptiles. I. The effect of temperature and CO_2 on the respiration of lizards (*Lacerta*). *J. Exp. Biol.* 38:301–14
57. Nolan, W. F., Frankel, H. M. 1982. Ventilatory responses to CO_2 at different body temperatures in the snake, *Coluber constrictor. Experientia* 38:943–45
58. Peterson, D. F., Fedde, M. R. 1968. Receptors sensitive to carbon dioxide in lungs of chicken. *Science* 162:1449–1501
59. Phillipson, E. A., Bowes, G. 1986. Control of breathing during sleep. *Handb. Physiol. Section 3,* 2:649
60. Phillipson, E. A., Duffin, J., Cooper, J. D. 1981. Critical dependence of respiratory rhythmicity on metabolic CO_2 load. *J. Appl. Physiol.* 50:45–54
61. Ray, P. J., Fedde, M. R. 1969. Response to alterations in respiratory P_{O_2} and P_{CO_2} in the chicken. *Respir. Physiol.* 6:135–43
62. Roberts, J. L. 1975. Active branchial and ram gill ventilation in fishes. *Biol. Bull.* 148:85–105
63. Roberts, J. L., Ballintijn, C. M. 1988. Sensory interactions with central 'generators' during respiration in the dogfish. *J. Comp. Physiol.* 162:695–704
64. Rovainen, C. M. 1974. Respiratory motoneurons in lampreys. *J. Comp. Physiol.* 94:57–68
65. Rovainen, C. M. 1977. Neural control of ventilation in the lamprey. *Fed. Proc.* 36:2386–89
66. Russell, D. F. 1986. Respiratory pattern generation in adult lamprey *(Lampetra fluviatilis)* interneurons and burst resetting. *J. Comp. Physiol.* 158:91–102
67. Scheid, P., Piiper, J. 1986. Control of breathing in birds. See Ref. 59, pp. 815–32
68. Shelton, D. 1970. The regulation of breathing. In *Fish Physiology, The Nervous System, Circulation and Respiration,* ed. W. S. Hoar, D. J. Randall, 4:293–359. New York: Academic
69. Shelton, G., Boutilier, R. G. 1982. Apnoea in amphibians and reptiles. *J. Exp. Biol.* 100:245–273
70. Shelton, G., Jones, D. R., Milsom, W. K. 1986. Control of breathing in ectothermic vertebrates. See Ref. 59, pp. 857–909
71. Smith, J. C., Feldman, J. L. 1987. Central respiratory pattern generation studied in an in vitro mammalian brain

stem-spinal cord preparation. In *Respiratory Muscles and Their Neuromotor Control,* ed. G. C. Sieck, S. Gondevia, W. C. Cameron, pp. 27–36. New York: Liss
72. St. John, W. M., Bartlett, D. Jr., Knuth, V., Hwang, J. C. 1981. Brain stem genesis of automatic ventilatory patterns independent of spinal mechanism. *J. Appl. Physiol.* 51:204–10
73. Sullivan, C. E., Kozar, F., Murphy, E., Phillipson, E. A. 1978. Primary role of respiratory afferents in sustaining breathing rhythm. *J. Appl. Physiol.* 45:11–17
74. Suzue, T. 1984. Respiratory rhythm generation in the in vitro brain stem-spinal cord preparation of the neonatal rat. *J. Physiol.* 354:135–52
75. Tahti, H., Soivio, A. 1975. Blood gas concentrations acid-base balance and blood pressure in hedgehogs in the active state and in hibernation with periodic respiration. *Ann. Zool. Fenn.* 12:188–92
76. Templeton, J. R., Dawson, W. R. 1963. Respiration in the lizard *Crotaphytus collaris. Physiol. Zool.* 36:104–21
77. Vitalis, T. Z., Milsom, W. K. 1986. Pulmonary mechanics and the work of breathing in the semi-aquatic turtle, *Pseudemys scripta. J. Exp. Biol.* 125:137–55
78. Vitalis, T. Z., Milsom, W. K. 1986. Mechanical analysis of spontaneous breathing in the semi-aquatic turtle, *Pseudemys scripta. J. Exp. Biol.* 125:157–71

Annu. Rev. Physiol. 1991. 53:107–35

ONTOGENY OF CARDIOVASCULAR AND RESPIRATORY PHYSIOLOGY IN LOWER VERTEBRATES

Warren W. Burggren

Department of Zoology, University of Massachusetts, Amherst, Massachusetts 01003-0027

Alan W. Pinder

Department of Biology, Dalhousie University, Halifax, Nova Scotia B3H 4J1 Canada

KEY WORDS: development, heart, lung, gill, gas exchange

INTRODUCTION

The ontogeny of cardiovascular and respiratory physiology in vertebrates has been, and continues to be, an area of intense study (45, 87, 124, 28, 105, see *Annual Review of Physiology* 1984. 46:617–703). While clinical benefits accrue from a knowledge of the developmental physiology of fetal mammals, much of the motivation for general vertebrate research on this topic stems from a fascination with the inherent complexity of developmental transitions of these systems. Indeed, some of the most radical developmental transitions of any organ system occur in heart, vasculature, and gas exchange organs of animals as they make the transition from embryonic/larval/fetal life to that of free-living animals.

This review examines the cardiovascular and respiratory transitions that accompany development in fishes, amphibians, and reptiles. In many cases these processes are very similar to those occurring in birds and mammals and reflect the strong commonalities of vertebrate development. There are also fascinating differences, however, that deserve emphasis. Unfortunately, all

0066-4278/91/0315-0107$02.00

too often the critical experiments remain to be performed, and therefore a major purpose of this review is to emphasize particular areas for fruitful future research.

WHY STUDY DEVELOPMENTAL PHYSIOLOGY IN LOWER VERTEBRATES?

Many aspects of the developmental transitions in cardiovascular and respiratory physiology are now well understood for mammals (although this must be qualified by recognizing that in reality it is primarily the late fetus rather than the mammalian embryo that is routinely investigated). The cardio-respiratory transitions in birds are also well appreciated, especially since the embryos of birds currently serve as the major model for investigation of the mammalian embryonic circulation (for reviews see 34, 35, 87). Far less is known about the developmental changes in cardio-respiratory physiology of fishes, amphibians, and reptiles, and virtually none of the tremendous diversity of physiology typical for these vertebrates has been described in a developmental context.

There are several important reasons for expanding this fragmentary knowledge of the developmental changes in the cardio-respiratory physiology of lower vertebrates. First, many lower vertebrates provide excellent experimental models that allow the investigator to distinguish physiologic changes associated with organogenesis, the differentiation of tissue and production of new tissues and organs, from processes associated with simple growth, in which tissue mass can increase without the qualitative change associated with tissue differentiation. "Immature animals are small—mature animals are big" is a truism, but the implications for studies of the development of cardio-respiratory physiology are often not recognized (or, if recognized, are often avoided). A vast body of literature deals with the considerable influence of body mass on physiologic processes in all vertebrates (32, 127, 112). Because the adults of a given species of bird and mammal almost always have a body mass that is far greater than that of embryos, larvae, and fetuses, and because developmental transitions usually occur at approximately the same body mass in all individuals, it is often difficult to distinguish between physiologic changes that occur simply because an animal has grown to a larger body mass from those that reflect true tissue differentiation. In many species of lower vertebrates, however, major developmental changes can occur at any of a variety of body masses. For example in the bullfrog, *Rana catesbeiana,* larval bullfrogs undergo metamorphosis to the juveniles when body mass ranges anywhere from about 5 g up to 50 or more g (similar situations arise in other amphibians and some fishes). Figure 1 shows heart mass (which is correlated with physiologic variables such as stroke volume) as a function of body mass. The effects of body mass on heart mass can be assessed independently for larvae and adults from an examination of the slope of the line for larvae and for post-metamorphic adults. In each of these two broad developmental groups, heart mass increases approximately in proportion to body mass. In the area of body mass overlap between the two developmental groups, however, metamorphosis to the adult body form *(vertical arrows)* results in an increase in the intercept of the line describing the relationship between heart mass and body mass. Thus metamorphic climax at constant body mass results in an increased heart mass in *Rana catesbeiana*—a pure developmental effect unrelated to scaling. By choosing species and designing similar experiments that emphasize rather than minimize variation in body mass, the specific effects of growth can begin to be separated from those of organogenesis (17).

A second compelling reason for studying the development of physiologic

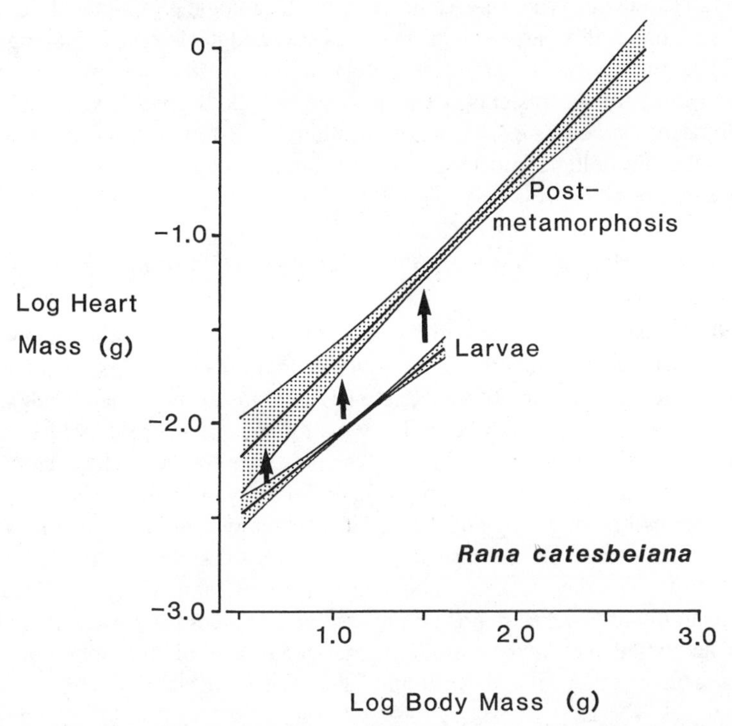

Figure 1 The relationship between heart mass and body mass in larvae and post-metamorphic juveniles and adults of the bullfrog, *Rana catesbeiana*. Linear regressions and 95% confidence intervals are provided. *Vertical arrows* from larvae to adults indicate the effect on heart mass of metamorphosis without change in body mass (essentially an upward shift in the Y-intercept of the relationship between these two variables). (W. Burggren, unpublished)

processes in lower vertebrates is that potentially they can provide important insights into the evolution of such processes (13, 14, 16–18). Of course, the concept that "ontogeny recapitulates phylogeny" is now widely recognized as overly simplistic and even anachronistic, but this does not mean that evolutionary biologists are uninterested in ontogeny. For example, the development of respiratory physiology in animals undergoing the developmental transition from water to air breathing can provide insights into feasible evolutionary steps towards air breathing and terrestriality (see 16, 18).

Finally, the study of immature stages of mammals or birds provides neither better nor worse insights into vertebrate development than does the study of the embryos and larvae of fishes, amphibians, and reptiles. There is no single vertebrate embryo that is truly representative of development in all vertebrates. For example, the current important role of the chick embryo is based as much on convenience and accessibility to material as on how representative it may be. The point is that we now need to expand our studies to understand the full extent and types of variation within physiologic development throughout vertebrates if we are to claim a general knowledge of vertebrate ontogeny.

Thus the study of cardio-respiratory ontogeny in lower vertebrates is compelling for the insights it can provide into both general vertebrate development as well as evolutionary questions. We now turn to the ontogeny of these physiologic processes in circulation and gas exchange in lower vertebrates.

THE CIRCULATION AND ITS REGULATION

The heart is the first organ to function in any vertebrate embryo, and the cardiovascular system is the first organ system to operate. This, plus the fact that the circulation in lower vertebrate embryos is prominent and easily observed through the embryonic body wall under the microscope, has made the embryonic circulation of lower vertebrates a source of fascination for anatomists for more than a century (see 66 for early literature). The ontogenetic changes in morphology of the cardiovascular system of amphibians (and, to a lesser extent, fishes) have been extensively described (see 11, 94–96, 103, 124). Yet, despite a substantial anatomical literature on the cardiovascular anatomy of lower vertebrate embryos, we know comparatively little about the hemodynamics and neural/hormonal regulation of the embryonic cardiovascular system of fishes, amphibians, and reptiles.

Heart Rate

RESTING HEART RATE Perhaps because it is the most easily quantified, developmental changes in heart rate (f_H) and the ontogeny of the cardiac regulatory system have received most attention. Invariably, resting f_H changes as development proceeds from embryo through larva to adult. The pattern of change, however, varies between species and does not correlate with vertebrate class or even with families. In larval rainbow trout, resting f_H at 10°C increases from around 60 beats/min at hatching to about 70 beats/min 3 days later, but then declines again to about 50 beats/min 21 days after hatching (75). A similar pattern of change in resting f_H during larval development occurs in the brown trout *Salmo trutta* (68), and f_H also decreases during the first 50 days of larval development in the Arctic char *Salvelinus alpinus* (102). Resting f_H at 18°C in the embryos of the skate *Raja erinacea* is about 40 beats/min when the heart first begins to beat in embryos (about 30 days after fertilization at body mass about 20–50 mg) (109a). With further growth, heart rate rises to 60 beats/min and then falls again to 35–40 beats/min before birth (about five months after fertilization and 5 g body mass). Unfortunately the mechanism(s) behind these changes in resting f_H in embryonic and larval fishes remains unknown. Possible explanations include developmental changes in the membrane permeability of the cardiac pacemaker (i.e. a change in the intrinsic rate of the heart) as well as the onset of sympathetic and parasympathetic cardiac tone.

Developmental changes in resting f_H also occur in anuran amphibians. In the bullfrog *Rana catesbeiana,* resting f_H in newly hatched larvae (about 40 mg body mass—stage I in the Taylor-Kollros (TK) staging system) is approximately 135 beats/min at 20–23°C, but falls sharply with further larval development (19). From TK stages IV–VII to metamorphic climax (body mass range 2–20 g), resting f_H remains at about 40–50 beats/min, but then shows a final development change by dropping to 20–30 beats/min in the mature bullfrog (400 g). When log heart rate is plotted against log body mass for *Rana catesbeiana,* the data for all animals, regardless of developmental stage, fall along a single line with the equation $y = -0.23x + 1.85$ (W. Burggren, unpublished). Resting heart rate thus scales with body mass to the exponent -0.23, compared with a value based on interspecific comparisons between adults of about -0.25 (32, 112, 127). This suggests that changes in resting f_H between newly hatched larvae and mature bullfrogs can be correlated almost entirely on the basis of allometry (scaling) rather than organogenesis or other qualitative changes associated with ontogeny.

Resting f_H in the direct developing frog *Eleuthrodactylus coqui* shows a particularly complex pattern of change with development (25). The first heart beats, recorded in intact 3 mg embryos by visual observation through the transparent egg capsule, occur at a frequency of about 50 beats/min at 24–25°C, but increase sharply to about 100 beats/min with a slight body mass increase and further embryonic development (Figure 2). During most of the remainder of embryonic development, which sees large increases in both body mass and tissue differentiation, resting f_H shows a relatively modest further increase to about 110–120 beats/min immediately before hatching as a

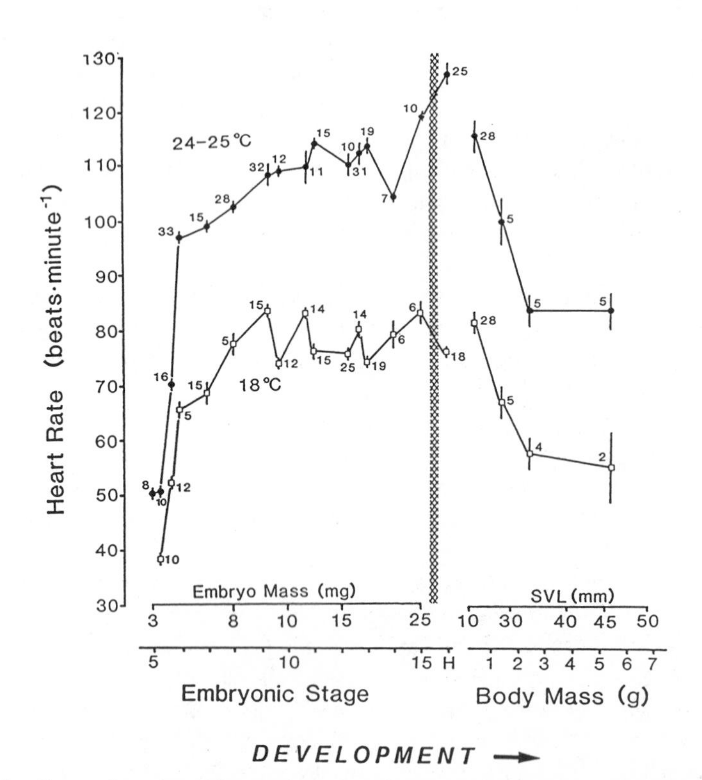

Figure 2 Changes in resting heart rate (mean ± 1 sec) during development in the Puerto Rican anuran frog *Eleutherodactylus coqui*. Heart rate data begin with the developmental stage in which the heart first beats. The *vertical hatched bar* indicates the point of development of the air-breathing adult morph (from Burggren et al, 25).

miniature adult. After hatching, resting f_H decreases from about 130 beats/min in hatchlings (<100 mg) to about 85 beats/min in the largest adults (6 g). Although at 18°C f_H is lower, this general pattern of development change in f_H persists. While changes in body mass alone no doubt influences f_H in *E. coqui,* especially after hatching, the sharp increase during early development with very little change in body mass indicates that heart rate is responding to undetermined developmental changes unrelated to simple changes in body mass.

The mechanism underlying these varying patterns of developmental changes in resting f_H in larvae of anuran amphibians awaits complete description, as it does for larval fishes. A vagal tone at rest appears in mid-larval development in *Rana catesbeiana* and results in a resting f_H about 10 beats/min lower than the intrinsic rate determined after combined cholinerginic and beta-adrenergic blockade (19). Interestingly, after metamorphosis, resting f_H is actually the intrinsic heart rate, since the sequential administration of atropine (a muscarinic cholinergic blocker) and propranolol (a beta-adrenergic blocker) to resting adult bullfrogs produces no change in f_H.

To our knowledge (and surprise), measurements of resting heart rate have yet to be made in intact reptile embryos, perhaps in part because of the opaque and generally more robust nature of the reptilian egg shell. Considerable literature exists on the metabolism and hydric relations of reptile embryos in their eggs (e.g. 135, 109), and physiologic observations of the ontogeny of the cardiovascular system should allow a much more integrated view of reptilian development prior to hatching.

HEART RATE AND ENVIRONMENTAL FACTORS Hypoxia challenges any cardiovascular and respiratory system and can occur in embryos within the specialized environments of the egg, oviduct, or uterus, which impose an additional diffusional boundary for respiratory gas transfer. Additionally, frequent and severe environmental hypoxia can characterize the freshwater habitats in which embryonic and larval fishes and amphibians develop. As adults, many lower vertebrates respond to environmental hypoxia with a bradycardia of varying magnitude (see 83, 106, 129). This response, however, appears to be absent in larval salmonid fishes (60, 75, 102) as well as in larval anuran amphibians beyond TK stage IV (50, 51, 56, 120, 143). Newly hatched larval *Rana catesbeiana* do show a sharp decrease in f_H when ambient PO_2 falls below about 40–50 mmHg, but this probably represents a direct cardiac depression caused by tissue hypoxia rather than a reflex slowing of heart beat (11).

The lack of a hypoxic bradycardia in lower vertebrate embryos does not, however, mean that the embryonic or larval heart is a metronome that is unresponsive to changes in the internal or external environment. Indeed, hypoxia results in a mild tachycardia in larval rainbow trout (75) and Arctic char (102). Voluntary locomotor activity produces a mild tachycardia even in one-day old larval trout (75). Voluntary activity has no effect on f_H in one-day old bullfrog larvae, but in all later developmental stages spontaneous movement is accompanied by a tachycardia (19). The mechanism behind exercise tachycardia has been investigated in the bullfrog. Experiments involving saline infusion into the central venous circulation of bullfrog larvae (i.e. increasing pre-load) produces a tachycardia in control larvae and also in larvae with confirmed cholinergic and beta-adrenergic blockade (19). This suggests that the tachycardia during exercise can result in part from direct effects of stretch on the cardiac pacemaker produced by enhanced venous return during activity. In the adult bullfrog, however, the activity tachycardia appears to result primarily from beta-adrenergic cardiac stimulation.

An increase in f_H occurs during the stress of hatching in the direct developing frog, *Eleuthrodactylus coqui* (25). Prior to hatching, the resting f_H in undisturbed animals within the egg is about 120 beats/min. The act of hatching, which is an explosive event requiring a few seconds of intense locomotor activity, results in an increase in f_H to nearly 160 beats/min within a min or less of hatching, and which persists for at least two hr following hatching. Because direct developing anurans like *E. coqui* hatch as miniature adults that are active predators, the hatchlings probably require all of the cardiovascular reflexes evident in the larger, mature adults.

CARDIO-RESPIRATORY COUPLING Interactions between cardiac and ventilatory events are commonplace in adult fishes, amphibians, and reptiles (83, 129, 142). Such interactions include phase locking between the ventilation cycle and the cardiac cycle, as well as diving bradycardia (or, alternatively, ventilation tachycardia) in intermittent air breathers. In some instances interactions between cardiac and ventilatory events are manifestations of reflex connections between peripheral chemo- and/or mechanoreceptors; in other instances they may represent the direct communication within the brain between cardiac and respiratory centers (see 57).

Cardio-respiratory phase coupling has been reported in larvae of the anurans *Xenopus laevis, Pachymedusa dacnicolor,* and *Rana berlandieri* (140), but its distinct absence has also been reported in larval *Rana catesbeiana* and *Rana berlandieri* (24, 144). Phase locking between cardiac and ventilatory cycles has not been reported in early larval stages of fishes or amphibians. This may reflect the fact that, at least in normoxia, the early buccal pumping movements that force water over the developing internal gills have an intermittent, erratic nature (e.g. 75, 102).

Ventilation tachycardia has been described repeatedly in adult air-breathing fishes (see 26, 27). Since air breathing starts relatively early in some air-breathing species, it would be of considerable interest to know if cardio-respiratory interactions develop equally early. Unfortunately, little is known about the ontogeny of the respiratory physiology of any air-breathing fish (see below). Virtually nothing can be said about the physiologic development of the complex cardiovascular system of air-breathing fishes, which generally have both gills and accessory gas exchange organs (lung, gas bladder, or modified branchial chamber). A noteworthy observation, however, involves the strictly aquatic larvae of the air-breathing fish *Monopterus albus* (93). In the early larval stages prior to establishment of internal gill ventilation, the pectoral fins produce a flow of water from anterior to posterior over the surface of the body wall. This in itself is not remarkable, and indeed water currents over the body surface have been observed in several fish larvae (see 124). In *Monopterus albus,* however, the flow of blood in the capillaries of the skin is from posterior to anterior. Thus cutaneous gas exchange operates as a countercurrent mechanism, which allows *Monopterus* to remove 40% of the available O_2 from the stream of water passing over the body surface. Whether such a mechanism occurs in other fishes, or indeed in larval amphibians where the ciliated surface of the embyro can generate a coordinated convective flow of perivitilline fluid over the body surface (12), begs further investigation.

In some larval amphibians, f_H is unaffected during bouts of intermittent lung ventilation, with ventilation tachycardia occurring only after metamorphosis to the final adult form (19, 143). Recent measurements on the giant larvae (up to 24 cm, 100 g) of the South American frog *Pseudis paradoxus* have shown that a mild ventilation tachycardia occurs as the larvae float at the water surface and take intermittent air breaths (W. Burggren, M. Glass, A. Abe, E. Bicudo, unpublished). Moreover, when the larvae are prevented from taking air breaths, f_H falls below the normal f_H recorded during the voluntary interbreath interval. Arterial blood PO_2 in unrestrained *Pseudis* varies from a low of 30 mmHg during voluntary breath holding up to 100 mmHg immediately following an air breath, but whether the cardiac reflexes are mediated by these changes in blood PO_2 (or the associated changes in blood O_2 content) awaits further investigation. Ventilation tachycardia has also been noted in larvae of the tiger salamander, *Ambystoma tigrinum* (71).

Pharmacology of the Embryonic and Larval Heart

The cholinergic and adrenergic sensitivity of the cardiac pacemaker changes with development in the bullfrog *Rana catesbeiana*. Dose-response curves for ACh using in situ preparations indicate that the pacemaker's cholinergic sensitivity increases progressively during larval development (20). At metamorphosis, however, there is a sharp decrease in cholinergic sensitivity to levels comparable to the earliest larval stages examined. Dose-response curves for atropine correspondingly indicate that cholinergic blockade of the chronotropic response requires higher dosages in both early larval and post-metamorphic stages than in late larval stages. In vitro studies, using isolated, spontaneously active atria from *Rana cartesbeiana,* indicate that both larval and adult hearts begin to show a heart rate acceleration at similar physiologic doses (about 10^{-7} M) of norepinephrine, but the atrial tissue of adults requires greater doses than does larval tissue to produce maximal adrenergic stimulation (86).

Interestingly, the pattern of developmental change for cholinergic inotropic responses of isolated ventricular strips from *Rana catesbeiana* differ markedly from the chronotropic responses of the intact heart of this species, since the ventricle of the adult bullfrog rather than of the larva is more sensitive to the inhibitory inotropic effects of ACh (S. Petrou, I. Walhquist, W. Burggren, unpublished). Complicating the situation still further, the pattern of developmental change for adrenergic inotropic responses of isolated ventricular strips in vitro is the opposite of inotropic responses produced by ACh—the adult heart is the least sensitive to the inotropic effects of epinephrine (S. Petrou, I. Walhquist, W. Burggren, unpublished).

Developmental changes in chronotropic and inotropic responses to acetylcholine and catecholamines may result from (*a*) changes in the number of receptors in the pacemaker cell membranes, (*b*) changes in affinity of each receptor site, or (*c*) both of these changes. Future investigations of developmental changes in cardiac pharmacology of lower vertebrate embryos should prove to be particularly rewarding.

Central Hemodynamics

The very small size of the heart and central vessels of vertebrate embryos has until recently precluded detailed physiologic measurements of central hemodynamics. The development of new microtechnologies such as pulsed-Doppler and laser blood flow monitoring and microelectrodes for measurement of blood pressure and blood gases has greatly expanded our ability to investigate cardiovascular physiology in vertebrate embryos, larvae, and fetuses. While most of this emerging technology has been applied to the investigation of the central hemodynamics in the chick embryo (see 34, 35, 87), the results of the relatively few measurements that have been made in lower vertebrate embryos are rather intriguing. Ventricular systolic blood pressure has been measured with a microelectrode recording technique in the embryos of the skate *Raja erinacea* (109a). Pressure increases from about 1 mmHg 30 days after fertilization (body mass 10 mg) to about 13 mmHg 144 days after fertilization (body mass 4.4 g), which is close to the end of the five to six month period of embryonic development at 18–20°C. Microelectrode measurements of blood pressure in the ventricle and conus arteriosus have also been made in pithed, immobilized larvae of the bullfrog *Rana catesbeiana* (109b). Marked seasonal differences may occur in the cardiac performance of these anurans. Measurements made during the fall months in early developmental stages (e.g. TK stage II) show that contraction of the conus rather than the ventricle produces the highest arterial pressure at systole. With further development, conal systolic pressures decrease while ventricular systolic pressures rise. By TK stage X–XIII of larval development, the central arterial hemodynamics are essentially the same as those of the post-metamorphic adult. Overall, there is a rise in systolic arterial pressure during larval development, from about 2 mmHg at TK stage II (about 0.3–0.4 g) to about 12 mmHg at TK stage XIV (about 10 g) (all values measured during the fall and winter months).

A similar rise in arterial systolic pressure with larval development has been confirmed using an indwelling sciatic artery cannula in intact, conscious larvae of the frog *Pseudis paradoxis* (W. Burggren, M. Glass, A. Abe, E. Bicudo, unpublished). In this species, however, larval body mass decreases rather than increases with larval development. Systolic pressure also increases by 50% from a mean pressure of about 20 mmHg to about 30 mmHg at metamorphosis, even though there is no body mass change during this final stage of metamorphosis in *Pseudis*. Changes in peripheral resistance, perhaps associated with changes in body mass, as well as developmental changes in gas exchange organs and their blood perfusion pattern may all interact in complex and as yet undetermined ways to alter blood pressure during development.

Finally, cardiac output has been measured in the larvae of the salamander *Ambystoma tigrinum* (76). To our knowledge, this is the only such measurement for lower vertebrate embryos. Cardiac output in conscious, restrained larvae is about 100 ml/kg/min at 20°C, which is within the range reported for adult *Rana, Xenopus,* and *Amphiuma*. Inter-individual variation in cardiac output in larval *Ambystoma tigrinum* results primarily from changes in stroke volume rather than heart rate. How cardiac output varies during locomotor activity, or in response to changes in environmental temperature or oxygen availability, in this, or other lower vertebrate species, awaits further research.

The Pheripheral Circulation

Compared even with our fragmentary knowledge of the ontogeny of central vascular hemodynamics in lower vertebrates, physiologic development of the peripheral circulation is practically unexplored. Many anecdotal observations of capillary recruitment, backwards surging during early diastole, and cessation of arterial flow during diastole have been made, especially for fish embryos and larvae (e.g. 75, 102). Blood flow in the capillary loops of the external gills of larval fishes and amphibians is particularly amenable to observation under the microscope, and velocity can even be measured in individual capillaries using pulsed-Doppler crystals (W. Burggren, unpublished), but few systematic studies have been attempted as yet.

In the larval bullfrog, *Rana catsbeiana,* catecholamines dilated the branchial vasculature of the larvae as early as stage III (86). The branchial vessels of the larvae of the anuran *Litoria ewingi* have an extensive network of shunt vessels (103), but the small size of the larvae is not conducive to pharmacological or physiologic investigation. The much larger size of the larvae of the salamander *Ambystoma* has permitted considerable investigation of the pharmacology of the peripheral vessels, however, especially those in the external gills (39, 94–96). The circulation to gas exchangers in *Ambystoma* is extremely complex (94, 95, 98). The lungs are both in parallel (through the pulmonary artery) and in series (through the ductus arteriosus) with the gill circulation. The gill circulation includes shunts around the gas-exchanging surfaces. The cutaneous circulation is in parallel with the systemic circulation and thus receives at least partially oxygenated blood. In larval *Ambystoma*, lung perfusion is primarily via the ductus arteriosus, in series with gill arches three; when the gills (but not the aortic arches originally supplying the gills) disappear at metamorphosis, the pulmonary artery becomes the source for pulmonary blood (98). In larval *Ambystoma*, severe aquatic hypoxia increases lung perfusion and decreases perfusion of the first gill, perhaps increasing pulmonary oxygen uptake and reducing oxygen loss through the gill. After metamorphosis, pulmonary perfusion is unaffected by aquatic hypoxia (98).

Branchial and proximal pulmonary arteries are under both cholinergic and adrenergic regulation in larval *Ambystoma* (94–96). Vagal stimulation and acetylcholine both vasoconstrict the branchial vessels. The pulmonary artery is constricted by acetylcholine (94, 96) and vagal stimulation (39), but is unaffected by catecholamines. Reciprocal changes in blood flow between the pulmonary and branchial vascular beds can be produced by changes in circulating levels of catecholamines, or neural stimulation, and by those effects on peripheral vascular resistance, as observed in adult amphibians (13, 53). Whether there is a capacity for autoregulation in the circulation of larval *Ambystoma* is unclear. Malvin (95) reports that local alterations in CO_2 and pH do not affect vasomotion in the branchial circulation, in contrast to Figge's (59) earlier studies on this species. Larval *Ambystoma* are obligate air breathers (cf. 13) and possess well-developed lungs even as quite small larvae.

Peripheral circulation in fish and amphibian embryos and larvae will be aided by the rhythmic swimming movements of the body, especially if the veins are extensively valved (a feature of embryonic/larval anatomy that is currently unknown). Evidence for blood convection caused by locomotor activity comes from quite unrelated investigations of cardiac pacemaker physiology. Normal embryonic development of heart structure occurs in so-called cardiac lethal mutants of the salamander *Ambystoma mexicanum*, but the cardiac pacemaker fails to depolarize spontaneously because of low membrane ion permeability (see 85 for review). Interestingly, the cardiac lethal mutants can develop to the point of hatching, and the larvae actually swim and survive for several days, without the heart beat ever beginning. Clearly, in extremely small larvae, a combination of diffusion of gases, nutrients, and wastes, combined with convection generated by body movements powered by skeletal muscles, can substitute effectively for cardiac-derived blood convection. This raises the question of how much the embryonic circulation actually contributes to the transport needs prior to hatching. While the basic physiology of development of cardiac pacemakers in vertebrate hearts has been considerably advanced by studies using these embryonic mutants, their use as a model system to examine the role of the embryonic circulation has been rather neglected to date.

RESPIRATION AND METABOLISM

Respiration and metabolism change dramatically over the course of development of all lower vertebrates. These changes occur in three major categories: (*a*) organogenesis and the differentiation of structures involved in gas exchange and transport; (*b*) increase in size, affecting both metabolic rate and the relative importances of convection and diffusion in gas exchange and transport; and (*c*) transitions in respiratory medium, most dramatically seen in amphibians metamorphosing from aquatic, primarily water-breathing larvae to terrestrial, air-breathing juveniles (Figure 3). At very small body size, diffusion is adequate for gas exchange (Figure 3*a*). At larger sizes and particularly in hypoxic environments, external gas conductance may be increased by external convection generated by cilia or body movements (Figure 3, stage *b*). Small larvae depend largely on cutaneous gas exchange with internal convection for gas transport (external convection is still important) (stage *c*). At larger body sizes, specialized gas exchangers (gills) develop to provide increased surface area for gas exchange, and they must be ventilated (stage *d*). Eventually air is used as an oxygen source and less commonly as a sink for CO_2, with concomitant changes in the gas exchange organ(s) and its regulation (stage *e*). Many fish end development at stage *d*, whereas reptiles pass through stages *a* to *c* in the egg and hatch at stage *e*.

Fish, amphibians, and reptiles differ greatly in their development at hatching (Figure 4). Fish hatch before what is usually thought of as embryonic development is complete; the digestive, respiratory, and cardiovascular sys-

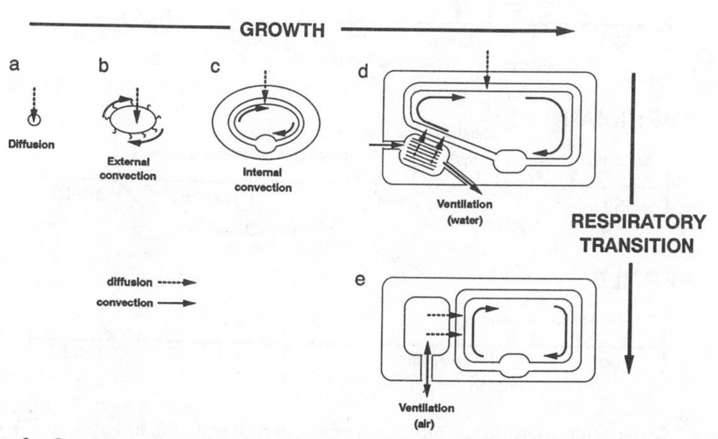

Figure 3 Overview of respiratory development in air-breathing lower vertebrates. Although innumerable variations exist (most of which have not been investigated), this common pattern of development is related to the increase in body size and (with the exception of strictly aquatic fishes and a few amphibians) the respiratory transition from an aquatic larva to an air-breathing or bimodally breathing adult.

tems are commonly not functional and the larva still carries a yolk sac. Fish and amphibians generally hatch as larvae and undergo a more-or-less radical change in body form, function, and life-style (metamorphosis). Reptiles are more completely developed, often appearing like a small version of the adult, and do not undergo metamorphosis. Cardiovascular and especially respiratory development differ greatly in fish, amphibians, and reptiles (Figure 4). Significant events include the initiation of blood circulation, appearance of hemoglobin, and organogenesis of gills and lungs. Except for the great majority of fishes and a few amphibians, air breathing becomes a significant source of oxygen before development to the adult. There is wide variation in the timing of these developmental events within each class (not shown in Figure 4), but even greater variation exists between classes. For example, most fish hatch into larvae before having a functional circulatory system; amphibians hatch into larvae with functional circulation and gills, and reptilian embryos hatch into air-breathing juveniles without any intervening larval stage. Not indicated in Figure 4 is the phenomenon of viviparity, which occurs in many lower vertebrates (see 89 for review).

Metabolism

Metabolic rate determines the rate at which respiratory gas exchange must occur. Metabolism has a number of peculiarities in rapidly growing and differentiating systems; in particular, in the rapid conversion of metabolically

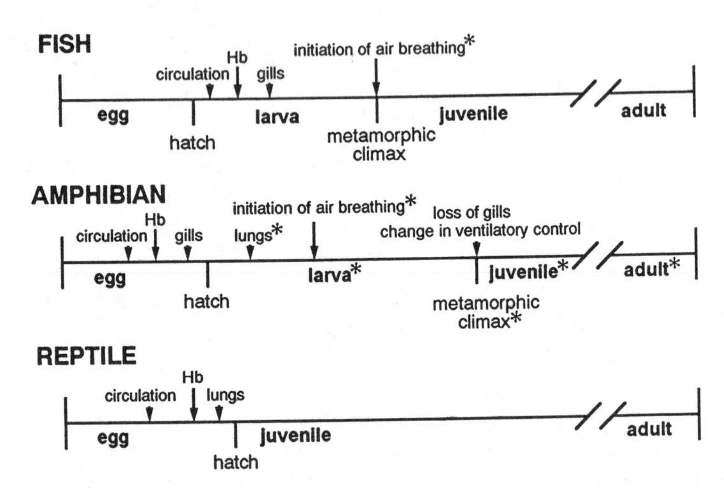

Figure 4 Cardiovascular and respiratory development in relation to life history stages in lower vertebrates. Developmental processes or stages that may or may not occur in a given species within the class are indicated by an *. As examples, most fishes remain strictly water breathers, some amphibians fail to develop lungs and breathe air, and some amphibians do not normally metamorphose to juvenile or adult forms.

inactive storage materials to metabolizing tissue, and in the large proportion of the energy budget going towards growth and biosynthesis (1). In contrast to mammalian embryos, which are closed systems only for the first few days of development and exchange materials with the mother thereafter, all materials necessary for growth and development (except water and oxygen) must be present at the time of laying in oviparous ectothermic vertebrates. Although environmental temperature has obvious effects on metabolism and development in ectotherms (6, 69, 148), this will not be considered in detail here.

METABOLIC DEVELOPMENT IN FISH Much of the available information on metabolic changes during development in lower vertebrates comes from fish, in which the major interest has been in establishing optimal conditions for aquaculture. Oxygen consumption ($\dot{M}O_2$) of the fish oocyte is very low; metabolism increases sharply upon fertilization. As the metabolizing cell mass increases at the expense of the mass of storage products, metabolic rate per embryo increases slightly more than proportionately (123–125, 138) so that the metabolic rate per gram of metabolizing tissue increases 20 to 50% before hatching (69). Some of this increase results from the start of muscle activity or cardiac work in the embryo (113, 138, 149). There is usually a sharp increase in metabolic rate, with hatching into a yolk sac larva, probably caused by increased spontaneous swimming (38, 42, 138, 141). Critical PO_2 increases throughout embryonic development because of the fixed resistance of the egg membranes and increasing oxygen uptake (124, 125). If environmental oxygen is lowered close to or below critical PO_2, hatching may occur sooner than normal, presumably to remove the resistance of the egg membranes to oxygen exchange and allow increased oxygen uptake (44, 92).

There may be a change in the scaling factor for metabolism between embryos, in which metabolism increases directly with body size, and adults, in which metabolism increases only as the 0.8 power of body size. In some larval fish (salmonids, mullet), routine and maximum metabolic rates increase in direct proportion to body mass (138, 147). In other fish (cyprinids, Oreochromis) mass-specific metabolic rates of larvae already decrease with size as is common in older animals (42, 148). The relative factorial scope for activity (maximum MO_2/routine MO_2) increases from two to four times during larval growth in trout, but is independent of body size in cyprinids (147, 148).

Respiratory enzyme activities and use of energy sources during development have been investigated in fish embryos (7). Of the energy stored in the yolk, 43% is catabolized; the remainder contributes to embryo mass (125). Unfertilized oocytes are glycolytic; after fertilization metabolism is supported both by glycolysis and oxidative phosphorylation of carbohydrates. Lipids are not used extensively until late in embryogenesis. Cells moving during gastrulation have much higher lactate dehydrogenase (LDH) activity than stationary cells (7). Protein catabolism is also important during late embryogenesis and the first few days after hatching, but lipid catabolism becomes dominant later (37).

Activities of aerobic enzymes are generally high and glycolytic enzyme activity low immediately after hatching in fish, which suggests that early larval activity is largely fueled aerobically (62, 73, 74). Glycolytic enzyme activities increase later in development, correlated with increased use of white muscle and increased versatility of swimming performance (47, 62). The detailed pattern of these changes in enzyme activity varies from group to group, apparently correlated with differences in life-style and activity patterns (47, 74).

METABOLIC DEVELOPMENT IN AMPHIBIANS AND REPTILES Metabolic changes during development in amphibians and reptiles are even more poorly understood than in fishes. The main determinant of resting $\dot{M}O_2$ in embryonic stages of anurans is body mass; $\dot{M}O_2$ increases directly with mass of metabolizing tissue in salamander embryos (132) and, as in fish, there is a large increase in $\dot{M}O_2$ with hatching, perhaps due to increased spontaneous activity (A. W. Smits, personal communication). In larval anurans, $\dot{M}O_2$ increases as the 0.83 power of body mass, although in some species there are stage-specific changes as well, which are probably correlated with change of life-style (49).

Metabolic development in reptile embryos shows at least two patterns (135, 145). All embryos show an initial exponential increase in $\dot{M}O_2$ (per unit fresh egg mass), probably reflecting an exponential increase in mass of metabolizing tissue. Some reptiles hatch at the end of this exponential growth, while others show a distinct decrease in metabolic rate before hatching, which is thought to be part of a mechanism allowing eggs that develop at slightly different rates to hatch simultaneously, or to allow for a waiting period for environmental cues (135, 145). There is no post-hatching biochemical metamorphosis in reptiles as there is in fish and amphibians, although there are gradual changes in aerobic scope for activity and the balance between aerobic and anaerobic capacity due to increasing body mass (5, 150).

Developmental Changes in Gas Exchange Sites

SIZE AND DIFFUSION In early stages of development, all vertebrates rely on diffusion for both exchange and transport of respiratory gases. In amphibians this dominance of cutaneous gas exchange may persist into the adult, but in most vertebrates cutaneous exchange is eventually eclipsed by lungs or gills. This change in gas exchange site is due to both increasing body size and organogenesis of the specialized gas exchangers (Figure 3). Size increase is a much more important factor in development of lower than higher vertebrates, since the mass of free-living lower vertebrates may increase more than six orders of magnitude between hatching and adulthood, for example in carp *(Cyprinus carpio)* from a one or two mg newly hatched larva to a >1 kg adult (108). Some amphibians increase in mass over three orders of magnitude even after metamorphosis, and this growth is correlated with changes in aerobic and anaerobic capacities and activity patterns (133). Most mammals grow less than two orders of magnitude between birth and adulthood. In general, body surface area to mass ratio and the diffusion distance for cutaneous gas exchange decreases with increasing mass while the surface area of gills increases, usually with a shorter blood-water distance than skin, which results in a switch of primary gas exchange site from skin to gills during larval development (78, 108, 119).

Diffusion is adequate for both gas exchange and transport between environment and mitochondria at body diameters of less than 1 mm (33), the approximate diameter of many fish at hatching (6). In newly hatched fish, the cardiovascular system is often rudimentary, does not extend throughout the body, and generally does not contain red cells. Fish usually hatch without gills, mouth, or opercular openings (6, 63, 107, 124). The degree of cardio-respiratory development at hatching is highly variable, probably correlated with oxygen availability in the spawning waters (124). Newly hatched fish move at low Reynolds number (Re), in which viscosity predominates, but move at progressively higher Re with growth, so that inertial effects become much more important. This affects locomotor energetics, activity patterns, optimal body shape for maximum thrust and minimum drag (4, 137, 141) and, most importantly for respiration, the relative thickness of the hydrodynamic and diffusion boundary layers surrounding the animal (54, 141). Total resistance to oxygen uptake is dominated by resistance to diffusion across the boundary layer at low Re in adult bullfrogs (117); boundary layers are likely to be of even greater importance to very small aquatic animals living at even lower Re (67). A possible reason for continuous swimming in larval anchovy *(Engraulis mordax)* is to dissipate the boundary layer and increase cutaneous gas exchange (141).

Diffusion distances between water and tissues are kept as short as possible and thus gradients as steep as possible. Larval fish swim by using a layer of red muscle fibers immediately under the epithelium that are directly supplied with oxygen by diffusion. These muscle fibers move to the midline (their normal location in adult fish) as the circulation and gills develop (4, 47, 74). *Neoceratodus* (Australian lungfish) larvae, as well as many amphibian larvae, have cilia on the body surface (21, 146). Cilia are only useful at low Reynolds number (thus small body size and low fluid velocities), but may be particularly useful in dissipating boundary layers since they move fluid very close to the body wall (137).

GILL DEVELOPMENT External gills precede internal gills in lungfish and some other primitive fish (27). In most fish internal gills first develop early in larval life as primary bars, with little surface for gas exchange (Figure 4). Primary lamellae quickly appear, and finally secondary lamellae do, both of which increase in number over the larval and juvenile life of the fish (36, 108). Branchial exchange surface increases much more rapidly than body mass while secondary lamellae are appearing (6, 47, 74, 108) so that mass-specific gill surface area increases rapidly. Over the same range of growth, mass-specific skin surface area decreases with an exponent of approximately −0.33, thus suggesting that gas exchange partitioning shifts from exclusively cutaneous to primarily branchial during larval growth. After metamorphosis, gill surface area increases with approximately the same allometric exponent as metabolic rate, while mass-specific body surface area continues to decrease (108), so that gas exchange partitioning shifts further toward the gills with increasing size. The small size of most fish larvae has precluded direct measurement of gill/skin gas exchange partitioning.

The developmental shift in partitioning may be accompanied by changes in oxygen-binding properties of blood as gas exchange switches from a primarily diffusion-limited exchanger (skin) to an actively ventilated, more perfusion-limited gas exchanger (gills). There are ontogenetic changes in expression of multiple hemoglobins in salmonids (64, 65), but the functional significance of these changes is unknown.

At hatching, amphibian larvae are usually larger than fish larvae (although still only 5–25 mg) and many amphibian species hatch more fully developed, with functional cardiovascular system and circulating red cells (11, 12, 28). In larval salamanders, external gills quickly appear and persist throughout larval development. Many anurans have external gills for a few days after hatching, then they degenerate and are replaced by internal gills (11, 97). Amphibian gills are morphologically different from fish gills, with leaf-like lamellae extending from finger-like primary gill bars in urodeles and tufts of finger-like lamellae extending from the gill bars in anurans (29, 97, 103). These gills are much more irregular than the regularly spaced, plate-like lamellae of fish gills. The upstream side of the branchial basket is often adapted for filter feeding in anuran larvae; gas exchange is not the sole function of the branchial basket (55, 103).

DEVELOPMENT OF AIR BREATHING: RESPIRATORY TRANSITIONS FROM WATER TO AIR Some fish, most amphibians, and all reptiles start to breath air at some point in their ontogeny (Figure 4). Lungs appear to be a primitive feature of bony fish and are retained in lungfish and some other primitive fish (27, 121). Most modern teleosts have a swim bladder, probably derived from the primitive lung, but many genera of teleost fish have secondarily developed other aerial gas exchangers, including modifications of the pharynx, intestine, and branchial chambers. Amphibian larvae have lungs for aerial gas exchange, although they may not contribute significantly to gas exchange until close to metamorphosis. Reptiles hatch as juveniles rather than larvae and have fully functional lungs (110). Changes may occur in aerobic and anaerobic scope (5), respiratory surface area (134), and hemoglobin isoforms (118) with growth in reptiles, but most remain primarily air breathers throughout life.

Because of the physico-chemical differences between water and air in density, capacitances for oxygen and carbon dioxide, and diffusion rates, the structures of gas exchangers for water and air are very different (40, 41). Water breathers have a much higher ventilation requirement because of the low oxygen capacitance of water. They have a low PCO_2 because CO_2 capacitance of water is 20–30 times higher than O_2 capacitance, and gas exchange is more diffusion-limited because of the much slower rate of diffusion in water and the formation of diffusion boundary layers. Regulation of ventilation usually occurs through oxygen-sensitive chemoreflexes (33, 40, 111). Air breathers, in contrast, have a lower ventilation requirement because of the relative abundance of oxygen in air. However, air breathing animals have a much higher blood PCO_2 because (*a*) they hypoventilate compared to water breathers, and (*b*) air-breathing organs (typically lungs or swim bladders) are often tidally ventilated, which is less effective than a unidirectionally ventilated system like gills. Air-breathing animals usually regulate ventilation through both CO_2/H^+-sensitive chemosensors and oxygen-sensitive chemosensors (33, 40).

AIR-BREATHING FISH Air-breathing fish are typically found in warm hypoxic waters. These fish generally use the air-breathing organ to augment oxygen uptake, but excrete almost all CO_2 through reduced gills because of the high capacitance and diffusion of CO_2 in water compared to O_2. (As a consequence the blood PCO_2 is so low that little CO_2 is excreted into air) (40, 121, 122). A few air-breathing fish can also excrete significant amounts of CO_2 into air (10, 101), but this is exceptional. Gas exchange partitioning depends on numerous factors, including gas partial pressures in air and water, ventilation of the gills and air-breathing organs, surface areas and diffusion distances in the gas exchangers, circulatory arrangement, and perfusion of the gas exchangers. No one study or series of studies has addressed all the important variables. Oxygen uptake partitioning may change rapidly during development as gas exchangers develop or degenerate. As in purely aquatic fish, newly hatched larvae respire cutaneously with both skin and gills as the gills develop. After two to three weeks, air-breathing organs appear (lungs, suprabranchial chambers, and so on), increase in surface area, and are finally ventilated. When air breathing starts, the rate of increase of gill surface area with body size decreases (from a scaling exponent of 2.4 to 0.8), body scales develop, probably reducing cutaneous gas exchange (77, 119), and aquatic oxygen uptake decreases (131). In the air-breathing swamp eel *Monopterus cuchia,* cutaneous surface area and probably cutaneous gas exchange is reduced upon start of air breathing because the large pectoral, dorsal, and ventral fins of the larva disappear (130).

AMPHIBIAN METAMORPHOSIS The most dramatic transition from water breathing to air breathing occurs in amphibians. Some amphibians, such as the tiger salamander *(Ambystoma tigrinum),* change very little during metamorphosis, from larvae with external gills and well-developed lungs to morphologically similar but gill-less adults. At the other extreme is *Bufo americanus,* whose larvae do not have functional lungs until close to metamorphic climax, but metamorphose into almost completely terrestrial, air-breathing juveniles in only a few days.

Ambystomid salamanders are highly aquatic both as larvae and adults. Large larvae obtain approximately 65% of their oxygen from water with roughly equal contributions from skin and gills, and 35% of oxygen through lungs; adults obtain approximately 35% of their oxygen through the skin from water and 65% through the lungs. The proportion of pulmonary gas exchange increases in both larvae and adults in response to hypoxia (70). In keeping with the relatively minor morphological changes associated with metamorphosis, there is no major change in Hb-O_2 affinity or other hematological measurements (31). Blood properties do change with body mass in larvae, however; oxygen carrying capacity and Hill's n both increased with increasing body mass (22).

Immediately after hatching anuran larvae respire exclusively with water using gills and skin. *Bufo americanus* larvae remain obligate water breathers until metamorphosis, while older *Xenopus* larvae in hypoxic water can obtain 100% of their oxygen requirement from air with their lungs (56, 139). The skin is the most important site of gas exchange throughout larval growth of bullfrog larvae, by providing around 60% of oxygen uptake and excreting a similar amount of CO_2. Gills provide the remaining 40% of oxygen in early stages, but unlike fish, they become progressively less important during larval growth as lungs become more important for oxygen uptake. Since the lungs are not as important for CO_2 excretion, cutaneous CO_2 excretion increases to over 80% (30).

Bullfrog larvae have gas in their lungs soon after hatching (46, R. L. Infantino, personal communication), but do not obtain much oxygen through them until TK stage XVI (30, 24). The lungs are at first simple thin-walled sacs, but in later stages (TK V to XXII) develop primary, secondary, and tertiary septa, which increase the surface area (3, 15, 46). At metamorphosis the gills involute, aquatic oxygen uptake decreases sharply, and pulmonary oxygen uptake increases from less than 20% in pre-metamorphic larvae to almost 70% in juveniles (30, 72). There is a change in hemoglobin types to lower affinity variants as metamorphosis occurs—this appears to be correlated with increased reliance on a high capacitance, highly stable gas exchange medium (9, 88, 115).

Regulation of Ventilation

Changes of ventilatory regulation with the developmental transition from water breathing to air breathing resemble these thought to have occurred during the evolutionary transition from water to air. With the shift in respiratory medium, the control system changes from being almost entirely oxygen-driven to a combination of acid-base and oxygen-driven. Acid-base status adjusts from one with low PCO_2 and low bicarbonate to high PCO_2 and high bicarbonate, with little change in pH.

Almost nothing is known of the development of ventilatory control in fish. Newly hatched dogfish (*Scyliohinus* sp.) decrease gill ventilation frequency in hypoxia, probably as a direct consequence of oxygen limitation (43), while adult fish increase ventilation during hypoxia (40, 111). It is not known when the chemoreceptor reflex responsible for this response becomes functional.

Early bullfrog larvae (TK stages I–X) are almost entirely aquatic, are insensitive to PCO_2, and increase gill ventilation in response to aquatic hypoxia (21, 79). The receptors mediating these responses are located both centrally (location unknown, but presumably in a central vascular compartment and/or the CNS) and on the gill arches. The presence of the latter has been confirmed by the extremely rapid time course (<2 sec) of ventilatory responses to step changes of PO_2 of inspired water (81) and by ablation of selected regions of the gill arches (X. Jia, unpublished).

The lungs of pre-metamorphic larvae and the air-breathing organs of bimodally breathing fish are used only as an auxiliary oxygen supply and are ventilated infrequently (21, 24, 79, 104, 121, 126). Air-breathing frequency and the proportion of aerial oxygen uptake increases during aquatic hypoxia (2, 10, 30, 58, 104, 121, 144). Unlike breathing in entirely aquatic fish, there may be a simultaneous decrease in gill ventilation in bimodal breathers, probably to reduce oxygen loss from the blood (56, 61, 142, 143). Commonly, there are also vascular shunts that reduce the amount of blood perfusing the gill during aquatic hypoxia (13, 94–96, 98).

Ventilation in bimodal breathers is complicated by non-respiratory factors. Many larvae are filter feeders, which may uncouple gill ventilation from respiratory requirements (55). Lung ventilation changes buoyancy and requires movement to the surface, which may decrease locomotor efficiency; it is energetically expensive, and may expose the animal to predators (52, 90, 91, 128, 139).

Most adult anurans are still bimodal breathers, but use skin and lungs rather than gills, skin, and lungs. Lung ventilation frequency of adults also increases in hypoxia, with a concomitant increase in the proportion of oxygen taken through the lungs (82, 116). Ventilation sometimes decreases in hyperoxia, which indicates that part of the normal drive for ventilation is due to oxygen (136). Cutaneous gas exchange with water is probably also regulated, although the degree of regulation and the route, i.e. skin ventilation, capillary recruitment, or perfusion rate, is as yet uncertain (7, 23, 53, 99, 100, 114, 117).

Anuran larvae entering metamorphic climax (TK stages XX–XXIV) change from larval to adult breathing pattern. Late-stage larvae (XVI–XIX) are obligate air breathers, increase lung ventilation, but not gill ventilation, in response to hypoxia, and start to show sensitivity to CO_2 (21, 79). As the gills involute between stages XX and XXIV and the tail is resorbed, respiratory surface area is lost for aquatic CO_2 excretion. Blood PCO_2 increases from 3–5 to 13–15 mmHg, compensated by an increase in HCO_3 so that pH does not change (3, 48, 84). Although most CO_2 is excreted through the skin in adults, control of CO_2 excretion and acid-base balance is by lung ventilation (21, 30, 80, 83). The switch to adult respiration appears to be between TK stages XXI and XXII, when the larval pattern of infrequent single lung ventilations changes within one or two days to the adult pattern of much more frequent ventilations, which are often grouped into bouts (R. L. Infantino, personal communication).

Ontogenetic changes in the pattern of ventilation in newly hatched or born reptiles have not been investigated to our knowledge.

CONCLUDING REMARKS

In spite of literally centuries of anatomical study of the embryos of fishes, amphibians, and reptiles, developmental changes in the cardio-respiratory physiology of these vertebrate classes are only beginning to be investigated in detail. The recent advent of miniaturized techniques for recording hemodynamics and blood gases in very small animals is making an important impact upon the field, and more sophisticated physiologic measurements on earlier developmental stages are emerging.

These studies clearly indicate that qualitative as well as quantitative differences in cardio-respiratory physiology separate embryonic and larval forms from the terminal adult. In many instances, the earliest embryonic stages are very simple, indeed, from both an anatomical and physiologic perspective. In contrast to the embryos of birds and mammals, however, the larvae of fishes and amphibians undergo most development only after hatching into free-living entities. This self-sufficient existence demands that, even as development progresses, the organism must be able to respond physiologically (as well as behaviorally) to the inevitable changes in both the external and internal environment. The notion that the adult is physiologically the most complex developmental stage in a species' life cycle should be discarded (or at the very least be verified on a species-by-species basis) because data on numerous fronts indicate that even quite early developmental stages may possess complex mechanisms for finely regulating cardiovascular and respiratory performance.

Major gaps exist in our knowledge of the cardio-respiratory physiology of lower vertebrates. Many of these deficiencies have been identified above, but some bear special emphasis. Ultimately, adjustments in heart rate, blood pressure, stroke flow, and so on serve to maintain oxygen transport homeostasis. Yet crucial factors in this homeostatic process—e.g. cardiac output, arterial and venous oxygen content—remain undescribed.

Another area demanding further attention involves the onset of physiologic function, rather than the continuing developmental changes. This gap exists for all vertebrates, including mammals. For example, most fetal physiology is based on relatively developed fetuses with nearly complete regulatory systems. The origins of cardio-respiratory processes in the early embryos deserve much further attention, although admittedly, these are also the most difficult stages to examine experimentally.

Finally, we are struck by the relative dirth of information on physiologic development in reptiles compared with fishes and amphibians. This is perhaps unexpected, since there is a vast literature on the physiology of adult reptiles. The embryos of some reptiles are often very large relative to those of amphibians and fishes (or even birds and mammals), which could permit physiologic measurements on embryos that might not be possible in other vertebrates. Thus an increased focus on reptilian embryos in the future would have the combined effects of adding to our specific knowledge of reptilian development as well as providing a paradigm for future investigations of basic aspects of vertebrate development.

Acknowledgments

This article was prepared while the authors were supported by National Science Foundation operating grant #DCB-8916938 (W.W.B.) and a National Science and Engineering Research Council (Canada) University Research Fellowship (A.W.P.).

Literature Cited

1. Adolph, E. F. 1983. Uptakes and uses of oxygen from gametes to maturity: an overview. *Respir. Physiol.* 53:135–60
2. Ar, A., Zacks, D. 1989. Alterations in the bimodal gas exchange of the African catfish *Clarias lazera*. In *Physiological function in special environments*, ed. E. V. Paganelli, L. E. Farhi, pp. 172–90. New York: Springer Verlag
3. Atkinson, B. G., Just, J. J. 1975. Biochemical and histological changes in the respiratory system of *Rana catesbeiana* larvae during normal and induced metamorphosis. *Dev. Biol.* 45:151–65
4. Batty, R. S. 1984. Development of swimming movements and musculature of larval herring *(Clupea harengus. J. Exp. Biol.* 110:217–29
5. Bennett, A. F., Seymour, R. S., Bradford, D. F., Webb, G. J. W. 1985. Mass-dependence of anaerobic metabolism and acid-base disturbance during activity in the salt-water crocodile, *Crocodylus porosus. J. Exp. Biol.* 118:161–71
6. Blaxter, J. H. S. 1988. Pattern and variety in development. In *Fish Physiology*, ed. W. S. Hoar, D. J. Randall. 11A:1–58. New York: Academic
7. Boulekbache, H. 1981. Energy metabolism in fish development. *Am. Zool.* 21:377–89
8. Boutilier, R. G., Glass, M. L., Heisler, N. 1986. The relative distribution of pulmocutaneous blood flow in *Rana catesbeiana:* Effects of pulmonary or cutaneous hypoxia. *J. Exp. Biol.* 126: 33–39

8a. Bradford, D. F., Seymour, R. S. 1988. Influence of environmental PO_2 on embryonic oxygen consumption, rate of development, and hatching in the frog *Pseudophyrne bibroni. Physiol. Zool.* 61:475–82

9. Broyles, R. H. 1981. Changes in the blood during amphibian metamorphosis. In *Metamorphosis, A Problem in Developmental Biology*, ed. L. I. Gilbert, E. Frieden, pp. 461–90. New York: Plenum
10. Burggren, W. W. 1979. Bimodal gas exchange during variation in environmental oxygen and carbon dioxide in the air breathing fish *Trichogaster trichopterus. J. Exp. Biol.* 82:197–213
11. Burggren, W. W. 1984. Transition of respiratory processes during amphibian metamorphosis: from egg to adult. In *Respiration and Metabolism of Embryonic Vertebrates*, ed. R. S. Seymour, pp. 31–53. Dordrecht, Netherlands: Dr W Junk
12. Burggren, W. W. 1985. Gas exchange, metabolism and 'ventilation' in gelatinous frog egg masses. *Physiol. Zool.* 58:503–14
13. Burggren, W. W. 1988. Role of the central circulation in regulation of cutaneous gas exchange. *Am. Zool.* 28:985–98
14. Burggren, W. W. 1988. Cardiac design in lower vertebrates: what can phylogeny reveal about ontogeny? *Experientia* 44:919–29
15. Burggren, W. W. 1989. Lung structure and function. In *Comparative Pulmonary Physiology: Current Concepts*, ed. S. C. Wood. *Lung Biology in Health and Disease*, ed. C. Lenfant, 39:153–92. New York: Dekker
16. Burggren, W. W. 1991. The importance of an ontogenetic perspective in physiological studies: amphibian cardiology as a case study. In *Strategies of Physiological Adaptation, Respiration, Circulation and Metabolism*, ed. R. E. Weber, S. C. Wood, A. Hargens, R. Millard, New York: Dekker
17. Burggren, W. W. 1991. Does comparative respiratory physiology have a role in evolutionary biology (and vice versa)? In *Physiological Strategies for Gas Exchange and Metabolism*, ed. A. Woakes, C. Bridges, M. Grieshaber, Cambridge: Cambridge Univ. Press
18. Burggren, W. W., Bemis, W. E. 1990. Studying Physiological Evolution: Paradigms and Pitfalls. In *Evolutionary Innovations*, ed. M. H. Nitecki, pp. 191–227. Chicago: Univ. Chicago Press
19. Burggren, W. W., Doyle, M. 1986. Ontogeny of heart rate regulation in the bullfrog, *Rana catesbeiana. Am. J. Physiol.* 251:R231–39
20. Burggren, W. W., Doyle, M. 1986. The action of acetylcholine upon heart rate changes markedly with development in the bullfrog. *J. Exp. Zool.* 240:137–40
21. Burggren, W. W., Doyle, M. E. 1987. Ontogeny of regulation of gill and lung ventilation in the bullfrog, *Rana catesbeiana. Respir. Physiol.* 66:279–91
22. Burggren, W. W., Dupré, R. K., Wood, S. C. 1987. Allometry of red cell oxygen binding and hematology in larvae of the salamander, *Ambystoma tigrinum. Respir. Physiol.* 70:73–84
23. Burggren, W. W., Feder, M. E. 1986. Effect of experimental ventilation of the

skin on cutaneous gas exchange in the bullfrog. *J. Exp. Biol.* 121:445–50

24. Burggren, W. W., Feder, M. E., Pinder, A. W. 1983. Temperature and the balance between aerial and aquatic respiration in larvae of *Rana berlandieri* and *Rana catesbeiana*. *Physiol. Zool.* 56:263–73
25. Burggren, W. W., Infantino, R. L., Townsend, D. P. 1990. Developmental changes in cardiac and metabolic physiology of the direct-developing frog *Eleutherodactylus coqui*. *J. Exp. Biol.* 152:129–48
26. Burggren, W. W., Johansen, K. 1987. Circulation and respiration in lungfishes. In *Biology and Evolution of Lungfishes*, ed. W. E. Bemis, W. W. Burggren, N. E. Kemp, pp. 217–36. New York: Liss
27. Burggren, W. W., Johansen, K., McMahon, B. R. 1986. Respiration in primitive fishes. In *Evolutionary Biology of Primitive Fishes*, ed. R. E. Foreman, A. Gorbman, J. M. Dodd, R. Olson, pp. 217–52. New York: Plenum
28. Burggren, W. W., Just, J. J. 1991. Developmental changes in amphibian physiological systems. In *Environmental Physiology of Amphibians*, ed. M. E. Feder, W. W. Burggren, Chicago: Univ. Chicago Press
29. Burggren, W. W., Mwalukoma, A. 1983. Respiration during chronic hypoxia and hyperoxia in larval and adult bullfrogs *(Rana catesbeiana)*. I. Morphological responses of lungs, skin and gills. *J. Exp. Biol.* 105:191–203
30. Burggren, W. W., West, N. H. 1982. Changing respiratory importance of gills, lungs, and skin during metamorphosis in the bullfrog *Rana catesbeiana*. *Respir. Physiol.* 47:151–64
31. Burggren, W. W., Wood, S. C. 1981. Respiration and acid-base balance in the tiger salamander, *Ambystoma tigrinum:* influence of temperature acclimation and metamorphosis. *J. Comp. Physiol.* 144(B):241–46
32. Calder, W. A. 1984. *Size, Function, and Life History*. Cambridge: Harvard Univ. Press. 431 pp.
33. Cameron, J. N. 1989. *The Respiratory Physiology of Animals*. New York: Oxford Univ. Press. 353 pp.
34. Clark, E. B. 1985. Ventricular function and cardiac growth in the chick embryo. In *Cardiac Morphogenesis*, ed. Y. J. Ferrans, G. Rosenquist, C. Weinstein, pp. 238–44. New York: Elsevier
35. Clark, E. B. 1984. Functional aspects of cardiac development. In *Growth of the Heart in Health and Disease*, ed. R. Zak. New York: Raven
36. Coughlan, D. J., Glass, S. P. 1984. Early morphological development of gills in smallmouth bass *(Micropterus dolomieui)*. *Can J. Zool.* 62:951–58
37. Dabrowski, K., Kaushik, S. J., Luquet, P. 1984. Metabolic utilization of body stores during the early life of whitefish, *Coregonus lavaretus* L. *J. Fish Biol.* 24:721–29
38. Davenport, J. 1983. Oxygen and the developing eggs and larvae of the lumpfish *Cyclopterus lumpus*. *J. Mar. Biol. Assoc.* 63:633–40
39. de Saint-Aubain, M. L. 1982. Vagal control of pulmonary blood flow in *Ambystoma mexicanum*. *J. Exp. Zool.* 221:155–58
40. Dejours, P. 1988. *Respiration in water and air*. New York: Elsevier. 179 pp.
41. Denny, M. W. 1990. Terrestrial versus aquatic biology: The medium and its message. *Am. Zool.* 30:111–22
42. DeSilva, C. D., Premawansa, S., Keemiyahetty, C. N. 1986. Oxygen consumption in *Oreochromis niloticus* (L.) in relation to development, salinity, temperature, and time of day. *J. Fish Biol.* 29:267–77
43. Diez, J. M., Davenport, J. 1987. Embryonic respiration in the dogfish (*Scyliorhinus canicula* L.) *J. Mar. Biol. Assoc.* 67:249–61
44. DiMichele, L., Powers, D. A. 1984. The relationship between oxygen consumption rate and hatching in *Fundulus heteroclitus*. *Physiol. Zool.* 57:46–51
45. Dunnigan, A., Hu, N. Benson, D. W., Clark, E. B., 1987. Effect of heart rate increase on dorsal aortic flow in the Stage 24 chick embryo. *Pediatric Res.* 22:442–44
46. Dupré, R. K., Taylor, R. F., Frazier, D. T. 1985. Static lung compliance during the development of the bullfrog, *Rana catesbeiana*. *Respir. Physiol.* 59:231–38
47. El-Fiky, N., Wieser, W. 1988. Life styles and patterns of development of gills and muscles in larval cyprinids (Cyprinidae; Teleostei) *J. Fish Biol.* 33:135–45
48. Erasmus, B. de W., Howell, B. J., Rahn, H. 1970/71. Ontogeny of acid-base balance in the bullfrog and chicken. *Respir. Physiol.* 11:46–53
49. Feder, M. E. 1982. Effect of developmental stage and body size on oxygen consumption of anuran larvae: a reappraisal. *J. Exp. Zool.* 220:33–42
50. Feder, M. E. 1983. Effect of hypoxia and body size on the energy metabolism of lungless tadpoles, *Bufo woodhousei*, an air-breathing anuran larvae. *J. Exp. Zool.* 228:11–19

51. Feder, M. E. 1983. Responses to acute aquatic hypoxia in larvae of the frog *Rana berlandieri*. *J. Exp. Biol.* 104:79–95
52. Feder, M. E. 1984. Consequences of aerial respiration for amphibian larvae. In *Respiration and Metabolism of Embryonic Vertebrates,* pp. 71–86. Dordrecht: Dr W Junk
53. Feder, M. E., Burggren, W. W. 1985. Cutaneous gas exchange in vertebrates: Design, patterns, control and implications. *Biol. Rev.* 60:1–45
54. Feder, M. E., Pinder, A. W. 1988. Ventilation and its effect on "infinite pool" exchangers. *Am. Zool.* 28:973–84
55. Feder, M. E., Seale, D. B., Boraas, M. E., Wassersug, R. J., Gibbs, A. G. 1984. Functional conflicts between feeding and gas exchange in suspension-feeding tadpoles, *Xenopus laevis*. *J. Exp. Biol.* 110:91–98
56. Feder, M. E., Wassersug, R. J. 1984. Aerial versus aquatic oxygen consumption in larvae of the clawed frog, *Xenopus laevis*. *J. Exp. Biol.* 108:231–45
57. Feldman, J. L., Ellenberger, H. H. 1988. Central coordination of respiratory and cardiovascular control in mammals. *Annu. Rev. Physiol.* 50:593–606
58. Fernandes, M. N., Rantin, F. T. 1989. Respiratory responses of *Oreochromis niloticus* (Pisces, Cichlidae) to environmental hypoxia under different thermal conditions. *J. Fish Biol.* 35:509–19
59. Figge, F. H. J. 1936. The differential reaction of the blood vessels of a branchial arch of *Amblystoma tigrinum* (Colorado Axolotl). I. The reaction to adrenalin, oxygen and carbon dioxide. *Physiol. Zool.* 9:79–101
60. Fischer, K. C. 1942. The effect of temperature on the critical oxygen pressure for heart beat frequency in embryos of Atlantic salmon and speckled trout. *Can. J. Res.* Set. D. 20:1–12
61. Fishman, A. P., Galante, R. J., Pack, A. I. 1989. Diving physiology: lungfish. See Ref. 15 pp. 645–76
62. Forstner, H., Hinterleitner, S., Mahr, K., Wieser, W. 1983. Towards a better definition of "metamorphosis" in *Coregonus* sp.: Biochemical, histological, and physiological data. *Can. J. Fish. Aquat. Sci.* 40:1224–32
63. Galman, O. R., Avtalion, R. 1989. Further study of the embryonic development of *Oreochromis niloticus* (Cichlidae, Teleostei) using scanning electron microscopy. *J. Fish Biol.* 34:653–64
64. Giles, M. A., Rystephanuk, D. M. 1989. Ontogenic variation in the multiple hemoglobins of Arctic char, *Salvelinus alpinus*. *Can. J. Fish. Aquat. Sci.* 46:804–9
65. Giles, M. A., Vanstone, W. E. 1976. Ontogenetic variation in the multiple hemoglobins of coho salmon *Oncorhynchus kisutch* and effect of environmental factors on their expression. *J. Fish. Res. Board Can.* 33:1144–49
66. Goodrich, E. W. 1930. *Studies on the Structure and Development of Vertebrates*. London: MacMillan. 837 pp.
67. Graham, J. B. 1990. Ecological, evolutionary, and physical factors influencing aquatic animal respiration. *Am. Zool.* 30:137–46
68. Grodzinsky, Z. 1950. Susceptibility of the heart in the sea trout embryo *Salmo trutta L.* to small changes in temperature. *Bull. Acad. Polon. Sci. Ser.* BII:173–82
69. Gruber, K., Wieser, W. 1983. Energetics of development of the Alpine char, *Salvelinus alpinus,* in relation to temperature and oxygen. *J. Comp. Physiol.* 149:485–93
70. Heath, A. G. 1976. Respiratory responses to hypoxia by *Ambystoma tigrinum* larvae, paedomorphs, and metamorphosed adults. *Comp. Biochem. Physiol.* 55:45–49
71. Heath, A. G. 1980. Cardiac responses of larval and adult tiger salamanders to submergence and emergence. *Comp. Biochem. Physiol.* 65A439–44
72. Hillman, S. S., Lea, M. S. 1983. Aerial activity oxygen consumption during metamorphosis of the bullfrog, *Rana catesbeiana*. *Copeia* 1983:407–10
73. Hinterleitner, S., Platzer, U., Wieser, W. 1987. Development of the activities of oxidative, glycolytic and muscle enzymes during early larval life in three families of freshwater fish. *J. Fish Biol.* 30:315–26
74. Hinterleitner, S., Thurner-Fler, J., Wieser, W., El-Fiky, N. 1989. Profiles of enzyme activity in larvae of two cyprinid species with contrasting life styles (Cyprinidae; Teleostei). *J. Fish Biol.* 35:709–18
75. Holeton, G. F. 1971. Respiratory and circulatory responses of rainbow trout larvae to carbon monoxide and to hypoxia. *J. Exp. Biol.* 55:683–94
76. Hoyt, R. W., Eldridge, M., Wood, S. C. 1984. Noninvasive pulsed Doppler determination of cardiac output in an unanesthetized neotenic salamander, *Ambystoma tigrinum*. *J. Exp. Zool.* 230:491–93
77. Hughes, G. M. General anatomy of the gills. See Ref. 6. pp. 1–72
78. Hughes, G. M., Munshi, J. S. D., Ohja,

J. 1986. Post-embryonic development of water and air-breathing organs of *Anabas testudineus* (Bloch). *J. Fish Biol.* 29:43–50

79. Infantino, R. L. 1989. Ontogeny of gill and lung ventilatory responses to oxygen and carbon dioxide in the bullfrog, *Rana catesbeiana*. *Am. Zool.* 29:57A (Abst.)
80. Jackson, D. C. 1978. Respiratory control and CO_2 conductance: Temperature effects in a turtle and a frog. *Respir. Physiol.* 33:103–14
81. Jia, X., Burggren, W. W. 1989. Developmental changes in gill ventilation reflexes in larval *Rana catesbeiana*. *Am. Zool.* 29(4):56A
82. Jones, D. R., Chu, C. 1988. Effect of denervation of carotid labyrinth on breathing in unrestrained *Xenopus laevis*. *Respir. Physiol.* 73:243–56
83. Jones, D. R., Milsom, W. K. 1982. Peripheral receptors affecting breathing and cardiovascular function in non-mammalian vertebrates. *J. Exp. Biol.* 100:59–91
84. Just, J. J., Gatz, R. N., Crawford, E. C. Jr. 1973. Changes in respiratory functions during metamorphosis of the bullfrog, *Rana catesbeiana*. *Respir. Physiol.* 17:276–82
85. Justus, J. T. 1978. The cardiac mutant: an overview. *Am. Zool.* 18:321–26
86. Kimmel, P. B. 1990. *Ontogeny of Cardiovascular Control Mechanisms in the Bullfrog, Rana catesbeiana*. PhD thesis. Amherst, Mass. Univ. Massachusetts
87. Kirby, M. L. 1988. Roll of extracardiac factors in heart development. *Experientia* 44:944–51
88. Kobel, H. R., Wolff, J. 1983. Two transitions of haemoglobin expression in *Xenopus:* from embryonic to larval and from larval to adult. *Differentiation* 24:24–26
89. Korsgaard, B., Wever, R. E. 1989. Maternal-fetal trophic and respiratory relationships in viviparous ectothermic vertebrates. In *Advances in Comparative Environmental Physiology,* 5:229–33. Berlin: Springer Verlag
90. Kramer, D. L. 1988. The behavioural ecology of air breathing by aquatic animals. *Can. J. Zool.* 66:89–94
91. Lannoo, M. J., Backman, M. D. 1984. On flotation and air breathing in *Ambystoma tigrinum* larvae: Stimuli for and relationship between these behaviours. *Can. J. Zool.* 62:15–18
92. Latham, K. E., Just, J. J. 1989. Oxygen availability provides a signal for hatching in the rainbow trout (*Salmo gairdneri*) embryo. *Can. J. Fish. Aquat. Sci.* 46:55–58
93. Liem, K. 1981. Larvae of air-breathing fishes as counter-current flow devices in hypoxic environments. *Science* 211: 1177–79
94. Malvin, G. M. 1985a. Vascular resistance and vasoactivity of gills and pulmonary artery of the salamander, *Ambystoma tigrinum*. *J. Comp. Physiol.* 155:241–49
95. Malvin, G. M. 1985b. Cardiovascular shunting during amphibian metamorphosis. In *Cardiovascular Shunts; Phylogenetic, Ontogenetic and Clinical Aspects*. ed. K. Johansen, W. Burggren, pp. 163–72. Copenhagen: Munksgaard
96. Malvin, G. M. 1985c. Adrenoceptor types in the respiratory vasculature of the salamander gill. *J. Comp. Physiol.* 155:591–96
97. Malvin, G. M. 1989. Gill structure and function: amphibian larvae. See Ref. 15 pp. 121–52
98. Malvin, G. M., Heisler, N. 1988. Blood flow patterns in the salamander, *Ambystoma tigrinum* before, during and after metamorphosis. *J. Exp. Biol.* 137:53–74
99. Malvin, G. M., Hlastala, M. P. 1986. Regulation of cutaneous gas exchange by environmental O_2 and CO_2 in the frog. *Respir. Physiol.* 65:99–111
100. Malvin, G. M., Hlastala, M. P. 1989. Effects of environmental O_2 on blood flow and diffusing capacity in amphibian skin. *Respir. Physiol.* 76:229–42
101. Martin, K. L. M., Lighton, J. R. B. 1989. Aerial CO_2 and O_2 exchange during terrestrial activity in an amphibious fish, *Alticus kirki* (Blenniidae). *Copeia* 1989:723–27
102. McDonald, D. G., McMahon, B. R. 1977. Respiratory development in Arctic char *Salvelinus alpinus* under conditions of normoxia and chronic hypoxia. *Can. J. Zool.* 55:1461–67
103. McIndoe, R., Smith, D. G. 1984. Functional morphology of gills in larval amphibians. In *Respiration and Metabolism of Embryonic Vertebrates,* ed. R. S. Seymour, pp. 55–69. Dordrecht: Dr W Junk
104. McMahon, B. R., Burggren, W. W. 1987. Respiratory physiology of intestinal air breathing in the teleost fish *Misgurnus anguillicaudatus*. *J. Exp. Biol.* 133:371–93
105. Metcalfe, J., Stock, M. K. 1988. In *Comparative Pulmonary Physiology,* ed. S. C. Wood, pp. 258–78. New York: Dekker
106. Nilsson, S. 1984. Innervation and pharmacology of the gills. In *Fish Physiology,* ed. W. S. Hoar, D. J. Ran-

dall, 10A:185–229. New York: Academic
107. O'Connell, C. P. 1981. Development of organ systems in the northern anchovy, *Engraulis mordax*, and other teleosts. *Am. Zool.* 21:429–46
108. Oikawa, S., Itazawa, Y. 1985. Gill and body surface areas of the carp in relation to body mass, with special reference to the metabolism-size relationship. *J. Exp. Biol.* 117:1–14
109. Packard, G. C., Packard, M. J. 1988. Water relations of embryonic snapping turtles *(Chelydra serpentina)* exposed to wet or dry environments at different times of incubation. *Physiol. Zool.* 61:95–106
109a. Pelster, B., Bemis, W. E. 1991. Ontogeny of heart function in the little skate, *Raja erinacea*. *J. Exp. Biol.* In press
109b. Pelster, B., Burggren, W. 1991. Central arterial hemodynamics in larval bullfrogs (*Rana catesbeiana*): Developmental and seasonal influences. *Am. J. Physiol.* In press
110. Perry, S. F., Darian-Smith, C., Alston, J., Limpus, C. J., Maloney, J. E. 1989. Histological structure of the lungs of the loggerhead turtle, *Caretta caretta*, before and after hatching. *Copeia* 1989: 1000–10
111. Perry, S. F., Wood, C. M. 1989. Control and coordination of gas transfer in fishes. *Can. J. Zool.* 67:2961–70
112. Peters, R. H. 1983. *The Ecological Implication of Body Size*. New York: Cambridge Univ. Press. 329 pp.
113. Peterson, R. H., Martin-Robichaud, D. J. 1983. Embryo movements of Atlantic salmon, *Salmo salar*, as influenced by pH, temperature, and state of development. *Can. J. Fish. Aquat. Sci.* 40:777–82
114. Pinder, A. W. 1987. Cutaneous diffusing capacity increases during hypoxia in cold submerged bullfrogs *(Rana catesbeiana). Respir. Physiol.* 70:85–95
115. Pinder, A. W., Burggren, W. W. 1983. Respiration during chronic hypoxia and hypernoxia in larval and adult bullfrogs *(Rana catesbeiana)*. II. Changes in respiratory properties of whole blood. *J. Exp. Biol.* 105:205–13
116. Pinder, A. W., Burggren, W. W. 1986. Ventilation and partitioning of oxygen uptake in the frog *Rana pipiens:* effects of hypoxia and activity. *J. Exp. Biol.* 126:453–68
117. Pinder, A. W., Feder, M. E. 1990. Effect of boundary layers on cutaneous gas exchange. *J. Exp. Biol.* In press
118. Pough, F. H. 1977. Ontogenetic change in molecular and functional properties of blood of garter snakes, *Thamnophis sirtalis*. *J. Exp. Zool.* 201:47–56
119. Prasad, M. S. 1988. Morphometrics of gills during growth and development of the air-breathing habit in *Colisa fasciatus* (Bloch and Schneider). *J. Fish Biol.* 32:367–81
120. Quinn, D. E., Burggren, W. W. 1983. Lactate production, tissue distribution and elimination following exhaustive exercise in larval and adult bullfrogs, *Rana catesbeiana*. *Physiol. Zool.* 56:597–613
121. Randall, D. J., Burggren, W. W., Farrell, A. P., Haswell, M. 1981. *The Evolution of Air Breathing in Vertebrates*. New York: Cambridge Univ. Press. 133 pp.
122. Randall, D. J., Cameron, J. N., Daxboeck, C., Smatresk, N. J. 1981. Aspects of bimodal gas exchange in the bowfin *Amia calva* L. (Actinopterygii: Amiiformes). *Respir. Physiol.* 43:339–48
123. Rombough, P. J. 1986. Mathematical model predicting the dissolved oxygen requirements of steelhead (*Salmo gairdneri*) embryos and alevins in hatchery incubators. *Aquaculture* 59:119–37
124. Rombough, P. J. 1988. Respiratory gas exchange, aerobic metabolism, and effects of hypoxia during early life. See Ref. 6 pp. 59–161
125. Rombough, P. J. 1988a. Growth, aerobic metabolism and dissolved oxygen requirements of embryos and alevins of the steelhead trout, *Salmo gairdneri*. *Can. J. Zool.* 66:651–60
126. Sacca, R., Burggren, W. W. 1982. Oxygen uptake in air and water in the air-breathing reedfish *Calamoichthys calabaricus:* role of skin, gill, and lungs. *J. Exp. Biol.* 97:179–86
127. Schmidt-Nielsen, K. 1984. *Scaling: Why Is Animal Size So Important?* New York: Cambridge Univ. Press. 241 pp.
128. Shannon, P., Kramer, D. L. 1988. Water depth alters respiratory behaviour of *Xenopus laevis*. *J. Exp. Biol.* 137: 597–602
129. Shelton, G., Boutilier, R. G. 1982. Apnoea in amphibians and reptiles. *J. Exp. Biol.* 100:245–74
130. Singh, B. N., Towheed, M. A., Munshi, J. S. D. 1989. Respiratory adaptations in the larvae of *Monopterus cuchia* (Ham.). *J. Fish Biol.* 34:637–38
131. Singh, R. P., Prasad, M. S., Mishra, A. P., Singh, B. R. 1982. Oxygen uptake through water during early life in *Channa punctatus* (Pisces Ophicephaliformes). *Hydrobiologia* 87:211–16
132. Smits, A. W. 1985. Metabolic com-

pensation to temperature in salamander embryos. *Am. Zool.* 136A (Abst.)

133. Taigen, T. L., Pough, F. H. 1985. Metabolic correlates of anuran behavior. *Am. Zool.* 25:987–97
134. Tenney, S. M., Tenney, J. B. 1970. Quantitative morphology of cold-blooded lungs: amphibia and reptilia. *Respir. Physiol.* 9:197–215
135. Thompson, M. B. 1989. Patterns of metabolism in embryonic reptiles. *Respir. Physiol.* 76:243–56
136. Toews, D. P., Kirby, S. 1985. The ventilatory and acid-base physiology of the toad, *Bufo marinus*, during exposure to environmental hyperoxia. *Respir. Physiol.* 59:225–29
137. Vogel, S. 1983. *Life in Moving Fluids.* Princeton: Princeton Univ. Press. 352 pp.
138. Walsh, W. A., Swanson, C., Lee, C.-S., Banno, J. E. Eda, H. 1989. O_2 consumption by eggs and larvae of striped mullet, *Mugil cephalus*, in relation to development, salinity, and temperature. *J. Fish Biol.* 35:347–58
139. Wassersug, R. J., Feder, M. E. 1983. The effects of aquatic oxygen concentration, body size and respiratory behaviours on the stamina of obligate aquatic (*Bufo americanus*) and facultative air-breathing (*Xenopus laevis* and *Rana berlandieri*) anuran larvae. *J. Exp. Biol.* 105:173–90
140. Wassersug, R. J., Paul, R. D., Feder, M. E. 1981. Cardio-respiratory synchrony in anuran larvae (*Xenopus laevis, Pachymedusa dacnicolor* and *Rana berlandieri*). *Comp. Biochem. Physiol.* 70A:329–34
141. Weihs, D. 1980. Respiration and depth control as possible reasons for swimming of northern anchovy, *Engraulis mordax*, yolk-sac larvae. *Fish. Bull.* 78: 109–17
142. Weintraub, M. J., MacKay, R. S. 1975. Respiratory and heartbeat synchrony studied by telemetry in the trout (*Salmo gairdneri*). *Copeia* 1975(1):78–85
143. West, N. H., Burggren, W. W. 1982. Gill and lung ventilatory responses to steady-state aquatic hypoxia and hyperoxia in the bullfrog tadpole *(Rana catesbeiana). Respir. Physiol.* 47:165–76
144. West, N. H., Burggren, W. W. 1983. Reflex interactions between aerial and aquatic gas exchange organs in the larval bullfrog. *Am. J. Physiol.* 244(6):R770–77
145. Whitehead, P. J., Seymour, R. S. 1990. Patterns of metabolic rate in embryonic crocodilians *Crocodylus johnstoni* and *Crocodylus porosus*. *Physiol. Zool.* 63:334–52
146. Whiting, H. P., Bone, Q. 1980. Ciliary cells in the epidermis of the larval Australian dipnoan *Neoceratodus*. *J. Linn. Soc. London Zool.* 68:125–37
147. Wieser, W. 1985. Developmental and metabolic constraints of the scope for activity in young rainbow trout (*Salmo gairdneri*). *J. Exp. Biol.* 118:133–42
148. Wieser, W., Forstner, H. 1986. Effects of temperature and size on the routine rate of oxygen consumption and on the relative scope for activity in larval cyprinids. *J. Comp. Physiol.* 156:791–96
149. Wieser, W., Platzer, U., Hinterleitner, S. 1985. Anaerobic and aerobic energy production of young rainbow trout (*Salmo gairdneri*) during and after bursts of activity. *J. Comp. Physiol.* 155B:485–92
150. Wright, J. C. 1986. Effects of body temperature, mass, and activity on aerobic and anaerobic metabolism in juvenile *Crocodylus porosus*. *Physiol. Zool.* 59:505–13

Annu. Rev. Physiol. 1991. 53:137–59

β-ADRENERGIC RECEPTOR REGULATION IN THE HEART IN PATHOPHYSIOLOGIC STATES: ABNORMAL ADRENERGIC RESPONSIVENESS IN CARDIAC DISEASE

Charles J. Homcy, Stephen F. Vatner, and Dorothy E. Vatner

Departments of Medicine and Pediatrics, Harvard Medical School, and the Cardiac Unit and Children's Service, Massachusetts General Hospital, Boston, Massachusetts 02114; Brigham and Women's Hospital, Boston, Massachusetts 02115; and The New England Regional Primate Research Center, Southborough, Massachusetts 01772

KEY WORDS: desensitization, GTP-regulatory proteins, adenylyl cyclase, catecholamines, heart failure

---

INTRODUCTION

Activation of the sympathetic nerves to the heart results in enhancement of the rate and force of its contraction (42). This occurs as the result of increased norepinephrine release at myoneuronal junctions, which leads to an increased agonist occupancy at postsynaptic β-adrenergic receptors. The resulting increase in intracellular cAMP levels promotes phosphorylation of several intracellular proteins responsible for a calcium-mediated increase in contractility (64). For some time, it has been appreciated that this system does not function normally in certain disease states, in particular heart failure. It has neither been clarified as to where and why the abnormalities in this signal transduction pathway develop, however, nor what is their functional im-

0066-4278/91/0315–0137$02.00

portance. It is the goal of this review to discuss this pathway in detail, particularly as to its regulation, and finally to consider the causes underlying its malfunction in diseased states.

PHARMACOLOGICAL AND BIOCHEMICAL ASPECTS OF THE β-ADRENERGIC RECEPTOR SYSTEM

The adrenergic receptors were classified functionally by Ahlquist in 1948 (1). Insights into these membrane proteins resulted initially from the synthesis of specific antagonists and agonists that allowed the identification of various receptor isoforms based on their functional activity, e.g. vasoconstriction vs vasodilation (7, 96). These chemical compounds eventually allowed biochemical approaches to be undertaken that identified these receptors, by photoaffinity labeling and by protein purification, as single polypeptide chains of approximately 50–60,000 kd (4, 5, 14, 16, 47, 59). A major achievement, however, was the cloning of a cDNA for the β-adrenergic receptor by the laboratories of Dixon & Lefkowitz (30) and Ross (129). This work demonstrated that the β-adrenergic receptor was a member of a large multigene family of receptor proteins that share a common feature; based on predicted secondary structure, each is presumed to consist of seven transmembrane spanning domains. This structure was initially deduced for bacterial opsin and rhodopsin to which the β-adrenergic receptor is homologous at the amino acid level (52, 65, 93). We now know that all receptors that transduce a signal through activation of a G protein share this putative structure (44, 70, 75; Figure 1). Based on a variety of deletional and site-directed mutagenesis studies, it is now known that the ligand binds to the intramembranous portion of the receptor by contacting specific residues in the transmembrane helices (20, 31–33, 39, 41, 110, 111). The extramembranous loops themselves play little or no role in ligand binding. In contrast, the intracellular loops are the elements that contact and modulate interaction with the G protein; the third loop which links spans five and six is the most important (66, 109), although the second cytoplasmic loop and carboxy-terminal tail are also involved (92). The third intracellular loop and the carboxy-terminal portion of the β-adrenergic receptor, for example, also contain the serine and threonine residues that undergo phosphorylation by a variety of protein kinases (10, 51). Phosphorylation of these residues appears intimately linked to the process of receptor desensitization and possibly down-regulation. Although the molecular dynamics and actual contact sites, especially for the interaction between the β-adrenergic receptor and G_s, the GTP-binding regulatory protein that mediates activation of adenylyl cyclase, have not been determined, intermediate steps in this process have been generally defined (44; Figure 2). Upon binding of agonist, the receptor forms a ternary complex with G_s

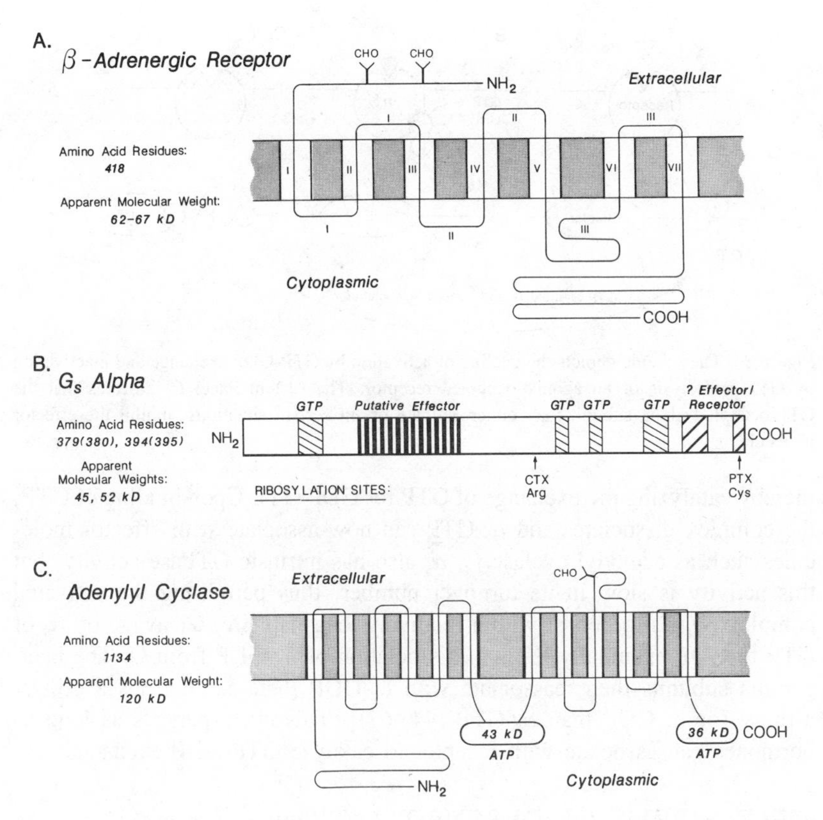

Figure 1 Panels *A-C* depict in simplified fashion the functional and structural domains of the β-adrenergic receptor signaling pathway. (*A*) The receptor's seven transmembrane-spanning alpha helices are shown. CHO indicates glycosylation sites present at the amino terminus of many adrenergic receptor subtypes where extended carbohydrate chains are co-translationally added and modified. Cytoplasmic loops II, III, and the COOH- terminal tail are involved in G protein interactions, particularly residues that are adjacent to the membrane. The third intracellular loop and COOH- terminal tail also contain the serines and threonines that are modified by either cAMP-dependent protein kinase or the β-adrenergic receptor kinase. (*B*) This figure graphs in linear fashion the regions of the alpha subunit, which interact with the GTP molecule (indicated by GTP), a putative effector domain, and the receptor-coupling domain, which is the best defined region at the COOH-terminal tail. This region may also play a role in effector coupling. The amino terminal portion of the molecule is likely involved in βγ interactions. The alpha subunits themselves do not contain extended hydrophobic regions and their association with the membrane may be mediated either by interactions with βγ, by covalent attachment of a fatty acid residue (e.g. myristoylation), or by a yet undefined mechanism (44). (*C*) The adenylyl cyclase molecule, based on the putative structure of brain adenylyl cyclase (68), is the least well-characterized of the three components. A putative glycosylation site (CHO) is shown on an extracellular loop. Of particular interest are the large intracellular domains (43 and 36 kd) that contain ATP-binding consensus sequences and are likely responsible for catalyzing the conversion of ATP to cAMP. (with permission, *Nature* 1987. 327: 188–89. Copyright © 1987 Macmillan Magazine Ltd.)

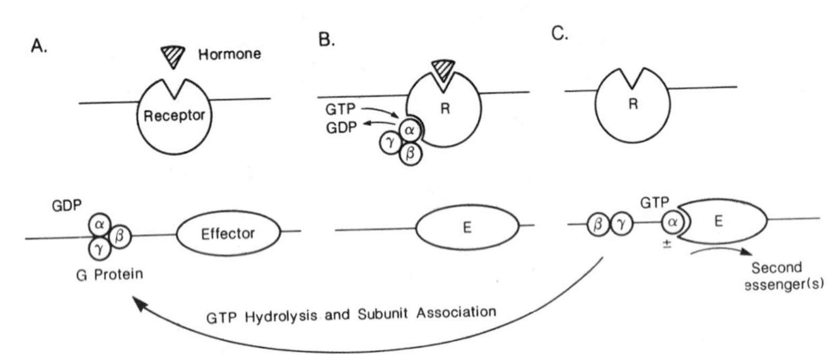

Figure 2 The scheme depicts the cycling of activation by GTP-GDP exchange and inactivation by GTP hydrolysis of an agonist-occupied receptor. The (±) in Panel *C* indicates that the GTP-occupied alpha subunit may either activate or, in certain situations, inhibit the effector molecule.

thereby catalyzing the exchange of GTP for GDP (11). Upon binding of GTP, the complex dissociates and α_s-GTP can now associate with effector molecules such as adenylyl cyclase C. α_s also has intrinsic GTPase activity, but this activity is slow in its turnover number, thus permitting the activated complex (α_s-C) to persist with a relatively long half-life. Cleavage by α_s of GTP to GDP eventually leads to dissociation of α_s-GDP from C. The beta-gamma subunits then reassociate with α_s-GDP [beta-gamma has a greater affinity for α_s-GDP than α_s-GTP (44, 67)]. This cycle persists as long as hormones can associate with receptor to catalyze GTP-GDP exchange.

MECHANISMS OF DESENSITIZATION

Down-regulation refers to the loss of cell surface receptors while desensitization, regardless of the mechanism, refers to the process whereby persistent exposure to an agonist results in a reduction in its net stimulatory effect. Desensitization could theoretically occur at any level, i.e. receptor, G protein, effector, or include mechanisms that enhance the rate of cAMP degradation. When the loss of stimulatory activity in the pathway is specific to the cell surface receptor being activated, it is termed homologous desensitization. This process usually involves modifications that are specific to the receptor protein itself. In contrast, if all pathways leading to activation of an effector are desensitized, then this more generalized effect is termed heterologous desensitization. It is thought that such a process would probably be at the level of the G protein or the effector enzyme itself, or possibly distal to these.

Occupancy of the β-adrenergic receptor by agonists triggers a variety of events that lead to homologous desensitization of the signaling pathway (2, 49, 70, 71, 98, 103). These include both translocation and phosphorylation of the receptor protein. The processes can be divided into rapid and delayed events. Down-regulation typically refers to a slower process, taking up to hours to occur, whereby receptor molecules are removed from the plasma membrane to the cell interior where they presumably are available to be recycled or, alternatively, degraded. There also appears to be a more rapid sequestration of receptors whereby receptors, although still detectable by hydrophobic ligands, are no longer identified by hydrophilic agents such as ^{3}H-CGP 12177 (19, 115, 124). The physical relationship of this sequestered pool to the plasma membrane has not been clarified. This process may be triggered by a phosphorylation event (2, 105) initiated upon agonist occupancy, which promotes a conformational change in the receptor molecule. In the homologous form of desensitization, it has been argued that agonist binds to receptor, which leads to its phosphorylation by a specific kinase termed BARK or β-adrenergic receptor kinase (6). An agonist-induced conformational change in the receptor is apparently necessary and sufficient for BARK to recognize the protein and to phosphorylate serine and threonine residues present in the carboxy-terminal tail of the protein, thus leading to an uncoupling of the receptor from its G protein (51). The early desensitization process, however, also can involve another phosphorylation event, which apparently is mediated via cAMP generation (3, 51).

METHODS EMPLOYED TO ASSESS THE COMPONENTS OF THE SIGNALING PATHWAY AND THEIR INTERACTIONS

A relatively pure membrane preparation that allows comparison among samples from normal and abnormal subjects is critical when comparisons of functional activities are made. It is clear that pathologic specimens can be inherently different than tissue obtained from normal animals in terms of fibrous components, other cell types, and the relative yield of membrane, as well as the components of the membrane obtained depending on the purification procedure. Basically two approaches to deal with this problem have been developed. One employs a partially purified membrane preparation in which the amount of sarcolemma obtained is relatively high, although still contaminated with other membrane components. The other approach is to use a highly enriched sarcolemma preparation (>90% pure), although the yield of sarcolemma is typically low (<10% total sarcolemma) (60, 118).

Ligand-binding methods for quantitating receptor concentration are now considered routine laboratory procedures. Nevertheless, certain guidelines should be considered to insure that specific receptor binding is being quantitated for a receptor population that has not been previously well-defined (58, 78). In addition to simply characterizing the type of receptor under study and its absolute concentration in a plasma membrane preparation, a variety of additional information concerning the functional aspects of a receptor can be obtained by ligand-binding studies. As discussed earlier, β-adrenergic receptors can be sequestered early during the course of desensitization. Also, certain ligands such as ^{125}I pindolol, because of their hydrophobic nature, can detect this sequestered component that in some manner remains associated with the plasma membrane. More hydrophilic ligands, however, such as ^{3}H CGP 12177 will not detect these sequestered components when experiments are carried out with intact cells. This kind of ligand binding approach allows one to quantitate directly the percentage of sequestered receptors. Another approach is to employ a competing ligand that allows this kind of specificity to be obtained. For example, a hydrophobic antagonist would compete with pindolol for all sites, while isoproterenol, a hydrophilic agonist, would only identify sites on the plasma membrane, but not sequestered receptors. Similarly, ligand-binding techniques in combination with appropriate membrane fractionation procedures have allowed a quantitation of receptors that have internalized or, at least moved, to another compartment within the cell. The physiologic implications of this are discussed more fully below. It has been observed that during the process of receptor down-regulation a pool of β-adrenergic receptors can be detected within a low density vesicular fraction that appears to be devoid of adenylyl cyclase or G protein activity (57, 115, 124). For example, in cardiac ischemia, Maisel et al (81) reported a decrease in this component in membrane preparations obtained from the heart as a mechanism underlying the increase in sarcolemmal β-adrenergic receptor content.

Ligand binding also allows one to assess more directly the interaction of the receptor with its G protein. It was recognized several years ago that the association of receptor, G protein, and hormone formed a high affinity state of agonist binding. That is, this ternary complex (27, 128) exhibits a higher affinity for agonist than does the receptor, which is uncoupled, i.e. not functionally associated with the G protein (27, 73). Loss of this high affinity state can be detected as an early event in the process of desensitization (104). The factors that regulate the percentage of receptors in the high affinity state among different membrane preparations are not well-understood, although they most likely reflect states of receptor phosphorylation, concentration of G proteins, and the relative stoichiometry of receptor to G protein. The basis for these differences is a particularly interesting question in itself. Nevertheless, one can determine whether the ability of the receptor to associate with a G protein has been altered in a pathophysiologic state by quantitating the percentage of receptors in the high and low affinity states. Differences in the ability to form a high affinity interaction could be secondary to a process of desensitization, that is, to phosphorylation of the receptor, or to an alteration in the concentration, or function of the G protein, or both. In our studies on animals with cardiac hypertrophy and heart failure, we have detected that there is a loss of this high affinity interaction between receptor and G protein although the concentration of antagonist binding sites have not decreased (121). Furthermore, a loss of G_s functional activity is also demonstrable (79). Whether another process that directly affects the receptor is also occurring, e.g. phosphorylation, has not yet been determined. Similarly, alteration in the fraction of high affinity beta receptors has also been attributed to a variety of other factors. For example, it has been shown that both steroid (26) and thyroid hormones (108) can modulate the interaction between receptor and G protein. Multiple mechanisms underly these effects, however (82, 97).

In addition to assessing the interaction of the receptor and the G protein, it is possible to quantitate directly the number of G protein molecules in a membrane preparation and their functional activity. Antibodies are now available to $G_{s\alpha}$, $G_{i\alpha}$, and their beta and gamma subunits that permit detection of these proteins by Western blotting with a great degree of sensitivity and specificity. Antipeptide antibodies have been raised to variable regions of the three known $G_{i\alpha}$ isoforms. Thus despite the overall homology among the various isoforms (75), this development has allowed antibodies with requisite specificity to be generated (46, 86). In addition to assaying the amount of a G protein in this manner, a functional assessment distinct from its receptor and effector interactions is valuable and suggests that direct modification of the G protein itself may underlie an alteration in its activity. With G_s, a reliable and relatively easy assay is available that uses the mutant S49 mouse lymphoma cell line termed cyc−, which is genetically deficient in $G_{s\alpha}$ (9, 107). This mutant cell line lacks the mRNA for $G_{s\alpha}$ (50). A more difficult assay to devise is one that reliably detects the functional activity of inhibitory G proteins in the membrane. For example, it is difficult in canine cardiac sarcolemma to assess G protein-mediated inhibition of adenylyl cyclase activity that is independent of receptor activation (120). The routine approach is to determine whether GTPγS, a nonhydrolyzable analogue of GTP, will inhibit forskolin-mediated cyclase stimulation. A direct assay that permits detection of G_i activity distinct from its effector is difficult to devise; at least one that does not require purification of the inhibitory G protein. This often is not feasible when limited amounts of membrane are available from a pathophysiologic model.

Cholera and pertussis toxin-mediated modification of $G_{s\alpha}$ and $G_{i\alpha}$, respectively, was among the earliest techniques developed to assay for these proteins. It is also clear, however, that these are not necessarily quantitatively reliable methods. For example, cholera toxin requires a variety of co-factors to carry out its enzymatic function of transferring an ADP-ribose group from NAD to an arginine residue in the $G_{s\alpha}$ molecule (15, 34).

Pertussis toxin catalyzes the ADP ribosylation of a cysteine residue in the carboxy terminus of all three $G_{i\alpha}$ isoforms and also of $G_{o\alpha}$ (75, 126). It has been shown that pertussis toxin-mediated ribosylation of $G_{i\alpha}$ is promoted when the alpha subunit is associated with beta-gamma (88). Thus, the presence of the heterotrimeric protein is one factor that determines the efficiency of toxin-mediated ribosylation. Because of these facts pertussis toxin labeling should also not be employed as a sole measure of $G_{i\alpha}$ levels. Several laboratories have developed antipeptide antibodies that both specifically and with sufficient sensitivity can be used in Western blotting of $G_{i\alpha}$ isoforms (46).

Toxin-mediated ribosylation of $G_{s\alpha}$ and $G_{i\alpha}$ has also been used to assess the functional activity of a particular pathway. In the case of G_i, it blocks the inhibitory pathway mediated by receptors such as muscarinic acetylcholine receptors in the heart. Pertussis toxin-mediated ribosylation of $G_{i\alpha}$ only uncouples this protein from its receptor (88). It does not interfere with the ability of G_i to inhibit adenylyl cyclase activity. For example, GTPγS can still activate the ADP-ribosylated alpha subunit of G_i to inhibit adenylyl cyclase.

The putative structure of the catalyst adenylyl cyclase and the existence of isoforms have been identified by molecular cloning (68; Figure 1). It is an integral membrane protein with multiple spans that traverse the plasma membrane. In fact, it has a structure not unlike an ion channel. The enzyme is particularly unstable when solubilized and dissociated from the stimulatory G protein (100), therefore direct measurements of its function are more difficult under these conditions. Although forskolin can directly stimulate catalytic unit activity, it is also clear that forskolin will enhance adenylyl cyclase activity to an even greater extent when the catalytic unit is associated with $G_{s\alpha}$ (21, 25, 101). Thus measurement of forskolin-stimulated adenylyl cyclase activity cannot be considered a direct assay of catalytic unit activity when $G_{s\alpha}$ is still associated with the catalytic unit. One approach has been to solubilize the cyclase catalytic unit in the presence of relatively high concentrations of manganese, which promotes the functional dissociation of the catalytic unit from its G protein and directly stimulates the catalytic unit. One can assess whether dissociation has been achieved by determining if GTPγS or fluoride will still stimulate catalytic unit activity (69, 74). If this G_s-mediated stimulatory effect has been abolished, then manganese-stimulated activity in the solubilized preparation can be considered a more reliable measure of cyclase catalytic unit activity. It is soon likely that appropriate antipeptide antibodies will be generated to allow direct quantitation of the number of molecules of the catalytic unit within the membrane. Reliable assessment of this functional activity is still wanting, however. It is clear that the catalytic unit is an important determinant of the overall activity of the β-adrenergic pathway and that its activity can be modified by post-translational processes such as phosphorylation (96, 130). Evidence from our laboratory suggests that the developmental activity of the β-adrenergic receptor signaling pathway in the rat heart reflects the activity of the cyclase catalytic unit to a greater extent than any other component (16a).

cDNA probes are now generally available for many receptors and G protein subunits. The reliable measurement of mRNA message levels for the various adrenergic receptors is made difficult by the fact that the steady-state concentration of their mRNAs is quite low, in the pg/μg total RNA range. Solution phase hybridization techniques have reported reliable measurements for even these low levels of message (48). For G protein subunits the mRNA levels of the alpha subunits are significantly higher than those reported for the β-adrenergic receptor (56). We have measured both $G_{s\alpha}$ and $G_{i\alpha 2}$ mRNA levels in the left ventricle of dogs. The $G_{s\alpha}$ mRNA level is five to sixfold higher than that of $G_{i\alpha 2}$, which is by far the predominant $G_{i\alpha}$ isoform in the canine left ventricle. With the use of a dot blotting protocol, one can accurately quantitate the concentrations of these mRNAs by comparison with a standard curve generated with pure G_α mRNAs obtained by in vitro transcription.

β-ADRENERGIC RECEPTORS IN CARDIAC DISEASE

When the heart is subjected to the stress of myocardial ischemia or pressure or volume overload, one generalized response is an activation of the sympathetic nervous system. In many instances, myocardial ischemia may be involved in the pathogenesis of myocardial hypertrophy and heart failure, which makes it important to consider these disease states in parallel. Furthermore, changes in the β-adrenergic receptor-adenylyl cyclase coupling may be related to acute or chronically altered catecholamine levels induced systemically or at the receptor site, thus requiring that desensitization mechanisms also be considered.

CONGESTIVE HEART FAILURE Increased stimulation of the heart by the sympathetic nervous system is one compensatory mechanism used to support the failing heart. As failure worsens, cardiac stores of norepinephrine are markedly depleted (17), but circulating plasma levels of norepinephrine are elevated and appear directly related to the degree of LV dysfunction (72, 113) and the subsequent risk of death (22). Even though the circulating levels of norepinephrine are elevated in response to the failing heart, inotropic responsiveness to catecholamines is abnormal. The source of this decreased responsiveness has been examined at several levels. Abnormalities in responsiveness to isoproterenol and several phosphodiesterase inhibitors, but normal responsiveness to acetystrophanthidin and forskolin, were noted in trabeculae carneae from the failing hearts of transplant recipients (37). The cause of contractile dysfunction in the failing heart was thought to be deficient cAMP and decreased myocardial β-adrenergic receptors in human hearts with end-stage heart failure, with a selective loss of β_1-adrenergic receptors (13), progressive β_1-adrenergic receptor down-regulation, dependent on the severity of the heart failure (38), and decreased responsiveness to isoproterenol (45). A similar loss of responsiveness in the failing human heart to isoproterenol, as well as milrinone, was related to loss of β-adrenergic receptors (8).

In some animal models of heart failure, the inotropic responses to norepinephrine and isoproterenol are also markedly depressed (91). In a guinea pig model of pressure overload heart failure, Karliner et al found increased myocardial β-adrenergic receptor density (61). In dogs with right heart failure, inotropic response to dobutamine was decreased and right ventricular β-adrenergic receptor density was decreased (35). In turkeys with congenital congestive cardiomyopathy, the β-adrenergic receptor-adenylyl cyclase system was shown to be defective before development of cardiac dilatation (106); after the development of severe cardiac dilatation, a global defect in adenylyl cyclase was observed.

In an aortic-banded model of pressure overload hypertrophy and failure in the dog (121), despite an increase in β-adrenergic receptor density, as assessed by using antagonist-binding techniques, the number of β-adrenergic receptors binding agonist with high affinity was markedly diminished. G_s levels and functional activity were reduced (79), and isoproterenol, forskolin, and sodium fluoride-stimulated adenylyl cyclase activity were reduced. In contrast, isoproterenol-stimulated adenylyl cyclase was specifically depressed in the failing human heart (12, 28), whereas forskolin- (28) and sodium fluoride-stimulated adenylyl cyclase (12) activity were unchanged from normal. Two groups have also found a selective increase in G_i, the inhibitory GTP-binding protein, in failing human heart (36, 90). While the experimental studies in canine heart failure caused by aortic banding found clear decreases in G_{sa}, insignificant increases in G_i were also observed (120).

In summary, the failing heart has defects in β-adrenergic receptor-adenylyl cyclase coupling, G-protein activity levels, and in some models, global decreases in adenylyl cyclase activity. The major difference between the results from aortic banding-induced heart failure in dogs and the human studies, which have predominantly studied cardiomyopathic or end-state heart disease, is the direction of β-adrenergic receptor density observed with antagonist binding. The ischemic myocardium is generally characterized by increased β-adrenergic receptor density, and the model of aortic banding-induced heart failure results in subendocardial ischemia, particularly during stress (54, 55).

Thus it remains to be determined if the model and etiology of heart failure are critical in determining the alterations of β-adrenergic receptor regulation. In any event, it appears that β-adrenergic receptor uncoupling and alteration in G_s may be major mechanisms responsible for the depressed β-adrenergic receptor activity in heart failure.

DESENSITIZATION One potential mechanism for the changes in the β-adrenergic receptor-adenylyl cyclase complex in the failing heart involves desensitization, secondary to the chronic high levels of circulating catecholamines found in heart failure. The topic of desensitization has been studied extensively in isolated organ and cellular systems. These studies have demonstrated two primary mechanisms of desensitization, which have been referred to as homologous and heterologous (49, 53, 71, 102; see above). Homologous desensitization is characterized by an attenuated responsiveness of adenylyl cyclase only to the specific desensitizing hormone without affecting the enzyme's responsiveness to other hormones. In contrast, heterologous desensitization is characterized by diminished responsiveness of adenylyl cyclase to a wide spectrum of activators, including other hormones as well as fluoride and guanine nucleotides.

Most studies on this topic have been conducted in vitro, and the majority have utilized isoproterenol rather than the physiologic neurotransmitter, norepinephrine, to induce desensitization. The majority of these studies on myocardial tissue has shown a specific, i.e. homologous, desensitization with an associated decrease of β-adrenergic receptor density (49, 53, 71, 102) and a loss of isoproterenol-stimulated adenylyl cyclase activity, although a generalized decrease in adenylyl cyclase activity has also been observed (116).

We recently examined this problem utilizing a different experiment design. In our study (122) the neurotransmitter, norepinephrine, was utilized as the agonist, and the study was performed in an intact, conscious, large animal model using chronic infusions of norepinephrine delivered over one month from implanted pumps. Physiologic desensitization, i.e. reduced inotropic responsiveness to isoproterenol, was observed in these conscious animals after one month of chronically maintained norepinephrine levels. The desensitization did not involve a decrease in β-adrenergic receptor density (receptor density was actually increased), however, but rather involved uncoupling of the β-adrenergic receptor as reflected by decreases in the number of receptor sites binding agonist with high affinity. Accompanying this decrease in coupled or high affinity receptors was a decrease in G_s activity as assessed by reconstitution as well as cholera-toxin labeling. In addition, these changes were associated with decreases in basal and stimulated adenylyl cyclase activation. Furthermore, adenylyl cyclase activity was depressed in animals with norepinephrine pumps, whether stimulated through the β-adrenergic receptor, or distally through the G_s protein, a pattern consistent with a complex mechanism for desensitization. These findings were strikingly similar to those observed in the aortic-banded model of heart failure (79, 121).

The mechanism clearly involved decreases in high affinity agonist binding, adenylyl cyclase activation, and depressed functional levels of G_s. Thus desensitization in response to acute, short term exposure to isoproterenol (49,

53, 71, 102) involves a specific, i.e. homologous, desensitization with an associated decrease in β-adrenergic receptor density and a loss of isoproterenol-stimulated adenylate cyclase activity. In contrast, desensitization in response to chronic elevation of norepinephrine levels occurs distal to the β-receptor.

Our recent studies also suggest that the mechanisms of desensitization are even more complicated than previously thought because the presence or absence of cardiac and/or arterial baroreceptor nerves play a major role in allowing the expression of functional desensitization to norepinephrine, but not to isoproterenol (89). It is interesting to speculate that these data have bearing on the state of chronic heart failure, which is often characterized by desensitization to catecholamines. It is important to note that heart failure is marked by elements of cardiac denervation, at least in terms of catecholamine depletion, and also by impaired arterial baroreflex control. Thus impaired neural control of the heart by cardiac nerves and arterial baroreflexes may be critical in the functional expression of catecholamine desensitization, not only in intact animals, but also in heart failure in general.

MYOCARDIAL ISCHEMIA Several studies have demonstrated major alterations in β-adrenergic receptor control in the presence of myocardial ischemia. It is conceivable that these changes in receptor regulation may be responsible for arrhythmias developing in the ischemic myocardium. The initial observation that ischemia increases β-adrenergic receptors was noted by Mukherjee et al (84, 85). This observation has been subsequently confirmed by most investigators (29, 80, 87, 112, 119), although a few studies have not found increases in β-adrenergic receptors with ischemia (40, 62, 63). These differences could be due to (*a*) the duration of ischemia, (*b*) whether reperfusion intervenes, and (*c*) the type of membrane preparation utilized.

It remains controversial whether the increased receptor density results in increased adenylyl cyclase activation. Maisel et al found enhanced isoproterenol-stimulated adenylyl cyclase activity (80, 81). Corr et al found increased cAMP only during the initial 20 min after coronary artery occlusion (24). Increased levels of cAMP (84) have been found with one hr of occlusion, followed by 15 min of reperfusion with isoproterenol, again suggesting that changes with ischemia are reversible by reperfusion and that the duration of coronary artery occlusion is also critical.

Only a few studies have examined the coupling of β-adrenergic receptors to adenylyl cyclase (40, 123), which requires agonist competition binding curves to determine the number of coupled β-adrenergic receptors that bind agonist with high affinity. Both of these studies demonstrate that high affinity β-adrenergic receptors were shifted into the low affinity state in ischemia as compared with the non-ischemic tissue. In a study of one hr of occlusion in conscious dogs from our laboratory (112), β-adrenergic receptor density increased and G_s levels and activity were significantly reduced. This finding suggests that the mechanism of the decrease in high affinity agonist-binding sites that results in uncoupling of the β-adrenergic receptor from adenylyl cyclase could involve the decrease of G_s activity. Whether an alteration (e. g. phosphorylation) in the receptor itself is playing a role has not been determined.

Relevance of Changes in the β-Adrenergic Receptor Signaling Pathway in Disease States

Classically β-adrenergic receptor regulation is thought to occur through up- and down-regulation of β-adrenergic receptor density. While these mechanisms may be important, other mechanisms also should be considered. These include β-adrenergic receptor cycling, as may occur in ischemia, and uncoupling of the β-adrenergic receptor from adenylyl cyclase, as may occur in heart failure, desensitization, and ischemia, which are associated with changes in G protein activity.

The interesting parallels among chronic desensitization, acute ischemia, and heart failure in canine models suggest that similar mechanisms are operating in these conditions (Table 1). All are characterized by a decrease in the number of receptors binding agonist with high affinity, decreased G_s activity and levels, and global decreases in adenylyl cyclase activity. To date these studies have demonstrated alterations in the β-adrenergic receptor-G protein-adenylyl cyclase complex that are potentially important adaptations of the β-adrenergic system to cardiac diseases.

Relationship of Physiologic Dysfunction to Biochemical Alterations in Receptor Signaling

NON-RECEPTOR-DEPENDENT MECHANISMS FOR DEPRESSED β-ADRENERGIC SENSITIVITY IN CONGESTIVE HEART FAILURE Depressed inotropic responsiveness to sympathomimetic amines in heart failure has been recognized for some time (17, 22, 23, 43, 45, 95, 99). It is generally assumed that the mechanism of the depressed function is simple down-regulation of β-adrenergic receptor number (12). While this mechanism may be important in certain models and in some disease states, it is certainly not the universal finding. There are several animal models of heart failure in which depressed inotropic responsiveness to sympathomimetic amines without a decrease in β-adrenergic receptor number were observed (121). In these studies, it appears that the mechanism was distal to the receptor and involved potential alterations in the catalytic unit of adenylyl cyclase as well as potential alterations in G proteins (79, 121). It is also conceivable that the mechanism

Table 1 Summary of results of alterations in the β-adrenergic receptor signaling pathway

Pathophysiology	β-adrenergic receptor density	Coupled or high affinity receptors	Funtional G_s activity	mRNA levels	Adenylyl cyclase activity
Hypertrophy	↑	ND	↓	↓	↓
Hypertrophy and heart failure	↑	↓	↓	↓	↓↓
Ischemia	↑	↓	↓	ND	↓
Chronic norepinephrine exposure	↑	↓	↓	ND	↓

ND = not determined.

This table summarizes the results of several studies from the authors' laboratories (79, 112, 119, 121, 122, 125) in which alterations in the β-adrenergic receptor signaling pathway have been identified. The similarity of the changes in at least three different pathophysiologic states (hypertrophy, ischemia, and desensitization) suggests that a common mechanism could be operative.

for depressed responsiveness occurs even distal to cyclase and G proteins and involves phosphorylation or alterations of calcium entry into the cell.

One other set of possibilities must be considered. There are other factors involved in the hypertrophied heart that may affect responsiveness to sympathomimetic amines. In some models of severe left ventricular hypertrophy and heart failure, fibrosis and replacement of myocytes with collagen occurs. This by itself will impair the ability to increase cardiac function in response to sympathetic stress. Another important mechanism is that of reduced subendocardial coronary reserve. It is generally well-recognized that reduced coronary reserve is associated with severe left ventricular hypertrophy and may not only be important in understanding the control of the hypertrophied heart, but may also be an important link in the pathogenesis of decompensation from compensated hypertrophy to failure (54). In this connection, in the presence of reduced subendocardial and coronary reserve, any inotropic stress that requires an increase in oxygen requirement and an increase in coronary blood flow might show depressed responsiveness because of the inability of the heart to meet the increased oxygen demands with the consequent production of intermittent bouts of myocardial ischemia. This subendocardial ischemia, in turn, will limit systolic function, particularly in response to sympathomimetic amines, and will also impair diastolic function. Altered diastolic function may also be important in limiting the ability of sympathomimetic amines to augment contractile function normally in the presence of severe hypertrophy and heart failure (55). These mechanisms, unrelated to β-adrenergic receptor regulation, may be equally important in determining the responsiveness to sympathetic stress in heart failure.

DIRECTIONS FOR THE FUTURE: APPROACH TO UNDERLYING MECHANISMS

It is now over a decade since the routine use of the radioligand-binding assay has allowed the quantitation and characterization of adrenergic receptors in a variety of pathophysiologic states involving the heart. Despite the ability to enumerate alterations in receptor number and to characterize the distal effector systems in pathophysiologic states including hypertrophy, ischemia, and hyperthyroidism, the functional consequences and significance of these changes at the physiologic level have remained inadequately defined. We do not know whether these alterations underlie important functional changes in terms of the pumping efficiency of the heart. For example, if β-adrenergic receptor density did not decrease in certain forms of heart failure, would cardiac function be more adequately maintained over a longer period of time? If desensitization did not occur at the receptor level, would β-adrenergic receptor agonists prove to be useful tools in treating heart failure? We can only define associations at this point, but we have been unable to assign cause and effect relationships. It is this inability to be certain of causal relationships that remains one of the significant deficiencies in this area of investigation.

A second aspect of this work that remains poorly defined is the biochemical and genetic mechanisms underlying these changes. For example, we know that β-adrenergic receptors can decrease in number at the level of the sarcolemma, or that they can uncouple from the effector pathway in heart failure. G_s functional activity can be reduced and adenylyl cyclase activation impaired. In none of these pathophysiologic models has the mechanism underlying these defects actually been defined, however. Recently we determined that the decrease in $G_{S\alpha}$ levels occurs in the state of compensated hypertrophy before heart failure ensues. Moreover, this reduction in $G_{S\alpha}$ is accompanied by a fall of similar magnitude in its mRNA levels (16a). Although the decrease in $G_{S\alpha}$ protein activity and its mRNA remains constant, basal and stimulated adenylyl cyclase activities decrease to an even greater extent when heart failure ensues. This pattern implicates an alteration in the adenylyl cyclase catalytic moiety itself as a principal mechanism underlying defective sarcolemmal cAMP generation in this disease model. However, we have not defined what underlies this alteration at the messenger RNA level. Measurements such as mRNA degradation rates or transcriptional synthetic rates as assessed by nuclear run-ons could possibly be carried out, but are difficult in these large animals models. Nevertheless, these kinds of approaches will be necessary if we are to understand the basis for these changes. Similarly, with alterations in receptor number, what is the initial process that leads to this down-regulation? Is phosphorylation of the receptor intimately involved with down-regulation in pathophysiologic states? What is the role of the sympathetic nerves in producing this effect? In fact, is abnormal function of the sympathetic nerves a requirement for the alterations in β-adrenergic receptor activity that have been delineated in certain types of heart failure in man? What are the temporal relationships among these events? Alternatively, do alterations in gene transcription underlie the reduction in β-adrenergic receptor content that has been defined in various disease states? Answering questions like these will be goals for the future in many laboratories.

The most direct way of defining cause and effect relationships however, may be through the use of transgenic animal models in which gene dosage is artificially altered. The effect of this maneuver can then be examined in terms of physiologic consequences. For example, one could encode for elevated levels of $G_{s\alpha}$ mRNA using a heterologous promoter element in a transgenic animal. In states of hypertrophy it could then be determined whether elevated $G_{s\alpha}$ levels prevent or alter the abnormalities in adenylyl cyclase that we have defined in our canine model of pressure overload-induced hypertrophy. Similarly, in relation to the role of β-adrenergic receptor down-regulation in heart failure, the β-adrenergic receptor gene could be expressed in a transgenic animal under the control of a heterologous promoter, even an inducible element such as the metallothionein promoter. If a pathophysiologic state is then induced and receptor down-regulation is identified, one could artificially increase receptor content by inducing the activation of this promoter. A variety of transcriptional regulatory elements could be utilized including metallothionein promoters and hormone response elements to list just a few (18, 83). This approach is not limited to mouse models, since work in several laboratories has indicated that transgenic miniswine can be developed that express the transgene at high levels (94, 127). The transgenic miniswine is a particularly valuable model in that it is of a sufficient size to allow careful physiologic measurements to be carried out both in acute and chronic experiments. The use of such an approach to examine the effect of overexpression of a particular gene product on cardiac function has several valuable features. The heart, more than any other organ, must be studied under conditions in which its intimate association with the vasculature is maintained. Preload and afterload are two of the most important determinants of overall cardiac pumping performance. Examination of the isolated myocyte alone suffers from an inability to adequately assess that property that constitutes the most critical function of the heart, its pumping action. Furthermore, gene expression at the level of the cardiocyte cannot be readily studied at the present time since these cells or even appropriate facsimiles cannot be continuously maintained in cell culture. The use of enhancer-promoter elements, therefore, that allow relatively selective expression of a transgene in the heart affords an alternative approach to examine the role of specific gene products on cardiac performance. The myosin promoter, which is known to be regulated in a tissue- and developmentally specific manner, is just one example of a regulatory element that may be potentially ideal for this kind of experimental approach (76, 77, 114). As more laboratories become adept with these methods, transgenic animal models may become routine in the physiology laboratory of the 1990s. It is this type of approach that should also usher in an exciting new era for the study of pathophysiologic processes involving the heart and cardiovascular system.

ACKNOWLEDGMENTS

This work was supported in part by U.S. Public Health Service grants HL-37404, HL-19259, HL-38070, HL-33107, and RR-00168 from the Division of Research Resources, and Grants-in-Aid from the American Heart Association, Massachusetts Affiliate. Dr. D. E. Vatner is currently supported by U.S. Public Health Service Research Career Development Award HL-01909.

Literature Cited

1. Ahlquist, R. P. 1948. A study of the adrenotropic receptors. *Am. J. Physiol.* 153:586–600
2. Benovic, J. L., Bouvier, M., Caron, M. G., Lefkowitz, R. J. 1988. Regulation of adenylyl cyclase-coupled β-adrenergic receptors. *Annu. Rev. Cell Biol.* 4:405–28
3. Benovic, J. L., Pike, L. J., Cerione, R. A., Staniszewski, C., Yoshimasa, T., et al. 1985. Phosphorylation of the mammalian β-adrenergic receptor by cyclic AMP-dependent protein kinase: Regulation of rate of receptor phosphorylation and dephosphorylation by agonist occupancy and effects on coupling of the receptor to the stimulatory guanine nucleotide regulatory protein. *J. Biol. Chem.* 260:7094–7101
4. Benovic, J. L., Shorr, R. G. L., Caron, M. G., Lefkowitz, R. J. 1985. The mammalian β_2-adrenergic receptor: Purification and characterization. *Biochemistry* 23:4510–18
5. Benovic, J. L., Stiles, G. L., Lefkowitz, R. J., Caron, M. G. 1983. Photoaffinity labelling of mammalian beta-adrenergic receptors: Metal-dependent proteolysis explains apparent heterogeneity. *Biochem. Biophys. Res. Commun.* 110: 504–11
6. Benovic, J. L., Strasser, R. H., Caron, M. G., Lefkowitz, R. J. 1986. β-adrenergic receptor kinase: identification of a novel protein kinase that phosphorylates the agonist-occupied form of the receptor. *Proc. Natl. Acad. Sci. USA* 83:2797–2801
7. Black, G. W., Stephensen, J. S. 1962. Pharmacology of a new adrenergic beta-receptor-blocking compound (Nethalide). *Lancet* ii:311–16
8. Böhm, M., Diet, F., Feiler, G., Kemkes, B., Kreuzer, E., et al. 1988. Subsensitivity of the failing human heart to isoprenaline and milrinone is related to β-adrenoceptor downregulation. *J. Cardiovasc. Pharmacol.* 12:726–32
9. Bourne, H. R., Coffino, P., Tomkins, G. M. 1975. Selection of a variant lymphoma cell deficient in adenylate cyclase. *Science* 187:750–52
10. Bouvier, M., Hausdorff, W. P., De-Blasi, A., O'Dowd, B. F., Kobilka, B. K., et al. 1988. Removal of phosphorylation sites from the β_2-adrenergic receptor delays onset of agonist-promoted desensitization. *Nature* 333: 370–73
11. Brandt, D. R., Ross, E. M. 1986. Catecholamine-stimulated GTPase cycle. *J. Biol. Chem.* 261:1656–64
12. Bristow, M. R., Ginsburg, R., Minobe, W., Cubicciotti, R. S., Sageman, W. S., et al. 1982. Decreased catecholamine sensitivity and β-adrenergic-receptor density in failing human hearts. *N. Engl. J. Med.* 307:205–11
13. Bristow, M. R., Ginsburg, R., Umans, V., Fowler, M., Minobe, W., et al. 1986. β_1- and β_2-adrenergic-receptor subpopulations in nonfailing and failing

human ventricular myocardium: Coupling of both receptor subtypes to muscle contraction and selective β_1-receptor down-regulation in heart failure. *Circ. Res.* 59:297–309

14. Caron, M. G., Srinivasan, Y., Pitha, J., Kociolek, K., Lefkowitz, R. J. 1979. Affinity chromatography of the β-adrenergic receptor. *J. Biol. Chem.* 254:2923–27
15. Cassel, D., Pfeuffer, T. 1978. Mechanism of cholera toxin action: Covalent modification of the guanyl nucleotide-binding protein of the adenylate cyclase system. *Proc. Natl. Acad. Sci. USA* 75:2669–73
16. Cerione, R. A., Strulovici, B., Benovic, J. L., Lefkowitz, R. J., Caron, M. G. 1983. Pure β-adrenergic receptor: The single polypeptide confers catecholamine responsiveness to adenylate cyclase. *Nature* 306:562–66

16a. Chen, C., Vatner, D. E., Vatner, S. F., Hittinger, L., Homcy, C. J. 1990. Decreased $G_{S\alpha}$ mRNA levels accompany the fall in G_S and adenylyl cyclase activities in compensated left ventricular hypertrophy. In heart failure, only the impairment in adenylyl cyclase activation progresses. *J. Clin. Invest.* In press

17. Chidsey, C. A., Braunwald, E., Morrow, A. G. 1965. Catecholamine excretion and cardiac stores of norepinephrine in congestive heart failure. *Am. J. Med.* 39:442–51
18. Chisari, F. V., Pinkert, C. A., Milich, D. R., Filippi, P., McLachlan, A., et al. 1985. A transgenic mouse model of the chronic hepatitis B surface antigen carrier state. *Science* 230:1157–60
19. Chuang, D.-M., Costa, E. 1979. Evidence for internalization of the recognition site of β-adrenergic receptors during receptor subsensitivity induced by (−)-isoproterenol. *Proc. Natl. Acad. Sci. USA* 76:3024–28
20. Chung, F.-Z., Wang, C.-D., Potter, P. C., Venter, J. C., Fraser, C. M. 1988. Site-directed mutagenesis and continuous expression of human β-adrenergic receptors. *J. Biol. Chem.* 263:4052–55
21. Clark, R. B., Goka, T. J., Green, D. A., Barber, R., Butcher, R. W. 1982. Differences in the forskolin activation of adenylate cyclase in wild-type and variant lymphoma cells. *Mol. Pharmacol.* 22:609–13
22. Cohn, J. N., Levine, T. B., Olivari, M. T., Garberg, V., Lura, D., et al. 1984. Plasma norepinephrine as a guide to prognosis in patients with chronic congestive heart failure. *N. Engl. J. Med.* 311:819–23
23. Colucci, W. S., Leatherman, G. F., Lundmar, P. L., Gauthier, D. F. 1987. β-adrenergic inotropic responsiveness of patients with heart failure: Studies with intracoronary dobutamine infusion. *Circ. Res.* 61:I82–86 (Suppl. I)
24. Corr, P. B., Witkowski, F. X., Sobel, B. E. 1978. Mechanisms contributing to malignant dysrhythmias induced by ischemia in the cat. *J. Clin. Invest.* 61:109–119
25. Darfler, F. J., Mahan, L. C., Koachman, A. M., Insel, P. A. 1982. Stimulation by forskolin of intact S49 lymphoma cells involves the nucleotide regulatory protein of adenylate cyclase. *J. Biol. Chem.* 257:11901–7
26. Davies, A. O., DeLean, A., Lefkowitz, R. J. 1981. Myocardial beta-adrenergic receptors from adrenalectomized rats: Impaired formation of high-affinity agonist-receptor complexes. *Endocrinology* 108:720–22
27. DeLean, A., Stadel, J. M., Lefkowitz, R. J. 1980. A ternary complex model explains the agonist-specific binding properties of the adenylate cyclase-coupled β-adrenergic receptor. *J. Biol. Chem.* 255:7108–17
28. Denniss, A. R., Marsh, J. D., Quigg, R. J., Gordon, J. B., Colucci, W. S. 1989. β-adrenergic receptor number and adenylate cyclase function in denervated transplanted and cardiomyopathic human hearts. *Circulation* 79:1028–34
29. Devos, C., Robberecht, P., Nokin, P., Waelbroeck, M., Clinet, M., et al. 1985. Uncoupling between beta-adrenoceptors and adenylate cyclase in dog ischemic myocardium. *Naunyn-Schmiedeberg's Arch. Pharmacol.* 331:71–75
30. Dixon, R. A. F., Kobilka, B. K., Strader, D. J., Benovic, J. L., Dohlman, H. G., et al. 1986. Cloning of the gene and cDNA for mammalian β-adrenergic receptor and homology with rhodopsin. *Nature* 321:75–79
31. Dixon, R. A. F., Sigal, I. S., Candelore, M. R. Register, R. B., Scattergood, W., et al. 1987. Structural features required for ligand binding to the β-adrenergic receptor. *EMBO J.* 6:3269–75
32. Dixon, R. A. F., Sigal, I. S., Rands, E., Register, R. B., Candelore, M. R., et al. 1987. Ligand binding to β-adrenergic receptor involves its rhodopsin-like core. *Nature* 326:73–77
33. Dohlman, H. G., Caron, M. G., Strader, C. D., Amlaiky, N., Lefkowitz, R.

J. 1988. Identification and sequence of a binding site peptide of the β_2-adrenergic receptor. *Biochemistry* 27:1813–17
34. Enomoto, K., Gill, D. M. 1980. Cholera toxin activation of adenylate cyclase. *J. Biol. Chem.* 255:1252–58
35. Fan, T.-H. M., Liang, C.-S., Kawashima, S., Banerjee, S. P. 1987. Alterations in cardiac β-adrenoceptor responsiveness and adenylate cyclase system by congestive heart failure in dogs. *Eur. J. Pharmacol.* 140:123–32
36. Feldman, A. M., Cates, A. E., Veazey, W. B., Hershberger, R. E., Bristow, M. R., et al. 1988. Increase of the 40,000-mol wt pertussis toxin substrate (G protein) in the failing human heart. *J. Clin. Invest.* 82:189–97
37. Feldman, M. D., Copelas, L., Gwarthmey, J. K., Phillips, P., Warren, S. E., et al. 1987. Deficient production of cyclic AMP: Pharmacologic evidence of an important cause of contractile dysfunction in patients with end-stage heart failure. *Circulation* 75:331–39
38. Fowler, M. B., Laser, J. A., Hopkins, G. L., Minobe, W., Bristow, M. R. 1986. Assessment of the β-adrenergic receptor pathway in the intact failing human heart: Progressive receptor down-regulation and subsensitivity to agonist response. *Circulation* 74:1290–1302
39. Fraser, C. M. 1989. Site-directed mutagenesis of β-adrenergic receptors. Identification of conserved cysteine residues that independently affect ligand binding and receptor activation. *J. Biol. Chem.* 264:9266–70
40. Freissmuth, M., Schütz, W., Weindlmayer-Göttel, M., Zimpfer, M., Spiss, C. K. 1987. Effects of ischemia on the canine myocardial β-adrenoceptor-linked adenylate cyclase system. *J. Cardiovasc. Pharmacol.* 10:568–74
41. Frielle, T., Daniel, K. W., Caron, M. G., Lefkowitz, R. J. 1988. Structural basis of β-adrenergic receptor subtype specificity studied with chimeric $\beta_1\beta_2$-adrenergic receptors. *Proc. Natl. Acad. Sci. USA* 85:9494–98
42. Fujii, A. M., Vatner, S. F. 1986. Sympathetic mechanisms regulating myocardial contractility in conscious dogs. In *The Heart and Cardiovascular System*, ed. H. A. Fozzard, E. Haber, R. B. Jennings, A. M. Katz, pp. 1119–32. New York: Raven Press
43. Gaffney, T. E., Braunwald, E. 1963. Importance of the adrenergic nervous system in the support of circulatory function in patients with congestive heart failure. *Am. J. Med.* 34:320–24
44. Gilman, A. G. 1987. G proteins: Transducers of receptor-generated signals. *Annu. Rev. Biochem.* 56:615–49
45. Ginsburg, R., Bristow, M. R., Billingham, M. E., Stinson, E. B., Schroeder, J. S., Harrison, D. C. 1983. Study of the normal and failing isolated human heart: Decreased response of failing heart to isoproterenol. *Am. Heart J.* 106:535–40
46. Goldsmith, P., Gierschik, P., Milligan, G., Unson, C. G., Vinitsky, R., et al. 1987. Antibodies directed against synthetic peptides distinguish between GTP-binding proteins in neutrophil and brain. *J. Biol. Chem.* 262:14683–88
47. Graham, R. M., Hess, H.-J., Homcy, C. J. 1982. Biophysical characterization of the purified α_1-adrenergic receptor and identification of the hormone binding subunit. *J. Biol. Chem.* 257:15174–81
48. Hadcock, J. R., Malbon, C. C. 1988. Down-regulation of β-adrenergic receptors: agonist-induced reduction in receptor mRNA levels. *Proc. Natl. Acad. Sci. USA* 85:5021–25
49. Harden, T. K. 1983. Agonist-induced desensitization of the beta-adrenergic receptor-linked adenylate cyclase. *Pharmacol. Rev.* 35:5–32
50. Harris, B. A., Robishaw, J. D., Mumby, S. M., Gilman, A. G. 1985. Molecular cloning of complementary DNA for the alpha subunit of the G protein that stimulates adenylate cyclase. *Science* 229:1274–77
51. Hausdorff, W. P., Bouvier, M., O'Dowd, B. F., Irons, G. P., Caron, M. G., Lefkowitz, R. J. 1989. Phosphorylation sites on two domains of the β_2-adrenergic receptor are involved in distinct pathways of receptor desensitization. *J. Biol. Chem.* 264:12657–65
52. Henderson, R., Unwin, P. N. T. 1975. Three-dimensional model of purple membrane obtained by electron microscopy. *Nature* 257:28–32
53. Hertel, C., Perkins, J. P. 1984. Receptor-specific mechanisms of desensitization of β-adrenergic receptor function. *Mol. Cell. Endocrinol.* 37:245–56
54. Hittinger, L., Shannon, R. P., Bishop, S. P., Gelpi, R. J., Vatner, S. F. 1989. Subendomyocardial exhaustion of blood flow reserve and increased fibrosis in conscious dogs with heart failure. *Circ. Res.* 65:971–80
55. Hittinger, L., Shannon, R. P., Kohin, S., Lader, A. S., Manders, W. T., et al. 1989. Isoproterenol-induced alterations in myocardial blood flow, systolic and diastolic function in conscious dogs with heart failure. *Circulation* 80:658–68

56. Holmer, S. R., Stevens, S., Homcy, C. J. 1989. Tissue- and species-specific expression of inhibitory G-proteins: Cloning of a full-length-cDNA from canine heart. *Circ. Res.* 65:1136–40
57. Homburger, V., Lucas, M., Cantau, B., Barabe, J., Penit, J., Bocaert, J. 1980. Further evidence that desensitization of beta-adrenergic-sensitive adenylate cyclase proceeds in two steps. Modification of the coupling and loss of beta-adrenergic receptors. *J. Biol. Chem.* 10436–44
58. Homcy, C. J., Graham, R. M. 1985. Molecular characterization of adrenergic receptors. *Circ. Res.* 56:635–50
59. Homcy, C. J., Rockson, S. G., Countaway, J., Egan, D. A. 1983. Purification and characterization of the mammalian β_2-adrenergic receptor. *Biochemistry* 22:660–68
60. Jones, L. R., 1988. Rapid preparation of canine cardiac sarcolemmal vesicles by sucrose flotation. In *Methods in Enzymology,* ed. S. Fleischer, B. Fleischer, 57:85–91. New York: Academic
61. Karliner, J. S., Barnes, P., Brown, M., Dollery, C. 1980. Chronic heart failure in the guinea pig increases cardiac α_1- and β-adrenoceptors. *Eur. J. Pharmacol.* 67:115–18
62. Karliner, J. S., Stevens, M., Grattan, M., Woloszyn, W., Honbo, N., Hoffman, J. I. E. 1986. Beta-adrenergic receptor properties of canine myocardium: Effects of chronic myocardial infarction. *J. Am. Coll. Cardiol.* 8:349–56
63. Karliner, J. S., Stevens, M. B., Honbo, N., Hoffman, J. I. E. 1989. Effects of acute ischemia in the dog on myocardial blood flow, beta receptors and adenylate cyclase activity with and without chronic beta blockade. *J. Clin. Invest.* 83:474–81
64. Katz, A. M., Takenaka, H., Watras, J. 1986. The sarcoplasmic reticulum. See Ref. 42, pp. 731–46
65. Khorana, H. G. 1988. Bacteriorhodopsin, a membrane protein that uses light to translocate protons. *J. Biol. Chem.* 263:7439–42
66. Kobilka, B. K., Kobilka, T. S., Daniel, K., Regan, J. W., Caron, M. G., Lefkowitz, R. J. 1988. Chimeric α_2-,β_2-adrenergic receptors: delineation of domains involved in effector coupling and ligand binding specificity. *Science* 240:1310–16
67. Kohnken, R. E., Hildebrandt, J. D. 1989. G protein subunit interactions: Studies with biotinylated G protein subunits. *J. Biol. Chem.* 264:20688–96
68. Krupinski, J., Coussen, F., Bakalyar, H. A., Tang, W.-J., Feinstein, P. G., et al. 1989. Adenylyl cyclase amino acid sequence: Possible channel- or transporter-like structure. *Science* 244:1558–64
69. Larner, A. C., Ross, E. M. 1981. Alteration in the protein components of catecholamine-sensitive adenylate cyclase during maturation of rat reticulocytes. *J. Biol. Chem.* 256:9551–57
70. Lefkowitz, R. J., Caron, M. G. 1987. Molecular and regulatory properties of adrenergic receptors. *Recent Progr. Horm. Res.* 43:469–497
71. Lefkowitz, R. J., Stadel, J. M., Caron, M. G. 1983. Adenylate cyclase-coupled beta-adrenergic receptors: structure and mechanisms of activation and desensitization. *Annu. Rev. Biochem.* 52:159–86
72. Levine, T. B., Francis, G. S., Goldsmith, S. R., Simon, A. B., Cohn, J. N. 1982. Activity of the sympathetic nervous system and renin-angiotensin system assessed by plasma hormone levels and their relation to hemodynamic abnormalities in congestive heart failure. *Am. J. Cardiol.* 49:1659–66
73. Limbird, L. E., Gill, D. M., Lefkowitz, R. J. 1980. Agonist-promoted coupling of the β-adrenergic receptor with the guanine nucleotide regulatory protein of adenylate cyclase system. *Proc. Natl. Acad. Sci. USA* 77:775–79
74. Limbird, L. E., Hickey, A. R., Lefkowitz, R. J. 1979. Unique uncoupling of the frog erythrocyte adenylate cyclase system by manganese. *J. Biol. Chem.* 254:2677–83
75. Lochrie, M. A., Simon, M. I. 1988. G-protein multiplicity in eukaryotic signal transduction systems. *Biochemistry* 27:4957–65
76. Lompre, A. M., Mercadier, J. J., Wisnewsky, C., Bouveret, P., Pantaloni, C., et al, 1981. Species- and age-dependent changes in the relative amounts of cardiac myosin isoenzymes in mammals. *Dev. Biol.* 84:286–90
77. Lompre, A. M., Nadal-Ginard, B., Mahdavi, V. 1984. Expression of the cardiac ventricular α- and β-myosin heavy chain genes is developmentally and hormonally regulated. *J. Biol. Chem.* 259:6437–46
78. Longabaugh, J. P., Vatner, D. E., Homcy, C. J. 1986. The beta-adrenergic receptor, adenylate cyclase system. See Ref. 42, pp. 1097–1117
79. Longabaugh, J. P., Vatner, D. E., Vatner, S. F., Homcy, C. J. 1988. Decreased stimulatory guanosine triphosphate binding protein in dogs with

pressure-overload left ventricular failure. *J. Clin. Invest.* 81:420–424

80. Maisel, A. S., Motulsky, H. J., Insel, P. A. 1985. Externalization of beta-adrenergic receptors promoted by myocardial ischemia. *Science* 230:183–86
81. Maisel, A. S., Motulsky, H. J., Ziegler, M. G., Insel, P. A. 1987. Ischemia- and agonist-induced changes in α- and β-adrenergic receptor traffic in guinea pig hearts. *Am. J. Physiol.* 253:H1159–66
82. Malbon, C. C., Hadcock, J. H. 1988. Evidence that glucocorticoid response elements in the 5' noncoding region of the hamster β_2-adrenergic receptor gene are obligate for glucocorticoid regulation of receptor mRNA levels. *Biochem. Biophys. Res. Commun.* 154:676–81
83. McGrane, M. M., de Vente J., Yun, J., Bloom, J., Park, E., et al. 1988. Tissue-specific expression and dietary regulation of chimeric phosphoenolpyruvate carboxykinase/bovine growth hormone gene in transgenic mice. *J. Biol. Chem.* 263:11443–51
84. Mukherjee, A., Bush, L. R., McCoy, K. E., Duke, R. J., Hagler, H., et al. 1982. Relationship between β-adrenergic receptor numbers and physiological responses during experimental canine myocardial ischemia. *Circ. Res.* 50:735–41
85. Mukherjee, A., Wong, T. M., Buja, L. M., Lefkowitz, R. J., Willerson, J. T. 1979. Beta adrenergic and muscarinic cholinergic receptors in canine myocardium: Effects of ischemia. *J. Clin. Invest.* 64:1423–28
86. Mumby, S. M., Kahn, R. A., Manning, D. R., Gilman, A. G. 1986. Antisera of designed specificity for subunits of guanine nucleotide-binding regulatory proteins. *Proc. Natl. Acad. Sci. USA* 83:265–69
87. Muntz, K. H., Olson, E. G., Lariviere, G. R., D'Souza, S., Mukherjee, A., et al. 1984. Autoradiographic characterization of beta adrenergic receptors in coronary blood vessels and myocytes in normal and ischemic myocardium of the canine heart. *J. Clin. Invest.* 73:349–57
88. Neer, E. J., Lok, J. M., Wolf, L. G. 1984. Purification and properties of the inhibitory guanine nucleotide regulatory unit of brain adenylate cyclase. *J. Biol. Chem.* 259:14222–29
89. Nejima, J., Uemura, N., Vatner, D. E., Homcy, C. J., Hintze, T. H., Vatner, S. F. 1990. Role of intact cardiac nerves and reflex mechanisms in desensitization to catecholamines in conscious dogs. *J. Clin. Invest.* In press
90. Neumann, J., Schmitz, W., Scholz, H., von Meyerinck, L., Doring, V., Kalmar, P. 1988. Increase in myocardial Gi-proteins in heart failure. *Lancet* 2:936–37
91. Newman, W. H. 1977. A depressed response of left ventricular contractile force to isoproterenol and norepinephrine in dogs with congestive heart failure. *Am. Heart J.* 93:216–21
92. O'Dowd, B. F., Hnatowich, M., Regan, J. W., Leader, W. M., Caron, M. G., Lefkowitz, R. J. 1988. Site-directed mutagenesis of the cytoplasmic domains of the human β_2-adrenergic receptor: Localization of regions involved in G protein-receptor coupling. *J. Biol. Chem.* 31:15985–92
93. Ovchinnikov, Y. A. 1982. Rhodopsin and bacteriorhodopsin: Structure-function relationships. *FEBS Lett.* 148:179–91
94. Polge, E. J. C., Barton, S. C., Surani, M. H. A., Miller, J. R., Wagner, T. E., et al. 1989. In *Biotechnology in Growth Regulation,* ed. R. B. Heap, C. G. Prasser, E. Lamming. pp. 189–199. London: Butterworth
95. Pouleur, H., Rousseau, M. F., Hanet, C., Marlow, H. F., Charlier, A. A. 1987. Left ventricular sensitivity to β-adrenoceptor: Stimulating drugs in patients with ischemic heart diseases and varying degrees of ventricular dysfunction. *Circ. Res.* 61(Suppl. I):I-91–95
96. Powell, C. E., Slater, I. H. 1958. Blocking of inhibitory adrenergic receptors by a dichloro analog of isoproterenol. *J. Pharmacol. Exp. Therap.* 122:480–88
97. Rapiejko, P. J., Watkins, D. C., Ross, M., Malbon, C. C. 1989. Thyroid hormones regulate G-protein β-subunit mRNA expression in vivo. *J. Biol. Chem.* 264:16183–89
98. Raymond, J. R., Hnatowich, M., Lefkowitz, R. J., Caron, M. G. 1990. Adrenergic receptors: models for regulation of signal transduction processes. *Hypertension* 15:119–31
99. Rector, T. S., Olivari, M. T., Levine, T. B., Francis, G. S., Cohn, J. N. 1987. Predicting survival for an individual with congestive heart failure using the plasma norepinephrine concentration. *Am. Heart J.* 114:148–52
100. Ross, E. M., Gilman, A. G. 1977. Resolution of some components of adenylate cyclase necessary for catalytic activity. *J. Biol. Chem.* 262:6966–69
101. Seamon, K., Daly, J. W. 1981. Activation of adenylate cyclase by the diterpene forskolin does not require the

guanine nucleotide regulatory protein. *J. Biol. Chem.* 256:9799–9801
102. Sibley, D. R., Daniel, K., Strader, C. D., Lefkowitz, R. J. 1987. Phosphorylation of the β-adrenergic receptor in intact cells: Relationship to heterologous and homologous mechanisms of adenylate cyclase desensitization. *Arch. Biochem. Biophys.* 258:24–32
103. Sibley, D. R., Lefkowitz, R. J. 1985. Molecular mechanisms of receptor desensitization using the β-adrenergic receptor-coupled adenylate cyclase system as a model. *Nature* 317:124–29
104. Stadel, J. M., DeLean, A., Mullikin-Kilpatrick, D., Sawyer, D. D., Lefkowitz, R. J. 1981. Catecholamine-induced desensitization in turkey erythrocytes: cAMP-mediated impairment of high affinity agonist binding without alteration in receptor number. *J. Cyclic Nucleotide Res.* 7:37–47
105. Stadel, J. M., Nambi, P., Shorr, R. G. L., Sawyer, D. F., Caron, M. G., Lefkowitz, R. J. 1983. Catecholamine-induced desensitization of turkey erythrocyte adenylate cyclase is associated with phosphorylation of the β-adrenergic receptor. *Proc. Natl. Acad. Sci. USA* 80:3173–77
106. Staley, N. A., Einzig, S., Noren, G. R., Surdy, J. E., Elsperger, J. 1987. β-adrenergic function in a congestive cardiomyopathy model. *Am. J. Physiol* 252:H334–39
107. Sternweis, P. C., Gilman, A. G. 1979. Reconstitution of catecholamine-sensitive adenylate cyclase: Reconstitution of the uncoupled variant of the S49 lymphoma cell. *J. Biol. Chem.* 254: 3333–40
108. Stiles, G. L., Lefkowitz, R. J. 1981. Thyroid hormone modulation of agonist-beta-adrenergic receptor interactions in the rat heart. *Life Sci.* 28:2529–36
109. Strader, C. D., Dixon, R. A. F., Cheung, A. H., Candelore, M. R., Blake, A. D., Sigal, I. S. 1987. Mutations that uncouple the β-adrenergic receptor from G_s and increase agonist affinity. *J. Biol. Chem.* 262:16439–43
110. Strader, C. D., Sigal, I. S., Candelore, M. R., Rands, E., Hill, W. S., Dixon, R. A. 1988. Conserved aspartic acid residues 79 and 113 of the β-adrenergic receptor have different roles in receptor function. *J. Biol. Chem.* 263:10267–71
111. Strader, C. D., Sigal, I. S., Register, R. B., Candelore, M. R., Rands, E., Dixon, R. A. F. 1987. Identification of residues required for ligand binding to the β-adrenergic receptor. *Proc. Natl. Acad. Sci. USA* 84:4384–88
112. Susanni, E., Manders, W. T., Knight, D. R., Vatner, D. E., Vatner, S. F., Homcy, C. J. 1989. One hour of myocardial ischemia decreases the activity of the stimulatory guanine nucleotide regulatory protein G_s. *Circ. Res.* 65: 1145–50
113. Thomas, J. A., Marks, B. H. 1978. Plasma norepinephrine in congestive heart failure. *Am. J. Cardiol.* 41:233–43
114. Thompson, W. R., Koren, G., Izumo, S., Mahdavi, V., Nadal-Ginard, B. 1989. Molecular regulation of myosin heavy chain switches: A model system for study of cardiac gene expression. *Proc. Symp. Etiology* Morphogenesis Congenital Heart Disease (III), ed. A. Takao, In press
115. Toews, M. L., Waldo, G. L., Harden, T. K., Perkins, J. P. 1984. Relationship between an altered membrane form and a low affinity form of the beta-adrenergic receptor occurring during catecholamine-induced desensitization: Evidence for receptor internalization. *J. Biol. Chem.* 259:11844–50
116. Tse, J., Powell, J. R., Baste, C. A., Priest, R. E., Kuo, J. F. 1979. Isoproterenol-induced cardiac hypertrophy: Modifications in characteristics of β-adrenergic receptor, adenylate cyclase, and ventricular contraction. *Endocrinology* 105:246–55
117. Deleted in proof
118. Van Alstyne, E., Bartschat, D. K., Wellsmith, N. V., Poe, S. L., Schilling, W. P., Lindenmayer, G. E. 1979. Isolation of a highly enriched sarcolemma membrane fraction from canine heart. *Biochim. Biophys. Acta* 553:388–95
119. Vatner, D. E., Knight, D. R., Shen, Y.-T., Thomas, J. X. Jr., Homcy, C. J., Vatner, S. F. 1988. One hour of myocardial ischemia in conscious dogs increases β-adrenergic receptors, but decreases adenylate cyclase activity. *J. Mol. Cell. Cardiol.* 20:75–82
120. Vatner, D. E., Lee, D. L., Schwartz, K. R., Longabaugh, J. P., Fujii, A. M., et al. 1988. Impaired cardiac muscarinic receptor function in dogs with heart failure. *J. Clin. Invest.* 81:1836–42
121. Vatner, D. E., Vatner, S. F., Fujii, A. M., Homcy, C. J. 1985. Loss of high affinity cardiac beta adrenergic receptors in dogs with heart failure. *J. Clin. Invest.* 76:2259–64
122. Vatner, D. E., Vatner, S. F., Nejima, J., Uemura, N., Susanni, E. E., et al. 1989. Chronic infusion of norepinephrine elicits desensitization by uncoupling the β-adrenergic receptor. *J. Clin. Invest.* 84:1741–48

123. Vatner, D. E., Young, M. A., Knight, D. R., Vatner, S. F. 1990. β-receptors and adenylate cyclase: Comparison of non-ischemic and postmortem tissue. *Am. J. Physiol.* 258:H140–44
124. Waldo, G. L., Northup, J. K., Perkins, J. P., Harden, T. K. 1983. Characterization of an altered membrane form of the β-adrenergic receptor produced during agonist-induced desensitization. *J. Biol. Chem.* 258:13900–8
125. Watkins, D. C., Northup, J. K., Malbon, C. C. 1987. Regulation of G proteins in differentiation: Altered ratio of α- to β-subunits in 3T3-L1 cells. *J. Biol. Chem.* 262:10651–57
126. West, R. E. Jr., Moss, J., Vaughan, M., Liu, T., Liu T.-Y. 1985. Pertussis toxin-catalyzed ADP-ribosylation of transducin. *J. Biol. Chem.* 260:14428–30
127. Wieghart, M., Hoover, J. L., McGrane, M. M., Hansen, R. W., Rottman, F. M. et al. 1990. *J. Repro. Fert. Suppl.* (Suppl. 41):89–96
128. Wreggett, K. A., DeLean, A. 1984. The ternary complex model: Its properties and application to ligand interactions with the D_2-dopamine receptor of the anterior pituitary gland. *Mol. Pharmacol.* 26:214–27
129. Yarden, Y., Rodriguez, H., Wong, S. K. F., Brandt, D. R., May, D. C., et al. 1986. The avian β-adrenergic receptor: Primary structure and membrane topology. *Proc. Natl. Acad. Sci. USA* 83:6795–99
130. Yoshimasa, T., Sibley, D. R., Bouvier, M., Lefkowitz, R. J., Caron, M. G. 1987. Cross-talk between cellular signalling pathways suggested by phorbol-ester-induced adenylate cyclase phosphorylation. *Nature* 327:67–70

Annu. Rev. Physiol. 1991. 53:161–77

CONTROL OF GROWTH AND DIFFERENTIATION OF VASCULAR CELLS BY EXTRACELLULAR MATRIX PROTEINS

David J. Carey

Weis Center for Research Geisinger Clinic Danville, Pennsylvania 17822

KEY WORDS: smooth muscle cells, endothelial cells, proliferation, extracellular matrix

---

INTRODUCTION

The extracellular matrix (ECM) has long been recognized as an important structural component of tissues. There is now considerable evidence that the ECM also plays an important role in modulating various aspects of cellular differentiation, including cell proliferation. Recent progress in the identification and structural characterization of ECM molecules and their cell surface receptors is beginning to provide a picture of ECM action at the molecular level. This review will summarize selected aspects of recent progress in our understanding of the role of ECM in modulating the growth and differentiation of cells of the vascular wall.

VASCULAR ECM

The histology of the vascular wall, with particular emphasis on the distribution of ECM, is shown schematically in Figure 1. The endothelium comprises a monolayer of polarized cells with different regions of the cell surface specialized for providing a non-thrombogenic lining for the blood vessel, cell-cell contacts or, at the basal surface, contact with the underlying basement membrane. External to the endothelium is the medial layer, which

0066-4278/91/0315-0161$02.00

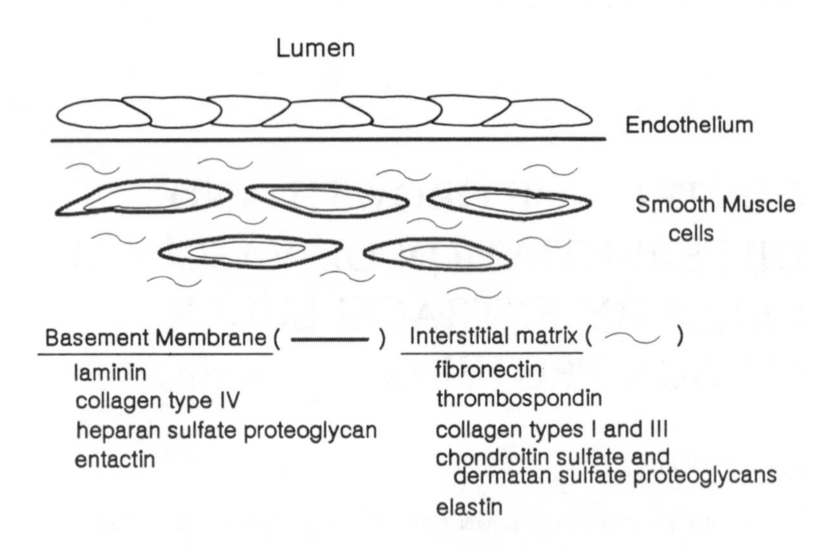

Figure 1 Schematic illustration of cell-ECM relationships in the vascular wall.

contains smooth muscle cells, i.e. spindle-shaped cells that are arranged in layers around the vessel circumference. The individual vascular smooth muscle (VSM) cells are covered by a layer of basement membrane and within the medial layer are embedded in and connected to a meshwork of interstitial ECM.

Figure 1 also lists the major molecular components of the two principal types of ECM: basement membrane and interstitial matrix. These matrices are formed by the self-assembly in the extracellular space of unique sets of macromolecules of three major types: collagens, proteoglycans and glycoproteins. In addition to the major components listed in Figure 1, these matrices contain quantitatively minor components that may be functionally important. For example, the subendothelial ECM contains vitronectin and von Willebrand Factor, both of which can mediate endothelial cell adhesion via specific cell surface receptors (15, 16). Their functions in vivo are not known. Both endothelial cells and VSM cells are active in ECM synthesis and are largely responsible for depositing the vascular ECM. Additional components may be absorbed from the circulation, e.g. proteins released by platelets or macrophages.

Most of the direct interactions between cells and the ECM appear to involve the matrix glycoproteins. Although the three glycoproteins that are prominent in the vascular wall, fibronectin (65), laminin (5), and thrombospondin (21), are not related in sequence, all are large, multisubunit, multidomain proteins that are capable of simultaneous interactions with a variety of molecules.

These include self-association into supramolecular aggregates as well as associations with other ECM molecules (e.g. collagens and proteoglycans) and cell surface receptors.

ECM RECEPTORS

Several different types of cell surface receptors for ECM molecules have been identified. In many cases more than one receptor type has been described that binds a given ECM molecule. Assigning individual receptor types to specific functions is an area of active research.

Integrins

The integrins, members of the large gene superfamily, are a group of sequence-related proteins that are involved in cell-ECM and cell-cell adhesion (31, 65). The ECM-receptor integrins are heterodimers composed of variable α and β subunits. To date eight α and three β subunits have been identified that bind ECM molecules. The subunits of the integrins are transmembrane proteins. The cytoplasmic domains of the integrin polypeptides appear to interact with cytoskeletal proteins inside the cell (29, 51), which may be an important function of these receptors (discussed below). Binding between integrin receptors and ECM molecules is dependent on divalent cations. Some of the integrin receptors are specific for a single ECM molecule (e.g. fibronectin), whereas others will bind several different molecules (the "promiscuous" receptors) (65, 77). In the majority of cases, the integrin receptors recognize a specific amino acid sequence in the ECM molecule (RGD). Synthetic peptides containing the RGD sequence have been used to block integrin-dependent binding phenomenona. The laminin-specific integrin receptor appears to be an exception to this rule because its binding appears to be RGD independent (23). Even for the RGD-binding integrins, however, additional sequence information in the ligand proteins affects the binding interaction (60). At least three kinds of integrin receptors have been identified in endothelial cells: $\alpha_2\beta_1$ (laminin and collagen receptor), $\alpha_5\beta_1$ (fibronectin receptor), and $\alpha v\beta_3$ (vitronectin and thrombospondin receptor) (4, 15, 16, 34, 40). One puzzling feature of integrin receptor function is that seemingly identical receptors exhibit different binding specificities when expressed in different cells (17, 34). The basis for this functional difference is not understood.

Cell Surface Proteoglycans

Nearly all cells, including endothelial and VSM cells, contain cell surface membrane-intercalated proteoglycans that may also function as ECM receptors. These usually contain heparan sulfate glycosaminoglycans (8, 26, 53), but cell surface chondroitin sulfate proteoglycans (14) as well as hybrid proteoglycans containing both glycosaminoglycans have also been identified (69). Although not as extensively studied as the integrin receptors, these have been shown to bind ECM molecules such as fibronectin, collagen, thrombospondin, and laminin (36, 68, 74). In most cases the binding is thought to occur between the carbohydrate chains of the proteoglycans and glycosaminoglycan binding domains of the ECM molecules that are distinct from integrin receptor binding sites. The available sequence information on cell surface proteoglycans indicates that they are transmembrane proteins (53, 65). Like the integrins, they appear to interact with cytoskeletal structures (9, 80). Some cells also possess heparan sulfate proteoglycans that are attached to the membrane via a glycosylphosphatidylinositol anchor (8). Whether these types of proteoglycans are expressed by vascular cells is not known.

Other Receptors

Other cell surface ECM binding proteins have been identified that are neither integrins nor proteoglycans. The most thoroughly characterized of these is a laminin-binding protein with an apparent mol wt of 69K (LB69). It is expressed by a variety of cells including endothelial and VSM cells (4, 82) and binds to a site on laminin that is distinct from that recognized by integrin receptors or proteoglycans. This receptor recognizes the amino acid sequence YIGSR, and synthetic peptides containing this sequence have been used to inhibit binding of laminin to this receptor (25, 37).

EFFECTS OF ECM ON VASCULAR CELLS

Vascular Smooth Muscle Cells

Interaction of cells with ECM or purified ECM molecules appears to mediate cell attachment and, in some cases, to promote cell migration, probably by providing an adhesive pathway for cell movement. In addition to these effects on cellular behavior, the ECM appears to modulate such activities as proliferation and specific gene expression.

Most studies examining the effects of ECM on VSM cells utilize primary or early passage cells grown in tissue culture. VSM cells will attach to and grow on plastic tissue culture dishes. They will also attach to dishes coated with purified ECM molecules, such as fibronectin, laminin, or collagen. Effects of individual ECM molecules on VSM cell behavior (e.g. proliferation) have been difficult to demonstrate, largely because the cultured cells rapidly synthesize and deposit their own complex ECM (Figure 2). The ECM deposited by cultured VSM cells is similar in composition to that seen in vivo, and contains several types of collagen, the adhesive glycoproteins fibronectin, laminin, and thrombospondin (26), and several types of secreted, cell-associated and ECM proteoglycans (26, 79).

Figure 2 Transmission electron micrographs of rat aortic vascular smooth muscle cells showing the multi-layered organization of the cells and extensive accumulation of ECM (*arrows*) in cultures grown in normal medium (*top panel*), and the absence of these features in cultures grown in the presence of an inhibitor of proteoglycan synthesis (*bottom panel*). The cells were sectioned at right angles to the culture dish surface.

Another difficulty in attempting to ascribe a specific function to an individual ECM molecule is the cooperative nature of ECM interactions. ECM glycoproteins can engage in multiple interactions, and this is probably an important aspect of their function (5, 21, 65). Thus interfering with one ECM molecule could have significant effects on the overall structure or assembly of the ECM, or on the ability of other ECM molecules to interact with cells.

Several experimental approaches have been used to study the effects of ECM molecules on VSM cell function. These include inhibition of ECM production by the cells, short-term culturing on pre-formed complex ECM, and addition of antibodies to specific ECM molecules.

EFFECTS OF INHIBITION OF ECM SYNTHESIS An interesting feature of VSM cells in culture is their propensity to form multi-layered cellular structures (Figure 2) that closely resemble the organization of the tissue in vivo. Experiments in which ECM accumulation is inhibited have demonstrated that the development of this cellular organization is dependent on the ECM.

Inhibition of ECM accumulation was achieved by using an inhibitor of proteoglycan synthesis. As a result of the cooperative nature of ECM assembly, inhibition of proteoglycan synthesis prevents, to a large extent, the accumulation of ECM in the cultures (26). This affects all the matrix proteins examined including fibronectin, laminin, and thrombospondin. These proteins continue to be synthesized and secreted by the cells, but are not incorporated into the VSM ECM. Inhibition of proteoglycan synthesis (and ECM deposition) does not significantly alter the rate of proliferation of subconfluent cells. In contrast, the post-confluent (multilayered) growth of the cells is almost completely inhibited (26; Figure 2). Effects on individual cells are also noted. For example, while the synthesis of a α-smooth muscle actin is not affected by inhibitor treatment, the assembly of a α-smooth muscle actin into fibrils is significantly reduced in the absence of ECM (26). These results demonstrate that the ECM plays an essential role in the generation of the three-dimensional organization of the tissue at both the cellular and multicellular levels. This may, in part, explain the increased deposition of ECM that occurs during the rapid growth of VSM cells under pathologic conditions (79).

EFFECTS OF COMPLEX ECM Another way to demonstrate effects of ECM on VSM cells has been to culture the cells on complex ECM previously synthesized by other cells. The ECM deposited by corneal endothelial cells promotes the growth of aortic VSM cells in the absence of serum (24). The proliferation of rat VSM cells in the presence of serum is stimulated by the ECM deposited by bovine aortic endothelial cells (28), or by VSM cells (72). Interestingly, the ECM deposited by VSM cells obtained from a strain of genetically hypertensive rats (SHR) is somewhat better at stimulating VSM cell growth than ECM deposited by cells from a normotensive strain (WKY) (72). This could potentially account for the increased rates of proliferation in the SHR VSM cells.

ECM contact can also modulate the responsiveness of cells to a particular mitogen. For example, VSM-derived ECM stimulates thymidine incorporation into rat VSM cells exposed to epidermal growth factor (EGF), which by itself is a poor mitogen for these cells (72). In this study evidence suggested that the factor in the ECM that is most responsible for this effect is thrombospondin. Additional effects of complex ECM on proliferation may be the result of ECM-bound growth factors (discussed below).

THROMBOSPONDIN AND VSM CELL PROLIFERATION One ECM macromolecule that appears to have a direct role in stimulating VSM cell proliferation is thrombospondin. Thrombospondin is a 450K homotrimeric, multidomain adhesive glycoprotein that is synthesized by a variety of cell types including platelets, endothelial cells, and smooth muscle cells (21).

Exposure of quiescent VSM cells to platelet-derived growth factor (PDGF) or serum results in a rapid, but transient, induction of thrombospondin synthesis (48). The induction appears to be a direct result of growth factor stimulation, since increases in thrombospondin mRNA levels are detected as early as 15 min after the addition of PDGF and occur in the presence of cycloheximide (51). The kinetics of thrombospondin mRNA induction are similar to that of the proto-oncogene c-*fos*. The dose response of thrombospondin mRNA induction by PDGF parallels the mitogenic activity of the growth factor (51).

Addition of exogenous thrombospondin does not augment the response of VSM cells to stimulation by PDGF. When added in the absence of growth factors, thrombospondin alone has little effect on VSM proliferation (49). When added in the presence of EGF, however, which by itself is a poor mitogen for rat VSM cells (12, 49), thrombospondin causes a stimulation of thymidine labeling of VSM cells almost as great as that caused by PDGF (49). Consistent with this, addition of anti-thrombospondin antibodies negates the enhancement of thymidine incorporation that results when EGF-stimulated VSM cells are plated on ECM (72). Evidence that thrombospondin may be essential for VSM proliferation comes from the observation that addition of monoclonal anti-thrombospondin antibodies to rat VSM cell cultures stimulated to proliferate by serum both prevents thrombospondin association with the cells and inhibits their proliferation (50). The association of fibronectin with the cells is not affected by the antibody.

The mechanism by which thrombospondin acts to stimulate VSM proliferation is not known. This is complicated by the multiplicity of interactions in which thrombospondin can participate (21). Addition of thrombospondin to VSM cell cultures has been reported to stimulate the phosphorylation of 40s ribosomal subunit protein S_6 (71). Activation of S_6 kinase activity is a commonly observed effect of treatments that stimulate cell proliferation, but its significance to the mechanism of stimulation is unclear. Thrombospondin also accelerates the turnover of inositol phospholipids (71), thus providing a potential mechanism for activation of protein kinase C. Many VSM cell mitogens are thought to act by protein kinase C-dependent pathways (12). Thrombospondin also binds to plasminogen and accelerates its activation by tissue plasminogen activator, thereby generating the potential to modify the ECM or to release other matrix-bound biologically active molecules.

INHIBITION OF VSM PROLIFERATION BY HEPARIN-LIKE MOLECULES The glycosaminoglycan heparin is a potent and somewhat specific inhibitor of VSM cell proliferation (11). Heparin-like glycosaminoglycans that are inhibitors of VSM cell proliferation are also produced by vascular cells, which suggests a potential mechanism for paracrine or autocrine regulation of VSM cell proliferation by ECM molecules.

Conditioned medium from confluent cultures of bovine aortic endothelial cells contains a glycosaminoglycan that inhibits VSM cell proliferation (10). The inhibitory activity of the glycosaminoglycan is abolished by digestion with heparinase, but it is stable to heat denaturation or digestion by protease or chondroitinase. Heparin-like glycosaminoglycans isolated from trypsin digests of rat aortic VSM cells also inhibit VSM cell proliferation, and are approximately 40 times more potent than commercial heparin (22). The anti-proliferative activity is significantly higher in post-confluent than sub-confluent VSM cultures, which suggests that the production of the active factor is regulated, perhaps by the growth state of the cell. Whether this represents induction of a new proteoglycan in post-confluent cells or structural modification of the glycosaminoglycans of a constitutively expressed proteoglycan is not known. The anti-proliferative activity of heparin is sensitive to structural modifications of the glycosaminoglycan chain (81). The nature of the proteoglycan that bears the anti-proliferative heparan sulfate is unknown. Recent evidence suggests that anti-proliferative heparan sulfates are part of hydrophobic cell surface proteoglycans and not matrix proteoglycans synthesized by VSM cells (H. Hamati, D. Carey, unpublished observations).

Because of the limited availability of endothelial or VSM cell-derived heparin-like inhibitors, almost all studies on the mechanism of inhibition have used commercially available heparin preparations. Several different mechanisms for heparin action have been proposed. Thrombospondin binds heparin with high affinity (21). Exogenous heparin has been reported to prevent the association of thrombospondin with VSM ECM without affecting the synthesis of thrombospondin (48). A thrombospondin-binding cell surface proteoglycan has been demonstrated in epithelial cells (74). Both cell surface and matrix proteoglycans synthesized by rat VSM cells also bind thrombospondin, but this property does not correlate with anti-proliferative activity (H. Hamati et al, unpublished observations).

It has also been proposed that heparin exerts its anti-proliferative effects by causing the release of transforming growth factor-β (TGF-β) from a complex with the serum protein α_2-macroglobulin (54). TGF-β is a potent modulator of VSM cell growth and strongly inhibits the proliferation of subconfluent VSM cells (47). It is difficult to explain all of heparin's activity by this mechanism, however. TGF-β has been reported to stimulate post-confluent VSM cell proliferation (47), whereas the anti-proliferative activity of heparin is independent of cell density (11). The strongest evidence for this mechanism comes from the observation that anti-TGF-β antibodies block the anti-proliferative activity of heparin in VSM cultures stimulated to proliferate by serum (54). Consistent with this idea is the observation in the above study that inhibition by heparin of VSM cell proliferation occurs only in the presence of serum. Others, however, have reported inhibition by heparin of proliferation triggered by PDGF and other mitogens in the absence of serum (12). The mechanism of inhibition of proliferation by TGF-β is not known. It has been proposed that many of the biological effects of TGF-β are mediated by its ability to regulate the synthesis of ECM proteins and their receptors (27). Epithelial cells exposed to TGF-β synthesize a modified form of the thrombospondin-binding cell surface proteoglycan (62). Whether this occurs in VSM cells and what the functional significance of this structural modification is remains unknown. Other studies suggest heparin may have a direct effect on VSM cells. Heparin binds with high affinity (kd approx 1 nM) to VSM cells and is internalized (13), which suggests the existence of a pathway for receptor-mediated endocytosis. Heparin's anti-proliferative activity has been suggested to be specific for mitogens that activate protein kinase C-dependent pathways, such as PDGF and phorbol esters and, at least in bovine cells, is less effective for EGF, which is thought to work via calcium-dependent pathways (12). Heparin has been shown to affect protein kinase C activity in vitro (18), but it is not clear whether this occurs in vivo. In rat VSM cells heparin does inhibit the stimulation of proliferation that is caused by EGF and thrombospondin (49). Thus it appears that heparin exerts multiple effects on cells. The relative importance of each may be species specific, which could account for some of the apparently disparate results.

Endothelial Cells

Numerous studies have demonstrated effects of complex ECM or purified ECM components on endothelial cell function, as well as effects of endothelial ECM on the behavior of endothelial and other cells. Endothelial cells derived from both large vessels and capillaries have been studied. In the former, the emphasis is usually on effects of ECM on such activities as cell attachment, migration, and cell proliferation. In the case of capillary endothelial cells, there is good evidence to indicate a role for ECM in control of capillary formation (angiogenesis).

GENERAL Endothelial cells have been shown to attach to and spread on a wide variety of ECM proteins, including fibronectin, laminin, collagen, vitronectin, and von Willebrand factor (15, 16, 43, 46, 82). Different matrix proteins appear to have diverse effects on endothelial cell phenotypic behavior. For example, culturing endothelial cells on a matrix composed of a mixture of interstitial collagens I and III enhances endothelial cell proliferation and migration, whereas culturing the cells on basement membrane collagens IV and V inhibits proliferation and stimulates aggregation into capillary-like tubes (45, 46).

In most cases where the endothelial cell receptors responsible for ECM interactions have been identified they appeared to be of the integrin type (15,

16, 34, 40), but the non-integrin laminin-binding protein (LB69) is also present in endothelial cells (4, 82). The specific functions of these two laminin receptors in bovine aortic endothelial cells were investigated by using receptor-specific antibodies and peptide inhibitors. The data suggest that the integrin receptors play a predominant role in mediating initial cell attachment to laminin-coated plates and in cell migration. The LB69 receptor appears to be important for longer term cell-laminin interactions, such as cell spreading (4).

ECM-BINDING GROWTH FACTORS Cultured endothelial cells synthesize and deposit their own complex ECM. One property of endothelial cell ECM that has received considerable attention is its ability to stimulate the proliferation of cells in the absence of serum or other growth factors. Recent studies have provided good evidence that at least some of the mitogenic properties of endothelial ECM result from the presence of matrix-bound growth factors deposited by the cells.

In cases where the mitogenic activity has been characterized, it derives from the presence of basic fibroblast growth factor (bFGF) (2, 3, 75). The amount of bFGF in endothelial ECM is significant, amounting to approximately 30% of that found in endothelial cell lysates (75). Incubation with anti-bFGF antibodies blocks 70–80% of the mitogenic activity of the ECM for bovine aortic endothelial cells (64). One important, but unresolved, question concerns the mechanism by which bFGF is deposited in the ECM. bFGF is synthesized without a signal sequence that would direct its secretion, and secretion of bFGF has not been described (63). Wounded endothelial cells have been shown to release bFGF (55). The extent to which this accounts for the ECM-bound growth factor in endothelial cultures is not known.

Binding of bFGF to ECM probably accounts for low affinity binding sites (57). Several lines of evidence indicate the growth factor binds to heparan sulfate molecules present in the ECM. Binding of exogenous bFGF is prevented if the ECM is pretreated with heparinase or heparitinase, but not when the ECM is pretreated with other glycosaminoglycan degrading enzymes (2, 3, 57). Binding of bFGF to ECM is inhibited by heparin or heparan sulfate, but not by other glycosaminoglycans (3). ECM-bound bFGF is rapidly released when the matrix is incubated with heparitinase, but not other glycosaminoglycan lyases (3). bFGF-binding heparan sulfate proteoglycans have been identified in endothelial ECM (66, 67).

ECM binding is neither necessary nor sufficient for stimulation of cells by bFGF. When binding to ECM sites is blocked by heparin, exogenous bFGF still binds to high affinity sites and elicits a biological response (57). Conversely, polyclonal anti-bFGF antibodies that inhibit binding of the growth factor to high affinity receptors, but not to heparin or low affinity ECM receptors, inhibit the biological activities of bFGF on capillary endothelial cells (38). It has been shown, however, that ECM-bound bFGF is metabolized by endothelial cells, although at a slower rate than growth factor bound to cellular receptors (58).

The function of ECM-bound bFGF is not known. It may provide a reservoir of growth factor to be released following the appropriate stimulus. Both plasminogen (35) and urokinase-type plasminogen activator (61) have been shown to be present in ECM. These enzymes can release ECM-bound bFGF in an active form from endothelial cell cultures (67). Binding of bFGF to endothelial cell-derived heparan sulfate protects the growth factor from proteolysis (66).

Additional evidence suggests that TGF-β may also be present in ECM. Both low and high affinity binding sites for TGF-β have been described, but only the high affinity sites appear to be directly involved in cellular responses to the factor. One class of low affinity sites has been shown to reside on a proteoglycan, designated betaglycan, that can exist as both a membrane-anchored and extracellular molecule (1). The functional significance of TGF-β binding to betaglycan is not known, but it could represent an extracellular reservoir of growth factor, similar to what has been proposed for bFGF.

ANGIOGENESIS The formation of capillary tubes by cultured endothelial cells is dependent on both a soluble stimulus (e.g. bFGF) and interactions with ECM. A common finding has been that ECM contact alters the qualitative response of the cells to growth factor stimulation. For example, endothelial cells plated on dishes coated with a relatively high concentration of fibronectin or gelatin and cultured in medium containing growth factor will proliferate to form monolayers (32, 44, 56). When the ECM to which the cells are attached is modified, the cells can be induced to cease proliferation and aggregate into capillary-like tubes. This can be achieved, for example, by culturing endothelial cells in a three-dimensional matrix of collagen type I (56). In this case, the endothelial cells deposit a basement membrane on their abluminal surfaces.

Capillary tube formation is also accelerated when endothelial cells are cultured on Matrigel (37), a reconstituted gel similar in composition and structure to basement membrane. There is evidence that in this case specific interactions between endothelial cells and laminin are important in triggering tube formation. Peptides corresponding to two different cell attachment sites on laminin were used to identify receptor-specific interactions that are important in this process. Peptides containing the sequence RGD, the attachment site for integrin ECM receptors, inhibit attachment of endothelial cells to Matrigel, whereas peptide containing the sequence YIGSR, the attachment site of the LB69 receptor, inhibit tube formation (25). These data suggest differential roles for domains of laminin that interact with distinct cell surface receptors.

Others have argued that induction of capillary tube formation by ECM does not require specific ECM protein-receptor interactions. Instead, the important effect of cell-ECM interactions is to alter the mechanical properties of the cells (32, 33). This is based, in part, on the observation that spontaneous tube formation in culture is enhanced under conditions that favor multicellular retraction of the cells, independent of the specific types of ECM molecules that are present (32). The simplest way to achieve this is to vary the concentration of ECM protein used to coat the cultures dishes. At low concentrations the cells attach, but do not spread and do not form tubes. At high concentration the cells spread fully and proliferate to form monolayers, but they do not form tubes. At intermediate concentrations the cells are balanced between spreading and retraction (resulting from the inherent contractile properties of the cells) and rapidly form capillary tubes (32). This behavior is independent of the specific ECM protein that is used and also occurs with fibronectin, collagen type IV, or type I.

GENERAL MECHANISMS TO EXPLAIN ECM ACTION

ECM-Cytoskeletal Interactions

Recently there has been considerable interest in the concept that many of the effects of ECM on cellular activity are caused by interactions between ECM molecules and the cytoskeleton. Evidence in support of this idea includes the observation that ECM contact induces cytoskeletal reorganization in cultured cells (73) and that in many cells the distributions of ECM proteins and intracellular actin-containing stress fibers are coincident (30).

ECM-cytoskeleton interaction appears to be mediated by transmembrane ECM receptors. The amino acid sequences of the cytoplasmic domains of the integrin ECM receptors have been highly conserved during evolution (52), which suggests an important conserved function. These receptors bind the cytoskeleton-associated protein talin (29). Binding of endothelial cells to dishes coated with fibronectin, laminin, or other adhesive proteins triggers a rapid clustering of the corresponding integrin receptors on the cell surface (4, 15). The cytoskeletal protein, talin, colocalizes with integrin receptor aggregates and may initiate assembly of adhesion plaques that contain other cytoskeletal proteins such as vinculin, α-actinin, and actin (59).

Other evidence suggests that cell surface proteoglycans also play a role in mediating ECM-cytoskeletal interactions. The amino acid sequences of the cytoplasmic domains of the transmembrane proteoglycan core proteins are also conserved (53, 69; T. Evans, D. Carey, unpublished observations), and association of cell surface proteoglycans with the cytoskeleton has been demonstrated (9). Cell surface proteoglycans have been shown to colocalize with actin-containing stress fibers (80). Glycosaminoglycan-deficient fibroblast cell lines are unable to form stress fibers on fibronectin-coated dishes (41).

Interaction between the ECM and the cytoskeleton is easy to reconcile with the effects of ECM on such functions as cell migration or cell spreading. Less clear is how ECM-cytoskeleton interactions would explain effects on cell proliferation or gene expression. One explanation suggests that matrix interactions modulate cellular activity by changing cell shape. Changes in cell shape have been shown to affect such activities as DNA synthesis (20) and specific protein expression (6). While a detailed mechanism that accounts for these effects cannot be given, it is becoming apparent that many cellular functions are dependent on structural filaments within the cell. For example, it has been shown that polyribosomes are associated with cytoskeletal filaments (42). The nucleus also contains structural filaments that interact with both nuclear DNA and RNA and are physically associated with cytoplasmic cytoskeletal elements (19). This suggests there is physical (and presumed functional) continuity between ECM structures outside the cell and structures inside the cell, with the ECM receptors and cytoskeleton as the connecting link.

Second Messenger Generation

Some evidence suggests that the ECM also modulates cellular activity through the generation of intracellular second messengers. Changes in cell shape (one of the effects of ECM contact in most cells) have been shown to affect cytoplasmic pH via activation of the Na/H antiporter (70). Many growth factors have a similar effect. Stretching cell membranes also activates other ion channels (39) as well adenylyl cyclase (76) and phosphatidylinisotol turnover (7).

There is also evidence that, at least in some cells, binding of ligand to the integrin fibronectin receptor stimulates specific gene expression in the absence of changes in cell shape (78). In this case stimulation does not occur with intact fibronectin, but with fibronectin fragments or anti-integrin antibodies. Interestingly, the products that are induced are matrix degrading proteases, thus suggesting this mechanism may play a role in ECM turnover.

CONCLUSIONS AND FUTURE DIRECTIONS

The ECM influences many aspects of vascular cell function, including proliferation and differentiation. The molecular mechanisms that underlie these effects of ECM have, in most cases, been elusive. This is due in large part, to the complexity and multiplicity of interactions of ECM molecules with one another and with cells. Progress in uncovering these mechanisms is being made as a result of advances in the isolation and structural characterization of ECM molecules and their receptors. The availability of specific probes for cell-ECM interactions (e.g. anti-receptor antibodies and inhibitor peptides) should enable continued progress. Important issues that remain include determination of the specific functions of the different types of ECM receptors (e.g. integrins, LB69, cell surface proteoglycans); understanding the regulation of expression of ECM molecules and their receptors during development; determining the mechanisms by which ECM contact alters cellular activity; and assessing the role of the ECM in cardiovascular disease.

ACKNOWLEDGMENTS

I want to thank Drs. Peter Watson and Gunay Cizmeci-Smith for reading the manuscript and for helpful suggestions on its contents. I also gratefully acknowledge the help of Brian Shoop, who provided Figure 1, and Brian Tucker, who provided the electron micrographs in Figure 2. Kathy Knarr, Nancy Petty, and Deb McCaffery provided excellent secretarial support.

Literature Cited

1. Andres, J. L., Stanley, K., Cheifetz, S., Massagué, J. 1989. Membrane-anchored and soluble forms of betaglycan, a polymorphic proteoglycan that binds transforming growth factor-β. *J. Cell Biol.* 109:3137–45
2. Baird, A., Ling, N. 1987. Fibroblast growth factors are present in the extracellular matrix produced by endothelial cells *in vitro*: implications for a role of heparinase-like enzymes in the neovascular response. *Biochem. Biophys. Res. Commun.* 142:428–35
3. Bashkin, P., Doctrow, S., Klagsbrun, M., Svahn, C. M., Folkman, J., Vlodavsky, I. 1989. Basic fibroblast growth factor binds to subendothelial extracellular matrix and is released by heparinase and heparin-like molecules. *Biochemistry* 28:1737–43
4. Basson, C. T., Knowles, W. J., Bell, L., Albelda, S. M., Castronovo, V., et al. 1990. Spatiotemporal segregation of endothelial cell integrin and nonintegrin extracellular matrix-binding proteins during adhesion events. *J. Cell Biol.* 110:789–801
5. Beck, K., Hunter, I., Engel, J. 1990. Structure and function of laminin: anatomy of a multidomain glycoprotein. *FASEB J.* 4:148–60
6. Ben-Ze'ev, A. 1984. Differential control of cytokeratins and vimentin synthesis by cell-cell contact and cell spreading in cultured epithelial cells. *J. Cell Biol.* 99:1424–33
7. Breuer, D., Wagener, C. 1989. Activation of the phophatidylinositol cycle in spreading cells. *Exp. Cell Res.* 182:659–63
8. Carey, D. J., Evans, D. M. 1989. Membrane anchoring of heparan sulfate proteoglycans by phosphatidylinositol and kinetics of synthesis of peripheral and detergent-solubilized proteoglycans in Schwann cells. *J. Cell Biol.* 108:1891–97
9. Carey, D. J., Todd, M. S. 1986. A cytoskeleton-associated plasma membrane heparan sulfate proteoglycan in Schwann cells. *J. Biol. Chem.* 261: 7518–25
10. Castellot, J. J. Jr., Addonizio, M. L., Rosenberg, R., Karnovsky, M. J. 1981. Cultured endothelial cells produce a heparinlike inhibitor of smooth muscle growth. *J. Cell Biol.* 90:372–79
11. Castellot, J. J. Jr., Karnovsky, M. J. 1987. Heparin and the regulation of growth of the vascular wall. In *Vascular Smooth Muscle in Culture,* ed. J. H. Campbell, G. R. Campbell, pp. 93–115 Boca Raton, FL: CRC
12. Castellot, J. J. Jr., Pukac, L. A., Caleb, B. L., Wright, T. C. Jr., Karnovsky, M. J. 1989. Heparin selectively inhibits a protein kinase C-dependent mechanism of cell cycle progression in calf aortic smooth muscle cells. *J. Cell Biol.* 109:3147–55
13. Castellot, J. J. Jr., Wong, K., Herman, B., Hoover, R. L., Albertini, D. F., et

al. 1985. Binding and internalization of heparin by vascular smooth muscle cells. *J. Cell. Physiol.* 124:13–20
14. David, G., Lories, V., Heremans, A., Van der Schueren, B., Cassiman, J.-J., Van den Berghe, H. 1989. Membrane-associated chondroitin sulfate proteoglycans of human lung fibroblasts. *J. Cell Biol.* 108:1165–75
15. Dejana, E., Colella, S., Conforti, G., Abbadini, M., Gaboli, M., Marchisio, P. C. 1988. Fibronectin and vitronectin regulate the organization of their respective Arg-Gly-Asp adhesion receptors in cultured human endothelial cells. *J. Cell Biol.* 107:1215–23
16. Dejana, E., Lampugnani, M. G., Giorgi, M., Gaboli, M., Federici, A. B., et al. 1989. von Willebrand factor promotes endothelial cell adhesion via an Arg-Gly-Asp-dependent mechanism. *J. Cell Biol.* 109:367–75
17. Elices, M. J., Helmer, M. E. 1989. The human integrin VLA-2 is a collagen receptor on some cells and a collagen/laminin receptor on others. *Proc. Natl. Acad. Sci. USA* 86:9906–10
18. Feige, J.-J., Bradley, J. D., Fryburg, K., Farris, J., Cousens, L. C., et al. 1989. Differential effects of heparin, fibronectin, and laminin on the phosphorylation of basic fibroblast growth factor by protein kinase C and the catalytic subunit of protein kinase A. *J. Cell Biol.* 109:3105–14
19. Fey, E. G., Krochmalnic, G., Penman, S. 1986. The nonchromatin substructures of the nucleus: the ribonucleoprotein (RNP)-containing and RNP-depleted matrices analyzed by sequential fractionation and resinless electron microscopy. *J. Cell Biol.* 102:1654–65
20. Folkman, J., Moscona, A. 1978. Role of cell shape in growth control. *Nature* 273:345–49
21. Frazier, W. A. 1987. Thrombospondin: a modular adhesive glycoprotein of platelets and nucleated cells. *J. Cell Biol.* 105:625–32
22. Fritze, L. M. S., Reilly, C. F., Rosenberg, R. D. 1985. An antiproliferative heparan sulfate species produced by postconfluent smooth muscle cells. *J. Cell Biol.* 100:1041–49
23. Gehlsen, K. R., Dillner, L., Engvall, E., Ruoslahti, E. 1988. The human laminin receptor is a member of the integrin family of cell adhesion receptors. *Science* 241:1228–29
24. Gospodarowicz, D., Ill, C. R. 1980. Do plasma and serum have different abilities to promote cell growth? *Proc. Natl. Acad. Sci. USA* 77:2726–30
25. Grant, D. S., Tashiro, K.-I., Segui-Real, B., Yamada, Y., Martin, G. R., Kleinman, H. K. 1989. Two different laminin domains mediate the differentiation of human endothelial cells into capillary-like structures in vitro. *Cell* 58:933–43
26. Hamati, H. F., Britton, E. L., Carey, D. J. 1989. Inhibition of proteoglycan synthesis alters extracellular matrix deposition, proliferation, and cytoskeletal organization of rat aortic smooth muscle cells in culture. *J. Cell Biol.* 108:2495–2505
27. Heino, J., Ignotz, R. A., Hemler, M. E., Crouse, C., Massagué, J. 1989. Regulation of cell adhesion receptors by transforming growth factor-β: concomitant regulation of integrins that share a common β_1 subunit. *J. Biol. Chem.* 264:380–88
28. Herman, I. M., Castellot, J. J. Jr. 1987. Regulation of vascular smooth muscle cell growth by endothelial-synthesized extracellular matrices. *Arteriosclerosis* 7:463–69
29. Horwitz, A., Duggan, K., Buck, C., Beckerle, M. C., Burridge, K. 1986. Interaction of plasma membrane fibronectin receptor with talin-a transmembrane linkage. *Nature* 320:531–33
30. Hynes, R. O. 1981. Fibronectin and its relation to cellular structures and behavior. In *Cell Biology of Extracellular Matrix,* ed. E. D. Hay, pp. 295–334. New York/London: Plenum
31. Hynes, R. O. 1987. Integrins: a family of cell surface receptors. *Cell* 48:549–54
32. Ingber, D. E., Folkman, J. 1989. Mechanochemical switching between growth and differentiation during fibroblast growth factor-stimulated angiogenesis in vitro: role of extracellular matrix. *J. Cell Biol.* 109:317–30
33. Ingber, D. E., Folkman, J. 1989. How does extracellular matrix control capillary morphogenesis? *Cell* 58:803–805
34. Kirchhofer, D., Languino, L. R., Ruoslahti, E., Pierschbacher, M. D. 1990. $\alpha_2\beta_1$ integrins from different cell types show different binding specificities. *J. Biol. Chem.* 265:615–18
35. Knudsen, B. S., Silverstein, R. L., Leung, L. L. K., Harpel, P. C., Nachman, R. L. 1986. Binding of plasminogen to extracellular matrix. *J. Biol. Chem.* 261:10765–71
36. Koda, J. E., Rapraeger, A., Bernfield, M. 1985. Heparan sulfate proteoglycan from murine mammary epithelial cells: cell surface proteoglycan as a receptor for interstial collagen. *J. Biol. Chem.* 260:8157–62
37. Kubota, Y., Kleinman, H. K., Martin, G. R., Lawley, T. J. 1988. Role of lami-

nin and basement membrane in the morphological differentiation of human endothelial cells into capillary-like structures. *J. Cell Biol.* 107:1589–98

38. Kurokawa, M., Doctrow, S. R., Klagsbrun, M. 1989. Neutralizing antibodies inhibit the binding of basic fibroblast growth factor to its receptor but not to heparin. *J. Biol. Chem.* 264:7686–91
39. Lansman, J. B., Hallam, T. J., Rink, T. J. 1987. Single stretch-activated ion channels in vascular endothelial cells as mechotransducers? *Nature* 325:811–13
40. Lawler, J., Weinstein, R., Hynes, R. O. 1988. Cell attachment to thrombospondin: the role of ARG-GLY-ASP, calcium, and integrin receptors. *J. Cell Biol.* 107:2351–61
41. LeBaron, R. G., Esko, J. D., Woods, A., Johansson, S., Hook, M. 1988. Adhesion of glycosaminoglycan-deficient Chinese hamster ovary cell mutants to fibronectin substrata. *J. Cell Biol.* 106:945–52
42. Lenk, R., Ransom, L., Kaufmann, Y., Penman, S. 1977. A cytoskeletal structure with associated polyribosomes obtained from HeLa cells. *Cell* 10:67–78
43. Macarak, E. J., Howard, P. S. 1983. Adhesion of endothelial cells to extracellular matrix proteins. *J. Cell Phys.* 116:76–86
44. Maciag, T., Kadish, J., Wilkins, L., Stemerman, M. B., Weinstein, R. 1982. Organizational behavior of human umbilical vein endothelial cells. *J. Cell Biol.* 94:511–20
45. Madri, J. A., Pratt, B. M. 1986. Endothelial cell-matrix interactions: in vitro models of angiogenesis. *J. Histochem. Cytochem.* 34:85–91
46. Madri, J. A., Williams, S. K. 1983. Capillary endothelial cell cultures: phenotypic modulation by matrix components. *J Cell Biol.* 97:153–65
47. Majack, R. A. 1987. Beta-type transforming growth factor specifies organizational behavior in vascular smooth cell cultures. *J. Cell Biol.* 105:465–471
48. Majack, R. A., Cook, S. C., Bornstein, P. 1985. Platelet-derived growth factor and heparin-like glycosaminoglycans regulate thrombospondin synthesis and deposition in the matrix by smooth muscle cells. *J. Cell Biol.* 101:1059–70
49. Majack, R. A., Cook, S. C., Bornstein, P. 1986. Control of smooth muscle cell growth by components of the extracellular matrix: autocrine role for thrombospondin. *Proc. Natl. Acad. Sci. USA* 83:9050–54
50. Majack, R. A., Goodman, L. V., Dixit, V. M. 1988. Cell surface thrombospondin is functionally essential for vascular smooth muscle cell proliferation. *J. Cell Biol.* 106:415–22
51. Majack, R. A., Mildbrandt, J., Dixit, V. M. 1987. Induction of thrombospondin messenger RNA levels occurs as an immediate primary response to platelet-derived growth factor. *J. Biol. Chem.* 262:8821–25
52. Marcantonio, E. E., Hynes, R. O. 1988. Antibodies to the conserved cytoplasmic domain of the integrin β_1 subunit react with proteins in vertebrates, invertebrates and fungi. *J. Cell Biol.* 106:1765–72
53. Marynen, P., Zhang, J., Cassiman, J.-J., Van den Berghe, H., David, G. 1989. Partial primary structure of the 48- and 90-kilodalton core proteins of cell surface-associated heparan sulfate proteoglycans of lung fibroblasts. *J. Biol. Chem.* 264:7017–24
54. McCaffrey, T. A., Falcone, D. J., Brayton, C. F., Agarwal, L. A., Welt, F. G. P., Weksler, B. B. 1989. Transforming growth factor-β activity is potentiated by heparin via dissociation of the transforming growth factor-β/α_2-macroglobulin inactive complex. *J. Cell Biol.* 109:441–48
55. McNeil, P. L., Muthukrishnan, L., Warder, E., D'Amore, P. A. 1989. Growth factors are released by mechanically wounded epithelial cells. *J. Cell Biol.* 109:811–22
56. Montesano, R., Orci, L., Vassalli, P. 1983. In vitro rapid organization of endothelial cells into capillary-like networks is promoted by collagen matrices. *J. Cell Biol.* 97:1648–52
57. Moscatelli, D. 1987. High and low affinity binding sites for basic fibroblast growth factor on cultured cells: absence of a role for low affinity binding in the stimulation of plasminogen activator production by bovine capillary endothelial cells. *J. Cell. Physiol.* 131:123–30
58. Moscatelli, D. 1988. Metabolism of receptor-bound and matrix-bound basic fibroblast growth factor by bovine capillary endothelial cells. *J. Cell Biol.* 107:753–59
59. Mueller, S. C., Kelly, T., Dai, M., Chen, W.-T. 1989. Dynamic cytoskeleton-integrin associations induced by cell binding to immobilized fibronectin. *J. Cell Biol.* 109:3455–64
60. Mugnai, G., Lewandowska, K., Carnemolla, B., Zardi, L., Culp, L. A. 1988. Modulation of matrix adhesive responses of human neuroblastoma cells

by neighboring sequences in the fibronectins. *J. Cell Biol.* 106:931–43
61. Pollanen, J., Saksela, O., Salonen, E.-M., Andreasen, P., Nielsen, L., et al. 1987. Distinct localizations of urokinase-type plasminogen activator and its type I inhibitor under cultured human fibroblasts and sarcoma cells. *J. Cell Biol.* 104:1085–96
62. Rasmussen, S., Rapraeger, A. 1988. Altered structure of the hybrid cell surface proteoglycan of mammary epithelial cells in response to transforming growth factor-β. *J. Cell Biol.* 107:1959–67
63. Rifkin, D. B., Moscatelli, D. 1989. Recent developments in the cell biology of basic fibroblast growth factor. *J. Cell Biol.* 109:1–6
64. Rogelj, S., Klagsbrun, M., Atzmon, R., Kurokawa, M., Haimovitz, A., et al. 1989. Basic fibroblast growth factor is an extracellular matrix component required for supporting the proliferation of vascular endothelial cells and the differentiation of PC12 cells. *J. Cell Biol.* 109:823–31
65. Ruoslahti, E. 1988. Fibronectin and its receptors. *Annu. Rev. Biochem.* 57:375–413
66. Saksela, O., Mosatelli, D., Sommer, A., Rifkin, D. B. 1988. Endothelial cell-derived heparan sulfate binds basic fibroblast growth factor and protects it from proteolytic degradation. *J. Cell Biol.* 107:743–51
67. Saksela, O., Rifkin, D. B. 1990. Release of basic fibroblast growth factor-heparan sulfate complexes from endothelial cells by plasminogen activator-mediated proteolytic activity. *J. Cell Biol.* 110:767–75
68. Saunders, S., Bernfield, M. 1988. Cell surface proteoglycan binds murine mammary epithelial cells to fibronectin and behaves as a receptor for interstitial matrix. *J. Cell Biol.* 106:423–30
69. Saunders, S., Jalkanen, M., O'Farrell, S., Bernfield, M. 1989. Molecular cloning of syndecan, an integral membrane proteoglyan. *J. Cell Biol.* 108:1547–56
70. Schwartz, M. A., Cragoe, E. J., Lechene, C. P. 1990. pH regulation in spread cells and round cells. *J. Biol. Chem.* 265:1327–32
71. Scott-Burden, T., Resink, T. J., Baur, U., Burgin, M., Buhler, F. R. 1988. Activation of S6 kinase in cultured vascular smooth muscle cells by submitogenic levels of thrombospondin. *Biochem. Biophys. Res. Commun.* 150: 278–86
72. Scott-Burden, T., Resink, T. J., Burgin, M., Buhler, F. R. 1989. Extracellular matrix: differential influence on growth and biosynthesis patterns of vascular smooth muscle cells from SHR and WKY rats. *J. Cell. Physiol.* 141:267–74
73. Sugrue, S. P., Hay, E. D. 1981. Response of basal epithelial cell surface and cytoskeleton to solubilized extracellular matrix molecules. *J. Cell Biol.* 91:45–54
74. Sun, X., Mosher, D. F., Rapraeger, A. 1989. Heparan sulfate-mediated binding of epithelial cell surface proteoglycan to thrombospondin. *J. Biol. Chem.* 264:2885–89
75. Vlodavsky, I., Folkman, J., Sullivan, R., Fridman, R., Ishai-Michaeli, R., et al. 1987. Endothelial cell-derived basic fibroblast growth factor: synthesis and deposition into subendothelial extracellular matrix. *Proc. Natl. Acad. Sci. USA* 84:2292–96
76. Watson, P. A. 1989. Accumulation of cAMP and calcium in S49 mouse lymphoma cells following hyposmotic swelling. *J. Biol. Chem.* 264:14735–40
77. Wayner, E. A., Carter, W. G. 1987. Identification of multiple cell adhesion receptors for collagen and fibronectin in human fibrosarcoma cells possessing unique α and common β subunits. *J. Cell Biol.* 105:1873–84
78. Werb, Z., Tremble, P. M., Behrendtsen, O., Crowley, E., Damsky, C. H. 1989. Signal transduction through the fibronectin receptor induces collagenase and stromelysin gene expression. *J. Cell Biol.* 109:877–89
79. Wight, T. N. 1989. Cell biology of arterial proteoglycans. *Arteriosclerosis* 9:1–20
80. Woods, A., Hook, M., Kjellen, L., Smith, C. G., Rees, D. A. 1984. Relationship of heparan sulfate proteoglycans to the cytoskeleton and extracellular matrix of cultured fibroblasts. *J. Cell Biol.* 99:1743–53
81. Wright, T. C., Castellot, J. J. Jr., Petitou, M., Lormeau, J.-C., Choay, J., Karnovsky, M. J. 1989. Structural determinants of heparin's growth inhibitory activity. *J. Biol. Chem.* 264: 1534–42
82. Yannariello-Brown, J., Wewer, U., Liotta, L., Madri, J. A. 1988. Distribution of a 69-kD laminin-binding protein in aortic and microvascular endothelial cells: modulation during cell attachment, spreading, and migration. *J. Cell Biol.* 106:1773–86

Annu. Rev. Physiol. 1991. 53:179–200

GROWTH FACTORS, PROTO-ONCOGENES, AND PLASTICITY OF THE CARDIAC PHENOTYPE

Thomas G. Parker[1] *and Michael D. Schneider*[1,2]

[1]Molecular Cardiology Unit, Departments of [1]Medicine, [2]Cell Biology, and [2]Molecular Physiology and Biophysics, Baylor College of Medicine, Houston, Texas 77030

KEY WORDS: fibroblast growth factors, transforming growth factors, heart, myocardium, gene expression

---

INTRODUCTION

The inability of cardiac muscle cells to replicate in adult myocardium confounds recovery from ischemic injury and contrasts with the excessive growth of vascular smooth muscle in atherosclerotic lesions. Growth of cardiac myocytes by cell enlargement, however, is one outcome of pressure and volume overload, which encompasses not only increased RNA, protein, cell volume and mass, but also plasticity of gene expression. Consequently, cardiac hypertrophy presents a challenging phenomenon to molecular geneticists, to explicate transducing mechanisms that couple mechanical load to long-term changes in cardiac function and structure.

Recent advances toward understanding trophic signals in the heart and remaining enigmas constitute the subject of this review. An ensemble of cardiac gene products exists, more extensive than recognized previously, which is coordinately regulated during experimental hypertrophy and myocardial disease. Whether such genetic responses signify a purely adaptive response or, instead, a shared regulatory program is controversial. Molecular signals that might initiate growth and alter gene expression after hemodynamic stress have been identified. Induction of nuclear oncogenes during cardiac

0066-4278/91/0315-0179$02.00

hypertrophy has suggested functional homology between mechanisms for growth factor signaling and transduction events initiated by mechanical stress. Cardiac myocytes, in addition, are targets for the action of peptide growth factors found in myocardium, thus suggesting an autocrine or paracrine model of the hypertrophic process (84).

PLASTICITY OF THE CARDIAC PHENOTYPE

Hypertrophy Recapitulates Ontogeny

Development of the embryonic heart and maturation after birth entail not only the neonatal loss of cardiac myocytes' proliferative capacity, but also sequential changes in expression of cardiac-specific genes (50, 78, 102). The canonical transitions involve isoforms of contractile proteins, which often result from selective transcription within multigene families; for other genes, alternative mRNA splicing is the basis for diversity (7). In rodent models, constriction of the aorta increases cardiac mass together with gene expression characteristic of the embryonic heart. The decreased myosin ATPase activity in overloaded myocardium (1) is now comprehended as a transition in synthesis from adult ($\alpha\alpha$, V1) to fetal ($\beta\beta$, V3) myosin heavy chains (MHC), whose actin-activated properties differ intrinsically (40, 106). Transcripts that encode α-actin itself are increased selectively for the skeletal muscle isoform (αSkA), which is associated with fetal myocardium (105). Also reactivated is the β-tropomyosin (41) gene, which is transcribed in the developing ventricle and ordinarily supplanted by alternate isoproteins. Thus, an ensemble of fetal contractile protein genes is re-expressed after increased load and contributes to novel sarcomeres, whose functional properties may differ (78).

The resurgence of fetal protein isoforms during cardiac hypertrophy may be more generalized, as illustrated for enzymes of myocardial metabolism [up-regulation of non-muscle subunits of creatine kinase (38) and lactate dehydrogenase (30), and (re-induction of the embryonic α3 isoform of the sarcolemmal Na^+/K^+ ATPase (138)]. Analogously, after pressure overload, inhibition of the sarcoplasmic reticulum (SR) slow/cardiac Ca^{2+} ATPase (54) and up-regulation of the secreted peptide, atrial natriuretic factor [ANF (41)], each restore the abundance of these transcripts found in embryonic hearts. Abnormal ultrastructure and electrophysiology also have been interpreted as fetal cardiac properties (63, 122).

Re-induction of βMHC in the ventricle also is common to diverse forms of cardiac hypertrophy—spontaneously hypertensive rats (37), compensatory growth after myocardial infarction (94), and Syrian hamster cardiomyopathy (43). Other embryonic transcripts including atrial myosin light chain-1 (MLC_1), ANF, and αSkA persist in this hereditary myopathy (48). Thus the generic response of fetal cardiac gene expression is not provoked exclusively by acute load. In contrast, βMHC does not appear in cardiac hypertrophy elicited by isometric exercise or thyroid hormone (120). Thus the underlying pathophysiology is likely to influence the specific subsets of cardiac genes, which are modulated, in addition to factors such as age or severity and duration of stress (121).

Plasticity of Adult Human Myocardium

Whether comparable transitions have equivalent significance in humans has been questioned, since βMHC predominates even in normal adult human ventricles (126) and αSkA expression may be inconsistent (107). Despite apparent counter-examples, the human myocardium, in fact, can modulate differentiated gene expression (Table 1). For instance, αMHC is principally expressed in human atrial muscle, but is also expressed at low abundance in an unexpectedly large proportion of ventricular myocytes, which decreases during pressure-overload hypertrophy (4a; cf 27). Conversely, βHMC, associated with embryonic, but not adult atria, is re-expressed in valvular disease in proportion to the atrial diameter (70). Novel ventricular isoforms of βMHC reportedly exist in human cardiomyopathy (126) and hypertensive baboons (34). Linkage analysis mapping a gene for familial hypertrophic cardiomyopathy to chromosome 14q1 is provocative, since the α and β MHC genes have been localized to 14q11.2–q13 (44). Structural mutations of cardiac MHC genes have been identified in two pedigrees with familial hypertrophic cardiomyopathy, and changes in the proportion of α vs β MHC are postulated as a basis for the variable phenotype in this form of hypertrophy (140).

That cardiac muscle responds locally to load is indicated by the appearance of ventricular MLC_1 in the right atrium during pulmonary hypertension, but in the left atrium during mitral valve regurgitation (58). Conversely, atrial MLC_1 is re-expressed in the hypertrophied human ventricle (35). Finally, as in rodent models, the ANF (98) and SR Ca^{2+} ATPase (71) genes are induced and repressed, respectively, in end-stage heart failure. Thus plasticity of gene expression in post-mitotic cardiac muscle provides a potential mechanism, both in animals and humans, for load or other trophic signals to produce long-term changes in myocardial performance, in contrast to beat-to-beat fluctuations caused by altered fiber length and short-term biochemical control of excitation-contraction coupling (50, 78).

Adaptation vs Atavism

During pressure overload hypertrophy, the diminished actin-activated ATPase activity of βMHC decreases the maximum velocity of shortening in unloaded muscle fibers (106), and the lower energetic cost of developed work is proposed to be advantageous during high oxygen demand (50, 78). Thus βMHC is paradigmatic for adaptive plasticity in cardiac muscle. By contrast, functional consequences of an α-actin isoform switch are not substantiated by

Table 1 Cardiac myocytes possess a continuum of responses to peptide growth factors, resembling fetal gene expression activated by a hemodynamic load

Gene/isoform	Agent[a]	Response[b]	Rodent ventricle[b,c] Embryonic	Rodent ventricle[b,c] Adult	Rodent ventricle[b,c] Hypertrophy	Human ventricle[b,c] Embryonic	Human ventricle[b,c] Adult	Human ventricle[b,c] Overload or failure	Human atrium[b,c] Adult	Human atrium[b,c] Overload
MHC										
α	aFGF, bFGF, TGFβ1	↓	—	+++	↓	+	+	↓	+++	↓
	NE	↔								
	T3	↑								
β	aFGF, bFGF, TGFβ1	↑	+++	—	↑	+++	+++	↔	+	↑
	NE	↑								
	T3	↓								
α-Actin										
Cardiac	bFGF, TGFβ1	↔	++	+++	↔	n.a.[d]	+++	↔	+++	n.a.
	NE	↔								
	T3	↔								
	aFGF	↓								
Skeletal	bFGF, TGFβ1	↑	++	—, +	↑	n.a.	+	variable	+	n.a.
	NE	↑								
	T3	↔, ↑								
	aFGF	↓								
Smooth	aFGF, bFGF, TGFβ1	↑	++	—	↑[e]	n.a.				
ANF	aFGF, bFGF, TGFβ1	↑	+++	—	↑	+++	—	↑	+++	↑
Slow/cardiac Ca^{2+} ATPase	aFGF, bFGF, TGFβ1	↓	+	+++	↓	+	+++	↓		

[a] aFGF, acidic fibroblast growth factor; bFGF, basic fibroblast growth factor; NE, norepinephrine; T3, thyroid hormone; TGFβ1, type β1 transforming growth factor.
[b] ↑, up-regulation; ↓, down-regulation; ↔, little or no change with trophic signals or myocardial disease.
[c] (+, ++, +++) relative or (—) absent expression in normal myocardium. For brevity the sequence of gene induction during cardiac myogenesis is omitted (cf. 97).
[d] n.a., not available or inconclusive.
[e] F. M. Black, L. H. Michael, R. Roberts, M. D. Schneider, unpublished results.

current in vitro assays, and over-expression of αSkA in Balb/C mice, which results from an upstream mutation in the α-cardiac actin (αCaA) gene, fails to provoke discernible abnormalities in cardiac structure or physiology (25). Paradoxically, while down-regulation of the SR Ca^{2+} ATPase is likely to be consequential, the resultant increase in intracellular calcium might augment systolic function, but impair myocardial relaxation. Thus cardiac load elicits a set of genetic responses whose outcome can be advantageous, indifferent, or maladaptive (50) and might reflect shared regulation, not adaptation, in common (78, 102).

Initiating Signals

The relative absence of hypertrophy in the right heart following aortic constriction and selective growth of right ventricular myocytes after pulmonary artery banding (66) suggest that circulating factors are unlikely to initiate hypertrophy in these forms of pressure overload. The potential role of local autocrine or paracrine mechanisms in the left ventricle remains open to question. Cardiac myocytes in cell culture have provided one means to overcome variables confounding in vivo studies and to identify regulators of cardiac growth and function. Adrenergic agonists, thyroid hormone, and angiotensin II each induce cardiac growth, yet differentially modulate cardiac-specific gene transcription (41, 49, 112). For example, thyroid hormone exerts pivotal and reciprocal control over α and β MHC (29), whereas norepinephrine selectively provokes αSkA (4; cf 130, 133).

The fact that perturbations induced by load are local argues for a contribution from mechanical stress itself (66). A passive stretch of cardiac myocytes on distensible membranes can induce protein synthesis (53), βMHC (45), and αSkA (I. Komuro, Y. Yazaki, personal communication), as seen with pressure overload in vivo (41). Certain models permit components of hypertrophy to be dissociated from load per se. Cardiac hypertrophy precedes hypertension in spontaneously hypertensive rats (24), and β-adrenergic blocking agents suppress the increase in cardiac mass, yet permit replacement of α by βMHC (37). After aortic constriction, normalization of left ventricle wall stress by increasing wall thickness does not extinguish βMHC, yet αSkA transcript levels subside (100). Thus signals alternative to load itself might potentiate or sustain hypertrophy and the fetal phenotype, possibly through local autocrine and paracrine mechanisms.

FIBROBLAST AND TYPE β TRANSFORMING GROWTH FACTORS

Originally characterized through their capacity to elicit proliferative or anchorage-independent cell growth, peptide growth factors are multifunctional agents that regulate differentiation and function in a lineage and stage-specific fashion (28, 93, 101, 102). Both fibroblast and type β transforming growth factors (FGF, TGFβ) are encoded by multigene families, are expressed in normal and abnormal myocardium, and provoke plasticity of cardiac gene expression, which resembles transitions produced in vivo during acute load or end-stage heart failure (Table 1). Basic and acidic FGF, potent mitogens for many cell lineages, have been purified from diverse sources. These peptides share 55% amino acid sequence homology, bind heparin, compete for receptor binding and, overall, have comparable biological effects (28). Like acidic FGF, basic FGF lacks a signal peptide sequence for secretion, yet accumulates in the extracellular matrix (28). In addition, basic FGF is released from cells after injury (68). Specific actions of acidic and basic FGF are contingent on the target cell, as illustrated by their shared ability to suppress differentiation of skeletal myoblasts (15, 59), yet promote differentiation in neurons (64). Additional members of the FGF family, whose potential expression and function in cardiac muscle are untested, include *int*-2, *hst*/KS3, FGF-5, FGF-6, and keratinocyte growth factor (28, 102).

Control of growth by TGFβ1 is dependent on cell age, cell density, and the presence of other growth factors. Typically, TGFβ1 induces transformed growth in agar yet inhibits mitotic growth in monolayer cultures (93). For example, TGFβ1 retards endothelial growth induced by FGF (74) and suppresses certain EGF-induced genes (16). Interestingly, TGFβ1 inhibits type II collagen production by mature chondrocytes, yet induces immature cartilage to differentiate (118). Related peptides include TGFβs 2 through 5, the decapentaplegic product, bone morphogenic proteins such as BMP2, Müllerian-inhibiting substance, activins and inhibins, and Vg1 and Vgr-1, maternally encoded mRNAs found in *Xenopus* and mouse oocytes, respectively (93, 102). More than 12 new members of the TGFβ family have been identified, using cDNA amplification by the polymerase chain reaction (125).

The apparent dichotomy between proliferative growth and differentiation in skeletal myocytes, the existence of representative permanent cell lines, and simple procedures for insertion of exogenous regulatory or reporter genes have contributed to the importance of skeletal muscle as a paradigm for the impact of growth factors during myogenesis (101; J. Florini, D. Ewton, K. Magri, this volume). Basic and acidic FGF are potent mitogens for skeletal myoblasts (15, 59) which, like TGFβ1 (10, 67, 80, 110), inhibit muscle-specific gene expression even in the absence of proliferative growth. Conversely, acidic and basic FGF cause differentiation of skeletal muscle precursor cells in the animal pole of *Xenopus* embryos, thus substituting for signals normally provided by vegetal pole cells (134). Thus, FGFs exert bifunctional control of differentiation in skeletal muscle, circumscribed by the underlying state of development. In agreement, TGFβ1 inhibits differentiation of skeletal myoblasts (10, 67, 80, 110), yet potentiates mesoderm induction by FGFs (115); the endogenous factor inducing dorsal mesoderm appears to be a TGFβ-related peptide, activin A (69, 116). Finally, in post-mitotic skeletal muscle, FGFs and TGFβ1 fail to modulate muscle-specific genes, although down-regulation of the corresponding receptors may be the outcome, not the cause, of terminal differentiation (15, 23, 81).

Although cardiac and skeletal myocytes share numerous muscle-specific gene products in common (especially in the embryo), particular distinctions suggest the potential for lineage-specific responses to growth factor binding. First, cardiac muscle cells synthesize tissue-specific proteins, even during proliferation (95). After birth, cardiac DNA synthesis is uncoupled from cell division, and subsequent growth occurs by hypertrophy alone (139). While the viral oncogene SV40 T antigen suppresses differentiation in skeletal muscle (21), cardiac myocytes, induced to grow by T antigen in culture, or in transgenic mice, retain a differentiated phenotype (108, L. Field, personal communication). Finally, peptide growth factors are likely to control skeletal muscle differentiation, at least in part, through the abundance or activity of *myc*-like determination proteins—MyoD1, myogenin, myf-5, and MRF4—which have not been detected in cardiac muscle (6, 18, 19, 91, 135) and are not thought to regulate gene expression in atrial or ventricular myocytes. Nonetheless, this discrepancy invites speculation that cardiac muscle might contain structural or functional homologues of MyoD1. A structurally unrelated gene, the proto-oncogene c-*ski,* likewise converts fibroblasts to the myogenic pathway, but is expressed in the developing and adult heart (86).

MYOCARDIAL GROWTH FACTORS

Expression and Localization

Indirect evidence favoring a functional role for growth factors in the heart has been proof of their expression within the myocardium, development control, and up-regulation in cardiovascular disease. Acidic and basic FGF have been purified from the heart (11, 89, 99) and are detected in dissociated cardiac myocytes (117). The paucity of basic FGF mRNA in myocardium, as in most tissues (111), contrasts with the abundance of this peptide in cardiac extracellular matrix (46). Acidic FGF is readily detected in cardiac myocytes, but not in cardiac fibroblasts and, like basic FGF, it accumulates in the extracellular matrix (132). A heart-derived growth factor for endothelial proliferation recently was identified as acidic FGF itself and was localized to cardiac myocytes in cultured myocytes and thin sections (99). Since the yield of acidic FGF in bovine heart was 500 $\mu g \cdot kg^{-1}$, adult cardiac muscle is one of the richest sources of this growth factor (99).

Along with transformed cells and platelets, cardiac muscle also highly expresses TGFβ1, which is found in cardiac myocytes, the endocardial cushion, and specialized conduction tissue (124). Like basic FGF (46), TGFβ1 is more highly expressed in the atrium than the ventricle (123), in parallel with the capacity for DNA synthesis. Intracellular staining for TGFβ1 in cardiac myocytes contrasts with extracellular staining of mesenchymal cells (123); however, during human embryogenesis, TGFβ mRNAs may be expressed preferentially in cardiac valves and the endocardium (26). Although TGFβs 1 through 5 each are found in the myocardium, variation exists between mammalian and non-mammalian hearts (42, 56, 124).

In addition, insulin-like growth factors I and II are both expressed, at least in neonatal myocardium, with IGF-II more abundant than IGF-I (22). The heart may also be the site of production for novel trophic peptides. Unique transcripts of TGFβ1 are found in murine, rat, and porcine hearts, although their protein products, if any, are unknown (123, 124). A potent mitogen with 66% homology to basic FGF also has been identified in mammalian myocardium (109). Three neurotrophic molecules are highly expressed in the heart—nerve growth factor, brain-derived neurotrophic factor, and neurotrophin-3 (65)—whose effects may not be limited exclusively to neurons (82).

Myocardial Development

Regulation of FGFs and TGFβs during cardiac development holds particular interest in view of the impact of these peptides on skeletal muscle determination. In embryonic mice, TGFβ1 is expressed at high levels in the endocardial cushion and cardiac valves (124). TGFβ3 and Vgr-1 also are expressed in mesenchymal cells of the endocardial cushion, 9–10 days post coitum, whereas BMP2 gene expression is localized to the outer myocardial layer (B. Hogan, personal communication). During chick embryogenesis, basic FGF at first may be restricted to developing myocardial cells and appears subsequently in the extracellular matrix [stages 9 and 15, respectively (85)]. Both basic FGF and TGFβs1–4 decrease in the adult vs neonatal ventricle (46, 124; S. Jakowlew, A. Roberts, personal communication). TGFβ5, investigated thus far only in *Xenopus*, is abundant in the neurula and tadpole and in adult heart (56). Both IGF-II gene expression and IGF receptor density rapidly decline in rat hearts 3–7 days after birth (22). Human fetal heart expresses high levels of acidic FGF mRNA, whose cellular distribution and temporal control are unknown (13).

Functional studies provide a more conclusive indication that these growth factors or other diffusible signals might contribute to induction of the cardiac myocyte lineage or other components of the heart. Formation of valve primordia in chick embryos (epithelial-mesenchymal induction) is elicited by TGFβ1 (87) or cardiac extracellular matrix containing FGFs (57). At the onset of gastrulation, excision of underlying endoderm, or injection of a factor inducing dorsal mesoderm, subsequently shown to be activin A, prevents the formation of cardiac muscle itself (17). Similarly, medium conditioned by endodermal cells causes the pluripotent embryonal carcinoma, P19, to form spontaneously beating muscle cells, and this induction of mesoderm resembling cardiac muscle is blocked by activin A (128).

Cardiac Disease

Measurements of increased expression with ischemia, infarction, or mechanical load have helped to establish interest in the possible functional consequences of myocardial growth factors. Chronic ischemia in the pig results in angiogenesis, concurrent with up-regulation of TGFβ in ventricular myocytes, and a precursor of acidic FGF in coronary vessels (89; M. Klagsbrun, P. D'Amore, this volume). Experimental infarction in the rat leads to loss of both TGFβ1 (123) and basic FGF (12) from the infarcted zone, with increased expression in adjacent surviving myocytes. An additional ~1.9 kb TGFβ transcript also appears after infarction in the rat (123), or pig (136), and perhaps appears in dilated cardiomyopathy as well (136). It has been postulated that these peptides aid healing, or angiogenesis, and benefit compensatory hypertrophy (12). Extracts from hypertrophied hearts provoke hypertrophy when infused in vivo, thus substantiating a role for trophic substances produced in response to load (31). Although up-regulation of angiotensinogen follows aortic constriction (61), expression of FGFs and TGFβs after a hemodynamic load is uncharacterized. Interestingly, acidic FGF increases five to tenfold in skeletal muscle with exercise conditioning (73).

CARDIAC MYOCYTES ARE TARGETS FOR THE ACTION OF PEPTIDE GROWTH FACTORS

Myocardial Differentiation is Induced by Mitogen Withdrawal

Dissociated cardiac myocytes in the absence of hemodynamic forces, innervation, and circulating hormones have facilitated the identification of molecules that regulate the cardiac phenotype and the dissection of signaling pathways. Historically, one clue was furnished by monolayer cultures in media containing fetal sera, which revert to a less differentiated phenotype (127). In contrast, serum-free media advance the maturation of neonatal cardiac muscle cells (84, 127) and maintain the differentiated properties of adult ventricular myocytes (8). Specific constituents of serum distinct from catacholamines and thyroid hormone induce cardiac myocyte hypertrophy and protein synthesis (112).

The response of cardiac myocytes to serum factors is developmentally regulated. Neonatal rat cardiac muscle cells, subjected to serum after mitogen withdrawal for 2, 7, or 15 days, exhibit three sequential phases of ventricular growth capacity: mitosis, DNA synthesis uncoupled from cell division, or suppression of both responses, in parallel with the corresponding loss of growth in vivo (127). In this model, proliferation is associated with down-regulation of both striated α-actins, whereas α-skeletal actin is induced by serum in older cultures, as seen in pressure overload hypertrophy. These data leave open to question the identity of serum components, which are trophic for cardiac myocytes and alter phenotypic properties.

Peptide Growth Factors Induce Fetal Cardiac Genes

The authors have established that neonatal rat cardiac myocytes possess a continuum of responses to TGFβ1, basic FGF, and acidic FGF (84; Table 1), which contrast with the uniform suppression of muscle-specific genes in skeletal myoblasts or biochemically differentiated myocytes (10, 20, 67, 80, 101, 110). Incubation with TGFβ1 provokes βMHC and inhibits αMHC, despite the presence of thyroid hormone. Similarly, αSkA is induced, with little or no change in α-cardiac actin. Thus the embryonic isoforms are up-regulated selectively, with essentially identical responses initiated by basic FGF. Both peptides also stimulated ANF and, conversely, inhibited sarcoplasmic reticulum Ca^{2+}-ATPase expression (83). Thus either alone differentially affected an ensemble of six genes, which corresponds to regulation of each gene seen in vivo with pressure-overload hypertrophy.

Despite activities comparable to basic FGF in other cell lineages, acidic FGF produced unexpectedly distinct effects in cardiac muscle. Although the α and β MHC, ANF and SR Ca^{2+}-ATPase genes responded similarly to acidic and basic FGF, both αSkA and αCaA were suppressed. [Vascular smooth muscle α-actin, perhaps the earliest molecular marker of cardiac myogenesis (97), in contrast, was upregulated by all three peptides.] Differential regulation of both striated α-actins by acidic and basic FGF stands in contrast to their shared effects on five other cardiac genes and establishes a model for FGF control of tissue-specific gene expression with specificity and discrimination unlike that reported in other systems.

Counter-regulation of Skeletal α-Actin Transcription in Cardiac Muscle by Two Fibroblast Growth Factors

Experiments utilizing transfected actin promoter-reporter genes indicate that αCaA transcription in cardiac muscle is unchanged by basic FGF, yet is suppressed by acidic FGF. By contrast, transcription of the αSkA promoter is counter-regulated by these two peptides—stimulated by basic FGF, but inhibited by acidic FGF. For both positive and negative modulation, growth factors thus control sarcomeric α-actin gene expression, at least in part, through transcriptional mechanisms. Recombinant acidic and basic FGF produced equivalent, dichotomous effects on αSkA transcription, thus verifying that the antithetical actions are intrinsic, not the consequence of contaminants such as other heparin-binding growth factors (83). The proximal 202 nucleotides of the chick αSkA promoter were sufficient for counter-regulation by basic and acidic FGF, with no additional contribution from elements further upstream (83), unlike the role of sequences distal to −450 for norepinephrine stimulation of the human αSkA promoter (N. Bishopric, personal communication). Positive vs negative control of a gene's transcription by two FGFs has not, to the authors' knowledge, been observed in other models, and warrants further attention to reconcile the basis for contradictory effects.

Together these studies underscore the likely importance of lineage-specific differences in growth factor control of cardiac vs skeletal muscle. Distinct effects of acidic vs basic FGF on αSkA transcription may provide insight into the sequential responses to serum seen in neonatal cardiac myocytes after differing intervals of serum withdrawal (127). As a whole, the coordinate regulation of an ensemble of genes by peptide growth factors can be described in the context of a fetal cardiac phenotype and gives credence to hypothesized autocrine and paracrine mechanisms during pressure-overload hypertrophy.

Cardiac Myocyte Growth

In the cultures of ventricular myocytes described above, acidic FGF, but not basic FGF, increased cell number at 24 hr; basic FGF increased cell protein; and TGFβ1 did not affect cell growth (84). No growth was seen in parallel cultures of cardiac fibroblasts. Thus, βMHC and ANF were highly expressed in proliferative cultures. Moreover, since TGFβ1 induced the same set of fetal cardiac genes as basic FGF, plasticity of gene expression can be dissociated from growth. Other laboratories confirm the ability of basic FGF to induce cardiac myocyte hypertrophy (114) or proliferation (47), which may be inhibited by TGFβ1 (47). Conversely, IGF-1 cooperates with basic FGF to induce proliferation of human fetal cardiac myoblasts (52). Thus results to date in rodent models are likely to have applicability to humans. In mice expressing a v-*fps* transgene, cardiac hypertrophy and failure are attributed to a paracrine factor from infiltrating monocytes, since v-*fps* was not transcribed in the ventricular myocytes themselves (137). Finally, the hypothesis that paracrine mechanisms might act on cardiac myocytes during hypertrophy receives particular support from the identification of a cardiac fibroblast-derived growth factor for cardiac muscle cells, distinct from basic and acidic FGF (114).

GROWTH FACTOR SIGNAL TRANSDUCTION BY CELLULAR ONCOGENES

Proto-oncogene Proteins Confer Trophic Signals to the Nucleus

Peptide growth factors control cell growth and differentiation through a cascade of proteins encoded by cellular (proto-) oncogenes, reviewed in detail elsewhere (131). First identified as counterparts in the normal vertebrate genome of the transforming genes of certain retroviruses, proto-oncogene products encompass growth factors, their receptors, coupling proteins, and nuclear transcription factors (131). Numerous cellular oncogenes are expressed in the heart, though the relative contribution of cardiac myocytes, smooth muscle, endothelium, and mesenchyme is uncertain (76, 113). Functional consequences of each oncogene generally are inferred from simpler, potentially contrasting systems.

A receptor for FGFs is encoded by *flg* [*a fms*-like gene; (60, 96)], and the existence of multiple homologous receptors is likely (90). Like platelet-derived growth factor receptor isoforms, which distinguish among related ligands (32), the FGF receptor may bind acidic and basic FGF with differing affinity (96). Whether this can account for discordant effects of acidic vs basic FGF in cardiac muscle awaits exploration. In addition, at least one putative receptor for FGFs lacks a tyrosine kinase domain (9). Developmental regulation of growth factor receptor isoforms in the heart could, in principle, contribute to the transition from hyperplastic to hypertrophic growth (cf 23, 81). Few observations have as yet been made of growth factor expression in diseased human myocardium. Recently down-regulation of the epidermal growth factor receptor in coronary microvasculature was observed in human cardiomyopathy, which suggests that decreased growth factor receptor abundance might restrict angiogenesis during ventricular enlargement (W. Schaper, personal communication).

Nuclear Oncogene Proteins in the Myocardium

Nuclear oncogene proteins—including c-*fos,* c-*myc,* and c-*jun*—are rapidly induced by growth factors or other trophic stimuli, are thought to couple transmembrane signaling to growth and transcriptional control, and are the focus of explicit attention in the context of cardiac growth and hypertrophy (41, 53, 55, 75, 76, 113, 119, 127). For example, down-regulation of c-*myc* in the embryonic heart parallels the loss of proliferative capacity (103); N- and B-*myc* also are down-regulated during cardiac development (102). Conversely, a hemodynamic load in vivo re-induces c-*myc* in adult cardiac muscle (75). In cultured ventricular myocytes, however, serum factors induce c-*myc* both in cells that undergo mitosis and in older cells incapable of cell division (127). Likewise, c-*myc* elicited by norepinephrine is associated with hypertrophy, not hyperplasia (119). Thus irreversible down-regulation of c-*myc* cannot account for cardiac myocytes' loss of proliferative potential. Conversely, up-regulation of c-*myc* precedes divergent responses and does not explain specific effects. In agreement, serum up-regulates the endogenous c-*myc* gene in post-mitotic skeletal muscle, without altering muscle-specific genes (20), and autonomous expression of c-*myc* delays, but does not prevent, differentiation of BC_3H1 muscle cells (104). Targeting a deregulated c-*myc* gene to the heart in transgenic mice increases cardiac size through myocyte hyperplasia, but neither produces ongoing proliferation after birth, nor immortalizes cardiac myocytes in culture (41a; J. Swain, personal communication). The c-*myc* transgene may potentiate other growth signals and augment thyroid hormone, but not isoproterenol (92). Although c-*myc* possesses a leucine repeat for dimer formation, and oligomers assemble in vitro, it is uncertain whether c-*myc* functions as a leucine zipper transcription factor like c-*fos* and c-*jun* (77).

Whereas little or no steady-state c-*fos* expression is seen in the developing myocardium, up-regulation of c-*fos* in the adult rat heart is triggered by load or diverse agonists and may accompany aging (2, 41, 55). Passive stretch itself induces c-*fos* in cultured cardiac myocytes (53), as well as c-*jun* (I. Komuro, S. Izumo, personal communication). *Jun*B and *jun*D are both expressed at relatively high basal levels in murine heart, although their response to trophic signals has not been reported (102). In most cell lineages, *fos* and *jun* are coinduced by growth factors and phorbol esters, yet some stimuli induce nuclear oncogenes more selectively: membrane depolarization activates c-*fos* and *jun*B but not c-*jun* in PC12 cells (3), and TGFβ1 preferentially induces *jun*B in skeletal muscle (62). In cardiac muscle, α_1- but not β-, adrenergic stimulation induces EGR-1, a zinc finger early response gene (39). Preliminary evidence suggests that acidic and basic FGF induce c-*fos*, c-*jun*, and *jun*B in cardiac muscle cells (T. Parker, M. Schneider, unpublished data). Distinct patterns of transcription factor induction could explain the contrasting effects of α_1- and β-adrenergic agonists, or acidic and basic FGF, on neonatal cardiac myocytes.

Nuclear oncogene induction by peptide growth factors, followed by growth and altered gene expression, does not by itself establish a causal relationship. In simpler systems, oncogene expression vectors, anti-sense RNA, and dominant negative mutations of the DNA-binding domain have proven that heterodimers of *fos* and *jun* *trans*-activate certain serum responsive genes, and that *jun*B can inhibit activation by c-*jun* (14). Furthermore, it appears likely that the function of these *trans*-acting nuclear phosphoproteins is regulated by their state of phosphorylation (36). Corresponding tests for the involvement of *fos* and *jun* in the control of myocardial gene expression await the application of these technologies to cardiac muscle.

SUMMARY AND IMPLICATIONS

Polypeptide growth factors are synthesized within the myocardium, in part by cardiac myocytes, are regulated during cardiac development, and are induced during myocardial disease. TGFβ1 and basic FGF alter the expression of at least six cardiac genes, each corresponding to adaptation during hemodynamic stress (84). While comprising an incomplete sample of the cardiac phenotype, these genes are representative of the proteins that are co-regulated in experimental cardiac hypertrophy or end-stage heart failure in humans. One interpretation of the available data is that certain intracellular transduction pathways, including nuclear proto-oncogenes, may be utilized in common by load and trophic peptides. Alternatively, specific growth factors formed in the myocardium could themselves play an autocrine or paracrine role in long-term responses to injury or mechanical load. Such a link is suggested by the ability of passive stretch to induce the secreted cytokine, JE, in cardiac myocytes (I. Komuro, S. Izumo, personal communication). Furthermore, differential responses to specific growth factors, illustrated by the discordant regulation of α-actin genes and cellular growth by basic vs acidic FGF, could account for observed anomalies in the response to pressure overload. For example, βMHC and αSkA transcripts differ in topographic distribution after aortic banding; induction of βMHC and ANF is bimodal (rising again after 8 days), whereas αSkA is expressed more transiently (40, 100); and ANF induction is relatively consistent in end-stage heart failure, while αSkA varies (40, 100, 107). Conceivably, peptide growth factors in the myocardium could sustain and modulate signals imposed initially by ischemia or mechanical load.

A series of intriguing questions remains unanswered, but amenable to experimental investigation. Is the expression or release of myocardial growth factors altered in the myocardium of animals after aortic constriction and, as a consequence of myocardial disease, in humans? Does the temporal and spatial distribution of growth factors correlate with changes in cardiac-specific genes? Can exogenous growth factors affect cardiac myocytes in vivo, as shown thus far only in cell culture, and modify the biological response to load, ischemia, and infarction? The complex and heterogenous control of cardiac-specific genes by growth factors departs from invariant suppression, as found in skeletal muscle cells. Along with counter-regulation of αSkA by acidic vs basic FGF, these observations suggest that cardiac myocytes offer particular advantages for analysis of the molecular events required for growth factor signal transduction. Do multiple receptor isoforms exist for FGFs, does their function differ, and are they regulated independently during cardiac development and disease? Are distinguishable intracellular pathways required for growth factors to regulate cardiac growth vs transcription? As one precedent, in aortic endothelial cells, the mitogenic pathway triggered by basic FGF is dependent on protein kinase C, but control of plasminogen-activator genes by basic FGF is not (88). It has not yet been tested directly whether stimulation of immediate-early response genes, including *fos* and *jun,* is either necessary or sufficient for growth factor effects in cardiac cells, and whether differential induction of these transcription factors can account for the divergent consequences of acidic vs basic FGF. In addition to the use of electroporation, calcium-phosphate transfection, retroviral vectors, and transgenic mice, the application to cardiac muscle of other gene transfer technologies, including anti-sense oligonucleotides (33) and high-velocity microprojectiles (51), now may be feasible.

Ultimately, it becomes critical to identify the specific *cis*-acting DNA sequences required for growth factor effects, to learn whether these motifs might be shared among cardiac-specific genes, and to understand the responsible *trans*-acting factors expressed in myocardial cells (e.g. 79). Transfection of αSkA deletion mutants indicates that the *cis*-acting sequences for tissue-specific expression in skeletal muscle—including, in particular, the downstream CCAAT box associated repeat (CBAR)—are also required in cardiac myocytes (T. Parker, K.-L. Chow, R. Schwartz, M. Schneider, unpublished), and provides a basis for more detailed analysis of putative growth factor response elements. The hypothesis that the downstream CBAR itself could function as a locus for growth factor control has been predicted by its similarity to the serum-response element of c-*fos* (5, 129), by identification of one actin promoter-binding protein as the c-*fos* promoter serum response factor (5), and by point mutations that abolish both muscle-specific expression and serum induction of αSkA in fibroblasts (129). A final challenge will be to learn whether peptide growth factors modulate an ensemble of cardiac genes through hierarchical mechanisms equivalent to MyoD1 and myogenin. The fact that a single peptide, such as recombinant acidic FGF, is sufficient to co-regulate at least seven cardiac genes heightens the interest in this issue. The possible involvement of MyoD-like proteins in cardiac myogenesis or plasticity of gene expression might be clarified through cDNA amplification, using the polymerase chain reaction (72).

ACKNOWLEDGMENTS

The authors are grateful to Drs. N. Bishopric, W. Casscells, W. Claycomb, L. Field, B. Hogan, S. Izumo, S. Jakowlew, L. Kedes, I. Komuro, A. Marks, E. Olson, A. Roberts, K. Schwartz, P. Simpson, M. Sporn, J. Swain, L. T. Williams, R. S. Williams, and Y. Yazaki for discussions of unpublished work; S. Terry for preparation of this manuscript; and R. Roberts for encouragement and support.

Supported by grants to M. D. S. from the American Heart Association, Texas Affiliate (85G-223, 87R-179), the National Science Foundation (DCB87-11313), and the National Institutes of Health (R01-HL39141). T. G. P. is a Fellow of the Medical Research Council of Canada and a Fellow of the American Heart Association-Bugher Foundation Center for Molecular Biology of the Cardiovascular System. M. D. S. is an Established Investigator of the American Heart Association.

Literature Cited

1. Alpert, N. R., Gordon, M. S. 1962. Myofibrillar adenosine triphosphastase activity in congestive heart failure. *Am. J. Physiol.* 202:940–46
2. Barka, T., van der Noen, H., Shaw, P. A. 1987. Proto-oncogene *fos* (c-*fos*) expression in the heart. *Oncogene* 1:439–43
3. Bartel, D. P., Sheng, M., Lau, L. F., Greenberg, M. E. 1989. Growth factors and membrane depolarization activate distinct programs of early response gene expression: dissociation of *fos* and *jun* induction. *Genes Dev.* 3:304–13
4. Bishopric, N., Simpson, P. C., Ordahl, C. P. 1987. Induction of the skeletal α-actin gene in α_1-adrenoreceptor-mediated hypertrophy of rat cardiac myocytes. *J. Clin. Invest.* 80:1194–99

4a. Bouvagnet, P., Mairhofer, H., Leger, J. O. C., Puech, P., Leger, J. J. 1989. Distribution pattern of α and β myosin in normal and diseased human ventricular myocardium. *Basic Res. Cardiol.* 84:91–102

5. Boxer, L. M., Prywes, R., Roeder, R. G., Kedes, L. 1989. The sarcomeric actin CArG-binding factor is indistinguishable from the c-*fos* serum response factor. *Mol. Cell. Biol.* 9:515–22
6. Braun, T., Buschhausen-Denker, G., Bober, E., Tannich, E., Arnold, H. H. 1989. A novel human muscle factor related to but distinct from MyoD1 induces myogenic conversion in 10T1/2 fibroblasts. *Cell* 51:987–1000
7. Breithart, R. E., Nadal-Ginard, B. 1987. Developmentally induced, muscle-specific *trans* factors control the differential splicing of alternative and constitutive troponin T exons. *Cell* 49: 793–803
8. Bugaisky, L. B., Zak, R. 1989. Differentiation of adult rat cardiac myocytes in cell culture. *Circ. Res.* 64:493–500
9. Burrus, L. W., Lueddecke, B. A., Zuber, M. E., Lieder, K. W., Olwin, B. B. 1990. Immunoaffinity purification and cDNA cloning of a putative receptor for acidic and basic fibroblast growth factors. *J. Cell. Biochem. Suppl.* 14E:71 (Abstr.)
10. Caffrey, J. M., Brown, A. M., Schneider, M. D. 1990. Ca^{2+} and Na^+ currents in developing skeletal myoblasts are expressed in a sequential program: Reversible suppression by transforming growth factor beta-1: An inhibitor of the myogenic pathway. *J. Neurosci.* 9:3443–53
11. Casscells, W., Speir, E., Sasse, J., Klagsburn, M., Allen, P., et al. 1990. Isolation, characterization, and localization of heparin-binding growth factors in the heart. *J. Clin. Invest.* 85:434–45
12. Chiba, M., Bazoberry, F., Speir, E. H., Sasse, J., Nesbitt, C. P., et al. 1989. Role of basic fibroblast growth factor in angiogenesis, healing and hypertrophy after rat myocardial infarction. *Circulation* 80:II-452 (Abstr.)
13. Chiu, I.-M., Wang, W.-P., Lehtoma, K. 1990. Alternative splicing generates at least two forms of mRNA coding for human heparin-binding growth factor 1. *J. Cell. Biochem. Suppl.* 14E:71 (Abstr.)
14. Chiu, R., Angel, P., Karin, M. 1989. Jun-β differs in its biological properties from, and is a negative regulator of, c-Jun. *Cell* 59:979–86
15. Clegg, C. H., Linkhart, T. A., Olwin, B. B., Hauschka, S. D. 1987. Growth factor control of skeletal muscle differentiation: commitment to terminal differentiation occurs in G1 phase and is repressed by fibroblast growth factor. *J. Cell Biol.* 105:949–56
16. Coffey, R. H., Bascom, C. C., Sipes, N. J., Graves-Deal, R., Weissman, B. E., et al. 1988. Selective inhibition of growth-related gene expression in murine keratinocytes by transforming growth factor β. *Mol. Cell. Biol.* 8:3088–93
17. Cooke, J. 1989. *Xenopus* mesoderm induction: Evidence for early size control and partial autonomy for pattern development by onset of gastrulation. *Development* 106:519–29
18. Davis, R. L., Cheng, P.-F., Lassar, A. B., Weintraub, H. 1990. The MyoD DNA binding domain contains a recognition code for muscle-specific gene activation. *Cell* 60:733–46
19. Edmondson, D. G., Olson, E. N. 1989. A gene with homology to the *myc* similarity region of MyoD1 is expressed during myogenesis and is sufficient to activate the muscle differentiation program. *Genes Dev.* 3:628–40
20. Endo, T., Nadal-Ginard, B. 1986. Transcriptional and post-transcriptional control of c-*myc* during myogenesis: Its mRNA remains inducible in differentiated cells and does not suppress the differentiated phenotype. *Mol. Cell. Biol.* 6:1412–21
21. Endo, T., Nadal-Ginard, B. 1989. SV40 large T antigen induces reentry of terminally differentiated myotubes into the

cell cycle. In *Cellular and Molecular Biology of Muscle Development,* ed. L. Kedes, F. Stockdale, pp. 95–104. New York: Liss

22. Engelmann, G. L., Boehm, K. D., Haskell, J. F., Khairallah, P. A., Ilan, J. 1989. Insulin-like growth factors and neonatal cardiomyocyte development: Ventricular gene expression and membrane receptor variations in normotensive and hypertensive rats. *Mol. Cell. Endocrinol.* 63:1–14
23. Ewton, D. Z., Spizz, G., Olson, E. N., Florini, J. R. 1988. Decrease in transforming growth factor-beta binding and action during differentiation in muscle cells. *J. Biol. Chem.* 263:4029–32
24. Frohlich, E. D. 1989. Left ventricular hypertrophy, cardiac diseases and hypertension: Recent experiences. *J. Am. Coll. Cardiol.* 14:1587–94
25. Garner, I., Sassoon, D., Vandekerchkove, J., Alonso, S., Buckingham, M. E. 1989. A developmental study of the abnormal expression of α-cardiac and α-skeletal actins in the striated muscle of a mutant mouse. *Dev. Biol.* 134:236–45
26. Gatherer, D., Baird, D., Akhurst, R. J. 1990. Expression of the transforming growth factor type beta gene family in human embryogenesis. *J. Cell. Biochem. Suppl.* 14E:57 (Abstr.)
27. Gorza, L., Mercadier, J.-J., Schwartz, K., Thornell, L. E., Sartore, S., et al. 1984. Myosin types in the human heart: An immunofluorescence study of normal and hypertrophied atrial and ventricular myocardium. *Circ. Res.* 54:694–702
28. Gospodarowicz, D., Ferrara, N., Schweigerer, L., Neufeld, G. 1987. Structural characterization and biological functions of fibroblast growth factor. *Endocr. Rev.* 8:95–114
29. Gustafson, T. A., Markham, B. E., Bahl, J. J., Morkin, E. 1987. Thyroid hormone regulates expression of a transfected alpha-myosin heavy-chain fusion gene in fetal heart cells. *Proc. Natl. Acad. Sci. USA* 84:3122–26
30. Hammond, G. L., Nadal-Ginard, B., Talner, N. S., Markert, C. L. 1976. Myocardial LDH isozyme distribution in the ischemic and hypoxic heart. *Circulation* 53:637–43
31. Hammond, G. L., Wieben, E., Markert, C. L. 1979. Molecular signals for initiating protein synthesis in organ hypertrophy. *Proc. Natl. Acad. Sci. USA* 76:2455–59
32. Hart, C. E., Forstrom, J. W., Kelly, J. D., Seifert, R. A., Smith, R. A., et al. 1988. Two classes of PDGF receptor recognize different isoforms of PDGF. *Science* 240:1529–31
33. Heikkila, R., Schwab, G., Wickstrom, E., Lake, S. L., Pluznik, D., et al. 1987. A c-*myc* antisense oligodeoxynucleotide inhibits entry into S-phase but not progress from Go to G1. *Nature* 328:445–49
34. Henkel, R. D., VandeBerg, J. L., Shade, R. E., Lewger, J. J., Walsh, R. A. 1989. Cardiac beta myosin heavy chain diversity in normal and chronically hypertensive baboons. *J. Clin. Invest.* 83:1487–93
35. Hirzel, H. O., Tuchschmid, C. R., Schneider, J., Krayenbuehl, H. P., Schub, M. 1985. Relationship between myosin isoenzyme composition, hemodynamics, and myocardial structure in various forms of human cardiac hypertrophy. *Circ. Res.* 57:729–40
36. Hunter, T., Boyle, B., Lindberg, R., Jaehner, D., Middlemas, D., et al. 1990. Signal-transducing protein kinases and their targets. *J. Cell. Biochem. Suppl.* 14E:139 (Abstr.)
37. Ieki, K., Yazaki, Y., Yamooki, K., Tsuchimochi, H., Yoskizumi, M., et al. 1989. Effect of long-term treatment with β-blocker on cardiac hypertrophy in SHR. *J. Mol. Cell. Cardiol. Suppl. V* 21:113–19
38. Ingwall, J. S., Kramer, M. F., Fifer, M. A., Grossman, W., Allen, P. 1985. The creatine kinase system in normal and diseased human myocardium. *N. Engl. J. Med.* 313:1050–54
39. Iwaki, K., Chien, K. R. 1989. Differential induction of the c-*fos,* c-*jun* and EGR-1 transcriptional factors during adrenergic stimulation of neonatal rat myocardial cells. *Circulation* 80:II-92 (Abstr.)
40. Izumo, S., Lompre, A.-M., Matsouka, R., Koren, G., Schwartz, K., et al. 1987. Myosin heavy chain messenger RNA and protein isoform transitions during cardiac hypertrophy. *J. Clin. Invest.* 79:970–77
41. Izumo, S., Nadal-Ginard, B., Mahdavi, V. 1988. Proto-oncogene induction and reprogramming of cardiac gene expression produced by pressure overload. *Proc. Natl. Acad. Sci. USA* 85:339–43

41a. Jackson, T., Allard, M. F., Sreenan, C. M., Doss, L. K., Bishop, S. P., Swain, J. L. 1990. The c-*myc* proto-oncogene regulates cardiac development in transgenic mice. *Mol. Cell. Biol.* 10:3709–16

42. Jakowlew, S. B., Dillard, P. J., Winokur, T. S., Marascalco, B. A., Flanders, K. C., et al. 1990. Expression of

TGF-βs in chondrocytes and myocytes of chicken embryos. *J. Cell. Biochem. Suppl.* 14E:59 (Abstr.)
43. Jandreski, M. A., Sole, M. J., Liew, C. C. 1987. Expression of alpha and beta myosin heavy chain genes in the cardiomyopathic Syrian hamster. *J. Mol. Cell. Cardiol. Suppl. IV* 19:S.33 (Abstr.)
44. Jarcho, J. A., McKenna, W., Pare, J. A. P., Solomon, S. D., Holcombe, R. F., et al. 1989. Mapping a gene for familial hypertrophic cardiomyopathy to chromosome 14q1. *N. Engl. J. Med.* 321:1372–78
45. Kaida, T., Komuro, I., Yazaki, Y. 1988. Increased protein synthesis and myosin isoform change in cultured cardiocytes by loading. *Circulation* 78:II-242 (Abstr.)
46. Kardami, E., Fandrich, R. R. 1989. Basic fibroblast growth factor in atria and ventricles of the vertebrate heart. *J. Cell Biol.* 109:1865–75
47. Kardami, E., Fandrich, R. R. 1989. Heparin-binding mitogen(s) in the heart; in search of origin and function. See Ref. 21, pp. 315–25
48. Katoh, Y., Komuro, I., Kurabayashi, M., Yamaguchi, H., Yazaki, Y. 1989. Re-expression of fetal type mRNAs in the ventricle of cardiomyopathic Syrian hamster. *Circulation* 80:II-458 (Abstr.)
49. Katoh, Y., Komuro, I., Shibasaki, Y., Yamaguchi, H., Yazaki, Y. 1989. Angiotensin II induces hypertrophy and oncogene expression in cultured rat heart myocytes. *Circulation* 80:II-450 (Abstr.)
50. Katz, A. M. 1990. Cardiomyopathy of overload: A major determinant of prognosis in congestive heart failure. *N. Engl. J. Med.* 322:100–10
51. Klein, T. M., Wolf, E. D., Wu, R., Sanford, J. C. 1987. High-velocity microprojectiles for delivering nucleic acids into living cells. *Nature* 327:70–73
52. Kohtz, D. S., Dische, N. R., Inagami, T., Goldman, B. 1989. Growth and partial differentiation of presumptive human cardiac myoblasts in culture. *J. Cell Biol.* 108:1067–78
53. Komuro, I., Kaida, T., Shibazaki, Y., Kurabayashi, M., Katoh, Y., et al. 1990. Stretching cardiac myocytes stimulates proto-oncogene expression. *J. Biol. Chem.* 265:3595–98
54. Komuro, I., Kurabayashi, M., Shibazaki, Y., Takaku, F., Yazaki, Y. 1989. Molecular cloning and characterization of a $Ca^{2+} + Mg^{2+}$-dependent adenosine triphosphatase from rat cardiac sarcoplasmic reticulum. *J. Clin. Invest.* 83:1102–8
55. Komuro, M., Kurabayashi, M., Takaku, F., Yazaki, Y. 1988. Expression of cellular oncogenes in the myocardium during the developmental stage and pressure-overload hypertrophy of the rat heart. *Circ. Res.* 62:1075–79
56. Kondaiah, P., Sands, M. J., Smith, J. M., Fields, A., Roberts, A. B., et al. 1990. Identification of a novel transforming growth factor-β (TGF-β5) mRNA in *Xenopus laevis*. *J. Biol. Chem.* 265:1089–93
57. Krug, E. L., Mjaatvedt, C. H., Markwald, R. R. 1987. Extracellular matrix from embryonic myocardium elicits an early morphogenetic event in cardiac endothelial differentiation. *Dev. Biol.* 120:348–55
58. Kurabayashi, M., Komuro, I., Tsuchimochi, H., Takaku, F., Yazaki, Y. 1988. Molecular cloning and characterization of human atrial and ventricular myosin alkali light chain cDNA clones. *J. Biol. Chem.* 263:13930–36
59. Lathrop, B., Olson, E. N., Glaser, L. 1985. Control by fibroblast growth factor of differentiation in the BC3H1 muscle cell line. *J. Cell. Biol.* 100:1540–47
60. Lee, P. L., Johnson, D. E., Cousens, L. S., Fried, V. A., Williams, L. T. 1989. Purification and complementary DNA cloning of a receptor for basic fibroblast growth factor. *Science* 245:57–60
61. Li, C., Prakash, O., Re, R. N. 1989. Altered regulation of angiotensin gene expression in the left ventricles of the hypertensive rats. *Circulation* 80:II-450 (Abstr.)
62. Li, L., Hu, J.-S., Olson, E. N. 1990. Different members of the *jun* proto-oncogene family exhibit distinct patterns of expression in response to type β transforming growth factor. *J. Biol. Chem.* 265:1556–62
63. Lin, H. L., Katele, K. V., Grimm, A. F. 1977. Functional morphology of the pressure- and the volume-hypertrophied rat heart. *Circ. Res.* 41:830–36
64. Machida, C. M., Rodland, K. D., Matrisian, L., Magun, B. E., Ciment, G. 1989. NGF induction of the gene encoding the protease transin accompanies neuronal differentiation in PC12 cells. *Neuron* 2:1587–96
65. Maisonpierre, P. C., Belluscio, L., Squinto, S., Ip, N. Y., Furth, M. E., et al. 1990. Neurotrophin-3: A neurotrophic factor related to NGF and BDNF. *Science* 247:1446–51
66. Marino, T. A., Brode, E., Lauva, I. K.,

Kent, R. L., Cooper, G. I. 1986. Reversibility of the structural effects of pressure overload hypertrophy of cat right ventricular myocardium. *Anat. Rec.* 214:141–47
67. Massagué, J., Cheifetz, T., Endo, S., Nadal-Ginard, B. 1986. Type β transforming growth factor is an inhibitor of myogenic differentiation. *Proc. Natl. Acad. Sci. USA* 83:8206–10
68. McNeil, P. L., Muthukrishnan, Warder, E. D., Amore, P. A. 1989. Growth factors are released by mechanically wounded endothelial cells. *J. Cell Biol.* 109:811–22
69. Melton, D., Sokol, S., Thomsen, G., Whitman, M. 1990. Embryonic induction and axial polarity in *Xenopus* development. *J. Cell. Biochem. Suppl.* 14E:35 (Abstr.)
70. Mercadier, J. J., de la Bastie, D., Menasche, P. 1987. Alpha-myosin heavy chain isoform and atrial size in patients with various types of mitral valve dysfunction: A quantitative study. *J. Am. Coll. Cardiol.* 9:1024–30
71. Mercadier, J.-J., Lompre, A.-M., Duc, P., Boheler, K. R., Fraysse, J.-B., et al. 1990. Altered sarcoplasmic reticulum Ca^{2+}-ATPase gene expression in the human ventricle during end-state heart failure. *J. Clin. Invest.* 85:305–9
72. Montarras, D., Pinset, C., Chelly, J., Kahn, A., Gros, F. 1989. Expression of MyoD1 coincides with terminal differentiation in determined but inducible muscle cells. *EMBO J.* 8:2203–7
73. Morrow, N. G., Kraus, W. E., Moore, J. E., Williams, R. S., Swain, J. L. 1990. Increased expression of fibroblast growth factors in a rabbit skeletal muscle model of exercise conditioning. *J. Cell. Invest.* 85:1816–20
74. Muller, G., Behrens, J., Nussbaumer, U., Bohlen, P., Birchmeier, W. 1987. Inhibitory action of transforming growth factor beta on endothelial cells. *Proc. Natl. Acad. Sci. USA* 84:5600–4
75. Mulvagh, S. L., Michael, L. H., Perryman, M. B., Roberts, R., Schneider, M. D. 1987. A hemodynamic load in vivo induces cardiac expression of the cellular oncogene, c-*myc*. *Biochem. Biophys. Res. Commun.* 147:627–36
76. Mulvagh, S. L., Roberts, R., Schneider, M. D. 1988. Cellular oncogenes in cardiovascular disease. *J. Mol. Cell. Cardiol.* 20:657–62
77. Murre, C., McCaw, P. S., Vaessin, H., Caudy, M., Jan, L. Y., et al. 1989. Interactions between heterologous helix-loop-helix proteins generate complexes that bind specifically to a common DNA sequence. *Cell* 58:537–44
78. Nadal-Ginard, B., Mahdavi, V. 1989. Molecular basis of cardiac performance: Plasticity of the myocardium generated through protein isoform switches. *J. Clin. Invest.* 84:1693–1700
79. Nemer, M., Ardati, A., Greenbaum, M., Drouin, J. 1990. A cardiac specific CTF like transcription factor binds to the ANF promoter and is regulated during cardiac differentiation. *J. Cell. Biochem. Suppl.* 14E:183 (Abstr.)
80. Olson, E. N., Sternberg, E., Hu, J. S., Spizz, G., Wilcox, C. 1986. Regulation of myogenic differentiation by type beta transforming growth factor. *J. Cell Biol.* 103:1799–1805
81. Olwin, B. B., Hauschka, S. D. 1988. Cell surface fibroblast growth factor and epidermal growth factor receptors are permanently lost during skeletal muscle terminal differentiation in culture. *J. Cell Biol.* 107:761–69
82. Otten, U., Ehrhard, P., Peck, R. 1989. Nerve growth factor induces growth and differentiation of human B lymphocytes. *Proc. Natl. Acad. Sci. USA* 86:10059–63
83. Parker, T. G., Chow, K.-L., Schwartz, R. J., Schneider, M. D. 1990. Differential regulation of skeletal α-actin transcription in cardiac muscle by two fibroblast growth factors. *Proc. Natl. Acad. Sci. USA* 87:7066–70
84. Parker, T. G., Packer, S. E., Schneider, M. D. 1990. Peptide growth factors can provoke "fetal" contractile protein gene expression in rat cardiac myocytes. *J. Clin. Invest.* 85:507–14
85. Parlow, M. H., Bolender, D. L., Lough, J. 1990. Localization of bFGF as particulate inclusions in developing heart cells of the early embryo. *J. Cell. Biochem. Suppl.* 14E:81 (Abstr.)
86. Pearson-White, S. H. 1990. *ski* Protooncogene expression during muscle development. *J. Cell. Biochem. Suppl.* 14E:111 (Abstr.)
87. Potts, J. D., Runyon, R. B. 1989. Epithelial-mesenchymal cell transformation in the heart can be mediated, in part, by transforming growth factor β. *Dev. Biol.* 134:392–401
88. Presta, M., Maier, J. A. M., Ragnotti, G. 1989. The mitogenic signaling pathway but not the plasminogen activator-inducing pathway of basic fibroblast growth factor is mediated through protein kinase C in fetal bovine aortic endothelial cells. *J. Cell Biol.* 109:1877–84

89. Quinkler, W., Maasberg, M., Bernotat-Danielowski, S., Luthe, N., Sharma, H. S., et al. 1989. Isolation of heparin-binding growth factors from bovine, porcine and canine hearts. *Eur. J. Biochem.* 181:67–73
90. Reid, H. H., Wilks, A. F., Bernard, O. 1990. Two forms of the basic fibroblast growth factor receptor-like mRNA are expressed in the developing mouse brain. *Proc. Natl. Acad. Sci. USA* 87:1596–1600
91. Rhodes, S. J., Konieczny, S. F. 1989. Identification of MRF4: A new member of the muscle regulatory factor gene family. *Genes Dev.* 3:2050–61
92. Robbins, R. J., Swain, J. L. 1989. Modulation of cardiac hypertrophy by the c-*myc* protooncogene in transgenic mice. *Circulation* 80:II-92 (Abstr.)
93. Roberts, A. R., Sporn, M. B., eds. 1990. The transforming growth factor-betas. In *Peptide Growth Factors and their Receptors. Handb. Exp. Pharmacol.,* 95: (Part 1)419–72 Heidelberg: Springer-Verlag
94. Rubin, S. A., Correa, M., Rabines, A., Fishbein, M. C. 1989. Beta blockade alters myosin heavy chain gene expression after rat infarction. *Circulation* 80:II-458 (Abstr.)
95. Rumyantsev, P. P. 1988. Interrelations of the proliferation and differentiation processes during cardiac myogenesis and regeneration. *Int. Rev. Cytol.* 51: 187–273
96. Ruta, M., Burgess, W., Givol, D., Epstein, J., Neiger, N., et al. 1989. Receptor for acidic fibroblast growth factor is related to the tyrosine kinase encoded by the *fms*-like gene. *Proc. Natl. Acad. Sci. USA* 86:8722–26
97. Ruzicka, D. L., Schwartz, R. J. 1988. Sequential activation of α-actin genes during avian cardiogenesis: vascular smooth muscle α-actin gene transcripts mark the onset of cardiomyocyte differentiation. *J. Cell Biol.* 107:2575–86
98. Saito, Y., Nakao, K., Arai, H., Nishimura, K., Okumura, K., et al. 1989. Augmented expression of atrial natriuretic polypeptide gene in ventricle of human failing heart. *J. Clin. Invest.* 83:298–305
99. Sasaki, H., Hoshi, H., Hong, Y.-M., Suzuki, T., Kato, T., et al. 1989. Purification of acidic fibroblast growth factor from bovine heart and its localization in the cardiac myocytes. *J. Biol. Chem.* 264:17606–12
100. Schiaffino, S., Samuel, J. L., Sassoon, D., Lompre, A. M., Garner, I., et al. 1989. Nonsynchronous accumulation of α-skeletal actin and β-myosin heavy chain mRNAs during early stages of pressure-overload-induced cardiac hypertrophy demonstrated by in situ hybridization. *Circ. Res.* 64:937–48
101. Schneider, M. D., Olson, E. N. 1988. Control of myogenic differentiation by cellular oncogenes. *Mol. Neurobiol.* 2:1–37
102. Schneider, M. D., Parker, T. G. 1990. Cardiac myocytes as targets for peptide growth factors. *Circulation* 81:1443–56
103. Schneider, M. D., Payne, P. A., Ueno, H., Perryman, M. B., Roberts, R. 1986. Dissociated expression of c-*myc* and a *fos*-related competence gene during cardiac myogenesis. *Mol. Cell. Biol.* 6: 4140–43
104. Schneider, M. D., Perryman, M. B., Payne, P. A., Spizz, G., Roberts, R., et al. 1987. Autonomous *myc* expression in transfected muscle cells does not prevent myogenic differentiation. *Mol. Cell. Biol.* 7:1973–77
105. Schwartz, K., de la Bastie, D., Bouveret, P., Oliviero, P., Alonso, S., et al. 1986. α-Skeletal muscle actin mRNAs accumulate in hypertrophied adult rat hearts. *Circ. Res.* 59:551–55
106. Schwartz, K., Lecarpentier, Y., Martin, J. L., Lompre, A. M., Mercadier, J. J., et al. 1981. Myosin isoenzyme distribution correlates with speed of myocardial contraction. *J. Mol. Cell. Cardiol.* 13: 1071–75
107. Schwartz, K., Schiaffino, S., Allen, P. D., Wisnewsky, C., Bouveret, P., et al. 1987. Expression of cardiac and skeletal actin genes in normal and failing human left ventricles. *J. Mol. Cell. Cardiol.* 19:S.34 (Abstr.)
108. Sen, A., Dunnmon, P., Henderson, S. A., Gerard, R. D., Chien, K. R. 1988. Terminally differentiated neonatal rat myocardial cells proliferate and maintain specific differentiated functions following expression of SV40 large T antigen. *J. Biol. Chem.* 263:19132–36
109. Sharma, H. S., Wunsch, M., Kandolf, R., Schaper, W. 1989. Angiogenesis by slow coronary artery occlusion in the pig heart: Expression of different growth factors mRNAs. *J. Mol. Cell. Cardiol. Suppl. III* 21:S24 (Abstr.)
110. Shih, H. T., Wathen, M. S., Bigo-Marshall, H., Caffrey, J. M., Schneider, M. D. 1990. Dihydropyridine receptor gene expression is regulated by inhibitors of myogenic differentiation and is relatively insensitive to denervation. *J. Clin. Invest.* 85:781–89

111. Shimasaki, S., Emoto, N., Koba, A., Mercado, M., Shibata, F., et al. 1988. Complementary DNA cloning and sequencing of rat ovarian basic fibroblast growth factor and tissue distribution study of its mRNA. *Biochem. Biophys. Res. Commun.* 157:256–63
112. Simpson, P., McGrath, A., Savion, S. 1982. Myocyte hypertrophy in neonatal rat heart cultures and its regulation by serum and by catecholamines. *Circ. Res.* 511:787–80
113. Simpson, P. C. 1989. Proto-oncogenes and cardiac hypertrophy. *Annu. Rev. Physiol.* 51:189–202
114. Simpson, P. C., Henrich, C. J., Karns, L. R., Long, C. S., Ordahl, C. P., et al. 1989. Growth factors in cardiac myocyte hypertrophy and gene expression. *J. Mol. Cell. Cardiol. Suppl. III* 21:S.25 (Abstr.)
115. Slack, J. M. W. 1989. Peptide regulatory factors in embryonic development. *Lancet* 1:1312–15
116. Smith, J. C., Green, J. B. A. 1990. Specification of cell types in *Xenopus* embryos by a morphogen gradient. *J. Cell. Biochem. Suppl.* 14E:35 (Abstr.)
117. Speir, E., Zhou, Y. F., Lee, M. 1989. Fibroblast growth factors are present in adult cardiac myocytes in vivo. *Biochem. Biophys. Res. Commun.* 159: 1336–40
118. Sporn, M., Roberts, A. 1988. Peptide growth factors are multifunctional. *Nature* 332:217–19
119. Starksen, N. F., Simpson, P. C., Bishopric, N., Coughlin, S. R., Lee, W. M. F., et al. 1986. Cardiac myocyte hypertrophy is associated with c-*myc* protooncogene expression. *Proc. Natl. Acad. Sci. USA* 83:8348–50
120. Swynghdauw, B. 1986. Developmental and functional adaptation of contractile proteins in cardiac and skeletal muscles. *Physiol. Rev.* 66:710–71
121. Takahaski, T., Isoyama, S., Izumo, S. 1989. Age-related differences in cardiac gene expression in response to pressure overload. *Circulation* 80:II-457 (Abstr.)
122. TenEick, R. E., Houser, S. R., Bassett, A. L. 1989. Cardiac hypertrophy and altered cellular electrical activity of the myocardium: Possible electrophysiological basis for myocardial contractibility changes. In *Physiology and Pathophysiology of the Heart,* ed. N. Sperelakis, pp. 573–588. New York: Kluwer
123. Thompson, N. C., Bazoberry, F., Speir, E. H., Casscells, W., Ferrans, V. J., et al. 1988. Transforming growth factor beta-1 in acute myocardial infarction in rats. *Growth Factors* 1:91–99
124. Thompson, N. L., Flanders, K. C., Smith, J. M., Ellingsworth, L. R., Roberts, A. B., et al. 1989. Expression of transforming growth factor-beta 1 in specific cells and tissues of adult and neonatal mice. *J. Cell Biol.* 108:661–69
125. Thomsen, G. H., Melton, D. A. 1990. Isolation of multiple new members of the transforming growth factor beta family from *Xenopus*. *J. Cell. Biochem. Suppl.* 14E:65 (Abstr.)
126. Tsuchimochi, H., Kuro-o, M., Koyama, H., Kurabayashi, M., Sugi, M., et al. 1988. Heterogeneity of beta-type myosin isozymes in the human heart and regulational mechanisms in their expression. *J. Clin. Invest.* 81:110–18
127. Ueno, H., Perryman, M. B., Roberts, R., Schneider, M. D. 1988. Differentiation of cardiac myocytes following mitogen withdrawal exhibits three sequential stages of the ventricular growth response. *J. Cell. Biol.* 107:1911–18
128. van den Eijnden-van Raaij, A. J. M. 1990. Induction and regulation of mesodermal and neural differentiation of embryonal carcinoma cells. *J. Cell. Biochem. Suppl.* 14E:129 (Abstr.)
129. Walsh, K. 1989. Cross-binding of factors to functionally different promoter elements in c-*fos* and skeletal actin genes. *Mol. Cell. Biol.* 9:2191–2201
130. Waspe, L. E., Ordahl, C. P., Simpson, P. C. 1990. The cardiac β-myosin heavy chain isogene is induced selectively in α_1-adrenergic receptor-stimulated hypertrophy of cultured rat heart myocytes. *J. Clin. Invest.* 85:1206–14
131. Weinberg, R. A. 1989. *Oncogenes and the Molecular Origins of Cancer,* Cold Spring Harbor, NY: Cold Spring Harbor Lab. 367 pp.
132. Weiner, H. L., Swain, J. L. 1989. Acidic fibroblast growth factor mRNA is expressed by cardiac myocytes in culture and the protein is localized to the extracellular matrix. *Proc. Natl. Acad. Sci. USA* 86:2683–87
133. Winegrad, S., Wisnewsky, C., Schwartz, K. 1990. The effect of thyroid hormone on the accumulation of mRNA for alpha skeletal and cardiac actin in hearts from normal and hypothysectomized rats. *Proc. Natl. Acad. Sci. USA* In press
134. Woodland, H. R. 1989. Mesoderm foundation in *Xenopus*. *Cell* 59:767–70
135. Wright, W. E., Sassoon, D. A., Lin, V. K. 1989. Myogenin, a factor regulating

myogenesis, has a domain homologous to MyoD. *Cell* 56:607–17

136. Wunsch, H., Sharma, H. S., Bernotat-Danielowski, S., Schott, R. J., Schaper, J., et al. 1989. Expression of transforming growth factor beta-1 (TGF-β1) in collateralized swine heart. *Circulation* 80:II-453 (Abstr.)
137. Yee, S.-P., Mock, D., Maltby, V., Silver, M., Rossant, J., et al. 1989. Cardiac and neurological abnormalities in v-fps transgenic mice. *Proc. Natl. Acad. Sci. USA* 86:5873–77
138. Zahler, R., Gilmore-Hebert, M., Benz, E. J. 1989. Regional variations in Na, K-ATPase isoform gene expression in normal and hypertrophied dog heart. *Circulation* 80:II-456 (Abstr.)
139. Zak, R. 1984. *Growth of the Heart in Health and Disease,* New York: Raven. 480 pp.
140. Tanigawa, G., Jarcho, J. A., Kass, S., Solomon, S. D., Vosberg, H.-P., et al. 1990. A molecular basis for familial hypertrophic cardiomyopathy: a α/β cardiac myosin heavy chain hybrid gene. *Cell* 62:991–98

Annu. Rev. Physiol. 1991. 53:201–16

HORMONES, GROWTH FACTORS, AND MYOGENIC DIFFERENTIATION

James R. Florini, Daina Z. Ewton, and Karen A. Magri

Biology Department, Syracuse University, Syracuse, New York 13244

KEY WORDS: myogenesis, insulin-like growth factors, transforming growth factor-β, fibroblast growth factor, myogenin, MyoD1

INTRODUCTION

The importance of hormones and growth factors in regulating the growth and differentiation of muscle cells is now widely recognized. This field has been summarized recently by two of the authors of this chapter (26), and other reviews of related topics (65, 69) provide additional information. Since our last review of the field, it has been revolutionized by the discovery of the myogenesis determination genes, which bring a new focus to the study of myogenesis.

Definitions and Concepts

MYOGENESIS DETERMINATION GENES MyoD1 (11) and *myd* (60) were first characterized as genes that control initial determination to the myogenic lineage. Subsequently, Myf-5 (7) and MRF4 (63)/herculin (51) have been added to the family of genes that are found exclusively in skeletal muscle and can convert nonmuscle cells to the myogenic lineage (6). However, MyoD1 is not expressed in BC_3H1 or L6 myoblasts (6), and MRF4 is not expressed in immortalized myogenic cell lines (63), so it appears that not all of these genes are essential for expression of the myogenic program in all muscle cells. In contrast, myogenin, which has been identified as a putative controller of terminal differentiation in both rat (85) and mouse (14) muscle cell lines, is expressed in every cell undergoing myogenic differentiation (6, 14, 85). In

0066-4278/91/0315-0201$02.00

addition, myogenin also induces nonmuscle cells to express muscle-specific genes (14, 85).

HORMONES AND GROWTH FACTORS The distinction between protein hormones and growth factors is arbitrary and has little biological significance. In general, hormones are synthesized and secreted by discrete endocrine glands, while growth factors are secreted by many different kinds of cells. All of these agents are relatively small peptides that act through a receptor on the cell membrane to generate an intracellular signal that is not yet understood. Until recently research on growth factors was severely restricted by the unavailability of purified materials in sufficient quantities. All of the growth factors discussed here are now commercially available, making possible experiments that could not be done in the past. The ready availability of these agents allows study of myogenic differentiation in well-defined systems that give answers much less ambiguous than was possible in the days of fetal bovine serum and chick embryo extract.

MUSCLE CELL LINES Most of the work on control of skeletal myogenesis has been done on three immortalized cell lines. The rat L6 line (86) has probably been the most widely used; it provides a useful combination of properties, with a convenient rate of differentiation that can be modified by medium components. Its major disadvantage is its lack of responsiveness to fibroblast growth factor (FGF). The mouse C2 line (87) differentiates more rapidly than L6 cells, and it is responsive to FGF. The mouse BC_3H1 line is unusual in several ways. It was initially isolated (70) from an intracranial tumor, and it does not fuse to form postmitotic myotubes, thus allowing study of the reversibility of myogenesis. In spite of their convenience, these cell lines have limitations. The fact that none of these cells exhibits senescence shows that they are different from normal diploid cells in at least one major property. For this reason, we feel strongly that all major conclusions should be verified in primary cultures of skeletal muscle cells.

Scope of This Review

This chapter concentrates on the differentiation of skeletal muscle and the growth factors that stimulate [insulin-like growth factors (IGFs)] and inhibit [FGF, transforming growth factor (TGF-β)] it. We mention those instances in which effects of hormones or growth factors on expression of the myogenic determination genes have been reported. The limited space allottment forces us to omit references to many publications that we consider important, and we apologize for the omissions.

EFFECTS OF SPECIFIC HORMONES AND GROWTH FACTORS

Insulin-like Growth Factors (IGFs)

CHEMISTRY AND SECRETION The IGFs (also known as somatomedins) are a family of small peptides similar in structure to proinsulin (reviewed in 28). As is true of all of the growth factors considered here, the IGFs were initially described as several different agents that were ultimately recognized as identical. The primary agents are IGF-I (70 amino acids, 7649 daltons), IGF-II (67 amino acids, 7471 daltons), and insulin (52 amino acids, 5733 daltons), listed in order of their potency in stimulating myogenic differentiation (20). Like the other growth factors described here, IGF-I is synthesized and apparently secreted by a number of cell types, although there is some reason to believe that the primary source of circulating IGFs is the liver (28). IGFs are also synthesized in substantial quantities by cultured muscle cells (78, 79).

ANABOLIC ACTIONS The IGFs exert pleiotypic anabolic actions on skeletal muscle cells (reviewed in 22), as they do on many other kinds of cells (3). These include stimulation of the following processes: amino acid uptake and incorporation into protein, uridine and thymidine incorporation into nucleic acids, glucose uptake, cell proliferation, etc. IGFs also suppress degradation of proteins. These activities occur in several cell lines as well as in primary myoblast cultures and satellite cells. Unlike FGF, IGFs stimulate myoblast proliferation in completely defined medium in the absence of other serum components.

STIMULATION OF DIFFERENTIATION The insulin-like hormones are unique among growth factors and hormones in that they stimulate, rather than inhibit, myogenic differentiation. It was first reported 25 years ago (12) that insulin (at μM levels) increased differentiation in chick embryo muscle cells and this finding was repeated in other laboratories (26). Ewton & Florini (20) first showed that physiological levels of IGFs stimulated L6 cell differentiation, both at the morphological (fusion) and biochemical (CK activity) levels, and suggested that the previous observations on insulin represented cross-reaction with the IGF-I receptor. This stimulation is not limited to cell lines; IGFs stimulate differentiation in chick embryo muscle cells (67) and in rat satellite cells (1). Thus the stimulation of differentiation by the insulin-like hormones is a general phenomenon, except in the case of cell lines such as C2 cells that secrete large amounts of these hormones (78, 79) and may thus stimulate their own differentiation by autocrine/paracrine mechanisms.

A curious aspect of the stimulation by IGFs, at least in L6 cells, is the biphasic concentration dependency (25). There is the expected increased stimulation from approximately 0.5 to 20 ng/ml, but this is followed by a rather sharp peak and lower levels of differentiation down to near control values at very high concentrations (360 ng/ml). Elevation of myogenin mRNA by IGF-I exhibited the same biphasic response (J. Florini et al, manuscript in preparation). Recent experiments (J. A. Foster, unpublished) show a similar biphasic response to IGF-I in the stimulation of expression of the elastin gene in aortic smooth muscle cells. The mechanism of this biphasic response is not apparent.

MECHANISM OF IGF STIMULATION OF DIFFERENTIATION

Possibilities that have been eliminated Some obvious explanations were considered soon after the discovery of the stimulation by IGF-I. One was that increased differentiation was a result of the greater culture density resulting from the mitogenic effects of IGF-I. This possibility was eliminated by two different approaches—use of inhibitors (80) and different plating densities (20). The possibility that the cells differentiated upon treatment with IGF-I because of generally better metabolic condition (the "happy cell" explanation) was eliminated by showing that differentiation was stimulated by IGF-I and IGF-II, even in serum concentrations that allowed high rates of cell proliferation (25). An extended study of effects of polyamines led to the conclusion that elevated polyamine levels are necessary but not sufficient for differentiation (18).

Induction of myogenin In our view the most likely mechanism of IGF-I action is induction of myogenin, the most universally expressed of the myogenesis determination genes. Recent work in this laboratory (J. Florini et al, manuscript in preparation) has shown that treatment of L6A1 cells with IGF-I gives a large (60-fold) increase in myogenin mRNA content at 30 to 40 hr, well before the elevation of creatine kinase. This is the only known case in which expression of the myogenin gene is increased, rather than inhibited, by a well-characterized agent. This elevation exhibits a concentration dependency like that of the stimulation of differentiation, including the sharply decreased stimulation at higher IGF-I concentrations. An antisense oligomer complementary to the first 15 nucleotides of the translated portion of myogenin mRNA blocks the stimulation of differentiation, so we conclude that increased myogenin gene expression is the primary mechanism by which IGF-I stimulates differentiation of muscle cells. The rather long time required for this elevation suggests that a rapid single step is not involved, i.e. that a substrate for the IGF-I receptor tyrosine kinase activity does not act directly on an enhancer for the myogenin gene.

IGF-I receptor Three different receptors—the IGF-I receptor, the IGF-II receptor, and the insulin receptor (for reviews see 62 and 66)—might mediate the stimulation of differentiation. The presence of all three receptors in cultured muscle cells has been demonstrated (2, 5, 13, 19). Our early experiments suggested that two different receptors might be involved in mediating various actions of IGFs on muscle, but we ultimately concluded (19) that all actions of IGFs were mediated by the type I receptor that exhibits the specificity IGF-I > IGF-II > insulin. Ballard (2) similarly concluded that the stimulation of protein and DNA synthesis in L6 cells was also mediated by the IGF-I receptor. Conclusive support for the primary role of the IGF-I receptor was provided by Kiess et al (37), who developed an antibody that specifically blocked the binding of IGF-II to the IGF-II receptor without affecting the binding of IGF-I to its receptor. This antibody did not alter the effects of IGF-II on amino acid or glucose uptake, or on leucine incorporation into proteins in L6 cells, thus indicating that the IGF-II receptor did not mediate these actions of the IGFs. An important theoretical paper (47) shows that differences in agonist potency for various actions mediated by the same receptor—some of the actions of IGF-I differ more than tenfold in the concentration required for half-maximal effect (19)—can be explained by differences in affinities of second messengers for their intracellular receptors.

IGF-II receptor The role of the IGF-II receptor remains unclear. It is present in large quantities in L6 cells (5), and it is strikingly elevated during differentiation in C2 cells (79), but no function has been shown for it in muscle cells. Its surprising identity to the mannose-6-phosphate receptor (which plays a role in targeting of lysosomal enzymes) is well established (52) and suggests that it may be involved in metabolism of IGF-II. This possibility was supported by the observation (37) that an antibody to the IGF-II receptor inhibited IGF-II degradation by 90% in L6 myoblasts. Other antibodies to the IGF-II/mannose-6-phosphate receptor blocked the insulin/IGF-I-induced decrease in protein catabolism of CHO cells, which suggests that this might result from a disruption of movement of lysosomal enzymes to lysosomes (40).

IGF binding proteins The IGFs are unlike other peptide hormones in that they circulate bound to a larger protein (3, 4). Initially it was believed that the binding protein functioned to decrease metabolism and regulate the concentration of free IGFs, and most early studies showed that binding proteins inhibited IGF actions (89). More recently, stimulatory effects of binding proteins have been reported (15), and a number of different binding proteins have been described (4). Human fetal myoblasts (32), as well as L6 and BC_3H1 myoblasts and porcine smooth muscle cells (49, 50), all secrete IGF binding proteins, and this secretion is regulated by insulin and IGF-I. Tollefsen et al (78, 79) found a 30-fold increase in binding proteins during differentiation of C2 cells. Thus binding proteins may play an important role in regulating the growth and differentiation of skeletal and smooth muscle, although the specifics of that role are not yet understood.

Effects on oncogene expression Increased oncogene expression is a frequently reported early effect of growth factors in many cells. In L6 cells, there is a fourfold increase in c-*fos* mRNA by IGF-I; several other oncogenes are not affected (58). The report (61) that elevated c-*fos* expression in transfected L6 myoblasts inhibited differentiation makes this an unlikely mediator of the IGF action considered here. There is induction of c-*myc* by high levels (1 μg/ml) of IGF-I (16), but at these levels differentiation of myoblasts is not stimulated (see discussion of the biphasic response above). A listing of oncogenes that exhibit changes during myogenic differentiation (26) and a more extensive treatment of the subject (68) are available in other reviews. The available evidence does not point to any oncogene likely to play a role in the stimulation of myogenic differentiation by IGF, although they may well be involved in proliferative and other anabolic responses.

We have taken a substantial step toward understanding the stimulation of differentiation with the discovery that IGFs stimulate expression of the myogenin gene. Major questions remain about events that occur between occupancy of the IGF receptor and increased myogenin mRNA levels that lead to terminal differentiation of muscle cells.

Transforming Growth Factor-β (TGF-β)

CHEMISTRY AND SECRETION TGF-β was initially characterized as an inducer of phenotypic transformation of fibroblastic cells, but it has subsequently been shown to have such a wide variety of actions that its name is clearly unduly restrictive (reviewed in 64). It is a member of a superfamily that includes several forms of TGF-β, activins, inhibins, and a number of other proteins (64, 84). It has also been found to be identical to several agents, including the myogenesis Differentiation Inhibitor discovered in this laboratory (17), that were initially described as having some other activity. At least five isoforms of TGF-β have been sequenced, and all members of the family consist of disulfide-linked dimers of 12,500 dalton peptide chains. TGF-β is present in relatively large quantities in the α granules of platelets, activated lymphocytes, and macrophages, and it has been found (at least in small quantities) in every cell line examined (64).

INHIBITION OF MYOBLAST DIFFERENTIATION The initial report of inhibition of terminal myogenic differentiation by a crude TGF-β preparation was made by Evinger-Hodges et al (17), but the low level of secretion of this growth factor by the BRL cell line prevented its identification as TGF-β.

Three independent reports (27, 48, 56) identifying TGF-β as an inhibitor of myogenic differentiation appeared virtually simultaneously, and all showed essentially the same results in L6A1, L6E9, C2, and BC_3H1 cell lines. The three reports agreed that TGF-β blocks all measured aspects of myogenic differentiation (fusion, elevation of creatine kinase activity, appearance of acetylcholine receptors, transition from β- and γ- to α-actin, and expression of other muscle-specific mRNAs and the corresponding proteins) in a concentration-dependent fashion. TGF-β has substantial effects on the morphology of L6 myoblasts, inducing formation of stress fibers and foci with numerous cells arrayed in a stelliform pattern (23). It also blocks the changes in ion transport associated with differentiation (8). The physiological significance of these observations with cell lines was demonstrated by the observation (1) that TGF-β also blocks differentiation of satellite cells prepared from adult rat skeletal muscle, as well as that of primary myoblast cultures from rat and quail embryos (17).

TGF-β is a potent inhibitor, with half-maximal inhibition at 6 pM (0.15 ng/ml) and complete inhibition at 20 pM (0.5 ng/ml) in L6A1 cells (27). Like FGF, it acts on a relatively early step (or steps) in the presumed cascade of events that lead to terminal differentiation; it is ineffective if added after the time required for commitment [defined by Nadal-Ginard (54) as attainment of a postmitotic state], and it apparently has no effect on subsequent steps in the pathway to expression of muscle-specific genes (27, 48, 56). We (D. Ewton, J. Florini, unpublished) find this critical step at about 24 to 30 hr after IGF-I addition for L6A1 cells and 18 hr for C2 cells. The inhibition of differentiation by TGF-β is reversible upon removal of the inhibitor with a time course reasonably close to that observed following addition of "differentiation medium" to myoblasts (17, 24, 56). This suggests that TGF-β induces a transient signal that is readily reversible, and it does not cause irreversible damage to myoblasts.

MECHANISM OF INHIBITION BY TGF-β One clue to the action of TGF-β is that its effects may be mediated by two oncogenes. In response to TGF-β, BC_3H1 cells showed a dramatic increase in *jun*B and a more modest rise in c-*jun* mRNA (44), as was also found to occur (59) in nonmuscle cell lines. Induction of *ras* expression (via an adjacent glucocorticoid response element in stably transfected C2 cells treated with dexamethasone) blocked differentiation (31), just as does TGF-β. Activation of *ras* blocked developmental induction of muscle-specific proteins (α-actin and desmin) and suppressed nonmuscle proteins (β- and γ-actin, and vimentin) (55). This inhibition of differentiation by H-*ras* is associated with down-regulation of expression of the MyoD1 gene (38). Thus all of these observations would be consistent with TGF-β acting by inducing expression of *jun* and/or *ras*.

This may be an oversimplification. Cotransfection with H-*ras* and MyoD1 gives at least partial restoration of differentiated functions, in contrast to TGF-β (and FGF), which inhibit differentiation in spite of high levels of MyoD1 mRNA in aza-C3H10T1/2-derived myoblasts (38). In C2C12 myoblasts, transfection with *ras* decreased myogenin mRNA, but this decrease could be reversed by cotransfection with a constituitively expressed MyoD1 (41). There were similar effects of expression of *fos* in aza-10T1/2 myoblasts. These results appear to indicate that either *ras* is not on the TGF-β/FGF signaling pathway, or that these inhibtors act by several pathways and *ras* is involved in only one of them. This view is supported by the report (33) that pertussis toxin inhibited induction of expression of several oncogenes by TGF-β, but had no effect on the stimulation of extracellular matrix protein gene expression in AKR-2B fibroblasts.

Possible roles of the most widely studied intracellular modulators of hormone actions have been eliminated by a number of investigations. For example, there was no change in intracellular cAMP levels in BC_3H1 cells following treatment with either TGF-β or FGF (34). Tetrahydrophorbol acetate does not inhibit differentiation in BC_3H1 cells (34) or C2 cells, nor do cyclooxygenase inhibitors (K. Magri, J. Florini, unpublished observations). There have been some indications of effects of TGF-β on established second messengers in other systems (64), but their relevance to muscle differentiation is by no means certain. The actions of TGF-β are so varied that is not likely to be useful to extrapolate from other systems, since there is no obvious reason to expect common mechanisms for such disparate actions.

Fibroblast Growth Factor

CHEMISTRY AND ACTIONS There are two forms of FGF, basic FGF (pI 9.6) and acidic FGF (pI 5.6) (reviewed in 29). Both are single peptide chains, with basic FGF composed of 146 amino acids and acidic FGF 140 amino acids. Basic FGF is the more widely distributed and (at least in the case of inhibition of myogenic differentiation) the more potent form. The FGFs are members of a family of related growth factors and have been described by at least 23 synonyms. They are mitogenic for cells of mesoderm- and neuroectoderm-derived tissues and have pleiotypic actions similar to those described above for IGFs. Like the other growth factors considered here, basic FGF is secreted by many kinds of cells. FGF is a potent inhibitor of differentiation, with half-maximal inhibition by 0.05 ng/ml basic FGF or 1 ng/ml acidic FGF (9).

RELATIONSHIP BETWEEN MITOGENIC AND DIFFERENTIATION-INHIBITING ACTIONS OF FGF The initial suggestion (39) that mitogens block terminal differentiation was based on the observation that differentiation occurred more rapidly in conditioned medium, from which the mitogens had presumably been metabolized. However, this point was not unambiguously demonstrated until it was shown (72) that medium conditioning decreases FGF concentrations from inhibitory levels to barely detectable amounts. Initial reports on inhibition of differentiation by FGF implied and often specifically stated that the effect was associated with its mitogenic activity (implying that other mitogens would also be inhibitors), but it was shown rather early that FGF could block differentiation under conditions in which it was not mitogenic, and this has been confirmed by several subsequent reports (9, 42, 43, 77). Thus, although the term mitogen removal is still used loosely in describing conditions used to promote myogenic differentiation, it is clear that there is no simple relationship between cell proliferation and differentiation to form postmitotic myotubes, except that the two are mutually exclusive. Indeed, except for two reports on effects of EGF on BC_3H1 cells (10, 82), FGF is the only purified mitogen that has been shown to inhibit myogenic differentiation, and one family of mitogens (the insulin-like growth factors) stimulates the process, as indicated above.

STAGE OF DIFFERENTIATION INHIBITED BY FGF FGF blocks an early step (or steps) in the events involved in terminal myogenic differentiation. Initial indications of this (46) have been followed by a report that removal of the growth factor for as little as two and one half hr (before readdition of FGF) allowed half of the MM14 myoblasts to become committed to terminal differentiation (9). These experiments also show that FGF (like TGF-β) has no effect on the subsequent expression of muscle-specific genes. It should be kept in mind that all of these studies on FGF actions have been done on cell lines; it has not yet been demonstrated that FGF acts on primary muscle cells by identical mechanisms, and FGF (unlike TGFβ) did not inhibit differentiation of rat muscle satellite cells when they were stimulated by IGF-I (1).

MECHANISM(S) OF INHIBITION BY FGF There is no mechanism yet generally accepted for the actions of FGF on myoblasts, and it has been suggested (75) that FGF actions are mediated by a novel signaling pathway not yet known. Lathrop et al (43) preincubated BC_3H1 myoblasts with FGF (in the absence of serum) and showed that this preincubation significantly decreased the lag period before initiation of ^{3}H-thymidine incorporation in response to serum. They concluded that FGF acted by "causing quiescent BC_3H1 cells to exit from the G_0 portion of the cell cycle, and to accumulate at a new restriction point 4 to 6 hours into the G_1 portion of the cell cycle." It is difficult to define this new restriction point in terms of biochemical mechanisms.

One attractive possibility is that increased expression of a cellular oncogene such as c-*fos* or c-*myc* in response to FGF (29) is involved in the inhibition of differentiation. However, elevation of c-*myc* did not repress expression of muscle-specific genes in myotubes (16), and persistent c-*myc* expression was not required for the inhibition of differentiation by FGF (or by TGF-β) (76). The observation (77) that cycloheximide blocks the down-regulation of CK in differentiated BC_3H1 cells in response to FGF suggests that the inhibition of differentiation by this growth factor requires protein synthesis.

It has been shown by several laboratories that FGF inhibits expression of the myogenesis determination genes MyoD1 (81) and myogenin (E. N. Olson, personal communication; J. Florini et al, unpublished observations). Thus each of the growth factors considered here affects myogenin expression in a direction consonant with its effect on terminal myogenic differentiation.

OTHER GROWTH FACTORS

Our literature searches have yielded few reports of actions of other growth factors on myogenesis. Platelet-derived growth factor (PDGF) has been shown to have a number of effects on smooth muscle cells, but we (J. R. Florini, unpublished observations) and C. D. Stiles (personal communication) could detect no effect of this agent on skeletal muscle cells. It has been reported to be produced by rat skeletal myoblasts (73), but the physiological significance of this is not apparent. As mentioned above, there are two reports that EGF inhibits expression of some differentiated functions in BC_3H1 cells (10, 82), but it has no effect on primary myoblasts (30) or muscle cell lines (45, 25). In many attempts, we have never observed any significant effects of EGF on L6 or C2 cells (25).

CHANGES IN RECEPTORS WITH DIFFERENTIATION

The finding that binding of EGF by mouse myoblasts decreases as these cells differentiate prompted Hauschka (45) to suggest that loss of growth factor receptors might account for the postmitotic state of myotubes. MM14 cells do not divide in response to EGF, so functional consequences of this decline in receptor number could not be demonstrated. Subsequently it was found that FGF receptors also disappear from the surfaces of differentiated MM14 cells (57). TGF-β receptors also disappear from several muscle cell lines as they differentiate (21). The parallel decrease in TGF-β-stimulated amino acid uptake in L6A1 myotubes showed that the receptors that disappeared were biologically functional. In contrast, there was only a 50% decrease in binding of TGF-β as BC_3H1 cells differentiated (21), and there was no decrease in FGF receptors (57), perhaps because these cells do not fuse. Uncoupling of biochemical and morphological differentiation by EGTA showed that the down-regulation of TGF-β receptors is associated with fusion, but not induction of muscle-specific proteins (35).

The generalization that mitogen receptors decrease with differentiation does not extend to the IGFs, which are very active mitogens for muscle cells. Under conditions in which TGF-β receptors virtually disappeared, we (21) detected little or no decrease in binding of ^{125}I-IGF-I and no change in responses to IGF-I. Beguinot et al (5) reported a decrease (about 70%) in IGF-I receptors with differentiation in a different subline of L6 cells, but this may be a result of their expressing binding on the basis of protein (which continues to accumulate in myotubes) rather than DNA content of the cultures. There is no decrease in binding of IGF-I and IGF-II to human muscle cells during differentiation (74), and there is a transient rise in IGF-I binding (78) and a dramatic increase in IGF-II binding (79) as C2 cells differentiate. Thus the decrease in FGF binding mentioned above is just one of many membrane changes that occur during differentiation, and it does not account for the postmitotic state of myotubes.

IN VIVO SIGNIFICANCE

All three growth factors considered in detail here are secreted by skeletal muscle, so it is possible that they might act by autocrine/paracrine mechanisms; current experiments (J. Florini et al, unpublished) indicate that IGF-II may play an important role in spontaneous differentiation of C2 cells incubated in 2% horse serum. Both at the mRNA and protein levels, genes for the IGFs have been shown to be expressed under conditions in which increased muscle growth occurs. These include regeneration (36) and hypertrophy induced by growth hormone administration (53). Allen & Boxhorn (1) showed that various combinations of IGF-I, TGF-β, and FGF could simulate the sequential phases of muscle regeneration. The TGF-β gene is expressed in mouse embryos at both the mRNA and protein (64) levels and (with FGF) is thought to play an important role in mesoderm formation in *Xenopus* oocytes (83). FGF levels in the chick embryo limb bud are high enough to inhibit differentiation of myoblasts (72), and FGF delays the onset of differentiation in muscle precursor cells from limb buds (71). Strohman's group (88) found that FGF is stored in the extracellular matrix of mature muscle and suggested that it plays a role in muscle hypertrophy. Although it is not yet possible to demonstrate conclusively that these agents affect normal growth and development of muscle, it seems very likely that they do.

SUMMARY AND CONCLUSIONS

Three families of growth factors/hormones have major effects on the differentiation of skeletal muscle cells. Two (FGF and TGF-β) are potent inhibitors, and the third (IGF) exhibits a biphasic stimulatory action (but is not inhibitory even at high concentrations). All of these affect the expression of myogenin, one of the recently discovered family of myogenesis controlling genes, and FGF and TGF-β have been shown to inhibit the expression of MyoD1 (and probably myf-5 and herculin) as well. These agents inhibit or stimulate (respectively) all measured aspects of myogenic differentiation—fusion, expression of a set of muscle-specific genes, and attainment of a postmitotic state—in all cells that are capable of these responses, whether cell lines or primary muscle cell cultures. It now seems clear that the myogenesis controlling genes regulate the entire family of muscle-specific proteins. Therefore the demonstration that expression of these genes is controlled (both positively and negatively) by specific growth factors that are now available at high purity and in useful quantities offers the possibility of understanding myogenic differentiation at a level of molecular detail that is very exciting.

ACKNOWLEDGMENTS

The preparation of this review was supported by grant HL11551 from the National Institutes of Health, United States Public Health Service. We thank the many colleagues who made manuscripts available to us prior to their publication.

Literature Cited

1. Allen, R. E., Boxhorn, L. K. 1989. Regulation of skeletal muscle satellite cell proliferation and differentiation by transforming growth factor-beta, insulin-like growth factor-I, and fibroblast growth factor. *J. Cell. Physiol.* 138: 311–15
2. Ballard, F. J., Read, L. C., Francis, G. L., Bagley, C. J., Wallace, J. C. 1986. Binding properties and biological potencies of insulin-like growth factors in L6 myoblasts. *Biochem. J.* 233:223–30
3. Baxter, R. C. 1988. The insulin-like growth factors and their binding proteins. *Comp. Biochem. Physiol.* 91B: 229–35
4. Baxter, R. C., Martin, J. L. 1989. Binding proteins for the insulin-like growth factors: structure, regulation and function. *Progr. Growth Factor Res.* 1:49–68
5. Beguinot, F., Kahn, C. R., Moses, A. C., Smith, R. J. 1985. Distinct biologically active receptors for insulin, insulin-like growth factor I, and insulin-like growth factor II in cultured skeletal muscle cells. *J. Biol. Chem.* 260:15892–98
6. Braun, T., Bober, E., Buschhausen-Denker, G. Kotz, S., Grzeschik, K.-H., Arnold, H. H. 1989. Differential expression of myogenic determination genes in muscle cells: possible autoactivation by the *myf* gene products. *EMBO J.* 8:3617–25
7. Braun, T., Buschhausen-Denker, G., Bober, E., Tannich, E., Arnold, H. H. 1989. A novel human muscle factor related to but distinct from myoD1 induces myogenic conversion in 10T1/2 fibroblasts. *EMBO J.* 8:701–9
8. Caffrey, J. M., Brown, A. M., Schneider, M. D. 1989. Ca^{2+} and Na^{+} currents in developing skeletal myoblasts are expressed in a sequential program: reversible suppression by transforming growth factor beta-1, an inhibitor of the myogenic process. *J. Neurosci.* 9:3443–53
9. Clegg, C. H., Linkhart, T. A., Olwin, B. B., Hauschka, S. D. 1987. Growth factor control of skeletal muscle differentiation: commitment to terminal differentiation occurs in G1 phase and is repressed by fibroblast growth factor. *J. Cell Biol.* 105:949–56
10. Connolly, J. A., Sarabia, V. E., Kelvin, D. J., Wang, E. 1988. The disappearance of a cyclin-like protein and the appearance of statin is correlated with the onset of differentiation during

myogenesis in vitro. *Exp. Cell Res.* 174:461–71
11. Davis, R. L., Weintraub, H., Lassar, A. B. 1987. Expression of a single transfected cDNA converts fibroblasts to myoblasts. *Cell* 51:987–1000
12. de la Haba, G., Cooper, G. W., Elting, V. 1966. Hormonal requirements for myogenesis in vitro: insulin and somatotropin. *Proc. Natl. Acad. Sci. USA* 56:1719–23
13. De Vroede, M. A., Romanus, J. A., Standaert, M. L., Pollett, R. J., Nissley, S. P., Rechler, M. M. 1984. Interaction of insulin-like growth factors with a nonfusing mouse muscle cell line: binding, action, and receptor down-regulation. *Endocrinology* 114:1917–29
14. Edmondson, D. G., Olson, E. N. 1989. A gene with homology to the *myc* similarity region of myoD1 is expressed during myogenesis and is sufficient to activate the muscle differentiation program. *Genes Dev.* 3:628–40
15. Elgin, R. G., Busby, W. H. Jr., Clemmons, D. R. 1987. An insulin-like growth factor (IGF) binding protein enhances the biological response to IGF-I. *Proc. Natl. Acad. Sci. USA* 84:3254–58
16. Endo, T., Nadal-Ginard, B. 1986. Transcriptional and posttranscriptional control of c-*myc* during myogenesis: its mRNA remains inducible in differentiated cells and does not suppress the differentiated phenotype. *Mol. Cell. Biol.* 6:1412–21
17. Evinger-Hodges, M. J., Ewton, D. Z., Seifert, S. C., Florini, J. R. 1982. Inhibition of myoblast differentiation in vitro by a protein isolated from liver cell medium. *J. Cell Biol.* 93:395–401
18. Ewton, D. Z., Erwin, B. G., Pegg, A. E., Florini, J. R. 1984. The role of polyamines in somatomedin-stimulated differentiation of L6 myoblasts. *J. Cell. Physiol.* 120:263–70
19. Ewton, D. Z., Falen, S. L., Florini, J. R. 1987. The type II IGF receptor has low affinity for IGF-I analogs: pleiotypic actions of IGFs on myoblasts are apparently mediated by the type I receptor. *Endocrinology* 120:115–24
20. Ewton, D. Z., Florini, J. R. 1981. Effect of somatomedins and insulin on myoblast differentiation in vitro. *Dev. Biol.* 86:31–39
21. Ewton, D. Z., Spizz, G., Olson, E. N., Florini, J. R. 1988. Decrease in transforming growth factor-β binding and action during differentiation in muscle cells. *J. Biol. Chem.* 263:4029–32
22. Florini, J. R. 1987. Hormonal control of muscle growth. *Muscle Nerve* 7:577–98
23. Florini, J. R., Ewton, D. Z. 1988. Actions of transforming growth factor-β on muscle cells. *J. Cell. Physiol.* 135:301–8
24. Florini, J. R., Ewton, D. Z., Evinger-Hodges, M. J., Falen, S. L., Lau, R. L., et al. 1984. Stimulation and inhibition of myoblast differentiation by hormones. *In Vitro* 20:942–58
25. Florini, J. R., Ewton, D. Z., Falen, S. L., Van Wyk, J. J. 1986. Biphasic concentration dependency of the stimulation of myoblast differentiation by somatomedins. *Am. J. Physiol.* 250:C771–78
26. Florini, J. R., Magri, K. A. 1989. Effects of growth factors on myogenic differentiation. *Am. J. Physiol.* 256: C701–11
27. Florini, J. R., Roberts, A. B., Ewton, D. Z., Falen, S. B., Flanders, K. C., Sporn, M. B. 1986. Transforming growth factor-β. A very potent inhibitor of myoblast differentiation, identical to the differentiation inhibitor secreted by buffalo rat liver cells. *J. Biol. Chem.* 261:16509–13
28. Froesch, E. R., Zapf, J. 1985. Insulin-like growth factors and insulin: comparative aspects. *Diabetologia* 28:485–93
29. Gospodarowicz, D., Ferrara, N., Schweigerer, L., Neufeld, G. 1987. Structural characterization and biological functions of fibroblast growth factor. *Endocr. Rev.* 8:95–114
30. Gospodarowicz, D., Mescher, A. L. 1977. A comparison of the responses of cultured myoblasts and chondrocytes to fibroblast and epidermal growth factors. *J. Cell. Physiol.* 93:117–28
31. Gossett, L. A., Zhang, W., Olson, E. N. 1988. Dexamethasone-dependent inhibition of differentiation of C2 myoblasts bearing steroid-inducible N-*ras* oncogenes. *J. Cell Biol.* 106:2127–38
32. Hill, D. J., Clemmons, D. R., Wilson, S., Han, V. K., Strain, A. J., Milner, R. D. 1989. Immunological distribution of one form of insulin-like growth factor (IGF)-binding protein and IGF peptides in human fetal tissues. *J. Mol. Endocrinol.* 2:31–38
33. Howe, P. H., Cunningham, M. R., Leof, E. B. 1990. Distinct pathways regulate transforming growth factor β1-stimulated proto-oncogene and extracellular matrix gene expression. *J. Cell. Physiol.* 142:39–45
34. Hu, J. S., Olson, E. N. 1988. Regulation of differentiation of the BC_3H1 muscle cell line through cAMP-dependent and independent pathways. *J. Biol. Chem.* 263:19670–77

35. Hu, J. S., Olson, E. N. 1990. Functional receptors for transforming growth factor-β are retained by biochemically differentiated C2 myocytes in growth factor deficient medium containing EGTA, but down-regulated during terminal differentiation. *J. Biol. Chem.* 265:7914–19
36. Jennische, E., Hansson, H.-A. 1987. Regenerating skeletal muscle cells express insulin-like growth factor I. *Acta Physiol. Scand.* 130:327–32
37. Kiess, W., Haskell, J. F., Greenstein, L. A., Miller, B. E., Aarons, A. L., et al. 1987. An antibody that blocks insulin-like growth factor (IGF) binding to the type II IGF receptor is neither an agonist nor an inhibitor of IGF-stimulated biologic responses in L6 myoblasts. *J. Biol. Chem.* 262:12745–51
38. Konieczny, S. F., Drobes, B. L., Menke, S. L., Taparowsky, E. J. 1989. Inhibition of myogenic differentiation by the H-*ras* oncogene is associated with the down regulation of the myoD1 gene. *Oncogene* 4:473–81
39. Konigsberg, I. R. 1971. Diffusion-mediated control of myoblast fusion. *Dev. Biol.* 26:133–52
40. Kovacina, K. S., Steele-Perkins, G. 1989. A role for the insulin-like growth factor II/mannose-6-phosphate receptor in the insulin-induced inhibition of protein catabolism. *Mol. Endocrinol.* 3: 901–6
41. Lassar, A. B., Buskin, J. N., Lockshon, D., Davis, R. L., Apone, S., et al. 1989. MyoD is a sequence specific DNA binding protein requiring a region of *myc* homology to bind to the muscle creatine kinase enhancer. *Cell* 58:823–31
42. Lathrop, B., Olson, E., Glaser, L. 1985. Control by fibroblast growth factor of differentiation in the BC_3H1 muscle cell line. *J. Cell Biol.* 100:1540–47
43. Lathrop, B., Thomas, K., Glaser, L. 1985. Control of myogenic differentiation by fibroblast growth factor is mediated by position in the G1 phase of the cell cycle. *J. Cell Biol.* 101:2194–98
44. Li, L., Hu, J. S., Olson, E. N. 1990. Different members of the *jun* proto-oncogene family exhibit distinct patterns of expression in response to type β transforming growth factor. *J. Biol. Chem.* 265:1556–62
45. Lim, R. W., Hauschka, S. D. 1984. A rapid decrease in epidermal growth factor-binding capacity accompanies the terminal differentiation of mouse myoblasts in vitro. *J. Cell Biol.* 98:739–47
46. Linkhart, T. A., Clegg, C. H., Lim, R. W., Merrill, G. F., Chamberlain, J. S., Hauschka, S. D. 1982. Control of mouse myoblast commitment to terminal differentiation by mitogens. In *Molecular and Cellular Control of Muscle Development,* ed. M. L. Pearson, H. F. Ebstein. 8:877–82. Cold Spring Harbor Conf.
47. Loeb, J. N., Strickland, S. 1987. Hormone binding and coupled response relationships in systems dependent on the generation of secondary mediators. *Mol. Endocrinol.* 1:75–82
48. Massagué, J., Cheifetz, S., Endo, T., Nadal-Ginard, B. 1986. Type beta transforming growth factor is an inhibitor of myogenic differentiation. *Proc. Natl. Acad. Sci. USA* 83:8206–10
49. McCusker, R. H., Camacho-Hubner, C., Clemmons, D. R. 1989. Identification of the types of insulin-like growth factor binding proteins that are secreted by muscle cells in vitro. *J. Biol. Chem.* 264:7795–7800
50. McCusker, R. H. Clemmons, D. R. 1988. Insulin-like growth factor binding protein secretion by muscle cells: effect of cellular differentiation and proliferation. *J. Cell. Physiol.* 137:505–12
51. Miner, J. H., Wold, B. 1990. Herculin, a fourth member of the myoD family of myogenic regulatory genes. *Proc. Natl. Acad. Sci. USA* 87:1089–93
52. Morgan, D. O., Edman, J. C., Standring, D. N., Fried, V. A., Smith, M. C., et al. 1987. Insulin-like growth factor-II receptor as a multifunctional binding protein. *Nature* 329:301–7
53. Murphy, L. J., Bell, G. I., Duckworth, M. L., Friesen, H. G. 1987. Identification, characterization, and regulation of a rat complementary deoxyribonucleic acid which encodes insulin-like growth factor-I. *Endocrinology* 121:684–91
54. Nadal-Ginard, B. 1978. Commitment, fusion, and biochemical differentiation of a myogenic cell line. *Cell* 15:855–63
55. Olson, E. N., Capetanaki, Y. G. 1989. Developmental regulation of intermediate filament and actin mRNAs during myogenesis is disrupted by oncogenic *ras* genes. *Oncogene* 4:907–13
56. Olson, E. N., Sternberg, E., Hu, J. S., Spizz, G., Wilcox, C. 1986. Regulation of myogenic differentiation by type beta transforming growth factor. *J. Cell Biol.* 103:1799–1806
57. Olwin, B. B., Hauschka, S. D. 1988. Cell surface fibroblast growth factor and epidermal growth factor receptors are permanently lost during skeletal muscle

terminal differentiation in culture. *J. Cell Biol.* 107:761–69

58. Ong, J., Yamashita, S., Melmed, S. 1987. Insulin-like growth factor I induces c-*fos* messenger ribonucleic acid in L6 skeletal muscle cells. *Endocrinology* 120:353–57
59. Petrovaara, L., Sistonen, L., Bos, T. J., Vogt, P. K., Keski-Oja, J., Alitalo, K. 1989. Enhanced *jun* gene expression is an early genomic response to transforming growth factor β stimulation. *Mol. Cell. Biol.* 9:1255–62
60. Pinney, D. F., Pearson-White, S. H., Konieczny, S. F., Latham, K. E., Emerson, C. P. Jr. 1988. Myogenic lineage determination and differentiation: evidence for a regulatory gene pathway. *Cell* 53:781–93
61. Rahm, M., Jin., P., Sumegi, J., Sejersen, T. 1989. Elevated c-*fos* expression inhibits differentiation of L6 rat myoblasts. *J. Cell. Physiol.* 139:237–44
62. Rechler, M. M., Nissley, S. P. 1985. The nature and regulation of the receptors for insulin-like growth factors. *Annu. Rev. Physiol.* 47:425–42
63. Rhodes, S. J., Konieczny, S. F. 1990. Identification of MRF4: A new member of the muscle regulatory factor gene family. *Genes Dev.* 3:2050–61
64. Roberts, A. B., Sporn, M. B. eds. 1990. The transforming growth factor-betas. In *Handbook Exp. Pharm.* 95: pp. 419–472. Heidelberg: Springer-Verlag
65. Rosenthal, N. 1990. Muscle cell differentiation. *Curr. Opin. Cell Biol.* In press
66. Roth, R. A. 1988. Structure of the receptor for insulin-like growth factor II: the puzzle amplified. *Science* 239:1269–71
67. Schmid, Ch., Steiner, Th., Froesch, E. R. 1983. Preferential enhancement of myoblast differentiation by insulin-like growth factors (IGF-I and IGF-II) in primary cultures of chicken embryonic cells. *FEBS Lett.* 161:117–21
68. Schneider, M. D., Olson, E. N. 1988. Control of myogenic differentiation by cellular oncogenes. *Molec. Neurobiol.* 2:1–39
69. Schneider, M. D., Parker, T. G. 1990. Cardiac myocytes as targets for the action of peptide growth factors. *Circulation.* In press
70. Schubert, D., Harris, J., Devine, C. E., Heinemann, S. 1974. Characterization of a unique muscle cell line. *J. Cell Biol.* 61:398–413
71. Seed, J., Hauschka, S. D. 1988. Clonal analysis of vertebrate myogenesis. VIII. Fibroblast growth factor (FGF)-dependent and FGF-independent muscle colony types during chick wing development. *Dev. Biol.* 128:40–49
72. Seed, J., Olwin, B. B., Hauschka, S. D. 1988. Fibroblast growth factor levels in the whole embryo and limb bud during chick development. *Dev. Biol.* 128:50–57
73. Sejersen, T., Betsholtz, C., Sjolund, M., Heldin, C-H, Westermark, B., Thyberg, J. 1986. Rat skeletal myoblasts and arterial smooth muscle cells express the gene for the A chain but not the gene for the B chain (c-*sis*) of platelet-derived growth factor. *Proc. Natl. Acad. Sci. USA* 83:6844–48
74. Shimizu, M., Webster, C., Morgan, D. O., Blau, H. M., Roth, R. A. 1986. Insulin and insulinlike growth factor receptors and responses in cultured human muscle cells. *Am. J. Physiol.* 251:E611–15
75. Smith, E. P., Hall, S. H., Monaco, L., French, F. S., Wilson, E. M., Conti, M. 1989. Regulation of c-*fos* messenger ribonucleic acid by fibroblast growth factor in cultured Sertoli cells. *Ann. NY Acad. Sci.* 564:132–39
76. Spizz, G., Hu, J.-S., Olson, E. N. 1987. Inhibition of myogenic differentiation by fibroblast growth factor or type β transforming growth factor does not require persistent c-*myc* expression. *Dev. Biol.* 123:500–7
77. Spizz, G., Roman, D., Strauss, A., Olson, E. N. 1986. Serum and fibroblast growth factor inhibit myogenic differentiation through a mechanism dependent on protein synthesis and independent of cell proliferation. *J. Biol. Chem.* 261:9483–88
78. Tollefsen, S. E., Lajara, R., McCusker, R. H., Clemmons, D. R., Rotwein, P. 1989. Insulin-like growth factors (IGF) in muscle development. Expression of IGF-I, the IGF-I receptor, and an IGF binding protein during myoblast differentiation. *J. Biol. Chem.* 264:13810–17
79. Tollefsen, S. E., Sadow, J. L., Rotwein, P. 1989. Coordinate expression of insulin-like growth factor II and its receptor during muscle differentiation. *Proc. Natl. Acad. Sci. USA* 86:1543–47
80. Turo, K. A., Florini, J. R. 1982. Hormonal stimulation of myoblast differentiation in the absence of DNA synthesis. *Am. J. Physiol.* 243:C278–84
81. Vaidya, T. B., Rhodes, S. J., Taparowsky, E. J., Konieczny, S. F. 1989. Fibroblast growth factor and transforming growth factor β repress transcription

of the myogenic regulatory gene MyoD1. *Mol. Cell. Biol.* 9:3576–79

82. Wang, Y.-C., Rubenstein, P. A. 1988. Epidermal growth factor controls smooth muscle α-isoactin expression in BC_3H1 cells. *J. Cell Biol.* 106:797–803
83. Woodland, H. R. 1989. Mesoderm formation in *Xenopus*. *Cell* 59:767–70
84. Wozney, J. M., Rosen, V., Celeste, A. J., Mitsock, L. M., Whitters, M. J., et al. 1988. Novel regulators of bone formation: Molecular clones and activities. *Science* 242:1528–34
85. Wright, W. E., Sassoon, D. A., Lin, V. K. 1989. Myogenin, a factor regulating myogenesis, has a domain homologous to myoD. *Cell* 56:607–17
86. Yaffe, D. 1968. Retention of differentiation potentialities during prolonged cultivation of myogenic cells. *Proc. Natl. Acad. Sci. USA* 61:477–83
87. Yaffe, D., Saxel, O. 1977. Serial passaging and differentiation of myogenic cells isolated from dystrophic mouse muscles. *Nature* 270:725–27
88. Yamada, S., Buffinger, N., DiMario, J., Strohman, R. C. 1989. Fibroblast growth factor is stored in fiber extracellular matrix and plays a role in regulating muscle hypertrophy. *Med. Sci. Sports Exerc.* 21:S173–80
89. Zapf, J., Schoenle, E., Jagers, E., Sand, I., Froesch, E. R. 1979. Inhibition of the actions of non-suppressible insulin-like activity on isolated fat cells by binding to its carrier protein. *J. Clin. Invest.* 63:1077–84

Annu. Rev. Physiol. 1991. 53:217–39

REGULATORS OF ANGIOGENESIS

Michael Klagsbrun[1]

Patricia A. D'Amore[2]

Laboratory for Surgical Research, Children's Hospital and Departments of Biological Chemistry[1] and Pathology[2], Harvard Medical School, Boston, Massachusetts 02115

KEY WORDS: growth factors, growth inhibitors, neovascularization, endothelial cells, fibroblast growth factors

INTRODUCTION

Biology of Angiogenesis

Proliferation of blood vessels is a process necessary for the normal growth and development of tissue (36). In the adult, angiogenesis occurs infrequently. Exceptions are found in the female reproductive system, where angiogenesis occurs in the follicle during its development, in the corpus luteum during ovulation, and in the placenta after pregnancy. These periods of angiogenesis are relatively brief and tightly regulated. Normal angiogenesis also occurs as part of the body's repair processes, e.g. in the healing of wounds and fractures. By contrast, uncontrolled angiogenesis can often be pathological. For example, the growth of solid tumors depends on vascularization (37), and in diabetic retinopathy vascularization of the retina often leads to blindness.

Given the physiologic and pathological importance of angiogenesis, much effort in the last twenty years has been devoted to the isolation, characterization, and purification of factors that can either stimulate or inhibit angiogenesis. Several bioassays have been developed to measure angiogenesis. The most common ones are endothelial cell migration (47) and proliferation (38) in vitro, and capillary growth in vivo in the developing chick chorioallantoic membrane (CAM) (4) and the cornea (45). The goal of this review is to describe those stimulators and inhibitors of angiogenesis that have been best-characterized.

0066-4278/91/0315-0217$02.00

STIMULATORS OF ANGIOGENESIS

A number of stimulators of angiogenesis have been purified and characterized (25, 39). Analysis of these factors strongly suggests that there must be several different mechanisms for stimulating angiogenesis. The family of angiogenesis factors includes polypeptides and non-peptides. The importance of the non-peptide angiogenesis factors has been hard to ascertain, however, since they are for the most part poorly characterized. Accordingly, this review describes primarily the biochemical and biological properties of polypeptide angiogenic factors that have been purified, sequenced, and cloned.

The Fibroblast Growth Factors

The fibroblast growth factors (FGF) constitute a family of mitogenic polypeptides (17, 39, 51, 124). The most intensively studied are basic FGF (bFGF) and acidic FGF (aFGF). bFGF (30, 50) is a cationic (pI of 9.6) 18-kd polypeptide. Higher molecular weight forms of bFGF also exist (35, 60, 86, 98). These are 21–25-kd forms of bFGF that are N-terminal extensions of the 18-kd form. The higher molecular weight forms of bFGF are unusual in that their synthesis is initiated at CUG rather that AUG start codons (35, 98). aFGF (also known as endothelial cell growth factor, ECGF) is an anionic (pI of 5) 18-kd polypeptide (46). bFGF and aFGF are structurally related, with a 53% absolute sequence homology (31). Several oncogenes have been described that encode for proteins that have a 40–50% homology to bFGF and aFGF. These include *int*-2 (27 kd), a product of integration of mammary tumor virus into the host genome (28); *hst* (23 kd), isolated from a human stomach cancer (139); K-*fgf*, isolated from a Kaposi's tumor (27); and FGF-5 (29 kd), isolated from a human bladder tumor (140). Another member of the FGF family, keratinocyte growth factor (KGF, 28 kd) (34), is a highly specific mitogen for epithelial cells and therefore is quite different than the other FGF family members in its target cell specificity.

bFGF and aFGF are characterized by their strong affinity for heparin (50, 66, 76, 117). The affinity of FGF for heparin might be important in terms of growth factor-cell interaction since it has been demonstrated that bFGF and aFGF bind to low affinity cell surface receptors ($K_d = 2 \times 10^{-9}$), which appear to be heparan sulfate proteoglycans (85).

FGF appears to be one of the most widely distributed growth factors in the body, and it is synthesized by many cells in culture. Biosynthetic studies indicate that bFGF is a cellular rather than a secreted protein (110, 131, 132). The lack of bFGF secretion is consistent with the absence of a consensus signal peptide in the open reading frame of bFGF (1). aFGF also lacks a signal peptide and is not secreted (64). Endothelial cells synthesize substantial amounts of bFGF (110, 132). The bFGF produced by these cells is not only cell-associated, but is found to be associated with the subendothelial cell extracellular matrix as well (7, 131). bFGF can be released from the extracellular matrix and basement membrane by displacement with heparin or by degradation with heparanases and proteinases (9). The association of bFGF with cells, extracellular matrix, and basement membrane has led to the speculation that bFGF may be a stored growth factor. The release of stored FGF might be a way to rapidly mobilize growth factor for the stimulation of angiogenesis and cell proliferation in reparative processes such as wound healing.

Angiogenesis in vivo is a complex process involving the degradation of the capillary basement membrane, the migration and proliferation of endothelial cells, and tube formation. FGF in vitro is mitogenic (51, 124) and chemotactic (123) for endothelial cells. It stimulates endothelial cell production of collagenase and plasminogen activator proteases capable of degrading basement membrane (82), and it induces capillary endothelial cells to migrate into three-dimensional collagen matrices to form capillary-like tubes (84). Both bFGF and aFGF are angiogenic factors in the chick chorioallantoic membrane (CAM) and cornea bioassays at levels as low as 10–100 ng (1, 31, 73, 116). bFGF has been shown to induce the formation of vascular granulation tissue containing highly dilated blood vessels in polyvinyl sponges implanted into rats (26). When anti-bFGF antibodies are incorporated into the sponges, angiogenesis is inhibited (16). aFGF complexed to gelatin induces angiogenesis in the neck and peritoneal cavities of the rat (125). In summary, both aFGF and bFGF are potent angiogenesis factors. Since they are both chemotactic and mitogenic for endothelial cells, they may be able to act directly on these cells to stimulate angiogenesis. It is not clear how bFGF and aFGF mediate angiogenesis in vivo. Since they are not secreted proteins, they have to be released from cells by alternative mechanisms. One of these may be cell lysis. Indeed, FGF might be released from cellular storage sites during injury and then repair the injury by stimulating connective tissue growth and angiogenesis.

Vascular Endothelial Growth Factor/Vascular Permeability Factor

A growth factor, highly specific as a mitogen for vascular endothelial cells, has been described by several laboratories (22, 23, 32, 49, 72, 127). This vascular endothelial cell growth factor has been termed VEGF and appears similar to a previously described vascular permeability factor (VPF). VPF contains a 24 amino acid insertion not present in VEGF (23). Although it is premature to assign a name to this new endothelial cell mitogen, the term VEGF/VPF will be used here. VEGF/VPF is a highly glycosylated cationic 46–48-kd dimer made up of two 24-kd subunits. VEGF/VPF is inactivated by sulfhydryl reducing agents, but is resistant to acid pH and to heating. It binds to immobilized heparin (elution with 0.6–1.2 M NaCl), but not as tightly as does FGF. VEGF/VPF cDNA has been cloned, and analysis of its nucleotide sequence suggests that VEGF/VPF is a member of the platelet-derived growth factor (PDGF) family. There is a 21–24% homology with the PDGF A and B chains and complete conservation of the eight cysteine residues found in both mature PDGF chains. PDGF differs from VEGF/VPF, however, in being a smooth muscle cell, but not an endothelial cell mitogen.

VEGF/VPF is a secreted protein that has been isolated from the conditioned media of a number of cell lines including bovine pituitary follicular cells (32, 49), guinea pig tumor (23), NB41 neuroblastoma (72), and rat glioma cells (22). The most striking property of VEGF/VPF is its specificity. It is mitogenic (at 1 ng/ml) for capillary and human umbilical vein endothelial cells, but not for adrenal cortex cells, lens epithelial cells, smooth muscle cells, corneal endothelial cells, granulosa cells, keratinocytes, BHK-21 fibroblasts, 3T3 cells, rat embryo fibroblasts, and human placental fibroblasts. VEGF/VPF stimulates angiogenesis in vivo in the rabbit cornea (1 μg), (72), in the rat cornea (4.2 μg) (23), on the CAM (50 ng) (32), and in a healing rabbit bone graft model (75 μg) (23). Besides being an endothelial cell mitogen and angiogenesis factor, VPF (and possibly VEGF) is a vascular permeability factor. It increases fluid leakage at the injection site (as measured using of Evan's blue dye) from blood vessels following intradermal injection (23). The relationship between stimulating endothelial cell proliferation, angiogenesis, and vascular permeability is not understood at present.

Platelet-Derived Endothelial Cell Growth Factor

The platelet-derived endothelial cell growth factor (PD-ECGF) is an acidic single chain 45-kd polypeptide (63, 83, 130). It is heat and acid labile, but resistant to sulfhydryl reducing agents. Unlike FGF and VEGF/VPF, PD-ECGF does not bind to heparin, and heparin does not potentiate its activity. Analysis of the PD-ECGF cDNA nucleotide sequence indicates the absence of a signal peptide sequence, a property similar to that of FGF. PD-ECGF was originally isolated from platelets and appears to be the major source of endothelial cell growth factor activity in those cells. In addition to platelets, PD-ECGF is synthesized by human foreskin fibroblasts, human squamous carcinoma cells, and anaplastic thyroid carcinoma cells. PD-ECGF is not secreted by these cells, but instead is sequestered intracellularly, consistent with its lack of a signal peptide. In the absence of active secretion, the mechanism by which PD-ECGF stimulates angiogenesis remains to be elucidated. Release from cells may occur as a result of cell lysis.

PD-ECGF is a specfic endothelial cell mitogen. It stimulates the proliferation of porcine and human endothelial cells (20 ng/ml), but not human fibroblasts. It is also chemotactic for bovine aortic endothelial cells at 1 ng/ml, but not for smooth muscle cells. Besides being an endothelial cell mitogen, PD-ECGF is also angiogenic on the CAM. In addition, when PD-ECGF is transfected into tumor cells, the tumors that develop in nude mice are highly vascular.

Epidermal Growth Factor/Transforming Growth Factor-Alpha

Epidermal growth factor (EGF), a 6-kd polypeptide, is found primarily in the mouse salivary gland and in biological fluids such as saliva, milk, and urine (19). Transforming growth factor-alpha (TGF-α) is a 5.5-kd single-chain polypeptide that is homologous (40%) to EGF and binds to the EGF receptor (81, 128). TGF-α is secreted by transformed fibroblasts, by a variety of tumor cells (128), and by normal cells such as macrophages (78). Both EGF and TGF-α stimulate the proliferation of bovine pulmonary endothelial and murine lung endothelial cells (1 ng/ml) in vitro and stimulate angiogenesis in vivo. TGF-α appears to be more potent than EGF in these effects. TGF-α injected subcutaneously into the hamster cheek pouch, at 0.3–1 μg, stimulates capillary proliferation and an increase in the labeling index of endothelial cells (109). The synthesis of TGF-α by tumors and macrophages coupled with its angiogenic activity suggest that TGF-α may be an important mediator of tumor vascularization and inflammation.

Angiogenin

Angiogenin is a cationic 14.1-kd single-chain polypeptide that stimulates angiogenesis in the CAM and in the rabbit cornea (33, 41, 67, 120). Structurally, angiogenin is related to pancreatic RNAse A. There is a 35% absolute homology between the two proteins and, including conservative replacements, the overall homology is 68%. The angiogenic and ribonucleolytic properties of angiogenin and pancreatic RNAse A differ considerably (112), however. Angiogenin is strongly angiogenic, but has relatively weak ribonucleolytic activity. Pancreatic RNAse A is not angiogenic. The ribonucleolytic activity of angiogenin appears to be important to its angiogenic activity since human placental RNAse inhibitor also inhibits the angiogenesis activity of angiogenin (114).

Angiogenin is a secreted protein that was first isolated from the conditioned medium of an established human adenocarcinoma cell line HT-29 (33). It has also been found in human plasma (60–150 μ/l) (113) and is produced by normal cells, such as WI-38, and by lymphocytes as well (41). Analysis of angiogenin mRNA suggests that it is made predominantly in adult liver (136). Angiogenin synthesis in rat liver is developmentally regulated: low in the developing fetus, higher in the neonate, and maximal in the adult. Thus, although angiogenin is an angiogenesis factor, its gene expression is not temporally related to vascular development in the rat, a process which is highest in the developing fetus and lowest in the adult.

Unlike FGF, VEGF/VPF, and PD-ECGF, angiogenin does not appear to stimulate endothelial cell migration or proliferation in vitro. Pulmonary artery endothelial cells do possess high affinity angiogenin receptors, however, which bind angiogenin with a K_d of 5×10^{-9} (5), and angiogenin does have some direct effects on endothelial cells. For example, it stimulates a transient, but significant increase in the intracellular concentration of diacylglycerol, which results from the activation of phospholipase C (13). Angiogenin is angiogenic in vivo. It stimulates blood vessel growth in the CAM at 0.5 ng/egg and in the rabbit cornea at 50 ng/eye (33). Mutations that increase the ribonucleolytic activity of angiogenin also increase its specific activity in the CAM assay (41). The potent angiogenic effects of angiogenin in the absence of any direct demonstrable effects on endothelial cell migration or proliferation in culture suggest that this growth factor might be acting to stimulate other endothelial cell functions that are important in blood vessel development. Alternatively, angiogenin might stimulate angiogenesis indirectly.

Angiotropin

Angiotropin is a copper-containing polyribonucleopolypeptide with a molecular weight of 4.5 kd (59). The polypeptide portion consists of 38 amino acids and the ribonucleic acid portion consists of 43 bases, although no purified sequence data are available at present.

Angiotropin has been purified from the conditioned medium of concanavalin A-activated peripheral porcine monocytes. Angiotropin is not an endothelial cell mitogen, but it does stimulate random capillary endothelial cell migration (chemokinesis) at 4–400 pg/ml. When added to confluent cultures of capillary endothelial cells, angiotropin stimulates, in a dose-dependent and reversible manner, capillary endothelial cells to actively migrate and to rapidly reorganize into tubular structures. The affects of angiotropin are specific for capillary endothelial cells. The factor does not stimulate 3T3 cells to migrate, proliferate, or differentiate. Unlike capillary endothelial cells, aortic endothelial cells do not form cord-like or tube-like structures in the presence of angiotropin.

A 250 pg dose of angiotropin induces angiogenesis in the CAM and corneal pocket bioassays. When injected into the dorsal skin of a rabbit ear lobe, angiotropin induces morphological changes in capillary and post-capillary venule endothelial cells, vascular dilation, and angiogenesis. These events occur in two stages: At two days post-injection, capillaries are highly dilated and by day eight, blood vessels are reduced to normal size but the number of microvessels is significantly increased. In addition, the angiogenesis is associated with epidermal and stromal proliferation, but not with tissue necrosis or scar formation. Thus angiotropin, a chemical mediator produced by macrophages, appears to initiate a cascade of inflammatory and wound healing events including angiogenesis. As with the other angiogenic factors that are not endothelial cell mitogens, e.g. TGF-β and TNF-α, the mechanism of angiotropin-mediated angiogenesis is not clear.

Transforming Growth Factor-Beta

Transforming growth factor-beta (TGF-β) is a homodimeric 25-kd polypeptide (119). Each monomer is a 112 amino acid polypeptide that represents the carboxy-terminal portion of a 390 amino acid precursor. Despite the nomenclature, TGF-β is a protein totally distinct from TGF-α. TGF-β constitutes a family of highly homologous polypeptides that include TGF-β 1, 2, 3, 4, and 5. An interesting property of TGF-β is that it is secreted in a biologically inactive latent form. The latent form can be activated in vitro by heat, acidification and proteases (70). Activation of latent TGF-β in vivo by proteases could be a regulatory mechanism for mediating TGF-β activity.

Although an inhibitor of endothelial cell proliferation, as will be discussed below, TGF-β stimulates angiogenesis in vivo. When injected subcutaneously into the nape of the necks of mice at a dose of 1 μg, TGF-β causes the formation of a highly vascular granulation tissue in two to three days (103). Neither EGF nor PDGF has a similar effect. Since TGF-β is not an endothelial cell mitogen, it is possible that TGF-β promotes angiogenesis by differentiating endothelial cells after their proliferative phase has ended, possibly by inducing the synthesis of matrix. Alternatively, TGF-β may stimulate angiogenesis indirectly. TGF-β is highly chemotactic for monocytes (133). These cells might infiltrate a wound site under the influence of TGF-β and produce angiogenesis factors that are mitogenic for endothelial cells.

Tumor Necrosis Factor-Alpha

Tumor necrosis factor-alpha (TNF-α) is an anionic 17-kd single-chain polypeptide (11). It is a secreted protein synthesized primarily by activated macrophages and by some tumor cells. It is structurally related to lymphotoxin (28% sequence homology), a lymphocyte product also known as TNF-β (52). TNF-α is a multifunctional polypeptide that is a pleiotropic mediator of inflammation and immunity. TNF-α induces cachexia and is also known as cachectin. The term cachectin/TNF-α is often used (11). TNF-α has a wide range of activities that affect endothelial cells and that may be important in the response of these cells to infection and injury. For example, TNF-α stimulates granulocyte-macrophage-colony stimulating factor (GM-CSF) synthesis, interleukin-1 synthesis, and the induction of intercellular adhesion molecule-1 (ICAM-1), which in turn promote leukocyte adhesion to endothelial cells (12, 90).

TNF-α is angiogenic in vivo (43, 71) and, in fact, is claimed to be responsible for the total angiogenesis activity of macrophages (71). In one study, it was demonstrated that TNF-α stimulated angiogenesis in the cornea at 3.5 ng and in the CAM at 1 ng without any evidence of inflammation (71). The TNF-α stimulated angiogenesis at lower concentrations than did FGF, angiogenin, EGF, and TGF-α. In another study, however, it was found that while TNF-α is angiogenic in the cornea, higher amounts (5 μg) were required compared to FGF (0.5 μg) (43). In terms of its effect on endothelial cells, TNF-α is similar in many ways to TGF-β: both polypeptides induce angiogenesis in vivo, promote tube formation in vitro, and inhibit endothelial cell proliferation in vitro. It may be that TNF-α and TGF-β influence angiogenesis by promoting endothelial cell differentiation, e.g. tube formation, matrix production, rather than proliferation. Alternatively, TNF-α stimulation of angiogenesis might occur by some indirect mechanism, such as by stimulating other cells to produce angiogenic factors.

Colony Stimulating Factors

Granulocyte-colony stimulating factor (G-CSF) (18 kd) and GM-CSF (14–35 k) are myeloid growth factors required for the survival, growth, and differentiation of hematopoetic precursor cells (21). GM-CSF may be a heparin-binding protein since it had been shown that the major sulfated glycosaminoglycan of mouse marrow stroma, heparan sulfate, can absorb GM-CSF (104). Recombinant G-CSF and GM-CSF, at 200–250 pM, stimulate the migration and proliferation of human endothelial cells (18). These stimulatory effects are modest, however, in comparison to bFGF, and no angiogenesis data are available to indicate that the colony-stimulating factors are angiogenic.

Low Molecular Weight Non-Peptide Angiogenesis Factors

A number of low molecular weight compounds are reported to be angiogenic. They have been isolated from tumors, macrophages, serum, and adipocytes to mention just a few sources. These factors include well-known metabolites such as prostaglandins and nicotinamide. Recently, 1-butyryl-glycerol (monobutyrin) was identified as the angiogenesis factor produced by adipocytes (29). It is difficult to ascertain the role of low molecular weight non-peptides in mediating angiogenesis. One question is whether these compounds are actually angiogenesis factors as opposed to co-factors and nutrients that promote or enhance the angiogenic response.

Mechanisms of Angiogenesis

In summary, there appear to be many stimulators of angiogenesis. Their properties, in particular the ability to stimulate endothelial cell migration and proliferation, their specificity, and their ability to be secreted, are summarized in Table 1. The effects of angiogenesis factors on endothelial cells in culture vary dramatically. FGF, VEGF/VPF, PD-ECGF, and TGF-α are examples of angiogenesis factors that directly stimulate endothelial cell migration and proliferation. Angiotropin stimulates migration, but not proliferation. Angiogenin seems to have no effect on endothelial cell migration and proliferation. TGF-β and TNF-α are inhibitors of endothelial cell proliferation, but they can induce three-dimensional tube formation and angiogenesis. Angiogenesis factors differ in target cell specificity. VEGF, PD-ECGF, and angiotropin are the only angiogenesis factors that appear to be specific for endothelial cells. Finally, with the exception of FGF and PD-ECGF, most of the angiogenesis factors are secreted, which suggests paracrine functions. FGF and PD-ECGF may be released by cell lysis. Thus it is clear from the different properties of these various factors that angiogenesis can be induced by different mechanisms, most of which have yet to be elucidated. Some factors influence angiogenesis by stimulating migration and proliferation, while others appear to be more active in the differentiation pathway. Some angiogenesis factors probably work directly on endothelium, while others most likely work indirectly by activating a secondary cell to produce angiogenesis factors. The large number of angiogenesis factors suggests redundancy in the vascularization process. The process of angiogenesis is sufficiently important so that tissues do not rely on one angiogenesis factor alone. The redundancy of angiogenesis factors, however, might make anti-angiogenesis therapy difficult. It will be of interest to see if the various angiogenesis factors act synergistically and are differentially regulated.

INHIBITORS OF ANGIOGENESIS

Over the past decade an increasing number of angiogenesis inhibitors have been described. In many cases, initial identification utilized in vitro assays examining the effect of the putative inhibitory substances on endothelial cell functions such as proliferation, migration, or protease production. In the end, however, bona fide demonstration of an anti-angiogenic activity requires the substances to be capable of blocking new vessel growth in any one of a number of in vivo assay systems (see Introduction) (Table 2).

Angiostatic Steroids

A series of studies using the CAM, where new vessel growth was promoted by heparin and prevented by protamine (122), led to the unexpected finding that the combination of heparin and cortisone could block angiogenesis in the CAM, cause regression of tumor masses, and prevent metastasis (40). A non-anticoagulant heparin fragment of six sugar units (40) as well as hex-

Table 1 Angiogenesis factors

Name	MW	Heparin-binding	Angiogenesis	EC migration	EC proliferation	EC specific	Secreted
FGF	18,000	+	+	+	+	o	o
VEGF/VPF	46,000 (dimer)	+	+	+	+	+	+
PD-ECGF	46,000	o	+	+	+	+	o
TGF-α	5,500	o	+	+	+	o	+
Angiogenin	14,100	o	+	o	o	nd	+
Angiotropin	4,500	nd	+	+	o	+	+
TGF-β	25,000 (dimer)	o	+	–	–	o	+
TNF-α	17,000	o	+	+	–	o	+

Abbreviations: + = yes; o = no; – = inhibitory; nd = not determined; EC = endothelial cell.

uronyl hexosaminoglycan sulfate (105), a heparin analogue, were able to substitute for whole heparin in this anti-angiogenic activity. Furthermore, whole heparin could be taken orally (and degraded in the gut into heparin fragments) and was efficacious in the presence of cortisone to inhibit tumor growth and metastasis. The heparin-cortisone combination was also found to inhibit vascularization in rabbit corneas stimulated by de-epithelialization as well as by autograph transplant (94). In subsequent studies, a novel class of steroids, lacking glucocorticoid and mineralocorticoid activity, was shown to be anti-angiogenic when administered in the presence of heparin or heparin fragments (24). Structural studies conducted with steroid analogues revealed that the anti-angiogenic activity was associated with the pregnant structure and was determined primarily by structural elements on the D-ring.

Table 2 Angiogenesis inhibitors

Factor	MW	Heparin-binding	Angiogenesis	EC migration	EC proliferation
Angiostatic steroids	na	na	–	nd	–
Platelet Factor IV	28,000	+	–	nd	–
TNF-α	17,000	o	+	+	–
Thrombospondin	160,000	+	–	–	nd
TGF-β	25,000 (dimer)	o	+	–	–
γ-interferon	50,000	o	–	–	–
Protamine	43,000	+	–	nd	–

Abbreviations: + = yes; o = no; – = inhibitory; nd = not determined; na = not applicable; EC = endothelial cell.

In an effort to understand the mechanism of inhibition in these experiments, studies were conducted to assess the effect of heparin, hydrocortisone, and their combination on thymidine incorporation into cerebral microvessel endothelium in vivo (10). The two agents had a slight inhibitory effect on DNA synthesis in endothelial cells. When a freeze lesion was created to induce endothelial proliferation, the administration of cortisone significantly reduced the labeling index of the endothelium. The addition of heparin to the cortisone did not lower the labeling, and heparin by itself did not alter the labeling frequency. Thus in this single set of in vivo experiments, the combination of heparin with cortisone did not appear to be any more potent as an inhibitor than the cortisone alone. In another series of tissue culture studies, heparin plus cortisone was shown to significantly inhibit endothelial cell proliferation (106). Extracts of tumors from untreated animals as well as animals treated with hydrocortisone in combination with the heparin analogue, hexuronyl hexosaminoglycan sulfate, were assayed for their effect on endothelial cell migration in vitro (105). Extracts from treated animals markedly reduced endothelial migration, whereas extracts from control animals or those treated with either agent alone were without effect. These data suggest that the heparin/cortisone combination acts to inhibit angiogenesis by altering the ability of the tumor to elicit new vessels.

An alternate mechanism of heparin-angiostatic steroid-induced inhibition of neovascularization was suggested by studies in which immunohistochemical methods were used to study basement membrane structure. These studies indicated that the steriods might work by inducing basement membrane breakdown which leads to capillary regression (62). The importance of an intact basement membrane to normal vascularization was further pointed out in experiments in which regression of growing capillaries was induced by the administration of proline analogues and an inhibitor of proxlyl hydroxylase, which interfere with collagen fibril formation and deposition (61). These two sets of observations suggest that the regression of capillaries may be induced by a loss of structural integrity of their underlying basement membranes.

ENDOTHELIAL CELL INHIBITORS

There are a number of peptide growth regulators (e.g. TGF-β, TNF-α) that act to inhibit the proliferation of vascular endothelial cells. Although it has been suspected that endothelial cell stimulators would be angiogenic, and that endothelial cell inhibitors would be anti-angiogenic, it does not appear that these activities are necessarily correlated.

Thrombospondin

Thrombospondin is a 160-kd adhesive glycoprotein found in platelet alpha granules, where it is suspected to participate in the stabilization of platelet aggregates (97). It is also synthesized by a number of cultured cells, which deposit it into their extracellular matrices (88). In an interesting series of studies thrombospondin was shown to inhibit neovascularization (48). These studies were initiated when an anti-angiogenic factor was identified in the conditioned media of hamster and hamster-human hybrid cells. This inhibitory activity appeared to be linked to the presence of an active cancer suppressor gene and was identified using a series of transformants and revertants as well as a temperature-sensitive transformant (101). Conditioned media from temperature-sensitive transformants were assayed in the corneal pocket and were shown to inhibit new vessel growth. Antibodies were made to the purified inhibitor, a molecule of 140 kd (Gp140). Gp 140 is shown to be homologous to the C-terminal portion of human thrombospondin, as well as to exhibit immunological cross-reactivity and functional similarity. Both human thrombospondin and Gp 140 inhibit the migration of endothelial cells in vitro and neovascularization in the rat corneal pocket assay (101). Although actual linkage between the tumor suppressor gene and the thrombospondin is not known, it is clear that thrombospondin is not a product of the suppressor gene. Instead the suppressor gene appears to promote Gp140 in *trans;* thrombospondin is located on chromosome 15 and the suppressor is on chromosome 1.

Platelet Factor IV (PFIV)

Platelet factor IV (PFIV), a 28-kd tetrameric protein found in platelet alpha granules and released during platelet aggregation, was initially characterized by its high degree of affinity for heparin (134). Early studies by Taylor & Folkman (122), in which this compound was used as a control for the effects of protamine, indicated that PFIV was a potent anti-angiogenic factor. A recent report using recombinant human PFIV has extended these initial observations and identified the anti-angiogenic portion of PFIV to the carboxyl-terminal heparin-binding region (79). The specificity of this effect was revealed by controls in which the inclusion of heparin in the CAM implant eliminated the anti-angiogenic effect. More recently, human recombinant PFIV has been shown to inhibit the growth of solid tumors (115). PFIV has also been shown to block growth factor-dependent stimulation of human umbilical vein endothelial cells, an action that could be antagonized by readdition of growth factor. The recent identification of PD-ECGF, a platelet-derived angiogenesis factor (63), has led to the suggestion (79) that a "balance of platelet proteins may be important for the control of angiogenesis."

Transforming Growth Factor Type-β

TGF-β is a 25-kd homodimer that is found at high levels in human platelets (3) and bone (111), as well as in placenta, kidney, and tumor cells. It is a multifunctional regulator and is known to have a variety of effects depending on cell type, by acting as both a stimulator of cell proliferation and an inhibitor and inducer of differentiation (for review, see 119). TGF-β was originally characterized by its ability to promote anchorage-independent growth of normal fibroblasts (128). TGF-β is a potent inhibitor of both large vessel (6, 42, 55) and microvessel (65, P. A. D'Amore, S. R. Smith, manuscript submitted) endothelial cells and inhibits both baseline and growth factor- (e.g. FGF) stimulated growth. Of the three forms of TGF-β that have been assayed, TGF-β1, TGF-β2, and TGF-β1.2, the β1 form has by far the most potent inhibitory effect on both large vessels (65) and microvessel endothelium (P. A. D'Amore, S. R. Smith, manuscript submitted). TGF-β blocks endothelial cell motility, both in a Boyden chamber and in response to wounding of a monolayer, and inhibits the ability of endothelial cells to invade collagen gels and form capillary-like structures (89). The effects of TGF-β on endothelial cells appear to be a function of the culture conditions. When capillary endothelial cells are grown in a three-dimensional collagen gel, TGF-β (0.5 ng/ml) induces the formation of complex, branching, tube-like structures, but has no influence on growth (77). Thus it appears that TGF-β may be an inducer of endothelial cell differentiation by inhibiting endothelial cell migration and proliferation and stimulating three-dimensional tube formation.

It seems paradoxical that the administration of TGF-β in any one of a number of in vivo systems acts to induce the growth of new blood vessels (see above discussion of angiogenic activity of TGF-β) while it inhibits endothelial cell growth in vitro. Some insight into this question is provided by the finding that TGF-β is an extremely powerful chemoattractant for monocytes (133). As such, it has been suggested that the angiogenic effects of TGF-β are indirect and are mediated by a second cell type, in this case, the macrophage/monocyte. Thus the administration of a bolus of TGF-β, either in an experimental system or via the platelet at a wound site, might act to induce chemotaxis of macrophages, which would release a variety of angiogenic factors, including FGF.

At the same time, we postulate that TFG-β in the microenvironment of capillary beds, in the absence of excess stimulators, might suppress endothelial cell growth, thereby inhibiting angiogenesis and maintaining a quiescent, differentiated microvascular bed. The mechanism of TGF-β at the cellular level is unknown, but may be mediated by the effects of TGF-β on increasing matrix accumulation (for review see 119). In support of this concept, we (96) have used a tissue culture model to show that the co-culture of capillary endothelial cells with either smooth muscle cells or pericytes inhibits the proliferation of the endothelial cells. We (2) and others (108) have determined that this inhibition is mediated by the activation of TGF-β that is dependent on contact between the two cell types. We postulate that this in vitro interaction mimics the contact that occurs between the vascular endothelium and the vessel wall cells (smooth muscle cells or pericytes) and that activated TGF-β may, in fact, be an important mediator of vascular differentiation in vivo. We further speculate that under these conditions the growth state of the vasculature is a net effect between levels of inhibitors such as TGF-β and stimulators such as FGF.

Interferons

Gamma interferon is a 50-kd glycoprotein, shown to be a powerful growth inhibitor for a variety of normal and transformed cells. Gamma interferon has been shown to inhibit aFGF-induced endothelial cell proliferation in a dose-dependent manner (44). Further, this inhibition is associated with a reduction in binding of aFGF to the endothelial cell surface, which indicates that the mechanism of inhibition may be via modulation of the FGF receptor. Gamma interferon has also been shown to inhibit interleukin 2 (IL2)-stimulated endothelial cell growth (58). Using an in vitro model of angiogenesis, γ-interferon was also shown to inhibit capillary formation (129) and endothelial cell growth (57) in a dose-dependent manner. Further, dramatic results have been obtained using alpha interferon in the treatment of hemangioendotheliomas (95, 137), thus indicating a role for interferon as an anti-angiogenic agent.

Tumor Necrosis Factor-Alpha

TNF-α is a polypeptide originally isolated from macrophages [for more details of TNF-α structure and non-endothelial functions see above and (11)]. This molecule induces a number of endothelial functions including expression of interleukin 1 (92) and GM-CSF (90). The ability of TNF-α/cachectin to cause tumor necrosis and regression (20) and to block metastasis (135) has led to the speculation that TNF-α might act by inhibiting endothelial proliferation and thus blocking angiogenesis. TNF-α reversibly blocks basal and FGF-stimulated growth of aortic and capillary endothelial cells with half-maximal inhibition at 1 ng/ml (43). The inhibitory activity is not specific for the endothelium as smooth muscle cell growth is inhibited by similar concentrations of TNF-α. Earlier observations had suggested that the inhibitory actions of TNF-α on endothelial cells might be due to cytotoxicity (107). Pre-labeling studies and the reversibility of the inhibition, however, suggest that this is not the case (43). The unexpected finding that this endothelial inhibitor acts to stimulate neovascularization (43) is reminiscent of the actions of TGF-β. The fact that both growth factors induce angiogenesis in association with inflammation strongly suggests a role for another cell type (perhaps macrophage) in mediating the angiogenic response.

Protamine

Protamine is a polycationic protein of 43 kd. It is isolated from sperm and is best known for its ability to bind with high avidity to heparin. Protamine has been shown to be a specific inhibitor of angiogenesis (122). When applied to five or six day CAMs, large avascular zones are observed. In contrast, no anti-angiogenic effect was observed when protamine was administered to older (ten day old) CAMs, which indicates that the anti-angiogenic effect required proliferating/remodeling blood vessels. Protamine prevented neovascularization that was induced by the implantation of a V2 carcinoma into the rabbit ear model. Protamine was also able to block angiogenesis induced by silica particles, thus indicating that it was also effective against inflammatory angiogenesis. Systemic administration of protamine was able to block tumor growth as well as metastasis in a number of animal tumor models (56, 80). Subcutaneous administration of protamine was shown to inhibit embryonic vascularization in a rat model, which resulted in significantly lower capillary densities and a larger variability in capillary spacing than in the untreated controls (100).

The mechanism of this protamine-mediated anti-angiogenic effect is unknown. The fact, however, that other heparin-binding molecules, such as PF IV and major basic protein, which also display a high affinity for heparin, are anti-angiogenic (122) suggests that the mechanism of these molecules might be via their heparin-binding ability. It is appealing to speculate that these factors may act by blocking the action of heparin-binding growth factors, such as the FGFs, but no data have been generated to support or refute this hypothesis. The fact that protamine does not directly affect the proliferation of the tumor cells does suggest a direct effect of protamine on the endothelium (80). Evidence for this comes from the fact that protamine sulfate has been shown to inhibit the mitogenic activity of both matrix-associated and soluble FGF (93).

Tissue-Derived Inhibitors

There are several tissues, including vitreous and cartilage, that are avascular under normal circumstances. Their avascular state has led to the hypothesis that these tissues contain naturally occurring inhibitors of angiogenesis. Over the past several decades a number of laboratories have attempted to purify anti-angiogenic factors from these tissues.

VITREOUS/LENS Implantation of a carcinoma into the rabbit vitreous led to tumor growth for several weeks as unvascularized three-dimensional aggregates. Only when the tumors reached the retinal surface did vascularization proceed and exponential tumor growth occur. This observation prompted the suggestion that normal vitreous may somehow act to inhibit capillary proliferation (15). In a subsequent study, extracts of vitreous were shown to inhibit tumor-induced neovascularization in the rabbit corneal pocket model (99). Vitreous (which is rich in hyaluronic acid) was compared with keratin sulfate, chondroitin sulfate, and hyaluronic acid for anti-angiogenic activity in the CAM assay. Vitreous caused a dose-dependent inhibition of a retinal extract-induced neovascularization, whereas the sulfated glycosaminoglycans showed no inhibitory activity. Bovine hyaluronic acid revealed some slight, but not statistically significant inhibition of neovascularization, and digestion of a vitreous with hyaluronidase had no influence on the inhibitory activity (75). In vitro studies using cultured endothelial cells revealed that vitreous contains activities that prevented cell proliferation (74, 102). At present, the identity of the vitreous-derived inhibitors is not clear.

Another avascular tissue of the eye is the lens. Clinicians have observed that following removal of the lens, diabetic eyes with proliferative retinopathy have an increased frequency of neovascularization of the iris, which leads to the suggestion that the lens may have a constitutively suppressive effect on blood vessel growth. Towards this end, the extracts of both bovine and human lenses have been studied for their effect on endothelial cell growth and have been shown to be inhibitory in a specific (no inhibition of smooth muscle cells) and reversible manner (138).

CARTILAGE The resistance of cartilage to tumor invasion has led to the examination of cartilage as a source of anti-angiogenic activity. Using the rabbit corneal pocket assay, an implant of neonatal scapular cartilage was shown to depress the rate of capillary growth by an average of 75% (14). Subsequently, a guanidine extract of cartilage was demonstrated to prevent tumor-induced neovascularization in the rabbit corneal pocket model (68), and local infusion of a partially purified cartilage extract onto corneas in which B2 carcinoma has been implanted led to inhibition of neovascularization to less than 3% of the untreated controls. Tissue culture studies revealed that the partially purified inhibitor had no effect when assayed directly on tumor cell growth, whereas partially purified extracts of bovine cartilage inhibited endothelial cell growth (118, 121). These studies provide strong evidence that the cartilage inhibitor acts directly to prevent angiogenesis (69). More recently, a 28-kd inhibitor of mammalian collagenase was isolated from bovine scapular cartilage (91). Assay of this cartilage-derived inhibitor revealed that it was effective in inhibiting the proliferation and migration of capillary endothelial cells in vitro as well as new blood vessel growth in the CAM assay (87). In support of a role for collagenase in angiogenesis, it had been earlier demonstrated that medroxyprogesterone could inhibit tumor growth and vascularization of a V2 carcinoma in the rabbit corneal pocket assay (53). The inhibitory action was associated with reduced release of collagenase into the culture media by explants of the treated tumors and by explants of the area of the cornea containing the tumor. In the process of angiogenesis, proteases are important both for facilitating the escape of the endothelial cells from the parent venule (54), as well as for allowing tumor cells to migrate through the vascular wall in the process of metastasis. Thus, the potential for protease inhibitors in influencing vessel growth is obvious.

SUMMARY AND FUTURE DIRECTIONS

The field of angiogenesis has seen dramatic progress over the past two decades since Folkman first pointed out the importance of this process to tumor vascularization (37). Initially it seemed that there might be an angiogenic factor unique to tumors. This concept was dispelled by the finding that at least one angiogenic factor (bFGF) had wide tissue distribution in both tumors and normal tissue. Furthermore, it is now obvious that there are a number of angiogenic factors. Since the distribution and action of these factors is not yet known, it is difficult to speculate on their relative contributions to angiogenesis. It is clear that our knowledge is fragmentary and that a number of important questions remain to be answered before a complete picture will be elucidated concerning the control of angiogenesis. For instance, two of the angiogenic factors described (the FGFs and PD-ECGF) lack signal sequences and the mechanism of their release is therefore unclear. Localization of FGF to cell-surfaces (85, 126) and matrix-associated (8, 131) heparin-like molecules has led to the speculation that these may act as easily accessible reservoirs of FGF. How does the FGF gain access to these sites? Since no significant functional differences have been demonstrated between acidic and basic FGF, what is the purpose of the two forms of FGF? Are there qualitative differences among the various kinds of angiogenesis (e.g. embryogenesis, wound healing, tumor vascularization, and so on)? How is the process of angiogenesis regulated? Is quiescence maintained by a balance between stimulators and inhibitors? If so, might one be able to induce or block neovascularization simply by interfering with this balance? Some insight into these questions will require the use of specific reagents that can specifically block or stimulate vessel growth. A good example is provided by studies in which neutralizing antibodies against bFGF were shown to block neovascularization induced by a sponge implant, which strongly implicates a role for bFGF in wound repair (16). Finally, although a variety of substances have been demonstrated to block angiogenesis using in vivo assays, none has been demonstrated to function physiologically.

ACKNOWLEDGMENTS

This work was supported by National Institutes of Health grants NCI CA 37392, NCI CA 45548 (MK), and NEI EY 05985 (PD'A). PD'A is an Established Investigator of the American Heart Association. We thank Carlene Pavlos for preparing the manuscript.

Literature Cited

1. Abraham, J. A., Mergia, A., Whang, J. L., Tumolo, A., Friedman, J., et al. Nucleotide sequence of a bovine clone encoding the angiogenic protein, basic fibroblast growth factor. *Science* 233: 545–48
2. Antonelli-Orlidge, A., Saunders, K. B., Smith, S. R. D'Amore, P. A. 1989. An activated form of TGF-β is produced by co-cultures of endothelial cells and pericytes. *Proc. Natl. Acad. Sci. USA* 86:4544–48
3. Assoian, R. K., Sporn, M. B. 1986. Type-beta transforming growth factor in human platelets: release during platelet degranulation and action on vascular smooth muscle cells. *J. Cell Biol.* 102:1217–23
4. Ausprunk, D. H., Knighton, D. R., Folkman, J. 1974. Differentiation of vascular endothelium in the chick chorioallantois: a structural and autoradiographic study. *Dev. Biol.* 38:237–48
5. Badet, J., Soncin, F., Guitton, J.-D., Lamare, O., Cartwright, T., Barritault, D. 1989. Specific binding of angiogenin to calf pulmonary artery endothelial cells. *Proc. Natl. Acad. Sci. USA* 86:8427–31
6. Baird, A., Durkin, T. 1986. Inhibition of endothelial cell proliferation by type β-transforming growth factor: interactions with acidic and basic fibroblast factors. *Biochem. Biophys. Res. Commun.* 138:476–82
7. Baird, A., Ling, N. 1987. Fibroblast growth factors are present in the extracellular matrix produced by endothelial cells in vitro: implications for a role of heparinase-like enzymes in the neovascular response. *Biochem. Biophys. Res. Commun.* 142:428–35
8. Deleted in proof
9. Bashkin, P., Doctrow, S., Klagsbrun, M., Svahn, C. M., Folkman, J., Vlodavsky, I. 1989. Basic fibroblast growth factor binds to subendothelial extracellular matrix and is released by heparitinase and heparin-like molecules. *Biochemistry* 28:1737–43
10. Beck, D. W., Jeffrey, J. O., Lindhardt, R. J. 1986. Effect of heparin, heparin fragments, and corticosteroids on cerebral endothelial cell growth in vitro and in vivo. *J. Neuropath. Exp. Neurol.* 45: 503–12
11. Beutler, B., Cerami, A. 1986. Cachetin and tumour necrosis factor as two sides of the same biological coin. *Nature* 320:584–88
12. Bevilacqua, M. P., Pober, J. S., Wheeler, M. E., Cotran, R. S., Gimbone, M. A. Jr. 1985. Interleukin 1 acts on cultured human vascular endothelium to increase the adhesion of polymorphonuclear leukocytes, monocytes and related leukocyte cell lines. *J. Clin. Invest.* 76:2003–11
13. Bicknell, R., Vallee, B. L. 1988. Angiogenin activates endothelial cell phosphlipase C. *Proc. Natl. Acad. Sci. USA* 85:5961–65
14. Brem, H., Folkman, J. 1975. Inhibition of tumor angiogenesis mediated by cartilage. *J. Exp. Med.* 141:427–39
15. Brem, S., Brem, H., Folkman, J., Finkelstein, D., Patz, A. 1976. Prolonged tumor dormancy by prevention of neovascularization in the vitreous. *Cancer Res.* 36:2807–12
16. Broadley, K. N., Aquino, A. M., Woodward, S. C., Buckley, S. A., Sato, Y., et al. 1989. Monospecific antibodies implicate basic fibroblast growth factor in normal wound repair. *Lab. Invest.* 61:571–75
17. Burgess, W. H., Maciag, T. 1989. The heparin-binding (fibroblast) growth factor family of proteins. *Annu. Rev. Biochem.* 58:575–606
18. Bussolino, F., Wang, J. M., Defilippi, P., Turrini, F., Sanavio, F., et al. 1989. Granulocyte- and granulocyte- macrophage-colony stimulating factors induce human endothelial cells to migrate and proliferate. *Nature* 337:471–73
19. Carpenter, G., Cohen, S. 1979. Epidermal growth factor. *Annu. Rev. Biochem.* 48:193–216
20. Carswell, E. A., Old, L. J., Kassel, R. L., Green, S., Fiore, N., Williamson, B. 1975. An endotoxin-induced serum factor that causes tumor necrosis. *Proc. Natl. Acad. Sci. USA* 72:3666–70
21. Clark, S. C., Kamen, R. 1987. The human hematopoietic colony-stimulating factors. *Science* 236:1229–37
22. Conn, G., Bayne, M. L., Soderman, D. D., Kwok, P. W., Sullivan, K. A., et al. 1990. Amino acid and cDNA sequences of a vascular endothelial cell mitogen that is homologous to platelet-derived growth factor. *Proc. Natl. Acad. Sci. USA* 87:2628–32
23. Connolly, D. T., Heuvelman, D. M., Nelson, R., Olander, J. V., Eppley, B.

L., et al. 1989. Tumor vascular permeability factor stimulates endothelial cell growth and angiogenesis. *J. Clin. Invest.* 84:1478–89
24. Crum, R., Szabo, S., Folkman, J. 1985. A new class of steroids inhibits angiogenesis in the presence of heparin or a heparin fragment. *Science* 230:1375–78
25. D'Amore, P. A., Klagsbrun, M. 1989. Angiogenesis: Factors and mechanisms. In *The Pathobiology of Neoplasia,* ed. A. E. Sirica. pp. 513–31. New York: Plenum
26. Davidson, J. M., Klagsbrun, M., Hill, K. E., Buckley, A., Sullivan, R., et al. 1985. Accelerated wound repair, cell proliferation, and collagen accumulation are produced by a cartilage-derived growth factor. *J. Cell Biol.* 100:1219–1227
27. Delli-Bovi, P., Curatola, A. M., Kern, F. G., Greco, A., Ittmann, M., Basilico, C. 1987. An oncogene isolated by transfection of Kaposi's sarcoma DNA encodes a growth factor that is a member of the FGF family. *Cell* 50: 729–37
28. Dickson, C., Smith, R., Brookes, S., Peters, G. 1990. Proviral insertions within the int-2 can generate multiple anomalous transcripts but leave the protein-coding domain intact. *J. Virol.* 64:784–93
29. Dobson, D. E., Kambe, A., Block, E., Dion, T., Lu, H., Castellot, J. J. Jr., Speigelman, B. M. 1990. 1-Butyrylglycerol: A novel angiogenesis factor secreted by differentiating adipocytes. *Cell* 61:223–30
30. Esch, F., Baird, A., Ling, N., Ueno, N., Hill, F., et al. 1985. Primary structure of bovine pituitary basic fibroblast growth factor (FGF) and comparison with the amino-terminal sequence of bovine brain acidic FGF. *Proc. Natl. Acad. Sci. USA* 82:6507–11
31. Esch, F., Ueno, N., Baird, A., Hill, F., Denoroy, L., et al. 1985. Primary structure of bovine brain acidic fibroblast growth factor (FGF). *Biochem. Biophys. Res. Commun.* 133:554–62
32. Ferrara, N., Henzel, W. J. 1989. Pituitary follicular cells secrete a novel heparin-binding growth factor specific for vascular endothelial cells. *Biochem. Biophys. Res. Commun.* 161:851–55
33. Fett, J. W., Strydom, D. J., Lobb, R. F., Alderman, E. M., Bethune, J. L., et al. 1985. Isolation and characterization of angiogenin, an angiogenic protein from human carcinoma cells. *Biochemistry* 24:5480–86
34. Finch, P. W., Rubin, J. S., Miki, T., Ron, D., Aaronson, S. A. 1989. Human KGF is FGF-related with properties of a paracrine effector of epithelial cell growth. *Science* 245:752–55
35. Florkiewicz, R. A., Sommer, A. 1989. Human basic fibroblast growth factor gene encodes four polypeptides: three initiate translation from non-AUG codons. *Proc. Natl. Acad. Sci. USA* 86:3978–81
36. Folkman, J. 1971. Tumor angiogenesis: therapeutic implications. *N. Engl. J. Med.* 285:1182–86
37. Folkman, J. 1972. Anti-angiogenesis: new concept of therapy of solid tumors. *Ann. Surg.* 175:409–16
38. Folkman, J., Haudenschild, C., Zetter, B. R. 1979. Long-term culture of capillary endothelial cells. *Proc. Natl. Acad. Sci. USA* 76:5217–21
39. Folkman, J., Klagsbrun, M. 1987. Angiogenic factors. *Science* 235:442–47
40. Folkman, J., Langer, R., Linhardt R. J., Haudenschild, C., Taylor, S. 1983. Angiogenesis inhibition and tumor regression caused by heparin or a heparin fragment in the presence of cortisone. *Science* 221:719–25
41. Fox, E. A., Riordan, J. F. 1990. The molecular biology of angiogenin. In *Molecular Biology of the Cardiovascular System,* ed. S. Chien. pp. 139–54. Philadelphia: Lea & Fabiger.
42. Frater-Schroder, M., Muller, G., Birchmeier, W., Bohlen, P. 1986. Transforming growth factor-beta inhibits endothelial cell proliferation. *Biochem. Biophys. Res. Commun.* 137:295–302
43. Frater-Schroder, M., Risau, W., Hallmann, R., Gautschi, R., Bohlen, P. 1987. Tumor necrosis factor type-α, a potent inhibitor of endothelial cell growth in vitro, is angiogenic in vivo. *Proc. Natl. Acad. Sci. USA* 84:5277–81
44. Friesel, R., Komoriya, A., Maciag, T. 1987. Inhibition of endothelial cell proliferation by gamma-interferon. *J. Cell Biol.* 104:689–96
45. Gimbrone, M. A. Jr., Cotran, R. S., Folkman, J. 1974. Tumor growth neovascularization: an experimental model using rabbit cornea. *J. Natl. Cancer Inst.* 52:413–27
46. Gimenez-Gallego, G., Rodkey, J., Bennet, C., Rios-Candelore, M., DiSalvo, J., Thomas, K. 1985. Brain-derived acidic fibroblast growth factor: complete amino acid sequence and homologies. *Science* 230:1385–88
47. Glaser, B. M., D'Amore, P. A., Seppa, H., Seppa, S., Schiffman, E. 1980.

Adult tissues contain chemoattractants for vascular endothelial cells. *Nature* 288:483–84
48. Good, D. J., Polverini, P. J., Rastinejad, F., Le Beau, M. M., Lemons, R. S., et al. 1990. A tumor suppressor-dependent inhibitor of angiogenesis is immunologically and functionally indistinguishable from a fragment of thrombospondin. *Proc. Natl. Acad. Sci. USA*. In press
49. Gospodarowicz, D., Abraham, J. A., Schilling, J. 1989. Isolation and characterization of a vascular endothelial cell mitogen produced by pituitary-derived folliculo stellate cells. *Proc. Natl. Acad. Sci, USA* 86:7311–15
50. Gospodarowicz, D., Cheng, J., Lui, G.-M., Baird, A., Bohlen, P. 1984. Isolation of brain fibroblast growth factor by heparin-Sepharose affinity chromatography: identity with pituitary fibroblast growth factor. *Proc. Natl. Acad. Sci. USA* 81:6963–67
51. Gospodarowicz, D., Ferrara, N., Schweigerer, L., Neufeld, G. 1987. Structural characterization and biological functions of fibroblast growth factor. *Endocr. Rev.* 8:95–114
52. Gray, P. W., Aggarwal, B. B., Benten, C. V., Bringman, T. S., Henzel, W. J., et al. 1984. Cloning and expression of cDNA for human lymphotoxin, a lymphokine with tumor necrosis activity. *Nature* 320:584–88
53. Gross, J., Azizkhan, G. G., Biswas, C., Bruns, R. R., Hsieh, D. S., Folkman, J. 1981. Inhibition of tumor growth, vascularization, and collagenolysis in the rabbit cornea by medroxyprogesterone. *Proc. Natl. Acad. Sci. USA* 78: 1176–80
54. Gross, J. L., Moscatelli, D., Rifkin, D. B. 1983. Increased capillary endothelial cell protease activity in response to angiogenic stimuli in vitro. *Proc. Natl. Acad. Sci. USA* 80:2623–27
55. Heimark, R. L., Twardzik, D. R., Schwartz, S. M. 1986. Inhibition of endothelial cell regeneration by type-beta transforming growth factor from platelets. *Science* 233:1078–80
56. Heuser, L. S., Taylor, S. H., Folkman, J. 1984. Prevention of carcinomatosis and bloody malignant ascites in the rat by an inhibitor of angiogenesis. *J. Surg. Res.* 36:244–50
57. Heyns, A. D., Eldor, A., Vlodavsky, I., Kaiser, N., Fridman, R., Panet, A. 1985. The antiproliferative effect of interferon and the mitogenic activity of growth factors are independent of cell cycle events: studies with vascular smooth muscle and endothelial cells. *Exp. Cell Res.* 161:297–306
58. Hicks, C., Breit, S. N., Penny, R. 1989. Response of microvascular endothelial cells of biological response modifiers. *Immunol. Cell. Biol.* 67:271–77
59. Hockel, M., Jung, W., Vaupel, P., Rabes, H., Khaledpour, C., Wissler, J. H. 1988. Purified monocyte-derived angiogenic substance (angiotropin) induces controlled angiogenesis associated with regulated tissue proliferation in rabbit skin. *J. Clin. Invest.* 82:1075–90
60. Iberg, N., Rogelj, S., Fanning, P., Klagsbrun, M. 1989. Purification of 18- and 22-kDa forms of basic fibroblast growth factor from rat cells transformed by the *ras* oncogene. *J. Biol. Chem.* 264:19951–55
61. Ingber, D., Folkman, J. 1988. Inhibition of angiogenesis through modulation of collagen metabolism. *Lab. Invest.* 59: 44–51
62. Ingber, D. E., Madri, J. A., Folkman, J. 1986. A possible mechanism for inhibition of angiogenesis by angiostatic steroids: induction of capillary basement membrane dissolution. *Endocrinology* 119:1768–75
63. Ishikawa, F., Miyazono, K., Hellman, U., Wernstedt, C., Hagiwara, K., et al. cDNA cloning and expression of a novel angiogenic factor - platelet-derived endothelial cell growth factor. *Nature* 338:557–62
64. Jaye, M., Howk, R., Burgess, W., Ricca, G. A., Chiu, I.-M., et al. 1986. Human endothelial cell growth factor: cloning, nucleotide sequence, and chromosome localization. *Science* 233: 541–45
65. Jennings, J. C., Mohan, S., Linkhart, T. A., Widstrom, R., Baylink, D. J. 1988. Comparison of the biological actions of TGF beta-1 and TGF beta-2: differential activity in endothelial cells. *J. Cell. Physiol.* 137:167–72
66. Klagsbrun, M., Shing, Y. 1985. Heparin affinity of anionic and cationic capillary endothelial cell growth factors: analysis of hypothalamus-derived growth factors and fibroblast growth factors. *Proc. Natl. Acad. Sci. USA* 82:805–9
67. Kurachi, K., Davie, E. W., Strydom, D. J., Riordan, J. F., Vallee, B. L. 1985. Sequence of the cDNA and gene for angiogenin, a human angiogenesis factor. *Biochemistry* 24:5494–99
68. Langer, R., Brem, H., Falterman, K., Klein, M., Folkman, J. 1976. Isolation of a cartilage factor that inhibits tumor neovascularization. *Science* 193:70–72
69. Langer, R., Conn, H., Vacanti, J.,

Haudenschild, C., Folkman, J. 1980. Control of tumor growth in animals by infusion of an angiogenesis inhibitor. *Proc. Natl. Acad. Sci. USA* 77:4331–35
70. Lawrence, D. A., Pircher, R., Jullien, P. 1985. Conversion of a high molecular weight latent beta-TGF from chicken embryo fibroblasts into a low molecular weight active beta-TGF under acidic conditions. *Biochem. Biophys. Res. Commun.* 133:1026–34
71. Leibovich, S. J., Polverini, P. J., Shepard, H. M., Wiseman, D. M., Shively, V., Nuseir, N. 1987. Macrophage-induced angiogenesis is mediated by tumour necrosis factor-alpha. *Nature* 329:630–32
72. Levy, A. P., Tamargo, R., Brem, H., Nathans, D. 1989. An endothelial cell growth factor from the mouse neuroblastoma cell line NB41. *Growth Factors* 2:9–19
73. Lobb, R. R., Alderman, E. M., Fett, J. W. 1985. Induction of angiogenesis by bovine brain derived class 1 heparin-binding growth factor. *Biochemistry* 24:4969–73
74. Lutty, G. A., Mello, R. J., Chandler, C., Fait, C., Bennett, A., Patz, A. 1985. Regulation of cell growth by vitreous humour. *J. Cell. Sci.* 76:53–65
75. Lutty, G. A., Thompson, D. C., Gallup, J. Y., Mello, R. J., Patz, A., Fenselau, A. 1983. Vitreous: an inhibitor of retinal extract-induced neovascularization. *Invest. Ophthalmol. Vis. Sci.* 24:52–56
76. Maciag, T., Mehlman, T., Friesel, R., Schrieber, A. 1984. Heparin binds endothelial cell growth factor, the principal mitogen in the bovine brain. *Science* 225:932–35
77. Madri, J. A., Pratt, B. M., Tucker, A. M. 1988. Phenotypic modulation of endothelial cells by transforming growth factor-beta depends upon the composition and organization of the extracellular matrix. *J. Cell Biol.* 106:1375–84
78. Madtes, D. K., Raines, E. W., Sakariassen, K. S., Assoian, R. K., Sporn, M. B., et al. 1988. Induction of transforming growth factor-α in activated human alveolar macrophages. *Cell* 53:285–93
79. Maione, T. E., Gray, G. S., Petro, J., Hunt, A. J., Donner, A. L., et al. 1990. Inhibition of angiogenesis by recombinant human platelet factor-4 and related peptides. *Science* 247:77–79
80. Majewski, S., Kaminski, M. J., Szmuro, A., Kaminska, G., Malejczyk, J. 1984. Inhibition of tumour-induced angiogenesis by systemically administered protamine sulphate. *Int. J. Cancer* 33:831–33
81. Marquadt, H., Hunkapiller, M. W., Hood, L. E., Todaro, G. J. 1984. Rat transforming growth factor type I: structure and relationship to epidermal growth factor. *Science* 223:1079–82
82. Mignatti, P., Tsuboi, R., Robbins, E., Rifkin, D. B. 1989. In vitro angiogenesis on the human amniotic membrane: requirement for basic fibroblast growth factor-induced proteinases. *J. Cell Biol.* 108:671–82
83. Miyazono, K., Okabe, T., Urabe, A., Takaku, F., Heldin, C.-H. 1987. Purification and properties of an endothelial cell growth factor from human platelets. *J. Biol. Chem.* 262:4098–4103
84. Montesano, R., Vassali, J. D., Baird, A., Guillemin, R., Orci, L. 1986. Basic fibroblast growth factor induces angiogenesis in vitro. *Proc. Natl. Acad. Sci. USA* 83:7297–7301
85. Moscatelli, D. 1987. High and low affinity binding sites for basic fibroblast growth factor on cultured cells: absence of a role for low affinity binding in the stimulation of plasminogen activator production by bovine capillary endothelial cells. *J. Cell. Physiol.* 131:123–30
86. Moscatelli, D., Joseph, S. J., Presta, M., Rifkin, D. B. 1988. Multiple forms of an angiogenesis factor: basic fibroblast growth factor. *Biochimie* 70:83–87
87. Moses, M. A., Sudhalter, J., Langer, R. 1990. Identification of an inhibitor of neovascularization from cartilage. *Science* 248:1408–10
88. Mosher, D. F., Doyle, M. J., Jaffe, E. A. 1982. Synthesis and secretion of thrombospondin by cultured human endothelial cells. *J. Cell. Biol.* 93:343–48
89. Muller, G., Behrens, J., Nussbaumer, U., Bohlen, P., Birchmeier, W. 1987. Inhibitory action of transforming growth factor beta on endothelial cells. *Proc. Natl. Acad. Sci. USA* 84:5600–4
90. Munker, R., Gasson, J., Ogawa, M., Koeffler, H. P. 1986. Recombinant human TNF induces production of granulocyte-monocyte colony-stimulating factor. *Nature* 323:79–82
91. Murray, J. B., Allison, K., Sudhalter, J., Langer, R. 1986. Purification and partial amino acid sequence of a bovine cartilage-derived collagenase inhibitor. *J. Biol. Chem.* 261:4154–59
92. Nawroth, P. P., Bank, I., Handley, D., Cassimeris, J., Chess, L., Stern, D. 1986. Tumor necrosis factor/cachectin interacts with endothelial cell receptors to induce release of interleukin 1. *J. Exp. Med.* 163:1363–75

93. Neufeld, G., Gospodarowicz, D. 1987. Protamine sulfate inhibits mitogenic activities of the extracellular matrix and fibroblast growth factor, but potentiates that of epidermal growth factor. *J. Cell. Physiol.* 132:287–94
94. Nikolic, L., Friend, J., Taylor, S., Thaft, R. A. 1986. Inhibition of vascularization in rabbit corneas by heparin: cortisone pellets. *Invest. Ophthalmol. Vis. Sci.* 27:449–63
95. Orchard, P. J., Smith, C. M. III, Woods, W. G., Day, D. L., Dehner, L. P., Shapiro, R. 1989. Treatment of haemangioendotheliomas with alpha interferon. *Lancet* 2:565–67
96. Orlidge, A., D'Amore, P. A. 1987. Inhibition of capillary endothelial cell growth by pericytes and smooth muscle cells. *J. Cell Biol.* 105:1455–62
97. Phillips, D. R., Jennings, L. K., Prasanna, H. R. 1980. Ca^{2+}-mediated association of glycoprotein G (thrombin-sensitive protein, thrombospondin) with human platelets. *J. Biol. Chem.* 255: 11629–32
98. Prats, H., Kaghad, M., Prats, A. C., Klagsbrun, M., Lelias, J. M., et al. 1989. High molecular mass forms of basic fibroblast growth factor are initiated by alternative CUG codons. *Proc. Natl. Acad. Sci. USA* 86:1836–40
99. Preis, I., Langer, R., Brem, H., Folkman, J. 1977. Inhibition of neovascularization by an extract derived from vitreous. *Am. J. Ophthalmol.* 84:323–28
100. Rakusan, K., Turek, Z. 1985. Protamine inhibits capillary formation in growing rat hearts. *Circ. Res.* 57:393–99
101. Rastinejad, F., Polverini, P. J., Bouck, N. P. 1989. Regulation of the activity of a new inhibitor of angiogenesis by a cancer suppressor gene. *Cell.* 56:345–55
102. Raymond, L., Jacobson, B. 1982. Isolation and identification of stimulatory and inhibitory cell growth factors in bovine vitreous. *Exp. Eye Res.* 34:267–86
103. Roberts, A. B., Sporn, M. B., Assoian, R. K., Smith, J. M., Roche, N. S., et al. 1986. Transforming growth factor type-beta: rapid induction of fibrosis and angiogenesis in vivo and stimulation of collagen formation in vitro. *Proc. Natl. Acad. Sci. USA* 83:4167–71
104. Roberts, R., Gallagher, J., Spooncer, E., Allen, T. D., Bloomfield, F., Dexter, T. M. 1988. Heparan sulphate bound growth factors: a mechanism for stromal cell mediated haemopoiesis. *Nature* 332:376–78
105. Rong, G. H., Alessandri, G., Sindelar, W. F. 1986. Inhibition of tumor angiogenesis by hexuronyl hexosaminoglycan sulfate. *Cancer* 57:586–90
106. Sakamoto, N., Tanaka, N. G., Tohgo, A., Ogawa, H. 1986. Heparin plus cortisone acetate inhibit tumor growth by blocking endothelial cell proliferation. *Cancer J.* 1:55–58
107. Sato, N., Goto, T., Haranaka, K., Satomi, N., Nariuchi, H., et al. 1986. Actions of tumor necrosis factor on cultured vascular endothelial cells: morphologic modulation, growth inhibition, and cytotoxicity. *J. Natl. Cancer Inst.* 76:1113–21
108. Sato, Y., Rifkin, D. B. 1989. Inhibition of endothelial cell movement by pericytes and smooth muscle cells: activation of a latent transforming growth factor-beta 1-like molecule by plasmin during co-culture. *J. Cell Biol.* 109: 309–15
109. Schreiber, A. B., Winkler, M. E., Derynck, R. 1986. Transforming growth factor-alpha: A more potent angiogenic mediator than epidermal growth factor. *Science* 232:1250–53
110. Schweigerer, L., Neufeld, G., Friedman, J., Abraham, J. A., Fiddes, J. C., Gospodarowicz, D. 1987. Capillary endothelial cells express basic fibroblast growth factor, a mitogen that promotes their own growth. *Nature* 325:257–59
111. Seyedin, S. M., Thomas, T. C., Thompson, A. Y., Rosen, D. M., Piez, K. A. 1985. Purification and characterization of two cartilage-inducing factors from bovine demineralized bone. *Proc. Natl. Acad. Sci. USA* 82:2262–71
112. Shapiro, R., Riordan, J. F., Vallee, B. L. 1986. Characteristic ribonucleolytic activity of human angiogenin. *Biochemistry* 25:3527–32
113. Shapiro, R., Strydom, D. J., Olson, K. A., Vallee, B. L. 1987. Isolation of angiogenin from normal human plasma. *Biochemistry* 26:5141–46
114. Shapiro, R., Vallee, B. L. 1987. Human placental ribonuclease inhibitor abolishes both angiogenic and ribonucleolytic activities of angiogenin. *Proc. Natl. Acad. Sci. USA* 84:8783–87
115. Sharpe, R. J., Byers, H. R., Scott, C. F., Bauer, S. I., Maione, T. E. 1990. Growth inhibition of murine melanoma and human colon carcinoma by recombinant human platelet factor 4. *J. Natl. Cancer Inst.* 82:848–53
116. Shing, Y., Folkman, J., Haudenschild, C., Lund, D., Crum, R., Klagsbrun, M. 1985. Angiogenesis is stimulated by a tumor-derived endothelial cell growth factor. *J. Cell. Biochem.* 29:275–87
117. Shing, Y., Folkman, J., Sullivan, R.,

Butterfield, C., Murray, J., Klagsbrun, M. 1984. Heparin affinity: purification of a tumor-derived capillary endothelial cell growth factor. *Science* 223:1296–98
118. Sorgente, N., Dorey, C. K. 1980. Inhibition of endothelial cell growth by a factor isolated from cartilage. *Exp. Cell Res.* 128:63–71
119. Sporn, M. B., Roberts, A. B. 1988. Peptide growth factors are multifunctional. *Nature* 332:217–19
120. Strydom, D. J., Fett, J. W., Lobb, R. R., Alderman, E. M., Bethune, J. L., et al. 1985. Amino acid sequence of human tumor derived angiogenin. *Biochemistry* 24:5486–94
121. Takigawa, M., Shirai, E., Enomoto, M., Hiraki, Y., Fukuya, M., et al. 1985. Cartilage-derived anti-tumor factor (CTAF) inhibits the proliferation of endothelial cells in culture. *Cell Biol. Int. Rep.* 9:619–25
122. Taylor, S., Folkman, J. 1982. Protamine is an inhibitor of angiogenesis. *Nature* 297:307–12
123. Terranova, V. P., DiFlorio, R., Lyall, R. M., Hic, S., Friesel, R., Maciag, T. 1985. Human endothelial cells are chemotactic to endothelial cell growth factor and heparin. *J. Cell Biol.* 101: 2330–34
124. Thomas, K. A., 1987. Fibroblast growth factors. *FASEB J.* 1:434–40
125. Thompson, J. A., Anderson, K. D., DiPietro, J. M., Zweibel, J. A., Zametta, M., et al. 1988. Site-directed neovessel formation in vivo. *Science* 141:1349–52
126. Thompson, R. W., Whalen, G. F., Saunders, K. B., Hores, T., D'Amore, P. A. 1990. Heparin-mediated release of fibroblast growth factor-like activity into the circulation of rabbits. *Growth Factors.* 3:221–29
127. Tischer, E., Gospodarowicz, D., Mitchell, R., Silva, M., Schilling, J., et al. 1989. Vascular endothelial growth factor: a new member of the platelet-derived growth factor gene family. *Biochem. Biophys. Res. Commun.* 165: 1198–1206
128. Todaro, G. J., Fryling, C., DeLarco, J. E. 1980. Transforming growth factors produced by certain human tumor cells: polypeptides that interact with epidermal growth factor receptors. *Proc. Natl. Acad. Sci. USA* 77:5258–62
129. Tsuruoka, N., Sugiyama, M., Tawaragi, Y., Tsujimoto, M., Nishihara, T., et al. 1988. Inhibition of in vitro angiogenesis by lymphotoxin and interferon-gamma. *Biochem. Biophys. Res. Commun.* 155:429–36
130. Usuki, K., Heldin, N.-E., Miyazono, K., Ishikawa, F., Takaku, F., et al. 1989. Production of platelet-derived endothelial cell growth factor by normal and transformed human cells in culture. *Proc. Natl. Acad. Sci. USA* 86:7427–31
131. Vlodavsky, I., Folkman, J., Sullivan, R., Fridman, R., Ishai-Michaeli, R., et al. 1987. Endothelial cell-derived basic fibroblast growth factor: synthesis and deposition into subendothelial extracellular matrix. *Proc. Natl. Acad. Sci. USA* 84:2292–96
132. Vlodavsky, I., Fridman, R., Sullivan, R., Sasse, J., Klagsbrun, M. 1987. Aortic endothelial cells synthesize basic fibroblast growth factor which remains cell associated and platelet-derived growth factor-like protein which is secreted. *J. Cell. Physiol.* 131:402–8
133. Wahl, S. M., Hunt, D. A, Wakefield, I. M., McCartney-Francis, N., Wahl, I. M., et al. 1987. Transforming growth factor-beta (TGF-β) induces monocyte chemotaxis and growth factor production. *Proc. Natl. Acad. Sci. USA* 84: 5788–92
134. Walz, D. A., Hung, G.-L. 1985. In vivo studies on the binding of heparin and its fractions with platelet factor 4. *Semin. Thromb. Hemostasis* 11:40–47
135. Watanabe, N., Niitsu, Y., Neda, H., Sone, H., Yamauchi, N., et al. 1985. Antitumor effect of tumor necrosis factor against various primarily cultured human cancer cells. *Jpn. J. Cancer Res.* 76:1115–19
136. Weiner, H. L., Weiner, L. H., Swain, J. 1987. The tissue distribution and developmental expression of the messenger RNA encoding angiogenin. *J. Cell. Physiol.* 102:267–77
137. White, C. W., Sondheimer, H. M., Crouch, E. C., Wilson, H., Fan, L. L. 1989. Treatment of pulmonary haemonagiomatosis with recombinant interferon alfa-2a. *N. Engl. J. Med.* 320:1197–1200
138. Williams, G. A., Eisenstein, R., Schumacher, B., Hsiao, K.-C., Grant, D. 1984. Inhibitor of vascular endothelial cell growth in the lens. *Am. J. Ophthalmol.* 97:366–71
139. Yoshida, T., Muramatsu, H., Muramatsu, T., Sakamoto, H., Katoh, O., et al. 1988. Differential expression of two homologous and clustered oncogenes, Hst1 and Int-2, during differentiation of F9 cells. *Biochem. Biophys. Res. Commun.* 157:618–25
140. Zhan, X., Bates. B. Hu, X. G., Goldfarb, M. 1988. The human FGF-5 oncogene encodes a novel protein related to fibroblast growth factors. *Mol. Cell. Biol.* 8:3487–95

Annu. Rev. Physiol. 1991. 53:241–58

METHODS FOR MEASUREMENT OF INTRACELLULAR MAGNESIUM: NMR AND FLUORESCENCE[1]

Robert E. London

Laboratory of Molecular Biophysics, National Institute of Environmental Health Science, Box 12233 Research Triangle Park, North Carolina 27709

KEY WORDS: FURAPTRA, APTRA, ATP, magnesium indicators, fluorine NMR

INTRODUCTION

Accurate and reproducible methods for the measurement of cytosolic free magnesium ion concentration, Mg_i, are required in order to assess its physiologic role. This review covers two methods, in vivo nuclear magnetic resonance (NMR) and fluorescence spectroscopy, which have provided useful means for the determination of Mg_i. The first section contains a general discussion of the extraction of Mg_i values from NMR or fluorescence data for magnesium ion chelators. Subsequent sections cover the use of endogenous NMR magnesium chelators, exogenous NMR Mg_i indicators, and fluorescent Mg_i indicators. Two recent reviews (2, 15) covered Mg_i determinations based on ATP measurements, but did not cover more recently developed fluorinated or fluorescent indicators. Other methods are covered in References 2 and 34. With the availability of new Mg_i indicators, our understanding of the role of magnesium in metabolic regulation and in the etiology of disease will undoubtedly increase in the near future.

GENERAL CONSIDERATIONS

For the general case of a ligand forming a 1:1 complex with a magnesium ion, an equilibrium expression can be written:

$$L + Mg^{2} \rightleftarrows L{-}Mg, \qquad 1.$$

with a corresponding dissociation constant $K_D = [L]\cdot[Mg^{2+}]/[L{-}Mg]$. The cytosolic magnesium level is then determined from the relation

$$[Mg^{2+}] = K_D \frac{[L - Mg]}{[L]} \qquad 2.$$

Hence, the free magnesium ion concentration is proportional to the ratio of the concentration of bound ligand to free ligand: [L−Mg]/[L]. For ligands observed by NMR spectroscopy, the extraction of the bound/free ratio from the spectrum is dependent on the kinetics of the interaction. In the slow exchange limit, which prevails when the chemical shift difference between free and complexed resonances in Hz is much larger than the reciprocal lifetimes of the free and complexed ligand, separate resonances corresponding to the bound and free ligand may be observed, and the ratio is determined by measuring the areas of the corresponding resonances. As discussed below, this slow exchange condition prevails for several of the fluorinated indicators such as 5F APTRA (22), as well as for Mg-ATP at very high fields and low temperatures (20, 28, 38). Alternatively, the kinetics of equilibrium (Equation 1) are often fast on the NMR time scale if the chemical shift difference between the free and magnesium complexed ligand is much smaller than the reciprocal lifetimes of the free and complexed ligand. In this case, the observed shift is a weighted average:

$$\delta_o = f\cdot\delta_b + (1-f)\cdot\delta_f, \qquad 3.$$

where δ_o, δ_b, and δ_f are the chemical shifts for the observed resonance, the fully complexed ligand, and the uncomplexed ligand, and f is the fraction of ligand that is complexed with magnesium. Solution of Equation 3 for the ratio $[L{-}Mg]/[L] = f/(1-f)$ and substitution into Equation 2 yields

$$[Mg^{2+}] = K_D\left(\frac{\delta_o - \delta_f}{\delta_b - \delta_o}\right). \qquad 4.$$

Equation 4 applies to the case of Mg-ATP observed at lower fields and higher temperatures, as well as to the carbon-13 resonances of citrate or the fluorine resonances of (+)-fluorocitrate (19) and 4F APTRA (22). As is apparent from the above relation, the determination of the Mg^{2+} ion concentration using indicators in the fast exchange limit requires that the limiting shifts for the uncomplexed and fully complexed ligand be determined. We note here that such a determination is somewhat more problematical for the case of Mg^{2+} than for Ca^{2+}, since for indicators designed so that $K_D(Mg^{2+})$ is near the basal Mg^{2+} level of about 0.5 mM, saturating the indicator with Mg^{2+} generally requires a significant perturbation of the ionic strength of the medium. In the opinion of this reviewer, NMR determinations based on the measurement of a chemical shift corresponding to a ligand-ion exchange that is fast on the NMR time scale, are generally less accurate than intensity measurements of slowly exchanging ligands, since the chemical shifts of intracellular molecules are subject to additional perturbations as a result of interactions with other cellular components.

For the case of a fluorescent indicator in which a change in the magnitude of the fluorescence at a given wavelength results from ion complexation, such as Mag-quin-2 [described by Molecular Probes (18)], the Mg^{2+} ion level is determined by a relation analogous to Equation 4:

$$[Mg^{2+}] = K_D\left(\frac{F - F_{min}}{F_{max} - F}\right), \qquad 5.$$

where F is the observed fluorescence, F_{min} corresponds to the fluorescence intensity in the absence of Mg^{2+}, and F_{max} to the fluorescence in the presence of saturating Mg^{2+}. This formalism is similar to that of Equation 4 because the observed fluorescence corresponds to the sum of the Mg^{2+} complexed and uncomplexed indicator. As discussed below, a formally similar expression can be developed to describe the ratio of fluorescence intensity observed or excited at two wavelengths. This apporach is useful for the description of chelators, such as the calcium ion chelator fura-2 (12) or the analogous magensium chelator FURAPTRA (33), that undergo an excitation shift upon ion complexation.

In practice, the accuracy of Mg^{2+} determinations based on Equation 2 is limited by several factors, particularly other interactions of the ligand with ions and various cellular components. We have found it useful to distinguish between two types of perturbation that limit the applicability of Equation 2. A type I perturbation alters the affinity of the ligand L for the ion and can be handled by using an appropriately corrected dissociation constant. In general, type I perturbations do not alter the spectral properties of the ligand. A type II perturbation alters both the affinity and the spectral characteristics of the ligand. If the spectral perturbations resulting from a type II interaction are sufficiently different from those that result from an interaction with the ion of interest, then such perturbations can be handled as a type I perturbation.

In order to illustrate the above points further, we consider a ligand protonation that is assumed to produce a negligible change in the spectrum of the ligand. It is probable that the protonation of the carboxyl groups (but not the nitrogens) of indicator molecules such as fura-2 or FURAPTRA corresponds to such a perturbation. Such protonation effects will, however, alter the affinity of the ligand for the ion (calcium or magnesium, respectively) by reducing the association rate constant. In the case of a single protonation, only two additional equilibria need to be considered, which correspond to the pK of the ligand and to the dissociation constant for magnesium ion from the protonated ligand. This gives

$$K_H = \frac{[H^+] \cdot [L]}{[LH^+]} \qquad K_D' = \frac{[Mg^{2+}] \cdot [LH^+]}{[LH^+ - Mg^{2+}]}. \tag{6}$$

Making the assumption, as noted above, that this protonation is a type I perturbation, we will actually be measuring the ratio $([L-Mg] + [LH^+-Mg])/([L] + [LH^+])$. That is, the magnesium complexed ligand species may actually comprise both a binary L−Mg complex and a ternary LH^+-Mg complex, while the free species actually includes both the unprotonated and the protonated ligand. Then solving Equations 1 and 6, we obtain

$$[Mg^{2+}] =$$

$$K_D \left(\frac{1 + 10^{pK-pH}}{1 + \left(\frac{K_D}{K_D'}\right) 10^{pK-pH}} \right) \left(\frac{[L-Mg] + [LH^+-Mg]}{[L] + [LH^+]} \right). \tag{7}$$

Since the assumption of this calculation is that the protonation of the ligand causes no significant spectral change, it is seen that the Mg^{2+} is again related to the observed bound/free indicator ratio by a pH-dependent effective dissociation constant, $K_D(pH)$, where

$$K_D(pH) = K_D \left(\frac{1 + 10^{pK-pH}}{1 + \left(\frac{K_D}{K_D'}\right) 10^{pK-pH}} \right). \tag{8}$$

For example, for the case of an NMR-active indicator in the fast exchange limit, Equation 7 becomes Equation 4 with K_D replaced by $K_D(pH)$. Analogous expressions can be written for the slow exchange limit or for fluorescent indicators as described above. Thus, in general, the correction to K_D depends on both the pK of the ligand and the dissociation constant K_D' of the protonated ligand for Mg^{2+}. It may be noted from Equation 8 that if $K_D = K_D'$, then the correction for K_D as a function of pH is identically equal to 1, so that the observation is pH independent. Alternatively, in the limit $K_D' \rightarrow \infty$, Mg^{2+} does not bind to the protonated ligand, so that the result of protonation is to decrease the effective ligand concentration available for binding. In this limit, $K_D(\mathrm{pH}) = K_D(1+10^{\mathrm{pK-pH}})$. Alternatively, if the dissociation constant used is not a true thermodynamic parameter but an apparent K_D that has been determined at a given $\mathrm{pH_o}$, then we can write (3):

$$K_D(\mathrm{pH}) = K_D(\mathrm{pH_o}) \frac{1 + 10^{\mathrm{pK-pH}}}{1 + 10^{\mathrm{pK-pHo}}}. \qquad 9.$$

A second type of correction that is designated as type II arises because of interactions that alter not only the affinity of the ligand for magnesium, but the spectral properties as well. For example, protonation of the nitrogen atom of APTRA (see below), or the $P\gamma$ of ATP, will not only alter the affinity for the ion, but will also lead to spectral changes. In general, corrections for type II perturbations are not straightforward, making ion selectivity an important consideration in the design of studies and interpretation of data. We consider here only the idealized case of an NMR indicator for which the kinetics of magnesium binding fall within the fast exchange limit. In this case, we again have three equilibria corresponding to Equations 1 and 6, as well as chemical shifts corresponding to the free unprotonated species, δ_1, the free protonated species, δ_2, the magnesium complexed unprotonated species, δ_3, and the ternary complex, δ_4. If we define the free shift as the weighted average of the first two parameters and the bound shift as the weighted average of the second two parameters, i.e.

$$\delta_f = \frac{\delta_1 + \delta_2 \cdot 10^{\mathrm{pK-pH}}}{1 + 10^{\mathrm{pK-pH}}}; \qquad \delta_b = \frac{\delta_3 + \delta_4 \left(\frac{K_D}{K_D'}\right) 10^{\mathrm{pK-pH}}}{1 + \left(\frac{K_D}{K_D'}\right) 10^{\mathrm{pK-pH}}}, \qquad 10.$$

then we recover Equation 7. Hence, we can use the same formalism given above for a type I perturbation. This procedure has frequently been used for the determination of an apparent dissociation constant and shift parameters in a physiologic model solution. Nevertheless, it is only absolutely valid at the pH for which the shifts δ_f and δ_b have been determined. If the pH varies during the study, and if δ_f and δ_b as well as δ_o are pH-sensitive, application of Equation 7 may lead to significant errors. In this case, it is more useful to use the full expression:

$$[Mg^{2+}] = K_D \frac{\delta_o(1 + 10^{pK-pH}) - \delta_1 - \delta_2 10^{pK-pH}}{\delta_3 + \delta_4 \left(\frac{K_D}{K_D'}\right) 10^{pK-pH} - \delta_o\left(1 + \left(\frac{K_D}{K_D'}\right) 10^{pK-pH}\right)}. \qquad 11.$$

Several simple cases are worth considering. If the kinetics of the interaction with the perturbing ion differ significantly from those of the interaction with the target ion, separation of nuclear resonances may allow treatment of a type II perturbation as a type I perturbation. The most clear cut example of this effect is the interaction of the calcium ion NMR indicator 5FBAPTA with protons or magnesium ions (36). In this case, two ^{19}F NMR resonances for the 5FBAPTA are observed, which correspond to the uncomplexed and calcium complexed species. In contrast, the weakly interacting Mg^{2+} ion is in fast exchange with the indicator and produces only a shift of the ^{19}F resonance corresponding to the free (i.e. not calcium complexed) species; such a shift does not interfere operationally with the determination of the intensity ratio of bound/free 5FBAPTA. Therefore the only effect that needs to be considered is the altered calcium K_D, which results from the interaction of the 5FBAPTA with the protons or with Mg^{2+} ions. A nearly analogous situation arises for the magnesium ion indicator 5FAPTRA (22). In this case, the exchange of the magnesium ion is slow (at typical magnetic field strengths such as 8.5 T), however, the exchange rate of protons is fast. Hence, protonation of the nitrogen leads to a chemical shift for the uncomplexed species, but does not interfere with a determination of the bound/free ratio. Similarly, the interaction with calcium ions is fast enough so that, at least at low calcium ion levels, the interaction of 5FAPTRA with calcium ions can be treated as a type I perturbation.

NMR STUDIES USING ENDOGENOUS CHELATORS

A number of small metabolites in cells exist in equilibrium between uncomplexed and Mg^{2+} complexed states. Since the resonances of such molecules may shift upon Mg^{2+} complexation, NMR spectra can provide information on the level of Mg^{2+} in the cell. As discussed above, the spectral perturbation that Mg^{2+} complexation produces depends, in general, on the kinetics of the interaction. Metabolites that have been used for the determination of Mg_i include ATP (2, 3, 13–17), ADP (21), citrate (6), phosphocreatine (7) and, for the case of red cells, diphosphoglycerate (DPG) (14, 30). Apparent dissociation constants for the interaction of Mg^{2+} with these molecules determined in model solutions are summarized in Table I. ATP is the most useful NMR indicator because of the presence of NMR sensitive ^{31}P nuclei and its high concentration and broad distribution in cells. The principal limitations of ATP as a Mg indicator are the significant mismatch of the magnesium K_D and the cytosolic Mg_i concentration and the existence of a pK for uncomplexed ATP near 7.0 (1, 29, 32, 37). It is worth noting that although nearly all applications of this type have assumed fast exchange kinetics, the ATP-Mg^{2+} exchange becomes sufficiently slow at high fields and/or low temperatures to yield separate ^{31}P resonances for uncomplexed and magnesium complexed ATP (19, 28, 38). Therefore caution must be exercised in making measurements under those conditions. The use of the ^{31}P shifts of ATP for determining cytosolic Mg^{2+} levels in cells has been extensively explored by Gupta & co-workers (2, 3, 13–17), who suggest using the observed shift difference between α and β phosphate resonances as the parameter of choice [since the β and γ phosphate groups are believed to be primarily involved in magnesium ion complexation (8, 39), and the α phosphate shift functions primarily as an internal standard]. Since the chemical shifts of ATP and MgATP are pH-dependent, changes in pH represent a type II perturbation, and the Mg^{2+} concentration can be calculated using Equation 11. Based on measured values of the chemical shift parameters: $\Delta_1 = \delta_\alpha - \delta_\beta$ for ATP^{4-} = 10.55 ppm; $\Delta_2 = \delta_\alpha - \delta_\beta$ for ATP^{3-} = 11.64 ppm; $\Delta_3 = \delta_\alpha - \delta_\beta$ for Mg-ATP^{2-} = 8.25 ppm; $\Delta_4 = \delta\alpha - \delta_\beta$ for Mg-ATP^{1-} = 10.62 ppm, a family of pH-dependent titration curves can be generated (Figure 1). Since typical Mg_i values are well above $K_D(Mg^{2+})$ and since the pK value for Mg-ATP^{2-} is very low, it is generally satisfactory to approximate Equation 11 with a pH-dependent dissociation constant as in Equations 4 and 8:

$$[Mg^{2+}] = K_D(pH)\left(\frac{\Delta_o - \Delta_f}{\Delta_b - \Delta_o}\right), \qquad 12.$$

where $\Delta_o = \delta_\alpha - \delta_\beta$ is the observed shift difference between P_α and P_β, Δ_b is the limit of this parameter for the fully complexed ATP, Δ_f the value for the uncomplexed ATP determined at physiologic pH, and K_D(pH) is calculated according to Equation 8 or 9. The value of $[Mg^{2+}]$ so determined is strongly dependent on both the limiting Δ_3 shift and the K_D value chosen. Reported thermodynamic K_D values for the equilibrium $Mg^{2+} + ATP^{4-} \leftrightarrow$ Mg-ATP^{2-} show significant variation (1, 29, 32); the most recent study that this reviewer is aware of reports a value of 51 μM (35). Tabulations of

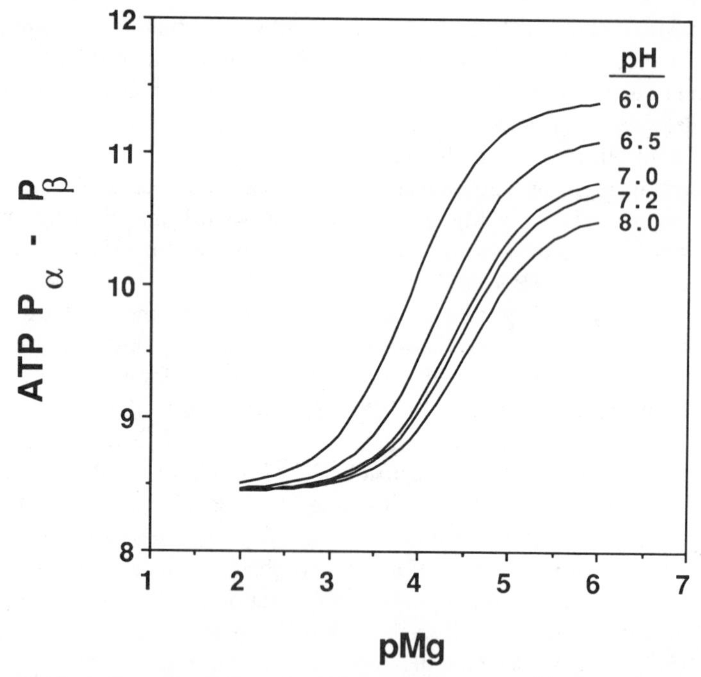

Figure 1 Dependence of the $Pa_\alpha - P_\beta$ shift on pMg = $-\log[Mg^{2+}]$. Calculation based on equation (11) with $K_D(Mg^{2+}) = 29\ \mu M$ for the binding of Mg^{2+} to ATP^{4-}, $K_{D'} = 6.54$ mM for the binding of Mg^{2+} to ATP^{3-}, pK = 6.53 for ATP (32, 21), and $P_\alpha - P_\beta$ shifts of 10.55 for ATP^{4-}, 11.64 for ATP^{3-}, 8.25 for Mg-ATP^{2-} and 10.62 for Mg-ATP^{1-}.

thermodynamic dissociation constants for other equilibria are given in (1, 10, 20, 29, 32, 35). Some reported apparent dissociation constants obtained in physiologic buffers are summarized in Table 1.

In addition to the dependence of ATP chemical shifts on Mg^{2+} concentration, the scalar $^{31}P - ^{31}P$ coupling constants also show significant sensitivity to Mg^{2+} (37). The reduction in the exchange contribution to the ^{31}P line widths of ATP at lower magnetic field strength makes it possible to obtain scalar coupling information under such conditions, as has been dramatically demonstrated at 1.5 T by Luyten et al (23). ATP coupling constants have also been determined at 7 T using two-dimensional J spectroscopy of perfused rat heart (41). Of course, as in the case of chemical shifts, the accuracy of such analysis is again limited by the mismatch between the dissociation constant of Mg-ATP and basal Mg_i levels.

The mismatch between the dissociation constant of ATP for Mg^{2+} and typical Mg_i values represents a significant limitation on the accuracy of the in vivo measurements, since chemical shifts measured in vivo are generally determined with less precision than in standard buffer solutions. From this

Table 1 Apparent Mg^{2+} dissociation constants for magnesium indicators

Indicator	K_D (mM)	Temperature (°C)	Reference
ATP	.038 ± 0.004	37	14[a]
	.046	37	42[b]
	.050	25	16[c]
	.086	37	24[d]
DPG	1.5 ± 0.3	37	14[a]
Citrate	0.48	35	6[e]
(+)-fluorocitrate	4.2	30	19[f]
Phosphocreatine	25	25	7, 21
MF-APTRA	1.0 ± 0.1	25	22[g,h]
MF-APTRA	0.6 ± 0.1	37	
5F-APTRA	1.8 ± 0.1	25	
5F-APTRA	0.9 ± 0.1	37	
4F-APTRA	4.8 ± 0.9	25	
4F-APTRA	3.1 ± 0.2	37	
FURAPTRA	1.5	37	33[i]

[a] $\mu = 0.14$, pH = 7.2; [b] 0.15 M KCl, 20 mM Bis-Tris, pH 7.2; [c] $K^+ = 0.15$ M, pH = 7.2 [d] I = 0.25, 3.5 mM P_i, 3.5 mM ATP, pH = 7.2; [e] 0.1 M KCl, 5 mM MOPS, pH 7.2, 3 mM citrate; [f] 0.1 M KCl, 25 mM Tris-acetate, pH 7.1; [g] Calcium K_D values for MF, 5F, and 4F APTRA under the same conditions were determined to be 12, 38, and 167 μM respectively, at 25°C, and 7, 25, and 86 μM at 37°C; [h] 0.115 M KCl, 20 mM NaCl, 10 mM HEPES/Tris pH 7.1; [i] 0.115 M KCl, 20 mM NaCl, 10 mM HEPES/Tris pH 7.05; Calcium K_D = 53 μM determined under the same conditions.

standpoint, ADP represents a more attractive indicator since its K_D is more closely matched to basal Mg_i levels (10, 21). The levels of free ADP in cells observed by ^{31}P NMR are generally below the detection threshold, however, and furthermore the chemical shifts of the P_α resonances of ADP and ATP are sufficiently close so that ADP P_α will generally not be resolvable. Nevertheless, the ADP P_β shift is sometimes resolved and has been used as an indicator of Mg_i in smooth muscle cells under ischemic and stimulated conditions (21). It is interesting to note in this context that the chemical shifts of the terminal P_β phosphate of ADP^{3-} and the P_γ phosphate of ATP^{4-} are almost completely unaffected by Mg^{2+} complexation. Significant shifts are observed, however, at physiologic pH values since uncomplexed ATP or ADP are partially protonated, and Mg^{2+} complexation displaces the proton. Thus, the terminal phosphate resonances are sensitive to the presence of Mg^{2+} in a strongly pH-sensitive manner.

A related question concerns the compartmentation of metabolites used for making Mg_i determinations. If resonances are observed from metabolites in several compartments, interpretation of the data depends on the exchange rates of Mg^{2+} with the ligand and on the exchange rate of the free or complexed ligand between compartments. For example, in ^{31}P NMR studies of suspended chromaffin cells, Painter et al (31) observed separate ATP resonances corresponding to ATP localized in the cytosol and in the chromaffin granules. In this case, differences in chemical shift arise because of differences in pH between the two compartments. Based on the ^{31}P NMR shifts of the intragranular ATP resonances and an intragranular pH of 5.6, comparison with the pH-dependent titration curves given in Figure 1 suggests that the free magnesium ion concentration in the granules is quite low. A more definite conclusion, however, would require the development of standard magnesium titration curves in media more representative of the granules, which contain high concentrations of catecholamines. In studies of isolated mitochondria, Ogawa et al (28) made use of the shift perturbation of ATP resonances by Mg^{2+} to distinguish intra- and extramitochondrial ATP pools. In general, the failure to observe separate ATP resonances from cytosolic and mitochondrial compartments in most cells may reflect the similarities of $[Mg^{2+}]$, as well as the limited resolution attainable at high magnetic field strengths caused by exchange broadening of the ATP resonances. Recent studies of ischemic liver, however, suggest that in intact cells, mitochondrial ATP resonances may not be observable (26). Studies at lower magnetic fields in which magnesium exchange does not broaden the ATP resonances as severely might be useful for further sorting out such effects. Analogous questions about compartmentation also apply to citrate, which has similarly been proposed to be useful for determining cytosolic Mg_i levels (6): significant levels of citrate are present in both mitochondria and cytosol (9). In the reported study (6), ^{13}C resonances of isotopically labeled citrate were used that required exposure of the system to ^{13}C labeled metabolic precursors. The ^{1}H resonances of citrate are also potentially useful, although the shift and coupling constant perturbations caused by Mg^{2+} complexation appear to be quite small (R. London, unpublished observations).

EXOGENOUS NMR INDICATORS FOR Mg_i

Exogenous indicators have also been used to measure cytosolic magnesium ion levels. The principal advantage of this strategy is that indicators can be designed with greater sensitivity and selectivity. Most NMR-active indicators are fluorinated compounds in order to take advantage of the essentially complete absence of fluorine background resonances, the high sensitivity of ^{19}F for NMR detection, the 100% natural abundance of ^{19}F, and the sensitivity of ^{19}F shifts to conformational and electronic changes in the molecule. Analogous to the use of citrate as a ^{13}C NMR indicator for Mg_i, Kirschenlohr et al (19) have utilized (+)-fluorocitrate as a magnesium ion indicator. The fluorocitrate was prepared as the triacetoxymethyl ester, a membrane permeant form that is hydrolyzed by intracellular esterases. There is increasing evidence that such esterase activity is not completely confined to the cytosol so that observations made utilizing this loading strategy may be subject to additional contributions from indicator localized in subcellular organelles. The ^{19}F NMR resonances are in fast exchange, thus Equation 4 is used to determine the level of Mg_i in the cell. Some data have been reported for perfused heart loaded with fluorocitrate, in which extracellular fluorocitrate was used as a shift standard. A principal point of caution concerns the need to use the (+) isomer rather than the highly toxic (−) isomer.

An alternative strategy analogous to the approach taken by R. Y. Tsien for the development of Ca_i indicators (40) involves modification of an existing chelator structure with the desired ion selectivity. By analogy with the case of calcium selective indicators, which have been developed by modifying EGTA, magnesium selective indicators were developed by modifying EDTA (Figure 2). As a consequence of difficulties in the preparation of o-phenylenediamine N,N,N',N'-tetraacetate, an ether oxygen was substituted for one of the nitrogen atoms, yielding an o-aminophenol-N,N,O-triacetate (APTRA) chelator (22). This chelator retains the smaller binding cavity size of EDTA and exhibits $K_D(Mg^{2+})/K_D(Ca^{2+})$ ratios similar to the parent EDTA structure (22). Furthermore, since the chelator contains the o-aminophenol group utilized for the calcium selective chelators such as 5FBAPTA and fura-2, it can be modified to include fluorine nuclei or fluorophores by analogy with these compounds. The ^{19}F resonances of the 5-fluoro and 4-methyl-5-fluoro derivatives shift by ~8.0 ppm upon magnesium ion complexation and are in slow exchange at 8.5 T. Hence, the bound/free chelator ratio can be determined directly from a measurement of the areas of the corresponding resonances if a sufficient relaxation delay is used to allow full relaxation, or if both resonances are saturated to the same extent. Inversion-recovery experiments have indicated that to within experimental error the magnesium-complexed and uncomplexed APTRA derivatives exhibit identical ^{19}F spin-lattice relaxation behavior, so that valid ratios can be obtained even under rapid pulsing conditions (22). The resonances are subject to considerable exchange broadening, and this contribution to the ^{19}F line width of the magnesium ion-chelator complex is proportional to the dissociation rate constant for the Mg^{2+}-APTRA complex: $\Delta\nu_{exch} = k_{-1}/\pi$. The line width of the uncomplexed species is dependent on the amount of magnesium ion in solution and can be expressed as $\Delta\nu_{exch} = (k_1 \cdot [Mg^{2+}])/\pi$. In contrast to the results for the 5-fluoro and 4-methyl,5-fluoro derivatives, magnesium exchange kinetics were found to fall into the fast exchange limit for the 4-fluoro derivative when studied at 8.5 T. For these indicators, the $K_D(Ca^{2+})$ is actually somewhat lower than the $K_D(Mg^{2+})$. The $K_D(Ca^{2+})$ is still 10^2–10^3 fold greater than the basal cytosolic Ca level of most cells, however, so that

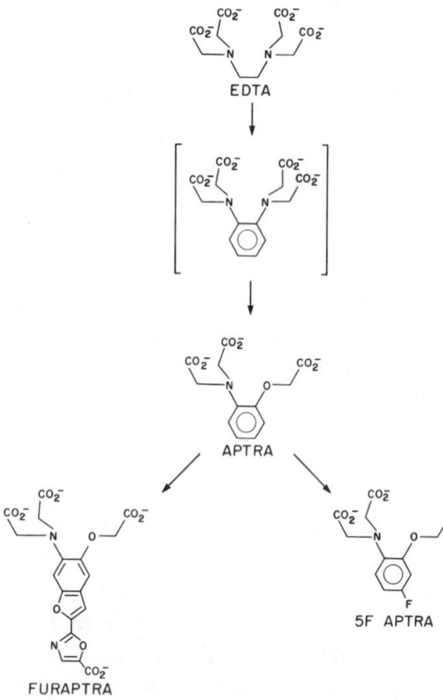

Figure 2 Modification of EDTA to give magnesium sensitive indicators. Replacement of the ethylene group with an aromatic ring provides a structural basis for further introduction of fluorophores or "NMRophores" such as ^{19}F. An additional substitution of an ether oxygen for one of the nitrogen atoms led to the chelator APTRA (o-*a*mino*p*henol-N,N,O-*tria*cetate), which is more readily synthesized, exhibits $K_D(Mg^{2+})$ values close to the basal Mg_i levels typical of most cells, and is less subject to interference from protonation near pH 7.0.

calcium ion binding will generally not be a significant problem. The exchange of calcium ions was found to occur on an intermediate time scale for the 5F and MF derivatives and in the fast limit for the 4F APTRA. Some calcium K_D values are given in the footnote to Table I.

One essential question in the use of exogenous indicators, such as those described above, is the extent to which loading and buffering effects of the indicator perturb levels being measured. It is noted first that the levels of Mg_i in cells of $\sim$ 0.5 mM are much higher than the levels of cytosolic ionized calcium, which are typically measured using analogous methods. Hence the ratio of indicator complexed Mg^{2+} to free Mg^{2+} is typically < 1; in contrast, the analogous ratio of indicator complexed Ca^{2+}/free Ca^{2+} can be as high as 5×10^3. Additionally, Corkey et al (9) have demonstrated the existence of high capacity, low affinity Mg^{2+} binding sites, which presumably will contribute to the maintenance of Mg_i levels subsequent to indicator addition. Consistent with these expectations, determination of Mg_i levels in perfused rat heart gave values similar to those based on ATP measurements (27). Additionally, Mg_i levels of perfused rat heart were found to be essentially independent of the indicator used, despite the fact that with differing K_D values the amount of indicator-complexed Mg^{2+} differed significantly from indicator to indicator. On the other hand, most evidence indicates that Mg^{2+} transport is slow, so that levels of cellular free Mg^{2+} depleted subsequent to indicator loading may not be rapidly replenished.

FLUORESCENT INDICATORS

Despite the high sensitivity of fluorescent indicators, until recently no fluorescent magnesium indicators had been described. As noted above, the development of the APTRA chelator provides a structure with sufficient magnesium ion selectivity to be useful as an indicator and, as shown in Figure 2, APTRA can be modified to yield a fluorescent indicator (33). As expected, the introduction of a furan ring structure analogous to that of fura-2 to yield FURAPTRA results in a magnesium selective chelator with spectral properties that are similar to those of fura-2. In the absence of divalent cations, FURAPTRA exhibits an excitation maximum at 370 nm, with the emission measured at 510 nm. Addition of Mg^{2+} causes a shift in the excitation spectrum such that the Mg-FURAPTRA complex has its excitation maximum at 335 nm, with an isosbestic point at 347 nm. A Hill plot was consistent with 1:1 binding of FURAPTRA to Mg^{2+} and gave a K_D value of 1.5 mM in a physiologic buffer (33). The significant excitation shift of FURAPTRA upon Mg^{2+} complexation allows magnesium ion concentration to be determined using the so-called ratio method, in which fluorescence intensities at two wavelengths, which are chosen to be at or near the maxima for the uncomplexed and the complexed inhibitor, are measured. Solution as in the case of fura-2 (12) then yields

$$[Mg^{2+}] = K_D\left(\frac{R - R_{min}}{R_{max} - R} \cdot \frac{S_{f2}}{S_{b2}}\right), \tag{13.}$$

where R is the fluorescence ratio at the wavelengths 335/370 for the sample, R_{min} and R_{max} are the corresponding parameters for uncomplexed and Mg^{2+} saturated conditions, and S_{f2} and S_{b2} are the fluorescence intensities at 370 nm for FURAPTRA with zero Mg^{2+} and with saturating Mg^{2+}. Determinations using this approach offer the major advantage of being independent of indicator concentration. The complexation of Ca^{2+} by FURAPTRA has also been studied (33). The addition of Ca^{2+} leads to changes in fluorescence spectra that are nearly identical to those resulting from Mg^{2+} complexation. The $K_D(Ca^{2+}) = 53\ \mu M$ for FURAPTRA is lower than the $K_D(Mg^{2+}) = 1.5$ mM (Table 1), but well above basal Ca^{2+} levels for most cells. Since Ca^{2+} and Mg^{2+} ions produce essentially identical changes in the fluorescence spectrum of FURAPTRA, the perturbation introduced by the presence of Ca^{2+} ions represents the extreme case of a type II perturbation, in which the measured fluorescence actually corresponds to an average of $[Mg^{2+}]$ and $[Ca^{2+}]$ concentrations weighted by their respective dissociation constants. Assuming that both Ca^{2+} and Mg^{2+} are in equilibrium with the FURAPTRA and noting that the measured bound/free indicator ratio is actually proportional to ([Mg−L] + [Ca−l)/[L], solution of the equations for the ratio of fluorescence at the two wavelengths yields

$$[Mg^{2+}] = K_D\left(\frac{R - R_{min}}{R_{max} - R} \cdot \frac{S_{f2}}{S_{b2}}\right) - \left(\frac{K_D}{K_D'}\right)[Ca^{2+}]. \qquad 14.$$

Thus there is a correction to the measured Mg^{2+} concentration that is equal to $-(K_D/K_{D'})\cdot[Ca^{2+}] = -28.3\cdot[Ca^{2+}]$. In order to deal with this limitation, Mg^{2+} indicators with greater Mg^{2+}/Ca^{2+} selectivity would be desirable. Efforts to develop such indicators are currently in progress.

In addition to FURAPTRA (designated as Mag-fura-2, see 18) Molecular Probes, Inc. has recently listed several fluorescent Mg^{2+} indicators. Mag-indo-1 is also a derivative of APTRA, which contains the same indo fluorophore utilized for the Ca^{2+} indicator, indo-1 (12). Like indo-1, Mag-indo-1 is reported to undergo a small excitation shift (from 354 nm to 338 nm; emission measured at 450 nm), and a larger emission shift (from 475 nm to 419 nm; excitation at 345 nm) upon Mg^{2+} complexation. Dissociation constants for Ca^{2+} were not given; however, since this indicator is also an APTRA derivative, similar ionic selectivity is expected. In addition, the Molecular Probes catalog (18) lists two chelators, Mag-quin-1 and Mag-quin-2, which are structurally related to the calcium indicator quin2 (40). Although at present there appears to be no characterization data beyond that provided in the catalog, we note that we have carried out some NMR studies on a fluorinated analogue of Mag-quin-2 and find that at neutral pH the ^{19}F resonance is subject to extreme broadening caused by titration of the ring nitrogen in the quinoline structure. This result is not surprising since the fluorinated quinoline ring structure has also been used as the basis for a pH indicator, Fquene (25). Hence, it is important to determine the pH sensitivity of these indicators and to determine whether variations in pH represent type I or type II perturbations.

CONCLUSIONS

The presence of endogenous, NMR-sensitive chelators for cytosolic Mg^{2+} enables a determination of Mg_i without the perturbations of buffering, toxicity, or other metabolic interference, which are inherent in the use of indicators. The technique suffers from the usual sensitivity constraint on NMR measurements that limits measurements to large populations of cells (typically $> 10^6$ cells/ml), as well as a time resolution of at least several minutes. Repetitive variations with a shorter periodicity may sometimes be observed using gating techniques (19). This may not be a significant limitation for Mg_i measurements, however, since there is little current evidence for rapid Mg_i transients, and hence it is more likely that changes in Mg_i occur on a slower time scale, which is more amenable to study by NMR. Although ATP is by far the most generally useful endogenous indicator that has been identified, the significant mismatch between $K_D(Mg^{2+})$ and basal Mg^{2+} levels (Figure 1) and inherent pH sensitivity are important limitations that need to be considered. These characteristics may explain some of the discrepancies in the literature (3, 4, 15, 42).

Generally, Mg_i values determined by these methods have been in good agreement, with more recent determinations converging on somewhat lower values than were obtained in some of the earlier studies. For example, an earlier analysis of ^{31}P NMR data for perfused guinea pig heart giving Mg_i = 2.5 mM (43) was subsequently reevaluated to give 0.6 mM (11), and a more recent study using the same method in perfused rat heart reported a basal level of 0.5 mM (5). This compares to a value of 0.85 mM using fluorinated APTRA derivatives (27) and 1.2 mM using (+)-fluorocitrate (19). Recent values for liver range from 0.37 mM (null point; 9), 0.46 mM (citrate NMR; 6), to 0.59 mM (FURAPTRA fluorescence; 33). Values for erythrocytes are somewhat lower, e.g. 0.2 mM (ATP; 15, 30, 42), 0.25 mM (MF-APTRA; 22).

The recent development of fluorescent indicators provides a means to measure intracellular magnesium ion levels and transients in cell suspensions or in individual cells using fluorescence microscopy. The principal limitation of FURAPTRA is the relatively high affinity for Ca^{2+}. The degree to which Ca^{2+} complexation will interfere with a determination of Mg^{2+} is dependent on the cell system under study and nature of the perturbations introduced. The magnitude of such effects can be evaluated using Equation 14 above. As noted, we have recently made progress toward the development of Mg^{2+} indicators that have enhanced selectivity for Mg^{2+} over Ca^{2+}, and hence should be less sensitive to Ca^{2+} interference.

The use of the fluorescent indicator FURAPTRA is in most respects analogous to the use of the Ca^{2+} indicator fura-2. In both cases, it is necessary to subtract cellular autofluorescence in order to obtain a true reading. This constraint is somewhat more important for FURAPTRA, which appears to have a somewhat lower fluorescence intensity (33). In cuvette systems, extracellular indicator arising from leakage or from cell lysis can lead to erroneous readings. In general, leakage will lead to an overestimation of the level of Mg^{2+} since extracellular chelator may be complexed with either Mg^{2+} or Ca^{2+}; this is analogous to the complexation of extracellular fura-2 by Ca^{2+}. As with fura-2, such effects can be dealt with in several ways, for example, using cell perfusion methods that wash away extracellular indicator. One particularly attractive aspect of the use of FURAPTRA for Mg_i measurements is the possibility of using indicator levels that are significantly below the Mg_i levels of the cell. Thus, in contrast to the case of Ca^{2+}, the ratio of indicator-complexed ion to free ion can be relatively low, reducing the buffering by the indicator. This is important because it is unclear how rapidly cells can restore basal Mg_i levels after depletion caused by loading of indicator.

Literature Cited

1. Alberty, R. A. 1969. Standard Gibbs free energy, enthalpy, and entropy changes as a function of pH and pMg for several reactions involving adenosine phosphates. *J. Biol. Chem.* 244:3290–3302
2. Alvarez-Leefmans, F. J., Giraldez, F., Gamino, S. M. 1987. Intracellular free magnesium in excitable cells: its measurement and its biologic significance. *Can. J. Physiol. Pharmacol.* 65:915–25
3. Bock, J. L., Wenz, B., Gupta, R. K. 1985. Changes in intracellular Mg adenosine triphosphate and ionized Mg^{2+} during blood storage: detection by ^{31}P nuclear magnetic resonance spectroscopy. *Blood* 65:1526–30
4. Bock, J. L., Yusuf, Y. 1988. Further studies on alterations in magnesium binding during cold storage of erythrocytes. *Biochim. Biophys. Acta* 941:225–31
5. Borchgrevink, P. C., Bergan, A. S., Bakoy, O. E., Jynge, P. 1989. Magnesium and reperfusion of ischemic rat heart as assessed by ^{31}P-NMR. *Am. J. Physiol.* 256:H195–H204
6. Cohen, S. M. 1983. Simultaneous ^{13}C and ^{3-31}P NMR studies of perfused rat liver. *J. Biol. Chem.* 258:14291–14308
7. Cohen, S. M., Burt, C. T. 1977. ^{31}P nuclear magnetic relaxation studies of phosphocreatine in intact muscle: Determination of intracellular free magnesium. *Proc. Natl. Acad. Sci. USA* 74:4271–75
8. Cohn, M., Hughes, T. R. 1962. Nuclear magnetic resonance spectra of adenosine di- and triphosphate. *J. Biol. Chem.* 237:176–81
9. Corkey, B. E., Duszynski, J., Rich, T. L., Matschinsky, B., Williamson, J. R. 1986. Regulation of free and bound magnesium in rat hepatocytes and isolated mitochondria. *J. Biol. Chem.* 261:2567–74
10. Dawson, R. M. C., Elliott, D. C., Elliott, W. H., Jones, K. M., eds. 1969. *Data for Biochemical Research,* p. 432. London: Oxford Univ. Press
11. Garfinkel, L., Garfinkel, D. 1984. Calculation of free-Mg^{2+} concentration in adenosine 5'-triphosphate containing solutions in vitro and in vivo. *Biochemistry* 23:3547–52
12. Grynkiewicz, G., Poenie, M., Tsien, R. Y. 1985. A new generation of Ca^{2+} indicators with greatly improved fluorescence properties. *J. Biol. Chem.* 260:3440–50
13. Gupta, R. K., Benovic, J. L., Rose, Z. B. 1978. Magnetic resonance studies of the binding of ATP and cations to human hemoglobin. *J. Biol. Chem.* 253:6165–71

14. Gupta, R. K., Benovic, J. L., Rose, Z. B. 1978. The determination of the free magnesium level in the human red blood cell by ^{31}P NMR. *J. Biol. Chem.* 253:6172–76
15. Gupta, R. K., Gupta, P. 1987. ^{31}P NMR measurement of intracellular free magnesium in cells and organisms. In *NMR Spectroscopy of cells and Organisms,* ed. R. K. Gupta, 2:33–43. Boca Raton, FL: CRC Press
16. Gupta, R. K., Gupta, P., Yushok, W. D., Rose, Z. B. 1983. On the noninvasive measurement of intracellular free magnesium by ^{31}P NMR spectroscopy. *Physiol. Chem. Phys. Med. NMR* 15: 265–88
17. Gupta, R. K., Yushok, W. D. 1980. Noninvasive ^{31}P NMR probes of free Mg^{2+}, MgATP, and MgADP in intact Ehrlich ascites tumor cells. *Proc. Natl. Acad. Sci. USA* 77:2487–91
18. Haugland, R. P., Ed. 1989. *Molecular Probes Catalog: Handbook of Fluorescent Probes and Research Chemicals, 1989–1991,* pp. 96–100. Eugene, OR: Molecular Probes, Inc.
19. Kirschenlohr, H. L., Metcalfe, J. C., Morris, P. G., Rodrigo, G. C., Smith, G. A. 1988. Ca^{2+} transient, Mg^{2+}, and pH measurements in the cardiac cycle by ^{19}F NMR. *Proc. Natl. Acad. Sci. USA* 85:9017–21
20. Klaus, W., Schlichting, I., Goody, R. S., Wittinghofer, A., Rosch, P., Holmes, K. C. 1986. ^{31}P-NMR studies on ATP Mg^{2+}, p21-nucleotide, and adenylate kinase nucleotide complexes. *Biol. Chem. Hoppe-Seyler* 367:781–86
21. Kushmerick, M. G., Dillon, P. F., Meyer, R. A., Brown, T. R., Krisanda, J. M., Sweeney, H. L. 1986. ^{31}P NMR spectroscopy, chemical analysis, and free Mg^{2+} of rabbit bladder and uterine smooth muscle. *J. Biol. Chem.* 261: 14420–29
22. Levy, L. A., Murphy, E., Raju, B., London, R. E. 1988. Measurement of cytosolic free magnesium ion concentration by ^{19}F NMR. *Biochemistry* 27: 4041–48
23. Luyten, P. R., Bruntink, G., Sloff, F. M., Vermeulen, J. W. A. H., van der Heijden, J. I., et al. 1989. Broadband proton decoupling in human ^{31}P NMR spectroscopy. *NMR Biomed.* 1:177–83
24. Malloy, C. R., Cunningham, C. C., Radda, G. K. 1986. The metabolic state of the rat liver in vivo measured by ^{31}P-NMR spectroscopy. *Biochim. Biophys. Acta* 885:1–11
25. Metcalfe, J. C., Hesketh, T. R., Smith, G. A. 1985. Free cytosolic Ca^{2+} measurements with fluorine labeled indicators using ^{19}F NMR. *Cell Calcium* 6:183–95
26. Murphy, E., Gabel, S. A., Funk, A., London, R. E. 1988. NMR observability of ATP: preferential depletion of cytosolic ATP during ischemia in perfused rat liver. *Biochemistry* 27:526–28
27. Murphy, E., Steenbergen, C., Levy, L. A., Raju, B., London, R. E. 1989. Cytosolic free magnesium levels in ischemic rat heart. *J. Biol. Chem.* 264:5622–27
28. Ogawa, S., Lee, T.-M. 1982. Proton stoichiometry of adenosine 5'-triphosphate synthesis in rat liver mitochondria studied by phosphorus-31 nuclear magnetic resonance. *Biochemistry* 21:4467–73
29. O'Sullivan, W. J., Smithers, G. W. 1979. Stability constants for biologically important metal-ligand complexes. *Methods Enzymol.* 63:294–336
30. Ouwerkerk, R., van Echteld, C. J. A., Staal, G. E. J., Rijksen, G. 1989. Intracellular free magnesium and phosphorylated metabolites in hexokinase- and pyruvate kinase-deficient red cells measured using ^{31}P-NMR spectroscopy. *Biochim. Biophys. Acta* 1010:294–303
31. Painter, G. R., Diliberto, E. J. Jr., Knoth, J. 1989. ^{31}P nuclear magnetic resonance study of the metabolic pools of adenosine triphosphate in cultured bovine adrenal medullary chromaffin cells. *Proc. Natl. Acad. Sci. USA* 86: 2239–42
32. Phillips, R. C., George, P., Rutman, R. J. 1966. Thermodynamic studies of the formation and ionization of the Magnesium(II) complexes of ADP and ATP over the pH range 5 to 9. *J. Am. Chem. Soc.* 88:2631–40
33. Raju, B., Murphy, E., Levy, L. A., Hall, R. D., London, R. E. 1989. A fluorescent indicator for measuring cytosolic free magnesium. *Am. J. Physiol.* 256:C540–48
34. Scarpa, A., Brinley, F. J. 1981. In situ measurements of free cytosolic magnesium ions. *Fed. Proc.* 40:2646–52
35. Sigel, H. 1987. Isomeric equilibria in complexes of adenosine 5'-triphosphate with divalent metal ions. Solution structures of $M(ATP)^{2-}$ complexes. *Eur. J. Biochem.* 165:65–72
36. Smith, G. A., Hesketh, R. T., Metcalfe, J. C., Feeney, J., Morris, P. G. 1983. Intracellular calcium measurements by ^{19}F NMR of fluorine-labeled chelators. *Proc. Natl. Acad. Sci. USA* 80:7178–82

37. Son, T. D., Roux, M., Ellenberger, M. 1975. Interaction of Mg^{2+} ions with nucleoside triphosphates by phosphorus magnetic resonance spectroscopy. *Nucleic Acids Res.* 2:1101–10
38. Sontheimer, G. M., Kuhn, W., Kalbitzer, H. R. 1986. Observation of Mg^{2+}·ATP and uncomplexed ATP in slow exchange by ^{31}P-NMR at high magnetic field. *Biochem. Biophys. Res. Commun.* 134:1379–86
39. Takeuchi, J., Murata, H., Harada, I. 1988. Interaction of adenosine 5'-triphosphate with Mg^{2+}: vibrational study of coordination sites by use of ^{18}O-labeled triphosphates. *J. Am. Chem. Soc.* 110:392–97
40. Tsien, R. Y. 1980. New calcium indicators and buffers with high selectivity against magnesium and protons. Design, synthesis, and properties of prototype structure. *Biochemistry* 19:2396–2404
41. Turner, C. J., Garlick, P. B. 1984. One- and two-dimensional ^{31}P spin-echo studies of myocardial ATP and phosphocreatine. *J. Magn. Reson.* 57:221–27
42. Woods, K. L., Walmsley, D., Heagerty, A. M., Turner, D. L., Lian, L.-Y. 1988. ^{31}P nuclear magnetic resonance measurement of free erythrocyte magnesium concentration in man and its relation to blood pressure. *Clin. Sci.* 74:513–17
43. Wu, S. T., Pieper, G. M., Salhany, J. M., Eliot, R. S. 1981. Measurement of free magnesium in perfused and ischemic arrested heart muscle. A quantitative phosphorus-31 nuclear magnetic resonance and multiequilibria analysis. *Biochemistry* 20:7399–7403

Annu. Rev. Physiol. 1991. 53:259–71

MECHANISMS OF MAGNESIUM TRANSPORT

Peter W. Flatman

Department of Physiology, University Medical School, Teviot Place, Edinburgh EH8 9AG, Scotland

KEY WORDS: Na-Mg antiport, magnesium pump, intracellular magnesium, red cells, squid axon

---

INTRODUCTION

Mg, the second or third most abundant intracellular cation, is an important constituent of cells and is a necessary cofactor for many enzymes especially those involved in the transfer of phosphate groups. In this role Mg is essential for Na and Ca pump activity. Recently it has been shown to regulate the activity of the Na,K,Cl (18) and K,Cl (39) co-transport systems and to influence ionic traffic through Ca (34), K (37), and Na (48) channels. Mg may thus be an important link between ion transport and metabolism, and it is likely that its cytoplasmic concentration is precisely regulated. This chapter will focus on how Mg crosses the membrane and on some of the factors that influence the process. It will show how models initially formulated to describe Mg transport in squid axon and barnacle muscle have been used to explain recent observations on red cells.

The earliest experiments on Mg transport suggested it was difficult to change cell Mg content. Several cell types had been incubated for long periods in media containing either high Mg concentrations or Mg chelators without significantly affecting cell Mg content. This, together with the observation that ^{28}Mg equilibrated very slowly across some cell membranes, suggested that membranes had a particularly low Mg permeability (17, 19)

0066-4278/91/0315-0259$02.00

and that specific Mg transport systems might not exist. New techniques allow a more detailed examination of Mg homeostasis and provide clear evidence for specific Mg transport.

Intracellular Mg exists in two forms. Some is ionized and the rest is bound to substances like ATP and RNA. In order to study Mg homeostasis, it is necessary to know the ionized as well as the total Mg concentration since it is ionized Mg that is regulated by transport systems. Analysis of the ionized intracellular Mg concentration ($[Mg^{2+}]_i$) also shows whether or not Mg is at equilibrium across the membrane. During the last decade it has become possible to measure $[Mg^{2+}]_i$ accurately using techniques such as ^{31}P and ^{19}F NMR (32, 40), null-point titrations (5, 16), ion-sensitive microelectrodes (1), and fluorescent indicators (49). The concentration in most mammalian cells is probably 0.2–1.0 mM. This represents less than 10% of total Mg, and since there is no evidence for sequestration of Mg within organelles (5), it suggests that Mg is well buffered within the cytoplasm. The data also show that in most cells, at resting membrane potential, $[Mg^{2+}]_i$ is maintained well below electrochemical equilibrium with the external ionized Mg concentration ($[Mg^{2+}]_o$) of about 0.5 mM (17). Thus Mg should slowly accumulate in cells if it simply leaks through the membrane. This accumulation has not been observed, and in red cells Mg content, in fact, decreases with age (19). It is clear that Mg transport systems exist and some of these systems must be capable of active Mg extrusion.

The chemistry of Mg poses unusual problems for transport systems. For instance, the exchange rate of water molecules in the inner hydration shell is about 10^4 times slower for Mg than for Na, K, or Ca ions (7). This reluctance to let go of water may influence the way Mg approaches and binds to transport sites. The hydrated ion can be imagined as being very large, whereas the unhydrated ion is very small and highly charged. Thus Mg ions may move slowly through channels, and it may be difficult to distinguish between carrier and channel behavior. Mg may also permeate channels for other ions at a slow yet finite rate. Very slow permeation may be one explanation for the Mg block of some K channels (37). Thus the permeability of membranes to Mg may be increased well above that of the phospholipid bilayer and provide a still greater need for active Mg transport systems.

MAGNESIUM TRANSPORT IN ISOLATED CELLS

Squid Axon

$[Mg^{2+}]_i$ is kept well below electrochemical equilibrium in squid axons, although the membrane is permeable to Mg, and there is net Mg influx during the action potential (3, 4). This indicates the presence of an active Mg transport system in the axolemma. The properties of the system have been explored in intact (4), injected (3, 6), and perfused (8, 23, 45, 46) axons. Mg efflux measured with ^{28}Mg is about 0.5–3 pmol cm^{-2} s^{-1} (3, 6, 8, 46). It is reversibly inhibited by D600 and La (6). A large component of efflux is inhibited by the removal of external Na (Na_o). Re-addition of Na to the medium activates Mg efflux with a $K_{0.5}$ of about 100 mM, assuming Na binds to a single site (3, 6). In the presence of Na_o, addition of external Mg (Mg_o) inhibits Mg efflux, whereas in the absence of Na_o, it stimulates efflux. This suggests that Mg-Mg exchange contributes to Mg efflux only when external Na concentration ($[Na]_o$) is low (3, 8). These data are consistent with Mg efflux through a Na-dependent transport system, which may be a Mg-pump or Na-Mg antiport.

Active transport may be driven either by energy from linked chemical reactions such as the hydrolysis of ATP, or by energy stored in ionic gradients realized by the movement of a cotransported ion. The source of energy for Mg transport is still controversial. Na-dependent Mg efflux requires internal ATP. Removal of ATP by chemical treatment (3, 6), or perfusion (8, 46), reduces Mg efflux that can be reactivated with a $K_{0.5}$ of about 0.35 mM when ATP is re-added to the perfusate. ATP can be replaced by adenosine 5'-o-(3-thiotriphosphate), which can act as a substrate for kinases but not for ATPases (8). This suggests that ATP activates the transporter (phosphorylation may change the ion-binding affinities) rather than provides energy by being hydrolysed during each transport cycle. There is no strong evidence for an ATP-hydrolysing Mg pump in squid axons (8) and thus an alternative source of energy is required. The movement of Na down its gradient on a Na-Mg antiport is an obvious candidate. The amount of energy available depends on the number of Na ions that move with each Mg ion. A number of different stoichiometries have been suggested either on thermodynamic grounds, or from the shape of curves relating Mg efflux to $[Na]_o$. Thermodynamics suggests that at least two Na ions should be transported for each Mg ion if all the energy for Mg transport comes from the Na gradient. On the other hand, the Na activation curves have been fitted assuming that the binding of a single Na ion is sufficient. These data, however, can also be fitted asssuming two or more Na ions bind (17). In squid, Mg efflux is not affected when the membrane potential is depolarized by incubation of the axons in high K media (4, 6), or by voltage clamp (8). This evidence has been interpreted as favoring electroneutral transport with a stoichiometry of 2Na : 1Mg. Reversal of Na-Mg exchange reveals components of Mg influx dependent on the internal Na concentration ($[Na]_i$) (3, 45) and components of Na efflux dependent on $[Mg^{2+}]_o$ (23). The properties of Mg-dependent Na efflux suggest a stoichiometry of 3Na : 1Mg (23). This observation is important as it provides one of the few demonstrations of the Na flux that must accompany Mg transport if the system is really a Na-Mg antiport. A similar flux has recently been reported in frog muscle (38).

There has been little work on Na-independent Mg transport. Recently, it was shown that in the absence of both ATP and Na, Mg efflux from an axon perfused with 3 mM ionized Mg is about 4–10 fmol cm^{-2} s^{-1} (8). This flux is surprisingly high and indicates a Mg permeability (recalculated $P_{mg} = 3-8 \times 10^{-8}$ cm s^{-1}) far in excess of that expected of lipid membranes. This may represent transport on other Mg-specific systems, or perhaps Mg permeation through the transport systems of other ions.

Barnacle Muscle

Mg transport in barnacle muscle resembles that in squid axon. Mg efflux (measured with ^{28}Mg) into a medium containing both Na and Mg is 6–12 pmol cm^{-2} s^{-1}, assuming that the fiber is a simple cylinder (2). This is equivalent to 0.4–0.8 pmol cm^{-2} s^{-1} if the area of the cleft system is taken into account. Efflux is reduced by high concentrations of external Mg, Ca, Mn, or Co. Trivalent cations, for instance La (1 mM), are potent inhibitors (2). Removal of Na_o (replaced with Li or choline) reduces Mg efflux (2, 53). Manipulation of $[Na]_i$ has produced equivocal results. Injection of sufficient Na to double $[Na]_i$ had no consistent effect (2), whereas reducing $[Na]_i$ from 80 to 2 mM by perfusion of the fiber more than doubled the efflux (53). The perfusates contained no ATP. These data are consistent with internal Mg being regulated by Na-Mg exchange. Recently, however, Mg fluxes have been measured by a stable isotope technique using thermal ionization mass spectrometry (44). Here barnacle muscle fibers have been shown to regulate their Mg content in the absence of Na_o. Mg_o stimulates Mg efflux, but this is not by Mg-Mg exchange since changes in Mg content are consistent with the efflux rate. The data suggest a Na-independent Mg transport system. P_{Mg} estimated for the inward leak in this study was 7×10^{-8} cm s^{-1}. Potassium may also play a role in regulating Mg in these fibers (43). Fiber Mg content does not change when muscles are incubated in media containing 100 mM Mg as long as K is also present. In the absence of K, the cells take up Mg. It is not clear whether the active efflux of Mg depends on maintenance of intracellular K, or the presence of external K per se.

Human Red Cells

Early studies attempting to measure ^{28}Mg uptake by human red cells suggested that Mg moves very slowly, if at all, across the membrane (19). Recently, Mg transport has been detected in human red cells loaded with extra Mg. In order to load cells, the membrane permeability to Mg was increased by using either A23187 (21, 42) or *p*-chloro-mercuribenzenesulfonic acid

(PCMBS) (10, 13, 15, 21). After loading to the desired level, A23187 was washed away with media containing albumin (42), and the effects of PCMBS were reversed by washing the cells and incubating them in media containing cysteine and metabolic substrates (13). It is unlikely that these treatments directly affect Mg transport to any great extent since both yield very similar results.

The observation that Mg can move across the human red cell membrane prompted careful exploration of the fluxes from cells with normal Mg content into media containing Na but nominally free of Mg. Fluxes ranging from about 4–7 μmol liter cell^{-1} hr^{-1} were detected after correction for hemolysis (13, 42). Although these fluxes are small, they are much higher than would be expected from passive diffusion through the lipid of the membrane. Their temperature sensitivity indicates an activation energy of about 55 kJ mol^{-1} (13). Mg efflux from Mg-loaded cells shows a strong dependence on $[Mg]_i$ and this efflux is greatly reduced when Na_o is replaced by K, choline, or Li (13, 42). Thus Mg efflux can be divided into at least two components, one dependent and one independent of Na_o. The V_{max} of the Na-dependent component varies widely between 35–500 μmol liter cell^{-1} hr^{-1}, depending on the donor (12, 13, 42). Red cell Mg transport, like Mg content, may well be influenced by genetic factors reflected in the HLA antigens (12). For instance, cells from subjects with B35+ antigens have a higher V_{max} than those cells from subjects with B35− (12). Mg efflux is well described if Na is assumed to bind to a single external site to activate transport with an apparent $K_{0.5}$ of 16–20 mM (13, 42). Problems in assessing $[Mg^{2+}]_i$ have resulted in disagreement over the nature of stimulation by intracellular Mg. $[Mg^{2+}]_i$ has been estimated from published Mg buffer data obtained with A23187 in fresh inosine-fed red cells, and these data may not be applicable to bank cells or to cells previously treated with PCMBS. By using the complete buffer equation, it is possible to show that Mg efflux is activated by the binding of at least two Mg ions (Hill coefficient of 2.5) with an apparent $K_{0.5}$ of 1.3 mM (42). Others have attempted to simplify the buffer equation and suggest that only one Mg ion needs to bind with an apparent $K_{0.5}$ of about 2.6 mM (13). This simplification may be erroneous, however, since it yields improbably high estimates of $[Mg^{2+}]_i$ for each total Mg content. Re-analysis of the published data using the full buffering equation indicates the binding of at least two Mg ions (Hill coefficient 2.5) and an apparent $K_{0.5}$ of 1 mM. The finding that two or more Mg ions activate transport does not imply that all of these ions are transported. It does, however, produce a steep activation curve. Transport systems are best able to maintain a particular concentration if it is similar to the $K_{0.5}$ of the transport binding site (52). The higher affinity model would allow the Mg transporter to operate in this range since $[Mg^{2+}]_i$ in human red cells varies between about 0.25 and 0.6 mM (16, 32). A recent model for the transporter suggests that the true dissociation constants for the external Na and internal Mg sites are 8 and 1 mM, respectively (21). There is competition for activation of the transporter between Na_o and Mg_i (21), between Na_o and Na_i (42), but not between Na_i and Mg_i (42).

The Na-dependent component is inhibited by quinidine, Mn (13), amiloride (42), imipramine, and several other tricyclic antidepressant drugs (15). It is not affected (13) by ouabain, bumetanide, furosemide, or 4,4'-diisothiocyanatostilbene-2,2'-disulfonic acid (DIDS). The component disappears when the cells are ATP-depleted by starvation or by treatment with iodoacetamide (13, 21, 42). It is reactivated by incorporating ATP into resealed ghosts with an apparent $K_{1/2}$ of 150 μM (21). It is not activated by AMP or by adenylyl (β,γ-methylene)disulfonate, a non-hydrolysable analogue of ATP (21). Low concentrations of vanadate, sufficient to inhibit the Na or Ca pumps, do not affect Na-dependent Mg transport (21). The evidence, therefore, suggests that ATP catalyses Na-dependent Mg efflux perhaps by phosphorylating the protein. There is no direct evidence to show that ATP is hydrolysed in each transport cycle, but if this does occur, there is more than sufficient Mg-dependent ATPase activity in red cell membranes to account for transport (42). The lack of inhibition by vanadate indicates that ATP does not interact with the transporter in the same way as it does with the Na or Ca pumps.

Evidence for Na-Mg exchange is clearer in red cells than in many other tissues. Even so, the stoichiometry of transport is difficult to assess because Na fluxes through Na-Mg exchange are tiny compared to those through other transporters. Thermodynamic arguments suggest that 1Na:1Mg provides more than sufficient energy for Mg regulation in both oxygenated and deoxygenated red cells. Careful kinetic analysis of activation curves also suggest 1Na:1Mg (21), but this kind of analysis is fraught with problems. The discovery that imipramine blocks Na-dependent Mg efflux perhaps offers a direct means of assessing stoichiometry (15). Comparison of imipramine-sensitive net Na and Mg fluxes in Mg-loaded, Na-depleted cells, treated with ouabain and bumetanide to inhibit the main Na transport systems, indicates a stoichiometry of 3Na:1Mg (15). Similar results are obtained with quinidine (15). The method yields an upper limit for stoichiometry as the drugs may inhibit other minor Na transport systems. Antiport with this stoichiometry would be very inefficient in human red cells because the energy available from the transport of three Na ions down their electrochemical gradient is far in excess of that needed to move a single Mg ion out. It would be far more efficient in other tissues, however, especially those with large negative membrane potentials. Experiments in red cells may reveal properties of a transport system that can operate under conditions that prevail in a wide range of tissues.

In spite of the arguments outlined above, which show that, in principle, all the energy needed for Mg transport could be harvested from the Na gradient, there is still doubt whether this, in fact, happens. Na-dependent Mg transport might obtain its energy from some other source. One objection to Na-Mg exchange is the observation that it is very difficult to reverse the direction of Mg transport even when both the Mg and Na gradients strongly favor Mg influx (42). This objection can be questioned on the grounds that Mg need not move at similar rates in both directions across the membrane. Inward movement of Mg may simply be very slow. Thermodynamic arguments dictate the direction of movement but not the rate. A second objection is that abolition of the Na gradient across the membrane by increasing $[Na]_i$ does not produce a large reduction in the rate of Mg efflux (21). Free energy changes, however, favor outward Mg movement in these experiments even if the stoichiometry of transport is assumed to be 3Na : 1Mg. Thus the problem is kinetic rather than thermodynamic and does not rule out a Mg transporter which, if necessary, can obtain energy from the Na gradient. In order to rule out Na-Mg exchange, it is necessary to show that Mg transport occurs when both the Na and Mg gradients oppose that movement. Interpretation of these experiments emphasizes the key issues of how the transporter harvests and uses energy and the relationship between available energy and the rate of ion transport. Most models assume a fixed stoichiometry; however, alternative schemes with variable stoichiometry may be possible. For instance, the transporter may have an oligomeric structure where one or more Na transporters can be associated with each Mg transporter depending on need. It is worth noting that objections to the Na gradient providing energy for transport are based on experiments using PCMBS.

Mg efflux in the absence of Na_o is small (13, 42), but may not simply represent leak through the lipid as the calculated permeability ($P_{Mg} = 10^{-9}$ cm s^{-1}) is larger than the ground permeabilities to Na or K (13). Possibly this efflux may represent other Mg transport systems or contributions from residual PCMBS or A23187. Analysis of Mg efflux from untreated cells suggests that P_{Mg} is about 10^{-10} cm s^{-1}; similar to the leak permeabilities for Na and K (41). Mg leak may be increased by removal of ATP (21). Recently it was shown that Mg efflux into (hypertonic) sucrose is about twice the flux into saline (29, 30). Efflux is reduced equally by isotonic replacement of sucrose by the Cl salts of choline, K, and Li but less so by NaCl (29). Efflux into sucrose is partially inhibited by amiloride and 4-acetamido-4'-isothiocyanatostilbene- 2,2'-disulfonic acid (SITS) (29, 30). It is suggested that the fluxes in sucrose reveal a Cl-dependent Mg transport system. An alternative explanation is that incubation of human red cells in sucrose depolarizes the membrane potential and activates a non-specific cation transport system (33). Mg may be able to move on this transporter. SITS may inhibit Mg efflux by reducing the membrane potential rather than by a direct effect on the transporter.

When human red cells are deoxygenated, $[Mg^{2+}]_i$ increases because of the increased binding of free ATP and 2,3 bisphosphoglycerate (2,3 BPG) by deoxyhemoglobin (16, 32). In normal red cells this increase simply reduces the inward Mg gradient. However, in the densest cells from patients with sickle cell disease (which also have reduced 2,3 BPG levels) the increase is so large that the gradient is reversed (47). This may result in a net loss of Mg from the dense cells because their Mg permeability is also markedly increased on deoxygenation (47). The cause and nature of the sickling-induced change in permeability has still to be elucidated.

Chicken Red Cells

Na-activated Mg transport has been demonstrated in chicken red cells loaded with Mg using A23187 (26, 31). Mg effux is activated by $[Mg^{2+}]_i$ (apparent $K_{1/2}$ 3.5 mM) and by Na_o (apparent $K_{1/2}$ 25 mM). It is inhibited by amiloride, Mn, high $[Mg^{2+}]_o$, and by metabolic inhibitors. It is unaffected by DIDS, ouabain, furosemide, PCMBS, N-ethylmaleimide (NEM), and acetazolamide. Amiloride not only blocks Mg transport, but also the phosphorylation of a 230-kd membrane protein, which is phosphorylated in Mg-loaded cells that have a high Mg efflux. It is not phosphorylated in control cells with low Mg efflux (27). Therefore this protein may be involved in Mg transport. Experiments following simultaneous changes in red cell Na and Mg content indicate a stoichiometry of 2Na:1Mg (31). This is an upper limit as the data were not corrected for Na transport on other systems. It has been suggested that the transporter does not obtain energy from the Na gradient since Mg efflux is unaffected by increasing $[Na]_i$ with PCMBS (26). An alternative conclusion is that the Na gradient was not changed sufficiently to affect Mg transport. In these particular experiments the Mg gradient was strongly outward and Na gradient still inward so that there was sufficient energy to drive outward Mg transport. Addition of ^{28}Mg to cell suspensions indicates that the transporter can also mediate amiloride-sensitive Mg-Mg exchange, which is stimulated when Na_o is replaced by K, and that there is competition between Mg_o and Na_o (28).

Other Red Cells

Rat red cells have a powerful capacity to transport Mg (14). The majority of efflux is dependent on Na_o ($K_{1/2}$ 11 mM) and has a V_{max} that varies widely between individual rats from 0.15–1.2 mmol liter-cell^{-1} h^{-1}. Na-dependent Mg efflux is inhibited by quinidine and is reduced when cells are ATP-depleted. In the absence of Na_o, external Mn stimulates Mg efflux ($K_{0.5}$ 35 μM) and Mg_o stimulates Mn efflux ($K_{o.5}$ 35 μM) from Mn-loaded cells. The properties of Mn-stimulated Mg efflux are similar to those of the Na-dependent component. Mn uptake can also be seen in the absence of Na_o. The data suggest that the transporter mediates an exchange of 1Mn : 1Mg and that it handles Mn in much the same way as Mg (14). They also indicate that, at least in rat red cells, Mn may be a useful probe for Mg transport. Co, but not Ni, Sr, Ca, or Ba, also stimulates Mg efflux in the absence of Na_o.

Substantial Mg efflux has also been observed in ferret red cells (20). Mg efflux shows a complex dependence on Na_o. Efflux increases as Na is replaced by choline or N-methyl-D-glucamine and reaches a peak at about 5–10 mM Na. Further reduction of $[Na]_o$ powerfully inhibits efflux. At very low $[Na]_o$, Mg influx is seen thus indicating that Mg transport can be reversed if the Na gradient is reversed sufficiently in these red cells. Mg efflux is partially inhibited by quinidine, amiloride, Co, and Mn. Efflux of Mg into nominally Mg-free media can proceed against substantial Na gradients in these high Na cells. Even so, these data and the physiologic $[Mg^{2+}]_i$ are consistent with antiport of 1Na : 1Mg.

Murine S49 Lymphoma Cells

Studies on Mg transport in murine S49 lymphoma cells demonstrate hormonal modulation of Mg transport (11). Influx, but not efflux, is inhibited by β-adrenergic agonists and prostaglandin E_1 and is stimulated by phorbol esters (11, 24). The actions of β-agonists are not mediated by cAMP. The transport system responsible for influx is very selective for Mg and is distinct from Ca transport systems (25). Influx requires internal ATP and is stimulated by removal of Na_o and by cytosolic alkalinization. It is not affected by the membrane potential. Influx may be mediated by a system similar to that responsible for Mg efflux in human red cells (R. D. Grubbs & M. E. Maguire, personal communication).

CONCLUSION

Mg transport has been observed in a wide range of tissues. Work on squid axon, barnacle muscle, synaptosomes (35), and red cells from several species indicates that Na-dependent Mg efflux may be the primary mechanism for keeping $[Mg^{2+}]_i$ below electrochemical equilibrium. Transport in these tissues shares many features, which suggests that, rather than many tissue-specific transport systems, a common system is widely distributed. The energy source for active Mg transport is still controversial. Evidence marginally favors Na-Mg antiport, which obtains all of its energy from the Na and Mg gradients. ATP may be necessary to maintain the transporter in a phosphorylated, active state, acting catalytically and not as a source of energy for transport. A Mg pump, however, that requires Na_o and obtains energy from ATP or some other high energy compound is compatible with most of the data, although it is not clear why it should apparently dissipate the Na gradient so fruitlessly. Resolution of this and several other problems associated with Na-dependent Mg transport may have to await the isolation and reconstitution of the system.

Na-dependent Mg transport shares many properties with the Na-Ca exchange, which is found widely in tissues. It has been suggested, therefore, that the same transporter may be responsible for both (see 46). There is some evidence against this idea. NEM inhibits Mg efflux, but not Ca efflux, in barnacle muscle (2); membrane potential does not affect the rate of Mg efflux, whereas it has a profound effect on Ca transport in squid axons (6, 8); Na-Ca exchange is influenced by external monovalent cations binding to a regulatory site, whereas Na-Mg exchange in squid axons is not (8); Mg is not transported by the Na-Ca exchanger in retinal rod outer segments (54); and, finally Na-Mg exchange, but not Na-Ca exchange, occurs in human red cells. Studies on squid axon (8), sarcoplasmic reticulum vesicles (50), and red cells (21) rule out the possibility that Mg moves through the Ca pump. Magnesium needs its own, separate transport system.

A major problem with investigating Mg transport is that a specific, potent inhibitor of the Na-dependent component has not yet been found. This makes it particularly difficult to investigate the hypothesis that Mg transport occurs through Na-Mg antiport where the direction of transport may reverse at low $[Na]_o$. Without a specific inhibitor, it is difficult to dissect Mg fluxes unambiguously into components via the Na-Mg exchanger and those through other pathways. Transport through these pathways may also be affected by Na_o. Thus defining Na-Mg exchange simply as the component of Mg efflux sensitive to removal of Na_o may lead to errors in estimation of both components. Consequently, there is little information about the leak fluxes of Mg. The lack of an inhibitor has also made it particularly difficult to assess whether Na is transported by the system and, if it is, to assess transport stoichiometry. Recent evidence suggests one to three Na ions transported per Mg ion (15, 22, 23, 26). Stoichiometries of 1Na:1Mg and 3Na:1Mg would imply that transport is electrogenic and should be affected by changes in membrane potential unless other, as yet unidentified, ions also move. The inability of moderate changes in membrane potential to alter net Mg efflux argues against simple models with a stoichiometry of 1:1 or 3:1 (6, 8), but does not rule out more complex schemes.

There have been few attempts to produce kinetic models of Mg transport. In principle, Na-dependent Mg transport can be described by consecutive or simultaneous models (see 36). In consecutive models the transporter exists in two interconvertible forms, one that binds and transports Mg, and one that binds and transports Na. In simultaneous models both Na and Mg must be bound concurrently for transport to occur. Consecutive models, so successful at explaining Na-pump kinetics, appear attractive on the surface since they immediately explain Mg-Mg exchange. Such a model has recently been used to describe Na-dependent Mg transport in human red cells where the energy for active Mg transport is assumed to come from ATP (42). If, however, it is assumed that the Na gradient supplies energy, then consecutive models do not make clear how this energy drives active Mg movement. It has to be assumed that the transport of Na down its gradient leaves the transporter in a high energy state and that this energy is then used to increase the chemical potential of Mg, which is bound in a separate step. The transfer of energy in this way has not been documented and even in the Na-pump the crucial transfer of energy to Na occurs when both Na and P_i are bound to the pump (see 52). If it is assumed that energy is transferred between bound ions, then a simultaneous model of Na-Mg exchange is required. Versions of this model can account for Mg-Mg exchange. Unfortunately, kinetic tests to distinguish between the models have not yet been made.

There is not yet sufficient information to form a coherent picture of the Na-independent Mg transport systems. A Mg-H antiport and a Mg uniport may be involved in the regulation of mitochondrial Mg levels (9, 17), and they may also be present in other membranes. The possibility that Mg may be transported bound to agents such as ATP or amino acids has received little attention.

A promising new approach to understanding Mg transport is molecular genetics. Three Mg transport systems, coded by the loci *corA*, *mgtA*, and *mgtB*, have been cloned from *Salmonella typhimurium* (51). Study of these transporters with techniques such as site directed mutagenesis may yield information about the nature of Mg binding sites that could have important implications for understanding Mg transport in eukaryotic systems. Interestingly, *mgtB* encodes for a product that shows 49% homology with a rat sarcoplasmic reticulum Ca pump (M. E. Maguire, personal communication).

ACKNOWLEDGMENT

I would like to thank The Wellcome Trust for support and V. L. Lew and J. Morris for reading the manuscript.

Literature Cited

1. Alvarez-Leefmans, F. J., Giraldez, F., Gamiño, S. M. 1987. Intracellular free magnesium in excitable cells: its measurement and its biologic significance. *Can. J. Physiol. Pharmacol.* 65:915–25
2. Ashley, C. C., Ellory, J. C. 1972. The efflux of magnesium from single crustacean muscle fibres. *J. Physiol.* 226:653–74
3. Baker, P. F., Crawford, A. C. 1972. Mobility and transport of magnesium in squid giant axons. *J. Physiol.* 227:855–74
4. Caldwell-Violich, M., Requena, J. 1979. Magnesium content and net fluxes in squid giant axons. *J. Gen. Physiol.* 74:739–52
5. Corkey, B. E., Duszynski, J., Rich, T. L., Matschinsky, B., Williamson, J. R.

1986. Regulation of free and bound magnesium in rat hepatocytes and isolated mitochondria. *J. Biol. Chem.* 261:2567–74
6. De Weer, P. 1976. Axoplasmic free magnesium levels and magnesium extrusion from squid giant axons. *J. Gen. Physiol.* 68:159–78
7. Diebler, H., Eigen, M., Ilgenfritz, G., Maass, G., Winkler, R. 1969. Kinetics and mechanism of reactions of main group metal ions with biological carriers. *Pure Appl. Chem.* 20:93–115
8. DiPolo, R., Beaugé, L. 1988. An ATP-dependent Na^{+}/Mg^{2+} countertransport is the only mechanism for Mg extrusion in squid axons. *Biochim. Biophys. Acta* 946:424–28
9. Diwan, J. J. 1987. Mitochondrial transport of K^{+} and Mg^{2+}. *Biochim. Biophys. Acta* 895:155–65
10. Dunn, M. J. 1974. Red blood cell calcium and magnesium: effects upon sodium and potassium transport and cellular morphology. *Biochim. Biophys. Acta* 352:97–116
11. Erdos, J. J., Maguire, M. E. 1983. Hormone-sensitive magnesium transport in murine S49 lymphoma cells: characterization and specificity for magnesium. *J. Physiol.* 337:351–71
12. Féray, J.-C., Franck, G., Garay, R., Henrotte, J.-G. 1989. Inter-individual differences in red cell Mg^{2+} contents are related to the activity of a Na^{+}:Mg^{2+} exchanger. Possible relationship with HLA-associated genetic factors. *Magnesium Res.* 2:124
13. Féray, J.-C., Garay, R. 1986. An Na^{+}-stimulated Mg^{2+}-transport system in human red blood cells. *Biochim. Biophys. Acta* 856:76–84
14. Féray, J.-C., Garay, R. 1987. A one-to-one Mg^{2+}:Mn^{2+} exchange in rat erythrocytes. *J. Biol. Chem.* 262:5763–68
15. Féray, J.-C., Garay, R. 1988. Demonstration of a Na^{+}:Mg^{2+} exchange in human red cells by its sensitivity to tricyclic antidepressant drugs. *Naunyn-Schmiedebergs Arch. Pharmakol.* 338:332–37
16. Flatman, P. W. 1980. The effect of buffer composition and deoxygenation on the concentration of ionized magnesium inside human red blood cells. *J. Physiol.* 300:19–30
17. Flatman, P. W. 1984. Magnesium transport across cell membranes. *J. Membr. Biol.* 80:1–14
18. Flatman, P. W. 1988. The effects of magnesium on potassium transport in ferret red cells. *J. Physiol.* 397:471–87
19. Flatman, P. W. 1988. The control of red cell magnesium. *Magnesium Res.* 1:5–11
20. Flatman, P. W., Smith, L. M. 1990. Magnesium transport in ferret red cells. *J. Physiol.* 431:11–25
21. Frenkel, E. J., Graziani, M., Schatzmann, H. J. 1989. ATP requirement of the sodium-dependent magnesium extrusion from human red blood cells. *J. Physiol.* 414:385–97
22. Fry, C. H. 1986. Measurement and control of intracellular magnesium ion concentration in guinea pig and ferret ventricular myocardium. *Magnesium* 5:306–16
23. Gonzalez-Serratos, H., Rasgado-Flores, H., Sjodin, R. A., Montes, J. G. 1988. Evidence for "reverse mode" Na/Mg exchange in dialysed giant squid axons. *Biophys. J.* 53:342a
24. Grubbs, R. D., Maguire, M. E. 1986. Regulation of magnesium but not calcium transport by phorbol ester. *J. Biol. Chem.* 261:12550–54
25. Grubbs, R. D., Wetherill, C. A., Kutschke, K., Maguire, M. E. 1985. Magnesium transport in murine S49 lymphoma cells: pharmacology and divalent cation selectivity. *Am. J. Physiol.* 248:C51–57
26. Günther, T., Vormann, J. 1985. Mg^{2+} efflux is accomplished by an amiloride-sensitive Na^{+}/Mg^{2+} antiport. *Biochem. Biophys. Res. Commun.* 130:540–45
27. Günther, T., Vormann, J. 1986. Probable role of protein phosphorylation in the regulation of Mg^{2+} efflux via Na^{+}/Mg^{2+} antiport. *Magnesium Bull.* 8:307–309
28. Günther, T., Vormann, J. 1987. Characterization of Na^{+}/Mg^{2+} antiport by simultaneous $^{28}Mg^{2+}$ influx. *Biochem. Biophys. Res. Commun.* 148:1069–74
29. Günther, T., Vormann, J. 1989. Na^{+}-independent Mg^{2+} efflux from Mg^{2+}-loaded human erythrocytes. *FEBS Lett.* 247:181–84
30. Günther, T., Vormann, J. 1989. Characterization of Mg^{2+} efflux from human, rat and chicken erythrocytes. *FEBS Lett.* 250:633–37
31. Günther, T., Vormann, J., Förster, R. 1984. Regulation of intracellular magnesium by Mg^{2+} efflux. *Biochem. Biophys. Res. Commun.* 119:124–31
32. Gupta, R. K., Benovic, J. L., Rose, Z. B. 1978. The determination of the free magnesium level in the human red blood cell by ^{31}P NMR. *J. Biol. Chem.* 253:6172–76
33. Halperin, J. A., Brugnara, C., Tosteson, M. T., Van Ha, T., Tosteson, D.

C. 1989. Voltage-activated cation transport in human erythrocytes. *Am. J. Physiol.* 257:C986–96
34. Hartzell, H. C., White, R. E. 1989. Effects of magnesium on inactivation of the voltage-gated calcium current in cardiac myocytes. *J. Gen. Physiol.* 94:745–67
35. Heinonen, E., Åkerman, K. E. O. 1987. Intracellular free magnesium in synaptosomes measured with entrapped eriochrome blue. *Biochim. Biophys. Acta* 898:331–37
36. Hilgemann, D. W. 1988. Numerical approximations of sodium-calcium exchange. *Prog. Biophys. Molec. Biol.* 51:1–45
37. Horie, M., Irisawa, H., Noma, A. 1987. Voltage-dependent magnesium block of adenosine-triphosphate-sensitive potassium channel in guinea-pig ventricular cells. *J. Physiol.* 387:251–72
38. Kennedy, B. G., Knight, S. D. 1988. External Mg stimulated Na efflux in skeletal muscle. *Biophys. J.* 53:344a
39. Lauf, P. K. 1985. K^+:Cl^- cotransport: sulfhydryls, divalent cations and the mechanism of volume activation in a red cell. *J. Membr. Biol.* 88:1–13
40. Levy, L. A., Murphy, E., Raju, B., London, R. E. 1988. Measurement of cytosolic free magnesium ion concentration by ^{19}F NMR. *Biochemistry* 27: 4041–48
41. Lew, V. L., Beaugé, L. 1979. Passive cation fluxes in red cell membranes. In *Membrane Transport in Biology,* ed. G. Giebisch, D. C. Tosteson, H. H. Ussing, 2:81–115. Berlin: Springer-Verlag
42. Lüdi, H., Schatzmann, H. J. 1987. Some properties of a system for sodium-dependent outward movement of magnesium from metabolizing human red blood cells. *J. Physiol.* 390:367–82
43. Montes, J. G., Sjodin, R. A., Gonzalez-Serratos, H., Rasgado-Flores, H. 1988. Evidence for potassium-activated magnesium extrusion in barnacle muscle fibers. *Biophys. J.* 53:344a
44. Montes, J. G., Sjodin, R. A., Yergey, A. L., Vieira, N. E. 1989. Simultaneous bidirectional magnesium ion flux measurements in single barnacle muscle cells by mass spectrometry. *Biophys. J.* 56:437–46
45. Mullins, L. J., Brinley, F. J. Jr. 1978. Magnesium influx in dialyzed squid axons. *J. Membr. Biol.* 43:243–50
46. Mullins, L. J., Brinley, F. J. Jr., Spangler, S. G., Abercrombie, R. F. 1977. Magnesium efflux in dialyzed squid axons. *J. Gen. Physiol.* 69:389–400
47. Ortiz, O. E., Lew, V. L., Bookchin, R. M. 1990. Deoxygenation permeabilizes sickle cell anaemia red cells to magnesium and reverses its gradient in the dense cells. *J. Physiol.* 427:211–26
48. Pusch, M., Conti, F., Stühmer, W. 1989. Intracellular magnesium blocks sodium outward currents in a voltage- and dose-dependent manner. *Biophys. J.* 55:1267–71
49. Raju, B., Murphy, E., Levy, L. A., Hall, R. D., London, R. E. 1989. A fluorescent indicator for measuring cytosolic free magnesium. *Am. J. Physiol.* 256:C540–48
50. Salama, G., Scarpa, A. 1985. Magnesium permeability of sarcoplasmic reticulum. *J. Biol. Chem.* 260:11697–705
51. Snavely, M. D., Florer, J. B., Miller, C. G., Maguire, M. E. 1989. Magnesium transport in *Salmonella typhimurium:* $^{28}Mg^{2+}$ transport by the CorA, MgtA, and MgtB systems. *J. Bacteriol.* 171:4761–66
52. Tanford, C. 1983. Mechanisms of free energy coupling in active transport. *Annu. Rev. Biochem.* 52:379–409
53. Vogel, D., Brinley, F. J. Jr. 1973. Mg and Ca fluxes in isolated dialyzed barnacle muscle fibres. *Biophys. J.* 13:104a
54. Yau, K.-W., Nakatani, K. 1984. Electrogenic Na-Ca exchange in retinal rod outer segment. *Nature* 311:661–63

Annu. Rev. Physiol. 1991. 53:273–87

CELLULAR MAGNESIUM AND Na/Mg EXCHANGE IN HEART CELLS

Elizabeth Murphy

Laboratory of Molecular Biophysics, National Institute of Environmental Health Science, Research Triangle Park, North Carolina 27709

Craig C. Freudenrich, and Melvyn Lieberman

Division of Physiology, Department of Cell Biology, Duke University Medical Center, Durham, North Carolina 27710

KEY WORDS: FURAPTRA/Mag-fura-2, ion selective microelectrodes, NMR, Mg transport

---

INTRODUCTION

The development of new methods capable of resolving important questions concerning the regulation and physiologic importance of cytosolic free magnesium (Mg_i), coupled with the convergence of several areas of research, makes this an exciting time in magnesium research. Numerous studies have shown that plasma magnesium concentration correlates with cardiovascular diseases such as ischemia, arrhythmias, and hypertension (3, 4, 43, 48, 67, 68). The questions that remain to be answered relate to whether the pathologic effects of altered plasma magnesium are mediated primarily by alterations in extracellular magnesium (Mg_o), by a secondary alteration in Mg_i, or by the combined effect of the two mechanisms (3, 43, 68). Mg_o is a Ca-channel blocker (43); consistent with this is the observation that changes in plasma magnesium cause reciprocal changes in cell calcium (3). Additional clarification is needed to resolve whether chronic alterations in Mg_o cause a change in Mg_i in cardiac muscle (3, 48) and, if so, can such changes affect cardiac function. In this regard, recent studies describe the effects of a change in Mg_i ($\sim$ 1 mM) on K and Ca channels (1, 40, 72, 82), Na, K ATPase activity (19,

0066–4278/91/0315–0273$02.00

69), and Ca release from the sarcoplasmic reticulum (54). These studies suggest that Mg_i may modulate cardiac function; however, if Mg is a modulator of cell function, Mg_i itself must change under physiologic or pathologic conditions.

Clearly, convenient methods to measure Mg_i are needed before we can examine the regulation of Mg_i and address whether changes in Mg_o alter Mg_i, and whether changes in Mg_i occur which in turn affect cardiac cell function. New, improved methods for measuring Mg_i are reviewed briefly in the following section (also see 9; R. E. London, this volume). With these methods several groups have begun to investigate the cellular processes underlying Mg_i regulation. Mechanisms that affect M_g transport across the plasma membrane or the redistribution of Mg_i either by altered binding or by uptake or release from intracellular organelles are also discussed. In the final section, we consider whether changes in Mg_i are associated with various physiologic and pathologic conditions such as hormonal stimulation, hypomagnesemia, and ischemia-induced ATP depletion.

MEASUREMENT OF Mg_i IN HEART

Measurements of Mg_i have been recently reviewed (5, 9, 24; R. E. London, this volume) and therefore we will only provide an update of research in this area (see Table 1). Just a few years ago, values for Mg_i in cardiac tissue were reported to be between 0.4 and 4.0 mM. In the last 18 months, values for Mg_i have narrowed to 0.5–1.2 mM. The reasons for the closer agreement between reported values are due primarily to the following factors: (*a*) improved resins for ion selective microelectrodes (ISME) (7, 8, 15, 16, 42, 53); (*b*) recognition in the ISME studies that averaging Mg concentrations or activities leads to erroneously high values of Mg_i, whereas averaging pMg or mV gives statistically proper values for Mg_i (29); (*c*) resolution of the K_d for Mg-ATP

Table 1 Measured values of Mg_i in heart

mM	Method	Reference
0.5	^{31}P NMR	Borchgrevink et al (1989)
0.6	^{31}P NMR	Kirkels et al (1989)
0.7	^{31}P NMR	Headrick & Willis (1989)
0.4	^{31}P NMR	Gupta (1990)
0.4	ISME (ETH)	Blatter & McGuigan (1988)
0.85	ISME (ETH 5214)	Blatter et al (1990)
1.2	^{19}F NMR (fluorocitrate)	Kirschenlohr et al (1988)
0.85	^{19}F NMR (F APTRA)	Murphy et al (1989)
0.5	Fluorescence (Furaptra)	Murphy et al (1989)

(30); and (*d*) availability of fluorescent and nuclear magnetic resonance (NMR) magnesium-sensitive indicators (46, 49, 57, 58, 63).

Ion Selective Microelectrodes (ISME)

Blatter & McGuigan (9) recently described how magnesium measurements using ISME with the ETH 1117 resin are critically dependent on the concentrations of K and Na in the calibration solutions. This sensitivity to Na and K can account for some of the variability of Mg_i measurements; for example, Blatter & McGuigan (9) reported that a value of 0.4 mM Mg_i in their calibration solution would correspond to a value of 2.1 mM Mg_i using the calibration solution of Hess et al (37). The sensitivity of the resin to Na and K also limits the accuracy of measurements of Mg_i when Na and K change. Fortunately, the newly available resin, ETH 5214 (42), is insensitive to Na and K, and the response is approximately Nernstian at magnesium concentrations $\geq$0.5 mM (7, 8). Values for Mg_i in cardiac preparations measured with this resin average 0.8 mM (15, 53). Another development that has shifted some Mg_i values closer to 1 mM is the realization that averaging data as Mg_i results in a value that is statistically higher than data averaged as pMg or mV (29).

^{31}P NMR Measurements

Mg_i can be measured by ^{31}P NMR since the binding of Mg to ATP causes an NMR chemical shift of the β-phosphate resonance of ATP relative to the α-phosphate resonance of ATP (34). The difference in the shift between the α and β phosphates of ATP, which is proportional to Mg_i, is reasonably comparable between data published from different laboratories. For example, under control conditions, Wu et al (83) reported a shift difference of 8.57 ppm, whereas Gupta et al (34) and Kushmerick et al (47) reported a difference of 8.50 ppm; however, these investigators calculated different values of Mg_i: 2.5 mM (83), 0.8 mM (34), and 1.4 mM (47), respectively. These differences in calculated Mg_i arise because of variations in the K_d values assumed for Mg-ATP. Garfinkel & Garfinkel (30) have extensively examined the Mg-ATP equilibrium and report a K_d value similar to that used by Gupta et al (34). Thus it would appear that the ^{31}P NMR data are consistent with a Mg_i value of ~1.0 mM in heart.

The K_d for Mg-ATP is pH-sensitive in the physiologic range (47); therefore care must be taken when determining Mg_i under conditions that cause a change in pH. The apparent K_d for Mg-ATP at pH 7.0 is reported to be in the range of 38 (34) to 78 μM (47). In heart muscle, this value is an order of magnitude below Mg_i. Thus at physiologic levels of Mg_i, ATP-Mg complexation is close to saturation and, therefore the shift of the β phosphate of ATP is relatively insensitive to an increase in Mg_i (see Figure 7A in reference 47).

New NMR and Fluorescent Indicators

Levy et al (49) and Raju et al (63) recently characterized three NMR indicators and a fluorescent indicator based on the chelator, o-aminophenol triacetate (APTRA). The indicators are synthesized as acetoxymethyl esters, and as such they freely permeate the plasma membrane. Once inside the cell the ester is cleaved, and the negatively charged indicator becomes trapped. These indicators have pK values ranging from 4.0 to 5.5, K_d values for Mg of 0.6 to 3.0 mM, and K_d values for Ca of 10–80 μM (49, 63). When magnesium binds to the NMR indicator (F-APTRA), the fluorine undergoes an NMR chemical shift. The NMR indicator has been loaded into perfused rat heart and yields a Mg_i value of 0.85 ± 0.10 mM (58).

The fluorescent indicator, FURAPTRA, contains a fura-2 fluorophore and undergoes an excitation shift upon binding Mg. We have reported that embryonic chick heart cells have a Mg_i concentration of 0.48 ± 0.03 mM (57). Molecular Probes Inc. (Eugene, OR) offers FURAPTRA under the name mag-fura-2, and other magnesium-sensitive indicators based on indo and quin fluorophores; however, at this time there are no published data on these indicators.

Kirschenlohr et al (46) used ^{19}F NMR and the (+) isomer of fluorocitrate to measure Mg_i in perfused ferret hearts. They report that Mg_i remains constant at 1.2 ± 0.1 mM during the cardiac cycle. Maguire & co-workers (51) have synthesized a magnesium indicator based on a tropolone structure that increases in absorbance upon binding Mg_i. Both the fluorocitrate and the tropolone can be introduced into cells as esters. Mg_i in heart has also been estimated from chemical equilibrium of Mg-dependent reactions (74); values fall within the range of 1 mM.

MECHANISMS FOR REGULATING Mg_i

Processes involved in regulating Mg_i include permeability of the plasma membrane, Mg transporters in the membrane, intracellular buffering by proteins, and transport across organelles (P. Flatman, this volume). Ultimately, steady-state Mg_i is controlled by the first two mechanisms, although Mg_i can be altered by buffering or transport by intracellular proteins and organelles, respectively. These processes will be reviewed individually even though we recognize the likelihood that they act in concert.

Magnesium Electrochemical Gradient and Permeability

If Mg_i were in electrochemical equilibrium with 1 mM Mg_o and a membrane potential of −80 mV, then Mg_i would be 188 mM, well above the measured 1 mM Mg_i. Even with a membrane potential of −40mV, Mg_i would be 20 mM. Thus unless the plasma membrane is impermeable to magnesium, some mechanism(s) must exist to extrude magnesium against its electrochemical gradient. A Na/Mg exchanger and Mg ATPase have been postulated as two such extrusion mechanisms (24).

Magnesium permeability has been measured by several investigators using a ^{28}Mg tracer (60, 61, 76). The percentage of total magnesium that exchanges and the rate of exchange vary considerably in different tissues (see 76). In perfused rat heart, Page & Polimeni (60) showed that, at 37°C and 0.56 mM Mg_o, within 20 hr 98% of all cellular magnesium exchanged with an initial rate constant of 0.15 ± 0.02 mmol/kg dry wt/min. Page & Polimeni also presented three observations that suggest carrier-mediated magnesium transport: a low passive Mg permeability, a hyperbolic relationship between the rate of exchange and Mg_o, and a dependence of magnesium efflux on Mg_o.

Low Mg permeability is also suggested by both the slow net loss of total magnesium that occurs in a Mg_o-free solution (60), and the recent ISME and fluorescent indicator measurements of Mg_i, which show that Mg_i is unaltered by 15–20 min of magnesium-free perfusion (28, 57).

Plasma Membrane Magnesium Transport Mechanisms

MG ATPASE Although evidence for a Mg ATPase in heart is lacking, this mechanism must still be considered, especially since Hmiel et al (38) have cloned several Mg ATPase transporters in *Salmonella typhimurium*. The presence of a Mg ATPase is difficult to establish because no specific Mg ATPase inhibitors exist, and an increase in Mg_i, evoked by ATP depletion, could also be interpreted as the loss of a magnesium buffer. Thus unless a specific inhibitor of Mg ATPase becomes available, or until we can identify the gene encoding for a Mg ATPase and modify its expression, the presence of Mg ATPase in heart will be difficult to establish.

NA/MG EXCHANGE At present much of our knowledge concerning Na/Mg exchange has been obtained from the squid axon. Mg efflux from squid axons that were dialyzed or injected with ^{28}Mg is inhibited 95% by ATP depletion and 75% by removal of Na_o (6, 19, 56). Furthermore, Mg efflux is also unaffected by changes in membrane potential (11), and Mg influx is stimulated by increasing Na_i (55). These data collectively support the existence of an electroneutral Na/Mg countertransport that uses the energy of the Na gradient to provide the driving force for the extrusion of Mg against its electrochemical gradient. Since in squid axons, ATP-γ-S can replace ATP in activating Na/Mg exchange, DiPolo & Beauge (20) suggest that ATP is required as a modulator of the Na/Mg transporter. In red blood cells, however, ATP may be used to generate the energy for the outward Mg movement (23, 26).

Evidence for Na/Mg exchange in heart is not as clearly defined. Fry (28), using ISME, reported evidence in support of Na/Mg exchange in guinea pig papillary and ferret ventricular muscle. When Mg_o was raised from 1 to 10 mM, intracellular sodium concentration in guinea pig papillary muscle fell from 9.5 ± 0.3 to 6.4 ± 2.0 mM with a concomitant rise in Mg_i from 2.4 ± 0.2 to 3.7 ± 0.5 mM. Fry (28) also showed that addition of ouabain caused an elevation in Na_i from 10 to 20 mM with an increase in Mg_i from 2.4 ± 0.2 to 2.8 mM. In the same preparation, raising K_o to 30 mM did not change Mg_i. Sodium-free superfusion of ferret ventricular muscle caused a decrease in Na_i from 8.5 to 2.5 mM and an increase in Mg_i from 2.0 to 2.8 mM. Reducing Mg_o to zero did not cause a change in Mg_i in either ferret ventricular muscle or guinea pig papillary muscle.

Na/Mg countertransport requires that an ion be transported against its electrochemical gradient driven by the electrochemical gradient of the counter ion. To demonstrate net ion movements, total intracellular ion contents must be measured because the cytosolic-free concentration or activity of the ion could be altered because of its uptake into intracellular organelles, or binding to intracellular sites, or by a change in cell volume. For example, removing Na_o lowers pH_i and elevates Ca_i. These ion alterations might influence Mg_i by competing for binding sites so that the increase in Mg_i, observed with Na-free perfusion, might not be due to Na/Mg exchange (57). Indeed, as discussed below, the increase in Mg that occurs in chick heart cells on Na-free perfusion is not affected by the concomitant removal of Mg_o, which suggests that this increase in Mg_i does not result from Mg entry via Na/Mg exchange. Likewise, the increase in Ca_i following ouabain addition could affect Mg_i through alterations in binding.

Reasonable evidence for Na/Mg exchange in guinea pig papillary muscle is provided by the concomitant decrease in Na_i and increase in Mg_i that occurs upon raising Mg_o from 1 to 10 mM (28). Under these conditions, the decrease in Na_i occurs against its electrochemical gradient and is driven by the increase in the transmembrane magnesium gradient. Measurements of Na_i are usually a good index of total cell Na because intracellular sodium is not tightly bound or sequestered. Furthermore, increasing Mg_o is unlikely to change pH_i or Ca_i, either of which might be expected to alter intracellular magnesium buffering. Recent results (15, 16) obtained from ferret ventricular muscle, however, do not show a decrease in Na_i upon elevating Mg_o to 10 mM. This finding suggests that the presence or activity of Na/Mg exchange in heart may vary even among different species.

Using the fluorescent magnesium indicator, FURAPTRA, Murphy et al (57) have also investigated the presence of Na/Mg exchange in cultured embryonic chick heart cells. Perfusion of these cells with a Na-free solution caused an increase in Mg_i from 0.48 ± 0.03 to 1.27 ± 0.24 mM. This increase cannot be attributed to Na/Mg exchange, however, because a similar increase in Mg_i occurred in cells perfused by a Mg-free, Na-free solution, and total cell magnesium (measured by atomic absorption spectroscopy) did not increase with Na_o-free perfusion (unpublished results, C. C. Freudenrich, E. Murphy, & M. Lieberman). Furthermore, the increase in Mg_i was largely attenuated when calcium was removed from the Na-free perfusate. These data would seem to suggest that Na/Mg exchange, if present in chick heart cells, is not a high capacity transporter. A low capacity transporter would suffice, however, given the low permeability of the cell membrane to magnesium. If a low capacity Na/Mg exchange exists in chick heart cells, Na-free perfusion may not enable the transport of sufficient Mg into the cell to increase either free or total magnesium. To determine whether a low capacity Na/Mg exchanger exists in cardiac preparations, the best approach might be to combine measurements of cytosolic free ion and total ion content. For example, assuming 0.825 kg cell water/kg wet wt (60) and a wet wt/dry wt ratio of 4, if total cell magnesium, reported to be in the range of 40 mmol/kg dry wt, were free in the cytosol (which is clearly not the case), it would be equivalent to 12 mM Mg. Total cell sodium is also in the range of 10 mM. If the stoichiometry of Na/Mg exchange is 1 : 1 then an exchange of 2 mM Na for 2 mM Mg should be detectable. However, changes in Na or Mg of less than 5% of the total (~0.5 mM) would be difficult to detect.

A possible means of increasing the sensitivity of these measurements is by isotopic uptake or release of ^{28}Mg; however, isotopic flux measurements, especially in multicompartmented cells, are not simply related to net uptake or efflux of an ion across the plasma membrane (12). Furthermore, this isotope has a very short half-life and its availability is limited. Another possible approach to establishing the presence of Na/Mg exchange in heart cells would be to load them with magnesium and determine the effect of changing extracellular sodium on magnesium efflux. Although methods exist for increasing Mg in red blood cells (35), elevated total cell magnesium in heart cells has not been reported.

Intracellular Magnesium Buffering/Binding

As discussed above, Na-free perfusion causes a threefold increase in Mg_i that can be blocked by the simultaneous removal of calcium (57). Eisner et al (21) have shown that Na-free perfusion rapidly increases Ca_i to ~ 1 μM, with a subsequent fall to a plateau level of 269 nM. Murphy et al (59) have reported that Na-free perfusion increases total cell Ca from 10 to 30 nmol/mg protein. This increase, if it were all ionized and assuming 7 μl H_2O/mg protein, would correspond to ~ 2.9 mM Ca, sufficient calcium to displace 1 mM Mg from binding sites. Thus cytosolic ion concentrations cannot be used as a measure of Mg or Ca entry via countertransport because greater than 90% of these divalent ions are bound or sequestered. The data also suggest that calcium and magnesium can compete for intracellular binding sites and that the magnesium displaced by the calcium results in a measurable increase in Mg_i. This conclusion is supported by the observation that the increase in Mg_i in the absence of Na is comparable to values obtained in a Na-free, Mg-free solution (15, 16, 57).

Changes in pH are also known to alter total cell Mg (31). Recently, Freudenrich et al (27) used the NH_4Cl prepulse method (13) to change pH_i and measure concomitant changes in Mg_i. Addition of NH_4Cl caused an alkalinization of 0.52 pH unit that was accompanied by a 0.13 mM decrease in Mg_i, whereas removal of NH_4Cl produced an acidification of 0.92 pH unit concomitant with a 0.13 mM increase in Mg_i. Thus the calcium and hydrogen ions appear to compete with magnesium for binding sites, such that an increase in H_i or Ca_i causes the displacement of bound magnesium and leads to an increase in Mg_i. Interestingly, 0.5 pH unit alkalinization causes the same net change in Mg_i as a 0.9 pH unit acidification (27). In addition, whereas increasing Ca_i increases Mg_i, decreasing Ca_i causes no change in Mg_i. These observations probably reflect variations in the buffering of H, Mg, and Ca. Changes in pH_i and Ca_i, however, are capable of inducing significant changes in Mg_i, and this may indeed be the means by which Mg_i is modulated under physiologic conditions.

Intracellular Organelles

Brierley & co-workers (14) have shown that isolated mitochondria can both take up and extrude magnesium by respiration-dependent, uncoupler-sensitive processes. Since neither ruthenium red nor diltiazem affect either the uptake or release of magnesium, it is likely that magnesium transport by mitochondria is distinct from that of calcium transport. Mitochondrial magnesium uptake is inhibited by potassium, ATP, ADP, and respiration; therefore magnesium uptake is very slow under in situ conditions (6). Hogue & Hansford (39) recently determined matrix free magnesium to be 0.82 ± 0.02 mM in isolated heart mitochondria, loaded with mag-fura-2 (FURAPTRA), and suspended in a medium containing 1 mM Mg, 1 mM phosphate, and 0.12 M KCl. They further reported that raising extramitochondrial magnesium to 2 mM did not change the matrix free magnesium. In agreement with the data of Corkey et al (18), these data suggest that Mg_i is similar to matrix free Mg, and thus only a small, if any, magnesium gradient exists across the mitochondrial membrane. Due to the large mitochondrial membrane potential (- 180 mV), there is a large electrochemical gradient.

Electron probe X-ray microanalysis (EPMA) has been used to measure total magnesium of in situ mitochondria of various cardiac preparations; values of 22 to 56 mM Mg/kg dry wt. were reported (10, 77–80). Wendt-Gallitelli et al

(79) found that the total magnesium of the junctional sarcoplasmic reticulum (SR) adjacent to the T-tubules was 18 mmol/kg dry wt in ventricular cells and 60 mmol/kg dry wt in guinea pig trabeculae. Somlyo & co-workers (17, 70) showed an influx of magnesium into the SR during calcium release in striated muscle.

Mg_i REGULATION OF CELL FUNCTION

Interest in Mg_i has been heightened by recent reports that small changes in Mg_i in the physiologic range can significantly modulate important cardiac cell functions such as stimulation of RNA translation (41), membrane K (40, 72, 73) and Ca (1, 81) channel activity, and Ca release from the sarcoplasmic reticulum (44, 54). If Mg_i modulates cell function, however, Mg_i must change under physiologic conditions. With the availability of improved methodology for measuring Mg_i, (see above) we can now begin to probe the mechanism(s) that regulate Mg_i and subsequently determine whether hormonal stimulation, altered cell volume, or altered plasma magnesium levels can induce changes in Mg_i.

Alteration of Cell Function by Mg_i

Since this topic is covered extensively elsewhere (Matsuda this volume; Morad & Agus this volume; 82), we will only briefly describe a few of the cell functions that are modulated by Mg_i. Horie & Irisawa (40) reported that 1 mM Mg at the inner surface of the patch membrane blocks K channels and causes inward rectification in single guinea pig atrial cells. White & Hartzell (81) used the whole-cell configuration of the patch-clamp technique on isolated frog ventricle cells to show that an increase in Mg from 0.3 to 3.0 mM causes a 50% decrease of the cAMP-dependent voltage-gated calcium current. Agus et al (1) also showed that varying Mg_o from 0 to 1.3 and 9.4 mM progressively shortens the action potential and suppresses the calcium current. Meissner & Henderson (54) showed that Mg can modulate calcium release from the sarcoplasmic reticulum. Mg is also suggested to alter the activity of (*a*) the Na, K ATPase (19, 69); (*b*) the pH_i regulator/anion transporter in barnacle muscle (66); (*c*) protein synthesis in oocytes (41); and (*d*) the conductance of excised patches of rod membranes (71).

Alterations in Mg_i

If Mg_i does regulate cardiac cell function, then not only must Mg alter cell processes (e.g. K channels), but changes in Mg_i must occur. In other words, if Mg_i does not change, Mg modulation of Ca and K channels may be of pharmacologic, but not physiologic interest. Therefore, an important area for future research will be to determine whether physiologic or pathologic alterations occur in Mg_i.

HORMONES Hormones could change Mg_i directly by affecting the transport of magnesium, for example (33). Alternatively, hormones could indirectly affect Mg_i through alterations of H and Ca, which could compete with Mg for intracellular binding sites. Several years ago, Erdos & Maguire (22) showed that β-agonists stimulated ^{28}Mg uptake into S49 lymphoma cells, and more recently Grubbs & Maguire (32) showed a similar response to phorbol esters. Vormann & Gunther (75) reported that isoproterenol causes Mg efflux from perfused rat heart, a finding supported by the recent observations of Romani et al (65), which show that the addition of epinephrine to ventricular myocytes causes a decrease in total magnesium. No changes of Mg_i following β-agonist addition have been reported, however.

HYPOMAGNESEMIA Numerous cardiovascular diseases, such as myocardial infarction and ventricular fibrillation are associated with hypomagnesemia (3, 4, 43, 48, 68). As discussed by Wallach (76), hypomagnesemia causes a marked decrease in the total Mg content of bone and skeletal muscle. In contrast, hypomagnesemia does not appear to have a large effect on total cardiac Mg content, although there is considerable variability (see Table IX of reference 76). Because cellular Mg is mostly bound or sequestered, large changes in Mg_i could occur without a significant change in total Mg. As discussed by Corkey (18), however, changes in total magnesium are usually accompanied by changes in Mg_i. Since Mg_i can modulate cell function, it would be of considerable interest to determine whether hypomagnesemia alters cardiac Mg_i.

In heart cells of several species, reducing extracellular magnesium nominally to zero for as long as 20 min did not change Mg_i (28, 57); however, Mg_i decreased from 0.48 to 0.21 mM (62) in cultured heart cells incubated for 16 hr in a solution containing 0.12 mM Mg. This demonstrates that long-term, low Mg_o incubation can reduce Mg_i; however, studies with less drastic reduction in Mg_o concentrations (0.25–0.5 mM) will be useful to determine whether hypomagnesemia leads to a decrease in cardiac Mg_i.

DECREASED ATP Cellular ATP is usually complexed to magnesium; therefore under conditions in which ATP is decreased, e.g. ischemia (11, 45, 58), the loss of this binding site could lead to an increase in Mg_i. In addition, because energy is required to maintain Mg below its electrochemical equilibrium level, a decrease in ATP (below the kd) would inhibit the putative Mg ATPase and the Na, K ATPase (which ultimately provide the energy to transport Mg against its gradient via Na/Mg exchange). Also, if, as in squid axon (20), ATP is required as a modulator of Na/Mg exchange, then a decrease in ATP could also affect Mg_i by altering the activity of Na/Mg.

Murphy et al (58) recently measured a basal Mg_i concentration of 0.85 ± 0.10 mM in perfused rat hearts loaded with the magnesium-sensitive NMR indicator, F APTRA. Within 15 min of ischemia, Mg_i rose nearly threefold to 2.1 ± 0.4 mM; this increase in Mg_i occurred over the same time course as the decrease in ATP. After 20 min of reperfusion, Mg_i declined to 1.5 ± 0.5 mM. This sustained elevation of Mg_i above basal levels could inhibit calcium release from the sarcoplasmic reticulum and thereby contribute to the well-documented impairment of mechanical function that occurs after a reversible period of ischemia. This increase in Mg_i could also modulate Ca and K channel activity and thus could be involved in the ionic and electrical changes observed during ischemia. Borchgrevink et al (11), using ^{31}P NMR and the shift of the β-ATP to measure Mg_i, similarly reported that during ischemia (6–9 min) Mg_i rose from a basal level of 0.5 to 2.5 mM. The initial reperfusion caused a decrease in Mg_i to 0.85 mM followed by a further gradual decrease to 0.55 mM. Borchgrevink et al (11) also reported that elevating Mg_o during reflow enhanced the rate of recovery of ATP, creatine phosphate, pH, and coronary blood flow. Likewise, Kirkels et al (45) used ^{31}P NMR to measure Mg_i and reported that 15 min of ischemia increased Mg_i from 0.6 to >6.0 mM. They also observed that the increase in Mg_i did not equal the total amount of magnesium liberated from ATP, which suggests that Mg is either bound to other intracellular sites or lost from the heart cells. After 30 min of ischemia, Kirkels et al (45) reported that reperfusion did not lead to a decrease in total cell magnesium. These investigators concluded that post-ischemic recovery is not limited by intracellular magnesium and that any beneficial effects of high magnesium during reperfusion may be related to sarcolemmal rather than intracellular sites. To summarize, in response to 10–15 min of myocardial ischemia, Mg_i increases at least threefold, but the relationship between this increase in Mg_i and the physiologic processes (e.g. Ca and K channel activity and Ca release from SR) remains to be documented.

CONCLUSION

The previous controversy surrounding the range of values for cytosolic free magnesium (Mg_i) appears to have been resolved with the general agreement that in most vertebrate myocardium, Mg_i is between 0.5 and 1.0 mM (7–9, 15, 16, 29, 36, 45, 57, 58). Mg_i can be altered either via plasma membrane transport or through intracellular redistribution, which results from either altered intracellular binding or uptake, or release from intracellular organelles. In guinea pig papillary muscle, elevation of Mg_o causes an increase in Mg_i and a concomitant decrease in Na_i. These data support a

Na/Mg countertransport mechanism; however, there appears to be some species differences because an increase in Mg_o does not cause a decrease Na_i in ferret ventricular muscle (15, 16). Future studies will be necessary to elucidate the magnesium transport mechanisms in heart, and attention should be given to other possible transporters such as Mg ATPase and Na K/Mg transporter (64). Mg_i can also be altered by changes in pH_i and Ca_i, and these could be important physiologic regulators (27, 57).

If Mg_i modulates cardiac function, then Mg_i itself must be altered under physiologic and pathophysiologic conditions. Interest in physiologic modulators of Mg_i has centered on hormonally-induced changes in total magnesium, but further studies are needed to determine if there are related changes in Mg_i. Good evidence exists to support pathologic alterations in Mg_i; several groups have shown that ATP depletion, which occurs during ischemia, is accompanied by a threefold increase in Mg_i. This increase in Mg_i could have important ramifications for altered cardiac function during ischemia and early reflow. A 50% reduction in Mg_i of cardiac myocytes occurs after reducing Mg_o to 0.12 mM for 16 hr; future studies will have to determine whether a decrease in Mg_i is responsible for the pathology associated with hypomagnesemia.

Magnesium research is poised to provide new information in the next few years. Although many important questions about magnesium transport remain to be answered, the availability of new methods should enhance our understanding of intracellular magnesium regulation.

Literature Cited

1. Agus, Z., Kelepouris, E., Dukes I., Morad, M. 1989. Cytosolic magnesium modulates calcium channel activity in mammalian ventricular cells. *Am. J. Physiol.* 256:C452–55
2. Deleted in proof
3. Ahmad, A., Bloom, S. 1989. Sodium pump and calcium channel modulation of Mg-deficiency cardiomyopathy. *Am. J. Cardiovasc. Pathol.* 2:277–83
4. Altura, B. M., Altura, B. T. 1981. Magnesium ions and contraction of vascular smooth muscle: relationship to some vascular diseases. *Fed. Proc.* 40:2672–79
5. Alvarez-Leefmans, F. J., Giraldez, F., Gamino, S. M. 1987. Intracellular free magnesium in excitable cells: Its measurement and its biologic significance. *Can. J. Physiol. Pharmacol.* 65:915–25
6. Baker, P. F., Crawford, A. C. 1972. Mobility and transport of magnesium in squid giant axons. *J. Physiol.* 227:855–74
7. Blatter, L. A. 1990. Intracellular free magnesium in frog skeleton muscle studied with new type of magnesium-selective micro-electrode: Interactions between magnesium and sodium in the regulation of $[Mg]_i$. *Pflügers Arch.* In press
8. Blatter, L. A., Buri, A., McGuigan, J. A. S. 1989. Free intracellular magnesium concentration in isolated ferret ventricular muscle and in frog skeletal muscle measured with ion-selective microelectrodes containing the new magnesium sensor ETH 5214. *J. Physiol.* 418:154P
9. Blatter, L. A., McGuigan, J. A. S. 1986. Free intracellular magnesium concentration in ferret ventricular muscle measured with ion selective microelectrodes. *Q. J. Exp. Physiol.* 71:467–78

10. Bond, M., Jaraki, A., Disch, C., Healy, B. P. 1989. Subcellular calcium in cardiomyopathic hamster hearts in vivo: an electron probe study. *Circ. Res.* 64:1001–12
11. Borchgrevink, P. C., Bergen, A. S., Bakoy, O. E., Jynge, P. 1989. Magnesium and reperfusion of ischemic rat heart as assessed by ^{31}P NMR. *Am. J. Physiol.* 256:H195–H204
12. Borle, A. B. 1975. Methods for assessing hormonal effects on calcium fluxes in vitro. *Meth. Enzymol.* 39:513–73
13. Boron, W. F., DeWeer, P. 1976. Intracellular pH transients in squid giant axons caused by CO_2, NH_3 and metabolic inhibitors. *J. Gen. Physiol.* 67:91–112
14. Brierley, G. P., Davis, M., Jung, D. W. 1987. Respiration-dependent uptake and extrusion of Mg^{2+} by isolated heart mitochondria. *Arch. Biochem. Biophys.* 253:322–32
15. Buri, A., McGuigan, J. A. S. 1989. The regulation of the intracellular free magnesium concentration in isolated ferret ventricular papillary muscles. *J. Physiol.* 418:113P
16. Buri, A., McGuigan, J. A. S. 1990. Intracellular free magnesium and its regulation, studied in isolated ferret ventricular muscle with ion selective microelectrodes. *Quart. J. Exp. Physiol.* In press
17. Chiesi, M., Ho, M. M., Inesi, G., Somlyo, A. V., Somlyo, A. P. 1981. Primary role of sarcoplasmic reticulum in phasic contractile activation of cardiac myocytes with shunted myolemma. *J. Cell Biol.* 91:728–42
18. Corkey, B. E., Duszynski, J., Rich, T. L., Matschinsky, B., Williamson, J. R. 1986. Regulation of free and bound magnesium in rat hepatocyte and isolated mitochondria. *J. Biol. Chem.* 261:2567–74
19. DeWeer, P. 1976. Axoplasmic free magnesium levels and magnesium extrusion from squid giant axons. *J. Gen. Physiol.* 68:159–78
20. DiPolo, R., Beaugé, L. 1988. An ATP-dependent Na^+/Mg^{2+} countertransport is the only mechanism for Mg extrusion in squid axons. *Biochim. Biophys. Acta* 946:424–28
21. Eisner, D. A., Orchard, C. H., Allen, D. G. 1984. Control of intracellular ionized calcium concentration by sarcolemmal and intracellular mechanisms. *J. Mol. Cell. Cardiol.* 16:137–46
22. Erdos, J. J., Maguire, M. E. 1983. Hormone-sensitive magnesium transport in murine S49 lymphoma cells: characterization and specificity for magnesium. *J. Physiol.* 337:351–71
23. Feray, J. C., Garay, R. 1986. An Na^+-stimulated Mg^{2+}-transport system in human red blood cells. *Biochim. Biophys. Acta* 856:76–84
24. Flatman, P. W. 1983. Magnesium transport across cell membranes. *J. Memb. Biol.* 80:1–14
25. Deleted in proof
26. Frenkel, E. J., Graziani, M., Schatzmann, H. J. 1989. ATP requirement of the sodium-dependent magnesium extrusion from human red blood cells. *J. Physiol.* 414:385–97
27. Freudenrich, C. C., Murphy, E., Levy, L. A., London, R. E., Lieberman, M. 1990. Modulation of cytosolic free magnesium by intracellular pH in cultured chick heart cells. *FASEB J.* 4:A293
28. Fry, C. H. 1986. Measurement and control of intracellular magnesium ion concentration in guinea pig and ferret ventricular myocardium. *Magnesium* 5: 306–31
29. Fry, C. H., Hall, S. K., Blatter, L., McGuigan, J. A. S. 1990. Analysis and presentation of intracellular measurements obtained with ion-selective microelectrodes. *Exper. Physiol.* 75:187–98
30. Garfinkel, L., Garfinkel, D. 1984. Calculation of free-Mg^{2+} concentration in adenosine 5'-triphosphate containing solutions in vitro and in vivo. *Biochemistry* 23:3547–52
31. Gilbert, D. L. 1960. Effect of pH on muscle calcium and magnesium. *J. Gen. Physiol.* 43:1103–18
32. Grubbs, R. D., Maguire, M. E. 1986. Regulation of magnesium but not calcium transport by phorbol ester. *J. Biol. Chem.* 261:12550–54
33. Grubbs, R. D., Maguire, M. E. 1987. Magnesium as a regulator cation: Criteria and evaluation. *Magnesium* 6:113–27
34. Gupta, R. K., Gupta, P., Moore, R. D. 1984. NMR studies of intracellular metal ions in intact cells and tissues. *Annu. Rev. Biophys. Bioeng.* 13:221–46
35. Gunther, T., Vormann, J., Forster, R. 1985. Mg efflux is accomplished by an amiloride-sensitive Na/Mg antiport. *Biochem. Biophys. Res. Commun.* 130:540–45
36. Headrick, J. P., Willis, R. J. 1989. Effect of inotropic stimulation on cytosolic Mg in isolated rat heart: A ^{31}P magnetic resonance study. *Mag. Res. Med.* 12:328–38

37. Hess, P., Metzger, P., Weingart, R. 1982. Free magnesium in sheep, ferret and frog striated muscle at rest measured with ion-selective micro-electrodes. *J. Physiol.* 333:173–88
38. Hmiel, S. P., Snavely, M. D., Miller, C. G., Maguire, M. M. 1986. Magnesium transport in *Salmonella typhimurium:* Characterization of magnesium influx and cloning of a transport gene. *J. Bacteriol.* 168:1444–50
39. Hogue, B. A., Hansford, R. G. 1990. Measurement of free Mg^{2+} in isolated heart mitochondria. *Biophys. J.* 57:186a
40. Horie, M., Irisawa, H. 1987. Rectification of muscarinic K^+ current by magnesium ion in guinea pig atrial cells. *Am. J. Physiol.* 253:H210–14
41. Horowitz, S. B., Tluczek, L. J. M. 1989. Gonadotropin stimulates oocyte translation by increasing magnesium activity through intracellular potassium-magnesium exchange. *Proc. Natl. Acad. Sci. USA* 86:9653–56
42. Hu, Z., Buhrer, T., Muller, M., Rusterholz, B., Rouilly, M., Simon, W. 1989. Intracellular magnesium ion-selective microelectrodes based on a neutral carrier. *Anal. Chem.* 61:574–76
43. Iseri, L. T., French, J. H. 1984. Magnesium: Nature's physiologic calcium blocker. *Am. Heart J.* 108:188–93
44. Ito, T., Ehara, T. 1987. Mg inhibits voltage and tension oscillation but potentiates twitch in depolarized myocardium. *Am. J. Physiol.* 253:H248–55
45. Kirkels, J. H., van Echteld, C. J. A., Ruigrok, T. J. C. 1989. Intracellular magnesium during myocardial ischemia and reperfusion: Possible consequences for postischemic recovery. *J. Mol. Cell. Cardiol.* 21:1209–18
46. Kirschenlohr, H. L., Melcalfe, J. C., Morris, P. G., Rodrigo, G. C., Smith, G. A. 1988. Ca^{2+} transient, Mg^{2+}, and pH measurements in the cardiac cycle by ^{19}F NMR. *Proc. Natl. Acad. Sci. USA* 85:9017–21
47. Kushmerick, M. J., Dillon, P. F., Meyer, R. A., Brown, T. R., Krisanda, J. M., Sweeney, H. L. 1986. ^{31}P NMR spectroscopy, chemical analysis, and free Mg^{2+} of rabbit bladder and uterine smooth muscle. *J. Biol. Chem.* 261: 14420–29
48. Levine, B. S., Coburn, J. W. 1984. Magnesium, the mimic/antagonist of calcium. *N. Eng. J. Med.* 310:1253–55
49. Levy, L. A., Murphy, E., Raju, B., London, R. E. 1988. Measurement of cytosolic free magnesium ion concentration by ^{19}F NMR. *Biochemistry* 27: 4041–48
50. Deleted in proof
51. Maguire, M. E. 1988. Magnesium and cell proliferation. In *Annuals of New York Academy of Science,* ed. T. Galeotti, A. Cittadini, G. Neri, A. Scarpa, 551:201–17. New York: New York Acad. Sci.
52. Deleted in proof
53. McGuigan, J. A. S., Blatter, L., Buri, A. 1990. The use of ion selective microelectrodes to measure intracellular free magnesium. *Proc. Symp. Magnesium.* In press
54. Meissner, G., Henderson, J. S. 1987. Rapid calcium release from cardiac sarcoplasmic reticulum vesicles is dependent on Ca^{2+} and is modulated by Mg^{2+}, adenine nucleotide, and calmodulin. *J. Biol. Chem.* 262:3065–73
55. Mullins, L. L., Brinley, F. J. 1978. Magnesium influx in dialyzed squid axons. *J. Memb. Biol.* 43:243–50
56. Mullins, L. J., Brinley, F. J., Spangler, S. G., Abercrombie, R. F. 1977. Magnesium efflux in dialyzed squid axons. *J. Gen. Physiol.* 69:389–400
57. Murphy, E., Freudenrich, C., Levy, L. A., London, R. E., Lieberman, M. 1989. Monitoring cytosolic free magnesium in cultured chicken heart cells by use of the fluorescent indicator furaptra. *Proc. Nat. Acad. Sci. USA* 86:2981–84
58. Murphy, E., Steenbergen, C., Levy, L. A., Raju, B., London, R. E. 1989. Cytosolic free magnesium levels in ischemic rat heart. *J. Biol. Chem.* 264:5622–27
59. Murphy, E., Wheeler, D. M., LeFurgey, A., Jacob, R., Lobaugh, L. A., Lieberman, M. 1986. Coupled sodium-calcium transport in cultured chick heart cells. *Am. J. Physiol.* 250: C442–52
60. Page, E., Polimeni, P. I. 1972. Magnesium exchange in rat ventricle. *J. Gen. Physiol.* 224:121–39
61. Polimeni, P. I., Page, E. 1973. Magnesium in heart muscle. *Circ. Res.* 18: 367–74
62. Rabkin, S. W., Quamme, G. A. 1990. Control of intracellular Mg by alteration of the influx pathway in isolated cardiac myocytes. *FASEB J.* 4:A293
63. Raju, B., Murphy, E., Levy, L. A., Hall, R. D., London, R. E. 1988. A fluorescent indicator for measuring cytosolic free magnesium. *Am. J. Physiol.* 256:C540–48
64. Rasgado-Flores, H., Gonzalez-Serratos, H. 1990. Evidence for NaK/Mg exchange in squid giant axons. *Biophys. J.* 57:187a

65. Romani, A., Secard, C., Fatholahi, M., Scarpa, A. 1990. Adrenergic stimulation induces magnesium efflux from liver and cardiac cells. *FASEB J.* 4:A294
66. Russell, J. M., Brodwick, M. S. 1988. The interaction of intracellular Mg^{2+} and pH on Cl^- fluxes associated with intracellular pH regulation in barnacle muscle fibers. *J. Gen. Physiol.* 91:495–513
67. Sheehan, J. P., Seelig, M. S. 1984. Interactions of magnesium and potassium in the pathogenesis of cardiovascular disease. *Magnesium* 3:301–14
68. Shine, K. I. 1979. Myocardial effects of magnesium. *Am. J. Physiol.* 237:H413–23
69. Skou, J. C. 1957. The influence of some cations on an adenosine triphosphatase from peripheral nerves. *Biochim. Biophys. Acta* 23:394–401
70. Somlyo, A. P., McClellan, G., Gonzalez-Serratos, H., Somlyo, A. V. 1985. Electron probe X-ray microanalysis of post-tetanic Ca^{2+} and Mg^{2+} movements across the sarcoplasmic reticulum in situ. *J. Biol. Chem.* 260:801–5
71. Stern, J. H., Knutsson, H., MacLeish, P. R. 1987. Divalent cations directly affect the conductance of excised patches of rod photoreceptors membrane. *Science* 236:1674–78
72. Tarr, M., Trank, J. W., Goertz, K. K. 1989. Intracellular magnesium affects I_K in single frog atrial cells. *Am. J. Physiol.* 257:H1663–69
73. Vandenberg, C. A. 1987. Inward rectification of a potassium channel in cardiac ventricular cells depends on internal magnesium ions. *Proc. Natl. Acad. Sci. USA* 84:2560–64
74. Veloso, D., Guynn, R. W., Oskarsson, M., Veech, R. L. 1973. The concentration of free and bound magnesium in rat tissue. *J. Biol. Chem.* 248:4811–19
75. Vormann, J., Gunther, T. 1987. Amiloride-sensitive net Mg efflux from isolated perfused rat hearts. *Magnesium* 6:220–24
76. Wallach, S. 1987. Magnesium exchangeability and bioavailability in magnesium deficiency. *In Magnesium in Cellular Processes and Medicine*, ed. B. M. Altura, J. Durlach, M. S. Seelig, pp. 27–49. Basal: Karger
77. Walsh, L. G., Tormey, J. M. 1988. Subcellular electrolyte shift during in vitro myocardial ischemia and reperfusion. *Am. J. Physiol.* 255:H917–28
78. Ward, J. 1988. Tissue electrolytes in the rabbit following chronic dietary potassium depletion. *Quart. J. Exper. Physiol.* 73:1005–8
79. Wendt-Gallitelli, M. F., Isenberg, G. 1989. X-ray microanalysis of single cardiac myocytes frozen under voltage-clamp conditions. *Am. J. Physiol.* 256: H574–83
80. Wheeler-Clark, E. S., Tormey, J. M. 1987. Electron probe X-ray microanalysis of sarcolemma and junctional sarcoplasmic reticulum in rabbit papillary muscles: low sodium-induced calcium alterations. *Circ. Res.* 60:246–50
81. White, R. E., Hartzell, H. C. 1988. Effects of intracellular free magnesium on calcium current in isolated cardiac myocytes. *Science* 239:778–80
82. White, R. E., Hartzell, H. C. 1988. Magnesium ions in cardiac function. Regulator of ion channels and second messengers. *Biochem. Pharmacol.* 38: 859–67
83. Wu, S. T., Pieper, G. M., Salhany, J. M., Eliot, R. S. 1981. Measurement of free magnesium in perfused and ischemic arrested heart muscle. A quantitative phosphorus-31 nuclear magnetic resonance and multiequilibria analysis. *Biochemistry* 20:7399–403

Annu. Rev. Physiol. 1991. 53:289–98

MAGNESIUM GATING OF THE INWARDLY RECTIFYING K^+ CHANNEL

Hiroko Matsuda

Department of Physiology, Faculty of Medicine, Kyushu University, Fukuoka 812, Japan

KEY WORDS: inward rectification, potassium channels, magnesium, ions

INTRODUCTION

The phenomenon of inward rectification, whereby the K^+ conductance increases under hyperpolarization and decreases under depolarization, was first discovered in skeletal muscle close to 40 years ago (21). Its discoverer, Katz, described these properties as "anomalous rectification" because the increase in K^+ conductance with hyperpolarization and the reduction with depolarization are opposite to the changes in K^+ conductance that are involved in the action potential and are expected from the greater concentration of K^+ inside the cells than outside. Inward rectification of the K^+ conductance or current has been demonstrated in a variety of cell types (9, 10, 20) and has been thought to play an important role in determining the resting potential and in permitting long depolarizing responses and subsequent rapid repolarization.

Several models have been proposed to explain the mechanism that allows K^+ to move readily into the cell, but not out: (*a*) the channels themselves rectify because of the asymmetric profiles of the energy barrier in the open pore (36); (*b*) the channels are gated by voltage and are closed under depolarization (4, 6, 22); and (*c*) there may be intracellular blocking particles or blocking ions that prevent K^+ efflux by moving into the inner mouth of the K^+ channel and are driven intracellularly again at negative voltage by inward-moving K^+ (1, 13, 32).

0066-4278/91/0315-0289$02.00

The idea that an intracellular blocking ion is at least partly responsible for inward rectification turns out to be correct in heart muscle (24, 27, 35) and skeletal muscle (3); the rectification-producing blocking ion is Mg^{2+}. Further, other K^+ channel types have been demonstrated in cardiac cells to be modulated by intracellular Mg^{2+} and to show modest to substantial inward rectification (5, 14–16). This paper will mainly review work on blocking by intracellular Mg^{2+} of the cardiac inwardly rectifying K^+ channel responsible for the resting K^+ conductance (inward rectifier K^+ channel) and, briefly, work on Mg^{2+} block in other cardiac K^+ channels.

OHMIC CONDUCTANCE THROUGH THE INWARDLY RECTIFYING K^+ CHANNEL

The inwardly rectifying K^+ channel responsible for the resting conductance was the first cardiac K^+ channel examined in single-channel recordings (34). Gating kinetics during hyperpolarization was studied earlier in detail (19, 31). Inward currents show characteristically long-lasting openings and the mean open time decreases with hyperpolarization. The outward single-channel current through the channel was not recorded in the cell-attached configuration (30), but has been demonstrated either from patches on an open-cell preparation, whose intracellular contents can be dialyzed (24, 27), or from inside-out patches (35). Current-voltage relations for the single channel become ohmic if the internal surface of the cell is exposed to a divalent ion-free solution, and inward rectification is restored when Mg^{2+} is added to the internal bathing solution at a physiologic free ion concentration of 0.5–1 mM.

The open-cell preparation was made by rupturing the cell membrane mechanically using a second patch pipette; the intracellular milieu then equilibrates with the bathing solution through the hole in the membrane. In this preparation the channel usually closes during a 130-ms depolarizing pulse in the absence of internal Mg^{2+} (the uppermost current trace in Figure 1) and, as a result, the average outward currents decay with a time course that could be fitted with a single-exponential function (24, 27). This indicates that a second mechanism described above as (*b*) does work, i.e. the channel is also gated by voltage to cause inward rectification of the steady-state. The open times of the channel in the outward direction tended to be prolonged with time after opening the cell to the bathing solution. This is ascribed to the washing away of a soluble gating component related to channel closing. Although the voltage dependence of the time constant for relaxation of the outward current was obscured by a progressive increase during the time required for measurement at various voltages, it decreased with depolarization, which suggests that the closing rate constant increases as the membrane potential becomes more positive (24).

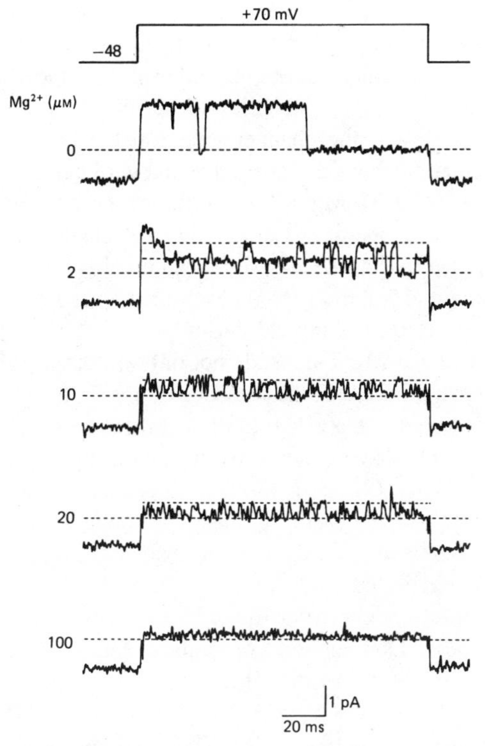

Figure 1 Effect of internal Mg^{2+} on the outward single-channel current. The *top trace* shows the voltage step. After recording the control trace while perfusing the open-cell patch membrane with Mg^{2+}-free solution, the Mg^{2+} concentration of the perfusing solution was progressively increased. Then Mg^{2+} was washed out, and recording at 0 and 2-μM Mg^{2+} was repeated. Traces for the illustration were obtained 55 min (0 μM), 65 min (2 μM), 30 min (10 μM), 40 min (20 μM), and 50 min (100 μM) after opening the cell membrane. The longer *dashed lines* indicate a zero-current level and the shorter ones show sublevels of the open-channel current. Guinea-pig ventricular cell; 15°C (from Reference 24).

INTRACELLULAR MAGNESIUM AS THE BLOCKING ION PRODUCING INWARD RECTIFICATION

Mg^{2+} Acts as an Open Channel Blocker

Figure 1 shows the current records in response to a clamp pulse stepped to +70 mV from a holding potential of −48 mV. Both pipette solution and internal solution (perfusing solution) contained about 150 mM K^+. In the absence of internal Mg^{2+}, full-size single-channel currents were observed on depolarization, usually followed by a closed state during 130-ms pulses. In the presence of internal Mg^{2+} at low levels, the channel no longer stayed either fully open or fully closed. Instead, it showed two discrete subconductance levels, equally spaced as indicated by the dotted lines, that fluctuated between four levels including these sublevels. As the Mg^{2+} concentration was increased, the channel stayed at the lower levels more frequently and fluctuations became faster. The outward current became noisy in the presence of 100 μM Mg^{2+}. It should be noted that internal Mg^{2+} prolonged the channel opening itself so that the channel activity was seen throughout the pulse. Also note that Mg^{2+} had no effect on the inward current at the holding potential. Internal Mg^{2+}, examined up to 1 mM (27) or 1.2 mM (35), had little effect on the inward current.

Blockage by internal Mg^{2+} depends not only on the Mg^{2+} concentration, but also on the test potential. In the presence of Mg^{2+}, the chord conductance was decreased at potentials positive to the equilibrium potential for K^+, and the current-voltage relationship showed a negative slope with an intermediate concentration of Mg^{2+} (25, 35). Voltage dependence was also evident in substate behavior. At increasingly positive voltages, the probability of observing the lower levels increased progressively, while that of observing the higher levels decreased (24).

A concentration-effect curve was fitted by assuming one-to-one binding of Mg^{2+} to a receptor. Dissociation constants averaged in three to four experiments at 25°C in 150 mM external and internal K^+ are 10.5 ± 1.7 μM at +30 mV, 3.2 ± 0.3 μM at +50 mV, 1.6 ± 0.2 μM at +70 mV, and 0.7 ± 0.1 μM at +90 mV, respectively (25). These values are much smaller than those obtained for the Mg^{2+} block of other cardiac K^+ channels (see below). In a semi-logarithmic plot of dissociation constant vs membrane potential, the data points were fitted by a straight line. Thus the dissociation constant (K_d) is described as

$$K_d(V) = K_d(0)\exp(-z\delta VF/RT),$$

where V is membrane potential, z the valence of the blocking ion, and δ the fractional electrical distance between the internal mouth of the aqueous pore and the binding site of the blocking ion (36, 37). F, R, and T have their usual meaning. The value of K_d at 0 mV, $K_d(0)$, was 37 μM and the slope of the regression line (e-fold decrease per 22 mV depolarization) gave a value of 0.57 for δ. Dissociation constants obtained in 30 mM external and 150 mM internal K^+ solutions were expressed by the same equation with $K_d(0)$ of 8.8 μM, thus suggesting that the Mg^{2+} block at a given voltage is increased by decreasing the external K^+ concentration (H. Matsuda, unpublished observation).

Voltage dependence of blockage by internal Mg^{2+} suggests that Mg^{2+} acts as an open channel blocker (12). Mg^{2+} moves into the inner mouth of the aqueous pore crossing an energy barrier, but it cannot pass through the pore to the outside of the membrane because of a high outer energy barrier. It stays at the site with the high affinity for Mg^{2+} (the energy well) to prevent K^+ efflux and is driven intracellularly again at a negative voltage by inward-moving K^+. The finding that internal Mg^{2+} prolonged the channel opening itself, in spite of its depressive effect on the outward current amplitude, also supports the idea that Mg^{2+} acts as an open channel blocker.

The cytosolic free Mg^{2+} concentration in cardiac muscle is reported to range from 0.5 to 3.5 mM (2, 7, 11). This concentration is sufficient to depress the outward currents (27, 35) and explains why outward currents were not recorded in the cell-attached configuration.

The voltage-dependent block by internal Mg^{2+} may be general for inward rectifiers, which have remarkably similar properties from one cell type to another (8, 33). The disappearance of inward rectification upon exposure of the internal surface of the membrane vesicle to a Mg^{2+}-free solution and restoration of inward rectification by adding Mg^{2+} to the internal bathing solution at the free ion concentration higher than 14 μM have been reported in the inwardly rectifying K^+ channel from rat skeletal muscle (3).

Substate Conductance in the Presence of Internal Mg^{2+}

The most characteristic finding in the Mg^{2+} block of the cardiac inwardly rectifying K^+ channel is the substate behavior, which is easily seen with low internal Mg^{2+} (24). As shown in Figure 1, sublevels with one or two thirds of the unitary amplitude were revealed by internal Mg^{2+} at micromolar levels. The current-voltage relation for each level is linear, and the slope conductances of the intermediate states are one to two thirds of the fully open channel conductance.

The appearance in the open channel of four equally spaced conductance levels (including the zero-current level) suggests that the cardiac inwardly rectifying K^+ channel consists of three identical conducting units. They usually function cooperatively to form a single channel, but Mg^{2+} enters and plugs up each subunit to produce the substate behavior at positive potentials. If the three subunits are blocked independently by internal Mg^{2+}, the open-state occupancies of each current level (the fraction of the total time for which the current stays at each level) should conform to a binomial distribution. At different probabilities for the blocked state, the distribution of the current levels showed a reasonable agreement with the binomial theorem (24). Sublevels with one or two thirds of the unit amplitude were induced in the inward current by the external application of Cs^+ or Rb^+, although, unlike Mg^{2+}

block of outward current, not in all channels (26). The open-state occupancies at each level followed approximately the binomial distribution, as in the Mg^{2+} block.

The kinetic properties of blockage accompanied with the substate behavior were studied based on the binomial scheme (24, 26). If the block of each subunit is described as

$$O \underset{\lambda}{\overset{\mu}{\rightleftharpoons}} B,$$

where O and B are the open and blocked states of each subunit, λ is the first-order unblocking rate and μ the second-order blocking rate, the open-state probability of subunit p is expressed as $\lambda/(\lambda + \mu)$ and transitions between substates during the open state of the channel can be described as

$$O_3 \underset{\lambda}{\overset{3\,\mu}{\rightleftharpoons}} O_2 \underset{2\,\lambda}{\overset{2\,\mu}{\rightleftharpoons}} O_1 \underset{3\,\lambda}{\overset{\mu}{\rightleftharpoons}} O_0,$$

where O_0, O_1, O_2, and O_3 are the substates in which all, two, one, and none of three subunits are blocked, respectively. In this scheme, the mean dwelling times in the substates are given:

$$\begin{aligned} 1/\tau_0 &= 3\,\lambda, \\ 1/\tau_1 &= 2\,\lambda + \mu, \\ 1/\tau_2 &= \lambda + 2\,\mu, \\ 1/\tau_3 &= 3\,\mu, \end{aligned}$$

where τ_0, τ_1, τ_2, and τ_3 represent the mean lifetimes in O_0, O_1, O_2 and O_3, respectively.

The rate constants are overdetermined in terms of the binomial model; five measurable quantities, τ_0, τ_1, τ_2, τ_3, and p yield calculations of only two rate constants. Therefore the validity of this model can be tested by calculating the rate constants from only some of the measurements and comparing the values that were not used for the calculation with the values predicted from these rate constants. The dwell-time histogram in each substate could be fitted by a single-exponential function. In Mg^{2+} block, λ and μ, which give the best fit to τ_1, τ_2, and p, were determined by a least-squares method. τ_3 predicted from the rate constants was not much different from the observed value, but predicted τ_0 was larger by two to three times than the observed value (24). A better agreement between the observed and predicted values was found in Cs^+ and Rb^+ block (26). Therefore there may be some interactions between the subunits in the Mg^{2+} block.

Although the effect of Mg^{2+} varied to some degree among the individual experiments, λ ranged between 50 and 90 s^{-1} and seemed independent of Mg^{2+}, while μ increased linearly with increasing Mg^{2+} (24). At +70 mV the blocking rate constant was 5×10^7 $s^{-1}M^{-1}$. The blocking rate increased with more positive potentials, while the unblocking rate constant seemed to decrease slightly. This result corresponds well with the idea of the open channel blocker. Voltage dependence of the blocking rate (e-fold increase per 40 mV depolarization) gives a value for the fractional electrical distance of an inner energy barrier of 0.3 (24).

As shown in Figure 1, the fully open current was frequently observed at the beginning of positive pulses, especially at the lower Mg^{2+} concentration, and then changed to lower substate levels. Average currents decline with a time course fitted with a single-exponential function. Because, in the presence of internal Mg^{2+}, the channel shows rapid transitions between substate levels throughout the depolarizing clamp pulse of 130 ms, the relaxation of the average current is ascribed to the voltage-dependent Mg^{2+} block rather than to the intrinsic gating kinetics. The observed time constants of relaxation were in close agreement with the time constants for block, $1/(\lambda + \mu)$, favoring the binomial model (24).

The average outward current with 2 μM Mg^{2+} reached a steady level of sizable amplitude after relaxation. This is in contrast to the average current without Mg^{2+}, which eventually approached the zero-current level. Such a difference results from the prolongation of the channel opening by Mg^{2+}, as noted earlier. The simplest explanation of these findings is to assume that the channel cannot close when any subunit of the channel is blocked by Mg^{2+} (i.e. the closed state is assumed to be to the left of the O_3 state in the sequential scheme) (see above) and that the block rate is much larger than the closing rate. Because the channel in substates O_1 and O_2 allows current of one third and two thirds of the unit amplitude, a partial block of the channel by low Mg^{2+} produces a larger steady-state current than without Mg^{2+}. Considering the small K_d for Mg^{2+}, it is unlikely that this mechanism works at the intracellular free Mg^{2+} concentrations reported so far.

An attempt to quantify the relative contributions of Mg^{2+} block and of intrinsic gating to the inward rectification was made using the oil-gap voltage clamp method (17). This method (29) enables fast voltage clamp and efficient internal perfusion, but has the disadvantage that the seal resistance of the oil gap is low (about 33 MΩ in the guinea pig ventricular cells). Analyses were made mainly on the macroscopic current upon repolarization, and the results were interpreted based on the same model as described above. The Mg^{2+} block, which was thereby deduced, showed a rather different appearance from that observed in single-channel recordings. Dissociation constants were 750 μM at +30 mV, 150 μM at +50 mV, 30 μM at +70 mV, and 6 μM at +90 mV (the voltage represents a deviation from the zero-current potential). A stronger voltage dependence of the dissociation constants (e-fold decrease per 12.5 mV depolarization) would presume a Mg^{2+}-binding site close to the external mouth of the aqueous pore ($\delta = 0.99$). The same voltage dependence (e-fold increase per 12.5 mV depolarization) was imposed on blocking rate constants for a simulation of the results.

It has been reported that internal Ca^{2+} at 0.1 μM induces the sublevel with three fourths of the unitary amplitude in the outward current (28). Sublevels with one quarter, half, or three quarters of the amplitude of the main conducting level were observed spontaneously in the inward current (19, 24, 30). Thus the substructure of the channel might not be so rigidly triple-barreled, but flexible enough to be, occasionally and according to the kind of blocking ion, two- or four-barreled.

MAGNESIUM BLOCK IN OTHER CARDIAC K^+ CHANNELS

Voltage-dependent block by internal Mg^{2+} was also observed in the ATP-regulated K^+ channel (5, 16), the muscarinic receptor-operated K^+ channel (14, 15), and the Na^+-activated K^+ channel (M. Horie, personal communication; Z. Wang, personal communication). Thus Mg^{2+} block seems to be a common mechanism that causes inward rectification of cardiac K^+ channels. In each channel type, the dose-response relation was fitted by a one-to-one binding curve. Table 1 summarizes the Mg^{2+} block of the cardiac K^+ channels reported so far.

Horie et al (16) analyzed a flickery outward open-channel current in the ATP-regulated channel using noise analysis. Much higher concentrations of

Table 1 Mg^{2+} block in cardiac K^+ channels

	δ	$K_d(\mu M)$	Rate constants: block $(M^{-1}s^{-1})$	Rate constants: unblock (s^{-1})	Other mechanisms of rectification	Referenc
Inward rectifier K^+ channel	0.57	10.5[a]	5×10^7	70[d]	Intrinsic gating, Ca block[f]	24, 25
Muscarinic receptor operated K^+ channel	0.63	290[b]			Weak intrinsic gating	14, 15
ATP-regulated K^+ channel	0.32	2000[c]	1.3×10^7	17600[e]	Na block	16

[a] +30 mV, 25°C; [b] +40 mV, 22–24°C; [c] +40 mV, 34°C; [d] +70 mV, 15°C; [e] 5.4 mM external K^+, 0 mV, 24
[f] Reference 28.

Mg^{2+} are needed in order to block this channel, and the blocking time constant is faster than in the inwardly rectifying K^+ channel (Table 1). This channel is also blocked by internal Na^+ (16, 18).

The dissociation constant for Mg^{2+} block of the muscarinic receptor-operated K^+ channel has an intermediate value (Table 1). Kinetics that are faster than in the ATP-regulated K^+ channel have been suggested (15). As in the inwardly rectifying K^+ channel, the muscarinic receptor-operated K^+ channel is also gated by voltage so that even in the absence of internal Mg^{2+}, the open state probability is reduced at more positive potentials (14). Internal Mg^{2+} acts not only as a blocker, but also as an activator of the channel by acting on GTP-binding proteins (14, 15, 23).

In conclusion, intracellular Mg^{2+} acts as an open channel blocker in the inwardly rectifying K^+ channel and produces inward rectification at physiologic concentrations. The Mg^{2+} block is not the only mechanism responsible for inward rectification: the channel is also gated by voltage. Substate behavior revealed by low internal Mg^{2+} suggests that the channel is composed of three identical conducting units and that each unit is blocked by Mg^{2+}.

ACKNOWLEDGMENT

I thank Professor A. Noma for reading the manuscript.

Literature Cited

1. Armstrong, C. M. 1975. Potassium pores of nerve and muscle membranes. In *Membranes: A Series of Advances,* ed. G. Eisenman, 3:325–58. New York: Dekker. 538 pp.
2. Blatter, L. A., McGuigan, J. A. S. 1986. Free intracellular magnesium concentration in ferret ventricular muscle measured with ion-selective microelectrodes. *Q. J. Exp. Physiol.* 71:467–73
3. Burton, F. L., Hutter, O. H. 1989. Properties of 'inwardly rectifying' potassium channels from rat muscle in absence of 'intracellular' Mg^{2+}. *J. Physiol.* 409:51P
4. Ciani, S., Krasne, S., Miyazaki, S., Hagiwara, S. 1978. A model for anomalous rectification: Electrochemical-potential-dependent gating of membrane channels. *J. Membr. Biol.* 44:103–34
5. Findlay, I. 1987. ATP-sensitive K^+ channels in rat ventricular myocytes are blocked and inactivated by internal divalent cations. *Pflügers Arch.* 410:313–20
6. Gunning, R. 1983. Kinetics of inward rectifier gating in the eggs of the marine polychaete, *Neanthes arenaceodentata*. *J. Physiol.* 342:437–51
7. Gupta, R. K., Gupta, P., Moore, R. D. 1984. NMR studies of intracellular metal ions in intact cells and tissues. *Annu. Rev. Biophys. Bioeng.* 13:221–46
8. Hagiwara, S. 1983. Anomalous rectification. In *Membrane Potential-Dependent Ion Channels in Cell Membrane. Phylogenetic and Developmental Approaches,* pp. 65–79. New York: Raven Press. 118 pp.
9. Hagiwara, S., Takahashi, K. 1974. The anomalous rectification and cation selectivity of the membrane of a starfish egg cell. *J. Membr. Biol.* 18:61–80
10. Hall, A. E., Hutter, O. F., Noble, D. 1963. Current-voltage relations of Purkinje fibres in sodium-deficient solutions. *J. Physiol.* 166:225–40
11. Hess, P., Metzger, P., Weingart, R. 1982. Free magnesium in sheep, ferret and frog striated muscle at rest measured with ion-selective micro-electrodes. *J. Physiol.* 333:173–88

12. Hille, B. 1984. Mechanisms of block. In *Ionic Channels of Excitable Membranes*, pp. 272–302. Sunderland: Sinauer. 426 pp.
13. Hille, B., Schwarz, W. 1978. Potassium channels as multi-ion single-file pores. *J. Gen. Physiol.* 72:409–42
14. Horie, M., Irisawa, H. 1987. Rectification of muscarinic K^+ current by magnesium ion in guinea pig atrial cells. *Am. J. Physiol.* 253:H210–14
15. Horie, M., Irisawa, H. 1989. Dual effects of intracellular magnesium on muscarinic potassium channel current in single guinea-pig atrial cells. *J. Physiol.* 408:313–32
16. Horie, M., Irisawa, H., Noma, A. 1987. Voltage-dependent magnesium block of adenosine-triphosphate-sensitive potassium channel in guinea-pig ventricular cells. *J. Physiol.* 387:251–72
17. Ishihara, K., Mitsuiye, T., Noma, A., Takano, M. 1989. The Mg^{2+} block and intrinsic gating underlying inward rectification of the K^+ current in guinea-pig cardiac myocytes. *J. Physiol.* 419: 297–320
18. Kakei, M., Noma, A., Shibasaki, T. 1985. Properties of adenosine-triphosphate-regulated potassium channels in guinea-pig ventricular cells. *J. Physiol.* 363:441–62
19. Kameyama, M., Kiyosue, T., Soejima, M. 1983. Single channel analysis of the inward rectifier K current in the rabbit ventricular cells. *Jpn. J. Physiol.* 33: 1039–56
20. Kandel, E. R., Tauc, L. 1966. Anomalous rectification in the metacerebral giant cells and its consequences for synaptic transmission. *J. Physiol.* 183:287–304
21. Katz, B. 1949. Les constantes électriques de la membrane du muscle. *Arch. Sci. Physiol.* 3:285–300
22. Kurachi, Y. 1985. Voltage-dependent activation of the inward-rectifier potassium channel in the ventricular cell membrane of guinea-pig heart. *J. Physiol.* 366:365–85
23. Kurachi, Y., Nakajima, T., Sugimoto, T. 1986. Role of intracellular Mg^{2+} in the activation of muscarinic K^+ channel in cardiac atrial cell membrane. *Pflügers Arch.* 407:572–74
24. Matsuda, H. 1988. Open-state substructure of inwardly rectifying potassium channels revealed by magnesium block in guinea-pig heart cells. *J. Physiol.* 397:237–58
25. Matsuda, H. 1990. Voltage-dependent block of cardiac inwardly rectifying K^+ channels by internal Mg^{2+}. In *Mg^{2+} and Excitable Membranes*, ed. P. Strata. Heidelberg: Springer-Verlag. In press
26. Matsuda, H., Matsuura, H., Noma, A. 1989. Triple-barrel structure of inwardly rectifying K^+ channels revealed by Cs^+ and Rb^+ block in guinea-pig heart cells. *J. Physiol.* 413:139–57
27. Matsuda, H., Saigusa, A., Irisawa, H. 1987. Ohmic conductance through the inwardly rectifying K channel and blocking by internal Mg^{2+}. *Nature* 325: 156–59
28. Mazzanti, M., DiFrancesco, D. 1989. Intracellular Ca modulates K-inward rectification in cardiac myocytes. *Pflügers Arch.* 413:322–24
29. Mitsuiye, T., Noma, A. 1987. A new oil-gap method for internal perfusion and voltage clamp of single cardiac cells. *Pflügers Arch.* 410:7–14
30. Sakmann, B., Trube, G. 1984. Conductance properties of single inwardly rectifying potassium channels in ventricular cells from guinea-pig heart. *J. Physiol.* 347:641–57
31. Sakmann, B., Trube, G. 1984. Voltage-dependent inactivation of inward-rectifying single-channel currents in the guinea-pig heart cell membrane. *J. Physiol.* 347:659–83
32. Standen, N. B., Stanfield, P. R. 1978. Inward rectification in skeletal muscle: A blocking particle model. *Pflügers Arch.* 378:173–76
33. Stanfield, P. R., Standen, N. B., Leech, C. A., Ashcroft, F. M. 1981. Inward rectification in skeletal muscle fibres. In *Advances in Physiological Sciences*, ed. E. Varga, A. Kövér, T. Kovács, L. Kovács, 5:247–62. New York: Pergamon. 320 pp.
34. Trube, G., Sakmann, B., Trautwein, W. 1981. Inward rectifying potassium currents recorded from isolated heart cells by the patch clamp method. *Pflügers Arch.* 391:R28
35. Vandenberg, C. A. 1987. Inward rectification of a potassium channel in cardiac ventricular cells depends on internal magnesium ions. *Proc. Natl. Acad. Sci. USA* 84:2560–64
36. Woodbury, J. W. 1971. Eyring rate theory model of the current-voltage relationships of ion channels in excitable membranes. In *Chemical Dynamics: Papers in Honor of Henry Eyring*, ed. J. O. Hirschfelder, pp. 601–17. New York: Wiley. 816 pp.
37. Woodhull, A. M. 1973. Ionic blockage of sodium channels in nerve. *J. Gen. Physiol.* 61:687–708

Annu. Rev. Physiol. 1991. 53:299–307

MODULATION OF CARDIAC ION CHANNELS BY MAGNESIUM

Z. S. Agus and M. Morad

Departments of Medicine and Physiology, University of Pennsylvania School of Medicine, Philadelphia, Pennsylvania 19104

KEY WORDS: calcium channel, potassium channels, rectification

---

INTRODUCTION

In large part stimulated by recent advances in the measurement of cytosolic magnesium activity, there has been a surge of interest in the effects of this ion on cardiac channel function. Studies have demonstrated potentially important effects on calcium channels and potassium channels that may have significant consequences on action potential duration and cell excitability. Here, we will briefly review the extracellular and intracellular effects of magnesium on the ionic currents in cardiac myocytes.

EXTRACELLULAR MAGNESIUM

Alterations in extracellular magnesium in cardiac tissue have been shown to alter ion channel currents in two ways. First, magnesium may enter the channel and reduce the current amplitude. Earlier studies demonstrated a blocking action of extracellular magnesium on the calcium channel (8, 17), and more recent studies have shown that magnesium is partly responsible for the negative slope of the inward rectifier K^+ channel in the guinea pig ventricular myocytes with extreme hyperpolarization (4). Second, extracellular magnesium may affect ion channels by altering or screening the membrane surface charge. For instance, 10–15 mM of extracellular Mg produces a shift in the voltage-dependent gating parameters of the calcium

0066–4278/91/0315–0299$02.00

channel by approximately 15 mV (14). Interestingly, recent studies in rat ventricular myocytes were unable to show a significant effect of increases of magnesium (up to 20 mM) on the voltage dependence of the transient outward K^+ current, which implies a possible specificity for the effects of magnesium on the calcium channel (1).

INTRACELLULAR MAGNESIUM

Recent studies employing both whole cell recording and excised patch single-channel recording have demonstrated that cytosolic magnesium has a number of effects on ion channels of atrial and ventricular myocytes from frog and guinea pig (Table 1). Two basic types are described and discussed separately below. Magnesium has been shown to produce inward rectification of at least four different potassium channels and to modulate the outwardly directed current through the potassium and the low-threshold calcium channels. While the mechanism of the former effect appears to be plugging of the open channel as outward current begins to flow, the mechanism of the latter modulatory effects is unclear. It is interesting to note, however, that the three channels that are markedly potentiated by phosphorylation (i.e. calcium, delayed rectifier K^+, and chloride channels) are all modulated by cytosolic magne-

Table 1 Effects of cytosolic magnesium activity on ion channels in cardiac cells

Channel description				Internal modulation		
Type		Cell[a]	Species	Phosphorylation	Rectifies[b]	Modifies[b]
Calcium	I_{Ca} (L)	VM	Guinea pig	Yes-cAMP	No	Yes
		VM	Frog	Yes-cAMP	No	Yes
	I_{Ca} (T)	VM	Guinea pig	No(?)	?	?
Sodium	I_{Na}	VM	Guinea pig	Yes-cAMP	?	?
Potassium	I_{to}	VM	Rat	No	No	No
	I_{K1}	VM	Guinea pig	No	Yes	Yes
	$I_{K(ACh)}$	AM	Guinea pig	Yes-cAMP	Yes	?
	$I_{K(ATP)}$	VM	Guinea pig	No	Yes	No
	$I_{K(Na)}$	VM	Guinea pig	?	?	?
	$I_{K(D)}$	AM	Frog	Yes-cAMP	No	Yes
		VM	Guinea pig	Yes-cAMP	No	Yes
	$I_{K\text{-}AA}$	AM	Rat	No	No	No
	$I_{K(Ca)}$	VM	Guinea pig	?	?	?
Chloride	I_{Cl}	VM	Guinea pig	Yes-cAMP	No	Yes
Pacemaker	I_f	PF	Dog	Yes-cAMP	?	?

[a] VM = ventricular myocyte, AM = atrial myocyte, PF = Purkinje fibers, [b] magnesium. See text.

sium (Table 1). There are no data as yet on effects of cytosolic magnesium on the cardiac sodium current, the pacemaker current (I_f), calcium- or Na^+-activated potassium current, or the T-type calcium channel (although Mg^{2+} alters the activity of the sodium channel (23) and calcium-activated potassium channel (25) in other tissues). Cytosolic magnesium (up to 10mM) appears to have no effect on the transient outward K^+ current in rat ventricular myocytes (1) and does not affect arachidonic acid-activated outwardly rectifying potassium current in neonatal rat atrial myocytes (15).

Inward Rectification of K^+ Channels

INWARD RECTIFIER This channel, which inwardly rectifies and passes little outward current at positive potentials, plays an important role in the maintenance of the resting potential in ventricular cells. In addition, the rectification allows for high membrane resistance during the plateau, which makes the inward current more effective in generating the plateau of the cardiac action potential. Cytosolic magnesium produces this rectification by blocking the open K^+ channel (12, 19, 20, 27). These studies are reviewed in detail by Matsuda in this volume.

ATP-SENSITIVE K^+ CURRENT A potassium channel inhibited by intracellular ATP concentrations in excess of 0.1 mM (22) has been described in mammalian atrial and ventricular myocytes. Intracellular magnesium has been shown to block the outward K^+ current through this channel in a voltage-dependent manner (11). Thus in the absence of internal magnesium and sodium, the current voltage relationship of this channel is virtually linear. Addition of magnesium to the internal (but not external solution) decreased only the outward, but not the inward, current through the channel. Thus as the membrane potential was made positive to E_K, the current rectified in the usual direction in a dose-dependent manner. When compared to the mean current measured at +40 mV in the absence of internal Mg^{2+}, the mean currents were 92, 75, 48, and 40% at $[Mg^{2+}]_i$ of 0.5, 1, 2, and 5 mM respectively. The voltage at which rectification occurred depended upon E_K, as expected for a model in which internal magnesium enters the mouth of the channel and produces a block of the outward current, whereas inward flow of potassium at potentials negative to E_K displaces magnesium from its blocking site and relieves the block. The K_d of the Mg^{2+} block varied from about 10 mM at −60 mV to 0.5 mM at +40 mV, at physiologic concentrations of potassium and E_K of −80 mV.

MUSCARINIC K^+ CURRENT Acetylcholine gates a current that inwardly rectifies in atrial cells, pacemaker cells, and cardiac Purkinje fibers. Similar to other rectifying K^+ channels, a voltage-dependent block by internal magnesium has been shown to underlie the rectification of the muscarinic K^+ channel. Recent studies have provided evidence for two effects of magnesium on the muscarinic K^+ current (9, 10, 16). In the absence of magnesium, but in the presence of GTP, the acetylcholine-induced current exhibits virtually ohmic conductance between −120 and +10 mV. Addition of 1 mM magnesium to the internal solution increased conductance at potentials negative to the E_K, but suppressed it at potentials positive to E_K, thus producing the typical inward rectification of the acetylcholine-induced current. The K_d for the Mg^{2+} block showed voltage dependence similar to the ATP-sensitive channel, but its value was an order of magnitude smaller, approximately 300 μM at +40 mV, which in turn is higher than that required to block the inward rectifier (discussed above). This suggests that the differences in blocking sensitivity may reflect different properties of the magnesium-binding sites associated with the degree of rectification of the respective currents. The second effect of magnesium on the acetylcholine-induced current appears to reflect an effect on G protein activation (9, 13); it is additive to that of GTP and has a K_d of 60–70 μM.

Modulation of Inward Currents

CALCIUM CHANNEL Magnesium modulation of the L type calcium channel appears to be somewhat different in mammalian and amphibian cardiac myocytes. In frog myocytes, dialysis of the cell with increasing concentrations of magnesium reduces the calcium current, but the effects are relatively small (28). For instance, increasing the pipette concentration from 0.3 to 3 mM only decreased the current by 26%. In cells where the calcium current was enhanced by cAMP, however, a similar increase in cytosolic magnesium activity produced a 63% inhibition. These data suggest that the effects of magnesium were exerted predominantly on the phosphorylated channels. In contrast, the effects of intracellular magnesium on the calcium current appear to be more prominent in mammalian myocytes. For instance, guinea pig ventricular myocytes dialyzed with 1.3 mM free Mg^{2+} exhibited less than 50% of the current generated by cells dialyzed with Mg^{2+}-free solutions (Figure 1). These effects of magnesium were observed on the basal (i.e. non-phosphorylated) channel (2). It appears, therefore, that in the mammalian preparation magnesium modulates the non-phosphorylated channel, since only 20% of the basal current is accounted for by protein kinase-mediated phosphorylation. Increasing cytosolic magnesium also inhibited the calcium current through phosphorylated (isoproterenol and/or cAMP) channels in guinea pig ventricular myocytes (2). The mechanism of these effects remains unclear. As the effects of Mg^{2+} do not appear to result from open channel block, shifts in voltage dependence of gating parameters, alterations in cAMP levels, or changes in the level of protein kinase-mediated phosphorylation (2,

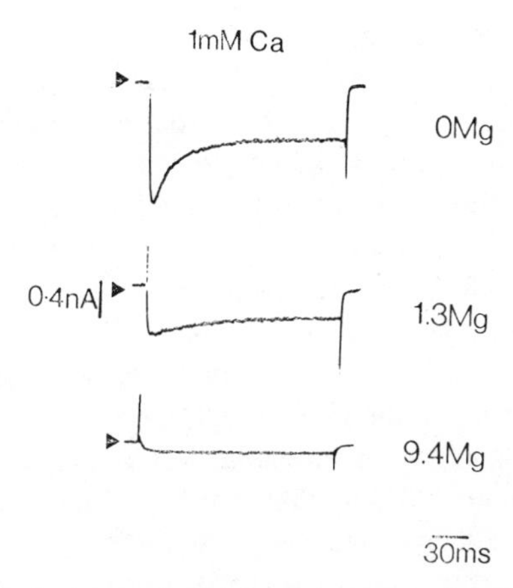

Figure 1 Magnesium and calcium channel. Inward current activated in guinea pig ventricular myocytes with depolarizing pulse to 0 mV from a holding potential of −80 mV internally dialyzed with nominally 0, 1.3, or 9.4 mM free Mg^{2+}. Reprinted with permission from Agus et al (2).

28), it is possible that magnesium modulates the availability of channels by a novel yet unknown mechanism.

INWARD RECTIFIER As discussed elsewhere in this volume (see Matsuda), the rectification of this channel in ventricular myocytes and the blockade of outward potassium current is critically dependent on micromolar concentrations of cytosolic magnesium. In addition, it appears that alterations of internal magnesium activity in the millimolar range may modulate the amplitude of the hyperpolarization-induced inward current (E. Kelepouris, Z. S. Agus, M. Morad, unpublished data). Increasing the cytosolic free magnesium in guinea pig ventricular myocytes inhibits the whole cell current carried by potassium at potentials more negative than the potassium equilibrium potential. Fifty percent inhibition of the inward current was apparent in cells dialyzed with 1.3 mM free magnesium. This concentration is comparable to that required for similar modulation of the calcium channel in the same cells and might represent a similar mechanism of action. It is not known whether this effect is seen in the other rectifying potassium channels in cardiac tissue.

Modulation of Outward Currents

DELAYED RECTIFIER Studies in frog atrial and guinea pig ventricular myocytes have demonstrated important modulatory effects of cytosolic free magnesium on the magnitude of the time-dependent outward current through the delayed rectifier K^+ channel. This current is augmented by both β-receptor agonists and adenylate cyclase stimulation and by protein kinase C activation. In two studies of dialyzed frog atrial cells, small increases in internal magnesium concentration in the physiologic range from 0.3 to 1.0mM suppressed the current by 50–60%, an effect quantitatively equivalent to the enhancing effect of isoproterenol (5, 26, 29). These effects were observed in non-stimulated cells and cAMP-treated cells, which suggests that the mechanism of these modulatory effects does not require channel phosphorylation. As voltage-independent modulation of both outward and inward currents through this channel was observed, and the rectification was not affected (26), the magnesium modulation of this channel resembles that of the calcium channel and does not appear to result from the open channel blocking effect observed in the inward rectifier K^+ channel. Similar striking effects have been observed in mammalian ventricular cells (I. Dukes, Z. S. Agus, M. Morad, unpublished observations). Figure 2 demonstrates the sensitivity of the peak delayed rectifier current recorded at +60 mV in guinea pig ventricular myocytes dialyzed with varying free magnesium concentrations. It is apparent that small changes in concentration of Mg^{2+} in the physiologic range of 0.6–0.8 mM produce significant alterations in the K^+ current. As in frog atrial cells, the suppressant effects are apparent in the presence or absence of cAMP. Similarly, the response to isoproterenol was completely blocked by high internal magnesium concentrations. It is not yet known if cytosolic free magnesium similarly modulates the regulation of the

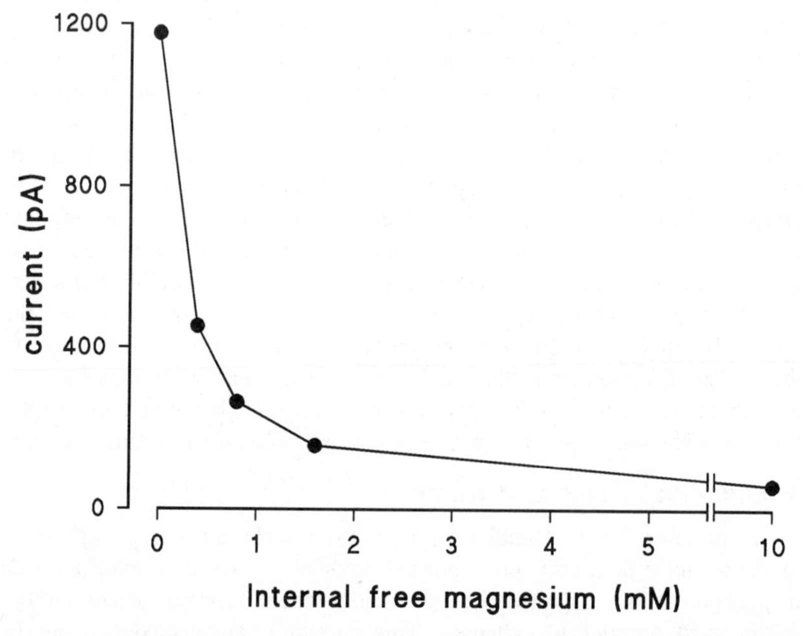

Figure 2 Magnesium and delayed rectifier. Mean data obtained with 400 ms depolarizing pulses to +80 mV from a holding potential of −40 mV in guinea pig ventricular myocytes dialyzed with differing concentrations of free Mg^{2+}.

K^+ channel by protein kinase C. Recent studies suggest that the delayed rectifier current in guinea pig ventricular myocytes actually consists of two currents (24). One current (I_{Kr}) activates more rapidly and exhibits inward rectification such that peak outward current occurs at 0 mV. The other current (I_{ks}) exhibits the classical characteristics of I_K. The mechanism of the inward rectification has not been directly studied, nor has the sensitivity of the outward current to either β-adrenergic stimulation or cytosolic magnesium been examined. Because most studies of the effects of magnesium were done using depolarizing pulses beyond 0 mV, it is not possible to characterize I_{Kr} from these data.

CHLORIDE CHANNEL Recent studies have uncovered another conductance in mammalian ventricular myocytes that is regulated by β-adrenergic agonists and protein kinase A (3, 6, 7). This conductance, which is negligible in the absence of kinase activation, appears to be selective for chloride, shows little rectification, and is time-independent. During β-adrenergic stimulation, at least in the rabbit and guinea pig, this current would represent another repolarizing influence on the action potential. Preliminary whole cell patch-clamp studies in guinea pig ventricular myocytes (R. Kasama, M. Morad, Z. S. Agus, unpublished data) suggest that this current is also modulated by cytosolic free magnesium in a manner similar to the calcium channel and the delayed rectifier currents.

SUMMARY AND PHYSIOLOGIC SIGNIFICANCE

Cytosolic magnesium activity is currently thought to approximate 0.5–0.8 mM. Variations around this range have recently been shown to alter current flow through several cardiac ion channels. Magnesium is responsible for inward rectification of the ventricular inward rectifier and the atrial muscarinic inward rectifier. In these channels, magnesium functions as an open channel blocker and completely prevents outward potassium current with a K_d in the micromolar range. In addition, magnesium modulates the inward current through this channel, but at much higher concentrations, with 1.5 mM producing an approximately 50% reduction of current amplitude. Another outwardly rectifying potassium channel, the ATP-sensitive channel, is also similarily modulated by intracellular magnesium with a K_d of 2–3 mM. Both the inward calcium current and the outward delayed rectifier potassium current are modulated by magnesium, and these effects appear to be independent of the phosphorylation state of the channel in mammalian myocytes, but seem to be more effective in phosphorylated channels in the frog myocyte. The calcium current is completely abolished when internal magnesium concentration is increased to 5–10 mM, while the delayed rectifier is exquisitely sensitive to changes around the normal level of 0.8 mM. The mechanism of these modulatory effects remains unclear. These changes do not appear to result from alteration of intracellular adenylate cyclase activity, or shifts in voltage dependence of gating parameters, and they are not reproduced by alterations in extracellular activity of Mg^{2+}. It seems likely, therefore, that these channels contain a binding site for magnesium that modulates their susceptibility to activation by changes in membrane potential.

Presently there is no evidence that cytosolic magnesium activity changes with physiologic events or hormonal stimulation. There are two pathophysiologic circumstances, however, that probably are associated with alterations in intracellular magnesium activity, namely magnesium depletion syndrome and ischemia. In the former, reduction in cytosolic magnesium activity would likely cause significant changes in the action potential. The net effect will vary from cell type to cell type and species to species, depending upon the channel composition. Thus in cells where repolarization depends on delayed rectifier current, magnesium will affect this component of the action potential, whereas in cells dependent on rapidly inactivating transient K^+ currents, repolarization will not be affected. It is unlikely that Mg^{2+} levels would ever fall enough to alter rectification of the inward rectifier. Small changes, however, could significantly increase the K^+ outward current through the delayed rectifier as well as the inward calcium current. The relative K_ds suggest that the predominant effect would be on potassium currents in this situation and result in shortening of the action potential and possibly changes in intracellular potassium activity. In ischemia, however, where cytosolic free magnesium levels increase significantly (21), multiple effects might be expected. Thus in addition to suppression of calcium current, modulation of the exposed ATP-sensitive outward current might be an important phenomenon. The net effects of these changes as well as potential effects of cytosolic magnesium efflux mechanism remain to be evaluated.

ACKNOWLEDGMENTS

This work was supported in part by an National Institutes of Health grant to M. M., HL-16152 and a grant from the W. W. Smith Charitable Trust to Z. S. A.

Literature Cited

1. Agus, Z. S., Dukes, I., Morad, M. 1989. Divalent cations modulate transient outward current in rat ventricular myocytes. *J. Physiol.* 418:28p
2. Agus, Z. S., Kelepouris, E., Dukes, I., Morad, M. 1989. Cytosolic magnesium modulates calcium channel activity in mammalian ventricular cells. *Am. J. Physiol.* 256:C452–55
3. Bahinski, A., Nairn, A. C., Greengard, P. O., Gadsby, D. C. 1989. Chloride conductance regulated by cyclic AMP-dependent protein kinase in cardiac myocytes. *Nature* 340:718–21
4. Biermans, G., Vereecke, J., Carmeliet, E. 1987. The mechanism of the inward-rectifying K current during hyperpolarizing steps in guinea-pig ventricular myocytes. *Pflügers Arch.* 410:604–13
5. Duchatelle-Gourdon, I., Hartzell, H. C., Lagrutta, A. A. 1989. Modulation of the delayed rectifier potassium current in

frog cardiomyocytes by β-adrenergic agonists and magnesium. *J. Physiol.* 415:251–74

6. Harvey, R. D., Hume, J. R. 1989. Autonomic regulation of a chloride current in heart. *Science* 244:983–85
7. Harvey, R. D., Hume, J. R. 1989. Isoproterenol activates a chloride current, not the transient outward current, in rabbit ventricular myocytes. *Am. J. Physiol.* 257:C1177–81
8. Hess, P., Lansman, J. B., Tsien, R. W. 1986. Calcium channel selectivity for divalent and monovalent actions. *J. Gen. Physiol.* 88:293–318
9. Horie, M., Irisawa, H. 1989. Dual effects of intracellular magnesium on muscarinic potassium channel current in single guinea-pig atrial cells. *J. Physiol.* 408:313–32
10. Horie, M., Irisawa, H. 1987. Rectification of muscarinic K^+ current by magnesium ion in guinea pig atrial cells. *Am. J. Physiol.* 253:H210–14
11. Horie, M., Irisawa, H., Noma, A. 1987. Voltage-dependent magnesium block of adenosine-triphosphate-sensitive potassium channel in guinea-pig ventricular cells. *J. Physiol.* 387:251–72
12. Ishihara, K., Mitsuiye, T., Noma, A., Takano, M. 1989. The Mg^{2+} block and intrinsic gating underlying inward rectification of the K^+ current in guinea pig cardiac myocytes. *J. Physiol.* 419:297–320
13. Iyengar, R., Birnbaumer, L. 1982. Hormone receptor modulates the regulatory component of adenylyl cyclase by reducing its requirement for Mg^{2+} and enhancing its extent of activation by guanine nucleotides. *Proc. Natl. Acad. Sci. USA* 79:5179–83
14. Kass, R. S., Krafte, D. S. 1987. Negative surface charge density near heart calcium channels. Relevance to block by dihydropyridines. *J. Gen. Physiol.* 89:629–44
15. Kim, D., Clapham, D. E. 1989. Potassium channels in cardiac cells activated by arachidonic acid and phospholipids. *Science* 244:1174–76
16. Kurachi, Y., Nakajima, T., Sugimoto, T. 1986. Role of intracellular Mg^{2+} in the activation of muscarinic K^+ channel in cardiac atrial cell membrane. *Pflügers Arch.* 407:572–74
17. Lansman, J. B., Hess, P., Tsien, R. W. 1986. Blockade of current through single calcium channels by Cd^{2+}, Mg^{2+}, and Ca^{2+}. *J. Gen. Physiol.* 88:321–47
18. Latorre, R. 1989. Ion channel modulation by divalent cations. *Acta Physiol. Scand.* 136:13–23
19. Matsuda, H. 1988. Open-state substructure of inwardly rectifying potassium channels revealed by magnesium block in guinea-pig heart cells. *J. Physiol.* 397:237–58
20. Matsuda, S., Saigusa, A., Irisawa, H. 1987. Ohmic conductance through the inwardly rectifying K channel and blocking by internal Mg^{2+}. *Nature* 325:156–59
21. Murphy, E., Steenbergen, C., Levy, L. A., Raju, B., London, R. E. 1989. Cytosolic free magnesium levels in ischemic rat heart. *J. Biol. Chem.* 264:5622–27
22. Noma, A. 1983. ATP-regulated K channels in cardiac muscle. *Nature* 305:147–48
23. Pusch, M., Conti, F., Stuehmer, W. 1989. Intracellular magnesium blocks sodium outward currents in voltage- and dose- dependent manner. *Biophys. J.* 55:1267–71
24. Sanguinetti, M. C., Jurkiewicz, N. K. 1990. Two components of cardiac delayed rectifier K^+ current: differential sensitivity to block by Class III antiarrhythmic agents. *J. Gen. Physiol.* In press
25. Squire, L. G., Petersen, O. H. 1987. Modulation of Ca^{2+}- and voltage-activated K^+ channels by internal Mg^{2+} in salivary acinar cells. *Biochim. Biophys. Acta* 899:171–75
26. Tarr, M., Trank, J. W., Goertz, K. K. 1989. Intracellular magnesium affects I_K in single frog atrial cells. *Am. J. Physiol.* 257:H1663–69
27. Vandenberg, C. A. 1987. Inward rectification of a potassium channel in cardiac ventricular cells depends on internal magnesium ions. *Proc. Natl. Acad. Sci. USA* 84:2560–64
28. White, R. E., Hartzell, H. C. 1988. Effects of intracellular free magnesium on calcium current in isolated cardiac myocytes. *Science* 239:778–80
29. White, R. E., Hartzell, H. C. 1989. Magnesium ions in cardiac function. Regulator of ion channels and second messengers. *Biochem. Pharmacol.* 38:859–67

Annu. Rev. Physiol. 1991. 53:309–19

CALMODULIN MUTANTS AND Ca^{2+}-DEPENDENT CHANNELS IN *PARAMECIUM*

Robin R. Preston, John A. Kink, Robert D. Hinrichsen,[1] Yoshiro Saimi, and Ching Kung

Laboratory of Molecular Biology and Department of Genetics, University of Wisconsin-Madison, Madison, Wisconsin 53706

[1]Fred Hutchinson Cancer Research Center, Seattle, Washington 98104

KEY WORDS: Ca^{2+}-dependent K^+ currents, Ca^{2+}-dependent Na^+ current, mutation, Ca^{2+}-binding proteins, channel regulation

---

INTRODUCTION

In 1958, Gárdos reported that Ca^{2+} stimulated the release of K^+ from human erythrocytes (9). The implications of this observation were not apparent until Meech (31) and Krnjevič & Lisiewicz (20) suggested that rises in intracellular Ca^{2+} could open K^+ channels directly. Ca^{2+}-dependent K^+ channels are now considered common, if not ubiquitous, membrane components. The two major Ca^{2+}-dependent K^+ channel classes and their varied functions have been reviewed recently (26). Ca^{2+}-dependent K^+ channels are the best-studied examples of channels that are gated by changes in internal Ca^{2+} concentration, but many non-selective cation channels (36), Cl^- channels (17, 43 and references therein), and several Na^+ channels (16, 21, 44) are also Ca^{2+}-sensitive. Despite this abundance of Ca^{2+}-dependent conductances, surprisingly little is known about how Ca^{2+}-sensitivity is conferred on a channel. Conceivably, Ca^{2+} could regulate a channel (*a*) by interacting with a Ca^{2+}-binding site on the pore-forming protein itself, (*b*) through a Ca^{2+}-binding protein, or (*c*) indirectly, perhaps by mobilization of other second messenger or enzyme pathways. This review describes how

0066-4278/91/0315-0309$02.00

combined genetic, electrophysiological, biochemical, and molecular studies have enhanced our understanding of how Ca^{2+}-dependent channel activity is governed in *Paramecium*. These studies implicate calmodulin (CaM) as being a key element in Ca^{2+}-dependent ion channel function.

CALMODULIN AND THE CALMODULIN GENE IN *PARAMECIUM*

CaM is a ubiquitous and highly-conserved Ca^{2+}-binding protein. Evidence from a variety of disciplines (6) suggests that 148 amino acid residues are arranged in a dumbbell conformation, each lobe of which contains two Ca^{2+}-binding loops. The N-terminal lobe contains Ca^{2+}-binding sites 1 and 2, the C-terminal lobe sites 3 and 4, and the two lobes are connected by a long, solvent-exposed alpha helix. When intracellular Ca^{2+} concentrations rise into the micromolar range, a Ca^{2+}/CaM complex is formed, triggering a conformational change that exposes hydrophobic patches on the protein's surface. These patches are suggested to both enable interaction of CaM with at least 20 different Ca^{2+}-dependent enzymes and confer specificity to the interaction, although the details of how CaM achieves such a high degree of specificity for so many effectors are uncertain. The activation of enzymes by CaM often entails a disinhibition, i.e. Ca^{2+}/CaM binding removes an inhibitory domain to expose the enzyme's catalytic site.

Paramecium CaM has been purified and sequenced; it is clearly similar to that of other organisms (51). It differs from *Tetrahymena* CaM by 8 amino acids, and from bovine brain CaM by 17 amino acids, with only conservative substitutions. The genes that encode CaM from a variety of species, including *Paramecium* (18), have now been cloned and characterized. *P. tetraurelia* possesses a single CaM gene, as do most organisms from yeasts to eel (6), which comprises a continuous open reading frame of 444 bases and no introns. The nucleotide sequence agrees with the peptide sequence determined previously. Northern analysis and protein studies suggest that there is only one CaM gene transcript in *P. tetraurelia*.

REGULATION OF MEMBRANE EXCITATION

The path that has led to the recognition of CaM as being critical for Ca^{2+}-dependent channel function originated in attempts to better understand *Paramecium* behavior. Swimming behavior in this unicell is tightly coupled to changes in membrane potential; several reviews on the subject are available (10, 15, 38, 47). Because *Paramecium* is a single-celled animal that lives in a variable freshwater habitat, membrane excitation in this organism is complex, which enables appropriate behavioral responses to a range of environmental stimuli. Membrane depolarization elicits a rapid, inward Ca^{2+} transient, mediated by a depolarization-activated Ca^{2+} conductance in the ciliary membrane (8, 29, 32). The resultant Ca^{2+} influx raises intracellular Ca^{2+} concentration from $< 10^{-7}$ M to $> 10^{-5}$ M (2). Depolarization also triggers the delayed activation of K^+ channels (32). The ensuing K^+ efflux short-circuits the Ca^{2+} action potential and facilitates membrane repolarization. Prolonged depolarization causes a Ca^{2+} concentration build-up within the cell that results in the slow activation of a Ca^{2+}-dependent K^+ current (45, 49). Two additional currents are activated by Ca^{2+}, a Ca^{2+}-dependent Na^+ current (44, 46) and a Ca^{2+}-dependent Mg^{2+} current (37, 37a). The Ca^{2+}-dependent Na^+ current helps maintain membrane depolarization when extracellular Na^+ concentrations are high, perhaps facilitating cell avoidance of potentially toxic conditions. The Ca^{2+}-dependent Mg^{2+} conductance has been characterized only recently, and its function is presently unclear. Hyperpolarizations elicit a similar, yet distinct, series of ionic events: first a novel hyperpolarization-activated Ca^{2+} conductance (44) and a hyperpolarization-activated K^+ conductance (33, 40), and later a Ca^{2+}-dependent K^+ current (40, 42).

CALMODULIN MUTATIONS ELIMINATE A Ca^{2+}-DEPENDENT K^+ CURRENT

In the wild type, the Ca^{2+}-dependent K^+ current seen upon depolarization activates slowly toward a plateau over a period of 1–2 sec. This current is activated by Ca^{2+} entering the cell through the depolarization-activated Ca^{2+} channels, hence it can be suppressed by treatments or mutations (the "pawns"; 49) that eliminate the Ca^{2+} current itself. There are also mutations that abolish the Ca^{2+}-dependent K^+ current while leaving the Ca^{2+} source intact. These mutations yield a behavioral phenotype called pantophobiac (13, 45). Among them are those that affect the structural gene of CaM.

A pantophobiac phenotype could conceivably result from defects in any one of many links in the chain of interactions that produce and maintain Ca^{2+}-dependent K^+ channels. The original pantophobiac strain, *pntA*, however, was found to be temporarily "cured" of its behavioral (and presumably electrophysiological) abnormality by injecting wild-type cytoplasm (13). Through a process of serial fractionation and microinjection, the cytoplasmic factor responsible for this curing was discovered to be CaM (14). When purified wild-type *Paramecium* CaM was injected into cam^1 (formerly *pntA* or $pntA^1$) cells, there was a temporary restoration of wild-type behavior and the Ca^{2+}-dependent K^+ current that is missing in this mutant (14). cam^1 cells injected with cam^1 CaM showed no such effect. These observations proved to be the first unequivocal evidence for a role of CaM in Ca^{2+}-dependent channel activity, a role that has been suggested by the effects of CaM and CaM antagonists on Ca^{2+}-dependent K^+ currents in various cell types (25,

34, 35). Wild-type and *cam*[1] CaMs show clear differences in their relative electrophoretic migration rates in certain gel systems (4, 14), but final confirmation that CaM is indeed the source of the *cam*[1] mutant's abnormalities came from sequence data. Peptide sequencing showed *cam*[1] to cause a single serine-to-phenylalanine substitution at residue 101 (50; Figure 1). Two other pantophobiac strains also have mutations in the CaM gene. The *cam*[2] mutation (formerly *pntD* or *pntA*[2]; 57) has been shown through both protein (28) and gene sequencing (18) to cause an isoleucine-to-threonine substitution at residue 136, whereas a base change in the *cam*[3] gene (formerly *fnaP:* 56) causes a methionine-to-valine substitution at residue 145 (18). The *cam*[2] mutation secondarily causes lysine 115 to be undermethylated (28, 57), a residue that is fully trimethylated in the wild type (51).

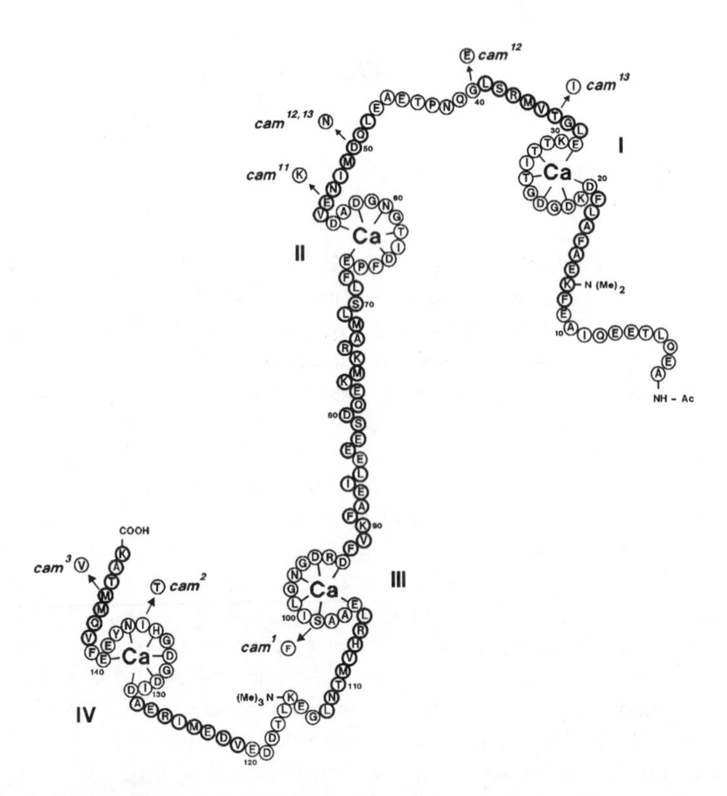

Figure 1 Amino acid sequence of wild-type *Paramecium* CaM and sites of mutation. Arabic numerals indicate relative positions of amino acid residues from the N-terminus, whereas the Roman numerals indicate Ca^{2+}-binding loops. Note that the substitutions caused by mutations *cam*[1], *cam*[2], and *cam*[3] all lie within the C-terminal lobe of the structure, whereas *cam*[11], *cam*[12], and *cam*[13] all affect residues located between Ca^{2+}-binding domains I and II of the N-terminal lobe. Data from references 18, 28, 50, 51. CaM design after Stoclet et al (53).

The *cam* mutations established that wild-type CaM is required for normal expression of the Ca^{2+}-dependent K^+ current, but their effects are not restricted to this current (see below). cam^1 additionally reduces the amplitude of the Ca^{2+}-dependent Na^+ current (41), whereas this current is enhanced by cam^2 and cam^3 (18, 41). These observations provided the first hint that CaM may also be involved in Na^+ channel regulation in *Paramecium*.

CALMODULIN MUTATIONS THAT ELIMINATE THE Ca^{2+}-DEPENDENT Na^+ CURRENT

The Ca^{2+}-dependent Na^+ current is unusual in its activation by Ca^{2+} rather than by voltage, but similar currents have been seen in other organisms (16, 21). As above, the Ca^{2+}-dependence of this current renders it susceptible to mutations and treatments that affect the Ca^{2+} current, but it can also be eliminated by mutating the structural gene for CaM. Mutations affecting the Na^+ current yield phenotypes traditionally dubbed fast-2 or paranoiac (23, 24, 56), which exhibit characteristic swimming behaviors in Na^+-rich solutions. Fast-2 mutants lack the Ca^{2+}-dependent Na^+ current (44), whereas this conductance may be enhanced in paranoiacs (18, 46). Genetic analyses showed a lack of complementation in the F1 progeny of a fast-2 × pantophobiac cross and also showed that no wild-type F2s segregated out after inducing autogamy (complete homozygosity) in the F1 (18). These results suggest that the two classes of mutants possess defects in the same gene and, indeed, all of the fast-2 mutants isolated to date express defective CaMs. Like the pantophobiacs, they exhibit multiple electrophysiological anomalies (R. R. Preston, unpublished). Parallel electrophoretic studies showed the CaM from some of these mutants migrating abnormally in certain electrophoretic gel systems (18). CaM genes of several fast-2 mutants have now been sequenced (18). cam^{11}, the first such mutant isolated (formerly *fna;* 23, 24), yields a glutamate-to-lysine substitution at residue 55 (Figure 1). The CaM defects of cam^{12} have been revealed by both peptide (18, 27) and gene sequencing: a glutamine-to-glutamate change at residue 40, and a second, aspartate-to-asparagine substitution at residue 50 (Figure 1). Interestingly, the cam^{13} mutation causes an identical change at position 50, while causing an additional threonine-to-isoleucine substitution at residue 35.

IMPLICATIONS OF THE PANTOPHOBIAC AND FAST-2 MUTATIONS FOR UNDERSTANDING CALMODULIN INTERACTIONS WITH EFFECTORS

One of the unanticipated benefits of studying these *Paramecium* behavioral mutants is that they may yield important insights as to how the specificity of CaM interaction with its targets is achieved. An intriguing pattern has emerged from elucidation of the sites of the pantophobiac and fast-2 CaM mutations (Figure 1). *cam*^{1}, *cam*^{2}, and *cam*^{3} all cause substitutions in the C-terminal lobe of CaM, whereas fast-2 mutations, *cam*^{11}, *cam*^{12}, and *cam*^{13}, all affect residues in the N-terminal lobe. Although the site and nature of CaM's involvement with the Ca^{2+}-dependent K^+ and Na^+ channels is unknown, these findings imply that the fast-2 mutations define a possible site of CaM interaction with a Ca^{2+}-dependent Na^+ channel, whereas the pantophobiac mutations define a different site that confers specificity for Ca^{2+}-dependent K^+ channels. Mutants lacking Ca^{2+}-dependent K^+ and Na^+ currents are readily obtained. By isolating and sequencing CaM from many such mutants, it may be possible to create a detailed map of sites on the CaM molecule that confer specificity to the interaction with these Ca^{2+}-dependent effectors. Such an achievement would significantly enhance our understanding of CaM association with other effectors.

OTHER EFFECTS OF CALMODULIN MUTATIONS

The discovery that these *Paramecium* mutations involved such a critical protein as CaM was surprising. While CaM genes from many organisms have been cloned and mutated, and the effects of these mutations tested in vitro (6, 7, 54), the *Paramecium* mutants are the first examples of CaM-defective cell lines that are viable and that have readily-recognized phenotypes. Moreover, aside from their behavioral abnormalities, there are few indications to suggest that they are mutants (18). Some cells show size and growth rate abnormalities, while others have difficulties in mating, but these changes are minor considering the purported vital and pivotal role of CaM in eukaryotes. Perhaps not so surprising was the finding that each CaM mutant expresses a unique set of ion current defects that provides it with a characteristic electrophysiological fingerprint (41; R. R. Preston, unpublished). Significantly, *cam*^{1} and *cam*^{2} mutants completely lack the Ca^{2+}-dependent K^+ current activated upon hyperpolarization (41). This current is kinetically and pharmacologically distinct from the depolarization-activated equivalent (39), which negates the possibility that the mutations act via a single species of channel to simultaneously eliminate both currents. This current is also greatly reduced by *cam*^{12}, whereas *cam*^{11} and *cam*^{13} cause the current to activate faster than in the wild type. *cam*^{12} additionally eliminates the voltage-dependent K^+ current that is activated upon hyperpolarization of the wild type. Many of these *cam* mutations also affect the Ca^{2+}-dependent Mg^{2+} current to some degree (R. R. Preston, unpublished). Lastly, *cam*^{1}, *cam*^{2}, and possibly other *cam* mutations, affect the inactivation properties of the Ca^{2+} currents (41). These latter observations are intriguing. Inactivation of the depolarization-activated Ca^{2+} current involves a rapid (within milliseconds) Ca^{2+}-dependent process (2) and a separate slow (on the order of seconds) inactivation that has been considered Ca^{2+}-independent (11). Surprisingly, the *cam* mutations alter the kinetics of slow inactivation, but have no effect on Ca^{2+}-dependent inactivation. This apparent contradiction might be reconciled by assuming that slow inactivation reflects channel phosphorylation (52), perhaps by a cGMP-dependent protein kinase. The guanylate cyclase that provides the cGMP stimulus for the protein kinase is strongly Ca^{2+}/CaM dependent (19), and may thus be a *cam* mutation-susceptible element in these events.

POSSIBLE SITES OF CALMODULIN INTERACTION WITH THE Ca^{2+}-DEPENDENT ION CHANNELS

Patch-clamp recordings have shown a variety of channel types to be active in isolated *Paramecium* membranes (30). These include a Na^+-selective and two K^+-selective activities whose properties approximate those of the whole-cell currents. All three channels are Ca^{2+}-dependent. The Ca^{2+}-dependent Na^+ channel has a conductance of ~ 20 pS and is selective for Na^+ and Li^+ over K^+ or Cs^+ (47a). This channel is particularly interesting because membrane patches exhibit a rapid loss of channel activity when maintained in low (10^{-8}M) Ca^{2+}. A priori, there are two likely causes of such an activity loss (commonly referred to as channel run-down): the channel may be inactivated by covalent modification, or Ca^{2+} may cause dissociation of an essential cofactor. It is tempting to speculate that this cofactor may be the Ca^{2+}/CaM complex. Indeed, the run-down could be reversed upon adding wild-type CaM to the cytoplasmic face of the membrane patch (47a). Presumably Ca^{2+}/CaM remains associated with the membrane following patch excision, but low Ca^{2+} promotes a conformational change that allows dissociation and loss of the endogenous protein into the bath solution.

How Ca^{2+}/CaM interacts with the channel is presently unclear, but a direct, physical coupling seems likely (47a). Channel activity is restored without any added ATP or enzymes, which excludes mediation by covalent modification. Thus parallels may be drawn between Ca^{2+}/CaM regulation of Na^+ channels in *Paramecium* and G protein regulation of Ca^{2+} and K^+ channels in other cells (3). In both examples, channel activation occurs independently of enzymatic reactions and is patch delimited: if there are additional cofactors or intermediaries, they must be membrane-, and possibly channel-, associated.

The hyperpolarization-activated Ca^{2+}-dependent K^+ channel exhibits two noteworthy features. First, membrane patches undergo a rapid loss of channel activity when exposed to $> 10^{-6}$M Ca^{2+} (48): the complete antithesis of conditions that promote Na^+ channel run-down. This run-down is not readily reversed, however (Y. Saimi, unpublished). Many Ca^{2+} channels share a similar fate upon loss of cytoplasmic contact (1). Evidence to date suggests that in these examples, phosphorylation-dephosphorylation reactions are involved (5). It is possible that similar covalent mechanisms regulate the Ca^{2+}-dependent K^+ channel of *Paramecium*.

The second feature of this channel is that limited proteolytic digestion of its cytoplasmic face causes an irreversible activity increase and a concomitant loss of Ca^{2+} sensitivity (22). This process is highly reminiscent of the effects of proteases on many Ca^{2+}/CaM-dependent enzymes (55). These observations might be explained by postulating that in the absence of Ca^{2+}, the activity of both Ca^{2+}-dependent enzymes and Ca^{2+}-dependent channels is suppressed by an inhibitory domain. Ca^{2+}/CaM binding activates the proteins by disinhibition, but the inhibitory domain and its Ca^{2+}/CaM binding site are removed by proteases to create a Ca^{2+}-insensitive, irreversibly activated state.

MUTATIONS THAT AFFECT THE Ca^{2+}-DEPENDENT CURRENTS INDEPENDENTLY OF CALMODULIN

At least two mutations affect the Ca^{2+}-dependent K^+ currents independently of CaM. The first, TEA-insensitive A *(teaA),* causes the depolarization-activated Ca^{2+}-dependent K^+ current to activate during depolarizations of a millisecond or less and with an amplitude that is significantly increased compared with that of the wild type (12). The wild-type current requires depolarizations lasting hundreds of milliseconds to activate. The restless mutation *(rst)* causes effects similar to *teaA,* but in this case, the hyperpolarization-activated Ca^{2+}-dependent K^+ current is enhanced (42). This current is also slow-activating in the wild type, but in restless, it is elicited by hyperpolarizations of a few milliseconds duration (39). Several strains containing two or more of the mutations described above have been constructed and analysed under voltage clamp (39). These studies show that the *teaA* mutation can restore both of the Ca^{2+}-dependent K^+ currents to cam^1 cells, but the depolarization-activated current is restored in a rapid-activating form that is characteristic of TEA-insensitive A. Similarly, cam^1, *rst* double-mutants express both Ca^{2+}-dependent K^+ currents, but the hyperpolarization-activated current is early-activating, as in restless. Combining the *teaA* and *rst* mutations creates a cell in which both the Ca^{2+}-dependent K^+ currents are fast-activating. Thus *teaA* and *rst* cause fundamental changes in the properties of the Ca^{2+}-dependent K^+ channels that cannot be readily corrected, which suggests that they may affect the channel structural proteins themselves. Patch-clamp recordings from restless membranes reveals the presence of a highly-active, Ca^{2+}-insensitive K^+ channel that bears a strong resemblance to the protease-digested K^+ channel of the wild type (A. Kubalski, C. Kung, unpublished). Thus *rst* possibly affects a putative K^+ channel inhibitory domain.

CONCLUDING REMARKS

Evidence to date suggests that Ca^{2+}/CaM regulates Ca^{2+}-dependent Na^+ channels in *Paramecium* by direct, physical interaction. Ca^{2+}-dependent K^+ channels are also functionally dependent upon CaM, but the nature and site of this dependence is uncertain at present. Clearly, the ability of CaM to restore the activity of Ca^{2+}-dependent K^+ channels in membrane patches needs to be tested. Many other questions also await answers. Are Ca^{2+}-dependent K^+ and Na^+ channels active in patches of membrane from the *cam* mutants and, if so, how does their activity compare with that of the wild type? How do the *cam* mutations affect the ability of CaM to restore Ca^{2+}-dependent K^+ and Na^+ channel activity? Since *cam*[1] and *cam*[2] mutations are in residues within the Ca^{2+}-binding domains of CaM, how do they affect the kinetics of Ca^{2+}-binding by CaM, and what are the consequences for CaM-activation of its effectors? Another exciting possibility lies in revertant analysis. By selecting mutations that suppress the phenotypes of the *cam* strains, it should be possible to identify proteins that interact with CaM. Following these protein threads through the fabric of membrane excitation of *Paramecium* may yield surprising new insights into ion channel regulatory mechanisms in general.

ACKNOWLEDGMENTS

We are grateful for the support of the National Institutes of Health (GM22714 & GM36386) and of the Lucille P. Markey Charitable Trust.

Literature Cited

1. Belles, B., Malécot, C. O., Hescheler, J., Trautwein, W. 1988. "Run-down" of the Ca current during long whole-cell recordings in guinea pig heart cells: role of phosphorylation and intracellular calcium. *Pflügers Arch.* 411:353–60
2. Brehm, P., Eckert, R. 1978. Calcium entry leads to inactivation of calcium channel in *Paramecium. Science* 202: 1203–6
3. Brown, A. M., Birnbaumer, L. 1990. Ionic channels and their regulation by G protein subunits. *Annu. Rev. Physiol.* 52:197–213
4. Burgess-Cassler, A., Hinrichsen, R. D., Maley, M. E., Kung, C. 1987. Biochemical characterization of a genetically altered calmodulin in *Paramecium. Biochim. Biophys. Acta* 913:321–28
5. Chad, J., Kalman, D., Armstrong, D. 1987. The role of cyclic AMP-dependent phosphorylation in the maintenance and modulation of voltage-activated calcium channels. In *Cell Calcium and the Control of Membrane Transport,* ed. L. J. Mandel, D. C. Eaton, 11:153–86. New York: Rockefeller Univ. Press. 303 pp.
6. Cohen, P., Klee, C. B. 1988. *Calmodulin.* New York: Elsevier. 371 pp.
7. Davis, T. N., Urdea, M. S., Masiarz, F. R., Thorner, J. 1986. Isolation of the yeast calmodulin gene: calmodulin is an essential protein. *Cell* 47:423–31

8. Dunlap, K. 1977. Localization of calcium channels in *Paramecium caudatum*. *J. Physiol.* 271:119–33
9. Gárdos, G. 1958. The function of calcium in the potassium permeability of human erythrocytes. *Biochim. Biophys. Acta* 30:653–54
10. Görtz, H.-D. 1988. *Paramecium*. New York: Springer-Verlag. 444 pp.
11. Hennessey, T. M., Kung, C. 1985. Slow inactivation of the calcium current in *Paramecium* is dependent on voltage and not internal calcium. *J. Physiol.* 365:165–79
12. Hennessey, T. M., Kung, C. 1987. A calcium-dependent potassium current is increased by a single-gene mutation in *Paramecium*. *J. Membr. Biol.* 98:145–55
13. Hinrichsen, R. D., Amberger, E., Saimi, Y., Burgess-Cassler, A., Kung, C. 1985. Genetic analysis of mutants with a reduced Ca^{2+}-dependent K^+ current in *Paramecium tetraurelia*. *Genetics* 111:433–45
14. Hinrichsen, R.D., Burgess-Cassler, A., Solvedt, B. C., Hennessey, T., Kung, C. 1986. Restoration by calmodulin of a Ca^{2+}-dependent K^+ current in a mutant of *Paramecium*. *Science* 232:503–6
15. Hinrichsen, R. D., Schultz, J. E. 1988. *Paramecium:* a model system for the study of excitable cells. *Trends Neurosci.* 11:27–32
16. Jaffe, L. A., Kado, R. T., Kline, D. 1986. A calcium-activated sodium conductance produces a long-duration action potential in the egg of a nemertean worm. *J. Physiol.* 381:263–78
17. Johansen, J., Kleinhaus, A. L. 1988. Voltage-clamp characterization of a calcium-dependent chloride conductance in a putative invertebrate motoneuron. *J. Comp. Physiol.* 162A:57–65
18. Kink, J. A., Maley, M. E., Preston, R. R., Ling, K.-Y., Wallen-Friedman, M. A., et al. 1990. Mutations in *Paramecium* calmodulin indicate functional differences between the C-terminal and the N-terminal lobes *in vivo*. *Cell* 62:165–74
19. Klumpp, S., Kleefeld, G., Schultz, J. E. 1983. Calcium/calmodulin regulated guanylate cyclase of the excitable ciliary membrane from *Paramecium*. *J. Biol. Chem.* 258:12455–59
20. Krnjevič, K., Lisiewicz, A. 1972. Injections of calcium ions into spinal motoneurones. *J. Physiol.* 225:363–90
21. Krüppel, T., Lueken, W. 1988. Membrane excitability and membrane currents in the marine ciliate *Euplotes vannus*. *Eur. J. Protistol.* 24:11–21
22. Kubalski, A., Martinac, B., Saimi, Y. 1989. Proteolytic activation of a hyperpolarization- and calcium-dependent potassium channel in *Paramecium*. *J. Membr. Biol.* 112:91–96
23. Kung, C. 1971. Genic mutants with altered system of excitation in *Paramecium aurelia*. I. Phenotypes of the behavioral mutants. *Z. Vergl. Physiol.* 71:142–64
24. Kung, C. 1971. Genic mutants with altered system of excitation in *Paramecium aurelia*. II. Mutagenesis, screening and genetic analysis of the mutants. *Genetics* 69:29–45
25. Lackington, I., Orrego, F. 1981. Inhibition of calcium-activated potassium conductance of human erythrocytes by calmodulin inhibitory drugs. *FEBS Lett.* 133:103–6
26. Latorre, R., Oberhauser, A., Labarca, P., Alvarez, O. 1989. Varieties of calcium-activated potassium channels. *Annu. Rev. Physiol.* 51:385–99
27. Ling, K.-Y., Burns, R., Strickland, M., Preston, R. R., Saimi, Y., Kung, C. 1990. A "fast" mutant of *Paramecium* has a G40E substitution on the second α helix in its calmodulin. *FASEB J.* 4:A640 (Abstr.)
28. Lukas, T. J., Wallen-Friedman, M., Kung, C., Watterson, D. M. 1989. *In vivo* mutations of calmodulin: a mutant *Paramecium* with altered ion current regulation has an isoleucine-to-threonine change at residue 136 and an altered methylation state at lysine residue 115. *Proc. Natl. Acad. Sci. USA* 86:7331–35
29. Machemer, H., Ogura, A. 1979. Ionic conductances of membranes in ciliated and deciliated *Paramecium*. *J. Physiol.* 296:49–60
30. Martinac, B., Saimi, Y., Gustin, M. C., Kung, C. 1988. Ion channels of three microbes: *Paramecium*, yeast and *Escherichia coli*. In *Calcium and Ion Channel Modulation*, ed. A. D. Grinnell, D. Armstrong, M. B. Jackson, pp. 415–30. New York: Plenum. 436 pp.
31. Meech, R. W. 1972. Intracellular calcium injection causes increased potassium conductance in *Aplysia* nerve cells. *Comp. Biochem. Physiol.* 42A:493–99
32. Oertel, D., Schein, S. J., Kung, C. 1977. Separation of membrane currents using a *Paramecium* mutant. *Nature* 268:120–24
33. Oertel, D., Schein, S. J., Kung, C. 1978. A potassium conductance activated by hyperpolarization in *Paramecium*. *J. Membr. Biol.* 43:169–85
34. Onozuka, M., Furuichi, H., Kishii, K., Imae, S. 1987. Calmodulin in the activa-

tion process of calcium-dependent potassium channel in *Euhadra* neurones. *Comp. Biochem. Physiol.* 86A:589–93
35. Pape, L., Kristensen, B. I. 1984. A calmodulin activated Ca^{2+}-dependent K^+ channel in human erythrocyte membrane inside-out vesicles. *Biochim. Biophys. Acta* 770:1–6
36. Partridge, L. D., Swandulla, D. 1988. Calcium-activated non-specific cation channels. *Trends Neurosci.* 11:69–72
37. Preston, R. R. 1989. A Ca^{2+}-sensitive Mg^{2+} current in *Paramecium tetraurelia. J. Cell Biol.* 109:255a (Abstr.)
37a. Preston, R. R. 1990. A magnesium current in *Paramecium. Science.* 250: 285–88
38. Preston, R. R., Saimi, Y. 1990. Calcium ions and regulation of motility in *Paramecium*. In *Ciliary and Flagellar Membranes,* ed. R. A. Bloodgood, 7:173–200. New York: Plenum. 431 pp.
39. Preston, R. R., Saimi, Y., Amberger, E., Kung, C. 1990. Interactions between mutants with defects in two Ca^{2+}-dependent K^+ currents of *Paramecium tetraurelia. J. Membr. Biol.* 115:61–69
40. Preston, R. R., Saimi, Y., Kung, C. 1990. Evidence for two K^+ currents activated upon hyperpolarization of *Paramecium tetraurelia. J. Membr. Biol.* 115:41–50
41. Preston, R. R., Wallen-Friedman, M. A., Saimi, Y., Kung, C. 1990. Calmodulin defects cause the loss of Ca^{2+}-dependent K^+ currents in two pantophobiac mutants of *Paramecium tetraurelia. J. Membr. Biol.* 115:51–60
42. Richard, E. A., Saimi, Y., Kung, C. 1986. A mutation that increases a novel calcium-activated potassium conductance of *Paramecium tetraurelia. J. Membr. Biol.* 91:173–81
43. Rogawski, M. A., Inoue, K., Suzuki, S., Barker, J. L. 1988. A slow calcium-dependent chloride conductance in clonal anterior pituitary cells. *J. Neurophysiol.* 59:1854–70
44. Saimi, Y. 1986. Calcium-dependent sodium currents in *Paramecium:* mutational manipulations and effects of hyper- and depolarization. *J. Membr. Biol.* 92:227–36
45. Saimi, Y., Hinrichsen, R. D., Forte, M., Kung, C. 1983. Mutant analysis shows that the Ca^{2+}-induced K^+ current shuts off one type of excitation in *Paramecium. Proc. Natl. Acad. Sci. USA* 80:5112–16
46. Saimi, Y., Kung, C. 1980. A Ca-induced Na current in *Paramecium. J. Exp. Biol.* 88:305–25
47. Saimi, Y., Kung, C. 1987. Behavioral genetics of *Paramecium. Annu. Rev. Genet.* 21:47–65
47a. Saimi, Y., Ling, K.-Y. 1990. Calmodulin activation of calcium-dependent sodium channels in excised membrane patches of *Paramecium. Science.* 249: 1441–44
48. Saimi, Y., Martinac, B. 1989. Calcium-dependent potassium channel in *Paramecium* studied under patch-clamp. *J. Membr. Biol.* 112:79–89
49. Satow, Y., Kung, C. 1980. Ca-induced K^+-outward current in *Paramecium tetraurelia. J. Exp. Biol.* 88:293–303
50. Schaeffer, W. H., Hinrichsen, R. D., Burgess-Cassler, A., Kung, C., Blair, I. A., Watterson, D. M. 1987. A mutant *Paramecium* with a defective potassium conductance has an altered calmodulin a nonlethal selective alteration in calmodulin regulation. *Proc. Natl. Acad. Sci. USA* 84:3931–35
51. Schaeffer, W. H., Lukas, T. J., Blair, I. A., Schultz, J. E., Watterson, D. M. 1987. Amino acid sequence of a novel calmodulin from *Paramecium tetraurelia* that contains dimethyllysine in the first domain. *J. Biol. Chem.* 262:1025–29
52. Schultz, J. E., Schade, U. 1989. Calcium channel activation and inactivation in *Paramecium* biochemically measured by cyclic GMP production. *J. Membr. Biol.* 109:259–67
53. Stoclet, J.-C., Gérard, D., Kilhoffer, M.-C., Lugnier, C., Miller, R., Schaeffer, P. 1987. Calmodulin and its role in intracellular calcium regulation. *Prog. Neurobiol.* 29:321–64.
54. Takeda, T., Yamamoto, M. 1987. Analysis and *in vivo* disruption of the gene coding for calmodulin in *Schizosaccharomyces pombe. Proc. Natl. Acad. Sci. USA* 84:3580–84
55. Tucker, M. M., Robinson, J. B. Jr., Stellwagen, E. 1981. The effect of proteolysis on the calmodulin activation of cyclic nucleotide phosphodiesterase. *J. Biol. Chem.* 256:9051–58
56. Van Houten, J., Chang, S.-Y., Kung, C. 1977. Genetic analysis of "paranoiac" mutants of *Paramecium tetraurelia. Genetics* 86:113–20
57. Wallen-Friedman, M. A. 1988. An ion current mutant of *Paramecium tetraurelia* with defects in the primary structure and post-translational N-methylation of calmodulin. PhD thesis. Univ. Wisc.-Madison. 231 pp.

Annu. Rev. Physiol. 1991. 53:321–39

ION CHANNELS AND COLONIC SALT TRANSPORT

David C. Dawson

Department of Physiology, The University of Michigan Medical School, Ann Arbor, Michigan 48109

KEY WORDS: ion absorption, ion secretion, electrolyte transport, intestinal ion transport

---

MODELS FOR COLONIC TRANSPORT: WORKING CLASS ION CHANNELS

The focus of this review is the ion transport functions of the vertebrate colon, in particular the role of ion channels in the maintenance and regulation of ion transport processes. A great deal has been learned in the last decade about the properties of ion channels in epithelial cells, and it seems appropriate to review our current understanding of the function of these elements in colonic epithelial transport. I like to think of epithelial ion channels in general, and colonic ion channels in particular, as "working class ion channels". While neuronal ion channels are up in the penthouse subserving a variety of cerebral functions, the channels that inhabit colonic epithelial cells are quietly at work doing the tedious, but nevertheless necessary, jobs associated with preserving electrolyte balance.

Absorption and Secretion

The vertebrate colon can effect the net transport of salt, and hence water, in either the absorptive or the secretory direction, depending on the hormonal status of the animal and the presence or absence of various pathogens (6). The ionic basis for this salt flow is relatively complex and at present incompletely understood, but it appears to involve active (metabolically linked) transport of Na, Cl, K, and HCO_3 as well as passive movements of these ions (6, 85). It seems likely that ion channels play an important role in each of these transport

0066-4278/91/0315-0321$02.00

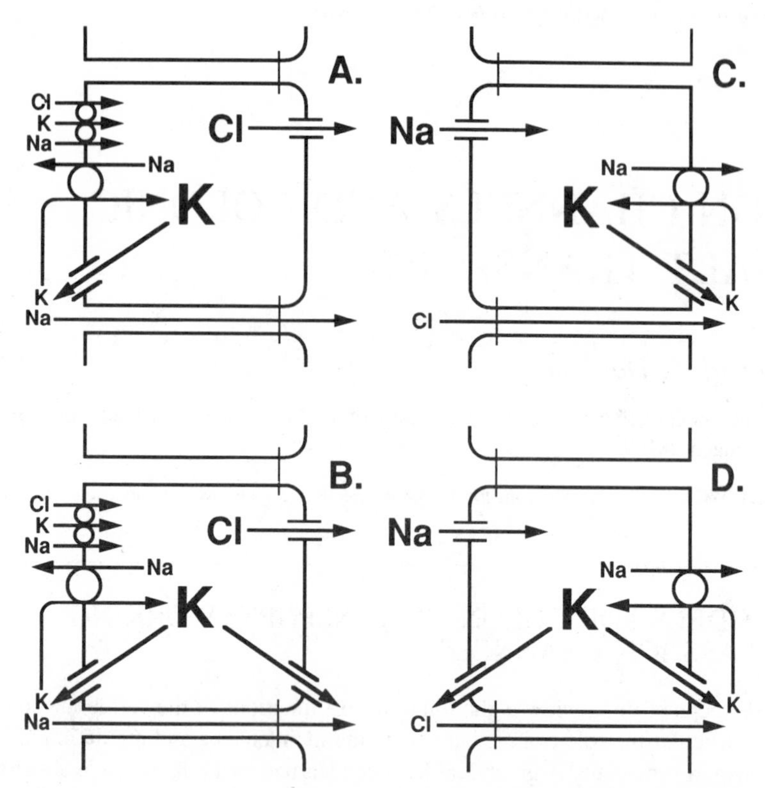

Figure 1 Ion channels and salt absorption and secretion. (*A*) Model for active Cl secretion. (*B*) Cl secretory cell with added apical K channel to allow for active K secretion. (*C*) Koefoed-Johnsen & Ussing's model for electrogenic Na absorption. (*D*) Addition of an apical K channel to the Koefoed-Johnsen & Ussing model allows for K secretion.

processes. Shown in Figure 1*C*, for example, is the now classic model of Koefoed-Johnsen & Ussing (54) for electrogenic Na absorption, a process exhibited to one degree or another by most vertebrate colons (18, 29). The polarity of the absorptive cell, which is essential to transcellular transport, is produced in part by the highly asymmetric disposition of specific classes of ion channels. The apical membrane is populated by amiloride-sensitive, Na-selective channels that facilitate Na entry into the cell down a favorable electrochemical potential gradient, whereas the basolateral membrane is dominated by K channels that permit the exit of K accumulated in the cell by the basolateral Na/K ATPase. It is worth noting that, if the stoichiometry of the Na/K ATPase is fixed at 3 Na: 2 K, then transcellular Na absorption can only occur to the extent that 2/3 of the inward Na current at the apical membrane is balanced by an outward K current across the basolateral membrane (19). Figure 1*D* illustrates the effect of adding apical K channels to the basic KJU model. The cell layer is now capable of active K secretion, and the balance between basolateral K recycling and apical K secretion will be determined by the relative K conductances and driving forces at the two membranes (39, 40).

In the mammalian colon, active Na absorption is thought to be a property of the surface cells, while salt secretion in thought to be localized to the Cl transporting cells of the crypts (6, 102). Figure 1*A* is the consensus model for active Cl secretion, the principal determinant of secretory salt and water flow. The membrane asymmetry required for secretory Cl transport is provided by localizing Cl channels in the apical membrane and K channels basolaterally. Here again transcellular transport requires not only apical Cl exit, but also outward basolateral K flow (19). In this model the burden of K recycling is even greater because K can enter the cell by way of the Na: K: 2Cl cotransporter as well as by the Na/K ATPase. Also the basolateral cotransporter is the route for Na recycling. In Figure 1*B* an apical K channel is added to the basic secretory model. It is interesting to contrast the K secretory capacity of model 1*B* to that of model 1*D*. Consider, for example, the limiting case in which all of the K that enters the cell across the basolateral membrane is secreted, i.e. apical K conductance is much greater than basolateral. The addition of the cotransporter increases the potential rate of basolateral K entry such that, for the same turnover rate of the Na/K ATPase and assuming fixed stoichiometries (3Na: 2K and 1Na: 1K: 2 Cl), the maximal, steady-state secretory rate for model 1*B* is more than double that for model 1*D*. Note that this result is based in part on the assumption that in model 1*B* all Na is recycled at the basolateral membrane.

Regulation of Ion Flows

The ability to record the currents associated with the opening and closing of single-ion channels has revolutionized the way in which we think about the regulation of transport. We now recognize channels as permissive elements: they are pores that are either open or closed. The impact of single-channel consciousness is perhaps best captured in the equation that relates the macroscopic conductance resulting from a particular population of ion channels to the conduction and gating properties of the individual channels, i.e.

$$g_i = \gamma_i N_i (P_o)_i$$

where g_i is the macroscopic conductance, γ_i is the single-channel conductance, N_i is the total number of channels, and $(P_o)_i$ is the probability of finding a channel in the open (conducting) state. This equation provides a powerful framework for the analysis of the regulation of ion flows. Membrane conductance can be altered by a change in γ_i, N_i, or $(P_o)_i$. For example, a cytosolic messenger, e.g. calcium, can act by modulating $(P_o)_i$, increasing or decreasing the fraction of time the channel spends in the conducting state. Changes in N_i can result from the insertion or deletion of membrane protein, or from transitions between active and inactive membrane pools. Finally, γ_i may be modulated by a messenger, reduced to zero by a blocker, or effectively altered by the activation of a different channel population.

The realization that epithelial membranes are inhabited by multiple channel types is the second great lesson of single channel recording (17, 19). The possibility of activating or inactivating different subpopulations (of K channels for example) not only introduces an additional subtlety into possible regulatory schemes, but also imposes the necessity to identify the roles played by particular ion channel populations in specific macroscopic transport functions. Initial efforts in this direction have relied on purely functional criteria, i.e. ion selectivity, blocker, agonist or messenger specificity, or voltage dependence, but the lack of specific tags for most epithelial channels has made this a formidable task. Recent advances in molecular biology (9, 61, 70) should soon provide more specific probes to be used in the implication of specific channel proteins in specific transport functions.

In the sections that follow I offer a partial catalogue of ion channels that have been identified in colonic cells and, where possible, provide some information as to possible modulatory influences that could be important for transport regulation. The relative lack of information about ion channels in the colon will make this chapter mercifully brief but will, I hope, point the way to some potentially interesting issues for future study.

APICAL MEMBRANES

Na Channels

A dominant feature of the apical membranes of the absorptive cells in colons from mammals (15, 32, 78, 86, 102, 107, 109), birds (13), reptiles (90, 103, 104), and amphibians (55–58) is a population of Na channels, although some portions of the mammalian colon may express few or none of these channels (14). Reversible blockade of these channels by amiloride and amiloride analogues, such as triamterene and CDPC (6-chloro-3-diamino-pyrazine-2-carboxamide), has permitted unequivocal identification of these channels in apical membranes and has set the stage for inquiry into the regulation of apical Na conductance. Macroscopic studies would suggest that these channels are highly selective for Na over K, but that Na and Li are roughly equally permeant (90). Colonic Na channels have not yet succumbed to patch-clamp analysis, but it seems reasonable to assume that they are similar to those recorded in the apical membranes of several renal epithelia. These channels exhibit conductances (26, 27, 34, 45, 74, 88) ranging from 5–10 pS, where γ is a saturable function of Na concentration (4, 83). Li is also conducted, and channel gating exhibits only a weak dependence on membrane potential.

In relation to the general nature of apical Na channels, it is interesting to note that in renal cells, particularly in primary culture or in cell lines, it has been possible to identify channels that are amiloride-sensitive, but lack the high Na/K selectivity that appears to be associated with a functional apical membrane (45, 49, 62). The significance of such observations is unclear at present, but the occurrence of such channels forms the basis for interesting speculations regarding the developmental origin of Na channels and a possible life cycle, including insertion into the apical membrane and subsequent degradation (64). It seems clear that A6 cells, for example, exhibit the highly selective apical Na channel only when they are induced to differentiate by growing them to confluence on permeable supports (26, 45).

The regulation of apical Na conductance in the colon, as in other epithelia, is poorly understood but available evidence suggests that this channel population is capable of varied and subtle forms of modulation that include not only responses to agonists, but also intrinsic autoregulatory responses. Autoregulation of apical Na conductance was first described by Helman & colleagues (1, 48) in frog skin, and it has been documented in the colon of amphibians (55) and reptiles (D. Dawson, W. Van Driessche, unpublished observation). The term refers to the fact that the reduction of apical Na entry, brought about by either an acute reduction of mucosal Na^+ concentration, or the addition of a Na channel blocker, evokes a compensatory increase in apical Na conductance that tends to restore the rate of active absorption. The response occurs with a time constant of about 10–20 min, and analysis of current fluctuations suggests that it involves the addition of channels to the active population. Recent experiments on A6 cells (63) suggest that a similar phenomenon can be evoked in single Na channels within a cell-attached patch if Na concentration is raised, or if amiloride is applied outside of the pipette, and that the effects may include a change in open probability in addition to the change in channel number. A related phenomenon is the self-inhibition of apical Na conductance that occurs when transport is inhibited, for example, by blocking the basolateral pump. In reptilian colon, apical Na conductance was preserved after pump inhibition only if apical Na concentration was reduced (2 mM). Raising mucosal Na concentration in this condition led to the disappearance of the apical conductance (53), and the time course of this effect suggested an effect of intracellular rather than extracellular Na concentration. In rabbit colon, a negative correlation was observed between apical Na permeability and apparent cytosolic Na concentration (92, 93).

The vertebrate colon is a well-known target for mineralocorticoids, which increase Na absorption. It is generally believed that an important early action of aldosterone is to induce an increase in apical Na conductance (15, 34, 50). The induction of amiloride-sensitive Na absorption is perhaps most striking in the rat colon (7, 106), which under normal dietary conditions absorbs NaCl by an electrically silent process, but develops an amiloride-sensitive absorptive component following salt deprivation or injection of mineralocorticoids (see also 72).

The molecular basis for the action of mineralocorticoids on apical Na conductance is at present obscure. The well-known effect of these hormones on protein synthesis naturally led to the hypothesis of channel insertion, but evidence for this is lacking. Single-channel recordings from A6 cells, in fact, provide evidence for a gating effect of aldosterone (52). In addition, the phenomenon of auto-regulation, discussed above, raises the possibility that the apical membranes of colonic cells contain a substantial pool of inactive channels that may be recruited into the active pool under a variety of conditions.

Electrogenic Na absorption also appears to be subject to inhibitory neural control via submucosal cholinergic nerves (16, 98, 119). In the reptilian colon, the cholinergic inhibition of Na transport appears to be a coordinate regulatory response, involving both apical Na conductance and basolateral K conductance (98, 103, 104). Fluctuation analysis of apical Na channels revealed that the inhibition of Na absorption was associated with a decrease in the number of active Na channels. Although the cellular basis for this regulation is unclear, it is of interest that a similar decline in transport and channel number was induced with the calcium ionophore A23187, or the phorbol ester PMA (D. Wilkinson, D. Dawson, unpublished).

Although not yet investigated in colonic cells, studies on frog skin (46) and renal tubules (74) suggest that apical Na channels are sensitive to cytosolic pH, such that cell acidification reduces apical Na conductance, and possibly that alkalinization of cytosolic pH may be a component of the regulatory mechanisms that accompany the action of aldosterone (46). Additionally, the basolateral membranes of the reptilian colon express a very high level of Na^+/H^+ exchange, a transport activity that could serve as a link between changes in cytosolic composition and apical Na entry (77).

K Channels

The phenomenon of colonic K secretion (3, 39, 40, 65, 66, 73, 88, 89, 107, 111) led to the identification of K channels in the apical membranes of the mammalian (107, 110, 111, 113, 114, 118) and reptilian colon (105) by fluctuation analysis. In the colon of the rabbit, apical K channel noise was only discernable in the presence of elevated concentrations of mucosal or serosal K, but the channel noise responded to changes in the applied potential as expected for an apical conduction path. Likewise, isolated human colon exhibited an apparent component of apical K channel noise in the presence of elevated mucosal K (110). In the reptilian colon, K secretion was variable under short circuit conditions, but was always induced by voltage clamping to a mucosa negative potential near the normal open circuit potential of the tissue

(39, 40). K secretion observed under short circuit or open circuit conditions was blocked by mucosal barium. Apical K channel noise (105) behaved in a similar fashion. When tissues were bathed by Na Ringers (K=2.5 mM), the appearance of a Lorentzian component in the power density spectrum, which could be attributed to K, was variable, but a Lorentzian was always induced by voltage clamping to a mucosal negative potential, by elevating serosal K, or by applying *serosal* barium. The Lorentzian was abolished by mucosal barium and was attenuated by raising mucosal K. All of these observations are consistent with the notions that the apical membrane contains a population of K channels that mediate conductive K exit from the cells and that the single channel currents exhibit the expected sensitivity to the apical K electrochemical gradient. The sensitivity of K exit to the apical membrane potential appears to be the basis for the inhibition of K secretion by amiloride under short circuit conditions (39, 40). Unfortunately, little can be said as to the identity of these apical K channels. Those in the turtle colon were apparently blocked by barium, while in the rabbit colon barium was ineffective, although Cs and TEA (tetraethyl-ammonium) produced partial block. In neither case, however, was it possible to identify a channel blocker that could be used to produce a blocker-induced Lorentzian of the sort necessary to perform more quantitative analysis of the single-channel currents or channel number (21). The regulation of apical K channels in the colon has not been investigated, but many possibilities emerge from the observation that K secretion, at least in the mammal, can be activated by a variety of secretagogues, including cAMP, prostaglandins, and calcium ionophores, as well as adrenergic agonists, cholinergic agonists, and aldosterone (41, 43, 69, 87, 88). In cells of the cortical collecting duct of the kidney, aldosterone appears to increase apical K conductance (71). In the mammalian colon a major component of the K secretion probably resides in the Cl secretory crypt cells (see Figure 1*B*) and is highly sensitive to loop diuretics, whereas in the non-Cl secreting reptilian colon, the smaller K secretion probably resides in Na absorptive cells (76, 79).

Cl Channels

Apical Cl channels appear to be a feature of secretory cells, in general, and colonic cells associated with Cl secretion are no exception (42, 43). Information pertaining to these channels is more extensive than for apical Na and K channels because of the existence of several colonic secretory cell lines that have been found appropriate for single-channel recording from the apical membranes. The apical membrane of the human colon carcinoma cell line, HT_{29}, was found to contain at least two types of Cl-selective channels (24, 47). One exhibited a conductance of about 15 pS in symmetric 147 mM Cl containing Ringers, but it was not characterized in detail. A second channel exhibited a larger conductance (50 pS), was highly anion selective, and was blocked reversibly by 5-nitro-2-(3 phenylpropyl-amino)-benzoate (NPPB). The gating of the channel was voltage-dependent, and P_o increased in response to depolarization.

Halm et al (44) conducted a detailed study of a Cl channel in the apical membrane of T84 cells, another colonic tumor cell line. The channel was outwardly rectifying in the presence of symmetric 160 mM NaCl solutions, and its slope conductance around zero mV was 40–45 pS. In addition to Cl, both I^- and Br^- were highly permeant. The open probability was voltage-dependent and increased with depolarization. The gating properties of this channel were somewhat unusual, particularly with regard to initial activation. In on-cell patches, Cl^- channels could be activated by exposing cells to forskolin, 8-Br-cAMP, or prostaglandin E_2 in accord with the notion that these channels can be activated by a rise in cytosolic cAMP. Channels were not detectable in the absence of secretagogues. In excised patches, however, the channels exhibited irreversible voltage-activation similar to that reported for Cl channels from tracheal cells (28, 30, 31, 84). Excised patches held at cell negative voltages for up to 20 min exhibited no channel activity, but in 50% of such patches depolarizing voltages of 60 mV applied for 0.5–10 min elicited channel openings which, after activation, exhibited typical voltage-dependence. Voltage activation could not be produced in cell-attached patches. In relation to the phenomenon of HCO_3 secretion, it is of interest that Cl channels in T84 cells can also conduct HCO_3 (89).

Activation by cytosolic cAMP and irreversible voltage activation, in addition to ion selectivity and rectification, are properties that suggest that apical Cl channels in colonic secretory cells are homologous to similar channels identified in other secretory cells, notably those of the airway (28, 30, 31). In apical patches from cultured normal human airway cells, single Cl channels can be activated by cAMP in the presence of the catalytic subunit of cAMP-dependent protein kinase (PKA). This activation step is inoperative, however, in cells from cystic fibrosis patients (83). This correspondence is of particular interest in view of recent studies suggesting that the cystic fibrosis secretory defect is also expressed in the human colon and rectum (4, 38). There is also evidence that increases in cytosolic calcium activity can activate apical Cl channels, but the mechanism does not seem to involve a simple ligand-binding interaction between calcium and the channel. Carbachol, a secretagogue in T84 cells, raises cytosolic calcium (115). Cl secretion is activated by calcium ionophores, and the same maneuver increases whole cell Cl conductance in isolated T84 cells (44). In detached, inside-out patches, however, apical Cl channels from T84 cells were insensitive to changes in calcium activity (D. Halm, personal communication). Intracellular calcium may be important for the neural activation of Cl secretion by acetylcholine or other transmitters released from submucosal nerves (5, 16, 29, 60).

The effect of phorbol esters on Cl secretion has raised the possibility of a role for protein kinase C (PKC) in apical Cl channel regulation, and studies on airway cells reveal an interesting interaction between PKC and cytosolic calcium activity (68). When calcium activity was low (< 10 nM), exposure of the cytoplasmic face of detached patches to PKC, PMA (phorbol 12-myristate 13-acetate), and ATP-activated Cl channels. If the calcium activity was raised to greater than 10 μM, however, the channels were inactivated. At 1 μM free Ca, channels activated by PKA were inactivated if exposed to PKC and diacylglycerol. At 1 μM Ca, PKC in the presence of ATP and diacylglycerol prevented voltage activation. Whole cell recordings from airway cells suggested that the secretory Cl channel could also be activated by cell swelling (67). In T84 cells, however, whole cell Cl currents activated by cell swelling were thought to reflect a population of channels distinct from those mediating secretion (117).

An anion-selective channel, which bears some resemblance to those identified in colonic cell lines, was reconstituted into planar lipid bilayers using a partially purified plasma membrane preparation from rat colon (80). The single-channel conductance was 50 pS in the presence of symmetric 200 mM NaCl and was weakly rectifying. Later studies of intact rat colonic mucosa using both isolated crypts and isolated cells disclosed several possible Cl channel types (23). The preparations precluded any precise definition of the location or function of the channels, but the study is noteworthy because it is one of the few reports of a successful single-channel recording from a reasonably intact colonic epithelium. It may be of interest that the Cl channels described in colon, like those in other cells, exhibit significant conductance to a variety of anions including I^-, Br^-, NO_3^-, and Scn^-. This property may be useful in the design of experimental strategies for separating anion conductive paths from non-conductive transport in radioisotope studies (99).

Although considerable effort has been devoted to the development of blockers for Cl channels, vexing problems remain with regard to the action of these compounds on colonic Cl channels. The disulfonic stilbene derivative DIDS (4'-4' diisothiocyanatostilbene—2,2' disulfonic acid) irreversibly blocked Cl channels reconstituted into planar bilayers from rat colon, while the non-covalently reactive analogue, DNDS, produced a flickery reversible block of the channel. Both compounds were active only at the side of the channel believed to correspond to the extracellular face of the membrane, but neither compound was effective in blocking Cl secretion by rat colon or T84 cell layers (8). This may reflect some alteration in the channel during the reconstitution process that produces increased access to the inhibitory binding site.

Derivatives of anthracene-9-carboxylic have been developed as blockers of Cl channels in renal cells (101) and have been shown to block Cl channels in detached patches from tumor cell lines (24) and to inhibit Cl secretion by rabbit colon (51).

Non-Selective Channels

The apical membrane of the amphibian colon (59) can express non-selective cation channels if the calcium activity in the lumenal bathing fluid is reduced by adding 0.5 mM EGTA to solutions, which contain no added calcium. The channel was identified by fluctuation analysis and resembles those studied extensively in the apical membrane of isolated toad bladder (2, 94, 95). The channel is apparently blocked by calcium and other divalent ions (Mg, Ba) as well as by quinidine, but its physiologic significance is unknown.

BASOLATERAL MEMBRANES

The basolateral membranes of colonic epithelial cells, despite being less accessible than the apical membranes, have nevertheless been studied in some detail primarily through the use of various permeabilized cell layers, which permit the basolateral membrane to be viewed, in a sense, through holes in the apical membrane (18, 21, 36, 37, 96, 109). These preparations have permitted the measurement of basolateral ionic currents and blocker-induced fluctuations, which provide evidence for an interesting diversity of conductive transport mechanisms, and establish a standard against which the properties of single channels, identified in isolated cells, planar bilayers, or by expression in amphibian oocytes, can be compared. The realization that cell isolation may dramatically alter the differentiated properties of epithelial cells may render the permeabilized cell layer an increasingly valuable tool for investigations of the basolateral membrane (33, 75).

K Channels

Models for electrogenic Na absorption and Cl secretion (see Figure 1) require outward basolateral K currents to balance conductive cation entry or anion exit at the apical membrane. Hence, it is not surprising that a consistent feature of colonic cells is a substantial basolateral conductance for K (19, 112). It is clear, however, that the nature of this conductance is more than that of a simple housekeeping mechanism for the recycling of cell K. It seems likely that we will find that this membrane contains several different populations of K channels that can be differentially regulated to provide subtle alterations in basolateral conductance.

The basolateral membrane of the reptilian colon is probably the most extensively studied, so I will consider it here in detail. This membrane appears to contain at least three distinct populations of K channels, although only one of these has been definitively identified at the single-channel level.

Cell layers apically permeabilized with amphotericin B exhibit a resting basolateral K conductance that does not discriminate appreciably between K and Rb, is blocked by barium, and is inactivated by cholinergic agonists (19, 36, 37, 98). The sensitivity of active Na transport to cholinergic agonists and the relative indifference of this process to substituting Rb for K suggests that this conductance supports normal transport. Another possible component of basolateral K conductance was disclosed as a transient activation of basolateral I_K by carbachol, which preceded the inactivation of the resting conductance. The fact that this same sequence of events could be evoked by the addition of calcium ionophores raised the possibility that the basis for this conductance was a population of calcium-activated K channels (98). Using cell layers apically permeabilized with digitonin it was possible to characterize a calcium-activated basolateral K conductance, but calcium-activated currents exhibited a peculiar pharmacological profile (10, 11). They were blocked by quinidine, but not by lidocaine, and both TEA and barium blocked them, but block occurred only from the cytosolic side. The inability of these last two agents to block from the extracellular side argues against this conductance being due to Ca-activated maxi channels. The conductance was also blocked by the anthranilic acid derivative, n-phenyl anthranilic acid (aka diphenylamine carboxylate or DPC). This observation proved to be more interesting than was at first apparent when it was found that DPC was relatively selective in its action on colonic K channels (82; N. Richards, D. Dawson, in preparation). The compound did not block Ca-activated maxi channels, nor did it block 20 pS channels activated by cell swelling (see below), but it did block a very flickery, 30 pS calcium-activated channel that could be identified in isolated cells. Thus this channel seemed to emerge as a candidate for the early carbachol response, but it may also be noteworthy that the DPC, although not effective on the swelling activated I_K, did block the resting I_K regardless of whether K or Rb was the current carrier (N. Richards, N. Kushman, D. Dawson, unpublished).

The basolateral membrane of turtle colon appears to contain a third K channel population that is not active under resting conditions, but can be activated by cell swelling (37). The conductance was initially distinguished on the basis of its sensitivity to quinidine and lidocaine and its high selectivity for K over Rb. Analysis of lidocaine-induced fluctuations in basolateral K current (20) was consistent with the notion that swelling activated this channel population. Single-channel recordings from isolated cells disclosed a 20 pS channel, which on the basis of its blocker specificity appears to be the basis for the conductance. Observations such as these suggest that a variety of K channels inhabit the basolateral membrane and provide the basis for a wide range of regulatory or homeostatic-control mechanisms.

Analysis of current fluctuations from nystatin-treated rabbit colon (108,

114) disclosed a population of basolateral K channels in this tissue, but a reversible blocker was not identified that would permit quantitative studies. In more recent studies a K channel was reconstituted into planar bilayers from rabbit colonic cell membrane vesicles enriched for basolateral membranes (91). The channel was a Ca-activated maxi K channel, but its physiologic significance was not clear as it was only open at depolarized membrane voltages, or rather high cytosolic calcium activities. Despite this ambiguity there is reason to believe that cytosolic calcium may be an important modulator of basolateral K conductance. The binding of carbachol to muscarinic receptors on T84 cells raised cell calcium and activated basolateral K conductance (22, 116). As indicated above, the digitonin-permeabilized reptilian colon exhibited a calcium-activated basolateral conductance that could be attributable to a DPC-sensitive K channel (82; N. Richards, D. Dawson, in preparation). The calcium-activated basolateral K channels in reptilian colon were also modulated by cytsolic pH (12). Acidification shifted the calcium activation curve to the right, thereby attenuating the conductance at any value of cell calcium. It is noteworthy that a basolateral K conductance in rabbit distal colon was also attenuated by reducing cytosolic pH (25). As indicated earlier, the presence in the basolateral membrane of Na/H exchangers raises the possibility that cytosolic pH may be at least a permissive regulator of both apical Na and basolateral K channels. Future experiments in this area could produce interesting results since there are suggestions that basolateral K conductance may vary with transport rate (19).

Cl Channels

Information about possible Cl channels in colonic basolateral membranes is fairly scarce. Patch-clamp recordings from dissociated crypts of rat colon registered single-channel Cl currents (23), but the role of these currents in cellular transport is not clear. The basolateral membranes of turtle colon cells can express a very large Cl conductance which, although its role in transport has not been precisely defined, is of interest because it is subject to inhibitory cholinergic control. The conductance is readily apparent in amphotericin-permeabilized cell layers, not as a transcellular current (because of the cation selectivity of the polyene pore), but as a large component of the small signal conductance. This conductance is inactivated by cholinergic agonists, but is specifically inhibited by experimental maneuvers that are expected to raise cellular cAMP, i.e. forskolin and phosphodiesterase inhibitors, and by exposure to cAMP analogues (97, 100). A possible physiologic role for these presumed channels emerged from experiments showing that some turtle colons exhibit a transcellular Cl conductance that behaves as a cellular leak path specific for Cl (97). This transcellular leak was inactivated by the same maneuvers that attenuated the basolateral conductance. When present in the cell layer, this conductance would enhance salt absorption by providing a path for transmural Cl flow with a conductance in excess of that of the paracellular shunt. Its inactivation, therefore, would provide an additional brake on the absorptive process. The significance of these observations is far from clear at present because the transcellular Cl-selective conductance was expressed in only a small portion of the colons examined. This raises the possibility of, as yet undiscovered, regulatory mechanisms as well as the possibility that membrane properties are modified somehow during the process of the removal of the muscle layer. In digitonin-permeabilized cell layers it was possible to identify a calcium-activated basolateral Cl conductance that was blocked by high concentrations (0.1–1.0 mM) of DPC. It is still unclear if this conductance is related to that detected in amphotericin-permeabilized layers (11).

Na Channels?

From a teleological perspective, a basolateral Na channel is not a transport element that has an obvious place in models for either Na absorption or Cl secretion. It would compromise transcellular Na flow in the former and coupled basolateral entry of Na, K, and Cl in the latter. Recently, however, experiments on permeabilized cell layers disclosed that it was possible to render the normally K-selective basolateral membrane of turtle colon, Na-selective (77). Cell layers were bathed in Cl-free solutions in which the impermeant gluconate was the principal anion, and were exposed to opposing gradients of Na (mucosal) and K (serosal). Apical permeabilization in this condition led to the development of a mucosa-to-serosa Na current that was blocked by serosal amiloride, but at a concentration 10–100-fold higher than required for apical Na channels. The nature and significance of the channels that underlie the current are unknown at present. The channels could represent some component of a volume regulatory response, as the conductance was associated with cell shrinkage, which also activated Na/H exchange. Alternatively the conductance could represent, not Na selective channels in the conventional sense, but rather a small component of uncoupled Na flow via the exchanger. A similar basolateral Na current was recorded in nystatin-permeabilized toad urinary bladder (35), but an association with Na/H exchange was not investigated.

SORTING OUT COLONIC ION CHANNELS

Although it has been possible in this review to catalogue a variety of ion channels that inhabit the plasma membranes of colonic cells, our understanding of the molecular details of the resultant ion transport processes and their regulation is rudimentary at best. This situation is due, at least in part, to the inherent cellular heterogeneity of the colon. The mammalian colon, for example, contains both secretory and absorptive machinery housed in different cell types. The crypt structure of the epithelium creates additional problems of accessibility of various membranes. This situation is exacerbated by the probable existence of a variety of channel types that are differentially expressed in different colonic cells, and for which Nature has not generally provided highly specific probes analogous to the toxins that recognize some of the channels in excitable membranes (9). It is not clear that it will be easy to defeat this complexity. Isolated cells can be studied, but in addition to losing their polarity, isolated cells may not retain their full complement of differentiated functions (33, 75). The simpler colons of cold-blooded vertebrates provide useful models for certain aspects of colonic transport, particularly electrogenic Na absorption, while cell lines or isolated crypts offer useful models for the secretory process. The problem remains, however, of understanding the function of an ensemble of transport elements in an integrated setting. It is hoped that the powerful techniques of molecular biology will provide one solution to this dilemma. Cloning of the cDNAs for specific channel proteins can, in principle, lead to the design of specific probes, which can be used to identify a specific transport protein in a complex setting. In addition, the information about the amino acid sequences of various channel subtypes may help us to identify familial relationships between channel proteins, which are not apparent on the basis of the rather crude criteria of blocker specificity and ion selectivity. Finally, it may be possible to reconstitute specific channels in simple environments that will facilitate the investigation of specific regulatory events (61). These exciting possibilities await us in the coming decade.

ACKNOWLEDGMENTS

The writing of this article and the research in the author's laboratory was supported by National Institute of Arthritis, Diabetes, and Digestive and Kidney Diseases, the University of Michigan G. I. Peptide Center, the Cystic Fibrosis Foundation, and the Michigan Heart Association.

Literature Cited

1. Abramcheck, R. J., Van Driessche, W., Helman, S. I. 1985. Autoregulation of apical membrane Na^+ permeability of tight epithelia. *J. Gen. Physiol.* 85:555–82
2. Aelvoet, I., Erlij, D., Van Driessche, W. 1988. Activation and blockage of a calcium-sensitive cation-selective pathway in the apical membrane of toad urinary bladder. *J. Physiol.* 398:555–74
3. Bastl, C., Kliger, A. S., Binder, H. J., Hayslett, J. P. 1978. Characteristics of potassium secretion in the mammalian colon. *Am. J. Physiol.* 234(1):F48–F53
4. Berschneider, H. M., Knowles, M. R., Azizkhan, R. G., Boucher, R. C., Tobey, N. A., Orlando, R. C., Powell, D. W. 1988. Altered intestinal chloride transport in cystic fibrosis. *FASEB J.* 2:2625–29
5. Biagi, B., Wang, Y. Z., Cooke, H. J. 1990. Effects of tetrodotoxin on chloride secretion in rabbit distal colon: tissue

and cellular studies. *Am. J. Physiol.* 258:G223–30
6. Binder, H. J., Sandle, G. I. 1987. Electrolyte absorption and secretion in the mammalian colon. In *Physiology of the Gastrointestinal Tract,* ed. L. R. Johnson, 2:1389–1418. New York: Raven. 1780 pp.
7. Bridges, R. J., Cragoe, E. J., Jr., Frizzell, R. A., Benos, D. J. 1989. Inhibition of colonic Na^+ transport by amiloride analogues. *Am. J. Physiol.* 256: C67–C74
8. Bridges, R. J., Worrell, R. T., Frizzell, R. A., Benos, D. J. 1989. Stilbene disulfonate blockade of colonic secretory Cl^- channels in planar lipid bilayers. *Am. J. Physiol.* 256:C902–12
9. Catterall, W. A. 1988. Structure and function of voltage-sensitive ion channels. *Science* 242:50–61
10. Chang, D., Hsieh, P. S., Dawson, D. C. 1988. Calcium: A program in basic for calculating the composition of solutions with specified free concentrations of calcium, magnesium, and other divalent cations. *Comput. Biol. Med.* 5:351–66
11. Chang, D., Dawson, D. C. 1988. Digitonin-permeabilized colonic cell layers: Demonstration of calcium-activated basolateral K^+ and Cl^- conductances. *J. Gen. Physiol.* 92:281–306
12. Chang, D., Dawson, D. C. 1988. Modulation of calcium-activated basolateral K^+ and Cl^- conductances by intracellular pH in turtle colon epithelial cells. *FASEB J.* 2:A1284
13. Christensen, O., Bindslev, N. 1982. Fluctuation analysis of short-circuit current in a warm-blooded sodium-retaining epithelium: site current, sensitivity and interaction with triamterene. *J. Membr. Biol.* 65:19–30
14. Clauss, W., Biehler, K. H., Schäfer, H., Wills, N. K. 1987. Ion transport and electrophysiology of the early proximal colon of rabbit. *Pflügers Arch.* 408:592–99
15. Clauss, W., Dürr, J. E., Krattenmacher, R., Hörnicke, H., Van Driessche, W., 1988. Circadian rhythm of apical Na-channels and Na-transport in rabbit distal colon. *Birkhäuser Verlag* 44:608–10
16. Cooke, H. J. 1989. Role of the "little brain" in the gut in water and electrolyte homeostasis. *FASEB J.* 3:127–38
17. Dawson, D. C. 1987. Properties of epithelial potassium channels. In *Curr. Top. Membr. Transp.* 28:41–71
18. Dawson, D. C., Chang, D., 1990. Turtle colon: Keeping track of transporters in the apical and basolateral membranes. *Methods Enzymol.* 192:734–45
19. Dawson, D. C., Richards, N. W. 1990. Basolateral K conductance: Role in regulation of NaCl absorption and secretion. *Am. J. Physiol.* 259:C181–95
20. Dawson, D. C., Van Driessche, W., Helman, S. I. 1988. Osmotically induced basolateral K^+ conductance in turtle colon: lidocaine-induced K^+ channel noise. *Am. J. Physiol.* 254:C165–74
21. Dawson, D. C., Wilkinson, D. J., Richards, N. W. 1990. Basolateral potassium channel noise: signals from the dark side. *Curr. Top. Membr. Transp.* 37:191–212
22. Devor, D. C., Simasko, S. M., Duffey, M. E. 1990. Carbachol induces oscillations of membrane potassium conductance in a colonic cell line, T84. *Am. J. Physiol.* 258:C318–26
23. Diener, M., Rummel, W., Mestres, P., Lindemann, B. 1989. Single chloride channels in colon mucosa and isolated colonic enterocytes of the rat. *J. Membr. Biol.* 108:21–30
24. Dreinhöfer, J., Gögelein, H., Greger, R. 1988. Blocking kinetics of Cl^- channels in colonic carcinoma cells (HT_{29}) as revealed by 5-nitro-2-(3-phenylpropylamino)benzoic acid (NPPB). *Biochim. Biophys. Acta* 946:135–42
25. Duffey, M. E., Devor, D. C. 1990. Intracellular pH and membrane potassium conductance in rabbit distal colon. *Am. J. Physiol.* 258:C336–43
26. Eaton, D. C., Hamilton, K. L. 1988. The amiloride-blockable sodium channel of epithelial tissue. *Ion Channels* 1:251–82
27. Frings, S., Purves, R. D., Macknight, A. D. C. 1988. Single-channel recordings from the apical membrane of the toad urinary bladder epithelial cell. *J. Membr. Biol.* 106:157–72
28. Frizzell, R. A. 1987. Cystic fibrosis: a disease of ion channels? *Trends Neurosci.* 10(5):190–93
29. Frizzell, R. A. 1977. Active chloride secretion by rabbit colon: calcium-dependent stimulation by ionophore A23187. *J. Membr. Biol.* 35:175–87
30. Frizzell, R. A., Halm, D. R. 1990. Chloride channels in epithelial cells. *Curr. Top. Membr. Transp.* 37:247–82
31. Frizzell, R. A., Halm, D. R., Rechkemmer, G., Shoemaker, R. L. 1986. Chloride channel regulation in secretory epithelia. *FASEB J.* 45:2727–31
32. Frizzell, R. A., Koch, M. J., Schultz, S. G. 1976. Ion transport by rabbit colon I. Active and passive components. *J. Membr. Biol.* 27:297–316
33. Fujimoto, T., Ogawa, K. 1982. Cell

surface alteration in dissociated frog urinary bladder epithelial cells. *J. Electron Microsc.* 31(2):171–84
34. Garty, H., Benos, D. J. 1988. Characteristics and regulatory mechanisms of the amiloride-blockable Na^+ channel. *Physiol. Rev.* 68:309–73
35. Garty, H., Warncke, J., Lindemann, B. 1987. An amiloride-sensitive Na^+ conductance in the basolateral membrane of toad urinary bladder. *J. Membr. Biol.* 95:91–103
36. Germann, W. J., Ernst, S. A., Dawson, D. C. 1986. Resting and osmotically induced basolateral K conductances in turtle colon. *J. Gen. Physiol.* 88:253–74
37. Germann, W. J., Lowy, M. E., Ernst, S. A., Dawson, D. C. 1986. Differentiation of two distinct K conductances in the basolateral membrane of turtle colon. *J. Gen. Physiol.* 88:237–51
38. Goldstein, J. L., Nash, N. T., Al-Bazzaz, F., Layden, T. J., Rao, M. C. 1988. Rectum has abnormal ion transport but normal cAMP-binding proteins in cystic fibrosis. *Am. J. Physiol.* 254: C719–24
39. Halm, D. R., Dawson, D. C. 1984. Potassium transport by turtle colon: active secretion and active absorption. *Am. J. Physiol.* 246:C315–22
40. Halm, D. R., Dawson, D. C. 1984. Control of potassium transport by turtle colon: role of membrane potential. *Am. J. Physiol.* 247:C26–C32
41. Halm, D. R., Frizzell, R. A. 1986. Active K transport across rabbit distal colon: relation to Na absorption and Cl secretion. *Am. J. Physiol.* 251:C252–67
42. Halm, D. R., Frizzell, R. A. 1990. Intestinal chloride secretion. In *Textbook of Secretory Diarrhea,* ed. E. Lebenthal, M. E. Duffy, pp. 47–85. New York: Raven
43. Halm, D. R., Frizzell, R. A. 1990. Ion transport across large intestine. In *Handbook of Physiology—The Gastrointestinal System IV,* ed. R. A. Frizzell, M. Fields, Bethesda: In press
44. Halm, D. R., Rechkemmer, G. H., Schoumacher, R. A., Frizzell, R. A. 1988. Apical membrane chloride channels in a colonic cell line activated by secretory agonists. *Am. J. Physiol.* 254:C505–11
45. Hamilton, K. L., Eaton, D. C. 1986. Single-channel recordings from two types of amiloride-sensitive epithelial Na^+ channels. *Membr. Biochem.* 6(2): 149–71
46. Harvey, B. J., Ehrenfeld, J. 1988. Role of Na^+/H^+ exchange in the control of intracellular pH and cell membrane conductances in frog skin epithelium. *J. Gen. Physiol.* 92:793–810
47. Hayslett, J. P., Gögelein, H., Kunzelmann, K., Greger, R. 1987. Characteristics of apical chloride channels in human colon cells (HT_{29}). *Pflügers Arch.* 410:487–94
48. Helman, S. I., Baxendale, L. M. 1990. Blocker-related changes of channel density: Analysis of a three-state model for apical Na channels of frog skin. *J. Gen. Physiol.* 95(4):647–78
49. Hillyard, S. D., Van Driessche, W. 1989. Effect of amiloride on the poorly selective cation channel of larval bullfrog skin. *Am. J. Physiol.* 256:C168–74
50. Hoffmann, B., Clauss, W. 1989. Time-dependent effects of aldosterone on sodium transport and cell membrane resistances in rabbit distal colon. *Pflügers Arch.* 415:156–64
51. Horvath, P. J., Ferriola, P. C., Weiser, M. M., Duffey, M. E. 1986. Localization of chloride secretion in rabbit colon: inhibition by anthracene-9-carboxylic acid. *Am. J. Physiol.* 250:G185–90
52. Kemendy, A. E., Eaton, D. C. 1989. Aldosterone affects apical Na^+ channel density and open probability in A6 epithelia. *FASEB J.* 3(3):3684
53. Kirk, K. L., Dawson, D. C. 1985. Passive cation permeability of turtle colon: Evidence for a negative interaction between intracellular sodium and apical sodium permeability. *Pflügers Arch.* 403:82–89
54. Koefoed-Johnsen, V., Ussing, H. H. 1958. The nature of the frog skin potential. *Acta Physiol. Scand.* 42:298–308
55. Krattenmacher, R., Clauss, W. 1989. Autoregulation of apical sodium entry in the colon of the frog *(Rana esculenta). Comp. Biochem. Physiol. A* 93:593–96
56. Krattenmacher, R., Clauss, W. 1988. Electrophysiological analysis of sodium-transport in the colon of the frog *(Rana esculenta). Pflügers Arch.* 411:606–12
57. Krattenmacher, R., Fischer, H., Van Driessche, W., Clauss, W. 1988. Noise analysis of cAMP-stimulated Na current in frog colon. *Pflügers Arch.* 412:568–73
58. Krattenmacher, R., Voigt, R., Clauss, W. 1990. Ca-sensitive sodium absorption in the colon of *Xenopus laevis. J. Comp. Physiol.* 160:161–65
59. Krattenmacher, R., Voigt, R., Heinz, M., Clauss, W. 1990. Electrolyte transport through a cation-selective ion channel in large intestinal enterocytes of *Xenopus laevis. J. Exp. Biol.* In press

60. Kuwahara, A., Bowen, S., Wang, J., Condon, C., Cooke, H. J. 1987. Epithelial responses evoked by stimulation of submucosal neurons in guinea pig distal colon. *Am. J. Physiol.* 252:G667–74
61. Lester, H. A. 1988. Heterologous expression of excitability proteins: Route to more specific drugs? *Science* 241:1057–1063
62. Light, D. B., McCann, F. V., Keller, T. M., Stanton, B. A. 1988. Amiloride-sensitive cation channel in apical membrane of inner medullary collecting duct. *Am. J. Physiol.* 255:F278–86
63. Ling, B. N., Eaton, D. C. 1989. Effects of luminal Na^+ on single Na^+ channels in A6 cells, a regulatory role for protein kinase C. *Am. J. Physiol.* 256:F1094–F1103
64. Loo, D. D. F., Lewis, S. A., Ifshin, M. S., Diamond, J. M. 1983. Turnover, membrane insertion, and degradation of sodium channels in rabbit urinary bladder. *Science* 221:1288–90
65. McCabe, R., Cooke, H. J., Sullivan, L. P., 1982. Potassium transport by rabbit descending colon. *Am. J. Physiol.* 242:C81–C86
66. McCabe, R. D., Smith, P. L., Sullivan, L. P. 1984. Ion transport by rabbit descending colon: mechanisms of transepithelial potassium transport. *Am. J. Physiol.* 246:G594–G602
67. McCann, J. D., Li, M., Welsh, M. J. 1989. Identification and regulation of whole-cell chloride currents in airway epithelium. *J. Gen. Physiol.* 94:1015–1036
68. McCann, J. D., Welsh, M. J. 1990. Regulation of Cl^- and K^+ channels in airway epithelium. *Annu. Rev. Physiol.* 52:115–35
69. McRoberts, J. A., Beuerlein, G., Dharmsathaphorn, K. 1985. Cyclic AMP and Ca^{2+}-activated K^+ transport in a human colonic epithelial cell line. *J. Biol. Chem.* 260:14163–72
70. Miller, C. 1989. Genetic manipulation of ion channels: A new approach to structure and mechanism. *Neuron* 2: 1195–1205
71. O'Neil, R. G. 1987. Adrenal steroid regulation of potassium transport. In *Potassium Transport: Physiology and Pathophysiology,* ed. G. Giebisch, 28:185–206. New York: Academic. 494 pp.
72. Pácha, J., Popp, M., Capek, K. 1987. Amiloride-sensitive sodium transport of the rat distal colon during early postnatal development. *Pflügers Arch.* 409:194–99
73. Pácha, J., Popp, M., Capek, K. 1987. Potassium secretion by neonatal rat distal colon. *Pflügers Arch.* 410:362–68
74. Palmer, L. G., Frindt, G. 1988. Conductance and gating of epithelial Na channels from rat cortical collecting tubule. *J. Gen. Physiol.* 92:121–38
75. Pisam, M., Ripoche, P. 1976. Redistribution of surface macromolecules in dissociated epithelial cells. *J. Cell Biol.* 71:907–20
76. Plass, H., Gridl, A., Turnheim, K. 1986. Absorption and secretion of potassium by rabbit descending colon. *Pflügers Arch.* 406:509–19
77. Post, M. A., Dawson, D. C. 1989. Basolateral Na^+/H^+ exchange and Na^+ conductance in turtle colon: Modulation by cell swelling. *FASEB J.* A549:1637
78. Rask-Madsen, J., Hjelt, K. 1977. Effect of amiloride on electrical activity and electrolyte transport in human colon. *Scand. J. Gastroenterol.* 12:1–6
79. Rechkemmer, G., Halm, D. R. 1989. Aldosterone stimulates K secretion across mammalian colon independent of Na absorption. *Proc. Natl. Acad. Sci. USA* 86:397–401
80. Reinhardt, R., Bridges, R. J., Rummel, W., Lindemann, B. 1987. Properties of anion-selective channel from rat colonic enterocyte plasma membranes reconstituted into planar phospholipid bilayers. *J. Membr. Biol.* 95:47–54
81. Deleted in proof
82. Richards, N. W., Dawson, D. C. 1989. N-phenylanthranilic acid blocks specific classes of K-conducting channels in colonic epithelial cells. *FASEB J.* 3:A1149
83. Sariban-Sohraby, S., Benos, D. J. 1986. The amiloride-sensitive sodium channel. *Am. J. Physiol.* 250:C175–90
84. Schoumacher, R. A., Shoemaker, R. L., Halm, D. R., Tallant, E. A., Wallace, R. W., Frizzell, R. A. 1987. Phosphorylation fails to activate chloride channels from cystic fibrosis airway cells. *Nature* 330:752–54
85. Schultz, S. G. 1984. A cellular model for active sodium absorption by mammalian colon. *Annu. Rev. Physiol.* 46:435–51
86. Sellin, J. H., De Soignie, R. 1987. Ion transport in human colon in vitro. *Gastroenterology* 93:441–48
87. Smith, P. L., McCabe, R. D. 1986. Potassium secretion by rabbit descending colon: effects of adrenergic stimuli. *Am. J. Physiol.* 250:G432–39
88. Smith, P. L., McCabe, R. D. 1984. Mechanism and regulation of transcellular potassium transport by the colon. *Am. J. Physiol.* 247:G445–56
89. Tabcharani, J. A., Jensen, T. J., Rior-

dan, J. R., Hanrahan, J. W. 1989. Bicarbonate permeability of the outwardly rectifying anion channel. *J. Membr. Biol.* 112:109–22

90. Thompson, S. M., Dawson, D. C. 1978. Cation selectivity of the apical membrane of the turtle colon. *J. Gen. Physiol.* 72:269–82
91. Turnheim, K., Costantin, J., Chan, S., Schultz, S. G. 1989. Reconstitution of a calcium-activated potassium channel in basolateral membranes of rabbit colonocytes into planar lipid bilayers. *J. Membr. Biol.* 112:247–54
92. Turnheim, K., Hudson, R. L., Schultz, S. G. 1987. Cell Na^+ activities and transcellular Na^+ absorption by descending colon from normal and Na^+-deprived rabbits. *Pflügers Arch.* 410: 279–83
93. Turnheim, K., Thompson, S. M., Schultz, S. G. 1983. Relation between intracellular sodium and active sodium transport in rabbit colon: Current-voltage relations of the apical sodium entry mechanism in the presence of varying luminal sodium concentrations. *J. Membr. Biol.* 76:299–309
94. Van Driessche, W., Aelvoet, I., Erlij, D. 1987. Oxytocin and cAMP stimulate monovalent cation movements through Ca^{2+}-sensitive, amiloride-sensitive channel in the apical membrane of toad urinary bladder. *Proc. Natl. Acad. Sci. USA* 84:313–17
95. Van Driessche, W., Simaels, J., Aelvoet, I., Erlij, D. 1988. Cation-selective channels in amphibian epithelia: electrophysiological properties and activation. *Comp. Biochem. Physiol. A* 90(4):693–99
96. Van Driessche, W., Wills, N. K., Hillyard, S. D., Zeiske, W. 1982. K^+ channels in an epithelial "single membrane" preparation. *Arch. Int. Physiol. Biochim.* 90:P12–P14
97. Venglarik, C. J., Dawson, D. C. 1987. A cellular Cl shunt pathway in turtle colon: Possible role in regulation of NaCl absorption. *Fed. Proc.* 46:636
98. Venglarik, C. J., Dawson, D.C. 1986. Cholinergic regulation of Na absorption by turtle colon: role of basolateral K conductance. *Am. J. Physiol.* 251: C563–70
99. Venglarik, C. J., Frizzell, R. A. 1990. A simple assay for agonist-regulated Cl and K conductances in salt-secreting epithelial cells. *Am. J. Physiol.* 259: C358–64
100. Venglarik, C. J., Keller, J. L., Dawson, D. C. 1986. Muscarinic inhibition of basolateral conductances to K and Cl in turtle colon: Possible roles for Ca^{++} and cAMP as intracellular mediators. *Fed. Proc.* 45:2083
101. Wangemann, P., Wittner, M., Di Stefano, A., Englert, H. C., Lang, H. J., Schlatter, E., Greger, R. 1986. Cl^--channel blockers in the thick ascending limb of the loop of Henle. Structure activity relationship. *Pflügers Arch.* 407:S128–141
102. Welsh, M. J., Smith, P. L., Fromm, M., Frizzell, R. A. 1982. Crypts are the site of intestinal fluid secretion. *Science* 218:1219–21
103. Wilkinson, D. J., Dawson, D. C. 1990. Cholinergic modulation of apical Na channels in turtle colon: Analysis of CDPC—induced fluctuations. *Am. J. Physiol.* 259:C668–74
104. Wilkinson, D. J., Dawson, D. C. 1989. Cholinergic modulation of apical Na channels in turtle colon: current fluctuation analysis. *FASEB J.* 3:A983
105. Wilkinson, D. J., Dawson, D. C. 1989. Apical K channels in turtle colon: Current fluctuation analysis. *FASEB J.* 4:A447
106. Will, P. C., Cortright, R. N., DeLisle, R. C., Douglas, J. G., Hopfer, U. 1985. Regulation of amiloride-sensitive electrogenic sodium transport in the rat colon by steroid hormones. *Am. J. Physiol.* 248:G124–32
107. Wills, N. K. 1985. Apical membrane potassium and chloride permeabilities in surface cells of rabbit descending colon epithelium. *J. Physiol.* 358:433–45
108. Wills, N. K. 1984. Mechanisms of ion transport by the mammalian colon revealed by frequency domain analysis techniques. *Curr. Top. Membr. Transp.* 20:61–85
109. Wills, N. K. 1981. Antibiotics as tools for studying the electrical properties of tight epithelia. *Fed. Proc.* 40:2202–2205
110. Wills, N. K., Alles, W. P., Sandle, G. I., Binder, H. J. 1984. Apical membrane properties and amiloride binding kinetics of the human descending colon. *Am. J. Physiol.* 247:G749–57
111. Wills, N. K., Biagi, B. 1982. Active potassium transport by rabbit descending colon epithelium. *J. Membr. Biol.* 64:195–203
112. Wills, N. K., Eaton, D. C., Lewis, S. A., Ifshin, M. S. 1979. Current-voltage relationship of the basolateral membrane of a tight epithelium. *Biochim. Biophys. Acta* 555:519–23
113. Wills, N. K., Zeiske, W., Van Driessche, W. 1982. Noise analysis reveals K^+ channel conductance fluctuations

in the apical membrane of rabbit colon. *J. Membr. Biol.* 69:187–97

114. Wills, N. K., Zweifach, A. 1987. Recent advances in the characterization of epithelial ionic channels. *Biochim. Biophys. Acta* 906:1–31
115. Wong, S. M. E., Lindemann, R. P., Parangi, S., Chase, H. S. Jr. 1989. Role of calcium in mediating action of carbachol in T84 cells. *Am. J. Physiol.* 257:C976–85
116. Wong, S. M. E., Tesfaye, A., DeBell, M., Chase, H. S. Jr. Carbachol increases basolateral K^+ conductance in T84 cells: Simultaneous measurements of cell [Ca] and g_k explore calcium's role. *J. Gen. Physiol.* In press
117. Worrell, R. T., Butt, A. G., Cliff, W. H., Frizzell, R. A. 1989. A volume-sensitive chloride conductance in human colonic cell line T84. *Am. J. Physiol.* 256:C1111–19
118. Zeiske, W., Wills, N. K., Van Driessche, W. 1982. Na^+ channels and amiloride-induced noise in the mammalian colon epithelium. *Biochim. Biophys. Acta* 688:201–10
119. Zimmerman, T. W., Dobbins, J. W., Binder, H. J. 1982. Mechanism of cholinergic regulation of electrolyte transport in rat colon in vitro. *Am. J. Physiol.* 242:G116–23

Annu. Rev. Physiol. 1991. 53:341–59

SURFACE CHARGES AND ION CHANNEL FUNCTION

William N. Green

Department of Cellular and Molecular Physiology, Yale University School of Medicine, 333 Cedar Street, New Haven, Connecticut 06510

Olaf S. Andersen

Department of Physiology and Biophysics, Cornell University Medical College, 1300 York Avenue, New York, New York 10021

KEY WORDS: permeation, selectivity, electrostatics, diffusion limitations, substrate steering

---

INTRODUCTION

Like other proteins, ion channels are charged. The amino acid sequence contains acidic and basic amino acids that are positively or negatively charged at physiologic pH. Other charges are added by posttranslational events such as the addition of sialic acid during complex carbohydrate trimming and phosphorylation. At least some of the charges appear to be essential for ion channel function as part of ligand and permeant ion binding sites and as the voltage sensor of voltage-gated channels (e.g. 35).

Surface charges also contribute to channel function in more subtle ways. Any charge on or near the surface of a channel will polarize the surrounding environment, thus establishing an electrostatic potential, i.e. the surface potential, between the channel and aqueous solution (e.g. 54). The surface potential will alter the surrounding ionic atmosphere and change the concentrations of all charged solutes (permeant ions, toxins, or ligands). Oppositely charged solutes (counterions) will be attracted to the charge and

0066-4278/91/0315-0341$02.00

increase their local concentration, while solutes of like charge will be repelled and decrease their concentration (25, 55, 36, 54, 30, 29, 80). In addition, surface potentials will alter the potential difference across the channel. The value of the surface potential will be added to (or subtracted from) the electrostatic potential on one side (or both sides) of the channel. The result is that the surface potential will offset the potential differences across the channel (25, 10, 36). If surface charges are near important functional sites, channel function can be modulated solely through the indirect actions of the surface potential on these sites. Changes in the local solute concentrations will alter the single-channel conductance and the channel's sensitivity to agonists, blocking ions and toxins. The offset in the membrane potential created by the surface potential will alter any voltage-dependent processes such as gating or ion channel block.

The purpose of this review is to summarize the data indicating that ion channel function is affected by electrostatic potentials emanating from surface charges (see also 35, 21). Despite overwhelming evidence for their existence, these charge effects are often overlooked or ignored when interpreting data and constructing models of channel permeation, selectivity and interactions with ligands and toxins. The importance of surface charge for channel gating will not be discussed since it is well established (e.g. 10, 36) and recently reviewed (28). Rather, this review will focus on the evidence that ion permeation is influenced by surface charges.

SOURCE AND DISTRIBUTION OF CHARGE

With the purification of many ion channel proteins and the sequencing of even more ion channel cDNAs and genes, substantial information exists about the types and number of charged groups on ion channels. To address the question "what is the chemical identity of ion channel surface charge?" we briefly examine the amino acid sequences and some posttranslational modifications of three different ion channels: the *Torpedo* nicotinic acetylcholine receptor (AChR), the bovine γ-aminobutyric acid ($GABA_A$) receptor, and the *Electrophorus* voltage-sensitive sodium channel (Table 1). The evidence that charges on phospholipids can affect channel function will also be discussed.

Acidic and Basic Amino Acids

Although amino acid sequences have been obtained, little is known of ion channel secondary and tertiary structure. Models of channel structure are based primarily on hydropathy profiles of deduced amino acid sequences. In these models charged amino acids and other hydrophilic residues are, for the most part, placed at or near the aqueous surfaces, while stretches of hydrophobic amino acids form lipid bilayer spanning α-helices (37, 49, 23).

Table 1 Surface charge estimates for the AChR, $GABA_A$ receptor, and the Na^+ channel

	Amino acid charges			Potential phosphorylation sites			Sialic acid residues (references)
Ligand-gated channels	Total	Extracellular	Intracellular	PKA[a]	PKC[b]	Tyrosine[c]	
Cationic AChR[d]							
α subunit	− 7.5	− 5	−2.5	—	—	—	no (66)
β subunit	− 8.5	− 6.5	−2	—	—	1 (38)	no (66)
γ subunit	−14	−16.5	+2.5	1 (38)	—	1 (38)	yes (66)
δ subunit	− 6.5	−10	+3.5	1 (38)	1 (38)	1 (38)	yes (66)
Anionic GABA receptor[d]							
α subunit	+14	+ 6	+8	—	—	—	N D[e]
β subunit	+11	+ 3.5	+7.5	1 (77)	—	—	N D
γ subunit	+ 9	+ 4	+5	—	—	1 (67)	N D
Voltage-gated channels							
Na^+ channel[f]	−37	ND	ND	3 (22)	—	—	yes; 113 ± 11 (56)

[a] Denotes protein kinase A; [b] denotes protein kinase C; [c] denotes tyrosine kinase.
[d] Total, extracellular and intracellular charge estimates based on the folding model with four membrane spanning α-helices (11, 19, 64). Glutamate and aspartate amino acids were assigned a charge of −1, arginines and lysines a charge of +1, and histadines a charge of +0.5.
[e] Not determined.
[f] Sequence from Noda et al (62).

Table 1 summarizes information on the overall number of charged residues as well as estimates of extra- and intracellular amino acid charges based on current structural models for the AChR (11, 19, 64) and $GABA_A$ receptor (77). The cation-selective AChR and sodium channels are negatively charged and the anion-selective $GABA_A$ receptor postively charged, which implies a role for some of the charge in ion selectivity (77, 85; see below).

Sialic Acid

Sialic acid residues are attached as the last step in the trimming of complex asparagine-linked oligosaccharide chains (47). Carbohydrate is added only to the extracellular domain of membrane proteins and may be a source of surface charge asymmetry. Sialic acids can make sizeable contributions to the net surface charge. The *Electrophorus* sodium channel contains large polysialic acid domains containing ~110 negative charges (56, 42). No function has been established for this negative charge, but its removal by the sialidase, neuraminadase, caused a large shift in the average midpoint potential of channel activation to more depolarized potentials and increased the frequency of the subconductance states of the *Electrophorus* sodium channel (51). The AChR also has a substantial amount of sialic acid on its γ and δ subunits (66), but the amount of charge contributed by sialic acid and its functional significance have not been determined.

Phosphates

All three channels in Table 1 contain potential phosphorylation sites determined from sequence analysis and/or in vitro phosphorylation experiments (38, 77, 67, 22). Protein phosphorylation adds two negative charges to a phosphorylation site on the cytoplasmic surface of the channel. Unlike amino acids and sialic acids, which are permanent fixtures on the polypeptide, phosphorylation is a transient event resulting from the combined actions of cellular kinases and phosphatases. The transient nature of phosphorylation is in keeping with its role in ion channel modulation (43). The established view has been that the covalent attachment of a phosphate group affects function through conformation changes. Recent studies indicate that function also can be affected by a direct electrostatic interaction between the negatively charged phosphate and charged substrates or ligands (83, 39), which suggests that a similar mechanism is possible for ion channels.

Charged Lipids

A net charge on the lipid headgroups in the surrounding bilayer can alter channel function. The single-channel conductance of bilayer-incorporated potassium channels from sarcoplasmic reticulum was increased in negatively charged bilayers and decreased in positively charged bilayers (6). The conductance changes were most prominent at low permeant ion concentrations, which suggests that the lipid charge changes the concentration of permeant ion at the mouth of the channel. The conductance of calcium-activated potassium channels (57) and, to a lesser degree, the L-type calcium channels (12) is also affected by charged lipid. The conductance of voltage-dependent sodium channels was unaffected, which suggests that its channel entrance is farther from the lipid than the other channel types (30). Interestingly, the sodium channel activation curve is affected (14), thus indicating that the voltage sensor lies close to the lipid bilayer.

ELECTROSTATIC POTENTIALS AT THE CHANNEL SURFACES

A precise mapping of the surface potential profile for ion channels is not possible without detailed structural information, which is unavailable. Detailed maps of the surface potentials of soluble proteins have been constructed, however, using high-resolution structures available for these proteins. These surface potential profiles show features that ion channels may have in common with soluble proteins.

Lessons from Soluble Enzymes

Charged residues are unevenly distributed over the surface of soluble proteins and clusters of charge are common (e.g. 82). The electrostatic potential thus varies with position over the protein surface, and the surface potential is a local, not a global, descriptor of the protein's electrostatic behavior. Detailed electrostatic maps, constructed using the Poisson-Boltzmann equation (e.g. 46), confirm that the electrostatic potential varies widely along the surface of the protein.

Functionally charge clusters near the enzyme active site seem to steer substrate flow towards and into the site (61). In this way, local charges affect the binding of substrates to the active site of subtilisin (74), calbindin (53), acetylcholine esterase (65), and Cu, Zn-superoxide dismutase (13). Substrate steering to Cu, Zn-superoxide dismutase is particularly well-characterized (26). At physiologic pH, these enzymes have many more negative than positive charges (75), which should produce an electrostatic barrier for the substrate O_2^-. Nonetheless, the catalytic (association) rate constant decreases as ionic strength increases (13), which indicates that O_2^- is attracted to the active site (and that no electrostatic barrier exists). A cluster of positively charged lysines at the entrance of the active site pocket appears to attract O_2^- (82, 46). Removing these charges through an acetylation reaction decreases the catalytic rate (13). After acetylation, the rate constant increases with ionic strength thus indicating that not only is the electrostatic attraction eliminated, but O_2^- is repelled from the modified enzyme.

Approximate Descriptions

In the absence of detailed structural information, the electrostatics of ion channels are usually described by one of two limiting models: the Gouy-Chapman theory of the diffuse double layer, or the Debye-Hückel theory of ionic solutions. For either model, the distribution of the ions (and thus the electrostatic potential profile) is calculated by balancing the electrostatic interactions between surface charge and ions in solution with the tendency of the ions to diffuse from high to low concentrations. At equilibrium the local concentrations are given by the Boltzmann equation:

$$[I] = [I]_b \cdot \exp(-z_i \cdot e \cdot V_s / kT) \qquad 1.$$

where $[I]_s$ and $[I]_b$ are the surface and bulk concentrations, respectively, V_s the surface potential, z_i the valence of the ion, e the elementary charge, k Boltzmann's constant, and T the temperature in Kelvin. Ions of the same charge as the surface charge are repelled from the channel, and $[I]_s$ will be less than $[I]_b$. Ions of opposite charge are attracted to the channel, and $[I]_s$ will be larger than $[I]_b$.

In the Gouy-Chapman theory, a channel's surface charges are assumed to be uniformly distributed (smeared) over a planar surface of infinite area. The relation between the surface potential (V_s), the charge density (σ), and the aqueous electrolyte composition is given by (e.g. 48)

$$\sigma = A \cdot \left\{ \sum_i [I]_i \cdot [\exp(-z_i \cdot e \cdot V_s/kT) - 1] \right\}^{0.5}, \qquad 2.$$

where the constant $A = (2 \cdot kT \cdot \epsilon_o \cdot \epsilon_r)^{0.5}$, ϵ_o is the permitivity of free space, ϵ_r the relative dielectric constant, $[I]_i$ and z_i the concentration and valence of ion species i.

In the Debye-Hückel theory, the surface charge is assumed to be distributed over a conducting, impenetrable sphere of radius a and valence z_s. The potential at the surface of the sphere is given by (e.g. 48).

$$V_s = z_s \cdot e/[4 \cdot \epsilon_o \cdot \epsilon_r \cdot a \cdot (1 + a/L_D)], \qquad 3.$$

where the Debye length, $L/_D = [(2 \cdot e/A)/\Sigma[I]_i \cdot z_i^2]^{0.5}$, is a measure of how far into the solution the potential change extends.

The magnitude of the surface potential (and the Debye length) decreases with increasing ionic strength. The reduction in surface potential is caused by shielding or screening of surface charges by the increased concentration of counterions nearby. Since ionic strength ($\Sigma[I]_i \cdot z_i^2$) increases as a second order function of an ion's valence (z_i), divalent or multivalent ions will be much more effective than monovalent ions at screening surface charges. At very high ionic strength both models predict that the surface potential approaches O mV and $[I]_s$ approaches $[I]_b$. The essential difference between the models occurs when the ionic strength approaches zero. According to the Gouy-Chapman theory (Equation 2), V_s will approach $\pm\infty$ in such a way that the interfacial counterion concentrations approach finite limiting values (e.g. 54). In contrast, the Debye-Hückel theory (Equation 3) predicts that V_s will approach $z_s \cdot e/(4 \cdot \pi \cdot \epsilon_o \cdot \epsilon_r \cdot a)$, and the interfacial counterion concentrations will approach zero.

Either model represents a simplification, but they nevertheless provide semi-quantitative estimates on the importance of surface potentials on channel function (see below). The most glaring deficiency is the neglect of structural features. Recently, models incorporating more realistic structural detail have been proposed (15, 7). For example, low resolution structural data for the AChR show that the extracellular entrance to the channel has an unusual topology. The entrance consists of a large funnel that extends out ~65 Å perpendicular to the plane of the membrane (45, 84). Electrostatic potentials at the channel entrances will be enhanced by this funnel shape (15). The electric field, believed to arise from rings of negative charge at the bottom of the funnel (40), is concentrated by the funnel walls and steers permeant ions to the channel entrance and thus increases the local cation concentration.

PERMEATION

Overcoming Diffusion Limitations

The primary function of ion channels is to provide selective yet rapid ion movement. The rates at which ions pass through a channel are limited by physical constraints. Ions cannot enter a channel faster than allowed by diffusion, which rate limits the approach to the channel entrance to 10^8–10^9(m sec)$^{-1}$. Still, channels achieve ion translocation rates on the order of 10^7–10^8 (sec)$^{-1}$ (35), values close to the diffusion-limited constraint, given the physiologic concentrations of permeant ions such as K^+,Na^+, and Cl^-. Such high translocation rates suggest that ions pass through the channels as fast as they reach the entrance. Interactions between ions and channel thus appear to be limited, and the channel has little time to discriminate among different ions. How then can a channel interact with and select among different ions if ion translocation is so fast?

Like other proteins, ion channels are subject to evolutionary, selective pressures to maximize function. Nature has molded the design of soluble enzymes to maximize the rate of catalysis (1). In a similar way, ion channels have evolved to deal with the problem of diffusion limitations and allow both maximal ion translocation rates and ion specificity. A major structural adaptation may be the large funnel-shaped entrances that are found in the AChR (45, 84) and in voltage-dependent sodium channels (18). It has been proposed that funnel-shaped entrances serve to increase the capture radius for incoming ions as compared to channels with long narrow pores (50). An increased capture radius will increase the overall translocation rate across the channel, but it will not increase the rate at which ions can access the region where the channel protein narrows and interacts with ions. In fact, the steric constraints imposed by a funnel will decrease the rate at which an ion diffuses to this part of the channel (76). If, however, the funnel is endowed with means to concentrate incoming ions, such as negative charge for a cation-selective channel, the funnel will increase ion access to the pore (2). In short, for a funnel-shaped entrance to increase ion access to a channel it must contain charges.

The question of how charges in the funnel affect the conductance has been analyzed (15). The low-dielectric protein walls of the funnel serve to constrain the field lines, and guide the ions down towards fixed charges at the entrance to the narrow region of the channel. These charges serve a similar function as the charges at the entrance to the active site channel in soluble enzymes. A charged channel entrance is thus similar to a charged catalytic site on a soluble enzyme, by increasing ion entry through an increase in the local ion concentration.

Evidence that Ion Channel Conductance is Increased by Surface Charge

Here we review experimental evidence that surface charges on ion channels enhance ion permeation and discuss problems involved in interpreting these data. The information is categorized by experimental technique. We start with the most general evidence that surface charges affect permeation and move through experiments designed to specify the chemical identity of the charged groups and their location on the polypeptide.

Changing Ionic Strength: Screening Surface Charge

CONDUCTANCE-CONCENTRATION RELATION: DEVIATIONS FROM SIMPLE SATURATION Surface potentials vary as a function of the ionic strength of the surrounding solution (see above). Increasing the ionic strength screens surface charge, which reduces the magnitude of the surface potential and the distance over which it affects permeating (or blocking) ions. Measurements of conductance as a function of the concentration of permeant and impermeant ions is, in principle, a simple test for surface charge effects on conductance. In the absence of electrostatic effects, the conductance-concentration relation for a singly occupied channel is described by a Michaelis-Menten curve (33, 34)

$$g = g_{max}/(1 + Kg/[\text{permeant ion}]), \qquad 4.$$

where g is the channel conductance, g_{max} is the maximal conductance value, and K_g is the permeant ion concentration at half-maximal conductance.

The conductance of AChRs (16) and batrachotoxin-modified sodium channels (30) deviate considerably from the simple rectangular hyperbola predicted by Equation 4. When ionic strength is varied by changing permeant ion concentration, the single-channel conductance at low permeant ion concentrations (20–100 mM) is larger than expected and is almost independent of concentration (see Figure 1). This is the behavior expected if negative charges are increasing permeant ion concentrations at the channel entrances. The conductance-concentration relation is well-described by several electrostatic models relating variations in bath concentrations with changes in the electrostatic potential at the channel entrances (15, 30, 7). Similar experiments on inward rectifying potassium channels (44), L-type calcium channels (69), and calcium-activated potassium channels (52) have led to similar conclusions about the existence of fixed charges near the entrances of these channels.

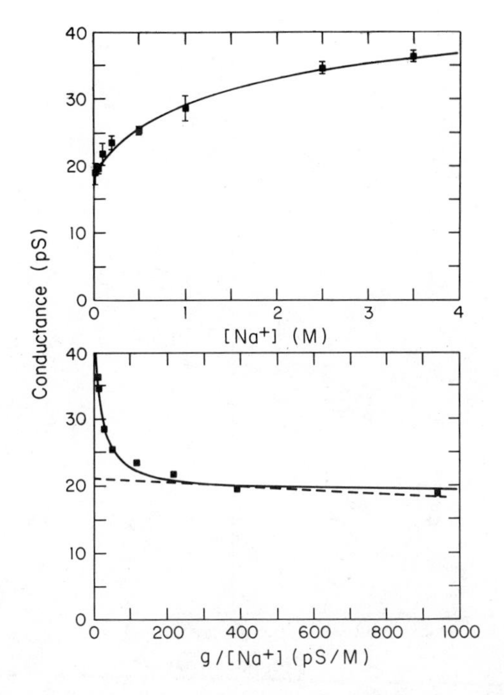

Figure 1 Single-channel conductance of batrachotoxin-modified sodium channels as a function of Na^+ concentration. *(top)* Conductance-[Na^+] relation for channels in phosphatidylethanolamine : phosphatidylcholine (4 : 1) membranes (no net charge). The points denote means ±S.D. The curve is a fit of Equations 1, 2, and 4 to the results assuming g_{max} = 45 pS; K_g = 1.5 M, and σ = 0.38 $e{\cdot}nm^{-2}$. *(bottom)* An Eadie-Hofstee plot of the same data. The *solid line* is a transform of the curve above. The *dotted line* is a nonlinear least-squares fit of Equation 4 to the results for 20 mM ≤ [Na^+] ≤ 100 mM, assuming σ = 0; g_{max} = 21 pS; and K_g = 3 mM. Reproduction from Green et al (30), *J. Gen. Physiol.* 1987. 89: 841–872, by copyright permission from The Rockefeller University Press.

For most of the channels, the negative charges must reside on the channel itself, not on the lipid. This is known for sodium channels and calcium-activated potassium channels since the channels were incorporated into planar bilayers composed of lipids carrying no net charge. For the AChR, the extracellular channel entrance is 6–7 nm from the membrane surface (84), too far for lipid charges to significantly affect permeant ions entering the AChR.

Additional evidence that surface charges increase channel conductance is obtained by measuring the conductance-concentration relation at constant ionic strength. Changing permeant ion concentrations at a constant ionic strength will keep the electrostatic potential profile constant, and the conductance-concentration relation should conform to the predictions of Equation 4. When the ionic strength was held constant, using the impermeant ion

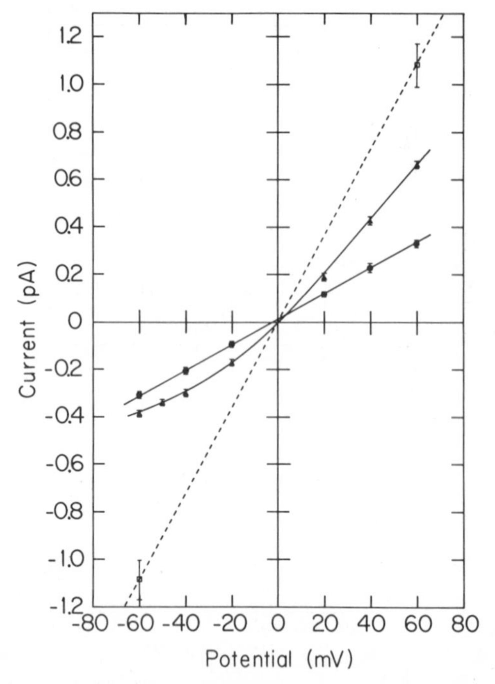

Figure 2 Effects of Ba^{2+} on the single-channel current of batrachotoxin-modified sodium channels. (Δ) i-*V* relation in symmetrical 20 mM Na^{+} with 5 mM Ba^{2+} added to the extracellular solution. (O) i-V relation in symmetrical 20 mM Na^{+} with 5 mM Ba^{2+} added to both solutions. The *dashed line* represents the average i-*V* relation in 20 mM Na^{+} in the absence of Ba^{2+}. Reproduction from Green et al (30) *J. Gen. Physiol.*, 1987. 89: 841–872, by copyright permission from The Rockefeller University Press.

TEA^{+}, the deviations from the ideal conductance-concentration relation for sodium (30) and L-type calcium channels (69) disappeared.

CHANGING DIVALENT CATION CONCENTRATION: CHANNEL BLOCK OR SCREENING OF SURFACE CHARGE. Changes in divalent cation concentration alter negative surface potentials to a much larger extent than the same change in monovalent cation concentration (see above). Another test for surface charge effects on conductance, therefore, has been to vary divalent cation concentrations. But divalent cations also can bind within the pore and block the channel (e.g. 86). Under certain experimental conditions, channel current reductions caused by divalent cation screening of surface charge and channel block are indistinguishable. This difficulty is illustrated in Figure 2 where the addition of 5 mM Ba^{2+} reduces the sodium channel conductance. When Ba^{2+} is added only to the extracellular solution *(closed triangles)*, the current-voltage (i-*V*) relation rectifies as if the Ba^{2+} causes a voltage-dependent block. When Ba^{2+} is applied symmetrically, however, the i-*V* relation is linear *(closed circles),* and the conductance is reduced by 70%. In contrast, symmetric application of the extracellular channel blockers Zn^{2+} and Ca^{2+} causes much larger reductions in the inward going current than in the outward current (58, 30).

The symmetry of the Ba^{2+}-induced current reduction suggests that Ba^{2+} does not block the sodium channel, but simply screens surface charges at the channel entrances. According to this interpretation, the Ba^{2+}-induced i-*V* rectification is caused by a combination of reduced local permeant ion concentration at the extracellular entrance and an offset of the transmembrane potential (25). Even this interpretation is too simple. At the concentrations Zn^{2+} and Ca^{2+} block the channel, they also must be screening surface charge. Further, divalent cations can directly bind to surface charges and reduce the charge density in addition to screening (e.g. 36). Conversely, it is likely that Ba^{2+} blocks the channel to some extent. Screening (along with binding to) charges and channel block are thus two extremes in a continuum.

At the single-channel level, block can be distinguished from screening by resolving discrete blocking events (59), or channel flicker caused by the blocker (88). When discrete blocking events are not evident, screening and block, in principle, can be distinguished by the shape and position of the dose-response curve for a suspected blocker on the channel conductance. With increasing concentration an impermeant blocker will reduce the conductance to zero over a concentration range highly dependent on the chemical identity of the blocker. If only screening is involved, the conductance decrease will approach a nonzero value (Figure 3) and the dose-response curve will be independent of the ion used. (The dose-response curve will vary with the ion species if the ion is binding to the surface charges.) This test was used to demonstrate the surface charge effects on AChR conductance. Increasing Ca^{2+}, Ba^{2+}, Sr^{2+}, or Mg^{2+} concentrations over the same range equally reduced the AChR single-channel conductance by only one half (41). Increasing divalent cation concentrations at inward rectifying (44) and calcium-activated potassium channels (52; Figure 3) yielded similar results and conclusions.

Changing pH: Neutralizing Surface Charge

Another approach is to study conductance as a function of pH. This relation can provide some information about the chemical identity of the surface charge. Lowering or raising pH will titrate acidic and basic groups that contribute to ion channel surface charge. One or more proton dissociation curves are fit in relation to those obtained from the changes in conductance as a function of pH (32, 27, 60, 36). The curve fit yields characteristic pK_a values that provide clues as to the chemical nature of the charge groups. The

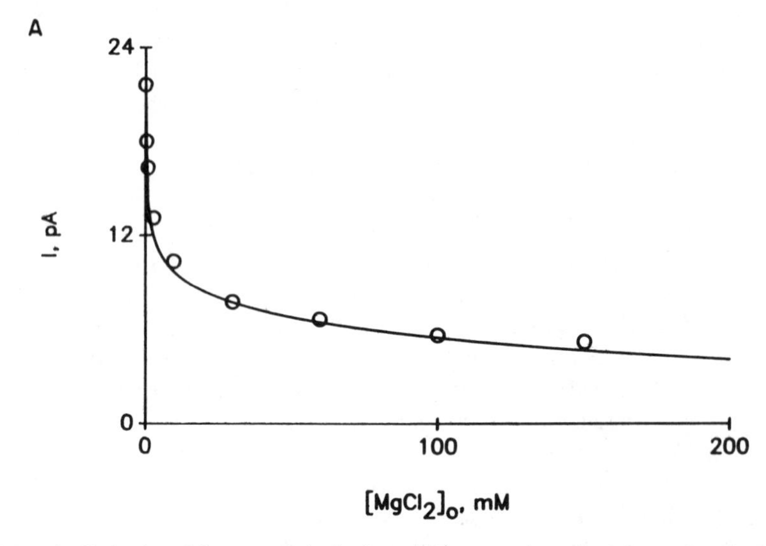

Figure 3 Reduction of the outward single-channel K^+ current through calcium-activated potassium channels by Mg^{2+}. The intracellular solution contained 150 mM KCl and the extracellular solution 4 mM MOPS-NaOH, pH 7.4, plus the indicated $[Mg^{2+}]$. Reproduction from MacKinnon et al (52), *Biochemistry* 1989, 28: 8092–8099, by copyright permission from the Am. Chem. Soc.

sodium channel conductance, for example, is reduced by lowering the extracellular pH (32). The data were well fit by a single H^+ dissociation curve with a pK_a of 5.2, which suggests that an acidic group is important for sodium channel conductance. In subsequent studies it was debated whether protons titrate surface charge at the channel entrance (32, 20, 8), or charge within the channel thus resulting in a voltage-dependent block (86, 8). It is experimentally difficult to distinguish between these two possibilities, and they are not mutually exclusive (17; see above).

Chemical Modifications: Eliminating Surface Charge Using Group Specific Agents

The chemical identity of surface charge groups can be probed using group-specific chemical reagents. Extracellular application of the carboxyl-specific reagents, carbodiimides, to sodium channels abolishes the channels' sensitivity to tetrodotoxin (78, 5, 71). Another carboxyl-specific reagent, trimethyloxonium (TMO), abolishes tetrodotoxin sensitivity and also reduces the single-channel conductance without affecting selectivity (81, 79, 31, 87). The latter results suggest that one or more carboxyl groups lie at the extracellular channel entrance where they contribute to the negative surface charge. Carbodiimides can reduce the single-channel conductance without altering tetrodotoxin sensitivity (9), further indicating that some of the carboxyl groups involved in the conductance change differ from those affecting tetrodotoxin sensitivity.

TMO modification of calcium-activated potassium channel conductance indicates that carboxyl groups are contributing to the electrostatic potential at that channel entrance (52). It was concluded that more than a single carboxyl group is involved because the single-channel conductance decrease occurred in discrete steps. The TMO effect on conductance depended on ionic strength. At low ionic strength, TMO caused a marked decrease in conductance, and a progressively smaller effect occurred with increasing ionic strength.

Site-Directed Mutations: Adding or Removing Specific Surface Charges

Specific charges that affect channel conductance have been identified using methods that alter the ion channel amino acid sequence. This approach was first applied to gramicidin A channels, which long have served as prototypical transmembrane ion channels (3). At the channel entrance, pyromellitic acid was attached to the ethanolamine, which is part of the carboxyl terminus of the peptide (4). This modification added three negative charges at the channel entrance. The single-channel conductance was increased at low permeant ion concentrations, but not at high concentrations, consistent with an increase in permeant ion concentration resulting from the negative charge. Essentially similar results were obtained with desethanolamine gramicidin A, which has a free carboxyl group at the entrance (72), and [taurine^{16}] gramicidin A, where the neutral ethanolamine has been replaced with the sulfur amino acid taurine (73).

Specific charge groups serving a similar function on AChRs have been located using recombinant DNA methods. A series of point mutations were performed that removed negatively charged amino acids thought to be situated at the extracellular and intracellular mouths of the AChR channel (40). Three sets of negatively charged amino acids, located on homologous positions on each of the four AChR subunits, were mutated by substituting neutral or positively charged amino acids. Because of the pentameric symmetry of the AChR, these acidic amino acids are thought to form rings of negative charge around the channel entrances. The results of the single-channel current measurements of the mutated AChRs support this structural hypothesis and are consistent with the charge rings increasing permeant ion concentrations through electrostatic interactions. Mutations in the extracellular ring of charge reduced the cell-inward current, and mutations in an intracellular ring reduced the cell-outward current. Each decrease in negative charge caused a decrease in current. The decrease depended primarily on the charge of the substituted amino acid, and to a lesser extent on its size and the subunit on which it was located. Additionally, the mutated channels were much less sensitive to the effects of divalent cations.

A single point mutation, changing a glutamate to glutamine, dramatically reduces the sodium channel's sensitivity to tetrodotoxin and decreases the cell inward current substantially more than the outward going current (63). The latter result indicates that the mutated glutamate could be near the extracellular channel entrance where it contributes to a negative electrostatic potential.

Is Channel Conformation Altered?

The experimental manipulations described above (changes in ionic strength, composition, or pH, chemical modifications or site-directed mutations) may impose strains on the channel structure. Conductance changes resulting from these manipulations may, therefore, be caused by changes in channel conformation instead of changes in the surface potential. Among the evidence that conformational changes can occur is the observation of single-channel subconductance states. At high ionic strength (1.0–3.5 M), batrachotoxin-modified sodium channels from dog brain exhibit a subconductance state about 20% of the size of the fully open state (30). A similar subconductance state is observed when Zn^{2+} is added to batrachotoxin-modified sodium channels from dog heart (70). Increasing the Zn^{2+} concentration causes the channel to spend progressively more time in a subconductance state, 15–25% as large as its fully open state. While these examples are most likely caused by conformational changes, it is possible that they result from changes in surface charge at the channel entrance. This is not the case for a subconductance state of the L-type calcium channel. A subconductance state, 25% as large as the fully open state, is observed when extracellular pH is lowered (68). A similar ion concentration dependence for both the fully open and subconductance state indicates that the subconductance state does not occur when surface charge at the channel entrance is titrated (69).

Subconductance states appear in many channel types. To the extent that their frequency is affected by changes in ionic composition (or the other experimental changes listed above), it is important to distinguish between conductance changes that are the direct result of changes in surface potential from those that result from channel conformational changes.

Relevance to Channel Selectivity

Charged groups at the entrance of an ion channel are a structural feature that helps determine whether a channel is cationic or anionic. A negatively charged entrance will increase the cation to anion concentration ratio at the entrance; a positively charged entrance will have the opposite effect. (As an example, a potential of –80 mV at the entrance will increase cation concentration over anion concentration by 400-fold, or vice-versa if the potential is + 80 mV.) Early evidence for the importance of this mechanism came from experiments on polyene-doped planar bilayers (24). Additional evidence in support of such a selection mechanism comes from a comparison of the charged regions at the entrance of the cationic AChR (40) with their structural counterparts from the anionic $GABA_A$ receptor (see Table 1). At both its extracellular and intracellular entrances, the *Torpedo* AChR is thought to have rings containing three negative charges. In the corresponding positions on the $GABA_A$ receptor (77, 67) there are at least seven positive charges at the extracellular entrance (α: +2, β: +2, γ: +3) and two positive charges at the intracellular entrance (α: +1, β: 0, γ: +1). Thus, the cation selective AChR has negatively charged entrances, and the anion selective $GABA_A$ receptor has positively charged entrances.

CONCLUSIONS

There is substantial evidence that ion permeation (and possibly ion selectivity) of many channels is enhanced by charges at the channel entrances. A striking parallel exists between the effect of these channel surface charges and the charges on soluble enzymes that steer substrate into the enzyme's active site. In both cases the effects of strategically located charge groups suggest that they result from evolutionary adaptations to overcome diffusion limited access to either the channel entrance or the enzyme active site. Given the very high ion translocation rates exhibited by ion channels, we believe that most, if not all, ion channels use surface charges to increase the rate in which ions enter the channel. Charge clusters at the entrances of ion channels, therefore, should be a common structural motif and could provide a landmark for locating a channel's entrance within its amino acid sequence.

ACKNOWLEDGMENTS

We thank Dr. E. Moczydlowski for providing data prior to publication. Preparation of this review was supported by a Osserman/McClure Fellowship from the Myasthenia Gravis Foundation (WNG) and National Institutes of Health grant GM40062 (OSA).

Literature Cited

1. Albery, W. J., Knowles, J. K. 1976. Evolution of enzyme function and the development of catalytic efficiency. *Biochemistry* 15:5631–40
2. Andersen, O. S. 1983. Ion movement through gramicidin A channels. Studies on the diffusion-controlled step. *Biophys. J.* 41:119–33
3. Andersen, O. S. 1984. Gramicidin channels. *Annu. Rev. Physiol.* 46:531–48
4. Apell, H., Bamberg, E., Alpes, H., Lauger, P. 1977. Formation of ion channels by a negatively charged analog of gramicidin A. *J. Memb. Biol.* 31:171–88
5. Baker, P. F., Rubinson, K. A. 1975. Chemical modification of crab nerves can make them insensitive to the local anaesthetics tetrodotoxin and saxitoxin. *Nature* 257:412–14
6. Bell, J., Miller, C. 1984. Effects of phospholipid surface charge on ion conduction in the K channel from sarcoplasmic recticulum. *Biophys. J.* 45:279–87
7. Cai, M., Jordan, P. C. 1990. How does

vestibule surface charge affect ion conductance and toxin binding in a Na channel? *Biophys. J.* 57:883–91
8. Cambell, D. T. 1982. Do protons block Na^+ channels by binding to a site outside the pore? *Nature* 298:165–67
9. Chabala, L. S., Green, W. N., Andersen, O. S., Borders, C. L. 1986. Covalent modification of external carboxyl groups of batrachotoxin-modified canine forebrain sodium channels. *Biophys. J.* 49:40a
10. Chandler, W. K., Hodgkin, A. L., Meves, H. 1965. The effect of changing the internal solution on sodium inactivation and related phenomena in giant axons. *J. Physiol.* 180:821–36
11. Claudio, T., Ballivet, M., Patrick, J., Heinemann, S. 1983. Nucleotide and deduced amino acid sequences of the *Torpedo californica* acetylcholine receptor γ subunit. *Proc. Natl. Acad. Sci. USA* 80:1111–15
12. Coronado, R., Affolter, H. 1986. Insulation of the conductance pathway of muscle transverse tubule calcium channels from the surface charge of the bilayer phospholipid. *J. Gen. Physiol.* 87:933–53
13. Cudd, A., Fridovich, I. 1982. Electrostatic interactions in the reaction mechanism of bovine erythrocyte superoxide dismutase. *J. Biol. Chem.* 257: 11443–47
14. Cukierman, S., Zinkand, W. C., French, R. J., Krueger, B. K. 1988. Effects of membrane surface charge and calcium on the gating of rat brain sodium channels in planar bilayers. *J. Gen. Physiol.* 92:431–47
15. Dani, J. A. 1986. Ion-channel entrances influence permeation. Net charge, size, shape, and binding considerations. *Biophys. J.* 49:607–618
16. Dani, J., Eisenman, G. 1987. Monovalent and divalent cation permeation in acetylcholine receptor channels. Ion transport related to structure. *J. Gen. Physiol.* 89:959–83
17. Daumas, P., Andersen, O. S. 1990. Effect of pH on the conductance and guanidinium toxin affinity of sodium channel from rat brain. *FASEB J.* 4: A12100
18. Denim, V. V., Grishkin, E. V., Kovalenko, V. A., Spadar, S. N. 1986. Electron microscopy studies of the fast sodium channel structure. In *Chemistry of Peptides and Proteins,* ed. W. Voelter, E. Bayer, Y. A. Ovchinnikov, V. T. Ivanov, pp. 363–370. Berlin: de Gruyter
19. Devillers-Thiery, A., Giraudat, J., Bentaboulet, M., Changeaux, J.-P. 1983. Complete mRNA coding sequence of the acetylcholine binding α-subunit of *Torpedo marmorata* acetylcholine receptor: a model for the transmembrane organization of the polypeptide chain. *Proc. Natl. Acad. Sci. USA* 80:2067–71
20. Drouin, H., Neumcke, B. 1974. Specific and unspecific charges at the sodium channels of the nerve membrane. *Pflügers Arch.* 351:207–29
21. Eisenman, G., Dani, J. A. 1987. An introduction to molecular architecture and permeability of ionic channels. *Annu. Rev. Biophys. Biophys. Chem.* 16:205–26
22. Emerick, M., Agnew, W. 1989. Identification of phosphorylation sites for adenosine 3',5'-cyclic phosphate-dependent protein kinase on the voltage-sensitive sodium channel from *Electrophorus electricus. Biochemistry* 28: 8367–80
23. Engelman, D. M., Steitz, T. A., Goldman, A. 1986. Identifying nonpolar transbilayer helices in amino acid sequences of membrane proteins. *Annu. Rev. Biophys. Biophys. Chem.* 15:321–53
24. Finkelstein, A., Holz, R. 1973. Aqueous pores created in thin lipid membranes by the polyene antibiotics nyastatin and amphotericin B. In *Lipid Bilayers and Antibiotics,* ed. G. Eisenman, pp. 377–408. New York: Dekker
25. Frankenhaeuser, B. 1960. Sodium permeability in toad nerve and in squid nerve. *J. Physiol.* 152:159–66
26. Fridovich, I. 1989, Superoxide dismutase: an adaptation to a paramagnetic gas. *J. Biol. Chem.* 264:7761–64
27. Gilbert, D. L., Ehrenstein, G. 1970. Use of a fixed charge model to determine the pK of the negative sites on the external membrane surface. *J. Gen. Physiol.* 55:822–25
28. Gilbert, D. L., Ehrenstein, G. 1984. Membrane surface charge. *Curr. Top. Memr. Trans.* 22:407–21
29. Green, W. N., Weiss, L. B., Andersen, O. S. 1987. Batrachotoxin-modified sodium channels in planar bilayers: characterization of saxitoxin- and tetrodotoxin-induced channel closures. *J. Gen. Physiol.* 89:873–903
30. Green, W. N., Weiss, L. B., Andersen, O. S. 1987. Batrachotoxin-modified sodium channels in planar bilayers: ion permeation and block. *J, Gen. Physiol.* 89:841–72
31. Gulden, K. M., Vogel, W. 1985. Three functions of sodium channels in the toad node of Ranvier are altered by trimetho-

xonium ions. *Pflügers Arch.* 401:13–20
32. Hille, B. 1968. Pharmacological modifications of the sodium channels of frog nerve. *J. Gen. Physiol.* 51:199–219
33. Hille, B. 1975. Ionic selectivity of Na and K channels of nerve membranes. In *Membranes—A Series of Advances,* ed. G. Eisenman, pp. 255–323. New York: Dekker
34. Hille, B. 1975. Ionic selectivity, saturation, and block in sodium channels. A four-barrier model. *J. Gen. Physiol.* 66: 535–60
35. Hille, B. 1984. *Ionic Channels of Excitable Membranes.* Sunderland, MA: Sinauer. 426 pp.
36. Hille, B., Woodhull, A. M., Shapiro, B. I. 1975. Negative surface charge near the sodium channels of nerve: divalent ions, monovalent ions, and pH. *Philos. Trans. R. Soc. London Ser. B* 270:301–18
37. Hopp, T. P., Woods, K. R. 1981. Prediction of protein antigenic determinants from amino acid sequence. *Proc. Natl. Acad. Sci. USA* 78:3824–28
38. Huganir, R. L., Miles, K., Greengard, P. 1984. Phosphorylation of the nicotinic acetylcholine receptor by an endogenous tyrosine-specific protein kinase. *Proc. Natl. Acad. Sci. USA* 81:6968–72
39. Hurley, J. H., Dean, A. M., Thorsness, P. E., Koshland, D. E., Stroud, R. M. 1990. Regulation of isocitrate dehydrogenase by phosphorylation involves no long-range conformational change in the free enzyme. *J. Biol. Chem.* 265:3599–3602
40. Imoto, K., Busch, C., Sackmann, B., Mishina, M., Konno, T., et al. 1988. Rings of negatively charged amino acids determine the acetylcholine receptor conductance. *Nature* 335:645–48
41. Imoto, K., Methfessel, C., Sackmann, B., Mishina, M., Mori, Y., et al. 1986. Location of a δ-subunit region determining transport through the acetylcholine receptor channel. *Nature* 324:670–74
42. James, W., Agnew, W. 1987. Multiple oligosaccharide chains in the voltage-sensitive Na channel from *Electrophorus electricus:* evidence for alpha-2,8-linked polysialic acid. *Biochem. Biophys. Res. Commun.* 148:817–26
43. Kaczmarek, L. K., Levitan, I. B. 1987. *Neuromodulation: The Biochemical Control of Neuronal Excitability.* Oxford: Oxford Univ. Press. 286 pp.
44. Kell, M. J., DeFelice, L. J. 1988. Surface charge near the cardiac inward-rectifier channel measured from single-channel conductance. *J. Membr. Biol.* 102:1–10
45. Kistler, J., Stroud, R. M., Klymkowsky, M. W., Lalancette, R. A., Fairclough, R. H. 1982. Structure and function of an acetylcholine receptor. *Biophys. J.* 37:371–83
46. Klapper, I., Hagstrom, R., Fine, R., Sharp, K., Honig, B. 1986. Focusing of electric fields in the active site of Cu-Zn superoxide dismutase: effects of ionic strength and amino-acid modification. *Proteins: Structure, Function, and Genetics.* 1:47–59
47. Kornfeld, R., Kornfeld, S. 1985. Assembly of asparagine-linked oligosaccharides. *Annu. Rev. Biochem.* 54:631–64
48. Koryta, J., Dvorak, J. 1987. *Principles of Electrochemistry.* New York: Wiley. 426 pp.
49. Kyte, J., Doolittle, R. F. 1982. A simple method for displaying the hydropathic character of a protein. *J. Mol. Biol.* 157:105–132
50. Latorre, R., Miller, C. 1983. Conduction and selectivity in potassium channels. *J. Membr. Biol.* 71:11–30
51. Levinson, S. R., Thornhill, W. B., Duch, D. S., Recio-Pinto, E., Urban, B. W. 1990. The role of nonprotein domains in the function and synthesis of voltage-gated sodium channels. In *Ion Channels,* ed. T. Narahashi, pp. 33–64. New York: Plenum
52. MacKinnon, R., Latorre, R., Miller, C. 1989. Role of surface electrostatics in the operation of a high-conductance Ca^{2+}-activated K^+ channel. *Biochemistry* 28:8092–99
53. Martin, S. R., Linse, S., Johansson, C., Bayley, P. M., Fosen, S. 1990. Protein surface charges and Ca^{2+} binding to individual sites in calbindin D_{9k} stopped-flow studies. *Biochemistry* 29:4188–93
54. McLaughlin, S. 1977. Electrostatic potentials at membrane-solution interphases. *Curr. Top. Membr. Trans.* 9: 71–144
55. McLaughlin, S. G. A., Szabo, G., Eisenman, G. 1971. Divalent ions and the surface potential of charged phospholipid membranes. *J. Gen. Physiol.* 58:667–87
56. Miller, J. A., Agnew, W. S., Levinson, S. R. 1983. Principle glycopeptide of the tetrodotoxin/saxitoxin binding protein from *Electrophorus electricus:* Isolation and partial physical and chemical characterization. *Biochemistry* 22: 462–70
57. Moczydlowski, E., Alvarez, O., Vegara, C., Latorre, R. 1985. Effect of

phospholipid surface charge on the conductance and gating of a Ca^{2+}-activated K^+ channel in lipid bilayers. *J. Membr. Biol.* 83:273–82

58. Moczydlowski, E., Uehara, A., Guo, X., Heiny, J. 1986. Isochannels and blocking modes of voltage-dependent sodium channels. *Ann. NY Acad. Sci.* 479:269–92
59. Neher, E., Steinbach, J. H. 1978. Local anaesthetics transiently block currents through single acetylcholine-receptor channels. *J. Physiol.* 277:153–76
60. Nelson, A. P., Colonomos, P., McQuarrie, D. A. 1975. Electrostatic coupling across a membrane with titratable surface groups. *J. Theor. Biol.* 50:317–25
61. Neuman, E. 1981. Dynamics of molecular recognition in enzyme-catalysed reactions. In *Structural and Functional Aspects of Enzyme Catalysis,* ed. H. Eggerer, R. Huber, pp. 45–58. Berlin: Springer-Verlag
62. Noda, M., Shimizu, S., Tanabe, T., Takai, T., Kayano, T., et al. 1984. Primary structure of *Electrophorus electricus* sodium channel deduced from cDNA sequence. *Nature* 312:121–27
63. Noda, M., Suzuki, H., Numa, S., Stuhmer, W. 1989. A single point mutation confers tetrodotoxin and saxitoxin insensitivity on the sodium channel II. *FEBS Lett.* 259:213–16
64. Noda, M., Takahashi, H., Tanabe, T., Toyosato, M., Kikyotani, S., et al. 1983. Structural homology of *Torpedo californica* acetylcholine receptor subunits. *Nature* 302:528–32
65. Nolte, H.-J., Rosenberry, T. L., Neumann, E. 1980. Effective charge on acetylcholinesterase active sites determined from the ionic strength dependence of association rate constants with cationic ligands. *Biochemistry* 19:3705–11
66. Nomoto, N., Takahashi, N., Nagaki, Y., Endo, S., Arata, Y., Hayashi, K. 1986. Carbohydrate structures of acetylcholine receptor from *Torpedo californica* and distribution of oligosaccharides among the subunits. *Eur. J. Biochem.* 157:233–42
67. Pritchett, D. B., Sontheimer, H., Shivers, B. D., Ymer, S., Kettenmann, H., et al. 1989. Importance of a novel $GABA_A$ receptor subunit for benzodiazepine pharmacology. *Nature* 338:582–85
68. Prod'hom, B., Pietrobon, D., Hess, P. 1987. Direct measurement of proton transfer rates controlling the dihydropyridine-sensitive Ca^{2+} channel. *Nature* 329:243–46
69. Prod'hom, B., Pietrobon, D., Hess, P. 1989. Interactions of protons with single open L-type calcium channels. Location of protonation site and dependence of proton-induced current fluctuations on concentration and species of permeant ion. *J. Gen. Physiol.* 94:23–42
70. Ravindran, A., Schild, L., Moczydlowski, E. 1990. Divalent cation selectivity for external block of voltage-dependent Na^+ channels prolonged by batrachotoxin. Zn^{2+} induces discrete substates in cardiac Na^+ channels. *J. Gen. Physiol.* Submitted
71. Reed, J., Raftery, M. 1976. Properties of the tetrodotoxin binding component in plasma membranes isolated from *Electrophorous electricus. Biochemistry* 15: 944–53
72. Reinhardt, R., Janko, K., Bamberg, E. 1986. Single channel conductance changes of desethanolamine-gramacidin through pH variations. In *Electric Double Layers in Biology,* ed. M. Blank, pp. 91–101. New York: Plenum
73. Roeske, R. W., Hrinyo-Pavlina, T. P., Pottorf, R. S., Bridal, T., Jin, X.-Z., Busath, D. 1989. Synthesis and channel properties of [Tau^{16}]gramacidin A. *Biochem. Biophys. Acta* 982:223–27
74. Russel, A. J., Ferst, A. R. 1987. Rational modification of enzyme catalysis by engineering surface charge. *Nature* 328:496–500
75. Salin, M., Wilson, W. W. 1981. Porcine superoxide dismutase. *Mol. Cell. Biochem.* 36:157–161
76. Samson, R., Deutch, J. M. 1978. Diffusion-controlled reaction rate to a buried active site. *J. Chem. Phys.* 68:285–89
77. Schofield, P. R., Darlison, M. G., Fujita, N., Burt, D. R., Stephenson, F. A., et al. 1987. Sequence and functional expression of the $GABA_A$ receptor shows a ligand-gated receptor super-family. *Nature* 328:221–227
78. Shrager, P., Profero, C. 1973. Inhibition of the receptor for tetrodotoxin in nerve membranes by reagents modifying carboxyl groups. *Biochem. Biophys. Acta* 318:141–46
79. Sigworth, F. J., Spalding, B. C. 1980. Chemical modification reduces the conductance of sodium channels in nerve. *Nature* 283:293–95
80. Smith-Maxwell, C., Begenisich, T. 1987. Guanidinium analogues as probes of the squid axon sodium pore. *J. Gen. Physiol.* 90:361–74

81. Spalding, B. 1980. Properties of toxin-resistant sodium channels produced by chemical modification in frog skeletal muscle. *J. Physiol.* 305:485–500
82. Tainer, J. A., Getzoff, E. D., Richardson, J. S., Richardson, D. C. 1983. Structure and mechanism of copper, zinc superoxide dismutase. *Nature* 306:284–87
83. Thorsness, P. E., Koshland, D. E., 1987. Inactivation of isocitrate dehydrogenase by phosphorylation is mediated by the negative charge of the phosphate. *J. Biol. Chem.* 262:10422–25
84. Toyoshima, C., Unwin, N. 1988. Ion channel of acetylcholine receptor reconstructed from images of postsynaptic membranes. *Nature* 336:247–50
85. Unwin, N. 1989. The structure of ion channels in membranes of excitable cells. *Neuron* 3:665–76
86. Woodhull, A. 1973. Ionic blockage of sodium channel in nerve. *J. Gen. Physiol.* 84:361–77
87. Worley, J. F., French, R. J., Krueger, B. K. 1986. Trimethyloxonium modification of single batrachotoxin-activated sodium channels in planar bilayers: Changes in unit conductance and in block by saxitoxin and calcium. *J. Gen. Physiol.* 87:327–49
88. Yellen, G. 1984. Ion permeation and blockade in Ca^{++}-activated K^+ channels of bovine chromaffin cells. *J. Gen. Physiol.* 82:157–86

Annu. Rev. Physiol. 1991. 53:361–73

REGULATION OF ION TRANSPORT ACROSS GALLBLADDER EPITHELIUM

Luis Reuss, Yoav Segal, and Guillermo Altenberg

Department of Physiology and Biophysics, University of Texas Medical Branch, Galveston, Texas 77550

KEY WORDS: fluid absorption, sodium transport, potassium transport, chloride transport

---

INTRODUCTION

Overview

Many of the transport mechanisms accounting for baseline salt transport in gallbladder epithelium have been characterized (37). Recent studies have focused on the means by which transport is regulated. The rate of transepithelial ion absorption is the result of the integrated activity of transporters in the cell membranes. Short- and/or long-term modulation of the activity of specific transporters can involve multiple factors and/or mechanisms, including membrane voltage, membrane stretch, effects of ions (e.g. H^+, Ca^{2+}) at modulatory sites, covalent modification (e.g. phosphorylation, methylation), direct modulation by regulatory proteins, and alterations in the surface density of transporting units. In epithelia, there is also the need for steady-state adjustment of the transport rates at both cell membrane domains if cell volume and composition are to be preserved when the rate of transepithelial transport is altered (46).

In gallbladder epithelium, the best understood regulatory mechanisms in-

0066-4278/91/0315-0361$02.00

volve intracellular factors such as pH_i, $Ca^{2+}{}_i$, and cyclic AMP (cAMP). Changes in intracellular levels of these and other agents mediate the effects of hormones and neurotransmitters on salt transport (see below). Our discussion will center on the effects of intracellular second messengers.

In this review, we summarize information on the regulation of specific transporters and discuss means by which regulation is integrated to eventually determine the overall rate of fluid transport. Historically gallbladder epithelium has served as a model for leaky epithelia. To the extent that there are parallels between transport regulation in gallbladder and in epithelia of greater homeostatic significance, such as the renal proximal tubule and the small intestine, studies on the former may enhance our understanding of the complicated means of maintenance of body fluid volume and composition. Perturbations such as large changes in HCO_3^-/CO_2 are unlikely to play a regulatory role in vivo, but will be discussed because their study can help understand the mechanisms by which other permeant buffers modulate salt transport (23).

There are significant differences in transepithelial transport processes in gallbladders of different species. While acknowledging these complications, we will focus our review on results obtained in the gallbladder of *Necturus maculosus* because ion transport mechanisms at the cell membrane level have been characterized extensively in this species.

Ion Transport in Gallbladder Epithelium

The main transport function of the gallbladder is the absorption of NaCl and water in near-isosmotic proportions (10). This involves apical membrane entry of Na^+ and Cl^- and basolateral membrane extrusion of both ions. The Na^+ and Cl^- influxes across the apical membrane are via parallel, independent Na^+/H^+ and Cl^-/HCO_3^- exchangers (35, 41, 60, 61, 65), although it is possible that there is also NaCl or NaKCl cotransport (8, 9, 24). Although quantitatively less important than NaCl absorption, the gallbladder epithelium also secretes K^+ and H^+ (10, 18, 33). In addition, in some mammalian species (e.g. the guinea pig) HCO_3^- is secreted instead of absorbed (62). Basolateral membrane Na^+ exit is mediated by the (Na^+,K^+)-activated ATPase, and Cl^- extrusion appears to result from both conductive transport (52, 55) and electroneutral KCl cotransport (5, 34). Both cell membranes are K^+ selective. Single K^+ channels originating from apical or basolateral membranes have been recently studied with the patch-clamp technique (see below).

The mechanisms of transepithelial transport in gallbladder have been reviewed (37–39, 45, 50) and are summarized for the case of *Necturus* gallbladder epithelium in Figure 1.

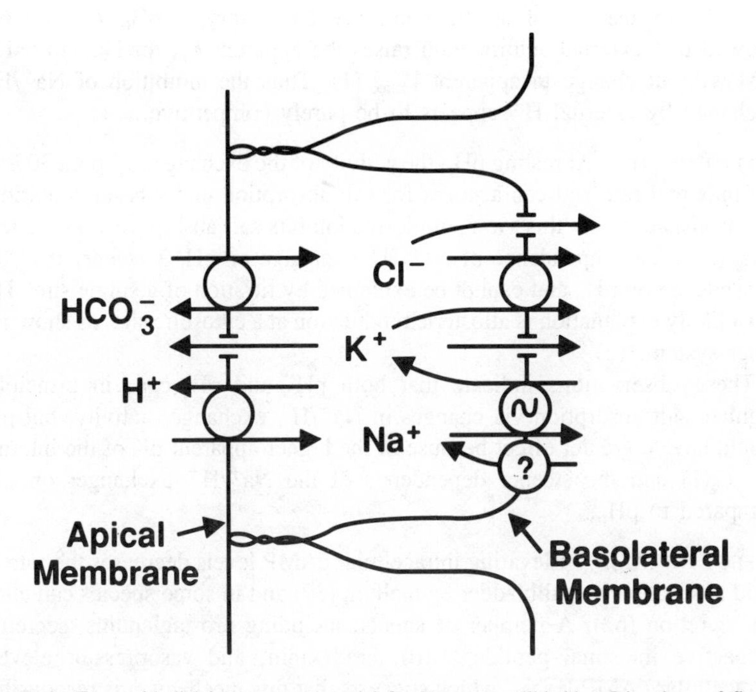

Figure 1 Transepithelial ion transport model for *Necturus* gallbladder. Directions of fluxes observed in steady state are depicted. Apical membrane NaCl entry is via parallel Na^+/H^+ and Cl^-/HCO_3^- exchangers. Basolateral Na^+ extrusion is via the Na^+ pump; Cl^- exit is by KCl cotransport and a Cl^- conductive pathway. There are K^+-selective channels in both membranes, but K^+ recycles mostly at the basolateral border, which has a much higher K^+ conductance. There is also some basolateral Na^+ recycling. A small apical Na^+ conductance is not shown (reproduced with permission of the American Physiological Society).

REGULATION OF APICAL MEMBRANE Na^+ AND Cl^- TRANSPORT

Regulation of the Rate of Apical Membrane Na^+/H^+ Exchange

EFFECT OF pH_o In tissues bathed in a medium containing 110 mM $[Na^+]_o$ and buffered with HEPES, reductions of mucosal solution pH cause decreases in intracellular Na^+ activity (aNa_i), which suggests that external pH (pH_o) can modify Na^+ entry and salt absorption under physiologic conditions (1). The relationship between pH_o and the rate of fall in aNa_i is compatible with titration of a single site with an apparent pK of 6.3.

The apparent K_m of the Na^+/H^+ exchanger for mucosal Na^+, determined from apical Na^+ entry and mucosal solution acidification, is about 15 mM (1,

60); kinetic analysis of apical membrane Na^+ entry at pH_o 7.5 and 6.5 showed that external acidification raises the apparent K_m for Na^+ to $\simeq$130 mM without change in apparent V_{max} (1). Thus the inhibition of Na^+/H^+ exchange by external H^+ appears to be purely competitive.

EFFECT OF pH_i At resting pH_i, the activity of the exchanger is about 30% of the maximal rate and can account for salt absorption under basal conditions (1). Consistent with this view, amiloride inhibits salt absorption and reduces aNa_i (35). The dependence of Na^+/H^+ exchange on pH_i is steeper than the dependence on pH_o and cannot be explained by titration of a single site. The most likely explanation is allosteric modulation at a cytosolic site, as shown in other systems (2).

These observations indicate that both pH_o and pH_i can, in principle, regulate salt absorption via changes in Na^+/H^+ exchanger activity, but pH_i would have a greater effect because of the higher apparent pK of the internal site (7.1) and the steeper dependence of the Na^+/H^+ exchanger on pH_i compared to pH_o.

EFFECT OF cAMP Elevating intracellular cAMP levels decreases the rate of fluid absorption by gallbladder epithelium (30) and in some species can elicit net secretion (62). A number of agents, including prostaglandins, secretin, vasoactive intestinal peptide (VIP), bradykinin, and vasopressin, elevate intracellular cAMP levels, which suggests that this mechanism is responsible for the effects of these agents on salt and water transport (28, 63).

Maximal elevations of cAMP, elicited by phosphodiesterase inhibition (theophylline), adenylyl cyclase stimulation (forskolin), or exposure to the permeant cAMP analogue 8-Br-cAMP, reduce apical membrane Na^+/H^+ exchange in *Necturus* gallbladder by about 50% (44). An inhibitory effect of cAMP on H^+ secretion has also been demonstrated in guinea pig gallbladder (31). The conclusion of inhibition of Na^+/H^+ exchange by cAMP in *Necturus* gallbladder is based on the following observations: (*a*) reduction of aNa_i upon elevation of intracellular cAMP levels, (*b*) decrease in the rate of fall of aNa_i upon lowering mucosal solution $[Na^+]$, (*c*) inhibition of the pH_i recovery from an acid load (the recovery is largely mediated by apical Na^+/H^+ exchange), and (*d*) reduction of mucosal solution acidification upon stopping mucosal superfusion. The inhibition of pH_i recovery from an acid load by cAMP involves a reduction in apparent V_{max}, without a change in apparent K_m for external Na^+ (44).

Regulation of the Rate of Apical Membrane Cl^-/HCO_3^- Exchange

EFFECTS OF pH_o AND pH_i The dependence of Cl^-/HCO_3^- exchange on pH_o and pH_i has not been studied in detail in gallbladder, but experiments in lymphocytes and Vero cells (27, 29) have shown that Cl^-/HCO_3^- exchange is exquisitely sensitive to pH_i. The steep increase of Cl^-/HCO_3^- exchange upon increasing pH_i in HEPES-buffered solutions suggests allosteric regulation by pH_i. The information available from *Necturus* gallbladder epithelium suggests that Cl^-/HCO_3^- exchange is affected by pH_i. When Na^+ is removed from the mucosal solution, the intracellular Cl^- activity (aCl_i) falls more slowly than aNa_i, thus indicating that the coupling between Na^+ and Cl^- entry through the apical membrane is indirect, probably via changes in pH_i and/or $[HCO_3^-]_i$ (35, 60). Amiloride inhibition of apical membrane Na^+/H^+ exchange also causes cell acidification, a fall in aNa_i, and a slower decrease of aCl_i (35, 60). The effect of intracellular HCO_3^- on Cl^-/HCO_3^- exchange is evident when gallbladders are incubated in HCO_3^-/CO_2 buffered solution instead of HEPES-Ringer (40). Regardless of the larger intracellular buffering power in tissues bathed in HCO_3^-/CO_2 media, the intracellular alkalinization elicited by removing mucosal solution Cl^- is increased, which indicates that the Cl^-/HCO_3^- exchanger is more active in physiologic solutions with higher $[HCO_3^-]$. The effect of pH_o on Cl^-/HCO_3^- exchange seems to be of minor importance since apical membrane Cl^- entry is not affected by pH_o reductions of 1 unit, i.e. by decreasing HCO_3^- from 10 to 1 mM, provided that the sum of the chemical gradients for Cl^- and HCO_3^- is kept constant by reducing simultaneously external $[Cl^-]$ (36).

EFFECT OF cAMP Increases in intracellular cAMP levels produced by theophyline, forskolin, or 8-Br-cAMP, reduce Cl^-/HCO_3^- exchange by about 50%, as demonstrated by a decrease in the rate of mucosal solution alkalinization when the Na^+/H^+ exchanger is blocked, and by a decrease in the voltage-independent rates of fall in aCl_i and $aHCO_3^-{}_i$ upon changing luminal solution $[Cl^-]$ or $[HCO_3^-]$ (36). This effect results from the reduction of the apparent V_{max} of the system without effect on the apparent K_m for external Cl^- (36).

Effect of cAMP on Apical Membrane Cl^- Conductance (gCl^-)

Increases in cAMP produce cell membrane depolarization and a decrease of the ratio of apical to basolateral membranes resistances, R_a/R_b (30, 36, 44). The underlying mechanism of these effects is an increase in apical membrane gCl^-, which is best evidenced by the large and rapid depolarization observed upon reducing mucosal solution Cl^-, an effect absent prior to cAMP treatment (30). In *Necturus* gallbladder, the cAMP-induced apical membrane gCl^- is insensitive to agents that block Cl^- channels in other cells (41, 58), but can be reduced by a monoclonal antibody raised against *Necturus* gallbladder epithelial cells (11). The cAMP-induced fall in aCl_i is due to the combined effects of inhibition of Cl^-/HCO_3^- exchange and stimulation of gCl^-.

Single Cl^- channels likely to account for the cAMP-induced gCl^- have been identified in gallbladder epithelial cells treated with theophylline or forskolin, but not in control tissues (47). More recently, monoclonal antibodies raised against *Necturus* gallbladder epithelial cells have allowed for isolation of proteins that when incorporated in planar lipid bilayers exhibit channel activity (56).

In guinea pig gallbladder, cAMP induces net secretion of both fluid and HCO_3^-. The latter effect is attributable to stimulation of Cl^-/HCO_3^- exchange, caused by the decrease in aCl_i, and enhanced conductive HCO_3^- exit (51). The possibility of a direct effect of cAMP on Cl^-/HCO_3^- exchange has not been explored in this preparation. It was claimed that cAMP increases apical membrane HCO_3^- conductance in *Necturus* gallbladder epithelium (64), but later experiments appear to rule out this possibility (36, 37).

REGULATION OF BASOLATERAL MEMBRANE Na^+ AND Cl^- TRANSPORT

Regulation of the Rate of the Na^+ Pump

Direct studies of the mechanisms of regulation of the rate of the Na^+ pump are lacking in gallbladder epithelium. It is clear, however, that changes in pump activity must occur in response to primary increases or decreases in the rate of Na^+ entry, i.e. an elevation of Na^+ entry is expected to stimulate the pump, and a reduction in Na^+ entry would inhibit it (see below). An obvious mechanism that would explain the relationship between apical Na^+ entry and basolateral Na^+ extrusion is the change in aNa_i elicited by alterations of apical entry. When Na^+ transport is stimulated by incubation in HCO_3^-/CO_2 media or inhibited by cAMP, however, there are no changes in aNa_i, or the changes are too small to account for the changes in pump activity predicted from the rate of fluid absorption. Hence, under these conditions it is likely that other factors influence the rate of active Na^+ transport across the basolateral membrane. On the basis of studies in other tissues, possible mechanisms include changes in cell volume and intracellular pH.

Regulation of Basolateral Membrane Cl^- Transport

EFFECT OF PERMEANT BUFFERS ON gCl^- In low-HCO_3^- media the basolateral membrane gCl^- is small, about 6% of the basolateral conductance (32). Incubating the tissues in media buffered with HCO_3^-/CO_2 increases R_a and decreases R_b (52); the former effect results from a decrease in apical membrane electrodiffusive K^+ permeability (P_K) and the latter from increases in basolateral membrane P_K and P_{Cl} (55). Consequently, in 10 mM

HCO_3^-/1% CO_2 about 50% of the total conductance of the basolateral membrane is due to Cl^- (55).

PH DEPENDENCE OF BASOLATERAL Cl^- CONDUCTANCE Lowering pH_o, by decreasing serosal solution $[HCO_3^-]_o$ at constant pCO_2, or by increasing pCO_2 at constant $[HCO_3^-]_o$, increases basolateral gCl^- and causes cell membrane depolarization (55). The depolarization occurs without measurable change in R_a/R_b, which suggests that if permeability changes are restricted to the basolateral membrane, they must involve both an increase in P_{Cl} and a decrease in P_K (55). Raising serosal solution pCO_2 and $[HCO_3^-]$ (constant pH_o) causes a fall in pH_i without changes in basolateral membrane voltage. Thus basolateral membrane P_{Cl} appears to be insensitive to pH_i changes, at least in the range of 7.4 to 7.1 (55).

REGULATION OF K^+ CONDUCTIVE PATHWAYS

Regulation of Macroscopic K^+ Conductances

The apical and basolateral cell membranes in amphibian (42, 43, 57) and mammalian (20, 57) gallbladder are predominantly K^+-conductive. As a result, the K^+ equilibrium potentials across these membranes determine both the cell membrane voltages and the electrical driving forces for ion transport. In *Necturus* and rabbit gallbladder, the apical membrane appears to provide a pathway for K^+ secretion, which amounts to a small fraction of Na^+ absorption (18, 33).

The apical membrane of *Necturus* gallbladder epithelium constitutes 60–90% of the total transcellular resistance under baseline conditions (52). In transepithelial current- and voltage-clamp studies, depolarization of the apical membrane decreases R_a/R_b. This effect is inhibited by adding the K^+ channel blocker TEA^+ to the mucosal bathing solution, which suggests that depolarization activates an apical membrane K^+ conductance (14, 48, 53). The apical membrane of guinea pig gallbladder also contains a voltage-activated K^+ conductance (17). In *Necturus* gallbladder, elevation of intracellular Ca^{2+} levels with Ca^{2+} ionophores enhances the effects of membrane depolarization, whereas lowering pH_o decreases them. These observations imply that gK^+ is increased by $[Ca^{2+}]_i$ and decreased by external H^+ (14).

The basolateral membrane conductance of *Necturus* gallbladder appears to be voltage-insensitive, as assessed in transepithelial voltage-clamp studies (14). Elevation of intracellular Ca^{2+} levels with A23187 or cyanide leads to a rapid hyperpolarization of the cell membrane voltages and an increase in the K^+ selectivity of the basolateral membrane (3), thus suggesting that K^+ channels in this membrane can be activated by internal Ca^{2+}. As noted earlier, acidification of the serosal bathing solution is likely to lead to a decrease in the absolute K^+ conductance of the basolateral membrane, concomitant with an increase in gCl^-. Evidence points to an external, rather than internal, modulatory site for H^+ (55).

Regulation of K^+ Channels

Potassium channels were first demonstrated in gallbladder epithelium by fluctuation analysis (15, 16). More recently, the patch-clamp technique has made it possible to identify and to characterize in detail single ion channels that account for some properties of the macroscopic apical and basolateral conductances.

In cell-attached patch-clamp experiments carried out on the apical membrane of *Triturus* (26) and *Necturus* (48) gallbladders, the most commonly observed channel is a large-conductance (~ 200 pS) maxi K^+ channel, which is largely inactive (open probability < 0.15) at the resting membrane voltage, and activates steeply with depolarization of the membrane patch. In cell-excised membrane patches, maxi K^+ channels from *Triturus* and *Necturus* are activated by membrane depolarization, or elevation of internal Ca^{2+} levels, like their counterparts in excitable cells, in which channels of this type were characterized originally (see 25). In *Necturus* gallbladder, maxi K^+ channels account for no more than 20% of the resting apical membrane conductance, assessed on the basis of the open probability at the resting membrane voltage, and simple models relating single-channel properties to the macroscopic conductance (48).

Maxi K^+ channels account for the voltage- and Ca^{2+}-sensitive components of apical membrane conductance, described above, and its pharmacological sensitivities (49). It is likely that these channels also participate in the overall response to cAMP, inasmuch as they would be activated by the depolarization elicited by this agent. For instance, the cAMP-induced reduction in cell volume (C. Cotton, L. Reuss, unpublished observations) could result in part from net KCl loss across the apical membrane. Apical membrane depolarization elicits K^+ secretion because of the change in electrochemical driving force and because of gating of voltage-sensitive K^+ channels. Although of minor importance in gallbladder, regulation of K^+ secretion is a major function of other epithelia, such as the renal collecting tubule. Recent experiments show that the open probability of maxi K^+ channels from the apical membrane of *Necturus* gallbladder epithelial cells is decreased by reductions of pH_i near the physiologic range (4).

K^+ channels underlying the resting apical membrane K^+ conductance in gallbladder epithelium have yet to be identified. Obstacles to their identification could arise from (*a*) low single-channel conductance, (*b*) low frequency of transitions between open and closed states, and/or (*c*) a tendency to run-down under the conditions of patch-clamp experiments. Low-conductance channels, which rarely close at the resting membrane voltage, have recently been described in several epithelia (e.g. 12).

Patch-clamp experiments on epithelial basolateral membranes are hindered by the presence of subepithelial connective tissue layers. In *Necturus* gallbladder, the recent development of a technique for exposing "clean" areas of basolateral membrane has permitted identification of several kinds of K^+ channels that are not yet fully characterized (59).

COORDINATED REGULATION OF APICAL AND BASOLATERAL MEMBRANE ION TRANSPORT

In the steady state, changes in the rate of transepithelial transport must involve parallel alterations of the rates of salt entry across the apical membrane and salt extrusion across the basolateral membrane. These adaptive mechanisms prevent large changes in cell volume and/or ion content in response to primary stimulation or inhibition of transport at either membrane domain (46). An obvious mechanism linking the transport rates across the two membranes is the change of intracellular ion activity resulting from the primary event. For instance, inhibition of Na^+/H^+ exchange will cause a fall in aNa_i, which in turn will cause a decrease in the rate of Na^+ pumping across the basolateral membrane. In some cases, however, there are no measurable changes in intracellular ion activity, or they are too small to account for the effect at the contralateral membrane. An example is the steady-state effect of galactose on Na^+ transport in amphibian small intestine: the short-circuit current is increased severalfold, whereas aNa_i does not change significantly (21). Examples in *Necturus* gallbladder epithelium are the effect of cAMP (fluid transport is virtually abolished while aNa_i is only moderately decreased, 44), the effect of ouabain (the long-term decrease in basolateral Na^+ extrusion causes a reduction in Na^+ entry across the apical membrane, 22), and the effect of HCO_3^-/CO_2 (net NaCl and fluid absorption increase without appreciable changes in aNa_i or aCl_i, 35, 61). Although the mechanisms linking transport rates at the cell membranes are not fully understood, it is useful to discuss two specific examples of parallel changes in apical and basolateral membrane ion transport.

Steady-State Inhibitory Effects of cAMP

The dominant effects of cAMP on gallbladder epithelial cells are exerted at the apical membrane and consist of activation and/or insertion of Cl^- channels and inhibition of both Na^+/H^+ and Cl^-/HCO_3^- exchangers (see above).

The observation that transepithelial fluid transport is abolished with maximal intracellular cAMP levels (30) implies that net transepithelial salt transport must be abolished as well. Therefore, in the steady-state, net Na^+

and Cl^- fluxes at each membrane are either zero or balanced by counterflux of another ion. For instance, net Na^+ absorption might be balanced by K^+ secretion and Cl^- absorption could be balanced by HCO_3^- secretion.

In *Necturus* gallbladder, the inhibition of Cl^-/HCO_3^- exchange, even by maximal concentrations of cAMP, is not complete (see above), which suggests that net apical membrane Cl^- influx via anion exchange is balanced by electrodiffusive Cl^- exit across the same membrane (37), or by secretion of another anion. Similarly, the maximal inhibition of apical membrane Na^+/H^+ exchange by cAMP is ~ 50%, which suggests that additional effects abolish net entry, or that cation (e.g. K^+) secretion balances Na^+ absorption. In either case, it is likely that net Na^+ extrusion across the basolateral membrane is reduced because of the fall in aNa_i and perhaps other factors.

Steady-State Stimulatory Effects of HCO_3^-/CO_2

In gallbladders from several species, exposure to HCO_3^-/CO_2-buffered solutions elevates the rate of fluid absorption. This effect is caused by stimulation of NaCl absorption and in some cases to $NaHCO_3$ transport per se (for review, see 13). Exposure to HCO_3^-/CO_2 stimulates NaCl entry across the apical membrane, as indicated by the increases in cell volume and cell Na^+ and Cl^- contents (6, 7). The most likely mechanism for these effects is stimulation of both cation and anion exchangers at the apical membrane (19, 35). Apical membrane Na^+/H^+ exchange could be stimulated by the decrease in pH_i in HCO_3^--buffered, compared to HEPES-buffered, solutions. The fall in pH_i is small, but in the range of highest sensitivity of the cation exchanger; extrapolations based on the measured effect of pH_i on Na^+ entry suggest that it could account for the increase in transepithelial Na^+ transport (1, 52). Certainly other factors could participate in the stimulation of Na^+ absorption. The stimulation of apical membrane Cl^-/HCO_3^- exchange in HCO_3/CO_2 media is probably a direct consequence of the elevation of intracellular HCO_3^- (40), but allosteric activation of a NaCl cotransporter has also been proposed for rabbit gallbladder (7).

Since both apical membrane Na^+ entry and transepithelial fluid transport increase in HCO_3^-/CO_2 media, basolateral membrane Na^+ extrusion must be stimulated in the absence of steady-state changes in aNa_i (35, 61). The mechanism of this effect is unknown.

Basolateral membrane gCl^- and gK^+ increase in 10 mM HCO_3^-/1% CO_2. The elevation of gCl^- contributes to the increase in transepithelial Cl^- transport and accounts almost exactly for the HCO_3^-/CO_2-dependent component of net Cl^- absorption (55). The parallel increases in K^+ and Cl^- extrusion across the basolateral membrane contribute to regulate cell volume and ionic composition in the face of the increased rates of NaCl entry across the apical membrane and K^+ uptake by the Na^+ pump (52, 54).

It is possible that the mechanisms of change in basolateral ion transport rates during cAMP-induced inhibition and HCO_3^-/CO_2-induced stimulation of transport involve changes in cell volume: cell volume decreases in response to elevation of cAMP levels and increases with elevation of mucosal solution CO_2 (C. Cotton, L. Reuss, unpublished observations). The links between cell volume and basolateral ion transport rates, however, have not been established.

ACKNOWLEDGMENTS

We thank Dr. C. U. Cotton for comments on a preliminary version of this review and L. Durant for secretarial help. This work was supported by National Institutes of Health grants DK-38734 and GM-07200. G. Altenberg is a post-doctoral fellow of Consejo Nacional de Investigaciones Científicas y Técnicas de la República Argentina.

Literature Cited

1. Altenberg, G. A., Reuss, L. 1990. Apical membrane Na^+/H^+ exchange in *Necturus* gallbladder epithelium: Its dependence on extracellular and intracellular pH and on external Na^+ concentration. *J. Gen. Physiol.* 95:369–92
2. Aronson, P. S., Nee, J., Suhm, M. A. 1982. Modifier role of internal H^+ in activating the Na^+-H^+ exchanger in renal mirovillus membrane vesicles. *Nature* 299:161–63
3. Bello-Reuss, E., Grady, T. P., Reuss, L. 1981. Mechanism of the effect of cyanide on cell membrane potential in *Necturus* gallbladder epithelium. *J. Physiol.* 314:343–57
4. Copello, J., Segal, Y., Reuss, L. 1991. Cytosolic pH regulates maxi K^+ channels in gallbladder epithelial cells. *J. Physiol.* In press
5. Corcia, A., Armstrong, W. McD. 1983. KCl cotransport: A mechanism for basolateral chloride exit in *Necturus* gallbladder. *J. Membr. Biol.* 76:173–82
6. Cremaschi, D., Hénin, S., Meyer, G. 1979. Stimulation of HCO_3^- of Na^+ transport in rabbit gallbladder. *J. Membr. Biol.* 47:145–70
7. Cremaschi, D., Meyer, G., Rosetti, C. 1983. Bicarbonate effects, electromotive forces and potassium effluxes in rabbit and guinea-pig gallbladder. *J. Physiol.* 335:51–64
8. Cremaschi, D., Meyer, G., Rosetti, C., Botta, G., Palestini, P. 1987. The nature of the neutral Na^+-Cl^- coupled entry at the apical membrane of rabbit gallbladder epithelium. I. Na^+/H^+, Cl^-/HCO_3^- double exchange and Na^+-Cl^- symport. *J. Membr. Biol.* 95:209–18
9. Davis, C. W., Finn, A. L. 1985. Effects of mucosal sodium removal on cell volume in *Necturus* gallbladder epithelium. *Am. J. Physiol.* 249:C304–12
10. Diamond, J. M. 1968. Transport mechanisms in the gallbladder. In *Handbook of Physiology: Section 6, Alimentary Canal, Bile, Digestion, Ruminal Physiology*, ed. W. Heidel, C. F. Cole, V:2451–2482. Bethesda, MD: Am. Physiol. Soc.
11. Finn, A. L., Tsai, L.-M., Falk, R. J. 1989. Monoclonal antibodies to the apical chloride channel in *Necturus* gallbladder inhibit the chloride conductance. *Proc. Natl. Acad. Sci. USA* 86:7649–52
12. Frindt, G., Palmer, L. G. 1988. Low-conductance K channels in apical membrane of rat cortical collecting tubule. *Am. J. Physiol.* 256:F143–51
13. Frizzell, R. K., Heintze, K. 1980. Transport functions of the gallbladder. In *International Review of Physiology: Liver and Biliary Tract Physiology I*, ed. N. B. Javitt. pp. 221–247. Baltimore: Univ. Park
14. García-Diaz, J. F., Nagel, W., Essig, A. 1983. Voltage-dependent K conductance at the apical membrane of *Necturus* gallbladder. *Biophys. J.* 43:269–78
15. Gögelein, H., Van Driessche, W. 1981. Noise analysis of the K^+ current through the apical membrane of *Necturus* gallbladder. *J. Membr. Biol.* 60:187–98
16. Gögelein, H., Van Driessche, W. 1981. The effect of electrical gradients on current fluctuations and impedance recorded from *Necturus* gallbladder. *J. Membr. Biol.* 60:199–209

17. Gunter-Smith, P. J. 1988. Apical membrane potassium conductance in guinea pig gallbladder epithelial cells. *Am. J. Physiol.* 254:C808–15
18. Gunter-Smith, P. J., Schultz, G. 1982. Potassium transport and intracellular potassium activities in rabbit gallbladder. *J. Membr. Biol.* 65:41–47
19. Heintze, K., Petersen, K.-U. 1980. Na/H and Cl/HCO_3^- exchange as a mechanism for HCO_3^--stimulated NaCl absorption by gallbladder. In *Hydrogen Ion Transport in Epithelia,* ed. I. Schultz, G. Sachs, J. G. Forte, K. J. Ullrich, pp. 345–354. Amsterdam: Elsevier/North Holland
20. Hénin, S., Cremaschi, D. 1975. Transcellular ion route in rabbit gallbladder. Electrical properties of the epithelial cells. *Pflügers Arch.* 355:125–39
21. Hudson, R. L., Schultz, S. G. 1984. Sodium-coupled sugar transport: effects on intracellular sodium activities and sodium-pump activity. *Science* 224: 1237–39
22. Jensen, P. K., Fisher, R. S., Spring, K. R. 1984. Feedback inhibition of NaCl entry in *Necturus* gallbladder epithelial cells. *J. Membr. Biol.* 82:95–104
23. Karniski, L. P., Aronson, P. S. 1985. Chloride/formate exchange with formic acid recycling: A mechanism of active chloride transport across epithelial membranes. *Proc. Natl. Acad. Sci. USA* 82:6362–65
24. Larson, M., Spring, K. R. 1983. Bumetanide inhibition of NaCl transport by *Necturus* gallbladder. *J. Membr. Biol.* 74:123–29
25. Latorre, R., Oberhauser, A., Labarca, P., Alvarez, O. 1989. Varieties of calcium-activated potassium channels. *Annu. Rev. Physiol.* 51:385–400
26. Maruyama, Y., Matsunaga, H., Hoshi, T. 1986. Ca^{2+}- and voltage activated K^+ channel in apical cell membrane of gallbladder epithelium from *Triturus*. *Pflügers Arch.* 406:563–567
27. Mason, M. J., Smith, J. D., García-Soto, J. De J., Grinstein, S. 1989. Internal pH-sensitive site couples Cl^--HCO_3^- exchange to Na^+-H^+ antiport in lymphocytes. *Am. J. Physiol.* 256: C428–33
28. O'Grady, S. M., Wolters, P. J., Hildebrand, K., Brown, D. R. 1989. Regulation of ion transport in porcine gallbladder: effects of VIP and norepinephrine. *Am. J. Physiol.* 257:C52–57
29. Olsnes, S., Tonnessen, T. I., Ludt, J., Sandvig, K. 1987. Effect of intracellular pH on the rate of chloride uptake and efflux in different mammalian cell lines. *Biochemistry* 26:2778–85
30. Petersen, K.-U., Reuss, L. 1983. Cyclic AMP-induced chloride permeability in the apical membrane of *Necturus* gallbladder epithelium. *J. Gen. Physiol.* 81:705–9
31. Petersen, K.-U., Wehner, F., Winterhager, J. M. 1985. Na/H exchange at the apical membrane of guinea-pig gallbladder epithelium: properties and inhibition by cyclic AMP. *Pflügers Arch.* 405: S115–20
32. Reuss, L. 1979. Electrical properties of the cellular transepithelial pathway in *Necturus* gallbladder. III. Ionic permeability of the basolateral cell membrane. *J. Membr. Biol.* 47:239–59
33. Reuss, L. 1981. Potassium transport mechanisms by amphibian gallbladder. In *Ion Transport by Epithelia,* ed. S. G. Schultz. pp. 108–128. New York: Raven
34. Reuss, L. 1983. Basolateral KCl cotransport in a NaCl-absorbing epithelium. *Nature* 305:723–26
35. Reuss, L. 1984. Independence of apical membrane Na^+ and Cl^- entry in *Necturus* gallbladder epithelium. *J. Gen. Physiol.* 84:423–45
36. Reuss, L. 1987. Cyclic AMP inhibits Cl^-/HCO_3^- exchange at the apical membrane of *Necturus* gallbladder epithelium. *J. Gen. Physiol.* 90:172–96
37. Reuss, L. 1989. Ion transport across gallbladder epithelium. *Physiol. Rev.* 69:503–45
38. Reuss, L. 1989. Regulation of transepithelial chloride transport by amphibian gallbladder epithelium. *Ann. NY Acad. Sci.* 574:370–84
39. Reuss, L. 1990. Salt and water transport by the gallbladder epithelium. In: *Handbook of Physiology, The Gastrointestinal System, Intestinal Transport,* 4: Bethesda, MD: Am. Physiol. Soc. In press
40. Reuss, L., Costantin, L. 1984. Cl^-/HCO_3^- exchange at the apical membrane of *Necturus* gallbladder. *J. Gen. Physiol.* 83:801–18
41. Reuss, L., Costantin, J. L., Bazile, J. E. 1987. Diphenylamine-2-carboxylate blocks Cl^--HCO_3^- exchange in *Necturus* gallbladder epithelium. *Am. J. Physiol.* 253:C79–89
42. Reuss, L., Finn, A. L. 1975. Electrical properties of the cellular transepithelial pathway in *Necturus* gallbladder. I. Circuit analysis and steady-state effects of mucosal solution ionic substitution. *J. Membr. Biol.* 25:115–39
43. Reuss, L., Finn, A. L. 1975. Electrical

properties of the cellular transepithelial pathway in *Necturus* gallbladder. II. Ionic permeability of the apical cell membrane. *J. Membr. Biol.* 25:141–61

44. Reuss, L., Petersen, K.-U. 1985. Cyclic AMP inhibits Na^+/H^+ exchange at the apical membrane of *Necturus* gallbladder epithelium. *J. Gen. Physiol.* 85: 409–25
45. Reuss, L., Stoddard, J. S. 1987. Role of H^+ and HCO_3^- in salt transport in gallbladder epithelium. *Annu. Rev. Physiol.* 49:35–49
46. Schultz, S. G. 1981. Homocellular regulatory mechanisms in sodium-transporting epithelia: avoidance of extinction by "flush-through". *Am. J. Physiol.* 241:F579–90
47. Segal, Y., Reuss, L. 1989. Cl^- channels in cyclic AMP-stimulated gallbladder epithelium. *FASEB J.* 3:A862
48. Segal, Y., Reuss, L. 1990. Maxi K^+ channels and their relationship to the apical membrane conductance in *Necturus* gallbladder epithelium. *J. Gen. Physiol.* 95:791–818
49. Segal, Y., Reuss, L. 1990. Ba^{2+}, TEA^+ and quinine effects on apical membrane K^+ conductance and maxi K^+ channels in gallbladder epithelium. *Am. J. Physiol.* 259:C56–68
50. Spring, K. R., Ericson, A.-C. 1982. Epithelial cell volume modulation and regulation. *J. Membr. Biol.* 69:167–76
51. Stewart, C. P., Winterhager, J. M., Heintze, K., Petersen, K.-U. 1989. Electrogenic bicarbonate secretion by guinea pig gallbladder epithelium apical membrane exit. *Am. J. Physiol.* 256: C736–49
52. Stoddard, J., Reuss, L. 1988. Dependence of cell membrane conductances on bathing solution HCO_3^-/CO_2 in *Necturus* gallbladder. *J. Membr. Biol.* 102: 163–74
53. Stoddard, J. S., Reuss, L. 1988. Voltage- and time-dependence of apical membrane conductance during current clamp in *Necturus* gallbladder epithelium. *J. Membr. Biol.* 103:191–204
54. Stoddard, J. S., Reuss, L. 1989. Electrophysiologic effects of mucosal Cl^- removal in *Necturus* gallbladder epithelium. *Am. J. Physiol.* 257:C568–78
55. Stoddard, J. S., Reuss, L. 1989. pH effects on basolateral membrane ion conductances in gallbladder epithelium. *Am. J. Physiol.* 256:C1184–95
56. Tsai, L.-M., Rosenberg, R. L., Finn, A. L., Falk, R. J. 1990. Reconstitution of a chloride channel from Necturus gallbladder (NGB); blockade by specific antibody. *FASEB J.* 4A550
57. Van Os, C. H., Slegers, J. F. G. 1975. The electrical potential profile of gallbladder epithelium. *J. Membr. Biol.* 24: 341–63
58. Wangemann, P., Wittner, M., DiStefano, A., Englert, H. C., Lang, H. J., et al. 1986. Cl^- channel blockers in the thick ascending limb of the loop of Henle. Structure activity relationship. *Pflügers Arch.* 407:S128–41
59. Wehner, F., Garretson, L., Dawson, K., Segal, Y., Reuss, L. 1990. A nonenzymatic preparation of epithelial basolateral membrane for patch clamp. *Am. J. Physiol.* 258:C1159–64
60. Weinmann, S. A., Reuss, L. 1982. Na^+-H^+ exchange at the apical membrane of *Necturus* gallbladder. Extracellular and intracellular pH studies. *J. Gen. Physiol.* 80:299–321
61. Weinmann, S. A., Reuss, L. 1984. Na^+-H^+ exchange and Na^+ entry across the apical membrane of *Necturus* gallbladder. *J. Gen. Physiol.* 83:57–74
62. Winterhager, J. M., Stewart, C. P., Heintze, K., Petersen, K.-U. 1986. Electroneutral secretion of bicarbonate by guinea pig gallbladder epithelium. *Am. J. Physiol.* 250:C617–28
63. Wood, J. R., Svanvik, J. 1983. Gallbladder water and electrolyte transport and its regulation. *Gut* 24:579–93
64. Zeldin, D. C., Corcia, A., Armstrong, W. McD. 1985. Cyclic AMP-induced changes in membrane conductance of *Necturus* gallbladder epithelial cells. *J. Membr. Biol.* 84:193–206
65. Zeuthen, T., Machen, T. 1984. HCO_3^-/CO_2 stimulates Na^+/H^+ and Cl^-/HCO_3^- exchange in *Necturus* gallbladder. In *Hydrogen Ion Transport in Epithelia,* ed. J. G. Forte, D. G. Warnock, F. C. Rector, Jr. pp. 97–108. New York: Wiley

Annu. Rev. Physiol. 1991. 53:375–94

STRUCTURES AND PROPERTIES OF THE SURFACTANT-ASSOCIATED PROTEINS

Samuel Hawgood

Department of Pediatrics and Cardiovascular Research Institute, University of California, San Francisco, California 94143

Kathleen Shiffer

Genentech, Inc., 460 Point San Bruno Blvd., South San Francisco, California 94080

KEY WORDS: surfactant apoproteins, lipid protein interactions, pulmonary surfactant

---

INTRODUCTION

The importance of surface forces to the mechanical properties of the lung were first recognized just over sixty years ago (80). The subject apparently received little attention for twenty years until a series of studies convincingly demonstrated the presence of a pulmonary surfactant and related the surface tension-surface area behavior of this secretion to the pressure-volume behavior of the lung (11, 52). These studies demonstrated a central role for pulmonary surfactant in maintaining the normal volume stability of the lung at low transpulmonary pressures. Soon thereafter abnormalities of surfactant function were found in certain types of fatal respiratory failure (1). Much of the research effort of the last thirty years has focused on the metabolism of surfactant and on efforts to understand the functional role of the many different surfactant components.

The fact that phospholipids, particularly phosphatidylcholines, make up the

0066–4278/91/0315–0375$02.00

major mass of surfactant was established soon after the material was first isolated (6, 45). It was not until 1973, however, that lung-specific proteins were also identified as a part of surfactant (42). In the last five years four surfactant-associated proteins have been purified and partially characterized. These proteins appear to influence many aspects of surfactant structure, function, and metabolism. It is important to emphasize at the outset of this review, which is focused primarily on the surfactant proteins, that phospholipids have a central role in the function of surfactant (reviewed in 29). Our major objective is to describe the structure and biochemical properties of the surfactant apoproteins. The introduction contains some additional commentary concerning the possible physiologic role of the surfactant apoproteins, but a detailed analysis of their roles in vivo has not been attempted. Relevant information concerning the molecular genetics, biosynthesis, and metabolism of the surfactant apoproteins can be found in the reviews by Mendelson & Boggaram, Haagsman & van Golde, and Wright & Dobbs in this volume.

The nomenclature proposed by Possmayer (59) to describe the surfactant apoproteins has become generally accepted and will be used throughout this review. The apoproteins of surfactant can be conveniently separated into two groups differentiated by their solubility in aqueous and organic solvents. The two water soluble proteins (SP-A and SP-D) are collagen-like proteins that belong to the family of C-type lectins. There is now considerable evidence that SP-A influences the structure and properties of surfactant lipids, but the role of SP-D in surfactant function is less clear. It seems likely that both proteins may also have immunological functions that are less clearly related to classical concepts of surfactant function (53, 74, 79). The two surfactant proteolipids (SP-B and SP-C) are small cationic hydrophobic proteins derived from much larger precursor proteins. Both proteolipids markedly affect the properties of phospholipids. Some basic characteristics of these proteins are shown in Table 1 and Figure 1. While these four proteins are our central focus, it is probable that future reviews on this subject will include information on additional proteins with roles in surfactant structure, function, or metabolism. In order to provide some biological background for a discussion of the properties of the individual surfactant apoproteins, current concepts of surfactant function and metabolism will be briefly discussed. Recent reviews of surfactant biology (29, 77, 95) and the review by Wright & Dobbs in this volume should be consulted for further detail.

OVERVIEW OF SURFACTANT BIOLOGY

Intracellular Assembly

The epithelium lining the alveolus is composed of two phenotypically different cell types. The relatively cuboidal type II cell is thought to be the only site

Table 1 Surfactant-associated proteins

	Chromosome	Gene (kb)	Primary translation product (Da)	Post-translation modifications	Protein monomer (Da)
Water Soluble					
SP-A	10	5	26,000	Signal peptide cleavage N-linked glycosylation proline hydroxylation gamma carboxylation[a] acetylation[a] sulfation[a] oligomerization	28,000–36,000
SP-D	NA	NA	NA	N-linked glycosylation proline hydroxylation lysine hydroxylation hydroxylysine glycosylation oligomerization	43,000
Proteolipids					
SP-B	2	6	40,000	signal peptide cleavage glycosylation proteolytic processing	9,000
SP-C	8	3	20,000	proteolytic processing acylation	4,000

NA — not available.
[a] in vitro observations that have not been confirmed in more than one species.

of surfactant lipid synthesis (64, 78). All four surfactant apoproteins are also synthesized in type II cells, but Clara cells lining respiratory bronchioles may also synthesize and secrete SP-A and SP-B (53, 56, 57, 71, 82). Despite considerable progress in our understanding of the biosynthesis of the separate surfactant components (reviewed by Haagsman & van Golde in this volume), we know little about how and where the lipids and proteins of surfactant are first assembled. Surfactant lipids and apoproteins are both found in a specialized secretory organelle of the type II cell known as a lamellar body, which suggests that they are co-assembled prior to secretion. Lamellar bodies, however, can apparently receive material from both synthetic (9) and endocytic pathways (91). Therefore the possibility that the assembly of some components of surfactant occurs extracellularly cannot be excluded.

The closely packed lipid lamellae in lamellar bodies have smooth internal fracture faces as seen by electron microscopy. Amorphous material that is of uncertain composition, but that is almost certainly proteinaceous, lies between the lamellae. Like secretory organelles in other cell types, lamellar bodies have an internal environment that is both acidic (8) and rich in calcium

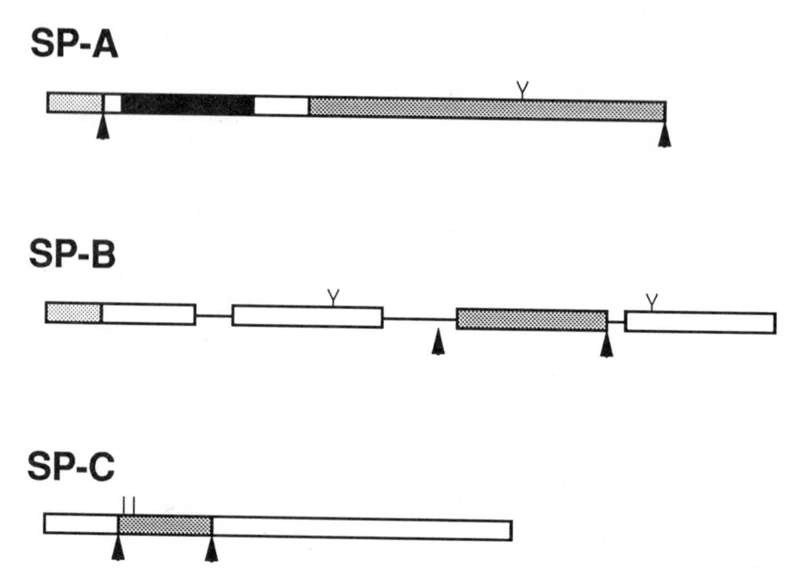

Figure 1 Schematic linear representation of the surfactant protein monomers. SP-A: The *lightly shaded region* represents the signal peptide; the *solid region* represents the collagenous domain; and the *Y* depicts the N-linked carbohydrate located in the carbohydrate recognition domain indicated by the *heavier stipling*. *SP-B:* The preproprotein is shown organized into four units based on the distribution of cysteine residues (see text for details). The *lightly shaded region* at the amino-terminus represents the signal peptide. The 79 amino acid form of SP-B associated with extracellular surfactant is depicted by *heavy shading*. The glycosylated residues in the regions flanking the fully processed form of SP-B are indicated by the *Y*. *SP-C:* The preprotein is shown with the 35 amino acids of the fully processed form of SP-C associated with extracellular surfactant depicted by *heavy shading*. The palmitic acids attached to the two adjacent cysteines in the processed form of SP-C are shown by a *I*. The location of the amino and carboxy terminus of the major extracellular form of each protein is marked with an *arrowhead*. The sequence and organization of SP-D has not been reported.

(19). This environment probably plays an important, but as yet undefined, role in regulating the nature of the intracellular interaction between the lipids and proteins of surfactant.

Secretion

Surfactant is secreted from type II cells by the exocytosis of lamellar bodies. Under resting physiologic conditions about 10% of the intracellular pool of surfactant is secreted per hour. The secretion rate of surfactant can be rapidly and dramatically increased in response to exercise, large inflations of the lung, in the immediate postnatal period, and in response to several pharmacological stimuli (reviewed in 95). In vitro there also appears to be some control over the rate of surfactant secretion from isolated type II cells exerted by the amount and composition of the surfactant overlying the cells. Current evidence suggests that the apoprotein SP-A may be the active component responsible for the feedback inhibition exerted by extracellular surfactant (16, 47, 62; Wright & Dobbs, this volume).

Extracellular Metabolism

A thin but continuous layer of fluid overlies the alveolar epithelium. Surfactant secreted into this fluid layer undergoes a series of dramatic structural rearrangements (25, 48, 49, 90). Secreted lamellar bodies freed of their limiting membranes expand into large ordered tubular aggregates known as tubular myelin, which are suspended in the alveolar lining fluid. This structure is particularly rich in surfactant apoproteins (36, 70, 93). The properties of tubular myelin have not been directly studied, but the structure is widely thought to be the immediate source of the lipids forming the film on the alveolar liquid surface (reviewed in 29).

The surface film itself has proven difficult to characterize in vivo (49, 76), but its properties have been ingeniously studied by observing the behavior of microdroplets of various liquids of known surface tensions applied directly onto the alveolar surface (67). These studies performed at different lung volumes suggest that the properties of the alveolar surface film in vivo are very similar to those of monomolecular films of surfactant phospholipids studied in vitro (11). Studies of this kind support the concept that the alveolar surface film is greatly enriched in disaturated phospholipids (reviewed in 29).

The liquid in the alveolar lining layer also appears to contain a wide variety of less-ordered vesicular structures (25, 49). When isolated from bronchoalveolar washings, these vesicular structures are relatively apoprotein poor, and despite their having a lipid composition similar to other forms of surfactant, they are quite surface inactive (48, 93). The exact origin of these vesicular structures is not certain, but it appears that they are a product of the complex movement of lipid into and out of the surface layer (30, 48).

Clearance

The clearance pathways of surfactant are reviewed in detail by Wright & Dobbs in this volume, but are briefly considered here because the surfactant apoproteins are thought to regulate the uptake of the surfactant lipids into both type II cells and alveolar macrophages. These two cell types appear to account for most of the surfactant leaving the alveolar luminal compartment. The structure or composition of the surfactant taken into either of these cells in vivo is unknown, but in vitro surfactant fractions containing SP-A associate more rapidly and to a greater extent with both type II cells and macrophages than do fractions of a similar lipid composition, but lacking in SP-A (96, 97). The characteristics of the interaction between SP-A and the cell surface of type II cells and macrophages suggest that specific receptors for SP-A may be involved in the regulation of both the endocytosis and the exocytosis of surfactant, but such molecules have yet to be isolated (47, 94).

Summary of Supposed Apoprotein Functions In Vivo

In the complex metabolic cycle of surfactant, the apoproteins appear to have multiple and at times overlapping functions. These putative functions can be summarized as follows. Both SP-A and SP-B appear to participate in the calcium-dependent transformation of lamellar body contents into tubular myelin. SP-A, SP-B, and SP-C appear to facilitate the formation of phospholipid surface films, and there is some evidence for cooperative interactions between apoproteins in this function. In addition to these primarily biophysical functions, the apoproteins, particularly SP-A, may have a regulatory role in the exocytosis, endocytosis, and intracellular movement of surfactant phospholipids. The physiologic role of SP-D is currently unknown. The mechanisms involved in each of these functions are to a large extent a mystery, but recently acquired information about the structure and properties of the apoproteins is beginning to provide some insight into their function. Throughout this review the sequences described are for the human proteins unless otherwise indicated, but the information provided is applicable to other species since the amino acid sequences of all the surfactant proteins are highly conserved between species.

SURFACTANT PROTEIN STRUCTURE AND FUNCTION

Water-Soluble Proteins

SP-A Two amino acid sequences for SP-A with different residues at 7 of the 248 positions have been described (24, 89). These proteins are probably distinct gene products, but only one gene, localized to the short arm of chromosome 10 (7, 22), has been characterized. The higher order protein structure of SP-A is unknown, but the amino acid sequence coupled with a number of biochemical studies provide a reasonable picture of the general structural organization of the protein. For the purposes of discussion, the SP-A sequence can be considered to be organized into four distinct regions (Figure 1).

Amino-terminal region A 20 residue signal peptide located at the amino-terminal end of SP-A is removed prior to secretion. The amino-terminal region of secreted SP-A consists of a short seven amino acid segment. A potential site for N-linked glycosylation is located in this region of SP-A in the dog (3) and rat (66), but not in the rabbit (5) and human (24, 89). This region also contains a single cysteine that contributes to an interchain disulfide bond (3), which may be important for the alignment of chains necessary for the oligomeric assembly characteristic of the mature protein. Although in most species this disulfide pair is the only point of covalent interaction between SP-A monomers, human SP-A has additional cysteines at positions 67 and 85 (variable residue) that also probably form interchain disulfide pairs. The amino-terminus of rat, but not dog, SP-A is partially acetylated by isolated type II cells in vitro (86), but there is no evidence that this modification occurs in vivo.

Collagen-like region The second structural region of SP-A consists of amino acids 8 through 80. The sequence of this part of the protein is arranged into 23 triplets of the sequence glycine-X-Y, where X is any amino acid and Y is hydroxyproline in 13 of the 23 repeats. This arrangement of residues is similar to that found in the collagen and collagen-like protein families. This homology suggests that this region of SP-A may be folded as a triple helix. The large negative extremum at 205 nm in the circular dichroic spectrum of SP-A is certainly consistent with this possibility (33, 44, 81), but other possible structural arrangements cannot be excluded. Electron micrographs of SP-A purified from surfactant and visualized by the rotary shadowing technique suggest that there is close lateral association between helices in the amino-terminal half of the collagen-like region such that 18 monomeric subunits or 6 triple helices are associated in the mature form of the protein (81). The nature of the forces stabilizing the SP-A oligomer in this region are uncertain, but there may be a role for the alternating bands of hydrophobic and charged residues, which become apparent when the sequence is arrayed as a helical net (33). All six of the variant amino acids predicted by the two different SP-A coding sequences that have been characterized (24) are located in this collagen-like region. A comparison between the isoelectric points of the products translated in vitro from the two cDNAs and those of SP-A isolated from lung lavage suggest that native SP-A is a heterotrimer of the two sequences (23). It is possible that this apparently minor sequence heterogeneity contributes to the stability of the interhelical interactions because a homotrimeric recombinant form of SP-A associates less efficiently into higher order oligomers than the native form of SP-A (33, 81). The sequence of repeating collagen-like tripeptides is interrupted between the thirteenth and fourteenth repeats by the sequence P-C-P-P. Photomicrographs of SP-A suggest that this break in the collagen-like sequence introduces a flexible kink in an otherwise rod-like arrangement of the helices (81). Beyond this kink there is no longer any apparent lateral interaction between helices, but rather the six individual triple helices fan out symmetrically from the tightly associated stem ($\sim$ 4.5 nm in diameter) to frame a cone with a diameter at its base of $\sim$ 28 nm (81). The precise geometry at the site of the kink is unknown, but the measurements obtained on SP-A adsorbed onto a mica support suggest that the formation of a 90° angle at the kink is possible (81). The behavior of SP-A during analytical ultracentrifugation (44) or non-denaturing gel-electrophoresis is consistent with this asymmetric organization and also supports the octadecameric assembly suggested by the ultrastructural study of Voss & colleagues (81).

Linking region A 24 amino acid segment of non-collagenous sequence follows the collagen-like region and precedes the fourth region of SP-A, which contains a carbohydrate-recognition domain (17). This stretch of SP-A is encoded by a single short exon (89). Based on studies with proteolytic fragments of SP-A, Ross & his colleagues have postulated that this region plays a role in phospholipid binding (65). It is interesting that other proteins in the family of C-type lectins also have short protein segments encoded by single small exons immediately preceding their carbohydrate-recognition domains (18). Although no obvious homology exists in the sequences of these linking regions between the various C-type lectins, it is possible that this region contributes to the ligand-recognition properties or the stability of the non-collagenous portion of SP-A.

Carbohydrate-recognition region The carboxy-terminal half of SP-A (124 amino acids) is encoded by a single exon (89). After translation, this region is modified by glycosylation and intrachain disulfide pairing. A complex predominantly triantennary oligosaccharide (50) is attached to the asparagine at position 187. The oligosaccharide attached to rat SP-A in primary type II cell cultures appears to be sulfated (87), but it is not known if this observation applies in vivo or to other species. Variable sialation of the oligosaccharide contributes to the charge heterogeneity of SP-A. Disulfide pairings form between the cysteines at positions 135 and 226 and 204 and 218 (33). The location of these disulfide pairs and the position of 13 other residues scattered throughout this region are conserved in a number of mammalian and invertebrate lectins (17). These lectins have variable sugar-binding specificities, but in all cases their binding is calcium-dependent at pH 7.4. Little further structural information for this region in SP-A or any of the other homologous C-type lectins is available. As visualized after rotary shadowing with heavy metal, this region appears relatively globular with an estimated diameter of 5–6 nm after correction for metal decoration (81). It is interesting and possibly relevant to ligand binding that this region of SP-A remains associated in non-covalently linked trimers even after the triple-helical stems have been removed (33).

PROPERTIES OF SP-A

Phospholipid binding Virtually all of the SP-A that is washed from the alveolus by lavage co-isolates with the surfactant lipids and appears to be tightly associated with them. The stoichiometry of phospholipid to SP-A in isolated surfactant is approximately 30:1 (wt to wt), but not all the lipid structures that make up surfactant have SP-A associated with them. The stoichiometry of the specific lipid SP-A complex is probably closer to 3–5:1 because among all the varied morphological forms present in isolated surfactant, only the tubular myelin structure reacts with antibodies directed against SP-A (M. Williams, S. Hawgood, unpublished observations). The association between SP-A and the lipids of native surfactant is not disrupted by increasing the ionic strength (41), or by the addition of a divalent cation chelator (4). This suggests that apolar interactions play an important role in the binding of SP-A to the lipids of surfactant.

This idea is supported by the results of experiments in which SP-A was reassembled with defined one or two component phospholipid vesicles (40, 43). In these studies the association of SP-A and phospholipids was favored at temperatures below the gel to liquid phase transition temperature (43). The binding of SP-A to any of the phospholipids was not dependent on the presence of calcium (40). The interaction of SP-A with multilamellar vesicles of dimyristoylphosphatidylcholine at a phospholipid to protein stoichiometry of close to 1:1 (wt to wt) is associated with a broadening of the lipid phase transition temperature and about a 30% reduction in the enthalpy of the transition (43). These results appear to suggest that a hydrophobic region in SP-A interacts with phospholipids in a way that is strongly dependent on the phase state of the lipid, but is little influenced by ionic interactions. The location of this putative hydrophobic binding site in SP-A is not known, but the potentially amphipathic stretch of amino acids between residues 81 and 117, which separate the collagen-like region and the carbohydrate-recognition region, has been proposed as one potential site (65). The strong dependence of binding on the phase state of the phospholipid does suggest a possible mechanism whereby the lipid-protein interactions in surfactant may be regulated since it is possible that the physical state of the major lipids in surfactant vary at different points in the surfactant cycle.

Ionic interactions do not appear to be required for the association of SP-A and phospholipids, but they do appear to have some role in the nature of the interaction since the addition of small amounts of phosphatidylglycerol to phosphatidylcholine markedly influences the stoichiometry of the reassembled SP-A/lipid complex even when both phospholipids are selected to have similar phase transition temperatures (40, 43). In addition, the reassembly experiments have revealed that the ionic conditions markedly influence the structure of SP-A/lipid complexes (20, 34, 40, 70). Calcium induces rapid and extensive aggregation of SP-A/phospholipid vesicles (40) at concentrations much below those required to aggregate the phospholipids alone (20, 34).

Calcium binding Several properties of SP-A are dependent on the presence of calcium in the micromolar to millimolar range. These include the effects on lipid vesicle structure described above, the carbohydrate binding described below, and the effects of SP-A on type II cells discussed by Wright & Dobbs in this volume. SP-A appears to have at least two distinct calcium-binding sites as determined by equilibrium dialysis in the presence of excess magnesium. The higher affinity site is located in the non-collagenous end of SP-A (32). It has been reported that rat SP-A contains the calcium-binding amino acid gamma carboxyglutamic acid (60), but studies with dog and human SP-A have not confirmed this observation (32, 83). The specific conformational change induced in SP-A by the binding of calcium is unknown, but two lines of evidence suggest that a significant change in the structure of the carboxy-terminal end of the protein occurs with occupancy of the high affinity site. Firstly, the isolated carbohydrate-recognition region of SP-A is markedly protected from proteolytic cleavage by calcium, but not magnesium and, secondly, there is a small blue shift and increase in intensity of the intrinsic fluorescence spectrum induced by calcium, but again not by magnesium (32, 40). As the only two tryptophans found in SP-A are located in the carboxy-terminal 38 amino acids, this result suggests that residues at this end of the protein participate in the calcium-induced conformational change. How such a change in conformation is translated into a biological effect is still unknown.

Carbohydrate binding The carboxy-terminal 120–130 amino acids of SP-A share partial sequence homology with proteins similar in their ability to bind carbohydrates in a calcium-dependent fashion (17). It is probable that the residues common to the proteins in this family, now known as C-type lectins, are important in defining the structural requirements of the carbohydrate-binding site. Notably, the location of the two intrachain disulfide bonds is identical in all the C-type lectins, and these bonds are necessary for binding activity (31). The residues that vary between C-type lectins may dictate the ligand specificity. The biological carbohydrate ligand recognized by SP-A is unknown, but the protein does bind with different avidity to a variety of immobilized monosaccharides. SP-A binds essentially quantitatively to immobilized mannose and fucose, less well to galactose and glucose and only poorly to N-acetyl sugars (31). Binding is calcium-dependent with a half-maximum requirement for calcium of approximately 0.8 mM. The oligomeric structure of SP-A may be relevant for the recognition of the biological ligand, which is presumably a complex oligosaccharide with multiple terminal sugars. Although in other C-type lectins the carbohydrate-recognition domain has been unequivocally localized to the sequence of residues common to the carboxy-terminal half of SP-A (37), there is evidence that the clustering of binding sites consequent to oligomeric assembly markedly affects the binding affinity (12). The possible role that carbohydrate-recognition plays in the biological function of SP-A remains to be clarified. SP-A binds in vitro to both type II cells and alveolar macrophages (47, 92, 94). These cells take up increased amounts of phospholipid (97) and bacteria (79), respectively, in the presence of SP-A, thus suggesting a potential role for SP-A in both surfactant clearance and alveolar immunity. Based on recent observations, it is tempting to speculate that carbohydrate-mediated events may have some role in these interactions. The strongest evidence for this at present is that binding and uptake of recombinant SP-A by macrophages derived in culture from peripheral blood monocytes can be inhibited by mannosyl-albumin (92). Although less compelling, there is the additional observation that at least one component of the binding of SP-A to type II cells appears to be mediated through the carbohydrate-recognition region (94). This finding is consistent with a role for carbohydrate recognition in this interaction, but it is important to note that other mechanisms cannot be excluded because as yet a sugar capable of blocking the binding of SP-A to type II cells has not been identified.

SP-D The characterization of this newly identified protein as a surfactant-associated protein is tentative because no property directly relevant to surfactant function has yet been ascribed to it. The protein does have some intriguing biochemical similarities to SP-A, however, and is secreted by type II cells into the alveolar lumen (53–55). The monomeric subunit of SP-D is a 43-kd protein containing both collagenous and non-collagenous regions of approximately equal size (55). SP-D subunits are assembled into disulfide-linked trimer (55) and probably, like other collagenous proteins, into higher order oligomers. Like SP-A, the protein is glycosylated by attachment of a sialylated oligosaccharide to an asparagine residue, but SP-D, unlike SP-A, also contains carbohydrate in the collagenous region in the form of hydroxylysine glycosides (54). SP-D binds to a number of saccharides in a calcium-dependent fashion (53) and therefore belongs with SP-A in the family of C-type lectins (17).

In contrast to SP-A, SP-D is quantitatively extracted from surfactant by EDTA or by a variety of saccharides (53). Therefore, it seems likely that the association of SP-D with surfactant is mediated by carbohydrate-dependent interactions, but at present neither the binding-site nor the functional importance of this association is known. The dynamic surface tension of surfactant is not apparently significantly affected by the selective extraction of SP-D (53). It is possible that SP-D like other collagenous C-type lectins, including SP-A, has a role in mediating the host's immune defense (75).

Surfactant Proteolipids

SP-B The human SP-B gene consists of 11 exons and is located on chromosome 2 (58). The protein sequences derived from the only two SP-B nucleotide sequences reported to date differ by only one residue, but interestingly this changes the potentially glycosylated threonine at position 131 to an isoleucine (27, 38). Identical non-conservative changes at this position have been found in SP-B cDNAs from the dog (35) and rat (21), which suggests that this variability resulting from a single nucleotide substitution may be of functional significance.

Preproprotein The primary translation product of SP-B mRNA is 381 amino acids long (21, 27, 35, 38), but the fully processed active form of SP-B consists of only 79 amino acids (14). The first 20–23 amino acids at the amino-terminus of the preproprotein probably serve as a signal peptide. Further processing of the proprotein involves the removal of extensive amino and carboxy-terminal flanking regions of approximately 180 and 102 amino acids, respectively. Both flanking regions of the proprotein are potentially glycosylated. Little is currently known about the site or regulation of SP-B proprotein processing. Unlike many other proproteins that are processed to their active forms in intracellular secretory organelles, the cleavage sites in SP-B are not marked by basic residues. The pair of glutamine residues immediately preceding the amino-terminus of the active form of SP-B is also found at the processing site of the serum apolipoprotein A1 proprotein (99). Isolated type II cells do process some newly synthesized SP-B to the 79 amino acid form through a series of larger molecular weight intermediates (88), but processing appears incomplete and significant amounts of preprotein and intermediate molecular weight forms are apparently secreted by these cultured cells. In contrast only the 79 amino acid form of SP-B is detectable in lamellar bodies (88) or alveolar surfactant. At present it is not possible to be certain if any forms of SP-B other than the fully processed protein are secreted in vivo.

Within the sequence of the SP-B proprotein, four regions each of approximately 80 amino acids defined by a similar distribution of cysteine residues can be identified. The fully processed form of SP-B consists of the third of these regions from residue 201 to 279 (Figure 1). This region of the proprotein is distinguished from the others by the relatively high content of both basic and hydrophobic residues. The possibility that other active proteins or peptides might be generated as products of SP-B proprotein processing cannot be excluded.

Fully processed SP-B The 79 amino acids that comprise the active form of SP-B associated with alveolar surfactant are noteworthy for their relatively high content of cysteine, basic, and hydrophobic residues. One or more disulfide bonds link this form of SP-B as a homodimer (35). Apart from the as yet uncharacterized disulfide pairing, no other post-translational modifications to the primary sequence of this region of SP-B have been identified. The strong amphipathic alpha helical potential of both the amino and carboxy-terminal ends of SP-B have been noted (84), but this or any other aspect of the higher order structure of SP-B remains uncertain.

SP-C The gene for SP-C has been assigned to chromosome 8 (28). Various cDNAs encoding SP-C proproteins with slightly different amino acid sequences have been identified (26, 85). The heterogeneity results from what is probably allelic variation at the gene locus (resulting in two amino acid changes) and the use of an alternate intron-exon splice site (resulting in a six amino acid deletion). All the variable amino acids are located in the regions flanking the fully processed form of the SP-C protein.

SP-C preprotein The SP-C proprotein is 197 amino acids long (28, 85). A relatively hydrophilic stretch of 24 residues precedes the amino-terminus of the processed SP-C protein isolated with surfactant lipids in lavage fluid. The scarcity of apolar residues in this amino-terminal flanking region of SP-C suggests that it would not function as a classical signal peptide. Despite the apparent absence of a signal sequence, SP-C, or some processed form of it, is secreted by mechanisms that remain to be defined. The predominant form of SP-C isolated with extracellular surfactant is composed of the 35 amino acids extending from residue 25 to 60 of the proprotein (Figure 1). Additional forms further shortened by one or more amino acids at both the amino and carboxy-ends are also present (39). SP-C mRNA has recently been exclusively localized to type II cells by in situ hybridization (57), but little more is currently known about the processing and secretion of the SP-C proprotein.

Fully processed SP-C Although the majority of the 35 amino acids that comprise SP-C are hydrophobic, some asymmetry in the apolar character of the protein is present. The 12 residues at the amino-terminal end of the protein contain some hydrophilic residues including a lysine-arginine pair. The following 23 residues are exclusively apolar in nature. The functional or structural significance of this apparent amphipathicity is not yet clear, but the arrangement of residues suggests that the 24 strongly hydrophobic amino acids at the tail of the protein may interact with the acyl chains of the surfactant phospholipids and leave the pair of basic residues to interact with other charged groups or ions in the plane of the phospholipid head groups. This or any other topographic model of SP-C will need to be further refined to accommodate the recently reported observation that the two cysteine residues located at positions five and six in the SP-C protein are linked through thioester bonds to a pair of palmitic acids (15). Clearly SP-C is a strikingly apolar molecule that is likely to have pronounced effects on the physical properties of associated lipids.

PROPERTIES OF SP-B AND SP-C In contrast to the rapid pace at which the primary structures of both SP-B and SP-C were derived using DNA cloning methodology, knowlege about the properties and functions of these proteins is only now being acquired. As a result there are few studies devoted to the biochemical or biophysical properties of either SP-B or SP-C in the reviewed literature.

Solubility To some extent the properties of these proteins have limited the scope of the biochemical studies undertaken. Both SP-B and SP-C are soluble in a variety of organic solvents including butanol and the mixtures of ether and ethanol or chloroform and methanol that are commonly used to extract the lipids from surfactant. SP-B is slightly more polar than SP-C and may precipitate from these solvents at low temperatures (38, 46). The physical state (monomer-oligomer) of these proteins in any solvent environment including lipid membranes is unknown. Because it has proven difficult to prepare totally delipidated and homogeneous preparations of SP-B and SP-C, many of the studies reported to date have been performed with preparations containing variable and usually undefined amounts of both SP-B and SP-C and trace, but possibly significant, amounts of lipid. The following observations should be evaluated with these reservations in mind.

Interactions with phospholipid vesicles A mixture of SP-B and SP-C added to phospholipid vesicles made from a wide variety of phospholipids promotes the movement of phospholipid from the vesicles into an air-liquid interface (73). This result indicates that one or both proteins will interact with many different phospholipids. Some specificity in the interaction with particular phospholipids is suggested, however, by the observation that leakage from the internal aqueous space of the vesicle occurs only if the vesicle has a negative surface charge (68). These studies did not distinguish which protein was responsible for this effect, but they did suggest that one or both proteins may have a specific interaction with anionic phospholipids. Spectroscopic studies utilizing the anisotropy of phospholipids with fluorescent reporter groups in the acyl chain region have recently provided more direct evidence for a specific interaction between SP-B and anionic phospholipids (2). The apparently preferential interaction of one or both of these cationic proteins with anionic phospholipids is of particular interest since surfactant is unusually enriched in phosphatidylglycerol. Considerably more work will be required to evaluate the functional significance, if any, of such interactions. The effects of SP-B and SP-C on the structure of phospholipid membranes are only now being evaluated. Electron microscopy suggests that both SP-B and SP-C may be able to aggregate, disrupt, and possibly fuse phospholipid membranes (63, 70). Spectroscopic measurements of membrane permeability and lipid mixing are consistent with this interpretation of the electron micrographs and again show that the effect of the proteins is strongly dependent on the presence of anionic phospholipids (68). A more detailed molecular picture of how SP-B and SP-C interact with phospholipids will undoubtedly emerge from studies currently in progress in several laboratories.

Effects of SP-B and SP-C on the surface properties of phospholipids Like other hydrophobic cationic proteins and peptides, both SP-B and SP-C promote the adsorption of phospholipids from suspended membranes to an air-liquid interface (13, 35, 51, 61, 69, 72, 73, 98). The effect of SP-B and SP-C on phospholipid adsorption is most marked in the presence of anionic phospholipids (73), but is not strongly calcium- or pH-dependent. It is possible that the mechanisms involved in the protein-mediated vesicle disruption and fusion also mediate the ability of these proteins to promote the formation of surface films from suspended lipid bilayers. It seems reasonable to suppose that protein-induced lipid-bilayer packing disorder and instability will be related to both processes. A role for one or other of these small intensely hydrophobic proteins in modulating the behavior of monolayers of phospholipids, even at the high surface pressures known to exist at the alveolar surface (67), should probably not be discounted. As yet such a possibility has not been experimentally tested.

evidence for interaction between apoproteins In vitro studies suggest that complex interactions dependent on the presence of more than one of the surfactant apoproteins are responsible for both the unusual structures present in surfactant and their surface properties. Suzuki & his colleagues have recently shown that the highly ordered three-dimensional lattice of tubular myelin is dependent on the presence of both SP-A and at least one hydrophobic protein that, although not unequivocally identified in their study, was probably SP-B (70). Consistent with the properties of the individual proteins that have been discussed in some detail herein, critical amounts of the anionic phospholipid phosphatidylglycerol and calcium were also required to successfully reassemble this structure (70). Studies with reassembled surfactant lipoproteins also suggest that cooperative interactions between apoproteins can markedly affect function. The surface properties of phospholipids, particularly the surface adsorption rate, are strongly dependent on the specific mix of apoproteins added to them (10, 35). It will be of great interest to discover whether these interdependent effects of the apoproteins are related to direct protein-protein interactions, or to separate but cooperative effects of the proteins on phospholipid structure.

CONCLUSIONS

This review has focused on the structure and biochemical properties of three of the surfactant apoproteins. Study of the proteins alone and in macromolecular complexes is beginning to provide some insight into their potential physiologic roles and the beginning of an understanding of the molecular mechanisms underlying their action. Clearly many challenges remain, including the identification and characterization of other proteins that may be a part of the surfactant system. The future directions for research in the field of surfactant apoproteins are many and, in most cases, readily apparent from the foregoing discussion. Other well-studied lipoprotein systems such as neural myelin and the serum lipoproteins will continue to be useful paradigms for surfactant researchers. The remarkable progress that has been made in these systems suggests, not surprisingly, that the tools of molecular and cell biology coupled with innovative biophysical studies will continue to be increasingly important to surfactant investigators. There is also a critical need to develop systems appropriate for the in vivo testing of ideas generated by these biochemical studies. Lessons learned from the study of the surfactant apoproteins are likely to be relevant to the larger group of investigators interested in lipid-protein interactions and may, in the not too distant future, lead to improved therapies for many forms of acute respiratory failure.

Literature Cited

1. Avery, M. E., Mead, J. 1959. Surface properties in relation to atelectases and hyaline membrane disease. *Am. J. Dis. Child.* 97:517–23
2. Baatz, J. E., Whitsett, J. A. Z., Dey, C. 1990. Effects of synthetic human surfactant protein SP-B polypeptide fragments on membrane bilayer surface order. *Am. Rev. Respir. Dis.* 141:A693
3. Benson, B., Hawgood, S., Schilling, J., Clements, J., Damm, D., et al. 1985. Structure of canine pulmonary surfactant apoprotein: cDNA and complete amino acid sequence. *Proc. Natl. Acad. Sci. USA* 82:6379–83
4. Benson, B. J., Williams, M. C., Sueishi, K., Goerke, J., Sargeant, T. 1984. Role of calcium ions in the structure and function of pulmonary surfactant. *Biochim. Biophys. Acta* 793:18–27
5. Boggaram, V., Qing, K., Mendelson, C. R. 1988. Major apoprotein of rabbit pulmonary surfactant. *J. Biol. Chem.* 263:2939–47
6. Brown, E. S. 1964. Isolation and assay of dipalmityl lecithin in lung extracts. *Am. J. Physiol.* 207:402–6
7. Bruns, G., Stroh, H., Veldman, G. M., Latt, S. A., Floros, J. 1987. The 35 kd pulmonary surfactant-associated protein is encoded on chromosome 10. *Hum. Genet.* 76:58–62
8. Chander, A., Johnson, R. G., Reicherter, J., Fisher, A. B. 1986. Lung lamellar bodies maintain an acidic internal pH. *J. Biol. Chem.* 261:6126–31
9. Chevalier, G., Collet, A. J. 1972. In vivo incorporation of choline-^{3}H, leucine-^{3}H and galactose-^{3}H in alveolar type II pneumocytes in relation to surfactant synthesis. A quantitative radioautographic study in mouse by electron microscopy. *Anat. Rec.* 174:289–310
10. Chung, J., Yu, S.-H., Whitsett, J. A., Harding, P. G. R., Possmayer, F. 1989. Effect of surfactant-associated protein-A (SP-A) on the activity of lipid extract surfactant. *Biochim. Biophys. Acta* 1002:348–58
11. Clements, J. A. 1957. Surface tension of lung extracts. *Proc. Soc. Exp. Biol. Med.* 95:170–72
12. Colley, K. J., Baenziger, J. U. 1987. Biosynthesis and secretion of the rat core-specific lectin. *J. Biol. Chem.* 262:3415–21
13. Curstedt, J., Jörnvall, H., Robertson,

B., Bergman, T., Berggren, P. 1987. Two hydrophobic low-molecular-mass protein fractions of pulmonary surfactant. *Eur. J. Biochem.* 168:255–62

14. Curstedt, T., Johansson, J., Barros-Soderling, J., Robertson, B., Nilsson, G., et al. 1988. Low-molecular-mass surfactant protein type I. *Eur. J. Biochem.* 172:521–25
15. Curstedt, T., Johansson, J., Persson, P., Eklund, A., Robertson, B., et al. 1990. Hydrophobic surfactant-associated polypeptides: SP-C is a lipopeptide with two palmitoylated cysteine residues, whereas SP-B lacks covalently linked fatty acyl groups. *Proc. Natl. Acad. Sci. USA* 87:2985–89
16. Dobbs, L. G., Wright, J. R., Hawgood, S., Gonzalez, R., Venstrom, K., Nellenbogen, J. 1987. Pulmonary surfactant and its components inhibit secretion of phosphatidylcholine from cultured rat alveolar type II cells. *Proc. Natl. Acad. Sci. USA* 84:1010–14
17. Drickamer, K., Dordal, M. S., Reynolds, L. 1986. Mannose-binding proteins isolated from rat liver contain carbohydrate-recognition domains linked to collagenous tails. *J. Biol. Chem.* 261:6878–87
18. Drickamer, K., McCreary, V. 1987. Exon structure of a mannose-binding protein gene reflects its evolutionary relationship to the asialglycoprotein receptor and nonfibrillar collagens. *J. Biol. Chem.* 262:2582–89
19. Eckenhoff, R. G. 1989. Perinatal changes in lung surfactant calcium measured in situ. *J. Clin. Invest.* 84:1295–1301
20. Efrati, H., Hawgood, S., Williams, M. C., Hong, K., Benson, B. J. 1987. Divalent cation and hydrogen ion effects on the structure and surface activity of pulmonary surfactant. *Biochemistry* 26:7986–93
21. Emrie, P. A., Shannon, J. M., Mason, R. J., Fisher, J. H. 1989. cDNA and deduced amino acid sequence for the rat hydrophobic pulmonary surfactant-associated protein, SP-B. *Biochim. Biophys. Acta* 994:215–21
22. Fisher, J. H., Kao, F. T., Jones, C., White, R. T., Benson, B. J., Mason, R. J. 1987. The coding sequence for the 32,000 dalton pulmonary surfactant-associated protein A is located on chromosome 10 and identifies two separate restriction-fragment-length polymorphisms. *Am. J. Hum. Genet.* 40:503–11
23. Floros, J., Phelps, D. S., Kourembanas, S., Taeusch, H. 1986. Primary translation products, biosynthesis, and tissue specificity of the major surfactant protein in rat. *J. Biol. Chem.* 261:828–31
24. Floros, J., Steinbrink, R., Jacobs, K., Phelps, D., Kriz, R., et al. 1986. Isolation and characterization of cDNA clones for the 35-kDa pulmonary surfactant-associated protein. *J. Biol. Chem.* 261:9029–33
25. Gil, J., Reiss, O. K. 1973. Isolation and characterization of lamellar bodies and tubular myelin from rat lung homogenates. *J. Cell Biol.* 58:152–71
26. Glasser, S. W., Korfhagen, T. R., Perme, C. M., Pilot-Matias, T. J., Kister, S. E., Whitsett, J. A. 1988. Two SP-C genes encoding human pulmonary surfactant proteolipid. *J. Biol. Chem.* 263:10326–31
27. Glasser, S. W., Korfhagen, T. R., Weaver, T., Pilot-Matias, T., Fox, J. L., Whitsett, J. A. 1987. cDNA and deduced amino acid sequence of human pulmonary surfactant-associated proteolipid SPL(Phe). *Proc. Natl. Acad. Sci. USA* 84:4007–11
28. Glasser, S. W., Korfhagen, T. R., Weaver, T. E., Clark, J. C., Pilot-Matias, T., et al. 1988. cDNA, deduced polypeptide structure and chromosomal assignment of human pulmonary surfactant proteolipid, SPL(pVal). *J. Biol. Chem.* 263:9–12
29. Goerke, J., Clements, J. A. 1986. Alveolar surface tension and lung surfactant. In *Handbook of Physiology—The Respiratory System III,* ed. P. T. Macklem, J. Mead, pp. 247–61. Washington DC: Am. Physiol. Soc.
30. Gross, N. J., Narine, K. R. 1989. Surfactant subtypes in mice: characterization and quantitation. *J. Appl. Physiol.* 66:342–49
31. Haagsman, H. P., Hawgood, S., Sargeant, T., Buckley, D., White, R. T., et al. 1987. The major lung surfactant protein, SP 28–36, is a calcium-dependent, carbohydrate-binding protein. *J. Biol. Chem.* 262:13877–80
32. Haagsman, H. P., White, R. T., Schilling, J., Lau, K., Benson, B. J., et al. 1989. Studies of the structure of lung surfactant protein SP-A. *Am. J. Physiol.* 257:L421–29
33. Haagsman, H. P., Sargeant, T., Hauschka, P. V., Benson, B. J., Hawgood, S. 1990. Binding of calcium to SP-A, a surfactant associated protein. *Biochemistry.* 29:8894–900
34. Hawgood, S., Benson, B. J., Hamilton, R. L. Jr. 1985. Effects of a surfactant-associated protein and calcium ions on the structure and surface activity of lung

surfactant lipids. *Biochemistry* 24:184–90

35. Hawgood, S., Benson, B. J., Schilling, J., Damm, D., Clements, J. A., White, R. T. 1987. Nucleotide and amino acid sequences of pulmonary surfactant protein SP 18 and evidence for cooperation between SP 18 and SP 28–36 in surfactant lipid adsorption. *Proc. Natl. Acad. Sci. USA* 84:66–70
36. Hook, G. E. R., Gilmore, L. B., Talley, F. A. 1986. Dissolution and reassembly of tubular myelin-like multilamellated structures from the lungs of patients with pulmonary alveolar proteinosis. *Lab. Invest.* 55:194–208
37. Hsueh, E. C., Holland, E. C., Carrera, G. M., Drickamer, K. 1986. The rat liver asialoglycoprotein receptor polypeptide must be inserted into a microsome to achieve its active conformation. *J. Biol. Chem.* 261:4940–47
38. Jacobs, K. A., Phelps, D. S., Steinbrink, R., Fisch, J., Kriz, R., et al. 1987. Isolation of a cDNA clone encoding a high molecular weight precursor to a 6-kDa pulmonary surfactant-associated protein. *J. Biochem.* 262:9808–11
39. Johansson, J., Curstedt, T., Robertson, B., Jörnvall, H. 1988. Size and structure of the hydrophobic low molecular weight surfactant-associated polypeptide. *Biochemistry* 27:3544–47
40. King, R. J., Carmichael, M. C., Horowitz, P. M. 1983. Reassembly of lipid-protein complexes of pulmonary surfactant. *J. Biol. Chem.* 258:10672–80
41. King, R. J., Clements, J. A. 1972. Surface active materials from dog lung. II. Composition and physiological correlations. *Am. J. Physiol.* 223:715–26
42. King, R. J., Klass, D. J., Gikas, E. G., Clements, J. A. 1973. Isolation of apoproteins from canine surface active material. *Am. J. Physiol.* 224:788–95
43. King, R. J., Phillips, M. C., Horowitz, P. M., Dang, S.-C. 1986. Interaction between the 35 kDa apolipoprotein of pulmonary surfactant and saturated phosphatidylcholines. Effects of temperature. *Biochim. Biophys. Acta* 879:1–13
44. King, R. J., Simon, D., Horowitz, P. M. 1989. Aspects of secondary and quaternary structure of surfactant protein A from canine lung. *Biochim. Biophys. Acta* 1001:294–301
45. Klaus, M. H., Clements, J. A., Havel, R. J. 1961. Composition of surface-active material isolated from beef lung. *Proc. Natl. Acad. Sci. USA* 47:1858–59
46. Kogishi, K., Kurozumi, M., Fujita, Y., Murayama, T., Kuze, F., Suzuki, Y. 1988. Isolation and partial characterization of human low molecular weight protein associated with pulmonary surfactant. *Am. Rev. Respir. Dis.* 137:1426–31
47. Kuroki, Y., Mason, R. J., Voelker, D. R. 1988. Pulmonary surfactant apoprotein A structure and modulation of surfactant secretion by rat alveolar type II cells. *J. Biol. Chem.* 263:3388–94
48. Magoon, M. W., Wright, J. R., Baritussio, A., Williams, M. C., Goerke, J., et al. 1983. Subfractionation of lung surfactant. Implications for metabolism and surface activity. *Biochim. Biophys. Acta* 750:18–31
49. Manabe, T. 1979. Freeze-fracture study of alveolar lining layer in adult rat lungs. *J. Ultrastruct. Res.* 69:86–97
50. Munakata, H., Nimberg, R. B., Snider, G. L., Robins, A. G., Van Halbeek, H., et al. 1982. The structure of the carbohydrate units of the 36K glycoprotein derived from the lung lavage of a patient with alveolar proteinosis by high resolution ^{1}H-NMR spectroscopy. *Biochem. Biophys. Res. Commun.* 108:1401–5
51. Notter, R. H., Shapiro, D. L., Ohning, B., Whitsett, J. A. 1987. Biophysical activity of synthetic phospholipids combined with purified lung surfactant 6,000 dalton apoprotein. *Chem. Phys. Lipids.* 44:1–17
52. Pattle, R. E. 1955. Properties, function and origin of the alveolar lining layer. *Nature* 175:1125–26
53. Persson, A., Chang, D., Crouch, E. 1990. Surfactant protein D is a divalent cation-dependent carbohydate-binding protein. *J. Biol. Chem.* 265:5755–60
54. Persson, A., Chang, D., Rust, K., Moxley, M., Longmore, W., Crouch, E. 1989. Purification and biochemical characterization of CP4 (SP-D), a collagenous surfactant-associated protein. *Biochemistry* 28:6361–67
55. Persson, A., Rust, K., Chang, D., Moxley, M., Longmore, W., Crouch, E. 1988. CP4: a pneumocyte-derived collagenous surfactant-associated protein. Evidence for heterogeneity of collagenous surfactant proteins. *Biochemistry* 27:8576–84
56. Phelps, D. S., Floros, J. 1988. Localization of surfactant protein synthesis in human lung by in situ hybridization. *Am. Rev. Respir. Dis.* 137:939–42
57. Phelps, D. S., Floros, J. 1990. Differential localization of surfactant protein mRNAS in rat and human lung. *Am. Rev. Respir. Dis.* 141:A694
58. Pilot-Matias, T. J., Kister, S. E., Fox, J. L., Kropp, K., Glasser, S. W., Whit-

sett, J. A. 1989. Structure and organization of the gene encoding human pulmonary surfactant proteolipid SP-B. *DNA* 8:75–86
59. Possmayer, F. 1988. A proposed nomenclature for pulmonary surfactant-associated proteins. *Am. Rev. Respir. Dis.* 138:990–98
60. Rannels, S. R., Gallaher, K. J., Wallin, R., Rannels, D. E. 1987. Vitamin K-dependent carboxylation of pulmonary surfactant-associated proteins. *Proc. Natl. Acad. Sci. USA* 84:5952–56
61. Revak, S. D., Merritt, T. A., Degryse, E., Stefani, L., Courtney, M., et al. 1988. Use of human surfactant low molecular weight apoproteins in the reconstitution of surfactant biologic activity. *J. Clin. Invest.* 81:826–33
62. Rice, W. R., Ross, G. F., Singleton, F. M., Dingle, S., Whitsett, J. A. 1987. Surfactant-associated protein inhibits phospholipid secretion from type II cells. *J. Appl. Physiol.* 63:692–98
63. Rice, W. R., Sarin, V. K., Fox, J. L., Baatz, J., Wert, S., Whitsett, J. A. 1989. Surfactant peptides stimulate uptake of phosphatidylcholine by isolated cells. *Biochim. Biophys. Acta* 1006:237–45
64. Rooney, S. A. 1985. The surfactant system and lung phospholipid biochemistry. *Am. Rev. Respir. Dis.* 131:439–60
65. Ross, G. F., Notter, R. H., Meuth, J., Whitsett, J. A. 1986. Phospholipid binding and biophysical activity of pulmonary surfactant-associated protein (SAP)-35 and its non-collagenous COOH-terminal domains. *J. Biol. Chem.* 261:14283–91
66. Sano, K., Fisher, J., Mason, R. J., Kuroki, Y., Schilling, J., et al. 1987. Isolation and sequence of a cDNA clone for the rat pulmonary surfactant-associated protein (PSP-A). *Biochem. Biophys. Res. Comm.* 144:367–74
67. Schürch, S., Goerke, J., Clements, J. A. 1976. Direct determination of surface tension in the lung. *Proc. Natl. Acad. Sci. USA* 73:4698–4702
68. Shiffer, K., Hawgood, S., Düzgünes, N., Goerke, J. 1988. Interactions of the low molecular weight group of surfactant-associated proteins (SP 5-18) with pulmonary surfactant lipids. *Biochemistry* 27:2689–95
69. Suzuki, Y., Curstedt, T., Grossmann, G., Kobayashi, T., Nilsson, R., et al. 1986. The role of the low-molecular weight (≤ 15000 daltons) apoproteins of pulmonary surfactant. *Eur. J. Respir. Dis.* 69:336–45
70. Suzuki, Y., Fujita, Y., Kogishi, K. 1989. Reconstitution of tubular myelin from synthetic lipids and proteins associated with pig pulmonary surfactant. *Am. Rev. Respir. Dis.* 140:75–81
71. Suzuki, Y., Kogishi, K., Fujita, Y., Kina, T., Nishikawa, S. 1986. A monoclonal antibody to the 15,000 dalton protein associated with porcine pulmonary surfactant. *Exp. Lung. Res.* 11:61–73
72. Takahashi, A., Fujiwara, T. 1986. Proteolipid in bovine lung surfactant: its role in surfactant function. *Biochem. Biophys. Res. Comm.* 135:527–32
73. Tanaka, Y., Takei, T., Aiba, T., Masuda, K., Kiuchi, A., Fujiwara, T. 1986. Development of synthetic lung surfactants. *J. Lipid. Res.* 27:475–85
74. Tenner, A. J., Robinson, S. L., Borchelt, J., Wright, J. R. 1989. Human pulmonary surfactant protein (SP-A), a protein structurally homologous to C1q, can enhance FcR- and CR1-mediated phagocytosis. *J. Biol. Chem.* 264:13923–28
75. Thiel, S., Reid, K. B. M. 1989. Structures and functions associated with the group of mammalian lectins containing collagen-like sequences. *FEBS Lett.* 250:78–84
76. Untersee, P., Gil, J., Weibel, E. R. 1971. Visualization of extracellular lining layer of lung alveoli by freeze-etching. *Respir. Physiol.* 13:171–85
77. van Golde, L. M. G. 1976. Metabolism of phospholipids in the lung. *Am. Rev. Respir. Dis.* 114:977–1000
78. van Golde, L. M. G., Batenburg, J. J., Robertson, B. 1988. The pulmonary surfactant system: biochemical aspects and functional significance. *Physiol. Rev.* 68:374–453
79. van Iwaarden, F., Welmers, B., Verhoef, J., Haagsman, H. P., van Golde, L. M. G. 1990. Pulmonary surfactant protein A enhances the host-defense mechanism of rat alveolar macrophages. *Am. J. Respir. Cell Mol. Biol.* 2:91–98
80. von Neergaard, K. 1929. Neue Auffassungen über einen Grundbegriff der Atemmechanik. Retracktionskraft der Lunge, abhängig von der Oberfläschenspunnung in den Alveolen. *Z. Gesamte Exp. Med.* 66:373–94
81. Voss, T., Eistetter, H., Schafer, K. P. 1988. Macromolecular organization of natural and recombinant lung surfactant protein SP 28-36. *J. Mol. Biol.* 201:219–27
82. Walker, S. R., Williams, M. C., Benson, B. 1986. Immunocytochemical localization of the major surfactant apoproteins in type II cells, Clara cells

and alveolar macrophages of rat lung. *J. Histochem. Cytochem.* 34:1137–48
83. Wallin, R., Seaton, M., Martin, L. F. 1988. No evidence for vitamin K-dependent carboxylation of canine surfactant apoproteins, 28-36 kDa. *Biochem. J.* 252:851–56
84. Waring, A., Taeusch, W., Bruni, R., Amirkhanian, J., Fan, B., et al. 1989. Synthetic amphipathic sequences of surfactant protein-B mimic several physicochemical and in vivo properties of native pulmonary surfactant proteins. *Peptide Res.* 2:308–12
85. Warr, R. G., Hawgood, S., Buckley, D. I., Crisp, T. M., Schilling, J., et al. 1987. Low molecular weight human pulmonary surfactant protein (SP5): isolation, characterization, and cDNA and amino acid sequences. *Proc. Natl. Acad. Sci. USA* 84:7915–19
86. Weaver, T. E., Hull, W. H., Ross, G., Whitsett, J. A. 1986. In vitro acetylation of rat pulmonary surfactant-associated glycoprotein(s) A primary translation products. *Biochim. Biophys. Acta* 869:330–36
87. Weaver, T. E., Kropp, K. L., Whitsett, J. A. 1987. In vitro sulfation of pulmonary surfactant-associated protein-35. *Biochim. Biophys. Acta* 914:205–11
88. Weaver, T. E., Whitsett, J. A. 1989. Processing of hydrophobic pulmonary surfactant protein B in rat type II cells. *Am. J. Physiol.* 257:L100–8
89. White, R. T., Damm, D., Miller, J., Spratt, K., Schilling, J., et al. 1985. Isolation and characterization of the human pulmonary surfactant apoprotein gene. *Nature* 317:361–63
90. Williams, M. C. 1977. Conversion of lamellar body membranes into tubular myelin in alveoli of fetal rat lungs. *J. Cell Biol.* 72:260–77
91. Williams, M. C. 1984. Uptake of lectins by pulmonary alveolar type II cells: subsequent deposition into lamellar bodies. *Proc. Natl. Acad. Sci. USA* 81:6383–87
92. Wintergerst, E., Manz-Keinke, H., Plattner, H., Schlepper-Schafer, J. 1989. The interaction of a lung surfactant protein (SP-A) with macrophages is mannose dependent. *Eur. J. Cell Biol.* 50:291–98
93. Wright, J. R., Benson, B. J., Williams, M. C., Goerke, J., Clements, J. A. 1984. Protein composition of rabbit alveolar surfactant subfractions. *Biochim. Biophys. Acta* 791:320–32
94. Wright, J. R., Borchelt, J. D., Hawgood, S. 1989. Lung surfactant apoprotein SP-A (26–36 kDa) binds with high affinity to isolated alveolar type II cells. *Proc. Natl. Acad. Sci. USA* 86:5410–5414
95. Wright, J. R., Clements, J. A. 1987. Metabolism and turnover of lung surfactant. *Am. Rev. Respir. Dis.* 135:426–44
96. Wright, J. R., Wager, R. E., Hamilton, R. L., Huang, M., Clements, J. A. 1986. Uptake of lung surfactant subfractions into lamellar bodies of adult rabbit lungs. *J. Appl. Physiol.* 60:817–825
97. Wright, J. R., Wager, R. E., Hawgood, S., Dobbs, L., Clements, J. A. 1987. Surfactant apoprotein M_r = 26,000–36,000 enhances uptake of liposomes by type II cells. *J. Biol. Chem.* 262:2888–2894
98. Yu, S. H., Wallace, D., Bhavnani, B., Enhorning, G., Harding, P. G. R., Possmayer, F. 1988. Effect of reconstituted pulmonary surfactant containing the 6000-dalton hydrophobic protein on lung compliance of prematurely delivered rabbit fetuses. *Pediatr. Res.* 23:23–30
99. Zannis, V. I., Karathanasis, S. K., Keutmann, H. T., Goldberger, G., Breslow, J. L. 1983. Intracellular and extracellular processing of human apolipoprotein A-I: secreted apolipoprotein A-I isoprotein 2 is a propeptide. *Proc. Natl. Acad. Sci. USA* 80:2574–78

Annu. Rev. Physiol. 1991. 53:395–414

REGULATION OF PULMONARY SURFACTANT SECRETION AND CLEARANCE

Jo Rae Wright

Department of Physiology and Cardiovascular Research Institute, University of California, San Francisco, California 94143

Leland G. Dobbs

Department of Medicine and Cardiovascular Research Institute, University of California, San Francisco, California 94143

KEY WORDS: pulmonary surfactant, pulmonary, type II cell, surfactant proteins, surfactant phospholipids

---

INTRODUCTION

Pulmonary surfactant functions in the lungs at the interface between the air and the liquid layer that covers the epithelial surface. Pulmonary surfactant is functionally, chemically, and morphologically heterogeneous. Although its best-defined function (and the one for which it is named) is to lower surface tension at the air/liquid interface within the lung, pulmonary surfactant is now believed to have additional functions, including mediating host defense against infection (100, 103). Chemically, surfactant consists of lipids (primarily phospholipids) and four specific surfactant-associated proteins: SP-A, SP-B, SP-C, and SP-D (reviewed by Hawgood & Shiffer, this volume). Several morphologic forms of surfactant have been identified in alveolar liquid in fetal lungs and in fluid obtained by endobronchial lavage (see 113 for review). Our understanding of the precise function of each of these forms as well as an accurate chemical characterization of them is incomplete.

0066-4278/91/0315-0395$02.00

A large body of evidence suggests that the alveolar type II cell is the major source of surfactant. Type II cells contain (47, 55) and secrete (19) material that is strikingly similar to surfactant isolated from endobronchial lavage. Both lipid and protein components of surfactant are synthesized by the type II cell and are stored prior to secretion in intracellular organelles called lamellar bodies. Secretion occurs by exocytosis, with fusion of the limiting membrane of the lamellar body to the apical plasma membrane of the cell and extrusion of lamellar body contents into the alveolar space. The secreted surfactant appears to undergo a series of complex transformations during its residence in the alveolus. After the lamellar body contents are secreted they are transformed into an extraordinary three-dimensional lattice-like structure called tubular myelin. The events responsible for this transformation in vivo are not understood, but in vitro the formation of tubular myelin requires calcium, phospholipids, and the surfactant proteins SP-A and SP-B (99). Indirect evidence suggests that tubular myelin is a precursor to the surface-tension-lowering monomolecular surface film, which is thought to be enriched in dipalmitoylphosphatidylcholine (reviewed in 113). It has been suggested that large/dense particles of surfacant become smaller/less dense particles during intra-alveolar metabolism (1, 2, 37, 38, 52, 79). The mechanisms by which these transformations occur are not known, although there appear to be changes in protein composition that correlate with changes in size as approximated by ease of sedimentation (111). Recent evidence suggests that enzymatic activity may play a role in the transformation of dense to light particles (39). As will be discussed below, different fractions of surfactant are cleared at different rates. It seems likely that various components of the fractions, such as surfactant proteins, may be involved in regulating alveolar surfactant pool size.

The surfactant system is in a state of continuous flux. The intra-alveolar pool of surfactant lipids turns over approximately every 5–10 hr (reviewed in (113)). Presumably, intra-alveolar surfactant undergoes alterations in its physical form as the surface area of the air-liquid interface changes within each breath during inhalation and exhalation. The pool size of surfactant must be adjusted so that an appropriate amount of material is present to meet changing demands. For example, the alveolar pool of surfactant increases substantially at birth when the fetus must make the transition from a fluid-filled lung, in which surface tension forces are negligible, to an air-filled lung in which the surface-tension-reducing properties of surfactant are required in order to effect efficient gas exchange. The size of the surfactant pool can also change dramatically with exercise (65); increasing by 60% during exercise and rapidly returning to pre-exercise levels after exercise has ceased. These and other observations suggest that some mechanisms must exist to maintain an appropriate amount of functional surfactant in the face of changing demands.

The overall goal of this article is to review the current understanding of the factors that regulate the alveolar pool size of surfactant. Specifically, we focus on the factors that regulate surfactant secretion into and clearance from the alveolar airspace. Although our understanding of these processes is somewhat limited, recent studies suggest that secretion and clearance of surfactant by the type II cell may be linked. Because massive amounts of membrane are inserted into the apical plasma membrane when exocytosis occurs and because added membrane is recycled by endocytosis, it seems reasonable to postulate that exocytic and endocytic events in type II cells are coordinatively regulated, as they are believed to be in other cell systems (29, 104).

SECRETION OF SURFACTANT

Secretion from cells can occur by both constitutive and regulated pathways (reviewed in 9). Constitutive secretion, in which substances are secreted continuously without prior concentration and storage, has not been studied in detail in type II cells. It is possible, although unstudied, that one or more components of surfactant are secreted by constitutive as well as regulated pathways and that the two pathways may be utilized to differing extents during various states of health and disease. Studies in type II cells have focused on regulated secretion, in which a stimulus causes previously synthesized material stored in cytoplasmic organelles to be released from the cell. In type II cells, regulated secretion occurs by a process described as classical exocytosis. Extracellular stimuli modulate intracellular chemical events, which result in movement of lamellar bodies towards the apical surface of the type II cell, apposition of lamellar bodies to the apical plasma membrane, fusion of the limiting membrane of the lamellar bodies with the plasma membrane, and extrusion of lamellar body contents into the alveolus. It is likely that various intracellular second messengers, cytoskeletal elements, protein phosphorylation and dephosphorylation, and membrane fusion proteins are all involved in exocytosis in type II cells. The steps linking the initial stimulus to the eventual secretion of lamellar bodies are incompletely understood.

Many different model systems have been used to study surfactant secretion. Morphometric techniques at the electron microscopic level have been used to estimate the cellular content of lamellar bodies before and after treatment with stimuli. Physical methods, i.e. measuring surface tension of alveolar lavage liquid, have also been used to estimate secretion. Chemical measurement of surfactant secretion has generally focused on secretion of one surfactant component because surfactant is chemically heterogeneous, and it is difficult to measure all surfactant components simultaneously. This approach appears to be valid because most surfactant components appear to be secreted together

(19). The majority of studies of control of surfactant secretion have used lipid components of surfactant as markers for secretion. Various classes of lipids have been used, in increasing order of selectivity: the entire lipid pool; the entire phospholipid pool; all phosphatidylcholines; and saturated phosphatidylcholines, in which fatty acids on both the C_1 and C_2 positions are saturated. There are very few studies of secretion of surfactant proteins (19, 107).

Systems involving whole animals, isolated lungs, lung slices, and cultured type II cells have all been used to study surfactant secretion. Each type of model system affords distinct advantages and disadvantages. Systems involving whole animals afford preservations of cell interactions both within the lung and among various organs, but do not easily permit direct effects on type II cells to be differentiated from effects that act indirectly on other cells, or on other organs. Model systems using isolated type II cells allow the direct study of type II cells, but it should be kept in mind that isolation and culture of cells can introduce artifacts and that effects observed in vitro are not necesssarily those that are important in vivo. Unfortunately, it has been difficult to correlate observations made in vitro with those made in vivo (see Table 1). Because the lung is sparsely innervated at the alveolar level, it seems unlikely that the nervous system directly affects type II cells. Both deep inflation of the lungs and circulating catecholamines probably modulate secretion in vivo (see Table 1). Unfortunately, naturally occurring substances that correspond to many pharmacologic agents active in vitro have not been identified.

Table 1 Factors that affect secretion and clearance of surfactant

Factor	Secretion	Clearance
Deep inflation	↑	↑
β-adrenergic stimulation	↑	↑
SP-A	↓	↑
Purinergic stimuli	↑	?
Calcium ionophores	↑	?
Activators of protein kinase C	↑	?
Alkalosis	↑	?
Leukotrienes	↑	?
Vasopressin	↑	?
Histamine	↑	?
Arachidonic acid metabolites	↑	?
Compound 48/80	↓	?

See text for references. A question mark indicates that factors have not been tested. Most factors have been shown to affect secretion or clearance only in vitro studies.

Stimuli of Secretion

DEEP INFLATION The normal pattern of breathing involves relatively shallow breaths at tidal volume punctuated by occasional deep inflations of the lung, termed sighs (4). Continuous shallow breathing without sighs causes diminished lung compliance, atelectasis, and hypoxemia (57). Thet & coworkers demonstrated that ventilation of a nonperfused isolated rat lung at a constant tidal volume for two hour results in atelectasis; atelectasis can be reversed by a single large breath (101). Several different lines of evidence in intact animals and in isolated lung models suggest that an increase in lung volume stimulates surfactant release. Doubling ventilation in anesthetized animals by increasing both tidal volume and frequency increases the amount of phospholipid that can be lavaged from the lungs (71). Nicholas & Barr (62, 63) showed that increasing tidal volume alone stimulated surfactant release. Hildebran et al (42) demonstrated that air inflation to total lung capacity of excised rat lungs increases the amount of phospholipid lavageable from the lungs. Nicholas, Power & Barr showed that a single large inflation of isolated perfused rat lungs can increase the amount of lavageable phospholipid from the alveolar pool (64). Morphologic evidence supports the concept that stimulation of surfactant secretion as well as opening of previous atelectatic areas is responsible for the increase in lavageable phospholipid when lungs are inflated because the volume density of lamellar bodies in alveolar type II cells decreases after inflation with large tidal volumes (56). It is still not known how deep inflation of the lungs increases surfactant secretion. In some (71) but not other (65) studies, various agents such as atropine, propranolol, and indomethacin can inhibit the stimulatory effect. One possible mechanism underlying the effect of deep inflation may involve direct effects of mechanical forces on type II cells. Recent studies of type II cells maintained in culture show that mechanical distortion of the cells, which results in an increase in mean cellular surface area by 15–25% (correlating to increases in cell diameter of 7–12%), leads to large increases in secretion of phosphatidylcholine. The stimulatory effect of a single stretch persists for up to 30 min and may be mediated by calcium released from intracellular stores (110), thus suggesting that direct distortion of type II cells results in prolonged secretion mediated by transient increases in cytosolic calcium.

β-ADRENERGIC STIMULI It is well-established that mechanisms that increase cellular cAMP stimulate surfactant secretion. Morphologic studies in rats (68, 102) demonstrate that injection of β-adrenergic agents causes a decrease in the number of lamellar bodies per type II cell. Both in isolated perfused lung models (6) and in primary cultures of type II cells (6, 21, 59), β-adrenergic agents stimulate secretion of phosphatidylcholine. The physiologic source of β-adrenergic stimuli is thought to be circulating catecholamines; the mechanism of action involves increasing cellular levels of cAMP (6, 58).

Not surprisingly, other agents that increase cellular cAMP also stimulate secretion. Analogues of cAMP (6, 21, 59), methyl xanthines (21), forskolin (81), and cholera toxin (58), all stimulate secretion in primary cultures of type II cells.

Presumably protein kinase A is involved in the stimulus-secretion pathway mediated by cAMP. Rice et al (81) showed that protein kinase A activation ratios increase in cells treated with terbutaline or forskolin. More detailed studies of patterns of changes in protein phosphorylation are likely to be forthcoming.

PURINERGIC STIMULI Adenosine compounds are potent secretagogues for phosphatidylcholine in cultured type II cells. Both adenosine (33, 34) and ATP (30, 88) stimulate secretion. ATP and TPA (see below) are the two most potent single secretagogues for surfactant in vitro. Gilfillan & Rooney (34) showed that the stimulatory effect of adenosine could be mimicked by nonmetabolizable adenosine analogues and could be blocked by 8-phenyltheophylline. The effects of adenosine analogues were not additive to those of terbutaline. Adenosine analogues also increase cellular cAMP content. These findings suggest that the stimulatory properties of adenosine occur via a P_1 purinoceptor mechanism. Recent observations further suggest that both the A_1 and A_2 subtypes of the P_1 receptor may regulate surfactant secretion, at least in cultured cells. The A_2 subtype appears to stimulate secretion (34), while the A_1 subtype may inhibit secretion (35).

ATP, which can act via both P_1 and P_2 purinergic receptors, appears to act via several intracellular pathways. Treatment with ATP stimulates cAMP (34, 105). However, ATP also causes a rise in intracellular free Ca^{2+} (23, 86, 88), which may be mediated by phosphatidylinositide hydrolysis and subsequent generation of IP3 (105). Rice & co-workers (80) also recently provided evidence that protein kinase C may be involved in mediating the stimulatory effect of ATP.

CALCIUM Early experiments (55) documented that the calcium ionophore A23187 stimulates surfactant secretion in cultured type II cells. In later experiments, both ionophores A23187 and ionomycin were shown to stimulate secretion in vitro, with approximately equal potency to β-adrenergic agents (18, 78, 96). Treatment with ionophores causes a rise in cytosolic calcium, as measured by fluorescent probes (78, 83, 96), although results of experiments with such probes must be interpreted with caution because some probes apparently are not evenly distributed throughout the cytoplasm (78). Warburton & co-workers (106) showed that verapamil, a calcium channel-blocking agent, has a multiphasic concentration effect on in vitro secretion, with a small stimulatory effect at low concentrations. Interestingly, cAMP concentrations were increased by verapamil. The stimulatory effects of both P_2 purinergic agents (83) and mechanical distortion of type II cells (110) appear to be mediated by mobilization of intracellular calcium.

12-O-TETRADECANOYL-13-PHORBOL-ACETATE (TPA, PMA) Tetradecanoylphorbolacetate (TPA) was one of the first substances found to act as a secretagogue for type II cells (21). TPA and ATP (see above) are the two most potent secretagogues for surfactant secretion in vitro. Sano et al (94) demonstrated that treatment with TPA or its analogues causes a translocation of protein kinase C from the cytoplasmic to membrane fractions of type II cells, from which it has been inferred that protein kinase C plays a role in stimulating surfactant secretion. Natural secretagogues having similar properties have not been identified.

ACID-BASE STATUS Studies with isolated perfused lungs suggest that intracellular alkalosis stimulates surfactant secretion (12). Findings with isolated type II cells are somewhat different in that varying the pH of the extracellular medium (54) does not modulate secretion in vitro. Furthermore, the regulation of intracellular pH by an amiloride-sensitive Na^+/K^+ antiporter does not appear to be involved with stimulated surfactant secretion in vitro (93, 95).

ARACHIDONIC ACID METABOLITES In some studies with hyperventilated rabbits (70), evidence suggests that arachidonic acid metabolites may be important in mediating stimulated secretion. Rooney & co-workers have presented evidence that leukotrienes play a role in stimulating surfactant secretion, both in vitro (31, 32) and in vivo (91).

OTHER SECRETAGOGUES

Histamine, antihistamines Both histamine (13) and antihistaminic agents (30) have been reported to stimulate surfactant secretion in cultured type II cells. These observations are difficult to interpret, particularly because there is not uniform agreement about whether histamine stimulates secretion (30).

Vasopressin Brown & Wood (8) recently reported that vasopressin is a potent stimulant for surfactant secretion in vitro.

Cytoskeletal Elements

It seems reasonable to assume that cytoskeletal elements play an important role in directing newly synthesized and recycled surfactant components to lamellar bodies, in regulating transport of lamellar bodies to the apical surface of the cell, and in modulating the apposition of the limiting membrane of the lamellar body to the plasma membrane of the type II cell. Inhibitors of various cytoskeletal elements such as colchicine and vinblastine inhibit secretion stimulated by various secretagogues in vitro (7, 20). These same agents may actually stimulate basal secretion in vitro. Cytochalasins can either stimulate (82) or inhibit (53, 102) secretion. Although there is no direct evidence to support such a hypothesis, it may be that stimulation of basal secretion occurs because cytoskeletal elements interposed between lamellar bodies close to the surface of the cell and the plasma membrane are disrupted, which allows fusion and exocytosis to occur. In contrast, stimulated secretion may be inhibited because cytoskeletal elements involved in lamellar body transport are disrupted.

Inhibitors of Secretion

The concept that surfactant secretion may be under inhibitory as well as stimulatory control has been attractive to many workers in the field. Rice (89) showed that compound 48/80 inhibits both basal secretion and secretion stimulated by either forskolin or cytochalasin D. The mechanisms by which 48/80 inhibits secretion remain uncertain. High concentrations of substance P, a small neuropeptide, also inhibit secretion in vitro (85).

SP-A, the major surfactant-associated protein, is a potent inhibitor of phosphatidylcholine secretion in vitro (22, 83). The mechanism by which SP-A inhibits secretion is unknown. Cellular cAMP levels are not affected by SP-A (77). Because SP-A inhibits secretion stimulated by every agonist thus far tested in vitro, it seems likely that its effects occur distally in the exocytic process, although effects on very early secretory events have not been excluded. Interest has also focused on what portion of the molecule confers its inhibitory properties. Because SP-A contains a lectin-like domain and has lectin-like properties (40), Rice & Singleton (87) examined the effects of various lectins on surfactant secretion. Several lectins, including concanavalin A, what germ agglutinin, and Maclura pomifera all inhibited stimulated secretion. The mechanism for these effects remains unknown. These effects were only partially reversed by incubation with the appropriate hapten sugar, thus leaving in question whether it was the sugar binding properties that caused the inhibitory effect.

Kuroki et al (48, 49) performed direct studies on SP-A in order to determine what portions of the molecule may cause the inhibitory secretory effect. Reduction of SP-A with mercaptoethanol resulted in a loss of biologic activity that could be restored by oxidation, which suggests that disulfide bonds are required for the inhibitory effect of SP-A. Alkylation of SP-A also abolished its inhibitory effect on secretion. Treatment with endoglycosidase F to remove the oligosaccharide portion of SP-A did not abolish its inhibitory effect. Because various monoclonal antibodies against SP-A have differing capabilities of blocking secretion (48, 49), it seems likely that studies using these antibodies will provide more detailed information about which portions of the SP-A molecule are responsible for its inhibitory effects.

Although it is clear that surfactant secretion can be inhibited in vitro, it remains a matter of conjecture to what extent similar mechanisms operate in vivo. Whether or not the processes have correlates in vivo, the study of the mechanisms by which secretion can be inhibited is likely to provide new insights into exocytic processes in type II cells.

INTRA-ALVEOLAR CONVERSION OF SURFACTANT FORMS

Surfactant components secreted as lamellar body contents undergo several morphologic transformations. The lamellar bodies unwind to form tubular myelin, which is believed to be the major precursor of the monomolecular film. Because lamellar bodies contain most if not all surfactant components and because the surface film is believed to consist of essentially pure dipalmitoylphosphatidylcholine, the various chemical components of surfactant must separate as the surface film is formed. The conversion of lamellar body contents to surface film may not always be complete. For these reasons, the fate of each surfactant chemical component (as well as the morphologically distinct forms) should ideally be studied separately. This type of analysis is intrinsically difficult and labor-intensive. Our overall understanding of the fate of each surfactant form and individual component is incomplete.

CLEARANCE OF SURFACTANT

Pathways of Surfactant Clearance

Secreted surfactant awaits at least three different fates: (*a*) recycling, in which components are not degraded, but are reutilized by being taken up by the type II cell, incorporated into lamellar bodies and then resecreted; (*b*) degradation and utilization of components to synthesize new surfactant lipids or proteins; and/or (*c*) removal from the surfactant system, either as intact molecules or as degradation products such as fatty acids (Figure 1). The cells involved in these pathways and the factors that regulate clearance via these pathways probably vary.

RECYCLING OF SURFACTANT COMPONENTS Evidence from several different experimental designs, including autoradiography (28), in vivo turnover studies (e.g. 41, 44), and studies with isolated type II cells (10) suggest that type II cells can internalize surfactant lipids. At least some of the internalized

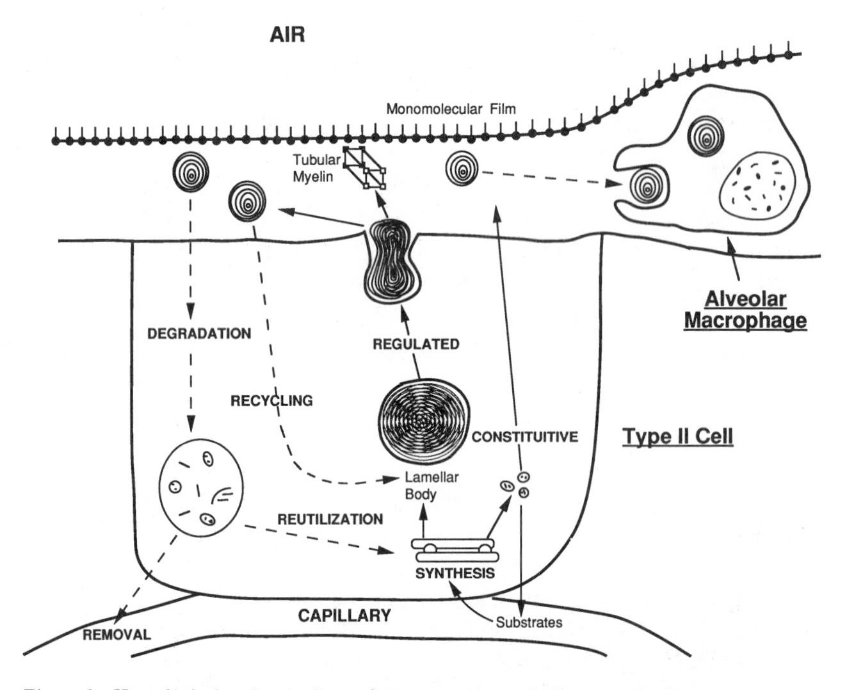

Figure 1 Hypothetical pathways for surfactant secretion and clearance. Surfactant components are synthesized by the alveolar type II cells and stored in lamellar bodies which, upon appropriate stimulation, are secreted into the alveolar airspace. It has not been determined if surfactant components are also secreted via constitutive pathways. The secreted lamellar body unwinds to form a unique three-dimensional lattice-like structure called tubular myelin. Tubular myelin (and perhaps other morphologic forms) can generate the surface active monomolecular film. The possible routes for surfactant clearance include uptake by the alveolar type II cell, uptake by the alveolar macrophage, and degradation and removal from the surfactant system, either by movement up the airways, or via other pathways. Some factors have been shown to affect both surfactant secretion and clearance, thus raising the possibility that the two processes may be coordinately regulated.

lipids are incorporated into lamellar bodies and are eventually resecreted. This uptake process in isolated type II cells is stimulated by SP-A, SP-B, and SP-C (14, 84, 115) and by phosphatidylglycerol (5).

The percentage of cleared material that is recycled varies with the age of the animal. The efficiency of reutilization has been estimated to be greater than 90% in newborn rabbits (44). The same researchers estimated that the efficiency of reutilization in adult rabbits ranged from 23 to 40% (43), although other groups have estimated the efficiency in adult rabbits and mice to be as high as 85% (36, 52). The factors that are responsible for age-dependent changes in efficiency of recycling are not known, but might include changes in the quantities of surfactant proteins or their putative receptors, enzymes involved in synthesis or degradation, and other unidentified factors.

The factors that direct internalized phospholipids to lamellar bodies for recycling are not known. Phosphatidylcholine internalized in the presence of SP-A by isolated type II cells is not significantly degraded, whereas some of the phospholipid that is internalized in the absence of SP-A is degraded (115). Thus it is possible that surfactant proteins or type II cell phospholipid transfer proteins (reviewed in 51) may play a role in directing phospholipids to either a recycling pathway through lamellar bodies, or a degradative pathway through lysosomes.

The concept that surfactant proteins may be reutilized has been less thoroughly investigated. SP-A (97, 116) instilled intratracheally in live animals is taken up and incorporated into lamellar bodies. The efficiency of this reutilization pathway has not been calculated. Ryan & co-workers (92) used microscopic cytochemical methods to demonstrate that SP-A is taken up by isolated type II cells. Internalized material was detected in coated pits, endosomes, and multivesicular bodies, but not in lamellar bodies. Thus it is possible that SP-A is not incorporated into lamellar bodies in isolated cells in primary culture. It is also possible, however, that SP-A could not be detected in lamellar bodies because of limitations of the technique. The fate of SP-B and SP-C await further investigation.

The mechanism of uptake of lipids and proteins is not known. Williams (109) demonstrated that lectins are internalized via an adsorptive endocytic pathway and deposited into lamellar bodies. Kalina & co-workers (46) recently demonstrated that surfactant complexed with colloidal gold was internalized by pathways similar to the endocytic pathways of lectins, except that coated vesicles rather than smooth vesicles were involved in the process of surfactant internalization. It remains to be established to what extent components of surfactant follow similar routes.

DEGRADATION AND UTILIZATION OF COMPONENTS TO SYNTHESIZE NEW SURFACTANT LIPIDS OR PROTEINS Some surfactant phospholipids are degraded during the clearance process and the constituents are incorporated into newly synthesized lipids. Possible sites of degradation include the alveolar type II cell, the alveolar macrophage, and the liquid hypophase that covers the alveolar epithelium.

Isolated type II cells have been shown to degrade phosphatidylcholine (10), possibly via the action of phospholipase A and lysophospholipase (11). The radiolabeled fatty acid appeared in a time-dependent fashion in other phospholipids, neutral lipids, and free fatty acids. Interestingly, basic amines, which have been shown to disrupt pH gradients in lysosomes and therefore were likely candidates as inhibitors of the degradative activity, did not affect the degradation (11). The mechanisms of degradation and the factors controlling this process remain unclear.

Alveolar macrophages internalize surfactant components (17, 61, 113).

Both tubular myelin and SP-A have been localized to phagocytic vesicles (15, 66, 98, 108). In vivo studies in which radiolabeled surfactant lipids or proteins have been injected into the airway suggest that little of the radiolabel becomes associated with macrophages (3, 17, 73, 111). One possible explanation for this seeming paradox is that macrophages may rapidly degrade internalized material and release the products into the extracellular environment. A recent study by Rider & co-workers (90) provides evidence to support that concept. It has been speculated that the macrophage may be important in removal of inactive or spent surfactant, although additional studies are required to define precisely the role of the macrophage in surfactant turnover.

The roles of other cells, such as the alveolar type I cell or the bronchiolar Clara cell, have not been thoroughly investigated.

Degradation of phospholipid in the alveolus does not appear to be a prerequisite for alveolar clearance since analogues of phosphatidylcholine that are resistant to phospholipases are cleared from the alveoli (70, 90) and reutilized to the same extent (45) as phosphatidylcholine that can be degraded. It has been reported that there are phospholipases in lavage fluid from rats, but not in lavage from several other species (60). Thus available evidence suggests that relatively little material is degraded within the alveolus.

REMOVAL FROM THE SURFACTANT SYSTEM, EITHER AS INTACT MOLECULES OR AS DEGRADATION PRODUCTS The rate of clearance of phospholipid from the whole lung is much slower than the rate of clearance from the alveoli. For example, Pettenazzo et al (75) reported that intratracheally administered radiolabeled rabbit surfactant is cleared from the whole lung at a rate of 56% of the administered dose/day. The same label was cleared from the alveolar wash at a rate of 90%/day. These results and others indicate that the flux of phospholipid through the alveoli is faster than the flux through the whole lung. These results suggest that some label must be removed from the surfactant system and reincorporated into non-surfactant lipids such as those in cell membranes.

Possible routes of clearance from the whole lung include movement up the muco-ciliary escalator to the esophagus where the surfactant could be swallowed, transfer across the epithelium/endothelium barrier into the blood or lymph, or degradation within the lung and transport of the degradation products to other organs. All of these routes appear to be involved to some extent. Intratracheally administered surfactant was cleared via the airways at a rate of 7% per day (74). A small amount of radiolabeled lipid was found in the blood stream after intratracheal instillation, and even smaller amounts appeared in the lung lymphatic system (16). The results of Rider & co-workers (90) and Fisher and co-workers (27) are consistent with the possibility that the phospholipid is degraded within the lung and the degradation products are taken up by other organs, such as liver and kidney (28, 74), and utilized to synthesize new lipid. Some label is excreted from the body (16, 28).

Factors Regulating Surfactant Clearance

The flux of surfactant through the alveolar compartment is fairly rapid. Estimates of pool size suggest that the reserves of material in either lamellar bodies or in alveoli are not large (reviewed in 113). These observations are consistent with a system in which pool size is tightly regulated in order to maintain an appropriate amount of functional surfactant. This idea is supported by an interesting study by Nicholas & co-workers (65). They found that exercise in the form of swimming significantly increased the pool size of alveolar phospholipid in rats and that pool size returned to normal values within four hr after cessation of swimming. In contrast to these findings are the observations of Oguchi & co-workers (67) that, when pool size is increased by administration of exogenous surfactant, the amount of phospholipid in the alveolar compartment remains elevated even for 72 hr. Although the reasons for these different results are not known, several possibilities exist. One explanation is that alterations via a physiologic mechanism (such as exercise) may elicit responses that are not triggered when pool size is increased by administration of an exogenous dose. Nevertheless, it does appear that the rates of clearance are under some form of control in some circumstances.

The factors that regulate clearance from the alveolar airspace may differ from the factors that regulate clearance from the whole lung. It has been shown that the rate of clearance from the whole lung is slower than the rate of clearance from the alveolar compartment (75). A recent study by Rider & co-workers (90) demonstrated that the rates of clearance of phosphatidylcholine and an ether analogue of phosphatidylcholine, which is resistant to degradation from the alveolar compartment, were similar. The rate of clearance of the ether analogue from the entire lung, however, was much slower. Surfactant particles that are enriched in SP-A are taken up from the alveolus into lamellar bodies to a greater extent than are fractions that do not contain SP-A (114). In contrast, fractions that contained SP-A were cleared from the whole lung at rates that were similar to preparations that contained little if any SP-A (67, 76). In addition, the rates of clearance from the two compartments differ by as much as twofold (75). How the rates of clearance from the alveoli and the whole lung are coordinated is not known.

SURFACTANT PROTEINS In vitro studies with isolated type II cells show that SP-A enhances lipid uptake in a time-temperature-, and protein concentration-dependent manner (84, 115). The stimulation of lipid uptake by SP-A was cell specific: SP-A enhanced uptake by type II cells and macrophages, but not by lung fibroblasts. Recent studies suggest that SP-A interacts with type II cells via a high affinity receptor-mediated process (50, 92, 112). SP-B, SP-C, (84) and lipid extracts of whole surfactant containing hydrophobic surfactant proteins (14) have also been shown to enhance lipid uptake. SP-B and SP-C both enhanced lipid uptake by type II cells and by lung fibroblasts. The enhancing effects of SP-B and SP-C were dose-dependent, but were not saturable and were similar at 4 and 37°C (84). The authors speculate that the enhancing effects of SP-B and SP-C may be related to changes in the physical form of the liposomes induced by the protein rather than by a receptor-mediated process.

The role of surfactant proteins in regulating alveolar pool size in vivo is unclear. Indirect evidence suggests that the proteins may be involved since fractions that were enriched in surfactant proteins were taken up into lamellar bodies to a greater extent than were fractions that contained no protein (114). In contrast, it was shown that liposomes that did not contain surfactant proteins were cleared from the alveolar compartment at the same rate as protein-containing surfactant that was purified from donor animals by lung lavage (67, 76). Several factors could contribute to these differences, including the size of the instilled particles used in the different studies, the manner in which the material was prepared and dispersed prior to instillation, the avidity with which the material associated with endogenous surfactant components, and the size of the dose. It is difficult to control these and other variables in physiological studies.

SP-A also enhances lipid uptake by alveolar macrophages (115). The fate of the material internalized by the macrophage in the presence of SP-A is not known. It is also not clear what signal directs SP-A to either the type II cell or the alveolar macrophage. One possibility is that SP-A may be modified, for example by an enzymatic process, in the alveolar subphase, and such a modification might target SP-A to the alveolar macrophage.

SURFACTANT LIPIDS Liposomes containing both phosphatidylglycerol and phosphatidylcholine are cleared more rapidly from the alveolar compartment (72) and are more rapidly taken up by isolated type II cells (5) than are liposomes comprised of only phosphatidylcholine. The mechanism by which phosphatidylglycerol may regulate clearance in vivo is not known, although it is interesting to hypothesize that the lipid composition of the different morphological forms of surfactant (e.g. tubular myelin, monolayer, etc) may change during intra-alveolar metabolism and that these changes may be involved in regulation of clearance. Available evidence suggests that there are only small differences in the phospholipid composition of surfactant subfractions, at least as they are purified by current techniques (1, 38, 52, 69). To the best of our knowledge, however, none of the fractions (e.g. tubular myelin) has been purified to homogeneity, and it is possible that subtle changes in phospholipid composition have not yet been detected.

FACTORS THAT AFFECT SURFACTANT SECRETION THAT ARE ALSO KNOWN TO AFFECT CLEARANCE If there is to be a balance between secretion and reuptake, it seems that secretion and clearance should be coordinately regulated. Results from in vitro studies are consistent with this hypothesis. For example, Fisher & co-workers (25–27) found that surfactant secretagogues such as isoproteronol, terbutaline, and others enhanced the clearance of radiolabeled phosphatidylcholine from the alveolar compartment of an isolated perfused lung model. Pettenazzo & colleagues (75) reported that the β-agonist metaproterenol enhanced the alveolar clearance in a whole animal model. Increases in ventilatory rate enhance both secretion and clearance (72). It is thought that ventilatory parameters may alter the balance between recycling and degradation (24).

The observation that SP-A enhances lipid uptake (115) and inhibits lipid secretion (see above) (22, 50, 83) has led to the speculation that SP-A may be involved in feedback regulation of surfactant pool size. In such a scenario, excess SP-A would inhibit secretion until enough material is taken up by an SP-A enhanced process at which time the inhibition of secretion would be removed and new material would be released into the alveolus. Because substantial evidence from in vivo studies is lacking to support this idea, the role of surfactant proteins in regulating pool size in vivo requires further investigation.

CONCLUSIONS

Considerable information about the factors that regulate surfactant secretion and clearance has been obtained from in vitro studies. To date, the factors responsible for regulation of pool size in vivo are not understood. It has been demonstrated that several mediators enhance lipid secretion by the type II cell and some of these mediators also affect uptake of lipids by lung cells. These observations raise the intriguing possibility that secretion and clearance may be coordinately regulated. How regulation of secretion and clearance are coupled with regulation of synthesis of new material is still unknown.

Acknowledgment

The authors thank Mr. Randy Decker for editorial assistance and preparation of the manuscript. This work was supported in part by National Heart, Lung, and Blood Institute Grants HL-30923 (J. R. W.), HL-24075 (L. G. D. & J. R. W.) and HL-41958 (L. G. D.). Dr. Wright is an Established Investigator of the American Heart Association.

Literature Cited

1. Baritussio, A., Bellina, L., Carraro, R., Rossi, A., Enzi, G., et al. 1984. Heterogeneity of alveolar surfactant in the rabbit: composition, morphology, and labelling of subfractions isolated by centifugation of lung lavage. *Eur. J. Clin. Invest.* 14:24–29
2. Baritussio, A., Carraro, R., Bellina, L., Rossi, A., Bruni, R., et al. 1985. Turnover of phospholipids isolated from fractions of lung lavage fluid. *J. Appl. Physiol.* 59:1055–60
3. Baritussio, A. G., Magoon, M. W., Goerke, J., Clements, J. A. 1981. Precursor-product relationship between rabbit type II cell lamellar bodies and alveolar surface-active material. Surfactant turnover time. *Biochim. Biophys. Acta* 666:382–93
4. Bartlett, D. 1971. Origin and regulation of spontaneous deep breaths. *Respir. Physiol.* 12:230–38
5. Bates, S. R., Ibach, P. B., Fisher, A. B. 1989. Phospholipids co-isolated with rat surfactant protein C account for the apparent protein-enhanced uptake of liposomes into lung granular pneumocytes. *Exp. Lung. Res.* 15:695–708
6. Brown, L. A. S., Longmore, W. J. 1981. Adrenergic and cholinergic regulation of lung surfactant secretion in the isolated perfused rat lung and in the alveolar type II cell in culture. *J. Biol. Chem.* 256:66–72
7. Brown, L. A. S., Pasquale, S. M., Longmore, W. J. 1985. Role of microtubules in surfactant secretion. *J. Appl. Physiol.* 58:1866–73
8. Brown, L. A. S., Wood, L. H. 1989. Stimulation of surfactant secretion by vasopressin in primary cultures of adult rat type II pneumocytes. *Biochim. Biophys. Acta* 1001:76–81
9. Burgess, T. L., Kelly, R. B. 1987. Constitutive and regulated secretion of proteins. *Annu. Rev. Cell Biol.* 3:243–93
10. Chander, A., Claypool, W. D. Jr., Strauss, J. F. III., Fisher, A. B. 1983. Uptake of liposomal phosphatidylcholine by granular pneumocytes in primary culture. *Am. J. Physiol.* 245:C397–404
11. Chander, A., Reicherter, J., Fisher, A. B. 1987. Degradation of dipalmitoyl phosphatidylcholine by isolated rat granular pneumocytes and reutilization for surfactant synthesis. *J. Clin. Invest.* 79:1133–38
12. Chander, A. 1989. Regulation of lung surfactant secretion by intracellular pH. *Am. J. Physiol.* 257:L354–L360
13. Chen, M., Brown, L. A. S. 1990. Histamine stimulation of surfactant secretion from rat type II pneumocytes. *Am. J. Physiol.* 258:L195–200
14. Claypool, W. D., Wang, D. L., Chander, A., Fisher, A. B. 1984. An ethanol/ether soluble apoprotein from rat lung surfactant augments liposome uptake by isolated granular pneumocytes. *J. Clin. Invest.* 74:677–84
15. Coalson, J. J., Winter, V. T., Martin, H. M., King, R. J. 1986. Colloidal gold immunoultrastructural localization of rat surfactant. *Am. Rev. Respir. Dis.* 133: 230–37
16. Davis, P. A., Gunther, R. A., Cross, C. E. 1987. Clearance of instilled surfactant lipid from the lungs of unanesthetized sheep: Lipids are differentially transported by nonlymphatic pathways. *J. Lab. Clin. Med.* 109:191–200
17. Desai, R., Tetley, T. D., Curtis, C. G., Powell, G. M., Richards, R. J. 1978. Studies on the fate of pulmonary surfactant in the lung. *Biochem. J.* 176:455–62
18. Dobbs, L. G., Gonzalez, R. F., Marinari, L. A., Mescher, E. J., Hawgood, S. 1986. The role of calcium in the secretion of surfactant by rat alveolar type II cells. *Biochim. Biophys. Acta* 877:305–13
19. Dobbs, L. G., Mason, R. J., Williams, M. C., Benson, B. J., Sueishi, K. 1982. Secretion of surfactant by primary cultures of alveolar type II cells isolated from rats. *Biochim. Biophys. Acta* 713:118–27
20. Dobbs, L. G., Mason, R. J. 1978. Stimulation of secretion of disaturated phosphatidylcholine from isolated alveolar type II cells by 12-*O*-tetradecanoyl-13-phorbol acetate. *Am. Rev. Respir. Dis.* 118:705–13
21. Dobbs, L. G., Mason, R. J. 1979. Pulmonary alveolar type II cells isolated from rats. Release of phosphatidylcho-

line in response to β-adrenergic stimulation. *J. Clin. Invest.* 63:378–87
22. Dobbs, L. G., Wright, J. R., Hawgood, S., Gonzalez, R., Venstrom, K., Nellenbogen, J. 1987. Pulmonary surfactant and its components inhibit secretion of phosphatidylcholine from cultured rat alveolar type II cells. *Proc. Natl. Acad. Sci. USA* 84:1010–14
23. Dorn, C. C., Rice, W. R., Singleton, F. M. 1989. Calcium mobilization and response recovery following P_2-purinoceptor stimulation of rat isolated alveolar type II cells. *Br. J. Pharmacol.* 97:163–70
24. Ennema, J. J., Reijngoud, D. J., Egberts, J., Mook, P. H., Wildevuur, C. R. H. 1984. High-frequency oscillation affects surfactant phospholipid metabolism in rabbits. *Respir. Physiol.* 58:29–39
25. Fisher, A. B., Dodia, C., Chander, A. 1985. β-adrenergic mediators increase pulmonary retention of instilled phospholipids. *J. Appl. Physiol.* 59:743–48
26. Fisher, A. B., Dodia, C., Chander, A. 1987. Degradation and reutilization of alveolar phosphatidylcholine by rat lungs. *J. Appl. Physiol.* 62:2295–99
27. Fisher, A. B., Dodia, C., Chander, A. 1989. Secretagogues for lung surfactant increase lung uptake of alveolar phospholipids. *Am. J. Physiol.* 257:L248–52
28. Geiger, K., Gallagher, M. L., Hedley-Whyte, J. 1975. Cellular distribution and clearance of aerosolized dipalmitoyl lecithin. *J. Appl. Physiol.* 39:759–66
29. Gibbs, E. M., Lienhard, G. E., Appleman, J. R., Lane, M. D., Frost, S. C. 1986. Insulin stimulates fluid-phase endocytosis and exocytosis in 3T3-L1 adipocytes. *J. Biol. Chem.* 261:3944–51
30. Gilfillan, A. M., Lewis, A. J., Rooney, S. A. 1987. Effects of thiazinamium chloride and other antihistamines on phosphatidylcholine secretion in rat type II pneumocyte cultures. *Biochem. Pharmacol.* 36:277–281
31. Gilfillan, A. M., Rooney, S. A. 1985. Arachidonic acid metabolites stimulate phosphatidylcholine secretion in primary cultures of type II pneumocytes. *Biochim. Biophys. Acta* 833:336–41
32. Gilfillan, A. M., Rooney, S. A. 1986. Leukotrienes stimulate phosphatidylcholine secretion in cultured type II pneumocytes. *Biochim. Biophys. Acta* 876:22–27
33. Gilfillan, A. M., Rooney, S. A. 1987. Purinoceptor agonists stimulate phosphatidylcholine secretion in primary cultures of adult rat type II pneumocytes. *Biochim. Biophys. Acta* 917:18–23
34. Gilfillan, A. M., Rooney, S. A. 1987. Functional evidence for adenosine A_2 receptor regulation of phosphatidylcholine secretion in cultured type II pneumocytes. *J. Pharmacol. Exp. Ther.* 241:907–14
35. Gobran, L. I., Rooney, S. A. 1990. Adenosine A_1 receptor-mediated inhibition of surfactant secretion in rat type II pneumocytes. *Am. J. Physiol.* 258:L45–51
36. Gross, N. J., Barnes, E., Narine, K. R. 1988. Recycling of surfactant in black and beige mice: Pool sizes and kinetics. *J. Appl. Physiol.* 64:2017–25
37. Gross, N. J., Narine, K. R. 1989. Surfactant subtypes of mice: metabolic relationships and conversion in vitro. *J. Appl. Physiol.* 67:414–21
38. Gross, N. J., Narine, K. R. 1989. Surfactant subtypes in mice: characterization and quantitation. *J. Appl. Physiol.* 66:342–49
39. Gross, N. J., Schultz, R. M. 1990. A serine protease mediates the extracellular metabolism of surfactant. *Am. Rev. Respir. Dis.* 141:A632 (Abstr.)
40. Haagsman, H. P., Hawgood, S., Sargeant, T., Buckley, D., White, R. T., et al. 1987. The major lung surfactant protein, SP 28-36, is a calcium-dependent, carbohydrate-binding protein. *J. Biol. Chem.* 262:13877–80
41. Hallman, M., Epstein, B. L., Gluck, L. 1981. Analysis of labeling and clearance of lung surfactant phospholipids in rabbit. Evidence of bidirectional surfactant flux between lamellar bodies and alveolar lavage. *J. Clin. Invest.* 68:742–51
42. Hildebran, J. N., Goerke, J., Clements, J. A. 1981. Surfactant release in excised rat lung is stimulated by air inflation. *J. Appl. Physiol.* 51:905–10
43. Jacobs, H. C., Ikegami, M., Jobe, A. H., Berry, D. D., Jones, S. 1985. Reutilization of surfactant phosphatidylcholine in adult rabbits. *Biochim. Biophys. Acta* 837:77–84
44. Jacobs, H., Jobe, A., Ikegami, M., Conaway, D. 1983. The significance of reutilization of surfactant phosphatidylcholine. *J. Biol. Chem.* 258:4156–65
45. Jacobs, H., Jobe, A., Ikegami, M., Miller, D., Jones, S. 1984. Reutilization of phosphatidylcholine analogues by the pulmonary surfactant system. The lack of specificity. *Biochim. Biophys. Acta* 793:300–9
46. Kalina, M., Socher, R. 1990. Internalization of pulmonary surfactant into lamellar bodies of cultured rat pulmonary type II cells. *J. Histochem. Cytochem.* 38:483–92

47. Kikkawa, Y., Yoneda, K., Smith, F., Packard, B., Suzuki, K. 1975. The type II epithelial cells of the lung. II. Chemical composition and phospholipid synthesis. *Lab. Invest.* 32:295–302
48. Kuroki, Y., Mason, R. J., Voelker, D. R. 1988. Chemical modification of surfactant protein A alters high affinity binding to rat alveolar type II cells and regulation of phospholipid secretion. *J. Biol. Chem.* 263:7596–602
49. Kuroki, Y., Mason, R. J., Voelker, D. R. 1988. Pulmonary surfactant apoprotein A structure and modulation of surfactant secretion by rat alveolar type II cells. *J. Biol. Chem.* 263:3388–94
50. Kuroki, Y., Mason, R. J., Voelker, D. R. 1988. Alveolar type II cells express a high-affinity receptor for pulmonary surfactant protein A. *Proc. Natl. Acad. Sci. USA* 85:5566–70
51. Lumb, R. H. 1989. Phospholipid transfer proteins in mammalian lung. *Am. J. Physiol.* 257:L190–94
52. Magoon, M. W., Wright, J. R., Baritussio, A., Williams, M. C., Goerke, J., et al. 1983. Subfractionation of lung surfactant. Implications for metabolism and surface activity. *Biochim. Biophys. Acta* 750:18–31
53. Marino, P. A., Ronney, S. A. 1980. Surfactant secretion in a newborn rabbit lung slice model. *Biochim. Biophys. Acta* 620:509–19
54. Mason, R. J., Cott, G. R., Robinson, P. C., Sugahara, K., Leslie, C. C., Dobbs, L. G. 1984. Pharmacology of alveolar type II cells. *Prog. Respir. Res.* 18:279–87
55. Mason, R. J., Williams, M. C., Greenleaf, R. D., Clements, J. A. 1977. Isolation and properties of type II alveolar cells from rat lung. *Am. Rev. Respir. Dis.* 115:1015–26
56. Massaro, G. D., Massaro, D. 1983. Morphologic evidence that large inflations of the lung stimulate secretion of surfactant. *Am. Rev. Respir. Dis.* 127:235–36
57. Mead, J., Collier, C. 1959. Relation of volume history of lungs to respiratory mechanics in anesthetized dogs. *J. Appl. Physiol.* 14:669–78
58. Mescher, E. J., Dobbs, L. G., Mason, R. J. 1983. Cholera toxin stimulates secretion of saturated phosphatidylcholine and increases cellular cyclic AMP in isolated rat alveolar type II cells. *Exp. Lung. Res.* 5:173–82
59. Mettler, N. R., Gray, M. E., Schuffman, S., LeQuire, V. S. 1981. β-adrenergic induced synthesis and secretion of phosphatidylcholine by isolated pulmonary alveolar type II cells. *Lab. Invest.* 45:575–86
60. Miles, P. R., Castranova, V., Bowman, L. 1985. Catabolism of rat surfactant disaturated phosphatidylcholines during incubation of alveolar lavage materials in vitro at 37°C. *Biochim. Biophys. Act.* 836:39–44
61. Miles, P. R., Ma, Y. C., Bowman, L. 1988. Degradation of pulmonary surfactant disaturated phosphatidylcholines by alveolar macrophages. *J. Appl. Physiol.* 64:2474–81
62. Nicholas, T. E., Barr, H. A. 1981. Control of release of surfactant phospholipids in the isolated perfused rat lung. *J. Appl. Physiol.* 51:90–98
63. Nicholas, T. E., Barr, H. A. 1983. The release of surfactant in rat lung by brief periods of hyperventilation. *Respir. Physiol.* 52:69–83
64. Nicholas, T. E., Power, J. H. T., Barr, H. A. 1982. The pulmonary consequences of a deep breath. *Respir. Physiol.* 49:315–24
65. Nicholas, T. E., Power, J. H. T., Barr, H. A. 1982. Surfactant homeostasis in the rat lung during swimming exercise. *J. Appl. Physiol.* 53:1521–28
66. Nichols, B. A. 1976. Normal rabbit alveolar macrophages. I. The phagocytosis of tubular myelin. *J. Exp. Med.* 144:906–19
67. Oguchi, K., Ikegami, M., Jacobs, H., Jobe, A. 1985. Clearance of large amounts of natural surfactants and liposomes of dipalmitoylphosphatidylcholine from the lungs of rabbits. *Exp. Lung. Res.* 9:221–35
68. Olsen, D. B. 1972. Neuro-hormonal secretory stimulation of pulmonary surfactant in the rat. *Physiologist* 15:230a (Abstr.)
69. Oulton, M., Fraser, M., Dolphin, M., Yoon, R., Faulkner, G. 1986. Quantification of surfactant pool sizes in rabbit lung during perinatal development. *J. Lipid. Res.* 27:602–12
70. Oyarzún, M. J., Clements, J. A. 1977. Ventilatory and cholinergic control of pulmonary surfactant in the rabbit. *J. Appl. Physiol.* 43:39–45
71. Oyarzún, M. J., Clements, J. A. 1978. Control of lung surfactant by ventilation, adrenergic mediators, and prostaglandins in the rabbit. *Am. Rev. Respir. Dis.* 117:879–891
72. Oyarzún, M. J., Clements, J. A., Baritussio, A. 1980. Ventilation enhances pulmonary alveolar clearance of radioactive dipalmitoylphosphatidylcholine in liposomes. *Am. Rev. Respir. Dis.* 121: 709–21

73. Pettenazzo, A., Ikegami, M., Seidner, S., Jobe, A. 1988. Clearance of surfactant phosphatidylcholine from adult rabbit lungs. *J. Appl. Physiol.* 64:120–27
74. Pettenazzo, A., Jobe, A., Humme, J., Seidner, S., Ikegami, M. 1988. Clearance of surfactant phosphatidylcholine via the upper airways in rabbits. *J. Appl. Physiol.* 65:2151–55
75. Pettenazzo, A., Jobe, A., Ikegami, M., Abra, R., Hogue, E., Mihalko, P. 1989. Clearance of phosphatidylcholine and cholesterol from liposomes, liposomes loaded with metaproterenol, and rabbit surfactant from adult rabbit lungs. *Am. Rev. Respir. Dis.* 139:752–58
76. Pettenazzo, A., Jobe, A., Ikegami, M., Seidner, S. 1988. Clearance of treatment doses of surfactant. Effect of lipid extraction and aggregate sizes. *Biol. Neonate* 53:23–31
77. Pian, M., Dobbs, L. G. 1989. Inhibition of surfactant secretion by SP-A is not mediated by an early effect on alveolar type II cells. *Pediatr. Res.* 25:322A (Abstr.)
78. Pian, M. S., Dobbs, L. G., Düzgünes, N. 1988. Positive correlation between cytosolic free calcium and surfactant secretion in cultured rat alveolar type II cells. *Biochim. Biophys. Acta* 960:43–53
79. Power, J. H. T., Barr, H. A., Jones, M. E., Nicholas, T. E. 1987. Changes in surfactant pools after a physiological increase in alveolar surfactant. *J. Appl. Physiol.* 63:1902–11
80. Rice, W. R., Dorn, C. C., Singleton, F. M. 1990. P_2-purinoceptor regulation of surfactant phosphatidylcholine secretion. Relative roles of calcium and protein kinase C. *Biochem. J.* 266:407–13
81. Rice, W. R., Hull, W. M., Dion, C. A., Hollinger, B. A., Whitsett, J. A. 1985. Activation of cAMP dependent protein kinase during surfactant release from type II pneumocytes. *Exp. Lung. Res.* 9:135–49
82. Rice, W. R., Osterhoudt, K. C., Whitsett, J. A. 1984. Effect of cytochalasins on surfactant release from alveolar type II cells. *Biochim. Biophys. Acta.* 805: 12–18
83. Rice, W. R., Ross, G. F., Singleton, F. M., Dingle, S., Whitsett, J. A. 1987. Surfactant-associated protein inhibits phospholipid secretion from type II cells. *J. Appl. Physiol.* 63:692–98
84. Rice, W. R., Sarin, V. K., Fox, J. L., Baatz, J., Wert, S., Whitsett, J. A. 1989. Surfactant peptides stimulate uptake of phosphatidylcholine by isolated cells. *Biochim. Biophys. Acta* 1006: 237–45
85. Rice, W. R., Singleton, F. M. 1986. Regulation of surfactant secretion from isolated type II pneumocytes by substance P. *Biochim. Biophys. Acta* 889: 123–27
86. Rice, W. R., Singleton, F. M. 1987. P_{2Y}-purinoceptor regulation of surfactant secretion from rat isolated alveolar type II cells is associated with mobilization of intracellular calcium. *Br. J. Pharmacol.* 91:833–38
87. Rice, W. R., Singleton, F. M. 1988. Regulation of surfactant phospholipid secretion from isolated rat alveolar type II cells by lectins. *Biochim. Biophys. Acta* 958:205–10
88. Rice, W. R., Singleton, F. M. 1986. P_2-purinoceptors regulate surfactant secretion from rat isolated alveolar type II cells. *Br. J. Pharmacol.* 89:485–91
89. Rice, W. R., Whitsett, J. A. 1984. Inhibition of surfactant release from isolated type II cells by compound 48/80. *Biochim. Biophys. Acta* 805:261–67
90. Rider, E. D., Ikegami, M., Jobe, A. H. 1990. Intrapulmonary catabolism of surfactant saturated phosphatidylcholine in rabbits. *Am. J. Physiol.* In press
91. Rooney, S. A., Gobran, L. I. 1988. Adenosine and leukotrienes have a regulatory role in lung surfactant secretion in the newborn rabbit. *Biochim. Biophys. Acta* 960:98–106
92. Ryan, R. M., Morris, R. E., Rice, W. R., Ciraolo, G., Whitsett, J. A. 1989. Binding and uptake of pulmonary surfactant protein (SP-A) by pulmonary type II epithelial cells. *J. Histochem. Cytochem.* 37:429–40
93. Sano, K., Cott, G. R., Voelker, D. R., Mason, R. J. 1988. The Na^+/H^+ antiporter in rat alveolar type II cells and its role in stimulated surfactant secretion. *Biochim. Biophys. Acta* 939:449–58
94. Sano, K., Voelker, D. R., Mason, R. J. 1985. Involvement of protein kinase C in pulmonary surfactant secretion from alveolar type II cells. *J. Biol. Chem.* 260:12725–29
95. Sano, K., Voelker, D. R., Mason, R. J. 1987. Tetradecanoylphorbol acetate and terbutaline stimulate surfactant secretion in alveolar type II cells without changing the membrane potential. *Biochim. Biophys. Acta* 902:317–26
96. Sano, K., Voelker, D. R., Mason, R. J. 1987. Effect of secretagogues on cytoplasmic free calcium in alveolar type II cells. *Am. J. Physiol.* 253:C679–86
97. Snyder, J. M., Rodgers, H. F., Nielsen,

H. C., O'Brien, J. A. 1988. Uptake of the 35 kDa major surfactant apoprotein (SP-A) by neonatal rabbit lung tissue. *Biochim. Biophys. Acta* 1002:1–7

98. Sueishi, K., Tanaka, K., Oda, T. 1977. Immunoultrastructural study of surfactant system. Distribution of specific protein of surface active material in rabbit lung. *Lab. Invest.* 37:136–42
99. Suzuki, Y., Fujita, Y., Kogishi, K. 1989. Reconstitution of tubular myelin from synthetic lipids and proteins associated with pig pulmonary surfactant. *Am. Rev. Respir. Dis.* 140:75–81
100. Tenner, A. J., Robinson, S. L., Borchelt, J., Wright, J. R. 1989. Human pulmonary surfactant protein (SP-A), a protein structurally homologous to C1q, can enhance FcR- and CR1-mediated phagocytosis. *J. Biol. Chem.* 264: 13923–28
101. Thet, L. A., Clerch, L., Massaro, G. D., Massaro, D. 1979. Changes in the sedimentation of surfactant in ventilated excised rat lungs. *J. Clin. Invest.* 64: 600–8
102. Tsilibary, E. C., Williams, M. C. 1983. Actin in peripheral rat lung: S_1 labeling and structural changes induced by cytochalasin. *J. Histochem. Cytochem.* 31:1289–97
103. van Iwaarden, F., Welmers, B., Verhoef, J., Haagsman, H. P., van Golde, L. M. G. 1990. Pulmonary surfactant protein A enhances the host-defense mechanism of rat alveolar macrophages. *Am. J. Respir. Cell Mol. Biol.* 2:91–98
104. von Grafenstein, H., Roberts, C. S., Baker, P. F. 1986. Kinetic analysis of the triggered exocytosis/endocytosis secretory cycle in cultured bovine adrenal medullary cells. *J. Cell Biol.* 103: 2343–52
105. Warburton, D., Buckley, S., Cosico, L. 1989. P_1 and P_2 purinergic receptor signal transduction in rat type II pneumocytes. *J. Appl. Physiol.* 66:901–5
106. Warburton, D., Parton, L., Buckley, S., Cosico, L. 1989. Verapamil: a novel probe of surfactant secretion from rat type II pneumocytes. *J. Appl. Physiol.* 66:1304–8
107. Whitsett, J. A., Ross, G., Weaver, T., Rice, W., Dion, C., Hull, W. 1985. Glycosylation and secretion of surfactant-associated glycoprotein A. *J. Biol. Chem.* 260:15273–79
108. Williams, M. C., Benson, B. 1981. Immunocytochemical localization and identification of the major surfactant protein in adult rat lung. *J. Histochem. Cytochem.* 29:291–305
109. Williams, M. C. 1984. Uptake of lectins by pulmonary alveolar type II cells: subsequent deposition into lamellar bodies. *Proc. Natl. Acad. Sci. USA* 81:6383–87
110. Wirtz, H. R. W., Dobbs, L. G. 1990. A single mechanical stretch of alveolar type II cells stimulates secretion of phosphatidylcholine. *Am. Rev. Respir. Dis.* 141:A633 (Abstr.)
111. Wright, J. R., Benson, B. J., Williams, M. C., Goerke, J., Clements, J. A. 1984. Protein composition of rabbit alveolar surfactant subfractions. *Biochim. Biophys. Acta* 791:320–32
112. Wright, J. R., Borchelt, J. D., Hawgood, S. 1989. Lung surfactant apoprotein SP-A (26-36 kDa) binds with high affinity to isolated alveolar type II cells. *Proc. Natl. Acad. Sci. USA* 86:5410–14
113. Wright, J. R., Clements, J. A. 1987. Metabolism and turnover of lung surfactant. *Am. Rev. Respir. Dis.* 135:426–44
114. Wright, J. R., Wagner, R. E., Hamilton, R. L., Huang, M., Clements, J. A. 1986. Uptake of lung surfactant subfractions into lamellar bodies of adult rabbit lungs. *J. Appl. Physiol.* 60:817–25
115. Wright, J. R., Wager, R. E., Hawgood, S., Dobbs, L., Clements, J. A. 1987. Surfactant apoprotein M_r = 26,000–36,000 enhances uptake of liposomes by type II cells. *J. Biol. Chem.* 262:2888–94
116. Young, S. L., Wright, J. R., Clements, J. A. 1989. Cellular uptake and processing of surfactant lipids and apoprotein SP-A by rat lung. *J. Appl. Physiol.* 66:1336–42

Annu. Rev. Physiol. 1991. 53:415–40

HORMONAL CONTROL OF THE SURFACTANT SYSTEM IN FETAL LUNG

Carole R. Mendelson and Vijayakumar Boggaram

Departments of Biochemistry and Obstetrics-Gynecology, The Cecil H. and Ida Green Center for Reproductive Biology Sciences, University of Texas Southwestern Medical Center at Dallas, 5323 Harry Hines Boulevard, Dallas, Texas 75235

KEY WORDS: developmental regulation, pulmonary, gene expression, glucocorticoids, multifactorial

---

INTRODUCTION

Pulmonary surfactant, a lipoprotein enriched in dipalmitoylphosphatidylcholine (DPPC) (21), is synthesized by the type II cells of the lung alveolus where surfactant glycerophospholipids and proteins function to reduce surface tension at the alveolar air-liquid interface. Surfactant contains several lung-specific proteins (84) that appear to act in concert with DPPC to reduce alveolar surface tension. The fetal lung acquires the capacity for surfactant synthesis relatively late in gestation; augmented surfactant synthesis and secretion are initiated after completion of 85–90% of gestation in all mammalian species thus far studied. In the human fetus, type II cells are first identifiable in the terminal sacs at 20–22 weeks of gestation; however, secretion of surfactant into the amniotic fluid is detectable only after 30–32 weeks of gestation. A consequence of surfactant deficiency in prematurely born infants is the respiratory distress syndrome (RDS), the leading cause of neonatal morbidity and mortality in developed countries (5). Although RDS is primarily associated with prematurity, term infants of diabetic mothers also manifest an increased incidence of RDS. On the other hand, premature infants of mothers afflicted with chronic or pregnancy-induced

0066–4278/91/0315–0415$02.00

hypertension commonly manifest a decreased propensity to develop RDS (106).

The cellular mechanisms involved in the initiation of surfactant synthesis by the fetal lung have not been defined; however, an expanding list of hormones and factors have been found to regulate in vivo and in vitro the synthesis and secretion of surfactant components by the fetal type II cell. In this chapter, we only briefly consider the regulation of surfactant glycerophospholipid synthesis in fetal lung tissue, since this topic has been reviewed extensively (6, 37, 89). Rather, we focus primarily on recent studies concerning the effects of hormones and factors on the regulation of surfactant protein synthesis and gene expression in fetal lung.

REGULATION OF SURFACTANT GLYCEROPHOSPHOLIPID SYNTHESIS IN FETAL LUNG

Developmental Regulation

Pulmonary surfactant is a unique lipoprotein because it is comprised of a high proportion of DPPC, the major surface-active component, which accounts for >50% of surfactant glycerophospholipids. In addition, the surfactant of most adult mammals, including man, contains a relatively large proportion of phosphatidylglycerol (PG), which comprises ~10% of surfactant composition (21). Both of these glycerophospholipid species are normally present only in trace amounts in other tissues. In most mammalian species, the surfactant that is synthesized initially by fetal lung tissue contains only small amounts of PG, although relatively large amounts of another acidic glycerophospholipid, phosphatidylinositol (PI), are present. With advancing gestation, the relative amount of PG in fetal surfactant increases, while the relative amount of PI declines (42). The reciprocal changes in these acidic glycerophospholipid species result from their synthesis from a common precursor, cytidine diphosphodiacylglycerol (CDP-diacylglycerol). It has been suggested that the decrease in PI synthesis in fetal lung tissue with advancing gestation results from the decreased availability of circulating *myo*-inositol. In studies with fetal rabbit lung tissue in vitro, it has been observed that synthesis of surfactant PI relative to PG is increased as the concentration of *myo*-inositol in the culture medium is increased (61). In addition, the PI synthase reaction is reversible in lung tissue and can be shifted in the direction of CDP-diacylglycerol by an increase in the levels of cytidine monophosphate (14), which is formed in association with augmented phosphatidylcholine (PC) biosynthesis that occurs in fetal lung tissue during the latter part of gestation (85). Thus the shift in a surfactant enriched in PI to one enriched in PG also may be due to an increase in the amount of CDP-diacylglycerol available for PG synthesis.

The role of PG in surfactant function has not been defined, although its presence in increased amounts in pulmonary surfactant is correlated with enhanced fetal lung maturity (42). The finding that inositol supplementation of drinking water of adult rabbits resulted in the synthesis of lung surfactant containing only minor amounts of PG (0.3%) and an increased proportion of PI (8.5%) with unaltered surface-active properties suggests that PG does not play an essential role in surfactant function (12). It should be noted that pulmonary surfactant of adult Rhesus monkeys contains relatively small amounts of PG (~1% of surfactant lipid composition) (26).

Regulation by Hormones

GLUCOCORTICOIDS The fundamental discovery by Liggins (57) that administration of synthetic glucocorticoids to fetal lambs resulted in accelerated lung maturation, followed by the findings that glucocorticoid treatment of fetal rabbits enhanced surfactant activity and accelerated the appearance of alveolar type II cells (54, 111), led to numerous studies that supported the concept that glucocorticoids are important in the regulation of surfactant glycerophospholipid synthesis in fetal lung tissue (see 6 for review). The results of the first clinical trial published by Liggins & Howie in 1972 provided evidence that administration of synthetic glucocorticoids to women in preterm labor prior to 34 weeks gestation caused a significant decrease in the incidence of RDS in their premature newborns (58).

The results of numerous in vivo and in vitro studies utilizing fetal lung tissues of a number of species suggest that surfactant glycerophospholipid synthesis by fetal lung is, in fact, subject to multifactorial control and that, in addition to glucocorticoids, prolactin, thyroid hormones, estrogens, androgens, growth factors, insulin, catecholamines acting through β-adrenergic receptors and cAMP are important in its regulation. Since this topic has been reviewed extensively (6, 37, 89), in this section we focus on some aspects of our own research and that of others on the multifactorial regulation of surfactant glycerophospholipid synthesis by fetal lung tissue.

MULTIFACTORIAL REGULATION We and others have utilized fetal lung in organ culture as a model system for study of the regulation of surfactant synthesis because the preservation of tissue architecture and appropriate cellular interactions appear to be essential for initiation and maintenance of type II cell differentiation (62, 105). Lung explants from midtrimester human abortuses (65, 99), or from 19–21 day gestational age fetal rabbits (104) differentiate and develop the capacity to synthesize surfactant after several days of organ culture in serum-free medium. Before the start of culture, the ductular epithelial cells of these tissues are columnar in form, contain abundant cytoplasmic glycogen, and have no lamellar bodies. Within four days of organ culture in serum-free defined medium, the epithelium lining the prealveolar ducts is comprised of differentiated type II cells that contain numerous lamellar bodies (65, 99, 104). These morphologic changes are associated with a marked increase in phosphatidate phosphohydrolase (PAPase) activity, an increased rate of PC and DPPC synthesis (99, 104), and induction of transcription of the gene encoding the major surfactant protein, surfactant protein A (SP-A) (15), with associated increases in the levels of SP-A mRNA and protein (15, 64, 102). Lamellar bodies isolated from human fetal lung explants maintained in organ culture for eight days have a glycerophospholipid composition similar to that of surfactant produced by the fetal lung at 36 to 38 weeks of gestation (101). The mechanisms that underly this phenomenon of in vitro differentiation are not known, although it is thought to result from the removal of the tissue from an inhibitory factor(s) that is present in vivo (99). A role for mesenchyme-derived factors in type II cell differentiation has been proposed by Smith (95), who identified a glucocorticoid-induced lung fibroblast-derived protein (~8 kd), fibroblast-pneumonocyte factor (FPF), that stimulated PC synthesis by type II cells. It has been further suggested that the stimulatory effect of FPF on type II cell PC synthesis is mediated by an effect to increase cellular levels of cAMP (97).

Studies from several laboratories using cultured fetal lung tissues from a variety of species suggest that surfactant glycerophospholipid synthesis by the fetal lung is under multifactorial control and that glucocorticoids in concert with a number of other hormones and factors play a major role in its regulation. In studies using fetal rabbit lung explants maintained in organ culture in serum-free medium, we observed that cortisol (10^{-7}) alone stimulated PC synthesis when lung tissues from 21–28 day gestational age fetal rabbits were utilized; however, a stimulatory effect of cortisol on lung explants from 19 day gestational age fetuses was observed only when fetal calf serum (10%) also was present in the culture medium (66, 104). These findings suggest that prior to day 21 of gestation in the rabbit, the capacity of the fetal lung to respond to glucocorticoids with increased PC synthesis is dependent upon exposure to a factor(s) present in fetal serum.

In studies using lung explants from 18 day gestational age fetal rats, Gross & Wilson (39) found that dexamethasone and the phosphodiesterase inhibitor, theophylline, each caused an approximate two and one-half fold increase in the rate of DPPC synthesis; whereas, a greater than sixfold increase in DPPC synthesis was found when the two agents were added together. A supra-additive effect on DPPC synthesis also was observed when lung explants were cultured in the presence of dexamethasone and Bt_2cAMP (39).

In studies using rat (39), rabbit (8), and human (38) fetal lung in vitro, additive or synergistic effects of glucocorticoids and triiodothyronine (T_3) on PC synthesis have been reported. An interactive effect of glucocorticoids and thyroid hormones on fetal lung maturation also was suggested by in vivo studies of Hitchcock (47), who found that intra-amniotic administration of thyroxine to fetal rats caused an enhanced rate of appearance of differentiated type II cells; this effect was greatly reduced when the mothers were adrenalectomized or treated with an inhibitor of glucocorticoid synthesis. By contrast, the stimulatory effects of maternal glucocorticoid treatment on fatty acid synthesis and glycogenolysis in fetal lung tissues were found to be antagonized by simultaneous administration of T_3 (83).

In human fetal lung in vitro, we found that cortisol, in combination with prolactin, insulin, or with prolactin + insulin, enhanced PC synthesis by two to threefold as compared to that of explants maintained in control medium, or in medium that contained either prolactin, cortisol, or insulin alone (65). The synthesis of DPPC in the human fetal lung explants was stimulated by these hormonal combinations in a similar manner; therefore, the ratio of DPPC to PC was relatively unaffected by hormone treatment. Upon morphologic examination of the cultured tissue, it was found that the stimulatory effects of these hormonal treatments on PC and DPPC synthesis were accompanied by a striking increase in the amount of secreted surfactant material within lumina of the prealveolar ducts (65). A stimulatory effect of prolactin on PC and DPPC synthesis also was reported in studies with fetal rat lung in vitro (67). On the other hand, other researchers (38) have been unable to find an effect of prolactin added in the absence or presence of glucocorticoids on PC synthesis by human fetal lung in vitro. A role for prolactin in lung maturation is suggested by the presence of prolactin receptors in fetal lung tissues (2, 10, 49, 92) and the findings that the marked increase in prolactin levels in human fetal plasma (3, 120) precedes the increase in the lecithin to sphingomyelin (L/S) ratio in amniotic fluid (43), an index of fetal lung surfactant synthesis. Also, significant negative correlations were found between the concentrations of prolactin in cord plasma and the incidence of RDS in premature newborns (36, 41, 43, 98).

As discussed above, the surfactant that is synthesized initially in fetal lung tissue is enriched in DPPC and PI and contains small amounts of PG. As gestation proceeds, the relative amount of PI in surfactant declines, whereas the relative amount of PG increases. Thus the ratio of PG to PI in human amniotic fluid increases from 0.04 at 35 weeks of gestation to 1.75 at term (42, 76). In studies to evaluate the hormonal regulation of surfactant glycerophospholipid composition, we observed that lamellar body lipid phosphorus content and relative rates of synthesis of lamellar body PG and PI also are subject to multihormonal regulation. Incubation of human fetal lung explants in medium that contained cortisol together with insulin, prolactin, or both hormones, resulted in a twofold increase in the amount of lamellar body lipid phosphorus isolated from the explants, as compared to tissues maintained in control medium or with either of the hormones alone (101). Furthermore, these hormones had profound effects on the relative rates of synthesis of lamellar body PG and PI in the human fetal lung in vitro. In lung explants maintained for seven days in control medium, the relative rate of synthesis of lamellar body PG to PI (PG/PI) was 0.4; whereas, the PG/PI of lamellar bodies isolated from insulin + cortisol + prolactin-treated fetal lung explants was increased to 1.6 (101). These findings suggest that surfactant synthesis by the human fetal lung is under multihormonal control; glucocorticoids act in concert with prolactin and insulin to stimulate surfactant DPPC synthesis and to alter the relative rates of synthesis of PG and PI, which result in the accumulation of increased numbers of lamellar bodies enriched in PG with reduced PI content.

As noted above, term infants of women with certain forms of diabetes have an increased incidence of RDS (87). Although the L/S ratio in amniotic fluid obtained from diabetic women between 35 and 37 weeks of gestation is frequently normal or even elevated, the levels of PG may be greatly reduced or absent (22). It has been suggested that the fetal hyperinsulinemia associated with maternal diabetes (72) exerts an antagonistic effect on fetal lung maturation. In studies using fetal rabbit lung cells, Smith & colleagues (96) observed that insulin antagonized the stimulatory effect of cortisol on DPPC synthesis. By contrast, our own studies using human fetal lung in vitro fail to support an inhibitory role of insulin either on surfactant PC and DPPC synthesis or on the synthesis of surfactant PG. As noted above, we observed that in fetal lung explants incubated with insulin + cortisol, lamellar body phospholipid synthesis was significantly increased as compared to that observed in human fetal lung tissues maintained in control medium or in medium that contained either insulin or cortisol alone (65, 101). In addition, the PG to PI ratio of lamellar bodies isolated from human fetal lung explants incubated with insulin + cortisol + prolactin (PG/PI = 1.6) was found to be greater than that of explants incubated with cortisol + prolactin (PG/PI = 1.0); the lamellar body PG/PI of insulin + cortisol-treated fetal lung explants (PG/PI = 1.4) was similar to that of tissues treated with cortisol alone. Thus our studies using human fetal lung in vitro provide no evidence for an inhibitory role of insulin on surfactant glycerophospholipid synthesis. On the other hand, the recent observations that SP-A levels in amniotic fluid of diabetic mothers are significantly reduced as compared to gestation matched non-diabetic women (50, 100) and that insulin causes a dose-dependent inhibition of SP-A synthesis in human fetal lung in vitro (103), may help to explain the increased incidence of RDS in newborn infants of diabetic mothers (see below).

REGULATION OF SURFACTANT PROTEIN SYNTHESIS AND GENE EXPRESSION IN FETAL LUNG TISSUE

Surfactant Proteins—Properties

Since the properties of the surfactant proteins and their genes are described in detail in other chapters of this volume (see Haagsman & van Golde; Hawgood & Shiffer) we only will provide a brief review of this topic. In recent years, several surfactant-associated proteins have been isolated and characterized (84). The major protein associated with pulmonary surfactant, SP-A ($M_r \sim$ 29–36,000), is a glycoprotein modified by N-linked oligosaccharide side-chains containing sialic acid residues (69). A variety of possible functions have been ascribed to SP-A, including a role coupled with calcium and the hydrophobic surfactant proteins, SP-B and SP-C, in the transformation of the secreted lamellar body into tubular myelin (44, 52) and in the reduction of alveolar surface tension (45). In addition, SP-A may mediate endocytosis and reutilization of secreted surfactant components through binding to specific high-affinity receptors on type II cells (55, 90) and, thereby, may act in a negative-feedback manner to regulate surfactant synthesis and secretion (24, 86).

The primary structures of human (31, 113), dog (11), rabbit (16), and rat (91) SP-A, determined by sequencing of complementary DNA (cDNA) clones, are found to be highly conserved and are comprised of 247–248 amino acids. SP-A can be subdivided into two distinct domains; the amino-terminal third of the protein is collagen-like (113), while the carboxy-terminal two-thirds has properties of a lectin (25).

Surfactant also contains several extremely hydrophobic polypeptides ($M_r \sim$ 5–18,000) or proteolipids that remain associated with the glycerophospholipids during organic solvent extraction. Two proteolipids, termed SP-B (35, 45, 48, 121) and SP-C (28, 34, 112), which have been isolated and characterized, are derived from two different precursor molecules by proteolytic cleavage at both amino- and carboxy-termini. The proteolipid derived from the SP-B precursor ($M_r \sim$ 40–42,000) has an apparent molecular weight of 18,000 in the non-reduced and 7,000 in the reduced form; whereas the proteolipid derived from the SP-C precursor ($M_r \sim$ 22,000) has an apparent molecular weight of 10,000 in the non-reduced and 5,000 in the reduced form. SP-C contains a unique polyvaline sequence (34) and two palmitic acids covalently linked to cysteine residues at the amino-terminus of the mature protein (23) that contribute to its extremely hydrophobic properties. These low molecular weight hydrophobic proteins markedly enhance the surface tension-lowering properties of surfactant glycerophospholipids (71, 107, 115, 122). The importance of these hydrophobic polypeptides is suggested by the findings of certain clinical trials, in which surfactant replacement therapy using bovine surfactant extracts containing these proteins was found to be more efficacious in the prevention and treatment of RDS in prematurely born infants than are synthetic phospholipid mixtures (70).

Recently, another structurally-unique surfactant-associated protein, termed SP-D ($M_r \sim$ 43,000; previously designated as CP4), has been identified (79). The complete primary sequence of SP-D has not as yet been determined. It is apparent, however, that, like SP-A, SP-D is a glycoprotein comprised of a collagen-like domain containing hydroxyproline residues that is secreted from type II cells as a multimeric complex held together in part by disulfide bonds (79). Also, like SP-A, SP-D has calcium-dependent carbohydrate binding properties (78).

Developmental Regulation in vivo

Expression of the SP-A gene is developmentally-regulated in fetal lung tissue. SP-A mRNA is undetectable in lung tissues of human abortuses at 16–20 weeks of gestation (7, 103). Differentiated type II cells containing few lamellar bodies can be observed in human fetal lung tissue as early as 22 weeks gestation; however, active secretion of surfactant occurs only after 30 weeks at which time SP-A can be detected in the amniotic fluid (50, 53, 56, 63, 94, 100). The levels of SP-A in amniotic fluid continue to increase throughout the remainder of gestation in association with an increase in the levels of surfactant glycerophospholipids. No significant differences were observed in amniotic fluid levels of SP-A on the basis of fetal sex (100). This is of interest in light of the increased risk of RDS in male as compared to female newborns (68) and apparent delay in lung maturation in males as reflected by a reduced L/S ratio and DPPC content of amniotic fluid (108).

In the rat, levels of SP-A mRNA and protein, which are first detectable on day 18 of gestation, increase markedly through day 21 to approximately 50% of adult levels, decline moderately during the first week of life, and then increase to adult levels by day 28 (93). No sex differences in the levels of SP-A or its mRNA were observed in fetal or adult lung tissues.

In the rabbit, SP-A gene expression is initiated in fetal lung tissue several days prior to the time when augmented surfactant glycerophospholipid synthesis occurs. SP-A gene transcription and mRNA levels are first detectable on day 24 of the 31 day gestation period (Figure 1) (15). SP-A gene transcription attains maximum levels by day 28 of gestation and then decreases slightly in the neonate; the levels of SP-A mRNA reach a maximum by day 30–31 and then decline somewhat after birth (16, 64). Parallel changes in the levels of immunoreactive SP-A in the fetal rabbit lung tissue also are observed. Immunoreactive protein, which is first detectable on day 24 of gestation, reaches peak levels by day 30, and declines modestly after birth (102). During gestation there are changes in the apparent molecular weight of the protein, which appear to result from changes in glycosylation state. In lung tissue homogenates from 24–28 day gestational age fetal rabbits, immunoreactive SP-A is present as a 29,000 M_r species, pI $\leq$ 5.6; whereas, in lung homogenates from 30 day fetal rabbits, neonates and adults, the major immunoreactive species is the fully glycosylated, 29–36,000 M_r form of the protein (102). Only the fully glycosylated form of SP-A is detectable in lamellar bodies isolated from lung tissues of 28–31 day fetal rabbits, neonates and adults,

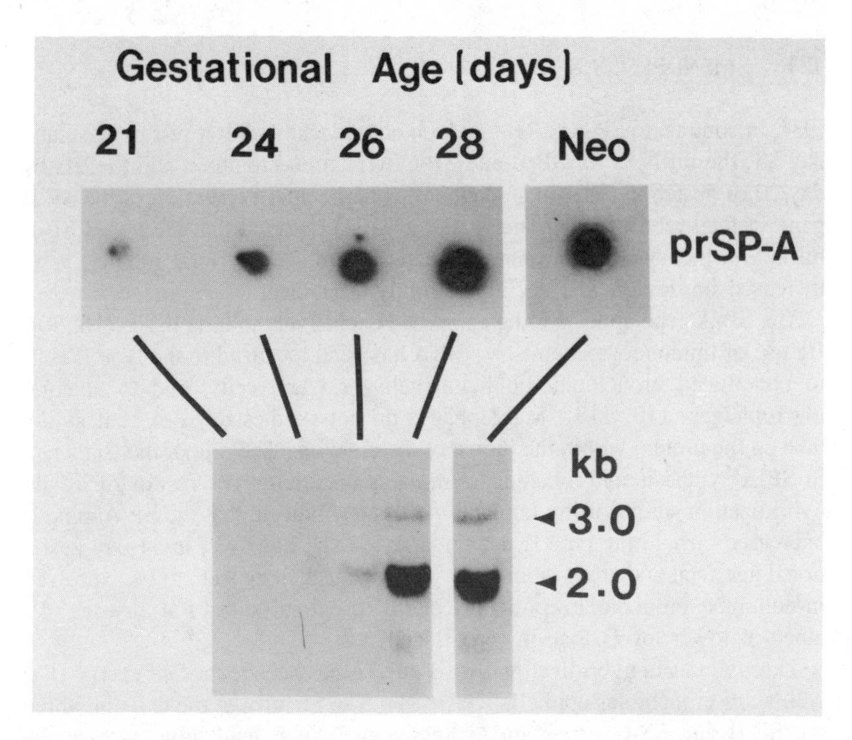

Figure 1 Changes in SP-A gene transcription and mRNA levels in rabbit lung tissue during development. *Upper Panel:* Transcriptional activity of the SP-A gene was assessed by transcription run-on analysis using nuclei isolated from lungs of fetal rabbits of 21–28 days gestational age and from neonates. *Lower Panel:* SP-A mRNA was analyzed by Northern blotting of total RNA isolated from the same lung tissues using a homologous ^{32}P-labeled SP-A cDNA insert. From Boggaram & Mendelson (15) with permission.

which suggests a role of posttranslational modification in transport of SP-A to the lamellar body (102). The time of initiation of SP-A gene expression in fetal lung tissue is correlated with the appearance of identifiable type II cells. It is uncertain, however, as to whether subsequent in vivo changes in SP-A mRNA levels are the result of an increase in SP-A gene expression per cell, or to increased numbers of type II cells, or to both.

In human fetal lung tissue, initiation of expression of the genes encoding SP-B and SP-C occurs at a much earlier time in development than is the case for SP-A. mRNAs for SP-B and SP-C are detectable in human fetal lung as early as 13 weeks of gestation (60, 117) and continue to increase during development, so that by 24 weeks, the levels of SP-B and SP-C mRNA are 50% and 15%, respectively, of the adult levels (60). In other mammalian species, this discrepancy in timing of developmental expression of genes encoding the precursors of the surfactant proteolipids (SP-B and SP-C) and SP-A is not as apparent. In rats, it was observed that SP-B mRNA was first detectable in fetal lung tissue on day 18 of gestation (as is the mRNA for SP-A); whereas, the mRNA for SP-C was readily detectable as early as day 17

(93). In contrast to SP-A mRNA, which only reaches adult levels by postnatal day 28, the mRNAs for SP-B and SP-C were found to attain adult levels by day 20 of gestation (93). In studies of developmental expression of the SP-B gene in fetal rabbit lung tissue, Xu et al (121) reported that the levels SP-B mRNA, which were first detected in tissues of 27 day fetal rabbits, were increased on day 30 and declined slightly after birth.

The SP-A gene appears to be expressed exclusively in lung tissue (16, 30). By use of immunocytochemistry, SP-A has been localized to the type II cell, to nonciliated bronchiolar epithelial cells or Clara cells, and to alveolar macrophages (110, 119). Macrophages do not synthesize SP-A, but avidly take up the protein within the lumen of the alveolus. The role of the Clara cell in SP-A synthesis and metabolism remains uncertain. The results of in situ hybridization studies using human lung tissues indicate that the SP-A gene is expressed only in the type II pneumonocyte (81); however, in 31-day gestational age fetal and adult rabbits, the SP-A gene also appears to be expressed in columnar bronchiolar epithelial cells of proximal and distal airways (4), albeit at lower levels than in type II cells.

Through in situ hybridization, SP-B mRNA has been identified in type II as well as in bronchiolar epithelial cells (81). The identity of the cells in which the SP-B and SP-C genes are expressed in human fetal lung prior to the appearance of differentiated type II cells is, at present, uncertain. The recent finding that immunoreactive SP-B is associated with surfactant-like particles secreted by intestinal enterocytes (27) suggests that SP-B gene expression may not occur exclusively in lung tissue.

Developmental Regulation in vitro

The spontaneous differentiation of fetal lung explants maintained in organ culture in serum-free medium is associated with a rapid induction of SP-A gene transcription and of the levels of SP-A mRNA and protein (15, 16, 64). In studies using fetal rat lung in organ culture, it was observed that the glucocorticoid receptor antagonist, RU 486, failed to block the spontaneous changes in morphology and increases in DPPC synthesis and SP-A mRNA accumulation (40). These findings suggest that spontaneous differentiation is not induced by the action of glucocorticoids retained within the cultured tissue (40). In recent studies, we found that human fetal lung tissue in organ culture produces large amounts of prostaglandin E_2 (PGE_2) (1). The prostaglandin synthesis inhibitor, indomethacin, was found to prevent the spontaneous induction of SP-A gene expression and markedly reduce cAMP formation by the cultured lung tissue (1). The finding that PGE_2 can markedly increase cAMP formation by the cultured tissue and that either PGE_2 or cAMP analogues could overcome the inhibitory effect of indomethacin on SP-A gene expression suggest that prostaglandins, acting through cAMP, may serve a role in the spontaneous induction of SP-A gene expression in human fetal lung in vitro (1).

As discussed above, SP-B and SP-C mRNAs are detectable in human fetal lung tissue as early as 13 weeks of gestation; the levels of SP-B mRNA increase in human fetal lung explants as a function of time in organ culture and reach adult levels after several days, whereas, the levels of SP-C mRNA decline as compared to preculture values (60). These findings are indicative that the genes encoding SP-A, SP-B and SP-C are independently regulated in human fetal lung tissue.

Regulation by Hormones

Although it is apparent that midgestation fetal lung explants differentiate spontaneously and develop the capacity to synthesize surfactant glycerophospholipids and proteins when placed in culture in serum-free medium, there is abundant evidence that hormones and bioactive substances can modulate the rate of biochemical and morphological differentiation.

EFFECTS OF cAMP ANALOGUES AND OF AGENTS THAT INCREASE THE CELLULAR LEVELS OF cAMP ON SP-A SYNTHESIS AND GENE EXPRESSION AND ON MORPHOLOGIC DEVELOPMENT OF FETAL LUNG Cyclic AMP greatly enhances SP-A synthesis and mRNA levels, as well as morphologic development of fetal lung tissues maintained in organ culture (16, 64, 74, 116). In rabbit fetal lung in vitro, SP-A synthesis is augmented by cAMP analogues and by agents that increase the accumulation of cAMP, such as isobutylmethylxanthine, which inhibits phosphodiesterase activity, and forskolin, which activates adenylyl cyclase directly (64). The cAMP induction of SP-A synthesis is associated with a rapid increase in SP-A mRNA levels (16, 64) and a comparable increase in SP-A gene transcription (15). The stimulatory effects of cAMP on SP-A gene transcription and mRNA levels are dependent upon ongoing protein synthesis, which suggests that a labile protein factor(s) mediates the stimulatory effects of cAMP on SP-A gene expression (15).

Cyclic AMP analogues also increase the levels of SP-A (74) and its mRNA (74, 116) in human fetal lung in culture. An autoradiogram of an immunoblot of the levels of immunoreactive SP-A in human fetal lung explants after two to six days of organ culture in the absence or presence of dibutyryl cAMP (Bt_2cAMP) is shown in Figure 2. Immunoreactive SP-A was first detectable in control tissues on day four of incubation and was present in increased amounts on day six. The spontaneous induction of SP-A synthesis in the human fetal lung explants was associated with an induction of surfactant glycerophospholipid synthesis, the enlargement of the prealveolar ducts, and the appearance of differentiated type II cells. Bt_2cAMP treatment increased

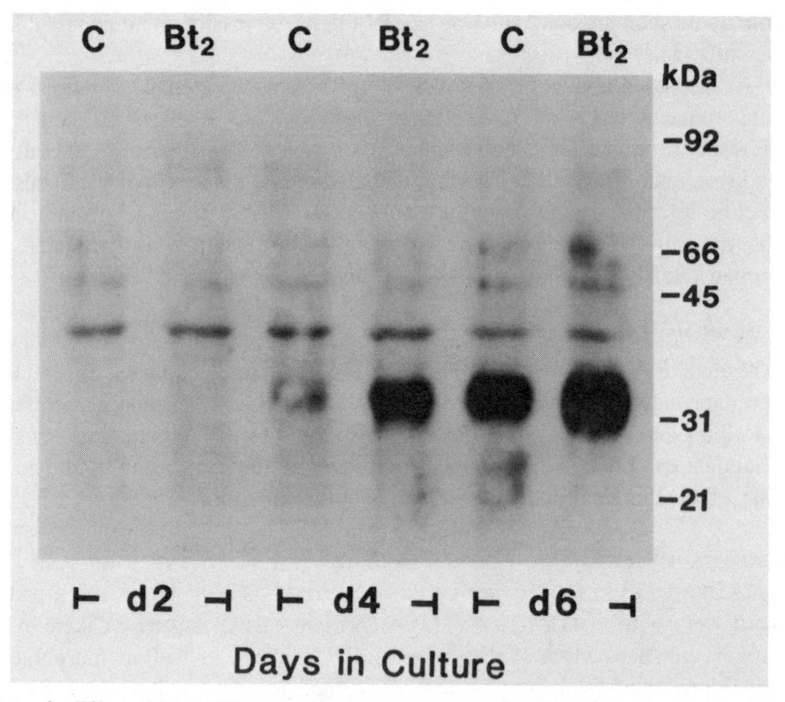

Figure 2 Effect of Bt_2cAMP on the levels of immunoreactive SP-A in human fetal lung in culture. Lung explants from midtrimester human abortuses were maintained in organ culture for up to six days in control medium (C) or in medium containing Bt_2cAMP (Bt_2, 1 mM). Specific content of immunoreactive SP-A was analyzed in equal amounts of homogenate protein (40 μg) by immunoblotting using specific antibodies against human SP-A. SP-A is the major band at 35 kd. From Odom et al (74) with permission.

the levels of immunoreactive SP-A on days four and six of incubation. The cAMP induction of SP-A accumulation in the fetal lung explants was associated with comparable increases in the levels of SP-A mRNA (74) and of SP-A gene transcription (17).

The stimulatory effects of Bt_2cAMP on SP-A gene expression in human fetal lung in vitro are associated with pronounced effects on morphology (74). In human fetal lung tissues incubated for two days in Bt_2cAMP-containing medium, a marked enlargement of the prealveolar ducts and decrease in the volume density of the interalveolar connective tissue was found, as compared to fetal lung tissues maintained for this period in control medium (Figure 3*A*,*B*). These differences between control and Bt_2cAMP-treated tissues were no longer evident after four and six days of incubation because the alveolar lumenal volume density of control explants was increased at these time points (Figure 3*B*). In cAMP-treated fetal lung explants there was an enhanced rate of appearance of differentiated type II cells (Figure 3*B*) and an increased

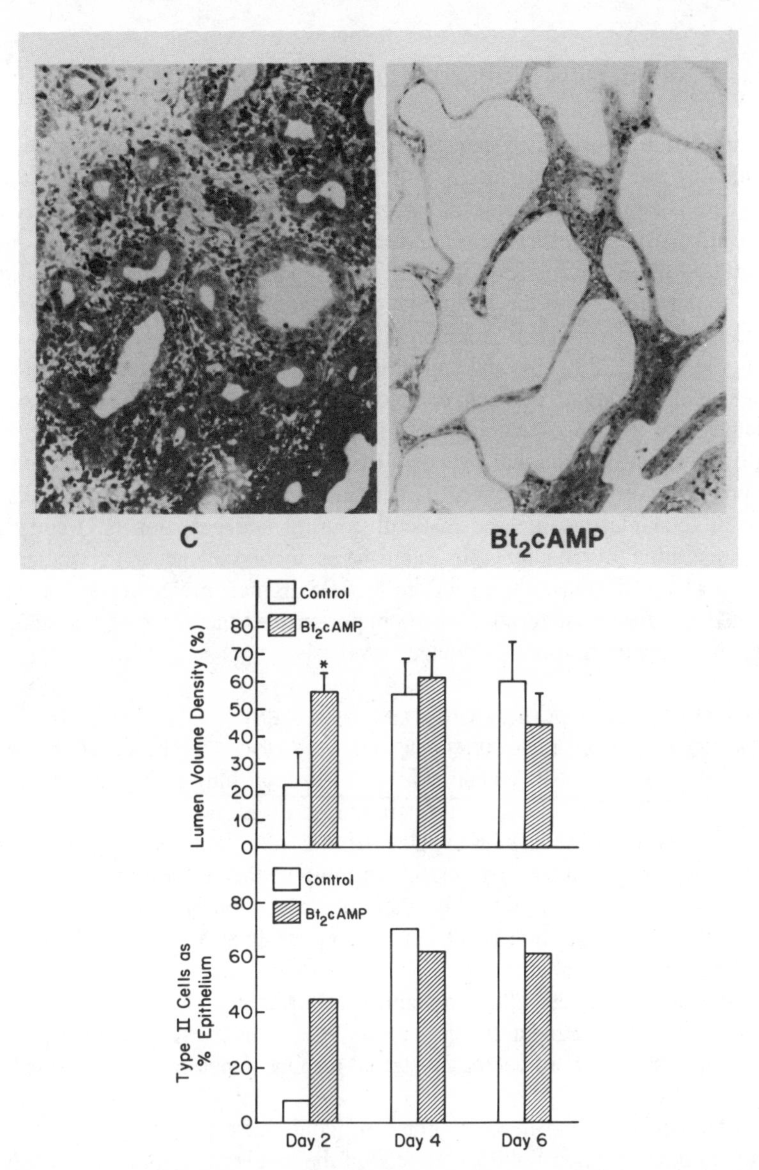

Figure 3 Effect of Bt_2cAMP on morphological development of human fetal lung in culture. *Upper panel:* Light micrographs (X340) of human fetal lung explants after two days of culture in control medium (C) or in medium containing Bt_2cAMP. *Lower panel:* Morphometric analysis at the light and electron microscopic levels of human fetal lung explants incubated for two to six days in the absence or presence of Bt_2cAMP. Data are the mean ± SEM (n = 6). * = $P < 0.001$. Six explants from two independent experiments were analyzed for each treatment at each time point to determine the relative volume density of the alveolar lumen (*upper graph*); each determination represents pooled data from 300 grid intersections scored for each explant. The proportion of type II cells (*lower graph*) was determined by ultrastructural analysis; 300 epithelial cells were scored as type II cells (one or more lamellar bodies) or as undifferentiated cells (no lamellar bodies) per treatment and time point in two independent experiments. From Odom et al (74) with permission.

accumulation of secreted lamellar bodies and tubular myelin within the lumina of the prealveolar ducts (74).

There is evidence that catecholamines, acting through β-adrenergic receptors and cAMP, may serve a role in the regulation of SP-A gene expression in fetal lung tissue during development. The β_2-adrenergic agonist, terbutaline, was found to increase the accumulation of immunoreactive SP-A in human fetal lung in vitro (74). β-Adrenergic receptors have been identified in fetal lung tissues (32, 88, 114) and appear to be concentrated on type II cells (88). The specific content of such receptors, as well as the responsiveness of adenylyl cyclase to catecholamines, is increased in fetal rabbit lung tissue with advancing gestational age (9). Receptor number also is increased in response to cortisol treatment (20). The findings that norepinephrine levels in human fetal plasma increase markedly during late gestation (77) and that administration of β-adrenergic agonists as tocolytic agents to women in preterm labor decrease the incidence of RDS in their premature infants (13, 18, 51) are further suggestive of the importance of the adrenergic system in fetal lung maturation and surfactant synthesis.

EFFECTS OF GLUCOCORTICOIDS ON SP-A GENE EXPRESSION AND ON MORPHOLOGIC DEVELOPMENT OF FETAL LUNG Glucocorticoids have complex actions on SP-A gene expression in fetal lung tissues that may be species-specific and dependent upon the stage of development at which treatment is initiated. In lung explants from 21-day fetal rabbits, glucocorticoids have acute but transient effects to inhibit SP-A gene transcription and mRNA levels that are followed by a stimulatory action on SP-A gene expression (15). Administration of dexamethasone to fetal and neonatal rats has been reported to enhance SP-A synthesis and mRNA levels in a dose-dependent manner (29, 80). No significant differences in responsiveness to dexamethasone treatment were observed as a function of postnatal age, although a trend toward decreased steroid responsiveness with increasing age was noted (29).

In human fetal lung in vitro, glucocorticoids have been reported to exert both stimulatory and inhibitory effects on the levels of SP-A and its mRNA that are dose- and time-dependent (7, 17, 59, 73, 116). We examined in detail the effects of dexamethasone in various concentrations on SP-A gene expression and on morphologic development of human fetal lung in vitro. Dexamethasone was found to have differential effects on the levels of SP-A and its mRNA in human fetal lung tissue that are dose-dependent; at concentrations of 10^{-10} and 10^{-9} M, a stimulatory effect was observed, while at concentrations $>10^{-8}$ M, the glucocorticoid was markedly inhibitory (73). Dexamethasone (10^{-7} M) also antagonized the action of Bt_2cAMP to increase the levels of SP-A and its mRNA. In recent studies, we observed that the

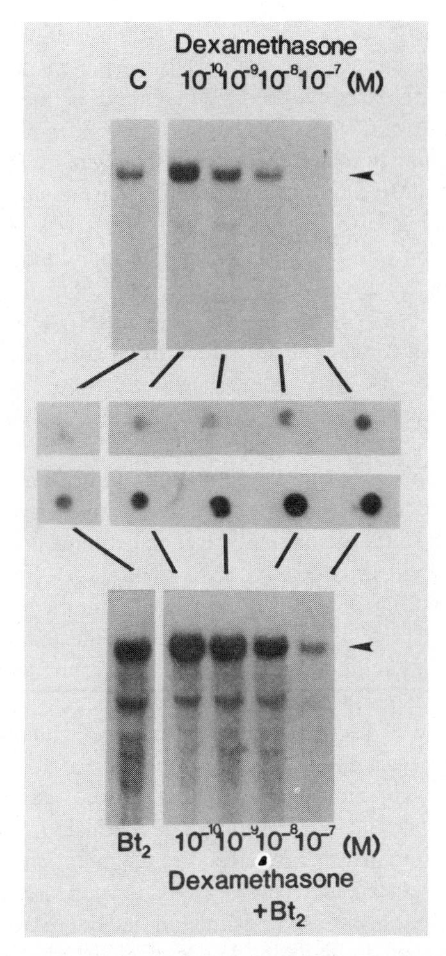

Figure 4 Effects of dexamethasone in the absence or presence of Bt_2cAMP (Bt_2) on SP-A gene transcription and on the levels of SP-A mRNA in human fetal lung in vitro. Human fetal lung explants were incubated for five days in the absence (C) or presence of dexamethasone (10^{-10} – 10^{-7} M) and in the absence or presence of Bt_2cAMP (1 mM). Nuclei isolated from the tissues were subjected to transcription run-on analysis using the rabbit SP-A cDNA as a probe (autoradiograms in center panels). Total RNA isolated from the same tissues was analyzed for SP-A mRNA transcripts by Northern blotting using ^{32}P-labeled SP-A cDNA as a probe (autoradiograms in upper and lower panels). From Boggaram et al (17) with permission.

effects of dexamethasone on SP-A gene transcription and mRNA levels in human fetal lung in vitro are, in fact, paradoxical (17). As shown in Figure 4 (*center panel*), dexamethasone caused a dose-dependent stimulation of SP-A gene transcription, with a maximum stimulatory effect evident at concentrations of 10^{-8}–10^{-7} M. Dexamethasone also acted synergistically with

Bt_2cAMP to increase the rate of SP-A gene transcription. On the other hand, dexamethasone at these concentrations caused a marked reduction in the levels of SP-A mRNA and reduced the magnitude of the stimulatory effect of Bt_2cAMP on SP-A mRNA accumulation (Figure 4, *upper and lower panels*). Furthermore, in human fetal lung explants that were maintained in culture for several days to induce SP-A gene expression, dexamethasone caused a rapid decline in the levels of SP-A mRNA; this effect was observed even in the presence of actinomycin D or cycloheximide, inhibitors of mRNA transcription and translation, respectively (17). Therefore, it is likely that the ability of dexamethasone ($>10^{-8}$ M) to reduce SP-A mRNA levels is mediated by a dominant action of the steroid to reduce SP-A mRNA stability (17).

Dexamethasone also has pronounced and dose-dependent effects on morphology of human fetal lung in vitro (73). As shown in the light micrographs and accompanying morphometric analyses in Figure 5*A* and *B*, a biphasic effect of dexamethasone on alveolar lumen size and on the volume density of type II cells was observed. At a concentration of 10^{-10} M, a stimulatory effect of the steroid on type II cell volume density and on alveolar lumen size was evident; whereas, at concentrations $\geq 10^{-7}$ M, type II cell volume density and alveolar lumen size were significantly reduced as compared to control explants (73). These findings indicate that elevated levels of glucocorticoids may inhibit human fetal lung development and SP-A synthesis, whereas low concentrations are stimulatory.

In consideration of the potential importance of glucocorticoids and catecholamines acting through cAMP in the regulation of SP-A gene expression in human fetal lung tissue, it is notable that fetal stress, associated with maternal hypertension and decreased uteroplacental perfusion, has been associated with accelerated lung maturation (106). Premature infants of mothers afflicted with pregnancy-induced and chronic hypertension are generally small for gestational age and manifest a decreased incidence of RDS (106). It is suggested that elevated circulating levels of glucocorticoids and other stress hormones (i.e. catecholamines, prolactin, vasopressin, adrenocorticotropin) in fetuses of hypertensive mothers may enhance lung maturation and, thereby, accelerate the developmental increase in SP-A gene expression and surfactant synthesis and secretion.

EFFECTS OF INSULIN AND GROWTH FACTORS ON SP-A GENE EXPRESSION IN FETAL LUNG As discussed above, fetal hyperinsulinemia associated with maternal diabetes has been suggested to exert a deleterious effect on fetal lung development and to predispose the neonate to an increased risk of developing RDS. The observation that the incidence of RDS is increased in newborn infants of diabetic mothers (87), despite amniotic fluid L/S ratios indicative of fetal lung maturity, suggests that a surfactant component other than PC is

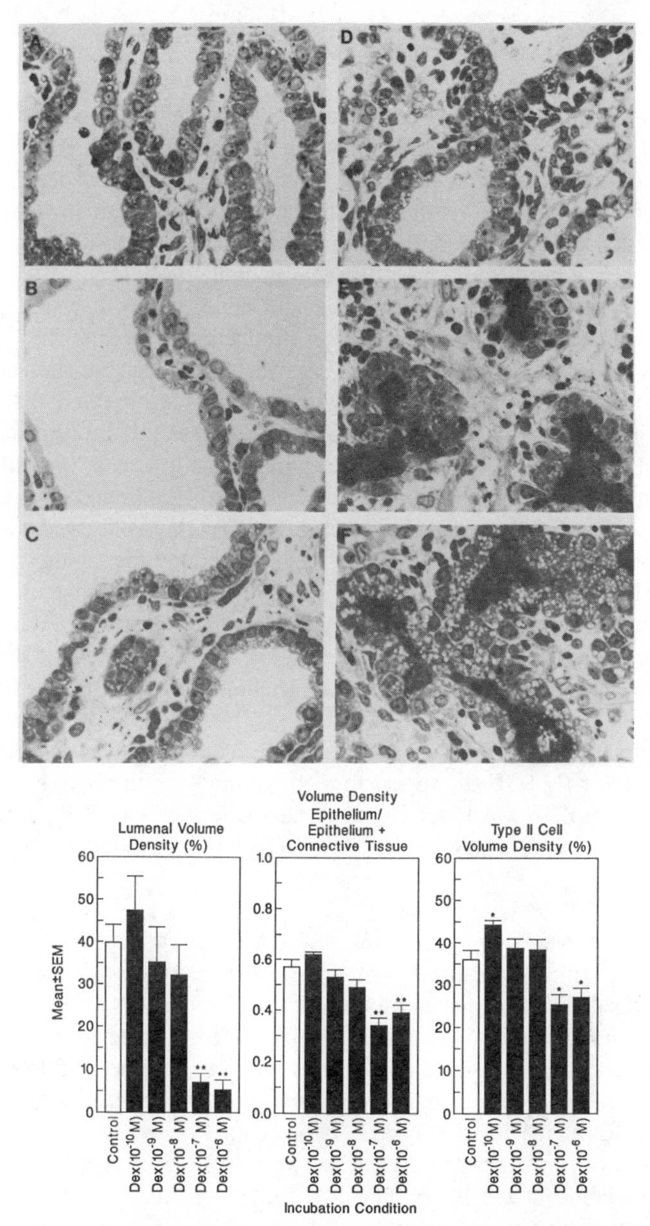

Figure 5 Effects of dexamethasone on morphologic development of human fetal lung in culture. *Top panels:* Light micrographs (X840) of human fetal lung explants after six days of incubation in control medium (A) or in medium containing dexamethasone at 10^{-10} (B), 10^{-9} (C), 10^{-8} (D), 10^{-7} (E) or 10^{-6} (F) M. *Bottom panel:* Morphometric analysis of the effects of dexamethasone on human fetal lung in vitro. Data are the mean ± SEM of six determinations. Each determination represents pooled data from 300 grid intersections scored for each explant; six explants from two independent experiments were analyzed per treatment (* = significantly different from control, $P < 0.01$; ** = significantly different from control, $P < 0.001$). From Odom et al (73) with permission.

affected. As discussed above, surfactant PG is markedly decreased in amniotic fluid samples from diabetic pregnancies; however, PG does not seem to serve an important role in surfactant function. In two independent studies it was found that SP-A levels in amniotic fluid of diabetic women were significantly reduced as compared to gestational age-matched non-diabetic subjects (50, 100). In a third study, no differences in amniotic fluid SP-A levels were observed between diabetic and non-diabetic subjects (63). It was suggested, however, that lung maturation and SP-A production in the infants of diabetic mothers in that study were unaffected because of improved metabolic control.

In studies using human fetal lung in culture, we observed that insulin caused a dose-dependent inhibition of SP-A synthesis (103). An inhibitory effect of insulin was observed at concentrations as low as 2.5 ng/ml. When fetal lung explants were incubated with combined insulin and cortisol (10^{-7} M), SP-A content was reduced to levels lower than those observed with either hormone alone. Interestingly, under such conditions the synthesis of surfactant PC was found to be increased significantly over that of explants maintained in control medium, or with either hormone alone (103). These findings suggest that the fetal hyperinsulinemia associated with maternal diabetes may cause production of a surfactant containing a reduced specific content of SP-A.

Growth factors, such as epidermal growth factor (EGF) and transforming growth factor-β (TGF-β), appear to regulate SP-A synthesis in human fetal lung in vitro. EGF was found to have a stimulatory effect on SP-A synthesis and on the levels of its mRNA, whereas, TGF-β was observed to be inhibitory (118).

THE SP-A GENE AND POTENTIAL REGULATORY REGIONS The human SP-A gene, which is localized on chromosome 10 (19), is ~5 kb in length and is comprised of five exons and four intervening sequences (113). Within the 5'-flanking region of the human SP-A gene, there is a sequence with homology to glucocorticoid regulatory elements that are characterized in other eukaryotic genes (113). In human lung tissue, there is evidence for two closely-related mRNA species that encode two proteins of 29,000 and 31,000 M_r (31). It has been suggested that these two mRNA species may result from allelic variation at the SP-A locus, or from a clustered family of closely related genes on chromosome 10 (19).

In the rabbit, SP-A is encoded by a single copy gene that is transcribed into two different size-species of mRNA by use of alternative polyadenylation signals (16). The 5'-flanking region of the rabbit SP-A gene contains two putative glucocorticoid regulatory elements (GREs) and a potential cAMP regulatory element (CRE) based on sequence homology with such regulatory elements in other eukaryotic genes (C. Chen, V. Boggaram, C. Mendelson, unpublished observations). These potential regulatory regions lie within 300 bp of the transcription initiation site.

EFFECTS OF cAMP ANALOGUES AND OF AGENTS THAT INCREASE cAMP ON SP-B AND SP-C SYNTHESIS AND GENE EXPRESSION IN FETAL LUNG TISSUE In contrast to their marked stimulatory effects on SP-A gene expression, cAMP analogues have modest effects on increasing the levels of SP-B and SP-C mRNA in human fetal lung in vitro (117). These apparent effects of cAMP analogues on SP-B and SP-C gene expression were unassociated with changes in the levels of the corresponding immunoreactive polypeptides (117). In studies by Liley et al (60), terbutaline and forskolin were found to modestly increase the levels of mRNA for SP-B in human fetal lung in culture; however, no effects of these agents on SP-C mRNA levels were observed.

EFFECTS OF GLUCOCORTICOIDS ON SP-B AND SP-C SYNTHESIS AND GENE EXPRESSION IN FETAL LUNG TISSUE Glucocorticoids have marked dose-dependent stimulatory effects on the levels of SP-B and SP-C mRNA in human fetal lung in vitro (60, 117). This is in contrast to their complex effects on SP-A gene expression. At concentrations of dexamethasone (10^{-7} M) that cause a pronounced inhibition of the levels of SP-A mRNA in human fetal lung explants, the levels of SP-B and SP-C mRNA are markedly stimulated. In studies with a human type II adenocarcinoma cell line, dexamethasone was observed to have a rapid and dose-dependent effect on increasing the levels of SP-B mRNA, while causing an equally rapid, dose-dependent inhibition of the levels of mRNA for SP-A (75).

THE SP-B AND SP-C GENES AND POTENTIAL REGULATORY REGIONS The precursor polypeptide for human SP-B is encoded by a gene that is localized on chromosome 2, which is composed of 11 exons and spans some 10 kb of DNA (82). Within the 5'-flanking region, one putative CRE and several GREs have been identified. The gene is transcribed into an mRNA of ~2 kb in size that encodes a precursor protein of ~40,000 M_r. Sequences encoding the hydrophobic 70 amino acid surfactant protein, SP-B, are present in exons six and seven of the gene.

The precursor for human SP-C is encoded by two highly homologous genes of ~3.0 kb in size (33). These genes, which have identical coding sequences, are composed of six exons and are localized on chromosome 8. The transcribed mRNA of ~1 kb in size encodes a precursor polypeptide of ~21,000 M_r. Sequences encoding the hydrophobic ~36 amino acid surfactant proteolipid, SP-C, which contains a stretch of 23 hydrophobic amino acids with six contiguous valines, is present within the second exon of the gene.

Although SP-C gene expression is only modestly regulated by cAMP, two regions with homology to CREs are present upstream of the SP-C precursor gene, within 500 bp of the site of transcription initiation. Paradoxically, no potential GRE has been identified within this 5'-flanking region (33).

SUMMARY

The synthesis of surfactant glycerophospholipids and proteins is under multifactorial control and is regulated by a number of hormones and factors, including glucocorticoids, prolactin, insulin, growth factors, estrogens, androgens, thyroid hormones and catecholamines acting through β-adrenergic receptors, and cAMP. In studies with human fetal lung in organ culture, glucocorticoids, in combination with prolactin and/or insulin, were found to increase the rate of lamellar body PC synthesis and increase the molar ratio of surfactant PG to PI to a value similar to that of surfactant secreted by the human fetal lung at term.

Recognition of the potential importance of the surfactant proteins SP-A, SP-B, and SP-C in the reduction of alveolar surface tension and in endocytosis and reutilization of secreted surfactant by type II cells has stimulated rapid advancement of knowledge concerning the structures of these proteins and their genes, as well as their developmental and hormonal regulation in fetal lung tissue. The genes encoding the surfactant proteins are expressed in a lung-specific manner and appear to be regulated independently during fetal development. SP-A gene expression is initiated in fetal lung tissue after 75–85% of gestation is completed in all mammalian species studied to date. In the human fetus, however, expression of the SP-B and SP-C genes is detectable prior to mid-gestation. In situ hybridization studies of human lung tissue indicate that the SP-A gene is expressed only in type II cells, whereas SP-B gene expression is detectable in bronchioalveolar epithelial cells as well.

Cyclic AMP and glucocorticoids have pronounced effects on the regulation of SP-A gene expression in human and rabbit fetal lung in culture. In human fetal lung in vitro, the effects of cAMP are primarily at the level of gene transcription. By contrast, glucocorticoids have stimulatory effects on SP-A gene transcription and inhibitory effects on SP-A mRNA stability. Furthermore, the combined effects of cAMP and glucocorticoids on SP-A gene transcription in human fetal lung in vitro are synergistic. Glucocorticoids appear to be of primary importance in the regulation of the genes encoding SP-B and SP-C. Elucidation of the molecular mechanisms involved in the regulation of expression of the surfactant protein genes in developing fetal lung will be of fundamental importance to our understanding of the developmental and tissue-specific regulation of eukaryotic gene expression.

ACKNOWLEDGMENTS

The authors' research is supported, in part, by National Institutes of Health Grant, HD-13912, by Basic Research Grant, 1-1183, from the March of Dimes Birth Defects Foundation, and by American Heart Association, Texas Affiliate Grant 89G-103.

Literature Cited

1. Acarregui, M. J., Snyder, J. M., Mitchell, M. D., Mendelson, C. R. 1990. Prostaglandins regulate surfactant protein A (SP-A) gene expression in human fetal lung *in vitro*. *Endocrinology* 127:1105–13
2. Amit, T., Barkey, R. J., Guy, J., Youdim, M. B. H. 1987. Specific binding sites for prolactin in adult rabbit lung. *Mol. Cell. Endocrinol.* 49:17–24
3. Aubert, M. L., Grumbach, M. M., Kaplan, S. L. 1975. The ontogenesis of human fetal hormones. III. Prolactin. *J. Clin. Invest.* 56:155–64
4. Auten, R. L., Watkins, R. H., Shapiro, D. L., Horowitz, S. 1990. Surfactant apoprotein A (SP-A) is synthesized in airway cells. *Am. J. Respir. Cell Mol. Biol.* 3:491–96
5. Avery, M. E., Mead, J. 1959. Surface properties in relation to atelectasis and hyaline membrane disease. *Am. J. Dis. Child.* 97:517–23
6. Ballard, P. L. 1986. Hormones and lung maturation. *Monogr. Endocrinol.* 28:1–354
7. Ballard, P. L., Hawgood, S., Liley, H., Wellenstein, G., Gonzales, L. W., et al. 1986. Regulation of pulmonary surfactant apoprotein SP 28-36 gene in fetal human lung. *Proc. Natl. Acad. Sci. USA* 83:9527–31
8. Ballard, P. L., Hovey, M. L., Gonzales, L. K. 1984. Thyroid hormone stimulation of phosphatidylcholine synthesis in cultured fetal rabbit lung. *J. Clin. Invest.* 74:898–905
9. Barrett, C. T., Sevanian, A., Kaplan, S. A. 1974. Adenylate cyclase activity in immature rabbit lung. *Pediatr. Res.* 8:244–47
10. Ben-Harari, R. R., Amit, T., Youdim, M. B. H. 1983. Binding of oestradiol, progesterone and prolactin in rat lung. *J. Endocrinol.* 93:301–10
11. Benson, B., Hawgood, S., Schilling, J., Clements, J., Damm, D., et al. 1985. Structure of canine pulmonary surfactant: cDNA and complete amino acid sequence. *Proc. Natl. Acad. Sci. USA* 82:6379–83
12. Beppu, O. S., Clements, J. A., Goerke, J. 1983. Phosphatidylglycerol-deficient lung surfactant has normal properties. *J. Appl. Physiol.* 55:496–502
13. Bergman, B., Hedner, T. 1978. Antepartum administration of terbutaline and the incidence of hyaline membrane disease in preterm infants. *Acta Obstet. Gynecol. Scand.* 57:217–21
14. Bleasdale, J. E., Johnston, J. M. 1982. CMP-dependent incorporation of [^{14}C]glycerol-3-phosphate into phosphatidylglycerol and phosphatidylglycerol phosphate by rabbit lung microsomes. *Biochim. Biophys. Acta* 710:377–90
15. Boggaram, V., Mendelson, C. R. 1988. Transcriptional regulation of the gene encoding the major surfactant protein (SP-A) in rabbit fetal lung. *J. Biol. Chem.* 263:19060–65
16. Boggaram, V., Qing, K., Mendelson, C. R. 1988. The major apoprotein of rabbit pulmonary surfactant: Elucidation of primary sequence and cAMP and developmental regulation. *J. Biol. Chem.* 263:2939–47
17. Boggaram, V., Smith, M. E., Mendelson, C. R. 1989. Regulation of expression of the gene encoding the major surfactant protein (SP-A) in human fetal lung in vitro: Disparate effects of glucocorticoids on transcription and on mRNA stability. *J. Biol. Chem.* 264: 11421–27
18. Boog, G., Brahim, M. B., Gandar, R. 1975. Beta-mimetic drugs and possible prevention of respiratory distress syndrome *Br. J. Obstet. Gynaecol.* 82:285–88
19. Bruns, G., Stroh, H., Veldman, G. M., Latt, S. A., Floros, J. 1987. The 35 kd pulmonary surfactant-associated protein is encoded on chromosome 10. *Hum. Genet.* 76:58–62
20. Cheng, J. B., Goldfien, A., Ballard, P. L., Roberts, J. M. 1980. Glucocorticoids increase pulmonary β-adrenergic

receptors in fetal rabbit. *Endocrinology* 107:1646–48
21. Clements, J. A., King, R. J. 1976. Composition of surface-active material. In *The Biochemical Basis of Pulmonary Function,* ed. R. G. Crystal, pp. 363–87. New York: Dekker. 534 pp.
22. Cunningham, M. D., Desai, M. S., Thompson, S. A., Greene, J. M. 1978 Amniotic fluid phosphatidylglycerol in diabetic pregnancies. *Am. J. Obstet. Gynecol.* 131:719–24
23. Curstedt, T., Johansson, J., Persson, P., Eklund, A., Robertson, B., et al. 1990. Hydrophobic surfactant-associated peptides: SP-C is a lipopeptide with two palmitoylated cysteine residues, whereas SP-B lacks covalently linked fatty acyl groups. *Proc. Natl. Acad. Sci. USA* 87:2985–89
24. Dobbs, L. G., Wright, J. R., Hawgood, S., Gonzalez, R., Venstrom, K., Nellenbogen, J. 1987. Pulmonary surfactant and its components inhibit secretion of PC from cultured rat alveolar type II cells. *Proc. Natl. Acad. Sci. USA* 84:1010–14
25. Drickamer, K., Dordal, M. S., Reynolds, L. 1986. Mannose-binding proteins isolated from rat liver contain carbohydrate-recognition domains linked to collagenous tails: Complete primary structure and homology with pulmonary surfactant apoprotein. *J. Biol. Chem.* 261:6878–87
26. Egberts, J., Beintema-Dubbeldam, A., de Boers, A. 1987. Phosphatidylinositol and not phosphatidylglycerol is the important minor phospholipid in Rhesus-monkey surfactant. *Biochim. Biophys. Acta* 919:90–92
27. Eliakim, R., DeSchryver-Kecskemeti, K., Nogee, L., Stenson, W. F., Alpers, D. H. 1989. Isolation and characterization of a small intestinal surfactant-like particle containing alkaline phosphatase and other digestive enzymes. *J. Biol. Chem.* 264:20614–19
28. Fisher, J. H., Shannon, J. M., Hofmann, T., Mason, R. J. 1989. Nucleotide and deduced amino acid sequence of the hydrophobic surfactant protein SP-C from rat: expression in alveolar type II cells and homology with SP-C from other species. *Biochim. Biophys. Acta* 995:225–30
29. Floros, J., Phelps, D. S., Harding, H. P., Church, S., Ware, J. 1989. Postnatal stimulation of rat surfactant protein A by dexamethasone. *Am. J. Physiol.* 257: L137–43
30. Floros, J., Phelps, D. S., Kourembanas, S., Taeusch, H. W. 1986. Primary translation products, biosynthesis and tissue specificity of the major surfactant protein in rat. *J. Biol. Chem.* 261:828–31
31. Floros, J., Steinbrink, R., Jacobs, K., Phelps, D., Kriz, R., et al. 1986. Isolation and characterization of cDNA clones for the 35-kDa pulmonary surfactant-associated protein. *J. Biol. Chem.* 261:9029–33
32. Giannopoulos, G. 1980. Identification and ontogeny of β-adrenergic receptors in fetal rabbit lung. *Biochem. Biophys. Res. Commun.* 95:388–94
33. Glasser, S. W., Korfhagen, T. R., Perme, C. M., Pilot-Matias, T., Kister, S. E., Whitsett, J. A. 1988. Two SP-C genes encoding surfactant proteolipid. *J. Biol. Chem.* 263:10326–31
34. Glasser, S. W., Korfhagen, T. R., Weaver, T. E., Clark, J. C., Pilot-Matias, T., et al. 1988. cDNA, deduced polypeptide structure and chromosomal assignment of human pulmonary surfactant proteolipid SPL(Val). *J. Biol. Chem.* 263:9–12
35. Glasser, S. W., Korfhagen, T. R., Weaver, T., Pilot-Matias, T., Fox, J. L., Whitsett, J. A. 1987. cDNA and deduced amino acid sequence of human pulmonary surfactant-associated proteolipid SPL(Phe). *Proc. Natl. Acad. Sci. USA* 84:4007–11
36. Gluckman, P. D., Ballard, P. L., Kaplan, S. L., Liggins, G. C., Grumbach, M. M. 1978. Prolactin in umbilical cord blood and the respiratory distress syndrome. *J. Pediat.* 93:1011–14
37. Gonzales, L. W., Ballard, P. L. 1989. Hormones and their receptors. In *Lung Cell Biology,* ed. D. Massaro, 41:539–89. New York/Basel:Marcel Dekker. 1431 pp.
38. Gonzales, L. W., Ballard, P. L., Ertsey, R., Williams, M. C. 1986. Glucocorticoids and thyroid hormones stimulate biochemical and morphological differentiation of human fetal lung in organ culture. *J. Clin. Endocrinol. Metab.* 62:678–91
39. Gross, I., Wilson, C. M. 1982. Fetal lung in organ culture. IV. Supra-additive hormone interactions. *J. Appl. Physiol.* 52:1420–25
40. Gross, I., Wilson, C. M., Floros, J., Dynia, D. W. 1989. Initiation of fetal rat lung phospholipid and surfactant-associated protein A mRNA synthesis. *Pediatr. Res.* 25:239–44
41. Grosso, D. S., MacDonald, C. P., Thomasson, J. E., Christian, C. D. 1980. Relationship of newborn serum prolactin levels to the respiratory distress syn-

drome and maternal hypertension. *Am. J. Obstet. Gynecol.* 137:569–74
42. Hallman, M., Kulovich, M., Kirkpatrick, E., Sugarman, R. G., Gluck, L. 1976. Phosphatidylinositol and phosphatidylglycerol in amniotic fluid: indices of lung maturity. *Am. J. Obstet. Gynecol.* 125:613–17
43. Hauth, J. C., Parker, C. R. Jr., MacDonald, P. C., Porter, J. C., Johnston, J. M. 1978. A role of fetal prolactin in lung maturation. *Obstet. Gynecol.* 51:81–88
44. Hawgood, S., Benson, B., Hamilton, R. L. Jr. 1985. Effects of a surfactant-associated protein and calcium ions on the structure and surface activity of lung surfactant lipids. *Biochemistry* 24:184–90
45. Hawgood, S., Benson, B. J., Schilling, J., Damm, D., Clements, J. A., White, R. T. 1987. Nucleotide and amino acid sequences of pulmonary surfactant protein SP 18 and evidence for cooperation between SP 18 and SP 28–36 in surfactant lipid absorption. *Proc. Natl. Acad. Sci. USA* 84:66–70
46. Deleted in proof.
47. Hitchcock, K. R. 1979. Hormones and the lung. I. Thyroid hormones and glucocorticoids in lung development. *Anat. Rec.* 194:15–40
48. Jacobs, K. A., Phelps, D. S., Steinbrink, R., Fisch, J., Kriz, R., et al. 1987. Isolation of a cDNA clone encoding a high molecular weight precursor to a 6-kDa pulmonary surfactant-associated protein *J. Biol. Chem.* 262:9808–11
49. Josimovich, J. B., Merisko, K., Boccella, L., Tobon, H. 1977. Binding of prolactin by fetal Rhesus cell membrane fractions. *Endocrinology* 100:557–70
50. Katyal, S. L., Amenta, J. S., Singh, G., Silverman, J. A. 1984. Deficient lung surfactant apoproteins in amniotic fluid with mature phospholipid profile from diabetic pregnancies. *Am. J. Obstet. Gynecol.* 148:48–53
51. Kero, P., Hirvonen, T., Välimäki, I. 1973. Prenatal and postnatal isoxuprine and respiratory distress syndrome. *Lancet* 2:198
52. King, R. J., MacBeth, M. C. 1981. Interaction of the lipid and protein components of pulmonary surfactant: Role of phosphatidylglycerol and calcium *Biochim. Biophys. Acta* 647:159–68
53. King, R. J., Ruch, J., Gikas, E. G., Platzker, A. C. G., Creasy, R. K. 1975. Appearance of apoproteins of pulmonary surfactant in human amniotic fluid. *J. Appl. Physiol.* 39:735–41
54. Kotas, R. V., Avery, M. E. 1971. Accelerated appearance of pulmonary surfactant in the fetal rabbit. *J. Appl. Physiol.* 39:358–61
55. Kuroki, Y., Mason, R. J., Voelker, D. R. 1988. Alveolar type II cells express a high-affinity receptor for pulmonary surfactant protein A. *Proc. Natl. Acad. Sci. USA* 85:5566–70
56. Kuroki, Y., Takahashi, H., Fukuda, Y., Mikawa, M., Inagawa, A., et al. 1985. Two-site "simultaneous" immunoassay with monoclonal antibodies for the determination of surfactant apoprotein in human amniotic fluid. *Pediatr. Res.* 19:1017–1020
57. Liggins, G. C. 1969. Premature delivery of foetal lambs infused with glucocorticoids. *J. Endocrinol.* 45:515–23
58. Liggins, G. C., Howie, M. B. 1972. A controlled trial of antepartum glucocorticoid treatment for prevention of respiratory distress syndrome in premature infants. *Pediatrics* 59:515–25
59. Liley, H. G., White, R. T., Benson, B. J., Ballard, P. L. 1988. Glucocorticoids both stimulate and inhibit production of pulmonary surfactant protein A in fetal human lung. *Proc. Natl. Acad. Sci. USA* 85:9096–9100
60. Liley, H. G., White, R. T., Warr, R. G., Benson, B. J., Hawgood, S., Ballard, P. L. 1989. Regulation of mRNAs for the hydrophobic surfactant proteins in human lung. *J. Clin. Invest.* 83:1191–97
61. Longmuir, K. J., Bleasdale, J. E., Quirk, J. G., Johnston, J. M. 1982. Regulation of lamellar body acidic glycerophospholipid biosynthesis in fetal rabbit lung in organ culture. *Biochim. Biophys. Acta* 712:356–64
62. Masters, J. R. W. 1976. Epithelial-mesenchymal interaction during lung development: The effect of mesenchymal mass. *Dev. Biol.* 51:98–108
63. McMahan, M. J., Mimouni, F., Miodovnik, K., Hull, W. M., Whitsett, J. A. 1987. Surfactant associated protein (SAP-35) in amniotic fluid from diabetic and non-diabetic pregnancies. *Obstet. Gynecol.* 70:94–98
64. Mendelson, C. R., Chen, C., Boggaram, V., Zacharias, C., Snyder, J. M. 1986. Regulation of the synthesis of the major surfactant apoprotein in fetal rabbit lung tissue. *J. Biol. Chem.* 261:9938–43
65. Mendelson, C. R., Johnston, J. M., MacDonald, P. C., Snyder, J. M. 1981. Multihormonal regulation of surfactant synthesis by human fetal lung *in vitro*. *J. Clin. Endocrinol. Metab.* 53:307–17
66. Mendelson, C. R., Snyder, J. M. 1985. Effect of cortisol on the synthesis of

lamellar body glycerophospholipids in fetal rabbit lung tissue *in vitro*. *Biochim. Biophys. Acta* 834:85–94
67. Mullon, D. K., Smith, Y. F., Richardson, L. L., Hamosh, P., Hamosh, M. 1983. Effect of prolactin on phospholipid synthesis in organ cultures of fetal rat lung. *Biochim. Biophys. Acta* 751:166–74
68. Naeye, R. L., Burt, L. S., Wright, D. L., Blanc, W. A., Tatter, D. 1971. Neonatal mortality, the male disadvantage. *Pediatrics* 48:902–6
69. Ng, V. L., Herndon, V. L., Mendelson, C. R., Snyder, J. M. 1983. Characterization of rabbit surfactant-associated proteins. *Biochim. Biophys. Acta* 754:218–26
70. Notter, R. H., Shapiro, D. L. 1987. Lung surfactants for replacement therapy: Biochemical, biophysical, and clinical aspects. *Clin. Perinatol.* 14:433–79
71. Notter, R. H., Shapiro, D. L., Ohning, B., Whitsett, J. A. 1987. Biophysical activity of synthetic phospholipids combined with purified lung surfactant 6000 dalton protein. *Chem. Phys. Lipids* 44:1–17
72. Obenshain, S. S., Adam, P. A. J., King, K. C., Teramo, K., Raivio, K. O., et al. 1970. Human fetal insulin response to sustained maternal hyperglycemia. *New Engl. J. Med.* 283:566–70
73. Odom, M. J., Snyder, J. M., Boggaram, V., Mendelson, C. R. 1988. Glucocorticoid regulation of the major surfactant-associated protein (SP-A) and its mRNA and of morphologic development of human fetal lung in vitro. *Endocrinology* 123:1712–20
74. Odom, M. J., Snyder, J. M., Mendelson, C. R. 1987. Adenosine 3',5'-monophosphate analogs and β-adrenergic agonists induce the synthesis of the major surfactant apoprotein in human fetal lung *in vitro*. *Endocrinology* 121:1155–63
75. O'Reilly, M. A., Gazdar, A. F., Morris, R. E., Whitsett, J. A. 1988. Differential effects of glucocorticoid on expression of surfactant proteins in a human lung adenocarcinoma cell line. *Biochim. Biophys. Acta* 970:194–204
76. Oulton, M., Martin, T. R., Faulkner, G. T., Stinson, D., Johnson, J. P. 1980. Developmental study of a lamellar body fraction isolated from human amniotic fluid. *Pediatr. Res.* 14:722–28
77. Peleg, E., Munsick, R. A., Diker, D., Goldman, J. A., Ben-Jonathan, N. 1986. Distribution of catecholamines between fetal and maternal compartments during human pregnancy with emphasis on l-dopa and dopamine. *J. Clin. Endocrinol. Metab.* 62:911–14
78. Persson, A., Chang, D., Crouch, E. 1990. Surfactant protein D is a divalent cation-dependent carbohydrate-binding protein. *J. Biol. Chem.* 265:5755–60
79. Persson, A., Chang, D., Rust, K., Moxley, M., Longmore, W., Crouch, E. 1989. Purification and biochemical characterization of CP4 (SP-D), a collagenous surfactant-associated protein. *Biochemistry* 28:6361–67
80. Phelps, D. S., Church, S., Kourembanas, S., Taeusch, H. W., Floros, J. 1987. Increases in the 35 kDa surfactant-associated protein and its mRNA following in vivo dexamethasone treatment of fetal and neonatal rats. *Electrophoresis* 8:235–38
81. Phelps, D. S., Floros, J. 1988. Localization of surfactant protein synthesis in human lung by in situ hybridization. *Am. Rev. Respir. Dis.* 137:939–42
82. Pilot-Matias, T. J., Kister, S. E., Fox, J. L., Kropp, K., Glasser, S. W., Whitsett, J. A. 1989. Structure and organization of the gene encoding human pulmonary surfactant proteolipid SP-B. *DNA* 8:75–86
83. Pope, T. S., Rooney, S. A. 1987. Effects of glucocorticoid and thyroid hormones on regulatory enzymes of fatty acid synthesis and glycogen metabolism in developing fetal rat lung. *Biochim. Biophys. Acta* 918:141–48
84. Possmayer, F. 1988. Pulmonary perspective: A proposed nomenclature for pulmonary surfactant-associated proteins. *Am. Rev. Respir. Dis.* 138:990–98
85. Quirk, J. G., Bleasdale, J. E., MacDonald, P. C., Johnston, J. M. 1980. A role for cytidine monophosphate in the regulation of the glycerophospholipid composition of surfactant in developing lung. *Biochem. Biophys. Res. Commun.* 95:985–92
86. Rice, W. R., Ross, G. F., Singleton, F. M., Dingle, S., Whitsett, J. A. 1987. Surfactant-associated protein inhibits phospholipid secretion from type II cells. *J. Appl. Physiol.* 63:692–98
87. Robert, M. F., Neff, R. K., Hubbell, J. P., Taeusch, H. W., Avery, M. E. 1976. Association between maternal diabetes and the respiratory distress syndrome in the newborn. *New Eng. J. Med.* 294:357–60
88. Roberts, J. M., Jacobs, M. M., Cheng, J. B., Barnes, P. J., O'Brien, A. T., Ballard, P. L. 1985. Fetal pulmonary beta-adrenergic receptors: Characterization in human and in vitro modulation

by glucocorticoids. *Pediatr. Pulmonol.* 1:S69–76
89. Rooney, S. A. 1985. The surfactant system and lung phospholipid biochemistry. *Am. Rev. Respir. Dis.* 131:439–60
90. Ryan, R. M., Morris, R. E., Rice, W. R., Ciraolo, G., Whitsett, J. A. 1989. Binding and uptake of pulmonary surfactant protein (SP-A) by pulmonary type II epithelial cells. *J. Histochem. Cytochem.* 37:429–40
91. Sano, K., Fisher, J., Mason, R. J., Kuroki, Y., Schilling, J., et al. 1987. Isolation and sequence of a cDNA clone for the rat pulmonary surfactant-associated protein (PSP-A). *Biochem. Biophys. Res. Commun.* 144:367–74
92. Scaglia, H. E., Margulies, M., Galimberti, D., Colombani, M., Spinedi, E., et al. 1981. Binding of prolactin to fetal human lung cell membranes. *Ric. Clin. Lab.* 11:279–82
93. Schellhase, D. E., Emrie, P. A., Fisher, J. H., Shannon, J. M. 1989. Ontogeny of surfactant apoproteins in the rat. *Pediatr. Res.* 26:167–74
94. Shelley, S. A., Balis, J. U., Paciga, J. E., Knuppel, R. A., Ruffolo, E. H., Bouis, P. J. 1982. Surfactant "apoproteins" in human amniotic fluid: an enzyme-linked immunosorbent assay for the prenatal assessment of lung maturity. *Am. J. Obstet. Gynecol* 144:224–28
95. Smith, B. T. 1979. Lung maturation in the fetal rat: Acceleration by injection of fibroblast-pneumonocyte factor. *Science* 204:1094–95
96. Smith, B. T., Giroud, C. J. P., Robert, M., Avery, M. E. 1975. Insulin antagonism of cortisol action by cultured fetal lung cells. *J. Pediatr.* 87:953–55
97. Smith, B. T., Sabry, K. 1983. Glucocorticoid-thyroid synergism in lung maturation: A mechanism involving epithelial-mesenchymal interaction. *Proc. Natl. Acad. Sci. USA* 80:1951–54
98. Smith, Y. F., Mullon, D. K., Hamosh, M., Scanlon, J. W., Hamosh, P. 1980. Serum prolactin and respiratory distress syndrome in the newborn. *Pediatr. Res.* 14:93–95
99. Snyder, J. M., Johnston, J. M., Mendelson, C. R. 1981. Differentiation of type II cells of human fetal lung *in vitro*. *Cell Tissue Res.* 220:17–25
100. Snyder, J. M., Kwun, J. E., O'Brien, J. A., Rosenfeld, C. R., Odom, M. J. 1988. The concentration of the 35-kDa surfactant apoprotein in amniotic fluid from normal and diabetic pregnancies. *Pediatr. Res.* 24:728–34
101. Snyder, J. M., Longmuir, K. J., Johnston, J. M., Mendelson, C. R. 1983. Hormonal regulation of the synthesis of lamellar body phosphatidylglycerol and phosphatidylinositol in fetal lung tissue. *Endocrinology* 112:1012–18
102. Snyder, J. M., Mendelson, C. R. 1987. Induction and characterization of the major surfactant apoprotein during rabbit fetal lung development. *Biochim. Biophys. Acta* 920:226–36
103. Snyder, J. M., Mendelson, C. R. 1987. Insulin inhibits the accumulation of the major lung surfactant apoprotein in human fetal lung explants maintained *in vitro*. *Endocrinology* 120:1250–57
104. Snyder, J. M., Mendelson, C. R., Johnston, J. M. 1981. The effect of cortisol on rabbit fetal lung maturation *in vitro*. *Dev. Biol.* 85:129–40
105. Sorokin, S. 1961. A study of development in organ cultures of mammalian lungs. *Dev. Biol.* 3:60–83
106. Stahlman, M. T. 1987. Acute respiratory disorders in the newborn. In *Neonatology,* ed. G. B. Avery, pp. 418–45. Philadelphia: Saunders. 1432 pp.
107. Takahashi, A., Fujiwara, T. 1986. Proteolipid in bovine lung surfactant: its role in surfactant function. *Biochem. Biophys. Res. Commun.* 135:527–32
108. Torday, J. S., Nielsen, H. C., Fencl, M. D., Avery, M. E. 1981. Sex differences in fetal lung maturation. *Am. Rev. Respir. Dis.* 123:205–8
109. Deleted in proof
110. Walker, S. R., Williams, M. C., Benson, B. 1986. Immunocytochemical localization of the major surfactant apoproteins in type II cells, Clara cells and alveolar macrophages of rat lung. *J. Histochem. Cytochem.* 34:1137–48
111. Wang, N. S., Kotas, R. V., Avery, M. E., Thurlbeck, W. M. 1971. Accelerated appearance of osmiophilic bodies in fetal lungs following steroid injection. *J. Appl. Physiol.* 30:362–65
112. Warr, R. G., Hawgood, S., Buckley, D. I., Crisp, T. M., Schilling, J., et al. 1987. Low molecular weight human pulmonary surfactant protein (SP5): Isolation, characterization, cDNA and amino acid sequences. *Proc. Natl. Acad. Sci. USA* 84:7915–19
113. White, R. T., Damm, D., Miller, J., Spratt, K., Schilling, J. et al. 1985. Isolation of and characterization of the human pulmonary surfactant apoprotein gene. *Nature* 316:361–63
114. Whitsett, J. A., Manton, M. A., Darovec-Beckerman, C., Adams, K. G., Moore, J. J. 1981. β-Adrenergic receptors in the developing rabbit lung. *Am. J. Physiol.* 240:E351–57

115. Whitsett, J. A., Ohning, B. L., Ross, G., Meuth, J., Weaver, T., et al. 1986. Hydrophobic surfactant-associated protein in whole lung surfactant and its importance for biophysical activity in lung surfactant extracts used for replacement therapy. *Pediatr. Res.* 20:460–67
116. Whitsett, J. A., Pilot, T., Clark, J. C., Weaver, T. E. 1987. Induction of surfactant protein in fetal lung: Effects of cAMP and dexamethasone on SAP-35 RNA and synthesis. *J. Biol. Chem.* 262:5256–61
117. Whitsett, J. A., Weaver, T. E., Clark, J. C., Sawtell, N., Glasser, S. W., et al. 1987. Glucocorticoid enhances surfactant proteolipid Phe and pVal synthesis and RNA in fetal lung. *J. Biol. Chem.* 262:15618–23
118. Whitsett, J. A., Weaver, T. E., Lieberman, M. A., Clark, J. C., Daugherty, C. 1987. Differential effects of epidermal growth factor and transforming growth factor-β on synthesis of $M_r = 35,000$ surfactant-associated protein in fetal lung. *J. Biol. Chem.* 262:7908–13
119. Williams, M. C., Hawgood, S., Schenk, D. B., Lewicki, J., Phelps, M. N., Benson, B. 1988. Monoclonal antibodies to surfactant proteins SP28-36 label canine type II and nonciliated bronciolar cells by immunofluoresence. *Am. Rev. Respir. Dis.* 137:399–405
120. Winters, A. J., Colston, C., MacDonald, P. C., Porter, J. C. 1975. Fetal plasma prolactin levels. *J. Clin. Endocrinol. Metab.* 41:626–29
121. Xu, J., Richardson, C., Ford, C., Spencer, T., Li-juan, Y., et al. 1989. Isolation and characterization of the cDNA for pulmonary surfactant-associated protein-B (SP-B) in the rabbit. *Biochem. Biophys. Res. Commun.* 160:325–32
122. Yu, S. H., Possmayer, F. 1986. Reconstitution of surfactant activity by using the 6 kDa apoprotein associated with pulmonary surfactant. *Biochem. J.* 236:85–89

Annu. Rev. Physiol. 1991. 53:441–64

SYNTHESIS AND ASSEMBLY OF LUNG SURFACTANT

Henk P. Haagsman and Lambert M. G. van Golde

Laboratory of Veterinary Biochemistry, University of Utrecht, Utrecht, The Netherlands

KEY WORDS: pulmonary surfactants, phospholipid metabolism, phosphatidylcholines, protein processing, alveolar type II cells

---

INTRODUCTION

The alveolar surfaces of the lungs are lined with a complex and highly surface-active material: pulmonary surfactant. This material consists of about 90% lipids and 5–10% surfactant-specific proteins. Pulmonary surfactant is synthesized and assembled by alveolar epithelial type II cells into lamellar bodies, the intracellular storage form of surfactant. Type II cells can be stimulated to secrete lamellar bodies into the fluid layer that covers the alveolar epithelium (reviewed by Wright & Dobbs, this volume). The surfactant lipids can subsequently spread as a monolayer at the air-liquid interface and, by decreasing surface tension, protect the alveoli against collapse at end-expiration. By reducing the contractile forces in the curved air-liquid interface, pulmonary surfactant also precludes alveolar edema. Most of the extracellular surfactant is recycled by the type II cell (106). Therefore, intracellular surfactant is not only assembled from newly synthesized surfactant components, but also from surfactant components that are taken up by the type II cells via endocytosis (Figure 1). Although the major physiologic function of pulmonary surfactant is undoubtedly to confer mechanical stability to the alveoli, there are important implications that the surfactant system also plays a role in pulmonary defense.

The purpose of this review is to summarize our current understanding of (*a*)

0066-4278/91/0315-0441$02.00

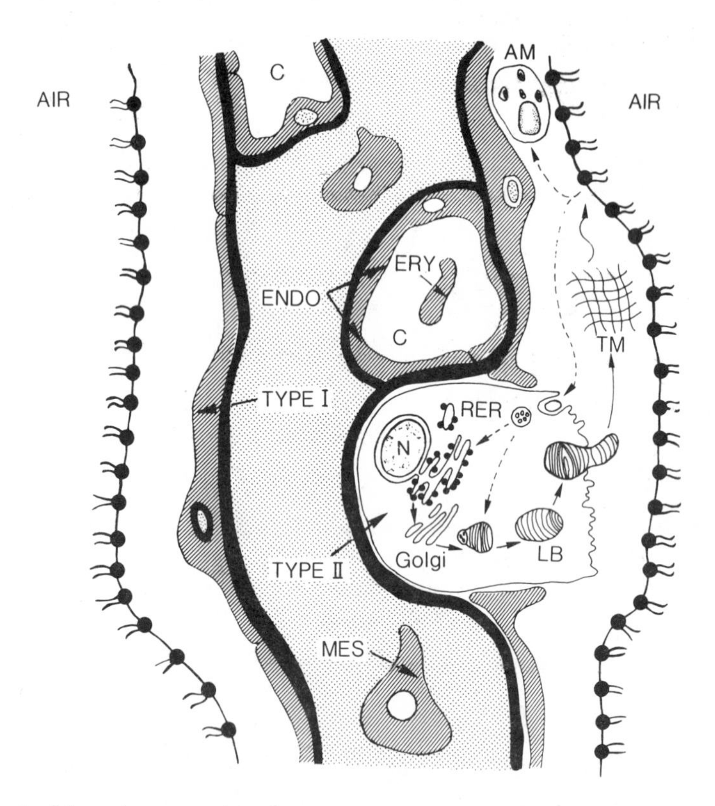

Figure 1 Schematic cross-section of an alveolar wall. TYPE I: type I pneumocyte; TYPE II: type II pneumocyte; ENDO: endothelial cell; MES: mesenchymal cell; ERY: erythrocyte; C: capillary; N: nucleus; RER: rough endoplasmic reticulum; LB: lamellar body; TM: tubular myelin; AM: alveolar macrophage.

the pathways and regulation of synthesis of surfactant lipids, (*b*) the synthesis and processing of surfactant proteins, and (*c*) the coalescence of these components to form lamellar bodies. First, we discuss the lipid and protein composition of surfactant followed by an introduction to type II cells and lamellar bodies. Next, an overview is given of the pathways of surfactant lipid production and the synthesis of surfactant proteins. Subsequently, we focus on the mechanisms by which these components may be assembled into lamellar bodies. In the final section we outline possibilities for future research.

COMPOSITION OF SURFACTANT

There are two major surfactant pools in the lung. The surfactant fraction that can be harvested by bronchoalveolar lavage represents the extracellular pool.

Table 1 Phospholipid composition of extracellular surfactant and lamellar bodies from rat lung

	Extracellular surfactant			Lamellar bodies		
Mol % of total phospholipids	PC 82.3	PG 7.5	PI 1.8	PC 72.9	PG 6.8	PI 1.5
Main molecular species (%)						
$C_{16:0}/C_{16:0}$	49.3	32.3		47.4	37.8	2.2
$C_{16:0}/C_{16:1}$	10.0	0.5		16.3	8.6	3.2
$C_{16:0}/C_{18:1}$	6.3	13.9		8.2	20.8	14.6
$C_{16:0}/C_{18:2}$	23.4	39.5		17.8	22.4	9.4
$C_{16:0}/C_{20:4}$	3.5	4.4		3.7	2.7	12.9
$C_{16:0}/C_{22:6}$	1.8	3.7		1.1	2.5	11.8
$C_{18:0}/C_{18:2}$	1.7	0.8		1.7	trace	trace
$C_{18:0}/C_{20:4}$	1.3	1.1		0.6	trace	31.5
$C_{18:1}/C_{18:2}$	0.8	2.1		0.7	2.5	13.4
Others	1.9	1.7		2.5	2.7	1.0

Data from Adachi et al (1).

This pool comprises a variety of morphologically different complexes, such as the actual monolayer at the air-water interface, tubular myelin, and surfactant components destined to be cleared from the alveolar spaces (see Figure 1 for a schematic overview). The intracellular surfactant pool resides in the lamellar bodies, the characteristic inclusion organelles in the alveolar type II cells. It is generally assumed that these organelles represent intracellular reservoirs of surfactant before this material is secreted into the alveolar space (106). This notion is corroborated by the fact that the phospholipid composition of lamellar bodies is similar to that of extracellular surfactant (Table 1).

Lipids

Of the lipids in surfactant, 80–90% is phospholipid, and cholesterol is the most abundant neutral lipid. There appears to be very little species variation as far as the phospholipid composition of lung tissue is concerned. Surfactant phospholipids contain much higher proportions of phosphatidylcholine (PC) and phosphatidylglycerol (PG) than lung tissue phospholipids, whereas the latter are richer in phosphatidylethanolamine (PE), phosphatidylserine (PS), and sphingomyelin. PC is the major phospholipid class in surfactant, and about 60% of the PC molecules contains two saturated acyl chains. The disaturated PC (DSPC) in lung surfactant is largely dipalmitoylphosphatidylcholine (DPPC; Table 1). This lipid is the major surface-active component of pulmonary surfactant that is responsible for decreasing surface tension to values below 10 mN/m at low lung volumes (12). It should be stressed that DPPC is not a surfactant-specific lipid as is often stated. It has been estimated that only 30% of DSPC in rat lung is present in the surfactant system (108). In addition, abundant levels of DPPC are also present in other tissues such as brain. Although the function of DPPC in surfactant is well-documented, there is less certainty about the role of the other surfactant lipids. The atypically high proportion of PG (about 10%) in surfactant of adult animals and humans is surprising. In other mammalian tissues this phospholipid serves primarily as a precursor for cardiolipin synthesis and usually does not accumulate. Several studies indicate that phosphatidylinositol (PI) can replace PG without affecting the most important physiologic and physicochemical properties of surfactant (7, 37). This would imply that charge rather than molecular structure of PG is important, at least for a part of the properties of surfactant.

Proteins

The primary structures of three different families of surfactant-associated proteins from several species have been determined. According to the recently proposed nomenclature, these proteins will be referred to as SP-A, SP-B, and SP-C (67). Very recently a new class of surfactant proteins was described: SP-D (62). The structure, properties, and possible functions of these proteins have been discussed by Hawgood & Shiffer in an other chapter of this volume.

The most abundant surfactant protein is the water-soluble surfactant protein A (SP-A). This glycoprotein was first described by King & co-workers in 1973 (50). The primary structure has been determined for SP-A from several species and is highly conserved (for review, see 39). SP-A is acidic and has isoelectric points ranging from pH 4.4 to pH 5.6. The presence of sialic acid contributes to this charge heterogeneity. The coding sequence for human SP-A has been localized to chromosome 10 (8, 26). SP-B and SP-C are hydrophobic surfactant proteins and were first detected in organic solvent extracts of lamellar bodies by Phizackerley & co-workers (66). Recently it became apparent that these proteins enhance the adsorption of phospholipids to an air-fluid interface. Mature SP-B is a basic cysteine-rich hydrophobic peptide, which consists of 79 amino acids. It is a dimer under non-denaturing conditions. Intra-chain disulfide bonds may be important in the formation of the active peptide since in all species studied so far, the positions of the cysteines are conserved (see 39). SP-B is processed from a glycosylated precursor of approximately 42,000 daltons (33, 42). The coding sequence of human SP-B is located on chromosome 2 (23). Human SP-C is a highly hydrophobic peptide characterized by a stretch of six contiguous valine residues. It is produced as a large, primary translation product of approximately 21,000 daltons (32, 91). Comparison of the primary structure of human SP-C with the primary structures of bovine (45), porcine (44), and rat (27) SP-C reveals a variable hydrophilic N-terminal part and a conserved hydrophobic region. The SP-C gene locus was assigned to chromosome 8 (32).

INTRACELLULAR SURFACTANT

Synthesis in Type II Cells

The synthesis of surfactant takes place in the alveolar epithelial type II cells. This cell type represents about 10% of the population of cells in the lung parenchyma (14). Characteristic of these cells are the surfactant storage organelles, the lamellar bodies (Figure 2). These organelles consist of stacked membranes organized around a protein-rich and electron-dense core. The organelle is surrounded by a limiting membrane that fuses with the plasma membrane upon secretion. The notion that type II cells are the sole producers of surfactant comes from many morphological and biochemical studies. The composition (49) and molecular species (1) of phospholipids in lamellar bodies is strikingly similar to that of lavage phospholipids (Table 1). Phospholipids secreted from isolated type II cells also have a composition similar to that of lavage phospholipids (21). Furthermore, cultured type II cells synthesize phospholipids from a variety of radioactive precursors with a high proportion of the typical surfactant phospholipids DSPC and PG (85). More evidence comes from the studies on the localization of surfactant protein synthesis. Hybridization in situ indicates that the only site of SP-A gene expression in the human lung is the type II cell (64). SP-A is synthesized and processed by isolated type II cells (98), and immunocytochemical studies show that SP-A is present throughout the biosynthetic route (2, 13, 81, 89, 102). SP-B also has been localized to type II cells (53, 94), and hybridization studies in situ suggest that SP-B is expressed in type II cells and possibly in nonciliated bronchiolar cells designated as Clara cells (64). Synthesis and processing of SP-B in isolated rat type II cells has also been described (94).

Lamellar Bodies as Storage Organelles

More evidence that lamellar bodies are the intracellular storage form of surfactant comes from morphological and secretion studies. Many investigators have shown that lamellar bodies are secreted by type II cells and unravel in the alveolar space to form tubular myelin, the extracellular form of surfactant that probably forms the phospholipid monolayer (Figure 1, 2; 52, 99, 102). The secretion of lamellar bodies is subject to control by a variety of factors as is discussed by Wright & Dobbs in an other chapter herein. Surfactant proteins are also present in lamellar bodies. SP-A has been localized morphologically to lamellar bodies (2, 13, 81, 89, 102). The electron-dense core of lamellar bodies does not contain SP-A (W. F. Voorhout et al, unpublished results). Lamellar bodies contain mature SP-B, but no

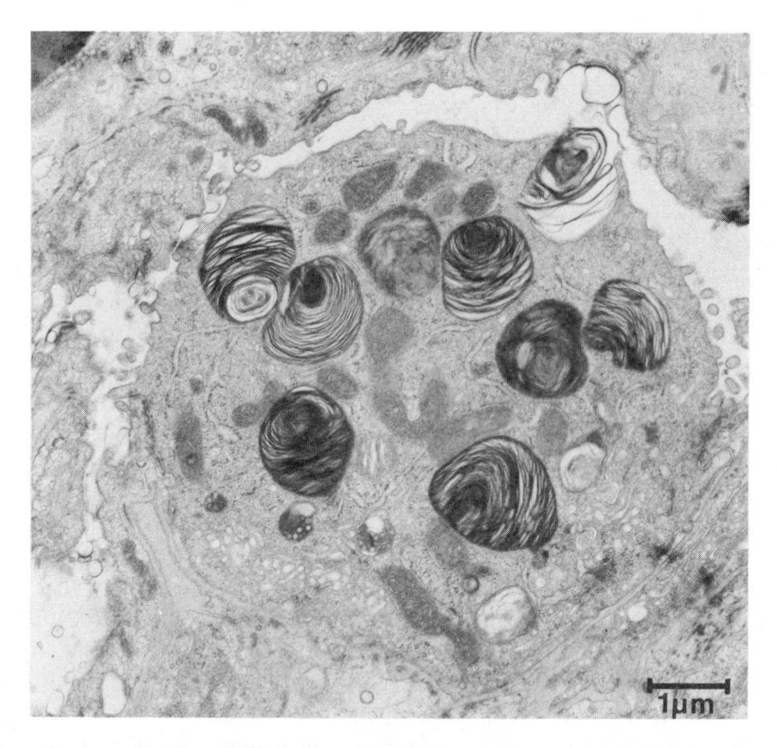

Figure 2 A type II cell caught by fixation while releasing the contents of a lamellar body. Bar: 1 μm (electron micrograph provided by W. F. Voorhout).

precursor forms of SP-B as was determined in isolated lamellar bodies (94) and in situ by immunogold electronmicroscopy (W. F. Voorhout et al, unpublished results). Recent work from our laboratory suggests that, compared to extracellular surfactant, SP-B and SP-C are more enriched in lamellar bodies than SP-A (M. A. Oosterlaken-Dijksterhuis et al, unpublished results).

Lamellar bodies are acidic organelles like lysosomes. The internal pH is maintained below 6.1 by an ATP-dependent process (10). By histochemical methods it was found that lamellar bodies contain hydrolytic enzyme activities. Biochemical studies by Hook & Gilmore indicate that a variety of lysosomal-type hydrolases are intrinsic to isolated lamellar bodies (40). Interestingly, a similar distribution of hydrolases was found in lamellar bodies and lysosomes. These observations indicate that the biogenesis of these organelles may be related. Support for this notion will be discussed below.

Human lamellar bodies contain at least two acid α-glucosidases; one with a high affinity to concanavalin A, similar to the lysosomal enzyme, and another lamellar body-specific isoenzyme with no affinity to concanavalin A (19).

Antibodies that reacted well with the lysosomal-type α-glucosidase reacted poorly with the lamellar body-specific enzyme. These two types of enzymes may be different gene products (20). The lamellar body-specific α-glucosidase could be a marker enzyme for lamellar bodies. Unfortunately, no concanavalin A negative α-glucosidase activity with a low pH optimum could be detected in lamellar bodies from lungs of rat, cow, pig, and guinea pig (M. A. Oosterlaken-Dijksterhuis, unpublished results). The biochemical hallmark of the lamellar body is its high phospholipid content, its specific phospholipid composition and, possibly, the presence of surfactant proteins.

SYNTHESIS OF SURFACTANT LIPIDS

The type II cell is the exclusive site of alveolar surfactant lipid synthesis. Therefore studies on the synthesis of surfactant lipids employing whole lung tissue or subcellular fractions of whole lung other than lamellar bodies should be interpreted with caution. Isolated type II cells have been used for many years to study the pathways and regulation of surfactant lipid synthesis. These studies focused primarily on the most important surfactant lipids PC, DPPC, and the acidic phospholipids PG and PI. In the subsequent paragraphs we will mainly review recent studies on the pathways and regulation of surfactant lipid synthesis that have been performed with pure preparations of isolated type II cells. For the less recent studies with whole lung preparations, we refer to other reviews (75, 84). The regulation of surfactant lipid synthesis during lung development has been discussed by Mendelson & Boggaram in another chapter of this volume.

Pathways

The glycerol backbone of surfactant glycerolipids is mainly derived from glucose that has been taken up from the blood. There is now strong evidence from studies with other tissues that glycerol-3-phosphate rather than dihydroxyacetone phosphate is the principal starting point for the synthesis of diacylglycerolipids (48). Glycerol-3-phosphate is mainly formed by reduction of dihydroxyacetone phosphate; formation of glycerol-3-phosphate from circulating glycerol by glycerol kinase plays only a minor role (25), but may be more important in diabetic animals (82). In the type II cells of the fetal lung, intracellular glycogen stores appear to be the major source of glycerol-3-phosphate that is required for surfactant glycerolipid synthesis. The blood supplies type II cells with fatty acids that are needed for surfactant lipid synthesis, but these cells can also synthesize fatty acids de novo, with lactate as an important source of acetyl groups. Although the relative importance of endogenously synthesized fatty acids for surfactant lipid formation remains unknown, there is evidence that lipogenesis is of particular importance to supply palmitate required for the formation of surfactant in prenatal lung (58). Acetyl CoA carboxylase, fatty acid synthase, and citrate lyase are involved in lipogenesis. Both activities and mRNA levels of these enzymes in whole lung showed increases toward term (6). The circulation also provides the lungs with the polar head group constituents of phospholipids such as choline and myo-inositol. Choline is efficiently taken up by isolated type II cells. This may be due to the fact that choline kinase, which converts choline into phosphocholine, is highly enriched in primary cultures of type II cells, when compared to whole lung (35).

The first step in the synthesis of phosphatidylcholines and the other phosphoglycerides involves the action of glycerol-3-phosphate acyltransferase, which catalyzes the conversion of glycerol-3-phosphate into 1-palmitoyl-sn-glycerol-3-phosphate. The activity of this enzyme in type II cell microsomes is substantially higher than that in whole lung microsomes (4). As in other cell types, glycerol-3-phosphate acyltransferase limits the rate of phosphatidic acid synthesis in type II cells, since the introduction of the second acyl moiety by 1-acylglycerol-3-phosphate acyltransferase proceeds much faster than the first acylation step. Phosphatidic acid occupies an important point in glycerolipid metabolism, where the pathways for the formation of PC and those of PG and PI diverge. Phosphatidate phosphatase catalyzes the formation of diacylglycerols from phosphatidic acid. Diacylglycerols are common precursors for both the synthesis of phosphatidylcholines and phosphatidylethanolamines.

SYNTHESIS OF PHOSPHATIDYLCHOLINES The CDP-choline route is undoubtedly the principal pathway involved in the synthesis de novo of PC in the lung. Cholinephosphotransferase catalyzes the formation of PC from diacylglycerols and CDP-choline. The CDP-choline required for this reaction is formed from choline by the sequential action of choline kinase and phosphocholine cytidylyltransferase. The formation of DPPC can either proceed by synthesis de novo or by remodeling of unsaturated PC species. Type II cell microsomes have the capability of synthesizing dipalmitoylphosphatidic acid from glycerol-3-phosphate and palmitoyl-CoA (4). More than 70% of the phosphatidic acid that is synthesized upon incubation of type II cell microsomes with [^{14}C]glycerol-3-phosphate and palmitoyl-CoA as the single exogenous acyl donor represents disaturated species. Since phosphatidate phosphatase (16) and cholinephosphotransferase (71) of type II cells show little if any specificity towards various molecular species of their substrates, type II cells have the potential to generate DPPC de novo. Microsomes of type II cells incubated in the presence of [^{14}C]glycerol-3-phosphate and a mixture of acyl-CoAs, of the same composition as endogenous acyl-CoAs, yielded phosphatidic acid of which ~40% was disaturated (18). From these studies it was estimated that about 45% of newly synthesized surfactant DPPC can be formed by type II cells via direct synthesis de novo.

The remaining portion is probably produced by remodeling of unsaturated PC species. The most direct evidence for this was provided by pulse-chase experiments with type II cells, which showed that unsaturated PC species were, indeed, transformed into DSPC (59). The remodeling most likely occurs through a deacylation-reacylation mechanism (85). The removal of the unsaturated fatty acyl-group from the 2-position of an unsaturated PC species can be accomplished by a microsomal Ca^{2+}-requiring phospholipase A_2, or by a cytosolic Ca^{2+}-independent phospholipase A_2. Unfortunately, phospholipase activities of type II cells have not yet been adequately characterized. Alternatively, the unsaturated acyl-group at the 2-position of an unsaturated PC species can be transferred to the vacant OH-group of a lysophospholipid via a CoASH-dependent transacylation (85). The resulting lysophosphatidylcholine, which will be largely 1-palmitoyl-lysophosphatidylcholine, can then be reacylated with palmitoyl-CoA to form DPPC. The activity of the enzyme catalyzing this reaction, lysophosphatidylcholine acyltransferase, is highly enriched in type II cells when compared to whole lung. The type II cell enzyme displays pronounced specificity towards palmitoyl-CoA as substrate (17).

SYNTHESIS OF ACIDIC SURFACTANT PHOSPHOLIPIDS Phosphatidate cytidylyltransferase catalyzes the synthesis of CDP-diacylglycerol from CTP and phosphatidic acid. This liponucleotide is a common precursor for both the formation of PG and PI. CDP-diacylglycerol can be converted into phosphatidylglycerophosphate by CDP-diacylglycerol glycerolphosphate phosphatidyltransferase. Phosphatidylglycerophosphate is rapidly dephosphorylated to form PG. The formation of PG in the lung can proceed both in the mitochondria and in the endoplasmic reticulum. Mitochondrial PG is used for cardiolipin synthesis in these organelles. It has been suggested that, in view of the similarity of the molecular species of PG from mitochondria, microsomes, and surfactant, PG is transported from mitochondria to lamellar bodies (79). Evidence from other studies indicated that PG destined for secretion as a surfactant component is synthesized at the endoplasmic reticulum of the type II cell rather than in mitochondria (5, 38). CDP-diacylglycerol can be converted into PI by CDP-diacylglycerol inositol phosphatidyltransferase. This reaction occurs at the endoplasmic reticulum. Comparison of the molecular species of PG and PI suggests that both phospholipids may be synthesized from a common CDP-diacylglycerol pool (76). These observations, however, were not confirmed by Adachi & co-workers. These investigators observed distinctly different molecular-species profiles of PG and PI in both lamellar bodies and extracellular surfactant (1). The dipalmitoyl species accounted for more than 30% of PG and less than 6% of PI, respectively (Table 1).

Regulatory aspects

The surfactant system is dynamic. Although surfactant lipids are recycled extensively, type II cells also possess the capacity to synthesize surfactant lipids in response to demand. Therefore the synthesis of lipid components of surfactant must be under rigorous and coordinated control. Our understanding of the hormonal and metabolic regulation of surfactant lipid synthesis and sorting is still in its infancy. Here we will give a brief overview of possible mechanisms by which the synthesis of the major phosphoglycerides is regulated in the adult type II cell. The regulation of phospholipid synthesis during lung development has been the subject of recent reviews (72, 85) and is also reviewed by Mendelson in this volume.

The availability of substrates is generally an important determinant of the rate of glycerolipid synthesis. Type II cells are equipped to synthesize large quantities of phospholipids to maintain surfactant homeostasis even at low substrate concentrations. Glycerol-3-phosphate acyltransferase catalyzes the first step in the synthesis of acyl phosphoglycerides. The activity of this enzyme is one of the factors that determine whether fatty acids are oxidized or esterified and its relatively low activity (35) indicates that it may be a regulatory enzyme. Although the activity of glycerol-3-phosphate acyltransferase is subject to hormonal control in other cells, it is not known whether it is hormonally regulated in type II cells. The activity of glycerol-3-phosphate acyltransferase may be rate-limiting for the synthesis of PC at choline concentrations in the upper physiologic range (35). Most studies on the regulation of surfactant phospholipid synthesis have been focused on the regulation of PC metabolism. Studies on the regulation of PG and PI synthesis have been mainly carried out with developing lung and have been discussed by Mendelson in this volume. The maximal rate of phosphatidylcholine synthesis by type II cells is high compared to that in hepatocytes (35). This may be related to the efficient uptake and phosphorylation of choline by type II cells.

At low choline concentrations, the rate of PC synthesis is determined by the supply of CDP-choline generated in the reaction catalyzed by phosphocholine cytidylyltransferase. There is ample evidence that this enzyme plays an important regulatory role in the synthesis of PC. Pulse-label and pulse-chase experiments with type II cells, using radioactively labeled choline as a precursor, showed that the formation of CDP-choline is rate-limiting in these cells (69). This conclusion was strongly endorsed by measurement of the pool sizes of choline and its intermediates in type II cells (70). Kinetic analysis of the data on the pool sizes showed that both choline kinase and phosphocholine cytidylyltransferase catalyze non-equilibrium reactions in the type II cell, whereas the reaction catalyzed by cholinephosphotransferase appears to operate near equilibrium. Recent results from work with cultured glioma cells suggest that individual steps of the CDP-choline pathway are functionally linked and that reaction intermediates are not freely diffusible within the cell, but are channeled to PC biosynthesis (31). The existence of several pools of substrates and intermediates in type II cells may complicate studies on the regulation of PC synthesis.

More support for the regulatory role of phosphocholine cytidylyltransferase comes from developmental and hormonal studies. Alterations in the rate of phosphatidylcholine synthesis are paralleled by changes in the activity of phosphocholine cytidylyltransferase (reviewed in 72, 85). Experiments with a variety of different cell types suggest that phosphocholine cytidylyltransferase is a so-called ambiquitous enzyme that occurs in an inactive cytosolic form and an active membrane-associated form. For a number of cells there is convincing evidence that stimulation of PC synthesis is accompanied by translocation of the enzyme from the cytosol to microsomes. It has been suggested that this translocation may be controlled by reversible phosphorylation of the enzyme and by fatty acids (83). Although there is also evidence from whole-lung studies (96) that favors such a translocation mechanism for the regulation of phosphocholine cytidylyltransferase, the results from experiments with type II cells designed to address this question are less conclusive. These studies indicated that enhanced synthesis of PC in type II cells exposed to either fatty acids (9) or dexamethasone (68) was, indeed, accompanied by augmented activity of microsome-associated phosphocholine cytidylyltransferase. There was little evidence, however, for a parallel decrease in the cytosolic activity of this enzyme. Recently, Weinhold & coworkers described two cytosolic forms of phosphocholine cytidylyltransferase in type II cells. The L-form, a dimer of the M_r 45,000 catalytic subunit is inactive in the absence of lipids in the assay. The H-form, the predominant cytosolic form in type II cells, is a high molecular lipoprotein complex of the L-form and may represent the physiologically active cytosolic cytidylyltransferase (95). Conversion of L-form to H-form may explain the observed discrepancies if enhanced activities measured in the microsomal fractions do not match cytosolic activities. Alternatively, translocation from the cytosol to the endoplasmic reticulum may not occur at all, and the enhanced activity in the microsomal fraction may represent cosedimentation of the H-form with this fraction.

INTRACELLULAR LIPID TRANSPORT Most studies thus far describe the pathways of phospholipid synthesis and remodelling in type II cells and the regulation of phosphatidylcholine synthesis in these cells, but nothing is known about the mechanisms of sorting and transport of newly synthesized lipids destined to be assembled into lamellar bodies. In general, mechanisms of intracellular lipid traffic are still poorly understood (87). Lamellar bodies do not contain all the enzymes required for the synthesis of glycerolipids as discussed previously (85). Therefore, lipids must be transported to nascent lamellar bodies, either by vesicular transport or by lipid transport proteins. Several phospholipid transport proteins have been described in type II cells (reviewed in 30, 56). It has been suggested that the selectivity of a lung phospholipid transfer protein for DSPC may be involved in the enrichment of this species in lamellar bodies (74).

The classic autoradiographic studies of Chevalier & Collet suggest that newly synthesized phosphatidylcholine may be transferred from the Golgi complex to lamellar bodies by small lamellar bodies, i.e. by vesicular transport (11). Pulse-label studies by Jobe & co-workers support the idea that surfactant phospholipids move sequentially through a series of high density subcellular particles toward the low density lamellar bodies (43). This suggestion was also supported by experiments of Magoon & co-workers (57), who showed by labeling studies in vivo that dense lamellar bodies with the lowest phospholipid-protein ratio developed into mature light lamellar bodies. It is surprising that relatively few studies are devoted to clarify the mechanisms of sorting and routing of surfactant lipids. This may be so because measurements of lipid flow are relatively difficult compared to studies on intracellular protein transport. With the emergence of new techniques to study the intracellular flow of fluorescent lipids, we may expect more research on the routing of surfactant lipids.

SYNTHESIS AND PROCESSING OF SURFACTANT PROTEINS

The structure of the genes, regulation of gene expression, and the relationship between structure and function of the proteins have been discussed in previous chapters of this volume. We focus here on the synthesis and processing of the surfactant proteins.

Surfactant Protein A

Expression of rat SP-A is specific to the lung (28). The exclusive site of SP-A gene expression in the human lung as determined by in situ hybridization is the alveolar type II cell (64). Although SP-A has been localized in the Clara cells of rats and dogs by immunocytochemistry, it is not clear whether this protein is synthesized by this cell type (2, 89, 104).

PRIMARY TRANSLATION PRODUCTS One genomic sequence of human SP-A has been characterized (97). Several complementary DNAs with minor sequence variations have been described, two of which are reported to be translated in vitro (29). SP-A is a large, multimeric protein consisting of 18 monomeric subunits that are assembled through interchain disulfide bonds and non-covalent interactions via the collagenous domains (36, 51, 88). The slightly different primary translation products may be required to form collagen triple helices, which consist of heterotrimers, as has been reported for complement factor C1q. Indeed, a recombinant SP-A obtained by transfection of Chinese hamster ovary (CHO) cells with a single genomic construct is not well-assembled into the oligomeric form although the protein is functionally active (36, 88).

PROCESSING SP-A is extensively modified after translation. The primary translation product may be N-acetylated co-translationally (29, 92). SP-A is glycosylated, and the oligosaccharide moiety may be sulfated (93). Proline residues in the collagenous domain are hydroxylated and inter- and intra-chain disulfide bonds are formed (15, 36). Vitamin K-dependent carboxylation of glutamic acid was reported for SP-A in isolated rat type II cells (73). Acetylation, sulfation, and carboxylation have only been demonstrated indirectly by labeling studies, and not chemically in the native proteins. Although it was reported that a protein with a similar molecular weight to SP-A in microsomes of type II cells was labeled in the presence of vitamin K and radioactive bicarbonate (73), no gamma-carboxyglutamic acid was detected in dog (90) or human SP-A (H. P. Haagsman et al, unpublished observations).

GLYCOSYLATION The synthesis and processing of SP-A has been studied mainly in isolated rat alveolar type II cells. These studies indicate that the protein is glycosylated rapidly to a endoglycosidase H-sensitive form (98). The high-mannose form is only slowly processed to an endoglycosidase H-resistant form that is sialylated. High mannose forms are detected even after 12–16 h of pulse-chase experiments. The slow transit through the secretory pathway of the type II cell may be a consequence of the complex folding required to form the triple-helical collagen-like structures and the assembly of the oligomer. On the other hand, it should be realized that type II cells in vitro differentiate rapidly, and synthesis and processing of SP-A may be affected during the process of differentiation. As for most proteins, the role of the carbohydrate moieties of SP-A is not clear. Intracellular transport and secretion of SP-A was not altered by inhibitors of carbohydrate processing (60).

It is not clear whether all SP-A is secreted into the alveolar space as part of lamellar bodies. The amount of SP-A found in lamellar bodies is much lower than the calculated SP-A content of tubular myelin if one assumes that all lamellar bodies transform into tubular myelin. Recent work indicates that SP-A may have functions other than a structural and metabolic role in surfactant homeostasis. SP-A is a collagenous carbohydrate-binding protein (34) with a similar structure (22) and a similar gene locus (78) as a serum mannose-binding protein. This acute phase protein was recently reported to play an important immunological role in serum (24). SP-A may play a similar role in alveolar defense by activation of alveolar macrophages and enhancement of phagocytosis of these cells (86). Therefore, SP-A synthesis and secretion may be regulated independently, as part of the alveolar defense system, from that of the other surfactant components. Indeed, it was recently reported that synthesis of SP-A can be enhanced by interferon-gamma without affecting the production of other components of the surfactant system (3).

Surfactant Protein B

SP-B has been localized to type II cells by immunohistochemistry (47, 53, 65). Hybridization studies in situ suggest that type II cells, and also bronchiolar cells, may be the site of synthesis of human SP-B (64). Mature SP-B is processed from a preprotein of 381 amino acids by removal of 200 amino acids at the N-terminus and 102 amino acids from the C-terminus. The [^{35}S]methionine-labeled preprotein is sensitive to digestion with endoglycosidase F, which indicates that the preprotein is glycosylated. Indeed, N-linked glycosidation is predicted by the deduced amino acid sequence. Interestingly, a second cDNA has been described that differs by one nucleotide and that results in an additional N-glycosylation site in the preprotein. In a human pulmonary adenocarcinoma cell line in which SP-B is processed, no glycosylation was found at this site (61). Translation of human and rat lung poly $(A)^+$ RNA in vitro followed by immunoprecipitation identified a protein with a molecular weight of 40 K (61, 94). Synthesis and processing of SP-B was studied by pulse-labeling experiments and immunoprecipitation in cells. Comparison of in vitro translation products and incubation of cells in the presence of tunicamycin suggest that the relatively hydrophobic N-terminal amino acid sequence is a signal sequence. Complete processing of SP-B to the alveolar mature peptide has been demonstrated by rat alveolar type II cells in vitro (94). Limited processing of SP-B has been found in a human pulmonary adenocarcinoma cell line (61). In contrast to SP-A, SP-B precursors were primarily detected as an endoglycosidase H-sensitive pool in these cells. Neuraminidase and endoglycosidase-sensitive forms of ProSP-B were detected in the medium of the human cell line and rat type II cells. Proteolytically processed forms of proSP-B that are generated by the cleavage of an N-terminal peptide were also detected in the culture media. Newly synthesized mature SP-B was found in the medium of type II cells. It is not clear whether the mature peptide found in the medium originates from the cleavage of the C-terminal peptide from the extracellular precursor. Lamellar bodies contain mature SP-B, but no precursor forms of SP-B (94). These observations are supported by recent work from our laboratory using immunogold electronmicroscopy. In these studies it was found that precursor forms of

SP-B were present in the endoplasmic reticulum and Golgi but not in the lamellar bodies (W. F. Voorhout et al, unpublished results).

Surfactant Protein C

The hydrophobic surfactant protein C is produced as a primary translation product consisting of 197 amino acids. The mature form of SP-C is about 36 amino acids long and begins at residue 24 of the human proprotein. The preprotein does not have an N-terminal domain with a characteristic signal sequence, but the primary structure of mature SP-C is reminiscent of signal peptides. Studies on the processing of SP-C are hampered by the lack of good antibodies against this peptide. Nothing is known about the N- and C-terminal trimming of proSP-C. Like mature SP-B, mature SP-C is highly enriched in lamellar bodies (M. A. Oosterlaken-Dijksterhuis et al, unpublished results).

Surfactant Protein D

This collagenous protein has recently been described to be a surfactant-specific protein. The protein is synthesized by alveolar type II cells (63) and is found in alveolar lavage in relatively low concentrations. In rat lavage, most of SP-D is in the soluble fraction and not associated with surfactant (62). The function of SP-D is unknown. No information is available that indicates that SP-D is associated with surfactant-specific structures like lamellar bodies or tubular myelin.

ASSEMBLY INTO LAMELLAR BODIES

From Newly Synthesized Surfactant Components

Chevalier & Collet used electron microscopic autoradiography to follow the time-dependent appearance of [^{3}H]choline, [^{3}H]leucine, and [^{3}H]galactose in organelles of type II cells (11). A label from [^{3}H]choline first appeared in the endoplasmic reticulum, rapidly transferred through the Golgi apparatus, and was stored in the lamellar bodies. The transport of PC between the Golgi and the lamellar bodies seemed to be carried out by small lamellar bodies. As was discussed above, support for this notion was provided by biochemical studies (43, 57). A label from injected [^{3}H]leucine followed a different route. After initial labeling of the endoplasmic reticulum, the leucine label migrated through the Golgi into multivesicular bodies that seemed to fuse with nascent lamellar bodies. The multivesicular bodies were never labeled following [^{3}H]choline injection (11). Because neither choline nor leucine incorporation is specific for the surfactant system, these studies should be interpreted with caution.

Nothing is known about the assembly of newly synthesized surfactant proteins into lamellar bodies. SP-A does not seem to be required to produce lamellar bodies. During mouse lung development in vivo and in vitro, the expression of SP-A did not appear to be a prerequisite for the biogenesis of precursor forms of lamellar bodies (80). Although SP-A has been localized to lamellar bodies, it is still puzzling how the oligomeric protein with a length of 20 nm can fit between the densely stacked membranes in lamellar bodies. It was recently found in our laboratory that lamellar bodies are highly enriched with the mature form of SP-B (M. A. Oosterlaken-Dijksterhuis et al, unpublished observations). These observations were confirmed by immunoelectronmicroscopy (W. F. Voorhout et al, unpublished observations). In contrast, pro-SP-B was detected in the endoplasmic reticulum and Golgi, but not in lamellar bodies. These observations indicate that mature SP-B is an intrinsic lamellar body protein and is processed before being assembled into lamellar bodies. Although mature SP-C is also highly enriched in isolated lamellar bodies, nothing is known about the processing of this protein.

Other organelles implicated in intracellular surfactant metabolism are composite bodies. These granules contain lamellae in addition to eccentrically positioned vesicles. Both multivesicular bodies and composite bodies may be precursors of lamellar bodies. Three-dimensional reconstruction and quantitative analysis of type II cells indicated a negative correlation between lamellar body volume and the volume of the presumed precursors (107). This suggests that the volume of these precursors is regulated as a response of depletion of the mature lamellar bodies. Lamellar body precursors are polarized in the type II cells. The composite bodies are located mainly toward regions of the cell farthest from the secretory surface; multivesicular bodies are strongly polarized close to the surface of Golgi regions (107). The quantitative localization of these lamellar body precursors from three-dimensional reconstructions is in line with the [^{3}H]leucine incorporation data of Chevalier & Collet (11). It is remarkable that after almost twenty years the work of Chevalier & Collet is still the only morphological study that addresses the flow of newly synthesized lipids and proteins in the secretory path.

From Recycled Surfactant Components

Surfactant components are recycled by type II cells (discussed by Wright & Dobbs, this volume). From the early studies in vivo it appeared that as much as 95% of alveolar PC is reutilized (41), and most of the radioactive PC was recovered in the lamellar bodies (reviewed in 106). [^{14}C]DPPC labeled subfractions that contain SP-A are preferentially taken up in vivo and recovered in the lamellar bodies. In line with these observations, it was observed that uptake of [^{14}C]DPPC by type II cells in vitro is greatly enhanced by SP-A. Recently, SP-A was shown to bind specifically to type II cells (54, 105). These studies suggest that phospholipids are taken up by SP-A-dependent endocytosis and are directed toward lamellar bodies. Studies by

Young & colleagues (109), using ^{125}I-labeled SP-A, suggest that both SP-A and lipids are taken up in vivo and preferentially incorporated into lamellar bodies. Other evidence that lamellar bodies may be asembled from recycled surfactant comes from the observations of Lecerf et al (55). These investigators observed a high activity of sphingomyelin synthesis by phosphocholine transfer from PC to ceramides. Plasma membranes have a relatively high activity of the enzyme that catalyzes the phosphocholine transfer reaction. Lamellar bodies may acquire this enzyme activity from endocytosed material.

Morphological studies indicate that not only endocytosed surfactant components end up in lamellar bodies after internalization by type II cells. Williams used compounds that specifically bind to the apical plasma membrane of type II cells to follow endocytosis. A ferritin-labeled lectin from *Maclura pomifera,* taken up by type II cells via adsorptive endocytosis, moves through multivesicular bodies and ends up in lamellar bodies (101). Multivesicular bodies labeled first lack detectable lysosomal enzymes, while those labeled later are reactive. Cationic, but not native, ferritin follows a similar route and is observed sequentially within small pinocytic vesicles, large electron-lucent multivesicular bodies, small electron-dense multivesicular bodies and, by 30 min of instillation, within the nonlamellar matrix of lamellar bodies (100). The tracer apparently escapes the degradative pathway, but does not seem to pass through the Golgi complex or *trans*-Golgi reticulum. A small part of the cationic ferritin enters the *trans*cytotic pathway. It should be realized that these electronmicroscopic studies were not done with native surfactant components. Indications that SP-A is taken up by type II cells via receptor-mediated endocytosis comes from the recent morphological work of Ryan & co-workers (77). Binding and uptake of biotinylated canine SP-A by isolated rat type II cells was studied after warming from 4 to 23°C. Biotinyl SP-A gold was seen in coated pits (0–2 min), coated vesicles (0.5–5 min), endosomes (1–60 min), multivesicular bodies (5–60 min), and in endosomes adjacent to lamellar bodies (10–60 min). In contrast with the in vivo tracer studies of Williams, no biotinyl SP-A gold was detected in the lamellar bodies. Cultured type II cells may have lost the capacity to deliver endocytosed material to lamellar bodies. Type II cells in culture have been shown to differentiate into cells that share some characteristics with type I cells such as lectin binding. In recent experiments Williams & Dobbs showed that the lectin from *Maclura pomifera,* in contrast with the studies in vivo, was not taken up by cultured type II cells. A lectin from *Ricinus communis* and concanavalin A was taken up by cultured type II cells, followed the early steps in the endocytic pathway, but did not enter lamellar bodies (103). As in the studies of Ryan & co-workers, tracer-loaded multivesicular bodies were found at short distances from the lamellar bodies. Recently, Kalina & Socher reported the uptake of colloidal gold-surfactant complexes by isolated type II cells (46). These investigators showed that both internalization of surfactant-gold and internalization of the gold-complexed lectin from *Maclura pomifera* resulted in labeling of lamellar bodies. The labeling was relatively slow, and only part of the lamellar bodies was labeled, even after 270 min incubation (46).

The deposition of endocytosed material in secretory granules is unique and indicates that lamellar bodies are assembled both from newly synthesized and recycled components. It should be realized that lamellar bodies contain many lysosomal enzymes and, for that matter, are probably part of the degradative route. The reason that fusion with a primary lysosome does not lead to the formation of a secondary lysosome may be the consequence of the special qualities of the surfactant proteins. It is clear that more experiments, in which the routing and sorting of the individual surfactant components is followed, need to be done both in vivo and in type II cells, cultured under conditions that prevent alterations of biosynthetic and endocytic routes.

FUTURE PERSPECTIVES

For many years the synthesis of surfactant was synonymous with the synthesis of surfactant lipids. In the past fifteen years phospholipid biosynthesis has been studied in type II cells. Much effort was devoted to elucidate the pathways of remodeling of phosphatidylcholines and the regulation of phospholipid synthesis in type II cells, and although our knowledge has increased, many questions still remain unanswered. Advances in the field of phospholipid metabolism are hampered by the fact that most enzymes involved in the synthesis of glycerolipids are membrane-bound and hard to purify. Some cDNA clones have been isolated for soluble enzymes involved in fatty acid and phospholipid synthesis. It will be a great challenge to purify important membrane-bound enzymes to study the regulation of phospholipid metabolism on a transcriptional level.

With the help of molecular biological techniques much has become known about the structure of surfactant proteins and the regulation of expression of these proteins. Interesting work was done to study the synthesis and processing of these unique proteins. Accumulating evidence suggests that surfactant proteins are important determinants of both surfactant structure and surfactant homeostasis. It is expected that in the next few years more information will be obtained about the interactions between lipids and surfactant proteins in the different structures of surfactant and also about the mechanisms of lamellar body assembly from de novo synthesized and recycled components. This information must come from a combination of morphological and biochemical approaches using both tagged and modified surfactant components and antibodies against surfactant proteins.

In many respects research of the surfactant system is reminiscent of work on the structure and metabolism of serum lipoproteins. In this latter field, research was first directed at lipid components and later at proteins that have both structural and metabolic roles. Despite much effort, the process of serum lipoprotein assembly is still poorly understood. It is clear that elucidation of the mechanisms of assembly and trafficking of surfactant in the type II cell will be very exciting, not only to surfactant researchers, but to all cell biologists.

ACKNOWLEDGMENTS

Research in the authors' laboratory was supported by the Netherlands Foundation for Chemical Research (SON) with financial aid from the Netherlands Organization for Scientific Research (NWO), by a C. and C. Huygens stipend (to H.P.H.) from NWO, and by the Dutch Asthma Foundation (Nederlands Astma Fonds).

Literature Cited

1. Adachi, H., Hayashi, H., Sato, H., Dempo, K., Akino, T. 1989. Characterization of phospholipids accumulated in pulmonary-surfactant compartments of rats intratracheally exposed to silica. *Biochem. J.* 262:781–86
2. Balis, J. U., Paterson, J. F., Paciga, J. E., Haller, E. M., Shelley, S. A. 1985. Distribution and subcellular localization of surfactant-associated glycoproteins in human lung. *Lab. Invest.* 52:657–69
3. Ballard, P. L., Liley, H. G., Gonzalez, L. W., Odom, M. W., Ammann, A. J., et al. 1990. Interferon-gamma and synthesis of surfactant components by cultured human fetal lung. *Am. J. Respir. Cell Mol. Biol.* 2:137–43
4. Batenburg, J. J., Den Breejen, J. N., Yost, R. W., Haagsman, H. P., van Golde, L. M. G. 1986. Glycerol 3-phosphate acylation in microsomes of type II cells isolated from adult rat lung. *Biochim. Biophys. Acta* 878:301–9
5. Batenburg, J. J., Klazinga, W., van Golde, L. M. G. 1985. Regulation and location of phosphatidylglycerol and phosphatidylinositol synthesis in type II cells isolated from fetal rat lung. *Biochim. Biophys. Acta* 833:17–24
6. Batenburg, J. J., Whitsett, J. A. 1989. Levels of mRNAs coding for lipogenic enzymes in rat lung upon fasting and refeeding and during perinatal development. *Biochim. Biophys. Acta* 1006: 329–34
7. Beppu, O. S., Clements, J. A., Goerke, J. 1983. Phosphatidylglycerol-deficient lung surfactant has normal properties. *J. Appl. Physiol.* 55:496–502
8. Bruns, G., Stroh, H., Veldman, G. M., Latt, S. A., Floros, J. 1987. The 35 kd pulmonary surfactant-associated protein is encoded on chromosome 10. *Hum. Genet.* 76:58–62
9. Burkhardt, R., von Wichert, P., Batenburg, J. J., van Golde, L. M. G. 1988. Fatty acids stimulate phosphatidylcholine synthesis and CTP:cholinephosphate cytidylyltransferase in type II pneumocytes isolated from adult rat lung. *Biochem. J.* 254:495–500
10. Chander, A., Johnson, R. G., Reicherter, J., Fisher, A. B. 1986. Lung lamellar bodies maintain an acidic internal pH. *J. Biol. Chem.* 261:6126–31
11. Chevalier, G., Collet, A. J. 1972. In vivo incorporation of choline-3H, leucine-3H and galactose-3H in alveolar type II pneumocytes in relation to surfactant synthesis. A quantitative radioautographic study in mouse by electron microscopy. *Anat. Rec.* 174: 289–310
12. Clements, J. A. 1977. Function of the alveolar lining. *Am. Rev. Respir. Dis.* 115:67–71
13. Coalson, J. J., Winter, V. T., Martin, H. M., King, R. J. 1986. Colloidal gold immunoultrastructural localization of rat surfactant. *Am. Rev. Respir. Dis.* 133:230–37
14. Crapo, J. D., Peters-Golden, M., Marsh-Salin, J., Shelburne, J. S. 1978. Pathologic changes in the lungs of ox-

ygen-adapted rats. A morphometric analysis. *Lab. Invest.* 39:640–53

15. Crawford, S. W., Mecham, R. P., Sage, H. 1986. Structural characteristics and intermolecular organization of human pulmonary-surfactant-associated proteins. *Biochem. J.* 240:107–14
16. Crecelius, C. A., Longmore, W. J. 1983. Phosphatidic acid phosphatase activity in subcellular fractions derived from adult rat type II pneumocytes in primary culture. *Biochim. Biophys. Acta* 750:447–56
17. Crecelius, C.A., Longmore, W. J. 1984. Acyltransferase activities in adult rat type II pneumocyte-derived subcellular fractions. *Biochim. Biophys. Acta* 795:238–46
18. Den Breejen, J. N., Batenburg, J. J., van Golde, L. M. G. 1989. The species of acyl-CoA in subcellular fractions of type II cells isolated from adult rat lung and their incorporation into phosphatidic acid. *Biochim. Biophys. Acta* 1002:277–82
19. De Vries, A. C. J., Schram, A. W., Tager, J. M., Batenburg, J. J., van Golde, L. M. G. 1985. A specific α-glucosidase in lamellar bodies of the human lung. *Biochim. Biophys. Acta* 837:230–38
20. De Vries, A. C. J., Schram, A. W., Tager, J. M., Batenburg, J. J., van Golde, L. M. G. 1986. Genetic relationship between lysosomal and lamellar body-specific α-glucosidase in human lung. *Biochim. Biophys. Acta* 878:288–91
21. Dobbs, L. G., Mason, R. J., Williams, M. C., Benson, B. J., Sueishi, K. 1982. Secretion of surfactant by primary cultures of alveolar type II cells isolated from rats. *Biochim. Biophys. Acta* 713: 118–27
22. Drickamer, K. 1988. Two distinct classes of carbohydrate-recognition domains in animal lectins. *J. Biol. Chem.* 263:9557–60
23. Emrie, P. A., Jones, C., Hofmann, T., Fisher, J. H. 1988. The coding sequence for the human 18,000 dalton hydrophobic pulmonary surfactant protein is located on chromosome 2 and identifies a restriction fragment length polymorphism. *Somat. Cell Mol. Genet.* 14:105–10
24. Ezekowitz, R. A. B., Kuhlman, M., Groopman, J. E., Byrn, R. A. 1989. A human serum mannose-binding protein inhibits in vitro infection by the human immunodeficiency virus. *J. Exp. Med.* 169:185–96
25. Fisher, A. B., Chander, A. 1982. Glycerol kinase activity and glycerol metabolism of rat granular pneumocytes in primary culture. *Biochim. Biophys. Acta* 711:128–33
26. Fisher, J. H., Kao, F. T., Jones, C., White, R. T., Benson, B. J., Mason, R. J. 1987. The coding sequence for 32,000 dalton pulmonary surfactant-associated protein A is located on chromosome 10 and identifies two separate restriction-fragment-length polymorphisms. *Am. J. Hum. Genet.* 40:503–11
27. Fisher, J. H., Shannon, J. M., Hofmann, T., Mason, R. J. 1989. Nucleotide and deduced amino acid sequence of the hydrophobic surfactant protein SP-C from rat: expression in alveolar type II cells and homology with SP-C from other species. *Biochim. Biophys. Acta* 995:225–30
28. Floros, J., Phelps, D. S., Kourembanas, S., Taeusch, H. W. 1986. Primary translation products, biosynthesis, and tissue specificity of the major surfactant protein in rat. *J. Biol. Chem.* 261:828–31
29. Floros, J., Steinbrink, R., Jacobs, K., Phelps, D., Kriz, R., et al. 1986. Isolation and characterization of cDNA clones for the 35-kDa pulmonary surfactant-associated protein. *J. Biol. Chem.* 261:9029–33
30. Funkhouser, J. D., Read, R. J. 1985. Phospholipid transfer proteins from lung, properties and possible physiological functions. *Chem. Phys. Lipids* 38: 17–27
31. George, T. P., Morash, S. C., Cook, H. W., Byers, D. M., Palmer, F. B. St. C., Spence, M. W. 1989. Phosphatidylcholine biosynthesis in cultured glioma cells: evidence for channeling of intermediates. *Biochim. Biophys. Acta* 1004:283–91
32. Glasser, S. W., Korfhagen, T. R., Weaver, T. E., Clark, J. C., Pilot-Matias, T., et al. 1988. cDNA, deduced polypeptide structure and chromosomal assignment of human pulmonary surfactant proteolipid, SPL(pVal). *J. Biol. Chem.* 263:9–12
33. Glasser, S. W., Korfhagen, T. R., Weaver, T., Pilot-Matias, T., Fox, J. L., Whitsett, J. A. 1987. cDNA and deduced amino acid sequence of human pulmonary surfactant-associated proteolipid SPL(Phe). *Proc. Natl. Acad. Sci. USA* 84:4007–4011
34. Haagsman, H. P., Hawgood, S., Sargeant, T., Buckley, D., White, R. T., et al. 1987. The major lung surfactant protein, SP 28-36, is a calcium-dependent carbohydrate binding protein. *J. Biol. Chem.* 262:13877–80
35. Haagsman, H. P., Schuurmans, E. A. J.

M., Batenburg, J. J., van Golde, L. M. G. 1988. Synthesis of phosphatidylcholines in ozone-exposed alveolar type II cells isolated from adult rat lung: Is glycerolphosphate acyltransferase a rate-limiting enzyme? *Exp. Lung Res.* 14:1–17
36. Haagsman, H. P., White, R. T., Schilling, J., Benson, B. J., Golden, J., et al. 1989. Studies of the structure of the lung surfactant protein, SP-A. *Am. J. Physiol.* 257:L421–29
37. Hallman, M., Enhorning, G., Possmayer, F. 1985. Composition and surface activity of normal and phosphatidylglycerol-deficient lung surfactant. *Pediatr. Res.* 19:286–92
38. Hallman, M., Epstein, B. L. 1980. Role of myo-inositol in the synthesis of phosphatidylglycerol and phosphatidylinositol in the lung. *Biochem. Biophys. Res. Commun.* 92:1151–59
39. Hawgood, S. 1989. Pulmonary surfactant apoproteins: a review of protein and genomic structure. *Am. J. Physiol.* 257:L13–L22
40. Hook, G. E. R., Gilmore, L. B. 1982. Hydrolases of pulmonary lysosomes and lamellar bodies. *J. Biol. Chem.* 257: 9211–20
41. Jacobs, H., Jobe, A., Ikegami, M., Conaway, D. 1983. The significance of reutilization of surfactant phosphatidylcholine. *J. Biol. Chem.* 258:4156–65
42. Jacobs, K. A., Phelps, D. S., Steinbrink, R., Fisch, J., Kriz, R., et al. 1987. Isolation of a cDNA clone encoding a high molecular weight precursor to a 6-kDa pulmonary surfactant-associated protein. *J. Biol. Chem.* 262:9808–11
43. Jobe, A., Ikegami, M., Sarton-Miller, I., Jones, S., Yu, G. 1981. Characterization of phospholipids and localization of some phospholipid synthetic and subcellular marker enzymes in subcellular fractions from rabbit lung. *Biochim. Biophys. Acta* 666:47–57
44. Johansson, J., Curstedt, T., Robertson, B., Jörnvall, H. 1988. Size and structure of the hydrophobic low molecular weight surfactant-associated polypeptide. *Biochemistry* 27:3544–47
45. Johansson, J., Jörnvall, H., Eklund, A., Christensen, N., Robertson, B., Curstedt, T. 1988. Hydrophobic 3.7 kDa surfactant polypeptide: structural characterization of the human and bovine forms. *FEBS Lett.* 232:61–64
46. Kalina, M., Socher, R. 1990. Internalization of pulmonary surfactant into lamellar bodies of cultured rat pulmonary type II cells. *J. Histochem. Cytochem.* 38:483–92
47. Katyal, S. L., Singh, G., Ryan, L., Gottron, S. 1988. Hydrophobic surfactant-associated proteins: electrophoretic and immunologic analyses and cellular localization in human lung. *Exp. Lung Res.* 14:655–69
48. Kennedy, E. P. 1986. The biosynthesis of phospholipids. In *Lipids and Biomembranes, Past, Present and Future,* ed. J. A. F. Op den Kamp, B. Roelofsen, K. W. A. Wirtz, pp. 171–206. Amsterdam: Elsevier
49. King, R. J. 1984. Isolation and chemical composition of pulmonary surfactant. In *Pulmonary surfactant,* ed. B. Robertson, L. M. G. van Golde, J. J. Batenburg, pp. 1–15. Amsterdam: Elsevier
50. King, R. J., Klass, D. J., Gikas, E. G., Clements, J. A. 1973. Isolation of apoproteins from canine surface active material. *Am. J. Physiol.* 224:788–95
51. King, R. J., Simon, D., Horowitz, P. M. 1989. Aspects of secondary and quaternary structure of surfactant protein A from canine lung. *Biochim. Biophys. Acta* 1001:294–301
52. Kliewer, M., Fram, E. K., Brody, A. R., Young, S. L. 1985. Secretion of surfactant by alveolar type II cells: morphometric analysis and three-dimensional reconstruction. *Exp. Lung Res.* 9:351–61
53. Kogishi, K., Kurozumi, M., Fujita, Y., Murayama, T., Kuze, F., Suzuki, Y. 1988. Isolation and partial characterization of human low molecular weight protein associated with pulmonary surfactant. *Am. Rev. Respir. Dis.* 137: 1426–31
54. Kuroki, Y., Mason, R. J., Voelker, D. R. 1988. Alveolar type II cells express a high-affinity receptor for pulmonary surfactant protein A. *Proc. Natl. Acad. Sci. USA* 85:5566–70
55. Lecerf, J., Fouilland, L., Gagniarre, J. 1987. Evidence for a high activity of sphingomyelin biosynthesis by phosphocholine transfer from phosphatidylcholine to ceramides in lung lamellar bodies. *Biochim. Biophys. Acta* 918:48–59
56. Lumb, R. H. 1989. Phospholipid transfer proteins in mammalian lung. *Am. J. Physiol.* 257:L190–94
57. Magoon, M. W., Wright, J. R., Baritussio, A., Williams, M. C., Goerke, J., et al. 1983. Subfractionation of lung surfactant. Implications for metabolism and surface activity. *Biochim. Biophys. Acta* 750:18–31
58. Maniscalco, W. M., Finkelstein, J. N.,

Parkhurst, A. B. 1989. Effects of exogenous fatty acids and inhibition of de novo fatty acid synthesis on disaturated phosphatidylcholine production by fetal lung cells and adult type II cells. *Exp. Lung. Res.* 15:473–89
59. Mason, R. J., Nellenbogen, J. 1984. Synthesis of saturated phosphatidylcholine and phosphatidylglycerol by freshly isolated rat alveolar type II cells. *Biochim. Biophys. Acta* 794:392–402
60. O'Reilly, M. A., Nogee, L., Whitsett, J. A. 1988. Requirement of the collagenous domain for carbohydrate processing and secretion of a surfactant protein, SP-A. *Biochim. Biophys. Acta* 969:176–84
61. O'Reilly, M. A., Weaver, T. E., Pilot-Matias, T. J., Sarin, V. K., Gazdar, A. F., Whitsett, J. A. 1989. In vitro translation, post-translational processing and secretion of pulmonary surfactant protein B precursors. *Biochim. Biophys. Acta* 1011:140–48
62. Persson, A., Chang, D., Rust, K., Moxley, M., Longmore, W., Crouch, E. 1989. Purification and biochemical characterization of CP4 (SP-D), a collagenous surfactant-associated protein. *Biochemistry* 28:6361–67
63. Persson, A., Rust, K., Chang, D., Moxley, M., Longmore, W., Crouch, E. 1988. CP4: a pneumocyte-derived collagenous surfactant-associated protein. Evidence for heterogeneity of collagenous surfactant proteins. *Biochemistry* 27:8576–84
64. Phelps, D. S., Floros, J. 1988. Localization of surfactant protein synthesis by in situ hybridization. *Am. Rev. Respir. Dis.* 137:939–42
65. Phelps, D. S., Heather, H. P. 1987. Immunohistochemical localization of a low molecular weight surfactant-associated protein in human lung. *J. Histochem. Cytochem.* 35:1339–42
66. Phizackerley, P. J. R., Town, M.-H., Newman, G. E. 1979. Hydrophobic proteins of lamellated osmiophilic bodies isolated from pig lung. *Biochem. J.* 183:731–36
67. Possmayer, F. 1988. A proposed nomenclature for pulmonary surfactant-associated proteins. *Am. Rev. Respir. Dis.* 138:990–98
68. Post, M. 1987. Maternal administration of dexamethasone stimulates choline-phosphate cytidylyltransferase in fetal type II cells. *Biochem. J.* 241:291–96
69. Post, M., Batenburg, J. J., Schuurmans, E. A. J. M., van Golde, L. M. G. 1982. The rate-limiting step in the biosynthesis of phosphatidylcholine by alveolar type II cells from adult rat lung. *Biochim. Biophys. Acta* 712:390–94
70. Post, M., Batenburg, J. J., Smith, B.T., van Golde, L. M. G. 1984. Pool sizes of precursors for phosphatidylcholine formation in adult rat lung type II cells. *Biochim. Biophys. Acta* 795:552–57
71. Post, M., Schuurmans, E. A. J. M., Batenburg, J. J., van Golde, L. M. G. 1983. Mechanisms involved in the synthesis of disaturated phosphatidylcholine by alveolar type II cells isolated from rat lung. *Biochim. Biophys. Acta* 750:68–77
72. Post, M., van Golde, L. M. G. 1988. Metabolic and developmental aspects of the pulmonary surfactant system. *Biochim. Biophys. Acta* 947:249–86
73. Rannels, S. R., Gallaher, K. J., Wallin, R., Rannels, D. E. 1987. Vitamin K-dependent carboxylation of pulmonary surfactant-associated proteins. *Proc. Natl. Acad. Sci. USA* 84:5952–56
74. Read, R. J., Funkhouser, J. D. 1984. Acyl-chain specificity and membrane fluidity. Factors which influence the activity of a purified phospholipid-transfer protein from lung. *Biochim. Biophys. Acta* 794:9–17
75. Rooney, S. A. 1985. The surfactant system and lung phospholipid biochemistry. *Am. Rev. Respir. Dis.* 131:439–60
76. Rüstow, B., Nakagawa, Y., Rabe, H., Waku, K., Kunze, D. 1988. Species pattern of phosphatidylinositol from lung surfactant and a comparison of the species pattern of phosphatidylinositol and phosphatidylglycerol synthesized de novo in lung microsomal fractions. *Biochem. J.* 254:67–71
77. Ryan, R. M., Morris, R. E., Rice, W. R., Ciraolo, G., Whitsett, J. A. 1989. Binding and uptake of pulmonary surfactant protein (SP-A) by pulmonary type II epithelial cells. *J. Histochem. Cytochem.* 37:429–40
78. Sastry, K., Herman, G. A., Day, L., Deignan, E., Bruns, G., et al. 1989. The human mannose-binding protein gene. Exon structure reveals its evolutionary relationship to a human pulmonary surfactant gene and localization to chromosome 10. *J. Exp. Med.* 170:1175–89
79. Schlame, M., Rüstow, B., Kunze, D., Rabe, H., Reichmann, G. 1986. Phosphatidylglycerol of rat lung. Intracellular sites of formation de novo and acyl species pattern in mitochondria, microsomes and surfactant. *Biochem. J.* 240:247–52
80. Slavkin, H. C., Johnson, R., Oliver, P., Bringas, P., Don-Wheeler, G. et al. 1989. Lamellar body formation precedes pulmonary surfactant apoprotein expression during embryonic mouse lung de-

velopment in vivo and in vitro. *Differentiation* 41:223–36
81. Sueishi, K., Tanaka, K., Oda, T. 1977. Immunoultrastructural study of surfactant system. Distribution of specific protein of surface active material in rabbit lung. *Lab. Invest.* 37:136–42
82. Uhal, B. D., Longmore, W. J. 1988. Glycerol as a substrate for phospholipid biosynthesis in type II pneumocytes isolated from streptozotocin-diabetic rats. *Biochim. Biophys. Acta* 961:122–28
83. Vance, D. E., Pelech, S. L. 1984. Enzyme translocation in the regulation of phosphatidylcholine biosynthesis. *Trends Biochem. Sci.* 9:17–20
84. van Golde, L. M. G. 1985. Synthesis of surfactant lipids in the adult lung. *Annu. Rev. Physiol.* 47:765–74
85. van Golde, L. M. G., Batenburg, J. J., Robertson, B. 1988. The pulmonary surfactant system: biochemical aspects and functional significance. *Physiol. Rev.* 68:374–455
86. van Iwaarden, F., Welmers, B., Verhoef, J., Haagsman, H. P., van Golde, L. M. G. 1990. Pulmonary surfactant protein A enhances the host-defense mechanism of rat alveolar macrophages. *Am. J. Respir. Cell Mol. Biol.* 2:91–98
87. van Meer, G. 1989. Lipid traffic in animal cells. *Annu. Rev. Cell Biol.* 5:247–75
88. Voss, T., Eistetter, H., Schäfer, K. P., Engel, J. 1988. Macromolecular organization of natural and recombinant lung surfactant protein SP 28–36. Structural homology with the complement factor C1q. *J. Mol. Biol.* 201:219–27
89. Walker, S. R., Williams, M. C., Benson, B. 1986. Immunocytochemical localization of the major surfactant apoproteins in type II cells, Clara cells, and alveolar macrophages of rat lung. *J. Histochem. Cytochem.* 34:1137–48
90. Wallin, R., Seaton, M., Martin, L. F. 1988. No evidence for vitamin K-dependent carboxylation of canine surfactant apoproteins, 28–36 kDa. *Biochem. J.* 252:851–56
91. Warr, R. G., Hawgood, S., Buckley, D. I., Crisp. T. M., Schilling, J., et al. 1987. Low molecular weight human pulmonary surfactant protein (SP5): isolation, characterization, and cDNA and amino acid sequences. *Proc. Natl. Acad. Sci. USA* 84:7915–19
92. Weaver, T. E., Hull, W. M., Ross, G., Whitsett, J. A. 1986. In vitro acetylation of rat pulmonary surfactant-associated glycoprotein(s) A primary translation products. *Biochim. Biophys. Acta* 869: 330–36
93. Weaver, T. E., Kropp, K. L., Whitsett, J. A. 1987. In vitro sulfation of pulmonary surfactant-associated protein-35. *Biochim. Biophys. Acta* 914:205–11
94. Weaver, T. E., Whitsett, J. A. 1989. Processing of hydrophobic pulmonary surfactant protein B in rat type II cells. *Am. J. Physiol.* 257:L100–8
95. Weinhold, P. A., Rounsifer, M. E., Charles, L., Feldman, D. A. 1989. Characterization of cytosolic forms of CTP:choline-phosphate cytidylyltransferase in lung, isolated alveolar type II cells, A549 cell and Hep G2 cells. *Biochim. Biophys. Acta* 1006:299–310
96. Weinhold, P. A., Rounsifer, M. E., Williams, S. E., Brubaker, P. G., Feldman, D. A. 1984. CTP:phosphorylcholine cytidylyltransferase in rat lung. The effect of free fatty acids on the translocation of activity between microsomes and cytosol. *J. Biol. Chem.* 259:10315–21
97. White, R. T., Damm, D., Miller, J., Spratt, K., Schilling, J., et al. 1985. Isolation and characterization of the human pulmonary surfactant apoprotein gene. *Nature* 317:361–63
98. Whitsett, J. A., Ross, G., Weaver, T., Rice, W., Dion, C., Hull, W. 1985. Glycosylation and secretion of surfactant-associated glycoprotein A. *J. Biol. Chem.* 260:15273–79
99. Williams, M. C. 1977. Conversion of lamellar body membranes into tubular myelin in alveoli of fetal rat lung. *J. Cell Biol.* 72:260–77
100. Williams, M. C. 1984. Endocytosis in alveolar type II cells. Effect of charge and size of tracers. *Proc. Natl. Acad. Sci. USA* 81:6054–58
101. Williams, M. C. 1984. Uptake of lectins by pulmonary alveolar type II cells: subsequent deposition into lamellar bodies. *Proc. Natl. Acad. Sci. USA* 81:6383–87
102. Williams, M. C., Benson, B. J. 1981. Immunocytochemical localization and identification of the major surfactant protein in adult rat lung. *J. Histochem. Cytochem.* 29:291–305
103. Williams, M. C., Dobbs, L. G. 1990. Endocytosis in alveolar type II cells in vivo and in vitro. *Prog. Respir. Res.* 25:81–90
104. Williams, M. C., Hawgood, S., Schenk, D. B., Lewicki, J., Phelps, M. N., Benson, B. 1988. Monoclonal antibodies to surfactant proteins SP 28-36 label canine type II and nonciliated bronchiolar cells by immunofluorescence. *Am. Rev. Respir. Dis.* 137:399–405
105. Wright, J. R., Borchelt, J. D., Hawgood, S. 1989. Lung surfactant apoprotein SP-A (26-36 kDa) binds with high

affinity to isolated alveolar type II cells. *Proc. Natl. Acad. Sci. USA* 86:5410–14

106. Wright, J. R., Clements, J. A. 1987. Metabolism and turnover of lung surfactant. *Am. Rev. Respir. Dis.* 136:426–44
107. Young, S. L., Fram, E. K., Craig, B. L. 1985. Three-dimensional reconstruction and quantitative analysis of rat lung type II cells: a computer-based study. *Am. J. Anat.* 174:1–14
108. Young, S. L., Kremers, S. A., Apple, J. S., Crapo, J. D., Brumley, G. W. 1981. Rat lung surfactant kinetics: biochemical and morphometric correlation. *J. Appl. Physiol.* 51:248–53
109. Young, S. L., Wright, J. R., Clements, J. A. 1989. Cellular uptake and processing of surfactant lipids and apoprotein SP-A by rat lung. *J. Appl. Physiol.* 66:1336–42

Annu. Rev. Physiol. 1991. 53:465–76

THE ELECTROPHYSIOLOGY OF HAIR CELLS

Jonathan F. Ashmore

Department of Physiology, School of Medical Sciences, University Walk, Bristol BS8 1TD, England

KEY WORDS: cochlea, hearing, vestibular system, ion channels, mechanotransduction

---

INTRODUCTION

Both the hearing and vestibular organs of vertebrates contain cells responsive to miniscule mechanical disturbances. The common element is the hair cell, a sensory cell with a specialized mechanoreceptor at its apical end and with a basolateral membrane designed to shape the receptor potential and control synaptic interaction at its basal pole. The way in which hair cells are assembled varies from species to species. This short review, with the main emphasis on hearing structures (see further 37, 38, 49, 50), will highlight some of the differences found between hair cells and describe the features that makes them effective transducers—their ability to convert mechanical stimuli into neural codes.

Multiple Hearing Mechanisms

The main purpose of any hearing organ is to separate and encode frequency, intensity, and phase information in a sound, and thus to act as a spectrum analyzer. Hearing is a sense in which the components have evolved to limits imposed by physical laws. Nevertheless, there is no single hearing mechanism that is found universally; different evolutionary solutions for differing species, but all based on hair cells, have developed. In lower vertebrates each frequency channel is determined peripherally by hair cells that are individual electrical or mechanical resonators. This arrangement is found in auditory

0066–4278/91/0315–0465$02.00

organs of turtles (17), chicks (28), fish (63), and in vestibular organs that double as frequency detectors, such as the sacculus of frogs (37, 44). In mammals, with small acoustic shadows, and in birds, living in acoustically noisy environments, there has been evolutionary pressure to exploit sound frequencies above 1 kHz. In these cases the mechanical interactions of the cells and their associated structures have been organized to prefilter the sound signal. In the mammalian cochlea in particular, the frequency selectivity and overall performance is believed to depend on the global mechanics of assemblies of cells (37, 40, 49, 50).

IONIC PROPERTIES OF THE APICAL MEMBRANE

Mechanotransduction: Kinetics

The requirements of sound transduction place strong constraints on hair cells. Like all devices designed to operate at high gain on small signals, hair cell structures are highly differentiated. With auditory ranges extending to 10 kHz or more, hair cells need to detect sounds at frequencies limited by channel kinetics. The most complete data on the cellular mechanisms of the hair cell transducer have been obtained from hair cells of the frog sacculus (34–38), from the turtle auditory papilla (15–17), and from the chick (46, 48), all cells that are specialized low (less than 1 kHz) frequency detectors. There are still questions to be answered before completing the picture for other systems.

The obvious feature common to all hair cells is the bundle of about 100 stereocilia, stiff, actin-filled processes on the cell apex, typically 2–8 μm long. A deflection of the bundle tip by 1–100 nm is sufficient to gate an inward flow of current through the few hundred transducer channels associated with the bundle (30). This small displacement is sufficient because the channels are directly linked to displacement with no second messenger mechanism involved. Neither the channel nor its coupling mechanism has been isolated. With one possible exception (48), single transducer channels have not been recorded. Instead the numbers and size of the channel have been inferred from analysis of the transducer noise (30), or the channel's permeability (14). The channel is selective for cations, both monovalent and divalent (48, 58). Calcium is approximately four times as permeant as other monovalent cations. Although the stereocilial membrane normally faces a fluid (endolymph) low in Ca, it has been proposed that Ca entry may play a critical role in resetting the dynamic range of the bundle deflection (10, 15).

The hair bundle, patterned like a ziggurat, needs to be deflected vectorially towards the tallest stereocilium to open the transducer channel. This is reflected developmentally in a highly ordered arrangement of hair cells in their epithelium. The current view favors a mechanical transducer channel in the stereocilial membrane that is similar to a stretch-activated channel (57), but spring-coupled to deflection (34, 35). This type of model predicts measurable forces as the transducer is gated between open and closed configurations.

The site of transduction is contentious. In lower vertebrates, the stereocilia are the only reported site for mechanosensitivity in the cells. Not surprisingly, the favored choice for a site in the stereocilia are at the tip and at the base. A tip site is indicated by mapping the current sink during stimulation: the data are best fitted by a model with a current entry at the stereocilial extremities (37). Further support comes from the observation that the tips of the processes are coupled by fine linkages (51), i.e. a single protein that can be digested by elastase. A more basal location for the transducer is suggested by calcium imaging experiments in which Ca entry appears to be concentrated around the bundle base (46; see, however, 36). There is a complex structure of cross-links associated with the stereocilia, however, and the definitive experiment has yet to be done.

Mechanotransduction: Adaptation

Prolonged deflection of the stereocilia leads to adaptation, and the receptor current slowly turns off (10, 15, 24). The time course in frog saccular hair cells is on the order of 30 ms (24). The question arises as to whether this is a modification of the mechanical stimulus applied to the channel, or to the subsequent ionic processes within the hair cell. Adaptation is associated with small realignments of the bundle, possibly associated with a myosin-based movement of the channel linkage (10). On the other hand, raising the buffering power of the cell for calcium or holding the cell at positive potentials, thereby reversing the gradient, lengthens the adaptation time course (15). In these experiments, the necessary calcium comes from the outside, whereas in vivo, the transducer faces low Ca (typically 30–100 μM), and adaptation processes may differ. There also may be other hair cell differences, for although cells of a vestibular origin show prominent resetting of their dynamic range (24), there is little sign in situ of transducer adaptation in auditory cells (17, 56).

Mechanotransduction in the mammalian cochlea is less well understood. The problems of studying sound transduction at frequencies up to 100 kHz, using current cellular technologies, are formidable. What is known in vivo has been restricted to intracellular recording from cells with fine microelectrodes. Promising systems for study in vitro include organ-cultured mouse cochleas (54, 55) and isolated outer hair cells (5).

In the mammal, mechanotransduction differs between inner and outer hair cells, the two distinct hair cell populations of the cochlea. Inner hair cells, as in lower vertebrates, show a markedly asymmetrical receptor potential (56). At rest only about 15% of the transducer channels are open, and a receptor potential is greater in the depolarizing direction than in the hyperpolarizing direction (20, 21, 54, 56). At high frequencies, when the membrane time constant filters the higher harmonic components of the receptor potential, a depolarizing pedestal remains to control the cell membrane potential and hence neurotransmitter release from the cell's synapse.

The outer hair cell transducer, on the contrary, seems to be biased as half-open at rest (54, but see 20). Thus at high frequencies there is virtually no steady receptor potential. The phasic responses of hair cells must be inferred by extraction of the signal using a lock-in amplifier, which makes data interpretation uncertain.

IONIC PROPERTIES OF THE BASOLATERAL MEMBRANE OF HAIR CELLS

Electrically Resonant Hair Cells

In lower vertebrates, the basolateral membrane of hair cells contains ionic mechanisms that produce an electrical resonance (Figure 1). There is little evidence to suggest that mammalian cells are resonant to the same degree

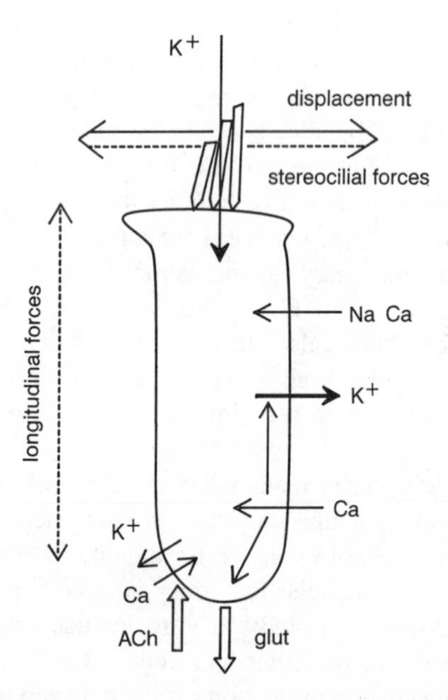

Figure 1 Schematic organization of the vertebrate hair cell. The membrane potential of the cell is controlled by entry of current, (mainly K), through the transducer on stereocilial displacement. The receptor potential is then shaped by further conductances in the basolateral membrane. The proportions of different conductances may differ significantly between cells of different origin. Neurotransmitters, afferent (labeled *glut*) and efferent (labeled *ACh*) are shown linked to the Ca metabolism of the cell. The *dashed lines* indicate directions of forces generated during reverse transduction.

Table 1 Summary of ionic currents in hair cells

Current	Hair cell type	Reference
Basolateral membrane		
K (outward rectifier)	Guinea pig, IHC	5, 42
I_A	Pigeon, crista	43
	Frog, sacculus	44
K (Ca)	Turtle, papilla	3
	Guinea pig, OHC	5
	Frog, sacculus	44
	Chick	28, 47
K (inward rectifier)	Chick, vestibular	47
	Frog, sacculus	14
Ca	Guinea pig, IHC	18
	Frog, sacculus	44
	Chick	27, 47
	Goldfish, sacculus	63
Na	Alligator, papilla	25
ATP-activated	Chick, papilla	61
	Guinea pig, OHC	45
ACh-activated	Toadfish, sacculus	62
	Frog, semicircular canals	31
	Turtle, papilla	2
Apical membrane		
transducer	Chick, papilla	46, 48
	Turtle, papilla	15, 16
	Frog, sacculus	10, 14, 34, 35, 39
	Mouse, cochlear explant	54
	Guinea pig, OHC	5

Data based on isolated cell experiments. Studies of the transducer in mammalian hair cells in vivo are included in references 11, 20, 21, 56.

(20), but isolated inner hair cells show a highly damped resonance (42). Such resonant mechanisms can arise from any voltage-gated conductance (7). In particular Ca and Ca-activated K-channels found in the cells (See Table 1) can act in a feedback loop to produce damped potential oscillations. The frequency of the oscillation depends on the voltage-dependence of the K conductance (3, 7, 44). The other critical parameter, the quality factor, Q, which measures the width of the resonance, depends upon the steepness of the K voltage activation curve and its activation time constant. In the case of K(Ca) currents, the Q can be large since a small influx of Ca can amplify activation of the K conductance. Other currents, such as the inactivating potassium current I_A, although present in hair cells, do not have the requisite activation kinetics and can only lead to highly damped oscillatory behavior outside the physiologic range of potentials (32, 42, 43, 63).

Many auditory structures, which show electrical resonant tuning, are organized tonotopically so that the best resonant frequency is mapped onto a unique place (3, 17, 27). The ionic current kinetics observed in these cells also depend on cell position (3). Those cells tuned to a higher frequency have larger currents and faster kinetics. Nevertheless, there is an intrinsic limitation to the frequencies at which electrically resonant cells can respond. Determined by the gating kinetics of the channels, the upper limit for cells that are electrically tuned seems to be about 800 Hz.

Non-resonant Hair Cells

Although most work suggests that hair cells have K, K(Ca), and Ca currents, a basis for electrical resonant behavior, not all hair cells are found to be resonant. Some examples of electrically excitable cells are found in the alligator, some hair cells exhibit a sodium action potential (27); in low frequency hair cells from the chick, a large Ca-dependent action potential (28) is apparent: regenerative spikes are also seen in cells from the goldfish sacculus (63). These action potentials are likely to be mechanisms that enhance the sensitivity of cells specialized to detect low frequency sounds.

Hair Cells from Non-auditory Organs

Some early intracellular work on efferent inhibition and on the mechanisms of mechanotransduction were successfully conducted on hair cells of the lateral line (26, 58). Relatively little research has continued with these systems except in the fish. Hair cells from fish (which possess well-developed acoustic and vestibular structures) exhibit a wide range of K currents (62, 63).

In the vestibular system proper there are two major classes of morphologically distinct cell types, classified type I and type II on the basis of their somatic morphology. In pigeons, the hair cells from the semicircular canals contain I_A, an inactivating K current, and Ca-activated K currents (43). A similar pattern of currents is seen in cells from the frog semicircular canals, (32). I_A is present in the frog sacculus (44), but dominated by a much large K(Ca) current, which generates resonant tuning. The situation in mammalian vestibular cells is less well-established. The phylogenetically more recent type I hair cells exhibit a novel K current, but type II cells contain an I_A (52a) whose functional significance is obscure.

Mammalian Hair Cells

Mammalian hearing, which operates at frequencies above those at which an electrical resonant mechanism would work, uses two classes of hair cell with functionally separate roles (21, 40, 50). Inner hair cells, the prime sensory cells of the auditory nerve, run in a single row along the cochlea. Outer hair cells, organized into three or four parallel rows, have a much poorer afferent innervation, but may instead be motor cells that provide a boost for the mechanics of the basilar membrane (11, 40, 56). How this works remains a topic hotly disputed by cochlear theoreticians.

INNER HAIR CELLS The inner hair cells, from the intact cochlea, have been studied directly with intracellular microelectrodes. The results obtained from the basal cells (20, 56) and the apical cells (20) indicate a membrane nonlinearity; the basis for this is only becoming apparent with more recent patch-clamp data. Isolated cells (5, 42, 59) with a range of voltage-gated channels have highly nonlinear current-voltage curves. As with other cells, the dominant current is carried by potassium, with a voltage-gated current that is activated at or around rest. The cell also exhibits a Ca current (18) with fast activation kinetics, perhaps involved in synaptic release.

OUTER HAIR CELLS Most recent evidence about outer hair cell conductances have been obtained using patch-clamp methods on isolated cells (5, 8, 9, 60). In situ, however, outer hair cell potentials can be recorded with fine microelectrodes from all turns of the cochlea (21, 56). Cells from the basal (high frequency) cochlear turns have low input resistances and short time constants. Cells recorded from the apical turns (20) are found to have higher resistances.

Whole cell patch recording of isolated cells reveals that the membrane is dominated by K conductances, (5, 9, 60). Such experiments reveal that as in other hair cells the currents are controlled in the cell by internal Ca. There is a TEA-sensitive current, and the basal area around the synapse contains K(Ca) channels (5). There is, in addition, a current that is cation selective (J. Ashmore, G. Housley, in preparation). This current, one of a class of currents also found in the chick (61), may be activated by ATP (45). Outer hair cells from along the cochlea have graded channel densities (8), with the basal cells having a channel density about ten times that found in cells from the cochlear apex. This is reminiscent of the gradient for ionic currents found in the turtle (3) and may suggest common developmental strategies in the cochlea.

Synaptic Interactions of Hair Cells

THE AFFERENT SYNAPSE Very little is known about the neurotransmitters that are released by and that act on hair cells (41). The best candidate for the afferent transmitter remains glutamate, based on experiments blocking afferent transmission and those experiments using immunocytochemical data to localize glutamate within the hair cells (1). Additional evidence for glutamate comes from patch recordings of cultured chick spiral ganglion cells, which indicate that NMDA receptors for glutamate are present on the postsynaptic neurons (64).

THE EFFERENT SYNAPSE Efferent innervation is found in most hair cell organs although its function remains enigmatic. The general finding is that physiologic activation of the whole efferent bundle detunes the cochlea (11). Efferent fiber activity is normally low (13) and, surprisingly, some patterns of chronic stimulation by implanted electrodes may lead to destruction of the target outer hair cells (23). The action on turtle (2), chick (61), and lateral line (26) hair cells is a hyperpolarization, which in the case of the turtle leads to a reduction of the electrical resonant tuning. The same experiment has yet to be reported for mammalian outer hair cells, either in the intact cochlea or on isolated cells.

There are few studies on isolated cells. In hair cells from the frog semicircular canals, application of ACh may lead to either inward or outward currents (31), which suggests at least two types of postsynaptic action. In toadfish, a similar ambiguity of action is also found (62). Equally perplexing, hair cells from the frog semicircular canals are also sensitive to histamine (33). Although the general action of ACh may, in part, result from an electrical shunt, the indications are that the efferents may act via a second messenger system and control basal calcium levels. A point in this direction has been the use of Ca imaging to detect agonist-induced changes in isolated chick papilla cells: 100 μM ACh increased intracellular Ca, an action inhibited by curare (61).

In the mammalian cochlea the efferent system terminates on the outer hair cells as a direct synaptic contact and on the postsynaptic afferent terminals of inner hair cells. Early work identified the efferent synapse as cholinergic on the basis of acetylcholinesterase staining (41) and more recently on the basis of choline acetyl transferase staining. Apart from two reports identifying enkephalins in the tunnel fibers (reported in 41), most evidence still favors a cholinergic mechanism. Indeed, antibodies raised against the acetylcholine receptor mark the synaptic region of the outer hair cell (52).

MICRO-MECHANICS OF HAIR CELLS: REVERSE TRANSDUCTION

Like physical devices designed to convert mechanical-to-electrical energy, hair cells operate in reverse as well. Electrical energy in the hair cell membrane can be converted into mechanical energy. Electromechanical conversion can be detected in squid axons (referenced in 4) and may be widespread, but it is of particular significance in hearing because the forces involved in the reverse transduction step may be of comparable magnitude to the mechanical stimulus forces themselves.

There are two different types of electromechanical conversion in hair cells, although they may be linked. The first is seen in stereocilial motion. In turtle, nanometer scale deflections of the stereocilia occur when current is injected into the cell (16). Since turtle hair cells show a pronounced potential resonance, the induced ringing in the turtle mechanical response suggests that such movements are potential driven. An analogous result is described in the semicircular canals of eels, where transepithelial current leads to a measurable deflection of the long stereocilia (53). The mechanics of the hair bundle is not that of a passive sprung pivot but has a stiffness that is position-dependent, a result used in the sacculus to infer the mechanical energy required to gate the transducer channel (34, 38). In mouse hair cells, direct displacement of the stereocilia is also associated with a change in stiffness of the bundle (55). The processes are active in the sense that the stereocilia show spontaneous mechanical movements (measured in picometers, but detectable by a new generation of laser differential interferometers) greater than thermal noise levels (22). In all these cases, however, the inferred total loop gain from mechanical-electrical mechanical energy appears to be less than unity, and the function of the reverse transduction is insufficient to reduce or boost mechano-electric transduction in a single cell significantly.

Another force-generating mechanism is found in isolated mammalian outer hair cells (4, 12) and associated with the basolateral membrane. This electromechanical process is of interest because of the possible role of the outer hair cells in altering the mechanics of the cochlear partition, even though the significance of the resulting motility has been questioned (59). Measurable length changes of about 4% of the cell length occur when the membrane is polarized, which shows that longitudinal forces are being produced in the cell. Virtually instantaneous, these forces are potential-driven (4, 60), but independent of cellular metabolism (29). There is as yet no molecular description of the force-generating steps, but there is an underlying charge movement similar to the type found in excitation-contraction coupling in muscle (6). Such observations suggest that there is an interesting molecular and cytoskeletal machinery yet to be explored within these hair cells.

CONCLUSION: WHERE DO WE GO FROM HERE?

Hair cells are seen as increasingly complex pieces of cellular machinery specialized to optimize the conversion of mechanical energy into neural signals. The application of the powerful techniques of molecular biology to these cells is in its infancy and has been hampered by the extremely small amount of material available. The future problems must include identification of the molecular structure of the transduction channel, whether it has similarities to the stretch-activated channels found in many other systems (57), and the precise site of the channel. At levels of integration above the single cell, there are still outstanding questions about the nature of the global interactions between hair cells. What factors contribute to make a functional mammalian cochlea? What are the developmental factors that regulate growth of such an incredibly orderly and precise structure?

Literature Cited

1. Altschuler, R. A., Sheridan, C. E., Horn, J. W., Wenthold, R. J. 1989. Immunocytochemical localization of glutamate immunoreactivity in the guinea pig cochlea. *Hear. Res.* 42:167–74
2. Art, J. J., Crawford, A. C., Fettiplace, R., Fuchs, P. A. 1985. Efferent modulation of hair cell tuning in the cochlea of the turtle. *J. Physiol.* 360:397–421
3. Art, J. J., Fettiplace, R. 1987. Variation of membrane properties in hair cells isolated from the turtle cochlea. *J. Physiol.* 358:323–48
4. Ashmore, J. F. 1987. A fast motile response in guinea-pig outer hair cells: the cellular basis of the cochlear amplifier. *J. Physiol.* 388:323–47
5. Ashmore, J. F. 1988. Ionic mechanisms in hair cells of the mammalian cochlea. *Prog. Brain Res.* 74:1–7
6. Ashmore, J. F. 1989. Transducer motor coupling in cochlea outer hair cells. In *Cochlear mechanisms: structure function and models,* ed. J. P. Wilson, D. T. Kemp. pp. 107–14 New York: Plenum
7. Ashmore, J. F., Attwell, D. 1985. Models for electrical tuning in hair cells. *Proc. R. Soc. London Ser. B* 226:325–44
8. Ashmore, J. F., Housley, G. D. 1989. Graded ionic properties of isolated hair cells from the guinea pig cochlea. *J. Physiol.* 417:83P
9. Ashmore, J. F., Meech, R. W. Ionic basis of membrane potential in outer hair cells of the guinea pig cochlea. *Nature* 322:368–71
10. Assad, J. A., Hacohen, N., Corey, D. P. 1989. Voltage dependence of adaptation and active bundle movement in bullfrog saccular hair cells. *Proc. Natl. Acad. Sci. USA* 86:2981–22
11. Brown, M. C., Nuttall, A. L., Masta, R. I. 1983. Intracellular recordings from cochlear inner hair cells: effects of stimulation of the crossed olivo-cochlear bundle. *Science* 222:69–72
12. Brownell, W. E., Bader, C. R., Bertrand, D., de Ribaupierre, Y. 1985. Evoked mechanical responses of isolated cochlear outer hair cells. *Science* 227: 194–96
13. Cody, A. R., Johnstone, B. M. 1982. Temporary threshold shift modified by binaural acoustic stimulation. *Hear. Res.* 6:199–205
14. Corey, D. P., Hudspeth, A. J. 1979. Ionic basis of the receptor potential in a vertebrate hair cells. *Nature* 281:675–77
15. Crawford, A. C., Evans, M. G., Fettiplace, R. 1989. Activation and adaptation on transducer currents in turtle hair cells. *J. Physiol.* 419:405–34
16. Crawford, A. C., Fettiplace, R. 1985. The mechanical properties of the ciliary bundles of turtle hair cells. *J. Physiol.* 364:359–80
17. Crawford, A. C., Fettiplace, R. 1981. An electrical tuning mechanism in turtle cochlear hair cells. *J. Physiol.* 312:377–412
18. Crawford, A. C., Kros, C. J. 1990. A fast calcium current with a rapidly inactivating component in isolated inner hair cells of the guinea pig. *J. Physiol.* 420:90P
19. Deleted in proof
20. Dallos, P. 1985. Membrane potential and response changes in mammalian cochlear hair cells during intracellular recording. *J. Neurosci.* 6:1609–15
21. Dallos, P. 1985. Response characteristics of mammalian hair cells. *J. Neurosci.* 6:1591–1608
22. Denk, W., Webb, W. W., Hudspeth, A. J. 1990. Mechanical properties of sensory hair bundles are reflected in their Brownian motion measured with a laser differential interferometer. *Proc. Natl. Acad. Sci. USA* 86:5371–75
23. Dodson, H. C., Walliker, J. R., Frampton, S., Douek, E. E., Fourcin, A. J., Bannister, L. 1986. Structural alteration of hair cells in the contralateral ear resulting from extracochlear stimulation. *Nature* 320:65–67
24. Eatock, R. A., Corey, D. P., Hudspeth, A. J. 1987. Adaptation of mechanoelectric transduction in hair cells of the bullfrog sacculus. *J. Neurosci.* 7:2821–36
25. Evans, M. G., Fuchs, P. A. 1987. Tetrodotoxin-sensitive, voltage dependent sodium currents in hair cells from the alligator cochlea. *Biophys. J.* 52:649–52
26. Flock, A., Russell, I. J. 1973. The postsynaptic action of efferent fibers in

the lateral line organ of the turbot, Lota lota. *J. Physiol.* 235:591–605
27. Fuchs, P. A., Mann, A. C. 1986. Voltage oscillations and ionic currents in hair cells isolated from the apex of the chick cochlea. *J. Physiol.* 371:31P
28. Fuchs, P. A., Nagai, T., Evans, M. G. 1988. Voltage oscillations and ionic conductances in hair cells isolated from the chick cochlea. *J. Neurosci.* 8:2460–67
29. Holley, M., Ashmore, J. F. 1988. On the mechanism of a high-frequency motile response in outer hair cells isolated from the cochlea of the guinea pig. *Proc. R. Soc. London Ser. B* 232:413–29
30. Holton, T., Hudspeth, A. J. 1986. The transduction channel of the bullfrog sacculus characterized by noise analysis. *J. Physiol.* 375:195–227
31. Housley, G. D., Norris, C. H., Guth, P. S. 1990. Cholinergically-induced changes in outward currents in hair cells isolated from the semicircular canals of the frog. *Hear. Res.* 43:121–34
32. Housley, G. D., Norris, C. H., Guth, P. S. 1989. Electrophysiological properties and morphology of hair cells isolated from the semicircular canal of the frog. *Hear. Res.* 38:259–76
33. Housley, G. D., Norris, C. H., Guth, P. S. 1989. Histamine and related substances influence neurotransmission in the semicircular canal. *Hear. Res.* 35: 87–98
34. Howard, J., Hudspeth, A. J. 1988. Compliance of hair bundle associated with gating of the mechanoelectric transduction channels in the bullfrog's saccular hair cell. *Neuron* 1:189–99
35. Howard, J., Roberts, W. M., Hudspeth, A. J. 1988. Mechano-electric transduction by hair cells. *Annu. Rev. Biophys. Chem.* 17:99–124
36. Huang, P. L., Corey, D. P. 1990. Calcium influx into hair cell stereocilia: further evidence for transduction channels at the tips. *Biophys. J.* 57:530a
37. Hudspeth, A. J. 1983. Mechanoelectrical transduction by hair cells of the acoustico-lateralis sensory system. *Annu. Rev. Neurosci.* 6:187–215
38. Hudspeth, A. J. 1989. How the ears works work. *Nature* 341:397–404
39. Hudspeth, A. J. 1983. Extracellular current flow and the site of transduction by vertebrate hair cells. *J. Neurosci.* 2:1–10
40. Kim, D. O. 1986. Active and nonlinear cochlear biomechanics and the role of the outer hair cell subsystem in the mammalian auditory system. *Hear. Res.* 22:105–14
41. Klinke, R. 1986. Neurotransmission in the inner ear. *Hear. Res.* 22:235–43
42. Kros, C. J., Crawford, A. C. 1990. Potassium currents in inner hair cells isolated from guinea-pig cochlea. *J. Physiol.* 421:263–92
43. Lang, D. G., Correia, M. J. 1989. Studies of solitary semicircular canal hair cells in the adult pigeon II. Voltage-dependent ionic conductances *J. Neurophysiol.* 62:935–45
44. Lewis, R. S., Hudspeth, A. J. 1983. Voltage- and ion-gated conductances in solitary vertebrate hair cells. *Nature* 304:538–41
45. Nakagawa, T., Akaike, N., Kimitsuki, T., Komune, S., Arima, T. 1990. ATP-induced current in isolated outer hair cells of guinea pig cochlea. *J. Neurophysiol.* 93:1068–74
46. Ohmori, H. 1988. Mechanical stimulation and FURA-2 fluorescence in the hair bundle of dissociated hair cells of the chick. *J. Physiol.* 399:115–38
47. Ohmori, H. 1984. Studies of ionic currents in the isolated vestibular hair cell of the chick. *J. Physiol.* 350:561–81
48. Ohmori, H. 1985. Mechano-electric transduction currents in isolated vestibular hair cells of the chick. *J. Physiol.* 359:189–217
49. Patuzzi, R., Robertson, D. 1988. Tuning in the mammalian cochlea *Physiol. Rev.* 68:1009–1082
50. Pickles, J. O. 1988. *An Introduction to the Physiology of Hearing.* London: Academic. 367 pp. 2nd ed.
51. Pickles, J. O., Comis, S. D., Osborne, M. P. 1984. Cross links between stereocilia in the guinea pig organ of Corti and their possible relation to sensory transduction. *Hear. Res.* 15:103–12
52. Plinkert, P. K., Gitter, A. H., Zimmerman, U., Kirchner, T., Tzartos, S., Zenner, H. P. 1990. Visualization and functional testing of acetylcholine receptor-like molecules in cochlear outer hair cells. *Hear. Res.* 44:25–34
52a. Rennie, K. J., Ashmore, J. F. 1990. *Soc. Neurosci. Abstr.* 16:1080
53. Rusch, A., Thurm, U. 1989. Cupula displacement, hair bundle deflection and physiological response in the transparent semicircular canal of the young eel. *Pflügers Arch.* 413:513–45
54. Russell, I. J., Richardson, G. P. 1987. The morphology and physiology of hair cells in organotypic cultures of the mouse cochlea. *Hear. Res.* 31:9–24
55. Russell, I. J., Richardson, G. P., Kossl, M. 1989. The responses of cochlear hair cells to tonic displacement of the sensory hair bundle. *Hear. Res.* 43:55–70

56. Russell, I. J., Sellick, P. 1983. Low frequency characteristics of intracellularly recorded receptor potentials in mammalian hair cells. *J. Physiol.* 284:261–90
57. Sachs, F. 1989. Ion channels as mechanical transducers In *Cell Shape: Determinants, Regulation and Regulatory Role,* ed. W. D. Stein, F. Bronner. pp. 63–92. San Diego: Academic
58. Sand, O. 1975. Effect of different ionic environments on the mechano-sensitivity of lateral line organs in the mudpuppy. *J. Comp. Physiol.* 102:27–42
59. Santos-Sacchi, J. 1989. Asymmetry in voltage-dependent movements of the isolated outer hair cell from the organ of Corti. *J. Neurosci.* 9:2954–62
60. Santos-Sacchi, J., Dilger, J. P. 1988. Whole cell currents and mechanical responses of isolated outer hair cells. *Hear. Res.* 35:143–50
61. Shigemoto, T., Ohmori, H. 1990. Muscarinic agonists and ATP increase intracellular Ca^{2+} in chick cochlear hair cells. *J. Physiol.* 420:127–48
62. Steinacker, A., Rojas, L. 1988. Acetylcholine modulated potassium channel in the hair cell of the toadfish saccule. *Hear. Res.* 35:265–70
63. Sugihara, I., Furukawa, T. 1989. Morphological and functional aspects of two different types of hair cells in the goldfish sacculus. *J. Neurophysiol.* 62:1–14
64. Yamaguchi, K., Ohmori, H. 1990. Voltage-gated and chemically gated ionic channels in the cultured cochlear ganglion neurone of the chick. *J. Physiol.* 420:185–206

Annu. Rev. Physiol. 1991. 53:477–96

STRATEGIES FOR STUDYING PERMEATION AT VOLTAGE-GATED ION CHANNELS

Henry A. Lester

Division of Biology, California Institute of Technology, Pasadena California 91125

KEY WORDS: heterologous expression, sodium/potassium/calcium channel excitable membranes, local anesthetics, site-directed mutagenesis

---

INTRODUCTION

Voltage-dependent ion channels are presently thought to consist of several distinct functional regions: (*a*) activation gates, (*b*) inactivation gates, and (*c*) permeation pathways. This chapter focuses on permeation pathways and may spur new ideas about experiments that use site-directed mutagenesis to probe the ion conduction pathway. Some hubris is required to attempt a survey of this field since individual families—K^+, Na^+, or Ca^{2+}—have been reviewed in detail (15, 68, 115, 127). My unified treatment is motivated by the structural similarity suggested by recent cDNA sequencing data on this group (see, for instance, 24). There have been many excellent previous treatments of ion channel permeation (6, 15, 34, 35, 51, 53, 68, 73, 74, 115, 127).

Most well-characterized voltage-dependent channels in animal cells are selective for cations and, as a class, these channels are more selective than the ligand-gated cation channels of postsynaptic membranes. At present there are few reports of pharmacological or genetic manipulations that affect the selectivity of ion channels, e.g. that change Na^+ to K^+ or Ca^{2+} channels. When successfully performed and interpreted, such manipulations will represent a triumph of the site-directed mutagenesis approach. It is already known that batrachotoxin and aconitine render Na^+ channels less selective for Na^+ than for many other ions (62).

0066-4278/91/0315-0477$02.00

A View of Permeation and Selectivity

I invoke the reviewer's privilege and responsibility to offer, before summarizing all the facts, a unified hypothesis for permeation and selectivity that emerges from much of the work discussed below (and that is explicitly stated in some of the papers). The problem is that high selectivity generally occurs via high-affinity binding, which in turn implies long-lived complexes, which are incompatible with high flux rates through a channel. For instance, if an ion bound with an apparent dissociation constant of 10 μM or less (95) at a diffusion-limited forward binding rate of 10^9 $M^{-1}s^{-1}$, it would remain bound for 100 μs or more, at least 1,000 times too long to account for the flux through most channels. An escape from this quandary is offered by the fact that the concentrations of ions are so high that their chemical potential also drives other less favorable processes, in this case mutual repulsion among bound ions in the channel. Channels appear to have a series of binding sites that, when unoccupied, have high affinity for the permeant ion (and much lower affinity for impermeant ones). When one such site is occupied, however, the affinity of neighboring sites decreases by several orders of magnitude, presumably because of electrostatic interactions among bound ions. Nonetheless, the high concentration of the permeant ion assures that neighboring sites are often simultaneously occupied. The brief residence times associated with the low affinity assure that ions hop rapidly among binding sites; the electrochemical driving force assures that the hops are predominantly in the direction of current flow. Recent modeling, involving Eyring rate theory and the concepts summarized above, provides a quantitative explanation for the process at Ca^{2+} channels (40). Similar analyses are available for a high-conductance Ca^{2+}-activated K channel (94, 95). It should be noted that different K^+ channels vary substantially in their permeation characteristics (127) and also that Na^+ channels may not normally function with multisite binding.

Several classes of measurement are available to count, localize, and define the binding sites in the permeation pathway. I summarize these measurements and the available results below.

Reversal Potentials

The use of reversal potentials to measure selectivity has been developed, applied experimentally, and reviewed by Hille (53), and will not be treated exhaustively here. A relative permeability P_B/P_A is obtained from measurements of the shift in reversal potential, $\Delta E_{rev} = (RT/zF)\ln(P_B[B]_o/P_A[A]_o)$, when cation A is replaced by cation B, both of valence z, in the external solution. What is the physical meaning of the result? Formally, the permeability coefficient P for an ion is a bulk property proportional to the water-membrane partition coefficient and to the diffusion coefficient within the membrane. In Eyring rate theory, a particle hops over energy barriers as it diffuses; the diffusion coefficient is proportional to a hopping frequency that decreases exponentially with the height of the barrier. Therefore, in the usual interpretation, permeability is dominated by the highest energy barrier that an ion must traverse in crossing the membrane. Because permeabilities measured in this way often seem to decrease monotonically with hydrated radius or other measures of molecular size, the critical energy barrier is usually identified with the narrowest region of the channel. This interpretation has given rise to many of the analyses that deduce the diameter of the selectivity filter based on the relative permeabilities for different ions. The reversal potential measurement is widely applicable because it is sensitive to neither block nor saturation in the channel. This insensitivity, however, also shows the limitations of reversal potential measurements for revealing details of the permeation process.

Current-Voltage Relations

THE MEANING OF RECTIFICATION In recent experiments on both acetylcholine receptors (58, 71) and K channels (81), some mutations have introduced rectification in the single-channel current-voltage (I-V) relation. Rectification allows one to deduce the approximate location of a new energy barrier (Figure 1). The additional energy barrier could be a narrow region, a change in dipole moment, or a change in charge—in general, something that makes ions pause as they move through the channel. If the barrier is sharp with a height ΔG^{+}, then the rate constant for crossing the barrier is $\kappa kT/h[\exp(-\Delta G^{+}/RT)]$. The reflection coefficient κ ($0 < \kappa < 1$) is unknown, but presumably it applies to a similarly shaped barrier anywhere along the channel.

The effect of this new barrier depends on its location. As shown in Figure 1, the new barrier is at an electrical distance δ from the extracellular surface of the membrane ($0 < \delta < 1$; $\delta = 1$ corresponds to the cytoplasmic surface). Ions experience an energy difference $zq\delta V$ between the base of the barrier and the external solution, where q is the elemental charge. This energy difference tends to accumulate ions at the extracellular-facing base of the barrier, relative to the extracellular solution, by the Boltzmann factor $\exp(-zq\delta V/kT)$. If V is -100 mV, $zq = +1$ electronic charge, and the barrier is located $\delta = 2/3$ of the distance to the intracellular face, then the accumulation is by a factor of 15. Now consider the case for an ion entering from the cytoplasmic face and driven in the opposite direction by the voltage gradient. In this case, the appropriate expression uses $\delta = 1/3$, and the accumulation at the intracellular base of the barrier is by only a factor of 3.7. Thus a new barrier, if located asymmetrically, can be overcome more easily by current in one direction. The

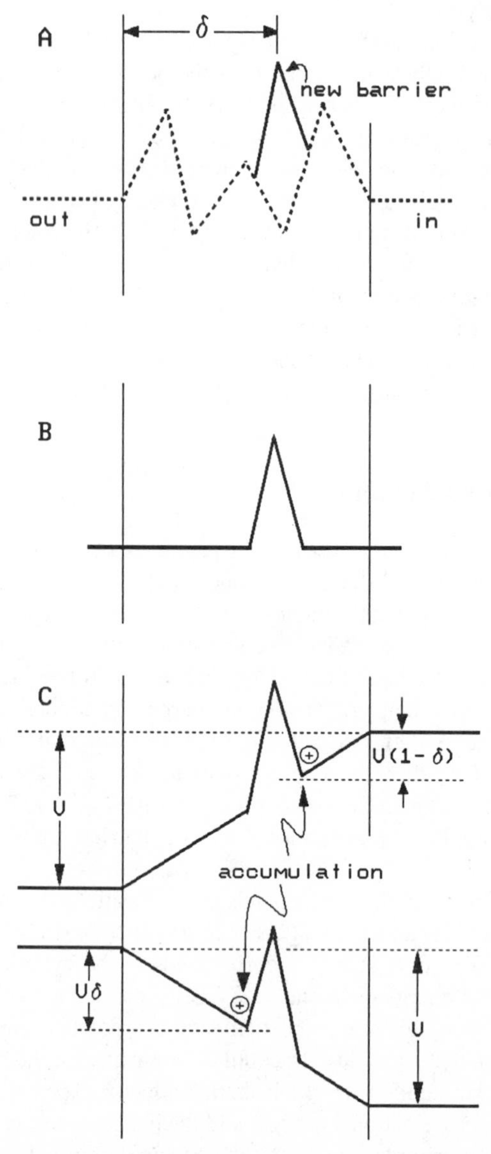

Figure 1 A diagram showing the energy experienced by an ion in a channel as a function of the distance *(horizontal axis)*. In (*A*) the normal channel is characterized by the *dashed line;* and a mutation introduces a localized extra barrier *(solid line)*. In (*B*) the extra barrier is shown in isolation for simpler analysis. (*C*) shows how the energy of the ion at the new barrier, relative to that in the solutions, is changed when a voltage is applied across the membrane. We assume here and in all figures (*a*) that the field in the membrane is constant and (*b*) that the barrier is so thin that the peak and bases are all roughly at the position δ.

resulting change in the current-voltage relation is diagnostic for the location of the new energy barrier.

SURFACE-CHARGE EFFECTS ON CURRENT-VOLTAGE RELATIONS Operationally, surface charge effects are suspected when all divalent cations (or higher concentrations of monovalent cations) produce a roughly equal concentration-dependent shift in a voltage-dependent parameter (85). The perturbation of the energy profile produced by surface charge differs from that produced by an energy barrier as discussed above: the potential well is (*a*) eccentric—confined to one surface of the membrane, and (*b*) asymmetric—there is a steep change in the solution near the membrane and a gradual one within the membrane (Figure 2). In the usual situation, substantial negative surface potential at the outer surface of the membrane tends to accumulate cations within one Debye length of the membrane. If this increased concentration occurs near a barrier that is rate-limiting for permeation (as in Figure 2),

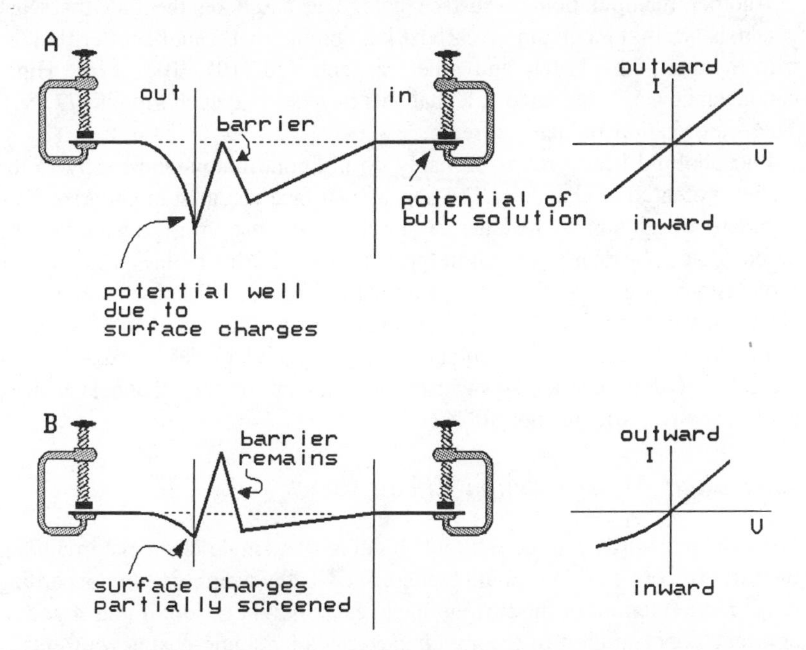

Figure 2 (*A*) This channel has two features. (*a*) It has a negative surface potential. In the external solution, this potential decreases to zero roughly within the Debye length (~ 8 Å). In the membrane, the potential gradient is much less. More than a few nm from the membrane, the potential is unaffected by the surface potential and is clamped to the value in the bulk solution. (*b*) The channel has an asymmetrically located energy barrier like the one in Figure 1. (*B*) Reduction of the surface potential cannot be directly detected by electrodes in the bulk solution. This change, however, allows the energy barrier to influence ion permeation more strongly, as in Figure 1.

increased current flow results. As another result of surface charge accumulation, the relation between zero-voltage channel conductance and permeant cation concentration shows a non-zero intercept as the ionic strength is lowered symmetrically (7, 16, 77, 89).

The typical experimental manipulation involving increased external divalent ion concentration leads to screening of negative surface charge and would therefore decrease inward current flow. For instance, in the study by Green et al (43), in the absence of divalent cations, reconstituted Na^+ channels showed a linear current-voltage relation. When Ba^{2+} was added to the external solution, the conductance decreased substantially more for inward than for outward currents. For K^+ channel mutants with threonine-449 replaced by lysine, arginine, or glutamine in an extracellular region, the reduction in external negative surface charge again leads to a greater decrease in inward than outward current (81). There is also some evidence for surface charge at the cytoplasmic face of the Na channels (105a).

Another manipulation of surface charge is based on the fact that Na^+ channels seem to contain a carboxylate group that can be esterified by trimethyloxonium (TMO) and other reagents (26, 105, 106, 123). High-conductance Ca^{2+}-activated K^+ channels have several such groups (77, 80). The esterification reduces currents.

Phospholipid head groups probably do not contribute significantly to the surface potential of channels. The negative surface potential might arise from aspartate or glutamate residues; it might also arise from sugars bearing carboxylate, phosphate, or sulfate groups. Most intrinsic plasma membrane proteins are glycosylated on their extracellular faces. All known subunits of electrically excitable Na^+ and Ca^{2+} channels, except for the αl and β subunits of the skeletal muscle Ca^{2+} channel, are glycosylated to a level of 20–40% by weight. The dominant acidic sugar in the α subunit of Na^+ channels is sialic acid in many (60), but not all (42), cases.

Anomalous Mole-Fraction Effects

For a channel with a unique saturable binding site, single-channel currents for mixtures of permeant ions could be described as the weighted sum (according to the mole fraction) of the current due to each individual ion: if ions A and B, at a total concentration of C_t, are characterized by single-channel currents i_A and i_B, then the current in a solution of $[A] + [B] = C_t$ and $[A]/C_t = \mu_A$ is $i = i_A\mu_A + i_B(1 - \mu_A)$. For Ca^{2+} channels (4, 19, 41, 50, 84) and for some K^+ channels (36, 48), on the other hand, currents go through a minimum as μ_A is varied. Recent studies confirm this anomalous mole-fraction effect at the single-channel level (28, 36, 40); it is not restricted to voltage-dependent cation channels. Although there are alternative explanations involving allosteric effects (22, 63, 64, 88), the most commonly accepted explanation is that the permeant ions are interacting within the lumen of a single-file pore.

The anomalous mole-fraction effect exists, like the frank blockade described in the next section, when one ionic species occupies the channel and prevents another from permeating it. The interaction between the two ions is expected to depend on the electrochemical driving force for occupancy of the sites within the channel. In particular, for a given extramembrane concentration of $[A]$, the saturation of a binding site also depends on the Boltzmann factor given above, in which membrane potential plays a role. Thus, the presence of an observable anomalous mole-fraction effect is also expected to depend on the membrane potential (21, 40). Theoretical modeling of these effects yields good agreement with the data if there are two, or perhaps three, (see 82) binding sites for permeant ions within the Ca^{2+} channel. For K^+ channels, there clearly are at least two sites and probably more.

Na^+ channels are generally thought not to exhibit anomalous mole-fraction effects, and there appear to be few interactions among permeant ions within the batrachotoxin-modified channels that are studied with bilayer reconstitution (e.g. reference 43). As pointed out by Hille (53), however, anomalous mole-fraction effects may occur only at extremes of concentration that do not allow the appropriate measurements. It is clear, nonetheless, that permeability ratios P_K/P_{Na} and P_{NH4}/P_{Na} decrease as the intracellular K^+ and NH_4 concentrations increase, as though the Na^+ channel can hold at least two ions simultaneously (15a). This fact is also revealed by experiments cited below on blockade by inorganic ions (reviewed in reference 15). Thus all voltage-dependent cation channels probably have at least two ion-binding sites. Are they at similar points in either the primary sequence or the three-dimensional structure?

Blockade within the Channel by Inorganic Ions

Evidence for mutually interacting binding sites also comes from analysis of inorganic blocking ions. One description is that the blocking ion is very slightly permeant. It visits some or all of the same sites that the normally permeant ion visits, but it remains at these sites so long that normally permeant ions are excluded from them (67).

A key concept in the view of such effects is the fact that blockade has vastly different signatures in single-channel records, depending on the time scale of blockade (53, 125, 126). A ligand that binds tightly at equilibrium (K_D rather small) often does so because its rate constant k_- for dissociation is quite slow ($K_D = k_-/k_+$). A reasonable rate constant for inorganic ion binding, 10^9 $M^{-1}s^{-1}$, implies that a blocker whose K_D is 1 μM has an average lifetime $1/k_-$ of 1 ms. Lifetimes one hundred times greater than this would have kinetics that are not easily distinguished from those of the channel gating;

lifetimes one hundred times less than this would be so brief that they appear to decrease single-channel current rather than produce observable flickers.

How does one know that the blocking ion is (*a*) physically blocking the conduction pathway rather than (*b*) binding elsewhere on the channel protein to change gating or permeation mechanism (as apparently occurs for proton block of Ca^{2+} channels; references 100, 101)? The conclusion that a blocker binds within the conduction pathway is presently based on circumstantial rather than direct structural evidence. For instance, the rate constant for termination of the open channel is increased by the amount $[I]k_+$, where $[I]$ is the blocking ion concentration, and this relationship holds at the highest $[I]$ observable (a plateau in the rate could imply an indirect binding of the ion that changes gating kinetics). In some special cases, it is possible to show that the channel must be in its open conformation to allow the blocker to bind or dissociate (87). The blocked time $1/k/_-$ does not change with concentration. The blocking kinetics or equilibrium blockade depend on voltage, which suggests that the blocker binds within the membrane field.

The voltage dependence of blockade is informative when inorganic ions are used to probe the conduction pathway (121). The analysis can proceed by invoking the same voltage-dependent Boltzmann factor described above. Alternatively, the equilibrium dissociation constant K_D for the blocker-channel binding is determined by the free energy change $\Delta G^+{}_{bound} - \Delta G^+{}_{free}$ between the solution and the binding site. One term in this energy comes from the interaction between the field in the membrane and the charge on the ion and equals $zq\delta V$. The relationship between free energy change and equilibrium binding affinity thus implies that the affinity is changed by the factor $\exp(-zq\delta V/kT)$. Thus, if a monovalent blocking ion binds halfway through the membrane field and can leave only via the route of entry (the channel tapers past the binding site), one expects the equilibrium affinity for binding to vary by *e*-fold for each 12.5 mV change in potential (at 300° K, $kT = 25$ meV). If the voltage dependence is greater than *e*-fold per 25 mV, this is good evidence for a more complex mechanism (25). If the blocking ion can actually leave the site by continuing through the membrane, then the analysis may be complicated by the existence of an additional rate-limiting step (121).

Single-channel measurements have proven particularly useful for understanding the blockade of Ca^{2+} channels by inorganic ions (83, 93). Lansman & colleagues (66, 67, 120) have conducted a series of experiments on the blockade of current through single-ion channels by Cd^{2+}, Mg^{2+}, Ca^{2+}, by trivalent lanthanides (La^{3+}, Nd^{3+}, Gd^{3+}, Dy^{3+}, and Yb^{3+}), and by divalent transition metals (Zn^{2+}, Fe^{2+}, Co^{2+}, and Ni^{2+}). The trivalent lanthanides provide a convenient series of ions with graded radii, coordination numbers similar to Ca^{2+}, and similar preferences for binding to oxygen donor groups. As the unhydrated radius decreases (from 1.16 Å for La^{3+} to 0.99 Å for Yb^{3+}), the forward rate constant for blocking decreases by 20-fold.

Because the entry rate does not depend on voltage, Lansman suggests that an energy barrier within the membrane is not the rate-limiting step in binding. Instead, the rate-limiting step may be dehydration, whose rate decreases with radius in the lanthanide series (32). The lifetime of the ion at its binding site increases for smaller ions, but seems to approach a maximum for ions of radius equal to or smaller than Ca^{2+}. These results show that the binding site is likely to be different in structure from the simplest model, EGTA, and to involve interactions distinct from electrostatic interactions based on size.

Another observation that supports the picture of a blocker occluding the actual conduction pathway is *trans*-enhanced dissociation (78); the blocker competes for its binding site with permeant ions added from the opposite side of the membrane. *Trans*-enhanced dissociation has been observed for K^+ channels with several blocking ions including Cs^+ (1, 18), Na^+ (125, 126), and Ba^{2+} (117), as well as for H^+ blockade of Na^+ channels (15b).

A thorough series of experiments on blockade by inorganic ions has utilized Ba^{2+} at K^+ channels (13, 14, 17, 33, 87, 94, 95, 117). Ba^{2+} can leave the channel either to the internal or the external solution. The particular favored direction depends on several factors, including the membrane potential and the concentration of permeant ions on either side of the membrane. The latter effect occurs because of a complement to the *trans*-enhanced dissociation effect. It is most obvious in K^+ channels because they usually hold several permeant ions at once. By occupying sites that the blocking ion must visit in order to leave the channel (and thereby relieve the block), the permeant ions exert a *cis*-suppressed dissociation (called lock-in by Neyton & Miller, 94). Findings of this sort should be distinguished from the effects of the ions on the gating equilibria (13, 94). Because the high-conductance K^+ channel allows measurements over a wide range of ionic conditions, it is possible to investigate the concentration- and voltage-dependence of *cis*-suppressed dissociation. The conclusion is that at least three permeant ions, in addition to a blocking ion, can occupy the channel simultaneously.

At Na^+ channels, inorganic blockers reveal the existence of at least two binding sites, for such blockers have different effects when added from different sides of the membrane (43, 65, 102). The site accessible from the external solution seems to lie within the membrane field. Recent studies suggest that Mg^{2+} can reach this site from the intracellular solution as well (102). In some studies the internal site seems to be outside the field and may be near the binding site for the inactivation gate; in other studies (15a,b), a voltage-dependent site is also accessible from the internal solution.

Blockade within the Channel by Organic Ions and Local Anesthetics

Tertiary and quaternary ammonium ions have diameters (4–8 Å) similar to those of hydrated cations. The clinically useful local anesthetics, which are mostly tertiary amines, are not the molecules of choice for mapping out permeation pathways. Terms such as the modulated receptor (52, 55) and the guarded receptor (110) emphasize that these drugs can reach their binding sites via at least two pathways—the external solution and the membrane—and when the channel is in several distinct states (52, 54).

Quaternary ammonium derivatives of these molecules, on the other hand, constitute excellent probes of open channels. They typically reach a blocking site on the cytoplasmic face of a Na^+ and K^+ channel only when the channel is open, like a plug in a drain (8, 11, 38). These channel blockers are characterized by many of the phenomena that apply to inorganic blockers. Their binding is voltage-dependent, often more strongly with divalent than with monovalent blockers (30, 86, 118). Their binding kinetics depend linearly and simply on the concentration; they exhibit *trans*-enhanced dissociation at both K^+ (9, 78) and Na^+ (20, 104) channels. On the other hand, the quaternary ammonium blocking ions themselves typically can reach their binding sites from only one side of the membrane and are totally impermeant. Series of related quaternary ammonium blocking compounds have traditionally been used in a pharmacological approach to mapping out the permeation pathway. Site-directed mutagenesis will enable "reverse pharmacology" in which the channel itself is modified while just one or a few compounds are studied.

K^+ CHANNELS One promising site for such studies is the cytoplasmic surface of K^+ channels. The existing data with various mono- and bis-quaternary ammonium derivatives indicate that this inner mouth may be about 12 Å in diameter for the squid axon delayed rectifier (38, 39), a K^+ channel from sarcoplasmic reticulum (86), and a Ca^{2+}-activated K^+ channel from T tubules (118).

Externally applied tetraethylammonium (TEA) blocks almost all K^+ channels much more strongly than do other quaternary ammonium ions (see, for instance, 118). Nonetheless K^+ channels display a wide spectrum of affinities for this blockade. The first fruits of reverse pharmacology are ripening. MacKinnon & Yellen (81) suggest, on the basis of site-directed mutagenesis on the S5-S6 loop of *Shaker* channels, that a single threonine side chain governs a substantial portion of this variability within the class of channels homologous to *Shaker*. Channels in which threonine is replaced by tyrosine, lysine, arginine, or asparagine at a particular position lack a high-affinity blockade by external TEA. The result recalls the important role played by hydroxyl-containing residues in the binding site for quaternary ammonium open-channel blockers at the nicotinic receptor (27, 71).

Most K^+ channels can close even while blocked by external TEA (31, 107–109). The exception is an inactivating, voltage-dependent K^+ channel of human lymphocytes (45). For this channel, TEA appears to act as a pure open-channel blocker: the channel cannot close when the blocker is bound. Furthermore, the blocker cannot bind to closed channels, i.e. there is no closed-blocked state. This interaction between the gates and a channel blocker gives rise to fascinating kinetic properties. At the single-channel level, the sum of all the open intervals remains constant. Single openings in the blocker's absence become lengthier bursts of openings in the blocker's presence. At the macroscopic level, relaxations are lengthened. The quantitative analysis of such kinetic effects provides a sensitive assay for the blocker-channel interaction (27, 71).

Na^+ CHANNELS The best studied quaternary ammonium channel blocker of Na^+ channels is QX-314 (37, 111; but see 29). Hille (53) has pointed out the distinction between smaller organic Na^+ channel blockers, such as QX-314, that allow gating to proceed, if with altered rates, and those so large [N-methylstrychnine, pancuronium, and thiazin dyes (12, 20, 104, 124)] that their presence within the channel completely hinders the operation of the gates. In a reverse pharmacological approach to Na^+ channel structure, I suggest the use of channels mutated or broken into two chains to eliminate inactivation, probed with one small blocker, such as QX-314, and with one large blocker, such as N-methylstrychnine.

Ca^+ CHANNELS The clinically useful organic Ca^{2+} channel blockers, like the local anesthetics, were designed to reach their receptors from the extracellular solution and to interact with both open and inactivated states of the channel. For a pharmacologically simple probe of the open Ca^{2+} channel, one should again turn to quaternary ammonium analogues, for instance the verapamil derivative D-890. This compound blocks open Ca^{2+} channels on the cytoplasmic surface analogously to the way quaternary ammonium ions block open Na^+ and K^+ channels (49, 70, 99).

Blockade by Guanidinium and Peptide Toxins

Electrically excitable Na^+ channels have several partially distinct binding sites for peptide toxins, lipid soluble toxins, and guanidinium toxins (23, 112). None of these sites is thought to lie within the permeation pathway. Interestingly, however, site-directed monoclonal antibodies and site-directed mutants have revealed that the binding sites for two of the best-characterized toxins, scorpion toxin and tetrodotoxin, are partially on the putative extracellular loop between the S5 and S6 membrane-spanning domains (96, 114). Extracellular blockade of neuronal Na^+ channels by tetrodotoxin (TTX) is voltage-dependent only for the case of channels modified by batrachotoxin, but this voltage dependence is thought to arise from a conformational change rather than from binding within the channel (43, 91, 122). Yet many workers think that TTX binds at the extracellular mouth of the channel (90). Evidence for this view is the similarity between the properties of Na^+ channels that are *O*-methylated by trimethyloxonium and those that are naturally resistant to TTX. Both have reduced single-channel conductance and reduced sensitivity to open-channel block by extracellular Ca^{2+} (105, 106, 119, 123). Conversely, the toxins and Ca^{2+} both protect against *O*-methylation (123). Single-hit kinetics with TMO suggest that a single carboxylate group is involved (but see 26). This may be glutamate-387 since the E387Q mutation decreases TTX sensitivity by $\sim 10^3$ (96). The mutant has altered macroscopic current-voltage properties; however, single-channel conductances were not reported.

It now appears that the region where charybdotoxin (CTX) binds to some K^+ channels is homologous to the region where TTX binds to the Na^+ channel (76, 79, 96). The evidence favors the view that this interaction occurs at the extracellular mouth of the channel and that charybdotoxin is physically plugging the channel, like the simpler local anesthetics described above. The interaction between charybdotoxin and a high-conductance Ca^{2+}-activated K^+ channel is well-described by a simple bimolecular binding; the association rate is sevenfold faster for the open than for the closed channel (5). Furthermore, the dissociation rate constant is increased as the intracellular concentration of permeant ions (K^+ or Rb^+), but not of impermeant ions (Na^+, Li^+, Cs^+, or arginine) is increased. This acceleration of dissociation is enhanced by membrane depolarization at a rate of *e*-fold/28 mV, as though the field is concentrating the permeant ions at a site near the extracellular mouth of the channel where they compete with charybdotoxin binding. TEA, which blocks the pore from the external solution, competitively prevents the binding of CTX at the *Shaker* K^+ channels (C. Miller, R. MacKinnon, personal communication). These facts motivated the site-directed mutagenesis experiments of MacKinnon & colleagues (76, 79, 81), which located the region between the S5 and S6 loops as part of the binding site for charybdotoxin.

At the risk of simplifying the structural picture too greatly, I therefore suggest that all the available evidence points to the loop between helices 5 and 6 as part of the extracellular binding site for toxins at two well-understood channels, Na^+ and K^+, and that these regions are quite close to the conduction pathway itself. These data do not yet bear directly on the hypothesis (44, 46, 47) that the channel protein crosses the membrane twice, perhaps with β strands, in this region. The loop between helices S5 and S6 has not yet been explored for Ca^{2+} channels.

Blockade by the Inactivation Flap

It has long been known that Na^+ channels have an intracellular region where proteolysis removes inactivation. This helped motivate the ball-and-chain model for inactivation (10) in which a part of the channel protein actually occludes ion flow through the open channel. I prefer the term flap to describe this region. If this model is correct, then the receptor for the flap is at the intracellular mouth of the channel. Because inactivation has little or no voltage dependence, the receptive region may lie only a small fraction of the way through the field (3).

The flap itself has been tentatively identified and seems to consist of the intracellular region between homology domains III and IV. Cuts in the primary sequence here, but not between domains II and III, remove inactivation (113); antibodies to this region block inactivation (116); and mutations of lysine to asparagine residues in this region accelerate inactivation (92).

Certain transient K^+ channels display similar effects. Inactivation is nearly independent of voltage, which suggests a ball-and-chain model in which the ball binds at the internal mouth of the channel (128). Mutations at the amino terminus of the protein abolish inactivation (2, 56, 57, 59) and thus the amino terminus of the K^+ channel's single homology domain seems to act like the flap between domains III and IV of the Na^+ channel. Hoshi et al (57) have synthesized the peptide corresponding to the amino-terminal sequence and applied it to *Shaker* K^+ channels mutated to remove the amino-terminus inactivation flap. This soluble version of the flap still caused inactivation at concentrations in the micromolar range. One may hope that site-directed mutations will identify the receptive region for the flap; will the same region be found for Na^+, Ca^{2+}, and K^+ channels?

Streaming Potentials

In a streaming potential experiment, an osmotic pressure gradient P_{osm} forces a water flux through open channels. The water flux drags permeant cations along, but anions remain behind, which leads to a charge separation and therefore to a potential difference across the membrane. This potential difference is most sensitively revealed as a change in reversal potential V_{str} compared with the value in the absence of an osmotic pressure gradient. The number N of water molecules associated with a single permeant cation is given by $N = (zFV_{str})/(WP_{osm})$ (75, 103). The measurements are performed with the largest possible cation, so that it completely fills the pore; N is then interpreted as the number of water molecules in front and back of the permeant ion, and it gives an idea about the length of the narrowest region. For the high-conductance K^+ channel, $N = 2$–3, and the narrowest region of the pore seems to be < 10 Å long (86). The theory does not rule out the presence of several equally narrow regions within the same channel.

Where and What are the Binding Sites?

WHERE? Efforts are now under way in many laboratories to localize the binding sites described here. The simplest question is whether the various sites are (*a*) within the membrane-spanning regions of the channel, or (*b*) in the protrusions into the extracellular and intracellular space. The first possibility presumably applies to those sites that are sensitive to the membrane field. A slightly tilted α-helix, with four amino-acid residues per turn, would have four or five turns exposed to the channel at intervals of about 5.4 Å. If each of these turns constitutes a distinct binding site for permeant or blocking cations, this would provide enough sites even to account for K^+ channels. The distance between turns is small enough to account for the postulated mutual repulsions included in several theories of permeation (72). The voltage-dependent local anesthetic-binding sites are indeed within the M2 membrane spanning region of nicotinic receptors (27, 71). In this example, the site is composed of hydroxyl side chains, but cationic blockers of voltage-dependent channels might bind to carboxylate side chains.

Other information about the importance of the membrane regions alone comes from information on channel-forming peptides. Peptides have been synthesized that contain only the uncharged amino acids of the putative M2 membrane-spanning region from the *Torpedo* ACh receptor δ subunit, flanked by two positively and one negatively charged residues from the putative extramembrane regions. These peptides presumably form homo-oligomeric aggregates in the membrane. The resulting channels show cation selectivity (97). In another case, nonselective cation channels were formed from a 22-mer corresponding to the S3 region of the electrically excitable Na^+ channel, including three flanking acidic groups (one of them poorly conserved) (98). Indeed, cation-selective channels are formed even if the peptides lack the flanking charged regions (69), thus favoring the membrane-spanning regions of the channel as binding sites. Two additional points, however, favor protrusions into the extracellular and intracellular space as binding sites. First, the putative extramembrane regions of channels have marked net charges (negative for most known cation channels). Second, the cation-selective nicotinic acetylcholine receptor channel is thought to be lined by the M2 helix, which is rich in hydroxyl-containing side chains. The homologous regions of the anion-selective GABA and glycine receptors are similar, which implies that charge selectivity occurs elsewhere.

Voltage-independent binding sites for cationic blockers could lie at the membrane surface or just a few residues away from it, like the three rings of charge identified in reference 58 (1, 2, and 5 residues from the M2 region). Charybdotoxin binding is influenced by groups 5, 10, and 14 residues from the S5 helix, and 5 and 8 residues from the S6 helix (76, 79). One of these, threonine-449, also affects blockade by external TEA and single-channel conductance (81). The glu residue that influences TTX binding to a Na^+ channel is 14 residues from the S6 helix (96). Many researchers now think that the S5-S6 loop actually lines the channel, but none of the sites thus far identified in this region is voltage-dependent.

WHAT? There are two (perhaps overlapping) views on the nature of the binding sites. (*a*) The sites could be formed from individual amino-acid side chains that make highly specific contacts with permeant ions and with blocking molecules. (*b*) The sites could be annuli whose properties are averaged from the four or five side chains projecting into the channel's lumen at a given depth. More specifically, one might ask how many subunits must contribute to a carboxylate or hydroxyl side chain to form a high-affinity binding site for Ba^{2+} within a K^+ channel? It is probably fruitless to approach such a question from first principles. Happily, the experimental approach to this question—and to many others presented in this chapter—using site-directed mutagenesis, is straightforward and now under way in several laboratories. Descriptions involving high-resolution structural techniques such as X-ray diffraction, however, are still several years away. When available, they will provide decisive tests for much of what has been deduced.

ACKNOWLEDGMENTS

I thank R. Aldrich and R. MacKinnon for sharing their work prior to publication, P. Lazarow for challenges on rectification, and N. Davidson, B. Hille, T. Begenisich, and members of my research group for many helpful comments. Preparation of this review was supported by grants from the Klingenstein Foundation, the Muscular Dystrophy Association, and the National Institutes of Health (GM-29836 and NS-11756).

Literature Cited

1. Adelman, W., French, R. L. 1978. Blocking of the squid axon potassium channel by caesium ions. *J. Physiol.* 276:13–25
2. Aldrich, R. W. 1990. Biophysical and molecular mechanisms of potassium channel gating. *Biophys. J.* 57:195a
3. Aldrich, R. W., Stevens, C. F. 1987. Voltage-dependent gating of single sodium channels from mammalian neuroblastoma cells. *J. Neurosci.* 7:418–31
4. Almers, W. A., McCleskey, E. W. 1984. Non-selective conductance in calcium channels of frog muscle: calcium selectivity in a single-file pore. *J. Physiol.* 353:585–608
5. Anderson, C. A., MacKinnon, R., Smith, C., Miller, C. 1988. Charybdotoxin block of single Ca^{2+}-activated K^+ channels: Effects of channel gating, voltage, and ionic strength. *J. Gen. Physiol.* 91:317–33
6. Andersen, O. S. 1989. Kinetics of ion movement mediated by carriers and channels. *Meth. Enzym.* 171:62–112
7. Apell, H. J., Bamberg, E., Lauger, P. 1979. Effects of surface charge on the conductance of the gramicidin channel. *Biochim. Biophys. Acta* 552:369–78
8. Armstrong, C. M. 1966. Time course of TEA^+-induced anomalous rectification in squid giant axons. *J. Gen. Physiol.* 50:491–503
9. Armstrong, C. M. 1971. Interaction of tetraethylammonium ion derivatives with the potassium channels of giant axons. *J. Gen. Physiol.* 58:413–37
10. Armstrong, C. M., Bezanilla, F. 1977. Inactivation of the sodium channel. II. Gating current experiments. *J. Gen. Physiol.* 70:567–90
11. Armstrong, C. M., Binstock, L. 1965. Anomalous rectification in the squid giant axon injected with tetraethylammonium chloride. *J. Gen. Physiol.* 48: 859–72
12. Armstrong, C. M., Croop, R. S. 1982. Simulation of Na channel inactivation by thiazin dyes. *J. Gen. Physiol.* 80:641–62
13. Armstrong, C. M., Swenson, R. P.,

Taylor, S. 1982. Block of squid axon K channels by internally and externally applied barium ions. *J. Gen. Physiol.* 80:663–82

14. Armstrong, C. M., Taylor, S. R. 1980. Interaction of barium ions with potassium channels in squid giant axons. *Biophys. J.* 30:473–88
15. Begenisich, T. 1987. Molecular properties of ion permeation through sodium channels. *Annu. Rev. Biophys. Biophys. Chem.* 16:247–63

15a. Begenisich, T., Cahalan, M. 1980. Sodium channel permeation in squid axons. II: Non-independence and current-voltage relations. *J. Physiol.* 307:243–57

15b. Begenisich, T., Danke, M. 1983. Hydrogen ion block of the sodium pore in squid giant axons. *J. Gen. Physiol.* 82:599–618

16. Bell, J. E., Miller, C. 1984. Effects of phospholipid surface charge on ion conduction in the K^+ channel of sarcoplasmic reticulum. *Biophys. J.* 45:279–88
17. Benham, C. D., Bolton, T. B., Lang, R. J., Takewaki, T. 1985. The mechanism of action of Ba^{2+} and TEA on single Ca^{2+}-activated K^+-channels in arterial and intestinal smooth muscle cell membranes. *Pflügers Arch.* 403:120–27
18. Bezanilla, F., Armstrong, C. M. 1972. Negative conductance caused by entry of sodium and cesium ion into the potassium channels of squid axons. *J. Gen. Physiol.* 60:588–608
19. Byerly, L., Chase, P. B., Stimers, J. R. 1985. Permeation and interaction of divalent cations in calcium channels of snail neurons. *J. Gen. Physiol.* 85:491–518
20. Cahalan, M. D., Almers, W. 1979. Block of sodium conductance and gating current in squid giant axons poisoned with quaternary strychnine. *Biophys. J.* 27:57–74
21. Campbell, D. L., Rasmusson, R. L., Strauss, H. C. 1988. Theoretical study of the voltage and concentration-dependence of the anomalous mole fraction effect in single calcium channels—new insights into the characterization of multi-ion channels. *Biophys. J.* 54:945–54
22. Carbone, E., Lux, H. D. 1988. Omega-conotoxin blockade distinguishes Ca from Na permeable states in neuronal calcium channels. *Pflügers Arch.* 413: 14–22
23. Catterall, W. A. 1980. Neurotoxins that act on voltage-sensitive sodium channels in excitable membranes. *Annu. Rev. Pharmacol. Toxicol.* 20:15–43
24. Catterall, W. A. 1988. Structure and function of voltage-sensitive ion channels. *Science* 242:50–61
25. Cecchi, X., Wolff, D., Alvarez, O., Latorre, R. 1987. Mechanisms of Cs^+ blockade in a Ca^{2+}-activated K^+ channel from smooth muscle. *Biophys. J.* 52:707–16
26. Chabala, L. D., Andersen, O. S. 1988. Evidence for a net negative charge near the guanidinium toxin binding-site and the entrance to rat-brain sodium-channels. *FASEB J.* 2:534
27. Charnet, P., Labarca, C., Leonard, R. J., Vogelaar, N. J., Czyzyk, L., et al. 1990. An open-channel blocker interacts with adjacent turns of α-helices in the nicotinic acetylcholine receptor. *Neuron* 4:87–95
28. Chesnoy-Marchais, D. 1985. Kinetic properties and selectivity of calcium-permeable single channels in *Aplysia* neurones. *J. Physiol.* 367:457–88
29. Cooper, E. C., Agnew, W. S. 1989. Reconstituted voltage-sensitive sodium channels from eel electroplax-activation of permeability by quaternary lidocaine, N-bromoacetamide, and N-bromosuccinimide. *J. Membr. Biol.* 111:253–64
30. Danko, M., Smith-Maxwell, C., McKinney, L., Begenisich, T. 1986. Block of sodium channels by internal mono- and divalent guanidinium analogues. *Biophys. J.* 49:509–19
31. DeCoursey, T. E., Chandy, K. G., Gupta, S., Cahalan, M. D. 1987. Two types of potassium channels in murine T lymphocytes. *J. Gen. Physiol.* 89:379–404
32. Diebler, H., Eigen, M., Ilgenfritz, G., Maas, G., Winkler, R. 1969. Kinetics and mechanism of reactions of main group metal ions with biological carriers. *Pure Appl. Chem.* 20:93–115
33. Eaton, D. C., Brodwick, M. S. 1980. Effect of barium on the potassium conductance of squid axons. *J. Gen. Physiol.* 75:727–50
34. Eisenman, G., Dani, J. A. 1987. An introduction to molecular architecture and permeability of ion channels. *Annu. Rev. Biophys. Biophys. Chem.* 16:205–26
35. Eisenman, G., Horn, R. 1983. Ionic selectivity revisited: the role of kinetic and equilibrium processes in ion permeation through channels. *J. Memb. Biol.* 76:197–225
36. Eisenman, G., Latorre, R., Miller, C. 1986. Multi-ion conduction and selectiv-

ity in the high-conductance Ca^{2+}-activated K^+ channel from skeletal muscle. *Biophys. J.* 50:1025–34

37. Frazier, D. T., Narahashi, T., Yamada, M. 1970. The site of the action and active form of local anesthetics. Experiments with quaternary compounds. *J. Pharmacol. Exp. Ther.* 171:45–51
38. French, R. J., Shoukimas, J. J. 1981. Blockage of squid axon potassium conductance by internal tetra-N-alkylammonium ions of various sizes. *Biophys. J.* 34:271–91
39. French, R. J., Shoukimas, J. J. 1985. An ion's view of the potassium channel. The structure of the permeation pathway as sensed by a variety of blocking ions. *J. Gen. Physiol.* 85:669–98
40. Friel, D. D., Tsien, R. W. 1989. Voltage-gated calcium channels: direct observation of the anomalous mole fraction effect at the single-channel level. *Proc. Natl. Acad. Sci. USA* 86:5207–11
41. Garnier, D., Rougier, O., Gargouil, Y. M., Coraboeuf, E. 1969. Analyse electrophysiologique du plateau des responses myocardiques: Mise en evidence d'un courant lent entrant en absence d'ions bivalents. *Pflügers Arch.* 313:321–42
42. Gordon, D., Merrick, D., Wollner, D. A., Catterall, W. A. 1988. Biochemical properties of sodium channels in a wide range of excitable tissues studied with site-directed antibodies. *Biochemistry* 27:7032–38
43. Green, W. N., Weiss, L. B., Andersen, O. S. 1987. Batrachotoxin-modified sodium channels in planar lipid bilayers. *J. Gen. Physiol.* 89:841–72
44. Greenblatt, R., Blatt, Y., Montal, M. 1985. The structure of the voltage-sensitive sodium channel. Inferences derived from computer-aided analysis of the *Electrophorus electricus* channel primary structure. *FEBS Lett.* 193:125–34
45. Grissmer, S., Cahalan, M. 1989. TEA prevents inactivation while blocking open K^+ channels in human T lymphocytes. *Biophys. J.* 55:203–6
46. Guy, H. R. 1989. Models of voltage- and transmitter activated membrane channels based on their amino acid sequences. In *Monovalent Cations in Biological Systems,* ed. C. A. Pasternak, pp. 32–58. Cleveland: CRC 32–58
47. Guy, H., Seetharamulu, P. 1986. Molecular model of the action potential sodium channel. *Proc. Natl. Acad. Sci. USA* 83:508–12
48. Hagiwara, S. 1983. In *Membrane Potential-Dependent Ion Channels in Cell Membrane. Phylogenetic and Developmental Approaches,* pp. 70–75. New York: Raven
49. Hescheler, J., Pelzer, D., Trube, G., Trautwein, W. 1982. Does the organic calcium channel blocker D600 act from inside or outside on the cardiac cell membrane. *Pflügers Arch.* 393:287–91
50. Hess, P., Tsien, R. W. 1984. Mechanism of ion permeation through calcium channels. *Nature* 309:453–56
51. Hille, B. 1975. Ionic selectivity of Na and K channels of nerve membranes. In *Membranes: A series of advances, Lipid bilayers and biological membranes: dynamic properties,* ed. G. Eisenman, 3:255–323. New York: Dekker
52. Hille, B. 1977. Local anesthetics: hydrophilic and hydrophobic pathways for the drug-receptor reaction. *J. Gen. Physiol.* 69:497–515.
53. Hille, B. 1984. In *Ionic Channels in Excitable Membranes*. Sunderland, MA: Sinauer
54. Hondeghem, L. M., Katzung, B. G. 1977. Time- and voltage-dependent interactions of antiarrhythmic drugs with cardiac sodium channels. *Biochim. Biophys. Acta* 472:373–98
55. Hondeghem, L. M., Katzung, B. G. 1984. Antiarrhythmic agents: the modulated receptor mechanism of action of sodium and calcium channel-blocking drugs. *Annu. Rev. Pharmacol. Toxicol.* 24:387–423
56. Hoshi, T., Zagotta, W. N., Aldrich, R. W. 1989. Mutations in the amino terminal variable domain alter inactivation of *Shaker B* potassium channels in *Xenopus* oocytes. *Soc. Neurosci. Abstr.* 15: 338
57. Hoshi, T., Zagotta, W. N., Aldrich, R. W. 1990. A synthetic peptide with *Shaker B* sequence restores inactivation in mutant channels that do not inactivate. *Soc. Neurosci. Abstr.* 16:4
58. Imoto, K., Busch, C., Sakmann, B., Mishina, M., Konno, T., et al. 1988. Rings of negatively charged amino acids determine the acetylcholine receptor channel conductance. *Nature* 335:645–48
59. Isacoff, E. Y., Jan, Y. N., Jan, L. Y. 1990. Structure-function studies on the *Shaker* K^+ channel. *Biophys. J.* 57:209a
60. James, W. M., Agnew, W. S. 1987. Multiple oligosaccharide chains in the voltage-sensitive Na channel from *Electrophorus electricus:* evidence for α-2,8-linked polysialic acid. *Biochem. Biophys. Res. Comm.* 148:817–26
61. Deleted in proof

62. Khodorov, B. I. 1985. Batrachotoxin as a tool to study voltage-sensitive sodium channels of excitable membranes. *Prog. Biophys. Mol. Biol.* 45:57–148
63. Kostyuk, P. G., Mironov, S. L. 1986. Some predictions concerning the calcium channel model with different conformal states. *Gen. Physiol. Biophys.* 6:649–59
64. Kostyuk, P. G., Mironov, S. L. Shuba, Y. M. 1983. Two ion-selecting filters in the calcium channel of the somatic membrane of mollusc neurons. *J. Membr. Biol.* 76:83–93
65. Krueger, B. K., Worley, J. F. III, French, R. J. 1986. Block of sodium channels in planar lipid bilayers by guanidinium toxins and calcium. *Ann. NY Acad. Sci.* 479:257–68
66. Lansman, J. B. 1990. Blockade of current through single calcium channels by trivalent lanthanide cations. *J. Gen. Physiol.* 95:679–96
67. Lansman, J. B., Hess, P., Tsien, R. W. 1986. Blockade of current through single calcium channels by Cd^{2+}, Mg^{2+}, and Ca^{2+}: Voltage and concentration dependence of calcium entry into the pore. *J. Gen. Physiol.* 88:321–47
68. Latorre, R., Miller, C. 1983. Conduction and selectivity in potassium channels. *J. Memb. Biol.* 71:11–30
69. Lear, J. D., Wasserman, Z. R., DeGrado, W. F. 1988. Synthetic amphiphilic peptide models for protein ion channels. *Science* 240:1177–81
70. Leblanc, N., Hume, J. R. 1989. D 600 block of L-type Ca^{2+} channel in vascular smooth muscle cells: comparison with permanently charges derivitive, D 890. *Am. J. Physiol.* 257:C689–95
71. Leonard, R. J., Labarca, C., Charnet, P., Davidson, N., Lester, H. A. 1988. Evidence that the M2 membrane-spanning region lines the ion channel pore of the nicotinic receptor. *Science* 242:1578–81
72. Levitt, D. G. 1978. Electrostatic calculations for an ion channel. II. Kinetic behavior of the gramicidin A channel. *Biophys. J.* 22:221–48
73. Levitt, D. G. 1984. Kinetics of movement in narrow channels. *Curr. Top. Membr. Trans.* 21:181–197
74. Levitt, D. G. 1986. Interpretation of biological ion channel flux data- reaction-rate versus continuum theory. *Annu. Rev. Biophys. Biophys. Chem.* 15:29–57
75. Levitt, D. G., Ellias, S. R., Hautman, J. M. 1978. Number of water molecules coupled to the transport of sodium, potassium and hydrogen ions via gramicidin, nonactin or valinomycin. *Biochim. Biophys. Acta* 512:436–51
76. MacKinnon, R., Heginbotham, L., Abramson, T. 1990. Mapping the receptor site for a pore-blocking potassium channel inhibitor. *Neuron.* In press
77. MacKinnon, R., Latorre, R., Miller, C. 1989. Role of surface electrostatics in the operation of a high-conductance Ca^{2+}-activated K^+ channel. *Biochemistry* 28:8092–99
78. MacKinnon, R., Miller, C. 1988. Mechanism of charybdotoxin inhibition of Ca^{++}-dependent K^+ channels. Specific competition by K^+. *J. Gen. Physiol.* 91:335–49
79. MacKinnon, R., Miller, C. 1989. Mutant potassium channels with altered binding of charybdotoxin, a pore-blocking peptide inhibitor. *Science* 245: 1382–85
80. MacKinnon, R., Miller, C. 1989. Functional modification of a Ca^{2+}-activated K^+ channel by trimethyloxonium. *Biochemistry* 28:8087–92
81. MacKinnon, R., Yellen, G. 1990. Mutations affecting blockade and ion permeation in voltage-activated potassium channels. *Science.* 250:276–79
82. Marban, E., Yue, D. T. 1989. Ion permeation in L-type Ca channels: evidence for triple-ion occupancy in the conduction pathway. *Biophys. J.* 55:594a
83. Matsuda, H. 1986. Sodium conductance of calcium channels of guinea pig ventricular cells induced by removal of external calcium ions. *Pflügers Arch.* 407:465–75
84. McDonald, T. F., Cavalie, A., Trautwein, W., Pelzer, D. 1986. Voltage-dependent properties of macroscopic and elementary calcium channel currents in guinea pig ventricular myocytes. *Pflügers Arch.* 406:437–48
85. McLaughlin, S. 1989. The electrostatic properties of membranes. *Annu. Rev. Biophys. Biophys. Chem.* 18:113–36
86. Miller, C. 1982. Bis-quaternary ammonium blockers as structural probes of the sarcoplasmic reticulum K^+ channel. *J. Gen. Physiol.* 79:869–91
87. Miller, C., Latorre, R., Reisin, I. 1987. Coupling of voltage-dependent gating and Ba^{++} block in the high conductance, Ca^{++}-activated K^+ channel. *J. Gen. Physiol.* 90:427–49
88. Mironov, S. L. 1988. In *Calcium and Ion Channel Modulation.* ed. A. D. Grinnell, A. Armstrong, M. B. Jackson, pp. 43–51. New York: Plenum
89. Moczydlowski, E., Alvarez, O., Vergara, C., Latorre, R. 1985. Role of surface electrostatics in the operation of a

high-conductance Ca^{2+}-activated K^+ channel. *J. Membr. Biol.* 83:273–82

90. Moczydlowski, E., Garber, S. S., Miller, C. 1984. Batrachotoxin-activated Na^+ channels in planar lipid bilayers. *J. Gen. Physiol.* 84:665–86
91. Moczydlowski, E., Hall, S., Garber, S. S., Strichartz, G., Miller, C. 1984. Voltage-dependent blockade of muscle Na^+ channels by guanidinium toxins. *J. Gen. Physiol.* 84:687–704
92. Moorman, J. R., Joho, R. H., Kirsch, G. E., Brown, A. M. 1990. Point mutations in the region linking domains II and III which speed inactivation of Na currents. *Biophys J.* 57:296a
93. Nelson, M. T., French, R. J., Krueger, B. K. 1984. Voltage-dependent calcium channels from brain incorporated into planar lipid bilayers. *Nature* 308:77–81
94. Neyton, J., Miller, C. 1988. Discrete Ba^{2+} block as a probe of ion occupancy and pore structure in the high-conductance Ca^{2+}-activated K^+ channel. *J. Gen. Physiol.* 92:569–86
95. Neyton, J., Miller, C. 1988. Potassium blocks barium permeation through a calcium-activated potassium channel. *J. Gen. Physiol.* 92:549–67
96. Noda, M., Suzuki, H., Numa, S., Stuhmer, W. 1989. A single point mutation confers tetrodotoxin and saxitoxin insensitivity on the sodium channel II. *FEBS Lett.* 259:213–16
97. Oiki, S., Danho, W., Madison, V., Montal, M. 1988. M2 δ, a candidate for the structure lining the ionic channel of the nicotinic cholinergic receptor. *Proc. Natl. Acad. Sci. USA* 85:8703–7
98. Oiki, S., Danho, W., Montal, M. 1988. Channel protein engineering: synthetic 22-mer peptide from the primary structure of the voltage-sensitive sodium channel forms ionic channels in lipid bilayers. *Proc. Natl. Acad. Sci. USA* 85:2393–97
99. Pelzer, D., Trautwein, W., McDonald, T. F. 1982. Calcium channel block and recovery from block in mammalian ventricular muscle treated with organic channel inhibitors. *Pflügers Arch.* 394: 97–105
100. Pietrobon, D., Prod'hom, B., Hess, P. 1988. Conformational changes associated with ion permeation in L-type calcium channels. *Nature* 333:373–76
101. Prod'hom, B., Pietrobon, D., Hess, P. 1987. Direct measurements of proton transfer rates to a group controlling the dihydropyridine-sensitive Ca^{2+} channel. *Nature* 329:243–46
102. Pusch, M., Conti, F., Stuhmer, W. 1989. Intracellular magnesium blocks sodium outward currents in a voltage-dependent and dose-dependent manner. *Biophys. J.* 55:1267–71
103. Rosenberg, P. A., Finkelstein, A. 1978. Interaction of ions and water in gramicidin A channels: Streaming potentials across lipid bilayer membranes. *J. Gen. Physiol.* 72:327–40
104. Shapiro, B. I. 1977. Effects of strychnine on the sodium conductance of the frog node of Ranvier. *J. Gen. Physiol.* 69:915–26
105. Sigworth, F. J., Spalding, B. C. 1980. Chemical modification reduce the conductance of sodium channels in nerve. *Nature* 283:293–95

105a. Smith-Maxwell, C., Begenisich, T. 1987. Guadidium analogues as probes of the squid axon sodium pore. Evidence for internal surface charges. *J. Gen. Physiol.* 90:361–74

106. Spalding, B. C. 1980. Properties of toxin-resistant sodium channels produced by chemical modification in frog skeletal muscle. *J. Physiol.* 305:485–500
107. Spruce, A. E., Standen, N. B., Stanfield, P. R. 1987. The action of external tetraethylammonium ions on unitary delayed rectifier potassium channels of frog skeletal muscle. *J. Physiol.* 393: 467–78
108. Standen, N. B., Stanfield, P. R., Ward, T. A. 1985. Properties of single potassium channels in vesicles formed from the sarcolemma of frog skeletal muscle. *J. Physiol.* 364:339–58
109. Stanfield, P. R. 1983. Tetraethylammonium ions and the potassium permeability of excitable cells. *Rev. Physiol. Biochem. Pharmacol.* 97:1–67
110. Starmer, C. F., Courtney, K. R. 1986. Modeling ion channel blockade at guarded binding sites: application to tertiary drugs. *Am. J. Physiol.* 251:H848–56
111. Strichartz, G. R. 1973. The inhibition of sodium currents in myelinated nerve of quaternary ammonium derivatives of lidocaine. *J. Gen. Physiol.* 62:35–37
112. Strichartz, G. R., Rando, T., Wang, G. K. 1987. An integrated view of the molecular toxinology of sodium channel gating in excitable cells. *Annu. Rev. Neurosci.* 10:237–67
113. Stuhmer, W., Conti, F., Suzuki, H., Wang, X., Noda, M., et al. 1989. Structural parts involved in activation of the sodium channel. *Nature* 339:597–603
114. Thomsen, W. J., Catterall, W. A. 1989. Localization of the receptor site for α-scorpion toxins by antibody mapping: implications for sodium channel topolo-

gy. *Proc. Natl. Acad. Sci. USA* 86: 10161

115. Tsien, R. W., Hess, P., McCleskey, E. W., Rosenberg, R. L. 1987. Calcium channels—mechanisms of selectivity, permeation, and block. *Annu. Rev. Biophys. Biophys. Chem.* 16:265–90
116. Vassilev, P., Scheuer, T., Catterall, W. A. 1989. Inhibition of inactivation of single sodium channels by a site-directed antibody. *Proc. Natl. Acad. Sci. USA* 86:8147–51
117. Vergara, C., Latorre, R. 1983. Kinetics of Ca^{2+}-activated K^+ channels from rabbit muscle incorporated into planar bilayers. *J. Gen. Physiol.* 82:543–68
118. Villarroel, A., Alvarez, O., Oberhauser, A., Latorre, R. 1988. Probing a Ca^{2+}-activated K^+ channel with quaternary ammonium ions. *Pflügers Arch.* 413: 118–26
119. Weiss, R. E., Horn, R. 1986. Functional differences between two classes of sodium channels in developing rat skeletal muscle. *Science* 233:361–64
120. Winegar, B., Kelly, R., Lansman, J. B. 1990. Block of single calcium channels in C2 myotubes by Zn, Fe, Co, and Ni. *Biophys. J.* 57:525a
121. Woodhull, A. M. 1973. Ionic blockage of sodium channels in nerve. *J. Gen. Physiol.* 61:687–708
122. Worley, J. F. III, Fiener, L. A., Jones, L., Nelson, M. T. 1986. Different types of calcium channels incorporated into planar lipid bilayers. *Biophys. J.* 49: 176a
123. Worley, J. F. III, French, R. J., Krueger, B. K. 1986. Trimethyloxonium modification of single batrachotoxin-activated sodium channel in planar bilayers. *J. Gen. Physiol.* 87:327–49
124. Yeh, J. Z., Narahashi, T. 1977. Kinetic analysis of pancuronium interaction with sodium channels in squid axon membranes. *J. Gen. Physiol.* 69:293–323
125. Yellen, G. 1984. Ionic permeation and blockade in Ca^{2+}-activated K^+ channels of bovine chromaffin cells. *J. Gen. Physiol.* 84:157–86
126. Yellen, G. 1984. Relief of Na^+ block of Ca^{2+}-activated K^+ channels by external cations. *J. Gen. Physiol.* 84:187–99
127. Yellen, G. 1987. Permeation in potassium channels: implications for channel structure. *Annu. Rev. Biophys. Biophys. Chem.* 16:227–46
128. Zagotta, W. N., Hoshi, T., Aldrich, R. W. 1989. Gating of single *Shaker* K^+ channels in *Drosophila* muscle and in *Xenopus* oocytes injected with *Shaker* mRNA. *Proc. Natl. Acad. Sci. USA* 86:7243–47

Annu. Rev. Physiol. 1991. 53:497–508

REGULATION OF ADRENERGIC RECEPTOR RESPONSIVENESS THROUGH MODULATION OF RECEPTOR GENE EXPRESSION

Sheila Collins, Marc G. Caron, and Robert J. Lefkowitz

Howard Hughes Medical Institute, Duke University Medical Center, Durham, North Carolina 27710

KEY WORDS: down-regulation, desensitization, mRNA regulation

INTRODUCTION

The adrenergic receptors mediate the diverse metabolic and neuroendocrine actions of the catecholamines, adrenaline and noradrenaline. They have served as excellent models for investigating the mechanisms of transmembrane signaling because of their widespread distribution and their ability to couple to well-defined effector systems. The genes for many receptors from this family have been cloned, thus providing the opportunity for direct analyses of the structural features required for G protein coupling, ligand-binding specificity, and the regulatory role of receptor phosphorylation (27, 34). In addition, several aspects of receptor regulation and hormonal responsiveness have been found to reside at the level of transcription of the receptor gene itself.

A FAMILY OF RECEPTORS

The adrenergic receptors are part of a large gene family that includes receptors for many hormones, drugs, and neurotransmitters. Cloning of several G protein-coupled receptors has revealed their striking topographical similarity

0066-4278/91/0315-0497$02.00

to rhodopsin, the visual receptor for light, which is coupled through a G protein (transducin) to a cGMP phosphodiesterase (2). This family of receptors is composed of a single polypeptide chain with seven transmembrane helical domains spanning the lipid bilayer (Figure 1). The details of the structural homologies between receptors and motifs important for ligand binding and G protein coupling are discussed in several recent reviews (27, 28, 34).

REGULATION OF HORMONAL RESPONSIVENESS

The G protein-coupled receptors serve to regulate the generation of various intracellular second messengers that affect cytoplasmic functions and gene expression. As a result, it is important for the responsiveness of the system to

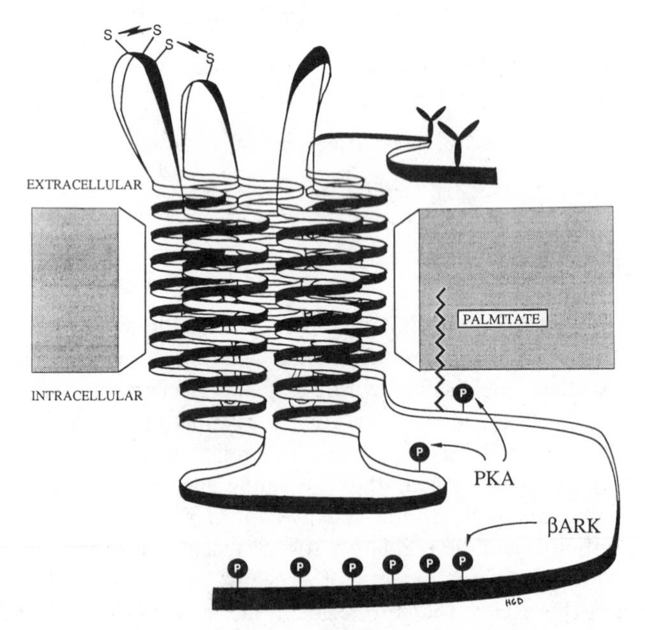

Figure 1 The seven-transmembrane helical model of the β_2AR and its post-translational modifications. On the extracellular side of this ribbon model of the receptor, *S-S* represents the proposed disulfide bridges in two extracellular loops. Toward the amino terminus the two consensus sites for N-glycosylation are shown. On the cytoplasmic side of this model are shown the various sites of phosphorylation by the regulatory cAMP-dependent protein kinase (PKA) and β-adrenergic receptor kinase (βARK). The *zigzag line* indicates the cysteine residue (CYS-341), which in the β_2-adrenergic receptor is palmitoylated.

be tightly controlled. Two major modes of regulation initiated by agonist occupancy and stimulation of the second messenger pathway are (*a*) the regulation of receptor number on the cell surface, and (*b*) the ability of these receptors to interact with their G proteins to alter cellular functions. Mechanisms underlying these aspects of regulation include post-translational modifications of the receptor, such as phosphorylation, as well as changes in rates of transcription of the receptor gene. Through heterologous regulation, a variety of other hormone systems (e.g. steroid and thyroid hormones) also contribute to physiological modulation of receptor number and, thus, adrenergic responsiveness. In these situations direct regulation of receptor gene transcription appears to be the major mechanism involved (8).

Desensitization

One major form of agonist-dependent regulation is desensitization. This is a general biological phenomenon wherein the response to a stimulus diminishes over time despite continued stimulation. Three processes shown to be associated with the development of β-adrenergic receptor (βAR) desensitization are rapid (seconds to minutes) uncoupling and sequestration of the receptor, and down-regulation. Rapid uncoupling of the receptor from effector units is mediated by phosphorylation. The cAMP-dependent protein kinase (PKA) and the β-adrenergic receptor kinase (βARK) are the two principle kinases involved at this step (6, 28, 29). Rapid sequestration of the receptor away from the cell surface is an agonist-dependent process, probably involving some conformational change in the receptor rather than phosphorylation. While receptor uncoupling and sequestration have been the subject of intense and extensive investigation and review (3, 28, 34), our discussion of desensitization focuses on the third pathway contributing to desensitization: down-regulation. Multiple mechanisms have been identified at this step, which include specific changes in receptor gene expression.

Down-Regulation

Down-regulation is defined as the loss of total receptor-binding sites in the cell with an accompanying loss in effector stimulation. Whereas uncoupling and sequestration are rapid processes that take place within seconds to minutes after agonist exposure, down-regulation occurs following more prolonged stimulation ($>$ 1 hr). Despite intense research efforts, the molecular mechanisms underlying down-regulation are poorly understood. Proteolytic degradation of the receptor is thought to contribute to down-regulation (4), and recovery from this condition is shown, in some cases, to require new protein synthesis while in other cases it is not (reviewed in reference 3, 34). There is evidence (30, 39, 42) that receptor-G_s coupling alone, in the absence of cAMP generation and the activation of PKA, can promote β_2AR down-regulation. The PKA pathway also appears to contribute to the process of down-regulation (4, 9, 18, 19). This overlap of pathways is reminiscent of the situation for rapid desensitization, where the participation of multiple mechanisms ensures prompt termination of signal transmission. New insight into the process of adrenergic receptor down-regulation has been obtained through the construction and expression of mutant receptors, and the use of the cloned receptor genes as probes for studying receptor gene expression during the course of down-regulation. In this manner the contributions of receptor-G_s coupling and the role of the PKA pathway are being evaluated at the molecular level.

AGONIST-DEPENDENT PATHWAY Several groups (30, 39, 42) have demonstrated that variants of the mouse S49 lymphoma cell series that either lack PKA activity (kin^-) or possess perturbed G_s-effector coupling (*H21a*) are, nevertheless, capable of β_2AR down-regulation. However, mutants with abnormal receptor-G_s coupling (cyc^-, unc) show a blunted (but not blocked) down-regulation of β_2AR. These studies raised the possibility that physical (protein-protein) interactions between β_2AR and G_s are more important than the actual functional coupling and activation of adenylyl cyclase for triggering receptor down-regulation. While these studies were descriptive in nature, they provided an important foundation for subsequent molecular approaches. Campbell et al (44) recently addressed the issue of physical receptor-G_s coupling in down-regulation using a collection of human β_2AR mutants generated by site-directed mutagenesis techniques. These mutant receptors displayed varying degrees of impairment in coupling to G_s. Their ability to undergo agonist-induced down-regulation appeared to reflect their capacities to physically couple to G_s. The most striking example of this apparent independence from the PKA pathway was demonstrated by a mutant β_2AR with completely normal physical coupling to G_s, but a dramatically impaired ability to mediate agonist-stimulated adenylyl cyclase activity (i.e. impaired functional G_s coupling; reference 21). This receptor still displayed a normal pattern of down-regulation. Mutant receptors with severely impaired functional G_s coupling produced a poor down-regulation response. Since such receptors are consequently incapable of stimulating adenylyl cyclase, it was reasoned that provision of exogenous cAMP (dibutyryl cAMP) and phosphodiesterase inhibitors might improve their abnormal down-regulation patterns. No significant increase in the rate or extent of down-regulation was obtained, however, thus implying that the primary defect was not a lack of PKA activation. Therefore, while the evidence to date supports the notion of a cAMP-independent pathway in βAR down-regulation, the mechanism of this process is unknown. Moreover, it is important to note that while the mutant receptors in these studies could be fully impaired in coupling to G_s, the down-regulation response was never completely blocked.

ROLE OF SECOND MESSENGER PATHWAYS The study of receptor gene expression during down-regulation has demonstrated that second messengers do, in fact, contribute to the process of down-regulation. Using the hamster smooth muscle cell line DDT_1MF-2, Hadcock & Malbon (18) and Collins et al (9) found that prolonged exposure to either β-adrenergic agonists or cAMP analogues (or agents such as forskolin, which directly stimulate adenylyl cyclase) produced a loss of receptor-binding sites that was accompanied by substantial decreases in β_2AR mRNA levels. Thus these groups showed that the second messenger cAMP, in the absence of any contribution from agonist occupancy, was able to promote β_2AR down-regulation. Hadcock & Malbon (18) observed that while agonist-promoted down-regulation of receptors was quite rapid and actually preceded the decline in mRNA levels, cAMP treatment resulted in a more modest decrease in β_2AR mRNA. The studies of Collins et al (9) indicated that decreases in β_2AR mRNA, either in response to prolonged agonist or cAMP treatment, tended to precede the loss of receptor number. In addition, treatment with dibutyryl cAMP or forskolin produced an equally effective reduction in β_2AR mRNA levels, although the effect on receptor density was clearly less dramatic. Since the role of agonist activation of the receptor is the stimulation of adenylyl cyclase and the generation of cAMP, the ability of cAMP to mimic the decrease in both receptor mRNA levels and, in part, receptor number suggests that the PKA pathway is intimately involved in these processes. Yet in both studies, the observation that agonists produce more rapid or more effective receptor down-regulation has been interpreted as further evidence for the apparent role of an agonist-promoted, cAMP-independent mechanism in receptor down-regulation, as noted earlier.

A good correlation between activation of the PKA pathway and decreases in β_2AR mRNA levels has been observed for the S49 mouse lymphoma mutants (19). Agonist or forskolin treatment of wild-type S49 cells reduced β_2AR mRNA levels by 50%, while β_2AR mRNA and receptor down-regulation were both unaffected in kin^- cells, which lack PKA activity. Receptor mRNA levels in the β_2AR-G_s coupling mutants, cyc^- and unc, were lowered only upon activation of PKA by forskolin. Unexpectedly, the novel mutant *H21a,* (normal receptor-G_s coupling but defective G_s-cyclase coupling) generated a more modest (~25%), but significant, decrease of β_2AR mRNA, which led the authors to propose that receptor-G_s activation of a PKA-independent pathway, such as calcium and potassium channels (5) may also serve to regulate β_2AR mRNA levels. Unfortunately, ligand-binding data for *H21a* or other mutants were not presented in this study; thus it was impossible to correlate receptor density with mRNA levels during down-regulation. Since the study of agonist-induced down-regulation by Campbell et al (44) also did not measure β_2AR mRNA levels, it is not possible to relate the effects of these coupling mutants to the partial decrease of β_2AR mRNA observed by Malbon & colleagues (19) for the *H21a* mutant of S49.

Evidence that post-transcriptional mechanisms regulate adrenergic receptor gene expression has recently appeared (4, 20, 35). Examining the role of cAMP alone in promoting β_2AR down-regulation in greater detail, Bouvier et al (4) compared wild-type β_2AR with mutated receptors in which one or both consensus sites for PKA phosphorylation were substituted with irrelevant amino acids. Since previous studies have clearly established the participation of PKA phosphorylation of the β_2AR in the process of rapid desensitization, it was of interest to know what role, if any, these same phosphorylation sites play in the cAMP-dependent down-regulation of β_2AR.

The functional consequences of these mutations were evaluated in cell lines expressing the receptor under the control of a viral promoter. After exposure to dibutyryl cAMP or forskolin, cAMP-induced phosphorylation of the mutant β_2ARs was completely abolished, but cAMP-induced down-regulation of the receptor was only moderately slowed relative to the wild-type cells. Thus the initial delay in the rate of down-regulation of the mutant receptor induced by cAMP is most likely due to an alteration in phosphorylation. It is clear from these results, however, that although phosphorylation contributes to the process of down-regulation, it is not the major factor. The more significant finding in this study was the dramatic decrease in β_2AR mRNA levels in both wild-type and mutant cells, which preceded the decline in receptor number. Therefore, since down-regulation of β_2AR mRNA in the transfected cells can occur in the absence of a promoter, we proposed (4) that post-transcriptional events must play a role in the regulation of β_2AR expression. Effects on mRNA stability have been demonstrated for a number of cAMP-regulated genes (22, 25, 40). Moreover, down-regulation of another G protein-coupled receptor, the thyrotropin releasing hormone receptor, was accompanied by a rapid decrease in the level of translatable receptor mRNA (35), and it was speculated that some form of post-transcriptional control was involved.

Recently these suggestions have been confirmed by Malbon & colleagues. They detected a decrease in the half-life of the β_2AR mRNA following prolonged agonist exposure of DDT$_1$MF-2 cells (20). The mechanisms responsible for this hormone-induced change in RNA stability await further investigation. It is tempting to speculate, however, that the 3'-untranslated region (UTR) of the mRNA for the β_2AR, as well as other G_s-coupled receptors, may be the focus of such regulation. Among the receptors cloned to date, i.e. those known to couple to stimulation of adenylyl cyclase, several β_2AR (26), D$_1$AR (15), LHR (31), and FSHR (41) contain 3'-UTRs that are rich in AU sequence and other features correlated with highly regulated, short-lived mRNAs (37, 38).

A post-transcriptional pattern of regulation may not be confined to the β_2AR. In a recent study of the α_1AR (α_{1B} subtype; 13), which is coupled to phosphatidyl inositol turnover and calcium mobilization via protein kinase C, down-regulation of α_1ARs in rabbit vascular smooth muscle cells (RSMC) was accompanied by a rapid, but transient, down-regulation of α_{1B} mRNA (24). Up to 80% of the receptor message was lost by 4 hr of treatment with the adrenergic agonist norepinephrine, followed by a gradual return to control levels by 24 hr. Regulation was specific to the α_1AR since the decrease in α_{1B} mRNA was blocked by prazosin, an α_1-antagonist, but not by the β-antagonist propranolol. Direct activation of the PKC pathway by phorbol esters thus bypasses the receptor and mimics the effects of norepinephrine on α_{1B}AR mRNA (N. Izzo, W. Colucci, unpublished observations). Since exposure of RSMC to phorbol esters or norepinephrine causes rapid uncoupling of the receptor from phosphatidyl inositol turnover and Ca^{+2} mobilization (11, 12), it is reasonable to expect that the second messenger pathways associated with α_1AR activation participate in the regulation of α_{1B}AR mRNA. Thus the transient nature of the effect of norepinephrine on α_{1B}AR mRN may be a consequence of this uncoupling event.

Up-Regulation and Endocrine Modulation

STEROID HORMONES Some of the first studies to address transcriptional control of adrenergic receptors focused on regulation by steroid hormones, whose major mode of action is the direct modulation of target gene transcription. Early studies demonstrated that glucocorticoids increase β-agonist-stimulated adenylyl cyclase activity and β_2AR number (reviewed in 8, 14). The cloning of the β_2AR made it possible to extend these original observations and directly address the role of regulation of β_2AR gene expression. Increases in β_2AR density and adrenergic responsiveness in DDT$_1$MF-2 smooth muscle cells treated with glucocorticoid agonists were preceded by a rapid elevation of β_2AR mRNA (7, 8). Direct increases in the rate of β_2AR gene transcription were shown to be the mechanistic basis for this increase (7). Sequence elements within the 5'-flanking region of the β_2AR gene with $> 85\%$ homology to a 15 bp glucocorticoid response element (GRE) consensus sequence may be responsible for this regulation (8).

In another report, treatment of cells with a combination of β-agonist and dexamethasone demonstrates the dynamic regulation and adaptation of β_2AR gene expression to multiple hormonal signals. In this study (20), Malbon & colleagues found that agonist-induced down-regulation of β_2AR and mRNA levels in DDT$_1$MF-2 cells described previously (9, 18) could be reversed by treatment with dexamethasone. The enhanced rate of β_2AR gene transcription in response to the steroid was sufficient to increase receptor mRNA levels and overcome the down-regulation. Conversely, receptor up-regulation, resulting from initial treatment with steroid, was gradually lowered by the subsequent addition of agonist and the development of down-regulation. This study was also interesting from a clinical perspective because treatment of asthmatics with β-agonists over time may result in refractoriness to this form of therapy, while glucocorticoids, which are frequently employed in the treatment of acute asthma, are potentially able to overcome this refractoriness (33).

The effects of sex steroids on adrenergic activity and receptor number have also been described. Catecholamines appear to be integral signaling components for maintaining steroid sensitivity (8, 17a) in the ventral prostate and other reproductive tissues. Studies in vivo have shown that expression of the β_2AR gene in the ventral prostate is regulated by androgens in a manner similar to that observed for glucocorticoids (8).

CYCLIC AMP Another aspect of adrenergic receptor up-regulation recently described is autoregulation: the ability of the receptor/effector complex to directly regulate the transcription of its own genes. The β_2AR is the first G protein-coupled receptor for which such a feedback loop has been demonstrated (10). Preliminary evidence indicates that such a process may exist for other G protein-coupled receptors as well (see below). Collins et al (10) observed that short-term (min) exposure to β-agonists or cAMP analogues produced a three to fivefold elevation in β_2AR mRNA. This increase resulted from direct transcriptional stimulation of the β_2AR gene, with no effect on β_2AR mRNA stability at these early times. These newly synthesized transcripts are efficiently translated as indicated by their localization to heavy polysomes (S. Collins, unpublished observations). The enhancement in mRNA levels was transient and upon more prolonged exposure was followed by a typical pattern of down-regulation, characterized by the reduction in receptor number and a shortening of β_2AR mRNA half-life as described above. For several other cAMP-regulated genes, which display early and transient accumulation of mRNA, dynamic changes in both the transcription rate and mRNA stability occur (22, 25). Thus the β_2AR gene conforms to this regulatory paradigm.

The transcriptional response of several genes to cAMP has been localized to a distinct DNA sequence termed the cAMP response element (CRE; 36) in their 5'-flanking promoter regions. Most CREs contain a variation of the palindromic sequence motif TGACGTCA, which is recognized by a 43-kd phosphoprotein (cAMP response element-binding protein, CREB) present in many cells. This protein has been purified (43), cloned (16, 23), and its ability to stimulate the transcription of target genes shown to be modified by phosphorylation (17), thus linking ligand-receptor interactions at the cell surface with the regulation of gene expression. Promoter-reporter gene fusions constructed between the 5'-flanking region of the human β_2AR gene

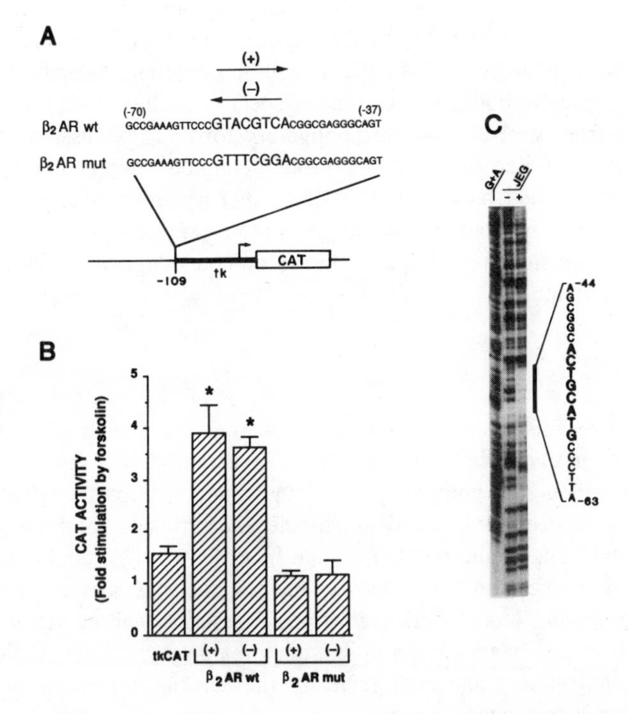

Figure 2 Identification of a cAMP response element (CRE) in the promoter of the β_2AR gene. (*A*) A single copy of a 34-bp oligonucleotide encompassing the wild-type (*wt*) β_2AR CRE (*large letters*) or a mutant version thereof (*mut*) plus flanking sequences (*smaller letters*) was inserted upstream of the thymidine kinase (*tk*) promoter in either the forward (+) or reverse (−) orientation relative to the direction of transcription (*raised arrow*) to generate the CAT reporter constructs β_2(+)CAT and β_2(−)CAT. (*B*) Stimulation of CAT activity by forskolin following transfection of the β_2AR wt and β_2AR mut constructs into JEG-3 cells. The results shown are the average of four to six experiments (*, $p < 0.001$). (*C*) DNase I footprinting analysis of the human β_2AR CRE with CREB-containing JEG-3 nuclear extract. In the presence (+) but not the absence (−) of JEG-3 extract, a protected region, centered on the sequence GTACGTCA at −57 bp to −50 bp, is visualized. A Maxam/Gilbert G+A sequencing reaction is included for orientation (see reference 7 for details).

and the coding region of the bacterial chloramphenicol acetyltransferase (CAT) gene conferred cAMP-inducible CAT activity (9), thus establishing that the promoter region of the β_2AR contains elements responsible for the transcriptional enhancing activity of cAMP.

To define this element more precisely, Collins et al (10) have shown by site-directed mutagenesis, gel-shift analysis, and DNA footprinting (Figure 2) that the sequence GTACGTCA in the β_2AR promoter is a CRE that is recognized and stimulated by the CREB transcription factor. This sequence thus serves as an enhancer of β_2AR gene transcription. The presence of comparable CRE sequences in the 5'-flanking regions of the three mammalian β_2AR genes cloned to date (1, 26, 32) suggests that this may be a fundamental regulatory mechanism for this gene. It will be important to establish the role of this sequence in both basal and tissue-specific expression of the β_2AR, as the CREs from several genes are obligatory for their expression (36). Evidence that other members of the G protein-coupled receptor family may be similarly modulated by cAMP (37a), or other second-messenger pathways (15a), has recently emerged and suggests the existence of common autoregulatory mechanisms involving the same second messenger cascades that these receptors activate.

SUMMARY

Multiple mechanisms contribute to the regulation of G protein-coupled receptors and their transmembrane signaling. Post-translational modifications of the receptors, such as phosphorylation, and changes in receptor gene expression can occur in either a strictly agonist-dependent fashion or through second messenger-mediated autoregulation. We have shown that modulation of receptor gene expression contributes to the responsiveness of adrenergic and related receptors. Recent evidence for post-transcriptional regulation, as well as the stimulation of transcription in an autoregulatory manner, indicates the unanticipated variety and complexity of mechanisms regulating adrenergic receptor responsiveness.

ACKNOWLEDGMENTS

We wish to thank Henrik Dohlman for the preparation of Figure 1 and Donna Addison and Mary Holben for secretarial assistance with the manuscript.

Literature Cited

1. Allen, J. M., Baetge, E. E., Abrass, I. B., Palmiter, R. D. 1988. Isoproterenol response following transfection of the mouse β_2-adrenergic receptor gene into Y1 cells. *EMBO J.* 7:133–38
2. Applebury, M. L., Hargrave, P. A. 1986. Molecular biology of the visual pigments. *Vision Res.* 26:1881–95
3. Benovic, J. L., Bouvier, M., Caron, M. G., Lefkowitz, R. J. 1988. Regulation of adenylyl cyclase-coupled β-adrenergic receptors. *Annu. Rev. Cell Biol.* 4:405–28
4. Bouvier, M., Collins, S., O'Dowd, B. F., Campbell, P. T., deBlasi, A., et al. 1989. Two distinct pathways for cAMP mediated down regulation of the β_2-adrenergic receptor: Phosphorylation of the receptor and regulation of its mRNA level. *J. Biol. Chem.* 264:16786–92
5. Brown, A., Birnbaumer, L. 1990. Ionic channels and their regulation by G protein subunits. *Annu. Rev. Physiol.* 52: 197–213
6. Clark, R. B., Kunkel, M. W., Friedman, J., Coka, T. S., Johnson, J. A. 1988. Activation of cAMP-dependent protein kinase is required for heterologous desensitization of adenylyl cyclase in S49 wild-type lymphoma cells. *Proc. Natl. Acad. Sci. USA* 85:1442–46
7. Collins, S., Altschmied, J., Herbsman, O., Caron, M. G., Mellon, P. L., Lefkowitz, R. J. 1990. A cAMP response

element in the β_2AR gene confers transcriptional autoregulation by cAMP. *J. Biol. Chem.* 265:19330–35

8. Collins, S., Bolanowski, M. A., Caron, M. G., Lefkowitz, R. J. 1989. Genetic regulation of β-adrenergic receptors. *Annu. Rev. Physiol.* 51:203–15
9. Collins, S., Bouvier, M., Bolanowski, M. A., Caron, M. G., Lefkowitz, R. J. 1989: Cyclic AMP stimulates transcription of the β_2-adrenergic receptor gene in response to short term agonist exposure. *Proc. Natl. Acad. Sci. USA* 86: 4853–57
10. Collins, S., Caron, M. G., Lefkowitz, R. J. 1988. β-Adrenergic receptors in hamster smooth muscle cells are transcriptionally regulated by glucocorticoids. *J. Biol. Chem.* 263:9067–70
11. Colucci, W. S., Alexander, R. W. 1986. Norepineprhine-induced alterations in the coupling of alpha$_1$-adrenergic receptor occupancy to calcium efflux in rabbit aortic smooth muscle cells. *Proc. Natl. Acad. Sci. USA* 83:1743–46
12. Cotecchia, S., Leeb-Lundberg, L. M. F., Hagen, P.-O., Lefkowitz, R. J., Caron, M. J. 1985. Phorbol ester effects on α_1 adrenoceptor binding and phosphatidylinositol metabolism in cultured vascular smooth muscle cells. *Life Sci.* 37:2389–98
13. Cotecchia, S., Schwinn, D. A., Randall, R. R., Lefkowitz, R. J., Caron, M. G., Kobilka, B. K. 1988. Molecular cloning and expression of the cDNA for the hamster alpha$_1$-adrenergic receptor. *Proc. Natl. Acad. Sci. USA* 85:7159–63
14. Davies, A. O., Lefkowitz, R. J. 1984. Regulation of β-adrenergic receptors by steroid hormones. *Annu. Rev. Physiol.* 46:119–30
15. Dearry, A., Gingrich, J. A., Falardeau, P., Fremeau, R. G., Bates, M. D., Caron, M. G. 1990. Molecular cloning and expression of the gene for a human D_1 dopamine receptor. *Nature* 347:72–76

15a. Fukamouchi, F., Hough, C., Chuang, D.-N. 1990. Regulation of M_2- and M_3-muscarinic receptor mRNA in cultured cerebellar granule cells. *FASEB J.* 4:A460 (Abst.)

16. Gonzalez, G. A., Montminy, M. R. 1989. Cyclic AMP stimulates somatostatin gene transcription by phosphorylation of CREB at serine 133. *Cell* 59:675–80
17. Gonzalez, G. A., Yamamoto, K. K., Fischer, W. H., Karr, D., Menzel, P., et al. 1989. A cluster of phosphorylation sites on the cAMP-regulated factor CREB predicted by its sequence. *Nature* 337:749–52

17a. Guthrie, P. D., Freeman, M. R., Liao, S., Chung, L. W. K. 1990. Regulation of gene expression in rat prostate by androgen and β-adrenergic receptor pathways. *Mol. Endocrinol.* 4:1342–53

18. Hadcock, J. R., Malbon, C. C. 1988. Down-regulation of β-adrenergic receptors: agonist-induced reduction in receptor mRNA levels. *Proc. Natl. Acad. Sci. USA* 85:5021–25
19. Hadcock, J. R., Ros, M., Malbon, C. C. 1989. Agonist regulation of β-adrenergic receptor mRNA. Analysis in S49 mouse lymphoma mutants. *J. Biol. Chem.* 264:13956–61
20. Hadcock, J. R., Wang, H., Malbon, C. C. 1989. Agonist-induced destablization of β-adrenergic receptor mRNA. Attenuation of glucocorticoid induced up-regulation of β-adrenergic receptors. *J. Biol. Chem.* 264:19928–33
21. Hausdorff, W. P., Hnatowich, M., O'Dowd, B. F., Caron, M. G., Lefkowitz, R. J. 1990. A mutation of the β_2-adrenergic receptor impairs agonist activation of adenylyl cyclase without affecting high affinity agonist binding. *J. Biol. Chem.* 265:1388–93
22. Hod, Y., Hanson, R. W. 1988. Cyclic AMP stabilizes the mRNA for phosphoenol pyruvate carboxykinase (GTP) against degradation. *J. Biol. Chem.* 263:7747–52
23. Hoeffler, J. P., Meyer, T. E., Yun, Y., Jameson, J. L., Habener, J. F. 1988: Cyclic AMP-responsive DNA-binding protein-structure based on a cloned placental cDNA. *Science* 242:1430–33
24. Izzo, N. J., Seidman, C. E., Collins, S., Colucci, W. S. 1990. α_1-Adrenergic receptor mRNA level is regulated by norepinephrine in rabbit aortic smooth muscle cells. *Proc. Natl. Acad. Sci. USA* 87:6268–71
25. Jungmann, R. A., Kelley, D. C., Miles, M. F., Milkowski, D. M. 1983. Cyclic AMP regulation of lactate dehydrogenase. *J. Biol. Chem.* 258:5312–18
26. Kobilka, B. K., Frielle, T., Dohlman, H. G., Bolanowski, M. A., Dixon, R. A. F., et al. 1987. Delineation of the intronless nature of the genes for the human and hamster β_2-adrenergic receptor and their putative promoter regions. *J. Biol. Chem.* 262:7321–27
27. Lefkowitz, R. J., Caron, M. G. 1988: Adrenergic receptors: Models for the study of receptors coupled to guanine nucleotide regulatory proteins. *J. Biol. Chem.* 263:4993–96

28. Lefkowitz, R. J., Hausdorff, W. H., Caron, M. G. 1990. Role of phosphorylation in desensitization of the β-adrenoceptor. *Trends Pharmacol. Sci.* 11:190–94
29. Lohse, M. J., Benovic, J. L., Caron, M. G., Lefkowitz, R. J. 1990. Multiple pathways of rapid β_2-adrenergic receptor desensitization: Delineation with specific inhibitors. *J. Biol. Chem.* 265:3202–9
30. Mahan, L. C., Koachman, A. M., Insel, P. A. 1985. Genetic analysis of β-adrenergic receptor internalization and down-regulation. *Proc. Natl. Acad. Sci. USA* 82:129–33
31. McFarland, K. C., Sprengel, R., Phillips, H. S., Kohler, M., Rosemblit, N., et al. 1989. Lutropin-choriogonadotropin receptor: An unusual member of the G protein-coupled receptor family. *Science* 245:494–99
32. Nakada, M. T., Haskell, K. M., Ecker, D. J., Stadel, J. M., Crooke, S. T. 1989. Genetic regulation of β_2-adrenergic receptors in 3T3-L1 fibroblasts. *Biochem. J.* 260:53–59
33. Nelson, H. S. 1986. Adrenergic therapy of bronchial asthma. *J. Allergy Clin. Immunol.* 77:771–785
34. O'Dowd, B. F., Collins, S., Bouvier, M., Caron, M. G., Lefkowitz, R. J. 1990. Structural, functional and genetic aspects of receptors coupled to G proteins. In *Molecular Biology of Receptors Which Couple to G-proteins,* ed. M. Brann, Cambridge: Birkhäuser Boston. In press
35. Oron, Y., Straub, R. E., Traktman, P., Gershengorn, M. D. 1987. Decreased TRH receptor mRNA activity precedes homologous down regulation: assay in oocytes. *Science* 238:1406–8
36. Roesler, W. J., Vandenbark, G. R., Hanson, R. W. 1988. Cyclic AMP and the induction of eukaryotic gene transcription. *J. Biol. Chem.* 263:9063–66
37. Ross, J. 1988. Messenger RNA turnover in eukaryotic cells. *Mol. Biol. Med.* 5:1–14
37a. Sakaue, M., Hoffman, B. B. 1990. Regulation of α_2-adrenergic receptor messenger RNA abundance by cAMP in HT-29 cells. *FASEB J.* 4:A460 (Abst.)
38. Shaw, G., Kamen, R. 1986. A conserved AU sequence from the 3' untranslated region of GM-CSF mRNA mediates selective mRNA degradation. *Cell* 46:659–667
39. Shear, M., Insel, P. A., Melmon, K. L., Coffino, P. 1976. Agonist-specific refractoriness induced by isoproterenol: Studies with mutant cells. *J. Biol. Chem.* 251:7572–76
40. Smith, J. D., Liu, A. Y.-C. 1988. Increased turnover of the messenger RNA encoding tyrosine aminotransferase can account for the desensitization and deinduction of tyrosine aminotransferase by 8-bromo-cyclic AMP treatment and removal. *EMBO J.* 7:3711–16
41. Sprengel, R., Braun, T., Nikolics, K., Segaloff, D. L., Seeburg, P. H. 1990. The testicular receptor for follicle stimulating hormone: Structure and functional expression of cloned cDNA. *Mol. Endocrinol.* 4:525–30
42. Su, Y. F., Harden, T. K., Perkins, J. P. 1980. Catecholamine specific desensitization of adenylyl cyclase: Evidence for a multiple step process. *J. Biol. Chem.* 255:7410–19
43. Yamamoto, K. K., Gonzalez, G. A., Biggs, W. H. III, Montminy, M. R. 1988. Phosphorylation-induced binding and transcriptional efficacy of nuclear factor CREB. *Nature* 334:494–98
44. Campbell, P. T., Hnatowich, M., O'Dowd, B. F., Caron, M. G., Lefkowitz, R. J., Hausdorff, W. P. 1991. Mutations of the human β_2-adrenergic receptor that impair coupling to G_s interfere with receptor down-regulation but not sequestration. *Mol. Pharmacol.* In press

Annu. Rev. Physiol. 1991. 53:509–30

EPITHELIAL Na^+ CHANNELS

P. R. Smith and D. J. Benos

Department of Physiology and Biophysics, University of Alabama at Birmingham, Birmingham, Alabama 35294

KEY WORDS: amiloride, transport, aldosterone, protein purification, protein reconstitution

---

INTRODUCTION

Electrically high resistance, Na^+ reabsorbing epithelia, such as the distal and collecting tubules of the kidney, descending colon, lungs, trachea, and sweat ducts, contain Na^+-specific channels situated within their apical membranes. These Na^+ channels are characteristically inhibited with high affinity by the diruretic amiloride and thus are referred to as amiloride-sensitive Na^+ channels. Amiloride-sensitive Na^+ channels mediate the entry of Na^+ from the luminal (apical) fluid into the cells during the first stage of electrogenic transepithelial Na^+ transport. In contrast to the Na^+ channels of excitable tissues, these Na^+ channels are voltage-independent. Their gating properties are regulated by hormones such as aldosterone, vasopressin, and atrial naturietic peptide, intracellular Ca^{2+}, Na^+, and pH levels, and by guanine nucleotide regulatory (G) proteins.

In this brief review we present our current understanding of epithelial Na^+ channels at both the biophysical and biochemical levels. We first discuss the biophysical characteristics of this ion channel and the use of amiloride and its analogues as tools for analyzing different classes of this channel. Next we discuss the biochemical purification of the Na^+ channel, including the production of antibodies and their use for immunolocalization of the channel within a variety of epithelia. This is followed by a discussion of the regulation of the channel by luminal factors, hormones, cytoplasmic ions, and G proteins. We conclude by comparing epithelial Na^+ channels with the voltage-dependent Na^+ channel and perspectives for further research. More extensive

0066-4278/91/0315-0509$02.00

reviews of this subject are presented in Garty & Benos (32) and Benos, Warnock & Smith (15).

Na^+ MOVEMENT THROUGH Na^+ CHANNELS

Macroscopic Characteristics

Transepithelial Na^+ transport was first examined using the short-circuit current techniques of Ussing & Zerahn (95). When an epithelium is placed in a Ussing chamber, bathed on both sides with an identical salt solution, and the transepithelial voltage is clamped at 0 mV, the short-circuit current is equal to net Na^+ influx (95). Although this technique has yielded information on the amiloride-inhibited influx, it was only through a variation of this technique, namely, transepithelial noise analysis, that it was first suggested the Na^+ entry pathway was an ion channel (61, 62). This technique gave single-channel conductance values of 5–20 pS.

Through the measurement of transepithelial potentials and tracer fluxes, the ion selectivity of the epithelial Na^+ channel was determined. These data revealed that the channel was highly selective for Na^+ over K^+ (Na^+/K^+ = 10:1 to 670:1) (53, 78) and that of the alkali metal cations, only Na^+ and Li^+ ions could enter the apical channels (11).

An important characteristic of ion movement through a transport pathway is that the relationship between the unidirectional ion influx and efflux should obey the Behn-Teorell-Ussing flux ratio equation (94). Benos et al (10) and Palmer (77) have demonstrated, using the frog skin and toad urinary bladder, respectively, that there is a strong correlation between the measured and predicted flux ratio of Na^+ over a wide range of electrochemical gradients. These data reveal that Na^+ movement through the epithelial Na^+ channel obeys this flux ratio equation and thus can be described by electrodiffusion.

The density of epithelial Na^+ channels in transporting epithelia has been measured using binding/displacement studies with [^{14}C] amiloride (26, 27), irreversible binding of [^{3}H] amiloride analogues (36, 82), and noise analysis (43). Using the binding/displacement technique, estimates of channel density were determined to be 130–400 and 312 sites/μm^2 in the frog skin and toad urinary bladder, respectively (26, 27). Analysis of channel densities using irreversible binding of radioactive amiloride analogues has yielded values of 450 sites/μm^2 for the toad bladder (36) and 70 sites/μm^2 for A6 epithelial cells (82), a cell line derived from the distal tubule of the toad. In contrast, noise analysis gives values of .02 to 38 sites/μm^2 for the toad bladder (43). As pointed out by Garty & Benos (32), the binding studies are based on the assumption that there is a 1:1 binding ratio of amiloride or analogue to channel. Available data suggest, however, that each channel may have multiple amiloride-binding sites. Furthermore, nonspecific binding could lead to an overestimation of channel number (32). The discrepancy between noise analysis and amiloride binding may be accounted for because noise analysis only measures (i.e. conducting) open channels, whereas the binding studies measure both open and closed channels.

Single-Channel Characteristics

The development of patch-clamp and planar lipid bilayer techniques allows the examination of Na^+ channels at the single-channel level. Using these techniques, the conductance, Na^+/K^+ selectivity, and open time probability can accurately be determined for individual Na^+ channels. Single-channel recordings of epithelial Na^+ channels were first achieved by Benos & collaborators, using channels from A6 membrane vesicles, which were incorporated into lipid bilayers (74, 85). Na^+ channels exhibited a single-channel conductance of 4–80 pS at 200 mM Na^+Cl^-. Channels were perfectly cation selective with a Na^+/K^+ selectivity ratio of 2:1. Amiloride interacted with the channel when added to either the *cis* or *trans* compartments of the bilayer. It reduced the open time conductance in a dose-dependent manner when in the *cis* compartment, with a K_i of 0.1 μM, and it induced a flickering response when present in the *trans* compartment.

Single-channel characteristics of amiloride-sensitive Na^+ channels were first examined using the patch-clamp technique in A6 epithelial cells (41). Subsequently, they have been measured in the rat cortical collecting duct (80), toad urinary bladder (29), rabbit straight proximal tubule (38), rat and porcine endothelia (98), porcine thyroid cells (97), human sweat ducts (40), and rat inner medullary collecting duct (58) in primary culture. A6 cells cultured on impermeable supports possess Na^+ channels with low Na^+/K^+ selectivity, moderately high conductances (9 pS), and short mean open times (in the milliseconds range) (41). In contrast, A6 cells grown on permeable supports have channels that are similar to those of the rat collecting tubule and toad urinary bladder, i.e. high Na^+/K^+ selectivity (19:1), low conductances (3pS), and longer open times (seconds) (29). The current voltage curves for these channels exhibit the rectification typical of a channel obeying the Goldman-Hodgkin-Katz constant field current equation. The differences in single-channel characteristics of A6 cells grown on plastic, when compared to those grown on permeable supports, may correlate with the lack of amiloride-sensitive $^{22}Na^+$ uptake exhibited by cells grown on plastic together with a low density of channels in the apical membranes of these cells. This observation suggests that expression of Na^+ channels in cultured cells may relate to cell-matrix interactions or basolateral nutrient requirements (32). Similarly, porcine thyroid cells (97), human sweat duct cells (40), and rat inner medullary collecting duct cells (58) grown in primary culture on impermeable supports all exhibit a low Na^+/K^+ selectivity that may possibly be equated with the culture conditions (i.e. impermeable supports).

Amiloride-sensitive Na^+ channels in the pars recta portion of the rabbit proximal tubule are characterized by a high Na^+/K^+ selectivity (> 19) and a moderately high unit conductance of 12 pS (38). The sensitivity of the channel to amiloride is much lower than that observed for other high amiloride-affinity channels. It should be stressed, however, that amiloride was added to the cytoplasmic side of the patches. The channels exhibited short mean open times, less than 500 ms. The low cation selectivity Na^+ channels that have been characterized from endothelial cells in primary culture (98) differ from those described above since they have a high conductance (23 pS) and an amiloride K_i of 10 μM; thus they belong to the class of channels that are characterized by low amiloride affinity (described below).

AMILORIDE AS AN INHIBITOR OF Na^+ CHANNELS

Amiloride and Its Analogues

The diuretic drug amiloride (3,5-diamino-6-chloropyrazainoylguanidine) is the most widely used inhibitor of epithelial Na^+ transport to date (8, 9, 15, 32, 45). The synthesis of amiloride and its analogues, of which there are approximately one thousand, was first described by Cragoe & associates (25), and the use of these drugs as tools in the study of epithelial Na^+ transport has been reviewed by Benos (8) and more recently by Kleyman & Cragoe (45) and Benos (9). Amiloride is a pyrazine ring compound possessing amino groups on the 3- and 5-positions, a Cl^- on the 6-position, and an acylguanidium moiety attached to the 2-position. Due to the presence of the guanidium moiety, amiloride exists either as a positively charged amine or as an undissociated base with a pK_a of 8.7 in aqueous solution. It is these acid-base properties that allow amiloride to penetrate biological and artificial membranes (12, 28).

Typically, amiloride inhibits Na^+ transport rapidly and reversibly. In addition to inhibiting the epithelial Na^+ channel, it inhibits the Na^+/H^+ exchanger, Na^+/Ca^{2+} exchanger, and Na^+-coupled solute transport (see 9, 15). The apparent equilibrium dissociation constant (K_i=concentration to block 50% of Na^+ transport) of amiloride is significantly different between the Na^+ channel and other amiloride-sensitive transport mechanisms, however. Typically epithelial Na^+ channels have a K_i of < 1 μM at high extracellular [Na^+], whereas the K_i for the Na^+/H^+ exchanger and for the Na^+/Ca^{2+} exchanger and Na^+-coupled solute transport systems are in the micromolar and millimolar concentrations, respectively (9, 15). Recently a new class of amiloride-sensitive Na^+ channels that have a K_i for amiloride of > 1 μM has been identified (see below).

The most specific inhibitors of epithelial Na^+ channels are the amiloride analogues, benzamil and phenamil, which bear hydrophobic substitutions of the terminal nitrogen atom of the guanidium moiety (15, 45). These analogues inhibit Na^+ transport with a K_i of approximately 10 nM (45).

To date, the mechanism by which amiloride blocks Na^+ conductance and its exact site of action remains enigmatic. For inhibition of Na^+ transport, amiloride must carry a net positive charge. Through the use of amiloride analogues, Li et al (54) suggest that the binding of amiloride to the Na^+ channel is facilitated by an interaction between the positively charged side chain of the molecule and the channel protein. This labile complex may either dissociate or be stabilized by an interaction of the Cl^- at the 6-position with another site, and thereby block the channel. Kinetic analysis of competition between Na^+ and amiloride suggests that the competition occurs at the level of the channel (41, 99); however, this analysis does not discern between interactions between cations at a site on or within the conduction pathway, the channel, or a Na^+-induced conformational change of the channel itself, which in turn diminishes amiloride binding to another site (32).

Palmer (79) presents a geometric model for the epithelial Na^+ channel based upon analysis of a voltage-dependent block of Na^+ currents by impermeant ions. In this model, the outer pore of the channel is envisaged as a negatively charged funnel that attracts cations indiscriminately. Farther into the channel the pore narrows to exclude all but the smallest cations, and a final narrowing excludes all ions except Na^+, Li^+, and H^+. Palmer (79) has formulated a kinetic model, based on this geometric model, that is consistent with the known electrophysiological data for the channel.

The positive charge of amiloride allows an estimation of the depth of its binding site in the channel through analysis of the voltage-dependence of blocking kinetics (55, 96). Such studies suggest that the guanidine group penetrates the channel from the luminal side (32). It should be noted, however, that there is a probability of a potential dependent conformational change in the channel protein, thereby affecting the binding of amiloride to a site situated outside of the electric field across the membrane (69). An additional approach that has been utilized to determine the location of the amiloride-binding site is to measure the effects of internal Na^+ on the blocking kinetics (55, 96). The inhibitory effect of amiloride should be prevented through the induction of a channel-mediated cell-to-lumen Na^+ flow, if amiloride does, in fact, block within the conduction pathway. Although such studies suggest that the amiloride-binding site is located within the channel, the results are by no means conclusive. Taken together, these data imply that the competition between amiloride and Na^+ arises from the molecules competing for a single site at the channel protein (32). An alternative view that must be considered is that amiloride and Na^+ may bind to different regions of the same channel protein (32). This awaits further clarification.

High Amiloride Affinity Channels

Characteristically, Na^+ channels from high resistance epithelia have a high affinity for amiloride with a K_i of $< 1\ \mu M$ at physiologic Na^+ concentrations (9, 15). Single-channel analysis reveals that amiloride inhibits Na^+ flow through these channels by either changing the probability of the channel being in the open or closed configuration, or by decreasing current flow through the single channel (15). As shown in Table 1 there are two types of high amiloride affinity channels that differ in their Na^+/K^+ selectivity and their open state conductances.

Low Amiloride Affinity Channels

Recently a second class of amiloride-sensitive Na^+ channels have been reported that has a low affinity for amiloride and can be only inhibited at concentrations of $> 1\ \mu M$. These Na^+ conductive pathways have been described in LLC-PK LLC-PK1 cells (70a), rabbit blastocyst trophectodermal cells (81), rat and porcine brain endothelia (98), rat (70a) and porcine kidney cortex (4–6), type II pneumocytes (65), rabbit proximal tubules (38), rat colonocytes (16), and the basolateral membrane of the toad urinary bladder (34). In addition to their low amiloride affinity, this class of channels differs significantly from high amiloride affinity Na^+ channels in their ion selectivity and kinetic properties. It may be that these two classes of epithelial Na^+ channels also differ in their biochemical composition.

Table 1 Properties of single amiloride-sensitive Na^+ channels in different tissues

Source	Open-state conductance ([NaCl] > 100 mM) (pS)	P_{Na}/P_K Selectivity	Amiloride K_i (μM)	Reference
A6 cells (bilayers)	4–80	2–3	0.1	74, 85
A6 cells (patch)	3–10	4–5/>20	≤0.5	29, 41
Rat cortical collecting tubules	5–8	≥10	<0.5	80
Rabbit straight proximal tubules	12	≥20	10	38
Rabbit inner medullary cells	28	1	<0.5	58
Rat and porcine brain endothelium	23	1.5	10	98
Porcine thyroid cells	3	1.2	0.15	97
Human sweat duct cells	15	3	<0.5	40
Toad urinary bladder cells	5	>20	.1	30

PURIFICATION OF THE AMILORIDE-SENSITIVE Na^+ CHANNEL

Methods of Purification

Benos & co-workers have purified an epithelial Na^+ channel from A6 epithelia and bovine kidney papilla to homogeneity using conventional biochemical techniques (13, 14, 82). Na^+ channels were solubilized using the ionic detergent CHAPS (3-[(3-cholamidopropyl) dimethylamino]-1-propanesulfonate) (82). Detergent solubilization from a tenfold enriched apical membrane preparation yields 100% recovery of specific amiloride-binding sites as determined by [^{3}H] methylbromoamiloride binding (13, 82). The solubilized extract was further purified using wheat germ agglutinin affinity chromatography and size exclusion HPLC. Both steps resulted in a single peak which has a molecular mass of 740 kd and contained all of the [^{3}H] methylbromoamiloride binding sites (13).

SDS/PAGE of the native channel under reducing conditions reveals that it is composed of six major polypeptides with average molecular mass values of 315, 150, 95, 71, 55, and 40 kd (14). It is believed that the subunits are covalently attached to one another through disulfide bridges because the native complex runs as a single band in the absence of reducing conditions. The 315, 150, and 95 kd subunits are heavily glycosylated and contain sialic acid homopolymers (32). Inhibition of glycosylation through the addition of tunicamycin to TMB cells (a cell line derived from the toad urinary bladder) causes a marked decrease in apical Na^+ reabsorption, which suggests that glycosylation is necessary for maintenance of functional Na^+ channels (100).

An amiloride-binding protein, which presumably represents an amiloride-sensitive Na^+ channel, has been identified from the pig kidney cortex using another amiloride analogue, [^{3}H] phenamil, by Barby & co-workers (4, 5). SDS/PAGE of the purified phenamil-binding protein under nonreducing conditions revealed a single polypeptide of molecular mass 180 kd, whereas reducing conditions suggests that it is a dimer composed of two identical subunits, each with a molecular mass of 90–105 kd (4, 5). The purified phenamil-binding protein was not part of a large molecular weight complex composed of several polypeptides cross-linked by disulfide bridges as found by Benos & co-workers (14) for the Na^+ channel isolated from bovine renal papillae and A6 cells (5). Studies of $^{22}Na^+$ uptake into membrane vesicles derived from pig kidney cortex demonstrate that amiloride inhibits $^{22}Na^+$ uptake with a K_i of 6–10 μM, which is characteristic of low amiloride affinity channels (6). Furthermore, the amiloride analogue, EIPA, which fails to block the high affinity channel, inhibits this channel with the same K_i as amiloride (6).

Subunit Composition

The advent of irreversible photosensitive amiloride analogues, which can be radioactively labeled, has provided a means to identify the amiloride-binding subunit. Kleyman et al (48) found that [^{3}H] bromobenzamil, a high affinity analogue of amiloride, binds to three polypeptides from bovine kidney cortical membrane preparations with molecular masses of 176, 77, and 47 kd. Photoincorporation of [^{3}H] bromobenzamil into these three polypeptides is inhibited by benzamil. The dose response of amiloride and its analogues (50; K_i values for benzamil, bromobenzamil, and amiloride of 4, 5, and 400 nM, respectively) for transport inhibition by the channel and the binding affinity of these analogues (K_d values of 5 and 6 nM for benzamil and bromobenzamil, respectively), further corroborates the evidence that [^{3}H] bromobenzamil labels subunits of an epithelial Na^+ channel (48).

Subsequently, Benos et al (14) found that [^{3}H] methylbromoamiloride, another photoactive amiloride analogue, predominantly binds to the 150-kd subunit of the purified channel. The 55-kd subunit was occasionally labeled, however. The apparent discrepancies in the molecular masses of the amiloride-binding sites between this study (150 kd) and that of Kleyman et al (48) (170 kd) may be caused by the variable degree of glycosylation between the subunits. The labeling of the lower molecular mass subunits suggests that either multiple amiloride-binding sites may be present within the channel complex, or that these small subunits are proteolytic products of the larger subunits. In fact, recent experiments by Kleyman et al (49), using yet another irreversible amiloride analogue, namely NMBA (9-2'-methoxy-5'nitrobenzamil), substantiate the claim that the 130–150 kd polypeptide binds amiloride. The 40- and 95-kd subunits of the Na^+ channel isolated from bovine renal papillae and A6 cells are ADP-ribosylated by pertussis toxin (PTX), a compound that specifically prevents activation of G proteins, thus suggesting that these subunits are, in fact, G proteins (3). Treatment of A6 monolayers with pertussis toxin inhibits transepithelial Na^+ transport (19). The 70-kd subunit can be induced by the adrenal hormone aldosterone, a stimulator of transepithelial Na^+ transport (91; B. Blazer-Yost, personal communication). It is suggested that this subunit functions as an effector protein, activating quiescent channels in response to aldosterone stimulation (see below).

Reconstitution of the Na^+ Channel

As presented above, epithelial Na^+ channels have several biophysical properties that are unique among membrane ion channels. Purified Na^+ channels should be inhibited by amiloride or its analogues, they should retain the ability to select Na^+ over other cations, and they should exhibit a characteristic single-channel conductance. Demonstration of these properties for epithelial Na^+ channels purified from bovine renal papillae and A6 cells has been achieved through reconstitution into lipid vesicles and planar lipid bilayers (13, 15). ^{22}Na uptake into phosphatidylcholine vesicles, following reconstitution of wheat germ agglutinin (WGA) affinity purified bovine kidney channel protein, was linear for 60 s and inhibited 73% ± 11% by 100 μM amiloride (13). Purified channels incorporated into planar lipid bilayers were also inhibited by 100 μM amiloride. Single-channel analysis revealed that the channel has an average conductance of 30 pS in 200 mM NaCl (15). The addition of 10 nM of bromoamiloride reduced the open time probability by 30%. There was no change, however, in single-channel conductance. The characteristics of purified bovine kidney Na^+ channel reconstituted into planar bilayers are similar to those reported for Na^+ channels transferred from A6 membrane vesicles to planar membranes (74, 85).

Recently, Sariban-Sohraby & Fisher (84) incorporated the 150-kd amiloride-binding subunit into liposomes and measured its single-channel conductance using the patch-clamp technique. Mean single-channel Na^+ conductance was 8 pS, which is similar to the mean conductance (10 pS) observed for solubilized apical membranes incorporated into liposomes. Effects of amiloride on the single-channel characteristics were not reported. These data suggest that the 150-kd subunit is capable of conducting Na^+ in the absence of the other subunits composing the channel.

Barby et al (5) succeeded in reconstituting the purified phenamil-binding protein from the pig kidney cortex into phosphatidylcholine vesicles. $^{22}Na^+$ uptake into the vesicles was linear for 20 min and inhibited 50% by 10 μM phenamil and amiloride. These K_i values are in agreement with those for the inhibition of $^{22}Na^+$ uptake into apical vesicles derived from the pig kidney cortex (6).

Antibodies Directed Against the Na^+ Channel

Two approaches have been utilized to generate antibodies for the localization and purification of the amiloride-sensitive Na^+ channel. The first method involves the production of anti-amiloride antibodies. Kleyman & co-workers (47) used an amiloride analogue that possesses a caproic acid group covalently bound to the guanidine moiety of amiloride as a hapten to raise anti-amiloride polyclonal antibodies. The anti-amiloride antibodies were found to reverse the inhibition of amiloride on Na^+ transport across toad urinary bladders, mounted in Ussing chambers, thereby suggesting that the anti-amiloride antibodies structurally resemble the amiloride-binding site of the Na^+ channel (47). In Western blots, the anti-amiloride antibodies recognize a 130-kd protein in bovine kidney and A6 membrane vesicles, which have been photolabeled with the amiloride analogue, NMBA (49). These anti-amiloride antibodies have been used to raise anti-idiotypic antibodies that may prove useful in identifying the amiloride-binding site of the Na^+ channel because they are capable of immunoprecipitating the channel complex from A6 membranes (46).

The second approach utilizes the generation of monoclonal and polyclonal antibodies against the amiloride-sensitive Na^+ channel purified from bovine renal papilla. Sorscher et al (90) have succeeded in producing monoclonal and polyclonal antibodies that show specificity against the amiloride-sensitive Na^+ channel in enzyme-linked immunoabsorbant assay (ELISA) and dot-blot assays. These antibodies are also capable of immunoprecipitating channel proteins. The polyclonal antibodies recognize four subunits on Western blots, the 300, 150, 95, and 40-kd polypeptides, and will also cross-react with channel protein isolated from A6 cells, principally the 300 and 150-kd subunits (90). In contrast, the monoclonal antibodies only recognize the 300-kd subunit of the bovine channel (90). Immunoaffinity chromatography suggests the potential usefulness of the polyclonal antibodies in purifying the channel from detergent-solubilized homogenates from a variety of tissues possessing the native amiloride-sensitive Na^+ channel. In addition to immunolocalization (see below), antibodies directed against the channel are being utilized in this laboratory to screen expression libraries of cDNA clones prepared from poly(A+) RNA from bovine kidney and A6 cells, thereby allowing the amino acid sequence of the channel to be determined.

An interesting observation is that an antibody directed against the α subunit of Na^+,K^+ATPase isolated from the toad kidney labels the apical membranes of the A6 and TMB cell lines (15), as well as the collecting duct of the rat kidney (39). Furthermore, in Western blots this antibody recognizes the purified amiloride-sensitive channel from the bovine renal papilla, specifically the 150-kd subunit (15). Based on these data, it is reasonable to speculate (64) that the amiloride-sensitive Na^+ channel shares a common antigenic site with the α subunit of Na^+,K^+ATPase.

IMMUNOCYTOCHEMICAL LOCALIZATION OF THE AMILORIDE-SENSITIVE Na^+ CHANNEL

Amiloride-sensitive Na^+ channels have been localized to the apical membranes of renal papillary collecting duct cells (18, 93), sweat duct cells (93), A6 epithelial cells (93), trophectodermal cells of the rabbit blastocyst (81), type II pneumocytes (66), olfactory epithelial cells (68), and the mammalian tongue (89) using anti-amiloride-sensitive Na^+ channel antibodies at either the light microscopic level using indirect immunofluorescence, the electron microscopic level using immunogold tagging, or both. These studies reveal that the Na^+ channels are predominantly localized to the apical microvilli, with little or no basolateral membrane tagging. Furthermore, intracellular vesicles do not stain, corroborating the view that Na^+ channels are always present at the cell surface whereupon stimulation of Na^+ transport, they are rendered functional by post-translational modification or through an effector protein (93; see below for further discussion).

REGULATION OF AMILORIDE-SENSITIVE Na^+ CHANNELS

Luminal Factors

Na^+ reabsorption is known to exhibit self-inhibition with an inverse relationship existing between (extracellular) luminal Na^+ concentrations and Na^+ permeability (63). Self inhibition may either be a direct effect of Na^+ ions on a regulatory site situated on the luminal face of the Na^+ channel, or it may be an indirect effect via intracellular second messengers. The effect of extracellular Na^+ ions on the regulation of Na^+ reabsorption has recently been examined by Ling & Eaton (63), using the patch-clamp technique. These authors were able to demonstrate that a reduction in external $[Na^+]$ increased open channel probability and increased the number of channels in a single patch. This increase in channel activity was prevented by the Ca^{2+} ionophore, A23187, and the protein kinase C activators, phorbol myristate (PMA) and oleyl-acetyl-glycerol (OAG). The protein kinase C inhibitor, sphingosine, increased the open time probability and number of channels. Ling & Eaton concluded that the regulation of apical Na^+ permeability by luminal Na^+ occurs by the second messengers, Ca^{2+} and protein kinase C. It is at present unknown whether protein kinase C directly induces phosphorylation of the Na^+ channels, or if it phosphorylates a regulatory protein such as a G protein.

The serine proteases, urokinase and kallikrein, are known to block amiloride-sensitive Na^+ channels. These two enzymes are secreted into the urine of mammals and amphibians by the distal tubule and alter the channels through proteolysis (51, 52). The presence of amiloride will protect the channels from inhibition by these enzymes. It has been proposed that cleavage of Na^+ channels by these enzymes may be involved in the physiologic regulation of Na^+ transport in the urinary bladder. The degradation process involves two steps: conversion of the Na^+ channel to a nonselective, amiloride-insensitive cationic channel, followed by a further proteolysis that leads to the loss of the channel into the urine (51). The loss of Na^+ channels through this process is dependent upon the concentration of urinary kallikrein, which is stimulated by corticoid hormones such as aldosterone. It is proposed that the number of channels in the distal tubule and urinary bladder can be regulated by this mechanism (51). Aldosterone can also increase the number of active channels in the apical membrane and down regulate the channels by an increased release of kallikrein into the urine.

Hormones

Vasopressin is known to increase Na^+ transport by stimulating adenylate cyclase activity and increasing intracellular cAMP levels (75, 76). Through the application of blocker-induced noise analysis, it has been demonstrated that vasopressin-induced Na^+ transport is due to an increased density of open channels situated in the apical membrane (42, 56). This increased density can be explained either through the recruitment of new channels into the apical membrane from an intracellular pool, or through a vasopressin-mediated opening of quiescent channels (32). Evidence supporting the former explanation comes from Garty & co-workers, who demonstrated that trypsinization, which blocks apical Na^+ conductance, does not alter vasopressin-induced Na^+ transport (33). These data suggest that vasopressin has stimulated insertion of new channels into the apical membrane. One caveat of these experiments is that pretreating the apical membranes of the epithelium with tyrosine-specific reagents inhibits vasopressin-stimulated Na^+ currents to the same extent as trypsinization. An explanation for this is that the channels may be continuously present in the apical membrane in a conformational state that prevents alteration by trypsin (32).

Vasopressin can activate a cAMP protein kinase in renal epithelia, which suggests that protein kinase A may directly phosphorylate a subunit(s) of the Na^+ channel that regulates open time probability (15, 32). Alternatively, cAMP-dependent kinase may phosphorylate other proteins that regulate the channel or induce insertion of new channels into the apical membrane (15, 32). Lester & co-workers (50) have shown that toad bladder apical membrane vesicles, into which purified cAMP-dependent protein kinase A, cAMP, and ATP were incorporated, failed to exhibit a stimulated Na^+ conductance. Their data favor the explanation that vasopressin-stimulated increase in Na^+ conductance arises through the phosphorylation of a mediator protein. Sariban-Sohraby et al (86), however, demonstrated that cAMP-dependent kinase directly phosphorylates the 315-kd subunit of the Na^+ channel both in vivo and in vitro. Further evidence corroborating a direct phosphorylation of the Na^+ channel comes from Frings et al (30). Using the patch-clamp technique, they demonstrated that the addition of protein kinase A, cAMP, and ATP to isolated patches of toad urinary bladder apical membranes activated quiescent channels.

Atrial natriuretic peptide (ANP), a hormone released from the atrium of the mammalian heart in response to volume expansion, inhibits Na^+ absorption by the inner medullary collecting ducts of the kidney. Light et al (59) recently used the patch-clamp technique to demonstrate that ANP acts via the second messenger cGMP to inhibit Na^+ reabsorption through the high conductance, nonselective cation channel of the inner medullary collecting duct. The cGMP inhibition of this channel occurs by two mechanisms: (*a*) a phosphorylation-independent mechanism, and (*b*) a phosphorylation-dependent mechanism involving cGMP-kinase and a G protein (60).

The adrenal steroid aldosterone is a regulator of Na^+ reabsorption in electrically tight epithelia. Aldosterone binds to an intracellular receptor, which in turn elicits a two to fourfold increase in Na^+ transport and a concomitant increase in protein synthesis. The response of an epithelium to aldosterone consists of three phases: (*a*) a latent period of 20–90 min in which intracellular events occur; (*b*) an early response in which there is a two to fourfold increase in Na^+ transport; and (*c*) a longer response (> 6 hr) in which there is de novo synthesis of Na^+,K^+ATPase. The initial increase in Na^+ transport is believed to arise from an increased density of open channels either by the activation of quiescent channels and/or induction of synthesis and insertion of new channels into the apical membrane (32).

Using either NMBA photolabeling together with anti-amiloride antibodies, or anti-amiloride anti-idiotypic antibodies alone, Kleyman et al (46, 49) demonstrated in A6 cells that the cellular pool of Na^+ channels is not significantly increased in response to aldosterone stimulation. These results suggest that increased Na^+ reabsorption is due to channel activation. Additional evidence corroborating activation of quiescent channels comes from Tousson et al (93), who have shown immunocytochemically, using polyclonal antibodies against the channel, that aldosterone treatment does not stimulate fusion of intracellular Na^+ channel-containing vesicles with the apical membrane. Although data suggest that aldosterone stimulates effector proteins that activate preexisting channels (1), one of the proteins induced by aldosterone is a 70-kd protein (92). This aldosterone-induced protein shows cross-reactivity with the 70-kd subunit of the purified bovine Na^+ channel in Western blots, which indicates that aldosterone may also directly modulate the channel. Kleyman & associates (46) have observed that although a 70-kd subunit of the channel is present in aldosterone treated A6 cells, a 70–80-kd doublet is present in the Na^+ channel in cells treated with spironalactone, an antagonist of aldosterone. They suggest that post-translational modification of the 70-kd subunit may be the mechanism by which aldosterone regulates the Na^+ channel (46).

The mechanism by which aldosterone activates Na^+ channels remains a mystery. Sariban-Sohraby et al (83) suggest that aldosterone stimulates transmethylation of the channel or surrounding lipids, which produces the early effect. Aldosterone would induce a specific methyltransferase or elevate the cellular concentration of S-adenosyl-L-methionine by acting upon cytoplasmic enzymes. Due to the limitations of the experimental design, however, aldosterone-induced methylation of the channel warrants further investigation.

Cytoplasmic Ions

It is well established that changes in intracellular Ca^{2+} levels, which are involved in the down regulation of apical Na^+ channels, are correlated with increases in cytoplasmic Na^+. The measurement of channel-mediated Na^+ fluxes in membrane vesicles has led to the identification of two different Ca^{2+}-dependent processes that directly regulate apical Na^+ channels. The first method is a direct, reversible Ca^{2+}-Na^+ channel interaction mediated by Ca^{2+} ions binding to a site on the cytoplasmic face of the channel proteins (22, 31). In the second method, protonation of the binding site through changes in intracellular pH prevents the Ca^{2+}-dependent blocking of the channel, whereas deprotonation yields the channel in the conductive state (31). Intracellular Ca^{2+} also regulates the channel by alternating cAMP levels by stimulation of prostaglandin synthesis (75) and through the activation of protein kinase C (2).

G Proteins

The guanine nucleotide-binding protein (G proteins) family is composed of three subunits (α, β, γ) that couple membrane receptors to a variety of enzymes and ion channels (17). Typically, their mechanism of action is as follows: Agonist binding to a membrane receptor induces a conformational change in the G protein, thereby facilitating GTP to replace GDP on the subunit. The GTP complex subsequently dissociates from the β- and γ-subunits and interacts with the effector, such as an ion channel, which produces a physiologic response. The GTPase activity of the subunit then hydrolyses GTP to GDP and the α-GDP complex reassociates with β-and γ-subunits, thus terminating the response (17).

A role for G proteins in the regulation of epithelial Na^+ channels was first suggested by Ausiello & collaborators (19, 70). Pertussis toxin (PTX), a compound that prevents receptor-dependent activation of G_i and G_o, was shown to reduce electrogenic Na^+ transport across LLC-PK1 (70) and A6 cells (19), both renal epithelial cell lines. Subsequently Garty et al (35), using membrane vesicles derived from toad bladder cells, demonstrated that GTPγs can stimulate amiloride-blocked Na^+ transport across the vesicles, whereas GDPβs can reverse the effect, thereby providing direct evidence for the role of G proteins in regulating amiloride-sensitive Na^+ channels.

Recently Light et al (57) and Cantiello et al (19), using the patch-clamp technique, revealed that the α-subunit of G_i directly activates an amiloride-sensitive, nonselective cation channel in renal medullary collecting duct cells and an amiloride-sensitive, Na^+ selective channel in A6 cells, respectively. Further evidence corroborating the role of G proteins in the regulation of epithelial Na^+ channels comes from Ausiello et al (3) who report that the 40 and 95-kd subunits of an epithelial Na^+ channel may be G proteins.

Two methods are currently proposed by which G proteins regulate apical Na^+ channels. First, there may be a receptor-G protein complex situated in the apical membrane that has a high basal activity or locally produced autocoids, such as lipoxygenase products, which bind to the receptor (57). PTX would inhibit receptor-dependent G protein activation and inactivate the channel. This hypothesis is supported by preliminary data of Cantiello et al (20), which suggest that G proteins regulating Na^+ channels in A6 cells are, in fact, activated by the 5-lipoxygenase pathway and its metabolites (i.e. arachidonic acid). The second possible method of G protein regulation of Na^+ channels may involve a unique mechanism because in polarized epithelial cells the apical G protein complex is geographically separated from the G protein receptor complexes situated in the basolateral membrane (57). Typically, hormones bind to receptors in the basolateral membrane and activate channels in the apical membrane. Therefore it is suggested that an effector activated by the G protein complex in the basolateral membrane may directly activate the G protein-Na^+ channel complex, or activate the G protein within the ion channel by phosphorylation. PTX would block the interaction between the apically situated G protein and the intracellular effector.

EXPRESSION OF FUNCTIONAL AMILORIDE-SENSITIVE Na^+ CHANNELS IN *XENOPUS* OOCYTES

The capability to express functional Na^+ channels through the injection of RNA into *Xenopus* oocytes is invaluable for verifying the functional characteristics of cDNA isolated by antibody screening techniques and for isolating the cDNA clones encoding the Na^+ channel by expression cloning. Microinjection of either total RNA or Poly$(A)^+$ mRNA isolated from A6 epithelial cells into *Xenopus* oocytes has led to the expression of functional amiloride-sensitive Na^+ channels (37, 44). Hinton & Eaton (44), using total RNA isolated from aldosterone-stimulated A6 cells, were able to induce an amiloride-sensitive Na^+ channel that has a high selectivity for Na^+, and an amiloride K_i of 50nM. These characteristics of the Na^+ current imply that the Na^+ channels expressed are of the high selectivity form, typical of high resistance epithelia. Injection of oocytes with RNA isolated from A6 cells that were not stimulated by aldosterone produced a current very similar to uninjected or H_2O-injected oocytes, which suggests that aldosterone is necessary for expression of Na^+ channels in oocytes.

Kraehenbuhl & collaborators (37) observed the expression of amiloride-sensitive Na^+ channels in *Xenopus* oocytes injected with Poly $(A)^+$ mRNA (1.4–4.4 kb in size) isolated from aldosterone-treated A6 cells. Expression of Na^+ channels was detected by measurement of $^{22}Na^+$ uptake, which was found to be inhibited by amiloride and benzamil with a K_i of 0.6 and 0.1 μM, respectively. The molecular mass of the polypeptides encoded by the mRNA size range of that injected is 50–150 kd, which would include several of the subunits that have been identified from purified and affinity labeled Na^+ channels (14). These authors conclude that the expression of functional Na^+ channels is independent of the translation of the 300-kd subunit, which corroborates the Na^+ conductance data of Sariban-Sohraby & Fisher for the 150-kd subunit reconstituted into liposomes (84).

Palmer et al (79a) recently extended these studies using the voltage clamp technique. Injection of Poly $(A)^+$ mRNA (sedimentation coefficient of 16–17s; 2.0–2.2 kb in size) from aldosterone-stimulated A6 cells into *Xenopus* oocytes induced amiloride-sensitive Na^+ channels with a high Na^+/K^+ selectivity and an amiloride K_i of 0.1 μM. In contrast to the previous study by this group (37), Palmer and co-workers concluded that the molecular mass of the protein encoded by the mRNA would be at most 70–80 kd. They suggested three possible explanations to account for the induction of Na^+ channels by this size range of mRNA. (*a*) One or more smaller components of the channel are needed for Na^+ transport; (*b*) high molecular weight components of the channel are already present in the oocyte and only the smaller ones are necessary to produce a functional channel; or (*c*) the channels are present in their entirety in an inactive form and the injected mRNA codes for a regulatory protein involved in the activation of the channel (79a).

COMPARISON OF THE AMILORIDE-SENSITIVE Na^+ CHANNEL TO THE VOLTAGE-DEPENDENT Na^+ CHANNEL

Comparison of the amiloride-sensitive Na^+ channel to the voltage-dependent Na^+ channel of excitable tissues reveals strong similarities. Before comparing the two channels, we will briefly review the structure of the voltage-dependent channel (see 7, 21 for reviews).

The voltage-dependent Na^+ channel is essential for the propagation of action potentials in excitable tissues. These channels open upon depolarization of the membrane and close again as inactivation sets in. Na^+ channels undergo abrupt transitions from the closed to open state with a typical single-channel conductance of 20 pS and Na^+/K^+ selectivity of 10 : 1 (7, 21). After remaining open for a variable time period (ms), the channel closes. The neurotoxins, tetrodotoxin (TTX) and saxitoxin (STX), inhibit transport through the channel with high affinity, and they have been used to isolate the channel proteins (7, 21).

The voltage-dependent channel has been isolated to homogeneity from the eel electroplax, rat brain, rabbit and rat skeletal muscle, and cardiac muscle (see 7, 21). The skeletal muscle and rat brain channels consist of an α subunit

(260 kd) plus two β subunits (β_1 of 36 kd; β_2 of 33 kd), whereas the cardiac muscle and eel electroplax consist only of the α subunit. Both TTX and STX bind to the α subunit, which is a glycosylated, transmembrane protein. The primary amino acid sequence has been deduced for the α subunit of the eel electroplax Na^+ channel (72) and three distinct Na^+ channels from the rat brain through the cloning of the cDNA (73). The α subunit possesses four homologous internal repeats each composed of six hydrophobic segments. Injection of mRNA for the α subunit of the rat brain Na^+ channel into *Xenopus* oocytes has shown that α subunit alone is sufficient for expression of functional Na^+ channels (71).

Voltage-dependent Na^+ channels are regulated by intracellular cAMP and Ca^{2+} (23, 88). Increased cAMP leads to phosphorylation of the α subunit of the channel via protein kinase A (23). The α subunit can also be phosphorylated by protein kinase C in response to increasing Ca^{2+} levels (24). Recently it was demonstrated that the β adrenergic modulation of cardiac Na^+ channels occurs through the G protein, G_s (87).

From the foregoing discussion, it can be seen that there are strong similarities between the two types of Na^+ channels. Both are large glycosylated molecules that bind their specific inhibitors at a single subunit. Both channels are regulated by intracellular Ca^{2+} levels and can be phosphorylated by cAMP-dependent protein kinase (kinase A). Furthermore, G proteins have been shown to regulate both these channels. Amino acid sequencing of the epithelial Na^+ channel will give further insight into whether these two channels do indeed show significant homology.

PERSPECTIVES

The recent advent of radiolabeled high affinity probes, patch-clamp and planar lipid bilayer reconstitution techniques, and the generation of specific antibodies, together with the biochemical purification of the channel and expression of functional channels transcribed from mRNA, have significantly advanced our understanding of epithelial Na^+ channels. With the successful sequencing of the channel subunits, we will be able to address the homology of the channels found in different tissues (i.e. low affinity and high amiloride affinity channels) and organisms as well as between the epithelial Na^+ channel and the voltage-dependent Na^+ channel, other amiloride-sensitive transporters, and Na^+,K^+ATPase. Once the amino acid sequence is known, one may be able to generate antibodies against synthetic peptides that correspond to specific parts of the channel. Furthermore, knowledge of the amino acid sequence will allow regions of the channel to be altered by site directed mutagenesis. This may provide insight into the function of subunits of the epithelial Na^+ channel. In fact, such technical approaches have already made it possible to identify the regions of the subunits involved in the activation and inactivation of the voltage-dependent Na^+ channel (67, 91). Furthermore, knowledge of the molecular biology of the epithelial Na^+ channel will allow us to address specific questions concerning the molecular interactions between amiloride and the channel, and between cations and the channel, as well as the regulation of the channel by hormones, other ions, or intracellular messengers.

ACKNOWLEDGMENTS

We thank Ms. Cathy Guy and Ms. Amy Burns for excellent secretarial service. The preparation of the review was supported by National Institutes of Health Grant DK 37206.

Literature Cited

1. Asher, C., Garty, H. 1988. Aldosterone increases the apical Na^+ permeability of toad bladder by two different mechanisms. *Proc. Natl. Acad. Sci. USA* 85: 7413–17
2. Ausiello, D. A., Orloff, J. 1982. Regulation of water and electrolyte movement by vasopressin and cyclic nucleotides in kidney. *Handb. Exp. Pharmacol.* 58: 271–303
3. Ausiello, D. A., Sorscher, E., Harlin, C., Benos, D. J. 1989. Subunits of the epithelial Na^+ channel may be G-proteins. *FASEB J.* 3:A228 (Abstr.)
4. Barbry, P., Chassande, O., Vigne, P., Frelin, C., Ellory, C., et al. 1987. Purification and subunit structure of the [^{3}H]phenamil receptor associated with the renal apical Na^+ channel. *Proc. Natl. Acad. Sci. USA* 84:4836–40
5. Barbry, P., Chassande, O., Marsult, R., Lazdunski, M., Frelin, C. 1990. [^{3}H]phenamil binding protein of the renal epithelium Na channel. Purification, affinity labelling, and functional reconstitution. *Biochemistry* 29:1039–45
6. Barbry, P., Frelin, C., Vigne, P., Cragoe, E. J. Jr., Lazdunski, M. 1986. [^{3}H]phenamil, a radiolabelled diuretic for the analysis of the amiloride-sensitive Na^+ channels in kidney membranes. *Biochem. Biophys. Res. Commun.* 135:25–32
7. Barchi, R. L. 1988. Probing the molecular structure of the voltage-dependent sodium channel. *Annu. Rev. Neurosci.* 11:455–95
8. Benos, D. J. 1982. Amiloride: a molecular probe of sodium transport in tissues and cells. *Am. J. Physiol.* 242:C131–45
9. Benos, D. J. 1988. Amiloride: chemistry, kinetics, and structure-activity relationships. In *Na^+/H^+ Exchange,* ed. S. Grinstein, pp. 121–36. Cleveland, OH: CRC
10. Benos, D. J., Hyde, B. A., Latorre, R. 1983. Sodium flux ratio through the amiloride-sensitive entry pathway in frog skin. *J. Gen. Physiol.* 81:667–85
11. Benos, D. J., Mandel, L. J., Simon, S. A. 1980. Cationic selectivity and competition at the sodium entry site in the frog skin. *J. Gen. Physiol.* 76:233–47
12. Benos, D. J., Reyes, J., Shoemaker, D. G. 1983. Amiloride fluxes across erythrocyte membranes. *Biochem. Biophys. Acta* 734:99–104
13. Benos, D. J., Saccomani, G., Brenner, B. M., Sariban-Sohraby, S. 1986. Purification and characterization of the amiloride-sensitive sodium channel from A6 cultured cells and bovine renal papilla. *Proc. Natl. Acad. Sci. USA* 83:8525–29
14. Benos, D. J., Saccomani, G., Sariban-Sohraby, S. 1987. The epithelial sodium channel. Subunit number and location of the amiloride binding site. *J. Biol. Chem.* 262:10613–18
15. Benos, D. J., Warnock, D. G., Smith, J. B. 1991. Amiloride-sensitive transport mechanisms. In *Membrane Transport in Biology,* Vol. 5, ed. G. Giebisch, H. H. Ussing, P. Kristensen, J. A. Schafer. New York: Academic. In press
16. Bridges, R. J., Cragoe, E. J. Jr., Frizzell, R. A., Benos, D. J. 1989. Inhibition of colonic Na^+ transport by amiloride analogues. *Am. J. Physiol.* 256:667–74
17. Brown, A., Birnbaumer, L. 1988. Di-

rect G-protein gating of ion channels. *Am. J. Physiol.* 254:H401–10
18. Brown, D., Sorscher, E. J., Ausiello, D. A., Benos, D. J. 1989. Immunocytochemical localization of Na^+ channels in rat kidney medulla. *Am. J. Physiol.* 256:F366–69
19. Cantiello, H. F., Patenaude, C. R., Ausiello, D. A. 1989. G-protein subunit, α_i-3, activates a pertussis toxin-sensitive Na^+ channel from the epithelial cell line, A6. *J. Biol. Chem.* 264:20867–70
20. Cantiello, H. F., Patenaude, C. R., Ausiello, D. A. 1990. G-protein activation of an epithelial Na channel is mediated via phospholipid metabolites. *Kidney. Int.* 37:213 (Abstr.)
21. Catterall, W. A. 1986. Molecular properties of voltage-dependent sodium channels. *Annu. Rev. Biochem.* 55:953–85
22. Chase, H. S. Jr., Al-Awqati, Q. 1983. Calcium reduces the sodium permeability of luminal membrane vesicles from toad bladder. Studies using a fast reaction apparatus. *J. Gen. Physiol.* 81:643–66
23. Costa, M. R., Catterall, W. A. 1984. Cyclic AMP-dependent phosphorylation of the alpha subunit of the sodium channel in synaptic nerve ending particles. *J. Biol. Chem.* 259:8210–18
24. Costa, M. R., Catterall, W. A. 1984. Phosphorylation of the alpha subunit of the sodium channel by protein kinase *C*. *Cell. Mol. Neurobiol.* 4:291–97
25. Cragoe, E. J. Jr., Woltersdorf, O. W. J., Bicking, J. B., Kwong, S. F., Jones, J. H. 1967. Pyrazine diuretics II. N-amidio-3-amino-5-substituted-6-holopyrazine carboximides. *J. Med. Chem.* 10:66–75
26. Cuthbert, A. W. 1973. An upper limit to the number of sodium channels in frog skin epithelium. *J. Physiol.* 228:681–92
27. Cuthbert, A. W. 1981. Sodium entry step in transporting epithelia: results of ligand binding studies. In *Transporting Epithelia,* ed. S. G. Schultz, pp. 181–96. New York: Raven
28. Dubinsky, W. P. J., Frizzell, R. A. 1983. A novel effect of amiloride on H^+-dependent Na^+ transport. *Am. J. Physiol.* 245:C157–59
29. Eaton, D. C., Hamilton, K. L. 1988. The amiloride blockable sodium channel of epithelial tissues. In *Ion Channels,* ed. T. Narahashi, pp. 251–82. New York: Plenum
30. Frings, S., Purves, R. D., Macknight, A. D. C. 1988. Single-channel recording from the apical membrane of the toad bladder epithelial cell. *J. Membr. Biol.* 106:157–72
31. Garty, H., Asher, C., Yeger, O. 1987. Direct inhibition of epithelial Na^+ channels by Ca^{2+} and other divalent cations. *J. Membr. Biol.* 95:151–62
32. Garty, H., Benos, D. J. 1988. Characteristics and regulatory mechanisms of the amiloride-blockage Na^+ channel. *Physiol. Rev.* 68:309–73
33. Garty, H., Edelman, I. S. 1983. Amiloride-sensitive trypsinization of apical sodium channels. Analysis of hormonal regulation of sodium transport in toad bladder. *J. Gen. Physiol.* 81:785–803
34. Garty, H., Warnke, J., Lindemann, B. 1987. An amiloride-sensitive Na^+ conductance in the basolateral membrane of toad urinary bladder. *J. Membr. Biol.* 95:91–103
35. Garty, H., Yeger, O., Yanovsky, A., Asher, C. 1989. Guanosine nucleotide-dependent activation of the amiloride-blockable Na^+ channel. *Am. J. Physiol.* 256:965–69
36. Garvin, J. L., Simon, S. A., Cragoe, E. J. Jr., Mandel, L. J. 1982. Binding of ^3H phenamil, an irreversible amiloride analog, to toad urinary bladder: effects of aldosterone and vasopressin. *J. Membr. Biol.* 90:107–13
37. George, A. L. Jr., Staub, O., Geering, K., Rossier, B., Kleyman, T. R., et al. 1989. Functional expression of the amiloride-sensitive sodium channel in *Xenopus* oocytes. *Proc. Natl. Acad. Sci. USA* 86:7295–98
38. Gögelein, H., Greger, R. 1986. Na^+ selective channels in the apical membrane of rabbit late proximal tubules (pars recta). *Pflügers Arch.* 406:198–203
39. Graves, J. S., Inabnett, T., Gerring, K., Simson, J. A. V. 1989. Cross-reactivity of an antiserum to the subunit of the Na^+, K^+ ATPase of toad *(Bufo marinus)* kidney with basal and apical membranes of transporting epithelia of the rat. *Cell. Tissue Res.* 258:137–45
40. Joris, L., Krouse, M. E., Hagiwara, G., Bell, C. L., Wine, J. J. 1989. Patch-clamp study of cultured human sweat duct cells: amiloride-blockable Na^+ channel. *Pflügers Arch.* 414:369–72
41. Hamilton, K. L., Eaton, D. C. 1985. Single-channel recordings from amiloride-sensitive epithelial sodium channel. *Am. J. Physiol.* 249:C200–7
42. Helman, S. I., Cox, T. C., Van Driessche, W. 1983. Hormonal control of apical membrane Na^+ transport in epithelia. *J. Gen. Physiol.* 82:201–20
43. Henrich, M., Lindemann, B. 1984. Vol-

tage dependence of channel currents and channel densities in the apical membrane of toad urinary bladder. In *Intestinal Absorption and Secretion,* ed. E. Skadhauge, K. Henitze, pp. 209–20. Lancaster, UK: MTP
44. Hinton, C. F., Eaton, D. C. 1989. Expression of amiloride-blockable sodium channels in *Xenopus* oocytes. *Am. J. Physiol.* 257:C825–29
45. Kleyman, T. R., Cragoe, E. J. Jr. 1988. Amiloride and its analogs as tools in the study of ion transport. *J. Membr. Biol.* 105:1–21
46. Kleyman, T. R., Ernst, S., Rossier, B., Kraehenbuhl, J. P. 1990. Aldosterone does not alter cell surface expression of the epithelial Na^+ channel in A6 cells. *Kidney Int.* 37:564 (Abstr.)
47. Kleyman, T. R., Rajagopalan, R., Cragoe, E. J. Jr., Erlanger, B. F., Al-Awqati, Q. 1986. New amiloride analogue as hapten to raise anti-amiloride antibodies. *Am. J. Physiol.* 250:C165–70
48. Kleyman, T. R., Yulo, T., Ashbaugh, C., Landry, D., Cragoe, E. J. Jr., et al. 1986. Photoaffinity labelling of the epithelial sodium channel. *J. Biol. Chem.* 261:2839–43
49. Kleyman, T. R., Cragoe, E. J. Jr., Kraehenbuhl, J. P. 1989. The cellular pool of Na^+ channels in the amphibian cell line A6 is not altered by mineralocortocoids. Analysis using a new photoactive amiloride analog in combination with anti-amiloride antibodies. *J. Biol. Chem.* 264:11995–12000
50. Lester, D. S., Asher, C., Garty, H. 1988. Characterization of cAMP-induced activation of epithelial sodium channels. *Am. J. Physiol.* 254:C802–8
51. Lewis, S. A., Alles, W. P. 1986. Urinary kallirein: a physiological regulator of epithelial Na^+ reabsorption. *Proc. Natl. Acad. Sci. USA* 83:5345–48
52. Lewis, S. A., Hanrahan, J. W. 1985. Apical and basolateral membrane ionic channels in rabbit urinary bladder epithelium. *Pflügers Arch.* 405(Suppl. 1):S83–88
53. Lewis, S. A., Wills, N. K. 1983. Apical membrane permeability and kinetic properties of the sodium pump in rabbit urinary bladder. *J. Physiol.* 341:169–84
54. Li, J. H.-Y., Cragoe, E. J. Jr., Lindemann, B. 1985. Structure-activity relationship of amiloride analogs as blockers of epithelial Na channels. 1. Pyrazine-ring modifications. *J. Membr. Biol.* 83:45–56
55. Li, J. H.-Y., Lindemann, B. 1982. Movement of Na^+ and Li^+ across the apical membrane of frog skin. In *Basic Mechanisms in the Action of Lithium,* ed. H. M. Emrich, J. B. Aldenhoff, H. D. Lux, pp. 23–35. Amsterdam: Excerpta Med.
56. Li, J. H.-Y., Palmer, L. G., Edelman, I. S., Lindemann, B. 1982. The role of sodium channel density in the natriferic response of the toad urinary bladder to an antidiuretic hormone. *J. Membr. Biol.* 64:77–89
57. Light, D. B., Ausiello, D. A., Stanton, B. A. 1989. Guanine nucleotide-binding protein α_{i-3} directly activates a cation channel in rat renal inner medullary collecting duct cells. *J. Clin. Invest.* 84: 352–56
58. Light, D. B., McCann, F. V., Keller, T. M., Stanton, B. A. 1988. Amiloride-sensitive cation channel in apical membrane of inner medullary collecting duct. *Am. J. Physiol.* 255:F278–86
59. Light, D. B., Schwiebert, E. M., Karlson, K. H., Stanton, B. A. 1989. Atrial natriuretic peptide inhibits a cation channel in renal inner medullary collecting duct cells. *Science* 243:383–85
60. Light, D., Corbin, J., Stanton, B. 1990. Atrial natriuretic peptide (ANP) inhibits a cation channel in the inner medullary collecting duct (IMCD) by activating cyclic GMP-dependent protein kinase (cGMP-kinase). *Kidney Int.* 37:119 (Abstr.)
61. Lindemann, B. 1984. Fluctuation analysis of sodium channels in epithelia. *Annu. Rev. Physiol.* 46:497–515
62. Lindemann, B., Van Driessche, W. 1978. The mechanism of Na^+ uptake through Na^+-selective channels in the epithelium of frog skin. In *Membrane Transport Processes,* ed. J. F. Hoffman, 1:155–78. New York: Raven Press
63. Ling, B. N., Eaton, D. C. 1989. Effects of luminal Na^+ on single Na^+ channels in A6 cells, a regulatory role for protein kinase C. *Am. J. Physiol.* 256:F1094–1103
64. Marxer, A., Stieger, B., Quaroni, A., Kashgarian, M., Hauri, H. P. 1989. (Na^+-K^+) ATPase and plasma membrane polarity of intestinal epithelial cells: Presence of a brush border antigen in the distal large intestine that is immunologically related to the β subunit. *J. Cell. Biol.* 109:1057–69
65. Matalon, S., Bridges, R. J., Benos, D. J. 1991. Na^+ uptake into alveolar type II membrane vesicles occurs through amiloride-inhibitable Na^+ channels. *Am. J. Physiol.* In press
66. Matalon, S., Kirk, K., Benos, D. J. 1989. Immunofluorescent localization of

Na^+ channel protein in type II pneumocytes. *J. Cell. Biol.* 109:130a (Abstr.)
67. Meiri, H., Spira, G., Sammar, M., Namir, M., Schwartz, A., et al. 1987. Mapping a region associated with Na^+ channel inactivation using antibodies to a synthetic peptide corresponding to a part of the channel. *Proc. Natl. Acad. Sci. USA* 84:5058–62
68. Menco, B. Ph. M., Benos, D. J. 1989. Freeze-substitution and freeze-etch cytochemistry on cilia and microvilli of the rat's olfactory epithelium. *J. Cell. Biol.* 109:254a (Abstr.)
69. Moczydlowski, E., Hall, S., Garber, S. S., Strichartz, G. S., Miller, C. 1984. Voltage-dependent blockade of muscle Na^+ channels by guanidinium toxins: Effect of toxin charge. *J. Gen. Physiol.* 84:687–704
70. Mohrmann, M., Catiello, H. F., Ausiello, D. A. 1987. Inhibition of epithelial Na^+ transport by atriopeptin, protein kinase C, and pertussis toxin. *Am. J. Physiol.* 253:F372–76
70a. Moran, A., Asher, C., Cragoe, E. J. Jr., Garty, H. 1988. Conductive sodium pathway with low affinity to amiloride in LLC-PK_1 cells and other epithelia. *J. Biol. Chem.* 263:19586–91
71. Noda, M., Ikeda, T., Suzuki, H., Takeshima, H., Takahashi, T., et al. 1986. Expression of functional sodium channels from cloned cDNA. *Nature* 322:826–28
72. Noda, M., Ikeda, T., Kayano, T., Suzuki, H., Takeshima, H., et al. 1986. Existence of distinct sodium channel messenger RNA's in rat brain. *Nature* 320:188–92
73. Noda, M., Shimizu, S., Tanabe, T., Takai, T., Kayano, T., et al. 1984. Primary structure of *Electrophorus electricus* sodium channel deduced from cDNA sequence. *Nature* 312:121–27
74. Olans, L., Sariban-Sohraby, S., Benos, D. J. 1984. Saturation behavior of single, amiloride-sensitive Na^+ channels in planar lipid bilayers. *Biophys. J.* 46: 831–35
75. Omachi, R. S., Robbie, D. E., Handler, J. S., Orloff, J. 1974. Effects of ADH and other agents on cyclic AMP accumulation in the toad bladder epithelium. *Am. J. Physiol.* 226:1152–57
76. Orloff, J., Handler, J. S. 1962. The similarity of effects of vasopressin, adenosisine-3,5 monophosphate (cAMP) and theophylline on the toad bladder. *J. Clin. Invest.* 41:702–9
77. Palmer, L. G. 1982. Na^+ transport and flux ratio through apical Na^+ channels in toad bladder. *Nature* 297:688–90
78. Palmer, L. G. 1987. Ion selectivity of the apical membrane Na^+ channel in the toad urinary bladder. *J. Membr. Biol.* 67:91–98
79. Palmer, L. G. 1990. Epithelial Na^+ channels: The nature of the conducting pore. *Renal Physiol. Biochem.* In press
79a. Palmer, L. G., Corrthesy-Theulaz, M., Gaeggeler, H.-P., Kraehenbuhl, J.-P., Rossier, B. 1990. Expression of epithelial Na channels in *Xenopus* oocytes. *J. Gen. Physiol.* 96:23–46
80. Palmer, L. G., Frindt, G. 1986. Amiloride-sensitive Na^+ channels from the apical membrane of the rat cortical collecting tubule. *Proc. Natl. Acad. Sci. USA* 83:2767–70
81. Robinson, D. J., Bubien, J. K., Smith, P. R., Benos, D. J. 1989. Whole-cell currents in six and seven day post coitus rabbit trophectodermal cells. *J. Cell. Biol.* 109:61a (Abstr.)
82. Sariban-Sohraby, S., Benos, D. J. 1986. Detergent solubilization, functional reconstitution, and partial purification of epithelial amiloride-binding protein. *Biochemistry* 25:4639–46
83. Sariban-Sohraby, S., Burg, M., Wiesmann, W. P., Chiang, P. K., Johnson, J. P. 1984. Methylation increases sodium transport into A6 apical membrane vesicles: possible mode of aldosterone action. *Science* 225:745–46
84. Sariban-Sohraby, S., Fisher, R. S. 1990. Single channel activity by the amiloride binding subunit of the epithelial Na^+ channel. *Biophys. J.* 57:87a (Abstr.)
85. Sariban-Sohraby, S., Latorre, R., Burg, M., Olans, L., Benos, D. 1984. Amiloride-sensitive epithelial Na^+ channels reconstituted into planar lipid bilayer membranes. *Nature* 308:80–82
86. Sariban-Sohraby, S., Sorscher, E. J., Brenner, B. M., Benos, D. J. 1988. Phosphorylation of a single subunit of the epithelial Na^+ channel protein following vasopressin treatment of A6 cells. *J. Biol. Chem.* 263:13875–79
87. Schubert, B., VanDongen, A. M. J., Kirsch, G. E., Brown, A. A. 1989. β-adrenergic inhibition of cardiac sodium channels by dual G-protein pathways. *Science* 245:515–19
88. Sherman, S. J., Catterall, W. A. 1984. Electrical activity and cytosolic calcium regulate levels of tetrodotoxin-sensitive sodium channels in cultured rat muscle cells. *Proc. Natl. Acad. Sci. USA* 81: 262–66
89. Simon, S. A., Holland, V. F., Benos, D. J., Zampighi, G. H. 1989. Transport properties and proteins in canine circum-

vallate papillae. *11th Ann. Meet. Chemoreception Sci.*, Sarasota, FL (Abstr.)

90. Sorscher, E. J., Accavitti, M. A., Keeton, D., Steadman, E., Frizzell, R. A., et al. 1988. Antibodies against the purified epithelial sodium channel from bovine renal papilla. *Am. J. Physiol.* 255:C835–43
91. Stühmer, W., Conti, F., Suzuki, H., Wang, X., Noda, M., et al. 1988. Structural parts involved in activation and inactivation of the sodium channel. *Nature* 339:597–603
92. Szerlip, H. M., Weisberg, L., Clayman, M., Neilson, E., Wade, J. B., et al. 1989. Aldosterone-induced proteins: purification and localization of GP65, 70. *Am. J. Physiol.* 256:C865–72
93. Tousson, A., Alley, C. D., Sorscher, E. J., Brinkley, B. R., Benos, D. J. 1989. Immunochemical localization of amiloride-sensitive sodium channels in sodium transporting epithelia. *J. Cell. Sci.* 93: 349–62
94. Ussing, H. H. 1949. The distinction by means of tracers between active transport and diffusion. *Acta Physiol. Scand.* 19:43–56
95. Ussing, H. H., Zerahn, K. 1951. Active transport of sodium as the source of electric current in the short-circuited isolated frog skin. *Acta Physiol. Scand.* 23:116–27
96. Van Driessche, W., Erlij, D. 1983. Noise analysis of inward and outward Na^+ currents across the apical barrier of ouabain-treated frog skin. *Pflügers Arch.* 398:179–88
97. Verrier, B., Champigny, G., Barbry, P., Gerard, C., Mauchamp, J., et al. 1989. Identification and properties of a novel type of Na^+-permeable amiloride-sensitive channel in thyroid cells. *Eur. J. Biochem.* 183:499–505
98. Vigne, P., Champigny, G., Marsault, R., Barbry, P., Frelin, C., et al. 1989. A new type of amiloride-sensitive cationic channel in endothelial cells of brain microvessels. *J. Biol. Chem.* 264:7663–68
99. Warncke, J., Lindemann, B. 1985. Voltage dependence of Na^+ channel blockade by amiloride: relaxation effects in admittance spectra. *J. Membr. Biol.* 86:255–65
100. Zamofing, D., Rossier, B. C., Geering, K. 1989. Inhibition of N-glycosylation affects transepithelial Na^+ but not Na^+-K^+-ATPase transport. *Am. J. Physiol.* 256:C958–96

Annu. Rev. Physiol. 1991. 53:531–47

THE CALCIUM PUMPING ATPase OF THE PLASMA MEMBRANE

Ernesto Carafoli

Laboratory of Biochemistry, Swiss Federal Institute of Technology (ETH), 8092 Zurich, Switzerland

KEY WORDS: calcium pump, calcium transport

INTRODUCTION

The first indication that the plasma membrane of eukaryotic cells contains a Ca^{2+}-dependent ATPase was provided thirty years ago by Dunham & Glynn (37). Five years later Schatzmann (119) showed that the ATPase actually transported Ca^{2+} out of erythrocytes, but it took a number of years before it became clear that the pump was, in fact, present in the plasma membranes of all eukaryotic cells. Table 1 shows an updated list of cells where the Ca^{2+} pump has been documented. Whereas the detailed properties of the pump have not been analyzed in all cell types mentioned, the essential characteristics are conserved in all tissues. Fine details of the pump structure and function may differ, however, as recent work on pump isoforms has shown. One pump type, that of the hepatocyte plasma membrane, may differ in a property that is considered essential, namely the sensitivity to calmodulin. Interestingly, the pump also has been found in the plasma membranes of heart and nervous cells, where an active $Na+/Ca^{2+}$ exchanger extrudes Ca^{2+} into the environment (5, 112).

This review should in principle privilege the pump of kidney cells. However, the pump in these cells has canonical properties: thus, no special effort will be made to single out the kidney enzyme, other than to mention special findings that pertain specifically to it.

0066-4278/91/0315-0531$02.00

Table 1 Calcium pumps in the plasma membrane of eukaryotic cells

Cell type	Approximate molecular mass	Reference
Skeletal muscle		
sarcolemma	140,000	85, 86, 133
T-tubules	nd	17, 56
Heart	140,000	20, 88
		21, 73, 75, 136
Smooth muscle	140,000	89, 107, 143, 144
Kidney tubules	140,000	31, 32, 33, 45, 48, 49, 50, 87
Nervous cells		
squid axon	nd	35
synaptosomes	140,000	55, 100, 128
optical nerve	nd	26
neurohypophysis	nd	32
Intestinal epithelium	115,000–130,000	29, 44, 46, 57, 92, 137, 141
Endocrine pancreas	nd	71, 104
Exocrine pancreas	100,000	2, 7, 59
Adipocytes	nd	105, 106
Osteoblasts	nd	124
Leucocytes		
lymphocytes	150,000	79, 116
monocytes	nd	90, 123
neutrophils	nd	99, 109, 139
Macrophages	132,500	77, 122
Ehrlich ascites cells	nd	68, 129
Plant cells	nd	34, 54, 84, 93
Hen shell gland	nd	28
Liver	70,000–105,000	4, 23, 60, 61, 72, 81

A series of studies by Kumar, Penniston and their associates have used monoclonal antibodies raised against the human erythrocyte pump to document the Ca^{2+} pump in several other cell types: reactivity has been observed in human osteoblasts (13); mammalian choroid plexus (11); eel gill chloride cells (12); and placental trophoblasts (10). An ATP-powered Ca^{2+} pump possibly exists also in the plasma membranes of other eukaryotic cells, e.g. thyroid (66) and the spermatozoon (18). As for platelets, some authors have ruled out a Ca^{2+} pump in the plasma membrane (130), but others have provided evidence in its favor (38, 40, 111).

GENERAL PROPERTIES OF THE Ca^{2+} PUMP

The general mechanism of the Ca^{2+} pump follows the pattern of that of all other P-type ion pumps (101, 102) (Figure 1). ATP phosphorylates an aspartic acid residue in a Ca^{2+}-dependent manner (67, 69). The phosphorylated protein has a molecular mass of about 140,000 kd (69) and has high Ca^{2+} affinity. Under optimal conditions the K_m(Ca) of the erythrocyte pump can be

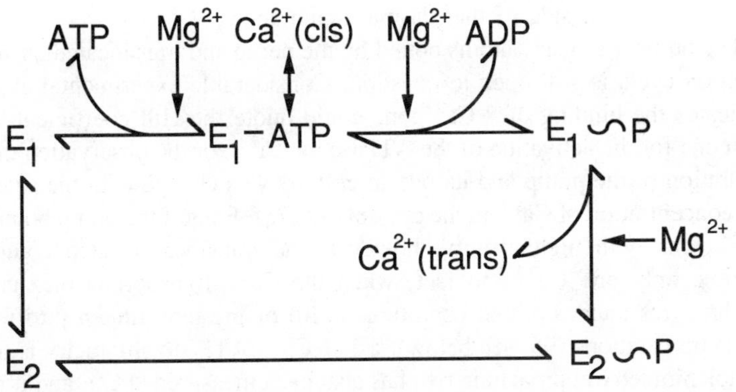

Figure 1 The reaction cycle of the plasma membrane Ca^{2+} pump. The Ca^{2+} translocating step is visualized in the $E_1{\sim}P \rightarrow E_2{\sim}P$ transition.

as low as 0.2 μM (134). ATP apparently interacts with the pump at two sites, one site having high affinity (K_m between 1 and 2.5 μM) (113), the other having much lower affinity ($K_m > 100 \mu$M), and probably playing a role in the decomposition of the aspartyl phosphate. Although not strictly essential for the formation of the phosphoenzyme, Mg^{2+} accelerates its formation (43). Mg^{2+} also accelerates the phosphoenzyme decomposition after ATP has been permitted to occupy the low affinity site.

One important aspect of the reaction cycle is the inhibition by La^{3+} (110, 117), which is associated with the increase of the steady-state level of the phosphoenzyme (134, 43), possibly resulting from the inhibition of the hydrolysis of the aspartyl phosphate. The effect is of interest methodologically since it permits the visualization of the phosphoenzyme in polyacrylamide gels at very low concentrations of the pump. Moreover, it easily allows the plasma membrane Ca^{2+} pump to be distinguished from the analogous Ca^{2+} pump in sarcoplasmic/endoplasmic reticulum in mixed membrane preparations, since the phosphoenzyme of the latter pumps is decomposed by La^{3+}. The other classical inhibitor of P-type ion pumps, vanadate (a pentacoordinate, trygonal bipyramid stereo analogue of phosphate), inhibits the plasma membrane Ca^{2+} pump at very low concentrations (2–3 μM) (9). It is generally assumed that vanadate inhibits by blocking the aspartic acid that forms the phosphorylated intermediate, and it has been shown to act as a non-competitive inhibitor of the binding of ATP to the high affinity site. In analogy with proposals on the other P-type ion pumps, vanadate interacts only with the E_2 conformer of the plasma membrane Ca^{2+} pumps and blocks the last step of the reaction cycle, which returns the enzyme to the starting E_1

conformation. Both La^{3+} and vanadate are assumed to interact with the pump from the internal side of the plasma membrane.

The number of Ca^{2+} atoms bound by the pump and translocated during the reaction cycle is still open to question. Considerable experimental evidence indicates the binding of 2 Ca^{2+}:one could quote the Hill coefficient higher than one for the activation of the ATPase by Ca^{2+}, or the observation that the saturation of the pump and its rate in erythrocytes change with the square of the concentration of Ca^{2+} in the cytosol (42, 78). Even if the pump bound two Ca^{2+} ions with high affinity, however, the translocation step could still involve only one Ca^{2+}. In fact, when the Ca^{2+} transport is measured in erythrocytes under optimal conditions (120) or in reconstituted purified enzyme preparations (95, see below), a 1:1 Ca^{2+}:ATP stoichiometry is found. A stoichiometry approaching two has also been measured (117), and it would be thermodynamically possible if one assumed a very tight coupling of Ca^{2+} transport to ATP hydrolysis and an extremely low Ca^{2+} leak through the membrane (121). The step in the reaction cycle during which the translocation of Ca^{2+} across the membrane occurs is unknown. It appears logical to relate this step to a conformational change in the pump molecule, i.e. to the step involving the $E_1{\sim}P \rightarrow E_2{\sim}P$ transition as indicated in Figure 1. The Ca^{2+}-binding site is necessarily located on the internal side of the plasma membrane prior to the translocation step, but must face the external side following translocation: whether this involves one single Ca^{2+}-binding site with varying Ca^{2+} affinity or two distinct sites is still an open question.

STIMULATION OF THE PUMP BY CALMODULIN AND OTHER TREATMENTS

Calmodulin stimulation of the plasma membrane Ca^{2+} pump was first described in 1977 (51, 65), and it was soon shown that the activation resulted from the direct interaction of the pump with calmodulin (82, 97). The binding of calmodulin to the pump has been used to measure its affinity for the activator and to estimate the number of pump units per red cell. Studies with ^{125}I-labeled calmodulin (1, 52), or azido-modified-^{125}I-calmodulin (58), have shown that (*a*) the kd for the interaction of the pump with calmodulin is in the nM range, and (*b*) that several thousand pump units are present in a red cell. Calmodulin decreases the K_m of the pump for Ca^{2+} from values in excess of 30 to below 1 μM, and increases the V_{max} of the enzyme up to tenfold (76, 91). It is generally assumed that these effects reflect the increased turnover of the enzyme.

In the absence of calmodulin, the Ca^{2+} pump can be activated by several alternative treatments. Among them is the exposure to acidic phospholipids and long chain polyunsaturated fatty acids (114). Since acidic phospholipids are present in the plasma membrane, the pump may be at least partially activated by them in vivo. Calculations on the reconstituted, purified enzyme have shown that the pump could be permanently half-maximally activated by the acidic phospholipids in the membrane environment (94). The phospholipids related to the metabolism of phosphatidyl-inositol (PI) are particularly attractive candidates for a role in the modulation of the pump in vivo, since the concentrations of PI and of its mono and bisphosphorylated derivatives (PIP, PIP_2) change in response to first messenger challenges to the cell. Since the activation of the pump increases in the order PI→PIP→PIP_2, and the products of PIP_2 hydrolysis are inactive (19, 24, 94; E. Carafoli, unpublished observations), an activation/deactivation cycle of the pump appears possible and has been proposed (103).

The activation of the pump by a tryptic treatment (135) was related to the removal of the calmodulin-binding domain from the pump molecule by Sarkadi & co-workers (41). More recent work using the intracellular Ca^{2+}-dependent protease calpain, which could well act on the pump in vivo, has also produced activation of the pump and calmodulin desensitization (3, 64, 142). Calpain treatment reduces the molecular mass of the pump by about 12 kd and leaves a fragment of apparent molecular mass 124 kd in the membrane that still binds calmodulin during the initial phases of calpain proteolysis. At later stages of proteolysis, the fragment of molecular mass 124 kd loses the ability to bind calmodulin. Work on the purified enzyme (64) has shown that calpain cleaves the pump sequentially at two locations. The first cut removes about one third of the calmodulin-binding domain, which accounts for the persistence of some calmodulin binding. A later cut removes the entire calmodulin-binding domain and produces a total loss of calmodulin reactivity.

Stimulation of the pump by the cAMP-dependent protein kinase was first observed in heart sarcolemma (21). The activation reduces the K_m (Ca) of the pump to about 1.2 μM and is linked to the phosphorylation of the pump in a domain near its C-terminus (63). Protein kinase C has also been claimed to activate the pump by stimulating its V_{max} (127). Although the cGMP-dependent protein kinase has been suggested to stimulate the pump in vascular smooth muscle (107, 118), recent work has shown that the activation is not linked to the phosphorylation of the pump molecule (6).

THE Ca^{2+} PUMP OF THE PLASMA MEMBRANE OF KIDNEY CELLS

The existence of a high Ca^{2+} affinity, calmodulin-sensitive Ca^{2+} pump in the plasma membrane of kidney cells has now been conclusively documented by a number of studies (31, 32, 33, 45, 48, 49, 50, 87). Since Ca^{2+} is handled differently in the proximal and distal tubules, differences could, in principle, exist in the activity of the pump in these two portions of the nephron. In particular, Ca^{2+} reabsorption is dependent on Na^+ reabsorption in the proximal tubule, but the two processes can be dissociated in the distal tubule (14, 15). In addition, pharmacological agents that affect the reabsorption of Ca^{2+} in the distal tubule fail to do so in the proximal tubule. That the Ca^{2+} pump is inhomogeneously distributed in the various kidney segments has been shown by experiments on microdissected nephrons (36), where it was found that the highest Ca^{2+} pumping activity (presumably of plasma membrane origin) was found in the distal tubules. In later studies monoclonal antibodies raised against the human erythrocyte Ca^{2+} pump were used to study the distribution of the pump in the different segments of the nephron (14, 30). It was found that in rat and human kidney epitopes for the plasma membrane, the Ca^{2+} pump was only present in the distal tubules. The absence or reactivity in the proximal tubule could be due to the insufficient levels of pump present in the plasma membranes, but the possibility has also been raised (15) that this portion of the nephron contains an immunologically distinct form of the pump.

PURIFICATION OF THE PLASMA MEMBRANE Ca^{2+} PUMP

In 1979 Niggli et al reported the purification of the plasma membrane Ca^{2+} pump from the erythrocyte membrane (96) by using a calmodulin affinity column that yielded a product that was functionally active. Phosphate was incorporated from γ-^{32}P-labeled ATP in a protein of molecular mass about 138,000. The purified pump was reconstituted into liposomes and shown to transport Ca^{2+} with a stochiometry to the ATP approaching one (95). One unexpected property of the purified pump was the absence of calmodulin stimulation. Calmodulin stimulation was, however, present in a preparation obtained by Gietzen et al (47), who essentially used the method of Niggli et al (131), but with phosphatidylcholine instead of phosphatidylserine as the stabilizing phospholipid. The difference in phospholipid was responsible for the different reactivity to calmodulin (94, 95), since the phosphatidylserine used in the original preparation of Niggli et al (96) had evidently already activated the pump to maximal levels. One important extension of the work on the reconstituted enzyme has been the demonstration that it functions as an obligatory H^+ exchanger (98), although it is not yet clear whether the exchange is electroneutral or partially electrogenic (115, 140). Another interesting finding on the purified erythrocyte pump (70) is its activation, concomitant with the loss of calmodulin sensitivity, under conditions that would favor its dimerization. In closing this section on purification of the

Ca^{2+} pump, it may be recalled that the enzyme has now been isolated using calmodulin affinity columns from a number of other plasma membranes, e.g. heart (22), skeletal muscle (85), and vascular smooth muscle (144). The procedure has been unsuccessful in hepatocytes, however, because the liver pump has peculiar properties, including the absence of a calmodulin response (4, 23, 60, 61, 72, 81, 80).

PROTEOLYTIC CLEAVAGE OF THE PURIFIED PUMP

A comprehensive study of the cleavage of the isolated erythrocyte pump by Zurini et al (145) showed that under controlled conditions trypsin progressively reduced the mass of the pump to fragments of molecular mass 90, 81, and 76 kd. Concomitantly, a stable fragment of molecular mass about 33 kd was also produced. The preparations enriched in the high molecular mass fragments were found to be functionally active, although their response to calmodulin varied. The 90 kd fragment was rapidly transient and behaved essentially like the intact pump, whereas the fragments of 81 and 76 kd, which tended to persist for longer times, had lost the ability to bind calmodulin. Thus it was proposed that the transition from 90 to 81 kd had removed a peripheral (probably C-terminal) fragment of about 9 kd that contained the calmodulin-binding domain. It was also proposed that the cut producing the fragment of about 33 kd occurred at the N-terminal end of the molecule. Later refinements of the work (8, 39) showed that an intermediate fragment of 85 kd, which retained calmodulin binding, but decreased calmodulin response, was also formed under special conditions. The fragment of 81 kd still retained phospholipid sensitivity, which became lost in the further transition to 76 kd.

Cyanogen bromide (CNBr) cleavage experiments on the isolated erythrocyte pump labeled with a bifunctional, radioactive, cleavable cross-linker conjugated to calmodulin have led to the sequencing of the entire calmodulin-binding domain (62). This is a fragment of ~30 amino acids that has a predominance of basic residues and the propensity to form an amphiphilic helix like other calmodulin-binding domains in calmodulin-modulated proteins.

PRIMARY STRUCTURE OF THE PUMP AND LOCATION OF FUNCTIONAL DOMAINS

In 1988 the complete amino acid sequence of the pump was deduced by Shull & Greeb from complementary DNA isolated from rat brain (125) and by Verma et al from human teratoma (138). The cDNA libraries were screened with oligonucleotides constructed from tryptic fragments of the human erythrocyte pump (138) or derived from the conserved amino acid sequence of

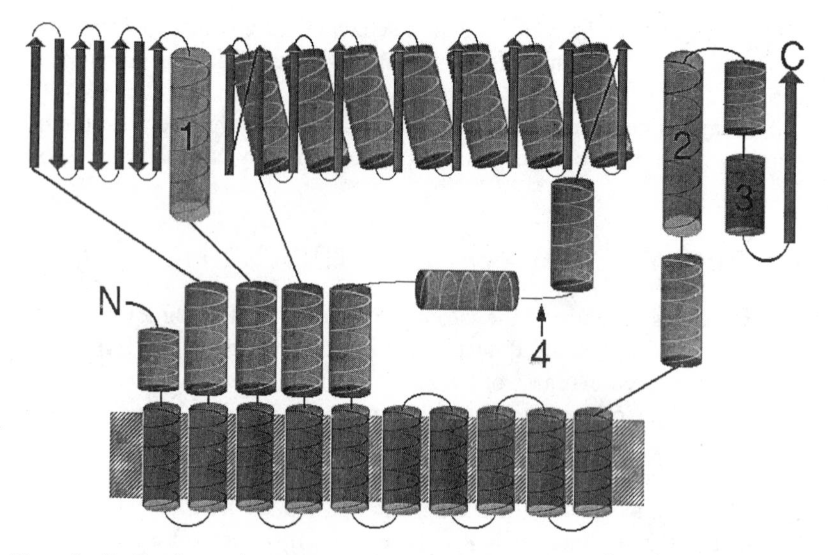

Figure 2 Predicted secondary structure of the plasma membrane Ca^{2+} pump, based on the model of the sarcoplasmic reticulum Ca^{2+} ATPase described in (138) and (139). As discussed in the text, the model is provisional and will have to be validated by direct experiments. The University of Wisconsin Genetic Computer Group sequence analysis software package was used, taking into account the alignments of P-type ATPases proposed by Green (53). α-helices are represented by cylinders, β-sheets by arrows. 1 = putative domain responsive to acidic phospholipids (see reference 146). 2 = calmodulin-binding domain. 3 = domain containing the substrate sequence for the cAMP-dependent protein kinase (reference 63). This sequence is not present in the major isoform of the pump expressed in human erythrocytes (see reference 143). 4 = flexible hinge, which permits the movement of the aspartyl-phosphate and of the ATP (FITC)-binding lysine (16, 83).

the fluorescein isothiocyanate (FITC)-binding site (125), which is commonly accepted to be part of the ATP-binding site of P-type ion pumps. The rat cDNA library has produced two isoforms of the pump, having 1176 and 1198 amino acids, respectively. The human cDNA library has produced an isoform containing 1220 amino acids, which is over 99% identical to the first rat isoform in the first 1117 residues, but differs substantially in the C-terminal domain. Differential RNA splicing involving a single exon at the C-terminal end of the corresponding gene (132) that accounts for this difference. A model of the pump showing the ten putative transmembrane helices and the secondary structure prediction for the extramembrane domains is shown in Figure 2.

The rat and human sequences are highly homologous in the catalytic domains. Both are assumed to contain ten putative transmembrane helices, assigned with the usual Kyte-Doolittle algorhythm (16), and are connected on the outside side of the membrane by short loops. The model is patterned on that of the sarcoplasmic reticulum pump and is provisional. It will have to be tested directly, e.g. with specific labels and/or antibodies. Recent work with site-directed antibodies (F. Hofmann, T. Vorherr, E. Carafoli, unpublished) has indicated that the transmembrane domains could be eight rather than ten. The model shows that large domains of the pump protrude into the intracellular space, the first domain connects transmembrane helices two and three and contains both α-helical and antiparallel β-sheet domains. It also contains a sequence found only in the plasma membrane Ca^{2+} pump, which represents the N-terminal difference between the tryptic fragments of 90, 85, 81 kd and that of 76 kd. This sequence identifies the N-terminal domain in the pump involved in regulation, i.e. the domain responsive to acidic phospholipids (146). The second regulating domain protrudes from transmembrane helix ten with about 160 residues and contains the calmodulin-binding region (residues 1086 to 1115) and the C-terminal sequence, which is phosphorylated by the cAMP-dependent protein kinase (63). The kinase phosphorylates a Ser residue, which is located about 50 residues away from the C-terminus of the pump (Ser 1178). The major unit protruding into the intracellular space (about 430 residues) connects transmembrane helices four and five and is predominantly arranged in α-helices and parallel β-sheets. It contains the aspartyl-phosphate residue (Asp 475 in the human teratoma isoform of the enzyme), the site of FITC binding (Lys 602 in the human teratoma isoform), and a domain called the hinge (83), which is generally conserved in all P-type ion pumps and is postulated to bring Asp 475 and Lys 609 close together during the catalytic cycle.

The calmodulin-binding domain is flanked by two acidic stretches that would be good candidates to bind Ca^{2+} (138). Although they could regulate the access of Ca^{2+} to the pump, i.e. functioning as Ca^{2+} filters, they do not contain the high affinity catalytic Ca^{2+}-binding sites because proteolytic treatments that remove these acidic stretches together with the calmodulin-binding domain from the enzyme leave a truncated pump that still has high Ca^{2+} affinity (see below). Most likely, the catalytic Ca^{2+}-binding sites reside within the transmembrane helices, in analogy with membrane-binding sites on the sarcoplasmic reticulum Ca^{2+} pump (25).

The functionally active trypic fragments of the pump (discussed above) have now been located within the pump structure by C- and N-terminal sequencing work (146). The N-terminus of the fragments of 90, 85, and 81 kd is Thr 315, that of the 76 kd fragment is Leu 349. The C-termini of these fragments have been found, as expected, near or within the calmodulin-binding domain. The C-terminus of the 90 kd fragment is Lys 1161, which shows that the 90 kd fragment contains the complete calmodulin-binding domain. The C-terminus of the 85 kd fragment is Lys 1105, i.e. this fragment has lost about 50% of the calmodulin-binding domain, which explains its weak response to calmodulin. The C-termini of the 81 and 76 kd fragments are identical (Lys 1066), i.e. these two fragments have lost the entire calmodulin-binding domain (and the acidic stretch N-terminal to it). Therefore, the difference in the reactivity of the 81 and 76 kd fragments to acidic phospholipids reflects the difference in their N-termini. As mentioned above, the difference is a highly charged α-helical sequence of about 50 residues in the loop connecting transmembrane domains two and three. Obviously this sequence must be located in the proximity of the membrane domain in order to interact with the phospholipid ambient. The C-terminus of the fragment of about 33 kd is Lys 314. Whether the latter fragment becomes separated from those of higher molecular mass after the cut between Lys 314 and Thr 315 has occurred is doubtful. While the cuts around the calmodulin-binding domain actually separate the latter (or portions of it) from the main body of the pump (96), the fragment of about 76 kd probably only separates from the remainder (i.e. the 33 kd N-terminal portion) of the pump under the denaturing conditions of the dodecyl-sulphate polyacrylamide gels. Thus the functional difference between the fragments of 76 and 81 kd would merely reflect the structural alteration of the domain between residues 314 and 359, rather than its separation from the remainder of the pump.

ISOFORMS OF THE PLASMA MEMBRANE Ca^{2+} PUMP

The existence of different isoforms of the pump in rat brain and human teratoma cells has been mentioned above (125, 138). Other isoforms have now been discovered that reflect alternative RNA splicing involving different exons in the pump gene, as well as the existence of multiple genes encoding the pump protein.

Alternative splicing of RNA involving a C-terminal exon produced the first rat brain isoform and the isoform characterized in human teratoma cells (see above). A more comprehensive investigation of the splicing at this exon in human fetal skeletal muscle has revealed that more than one splicing mode may occur that leads to the insertion of 29 or 38 amino acids in the middle of the calmodulin-binding domain (132). Although no protein data are available on these splicing products as yet, they probably have altered calmodulin response. Recently, a second isoform has been found to be expressed in human erythrocytes in addition to the isoform first found in human teratoma cells (131). It contains 1205 amino acids, shows about 75% identity with the first human isoform, and appears to be the major erythrocyte isoform. Most interestingly, it lacks the sequence that is phosphorylated by the cAMP-dependent protein kinase. The sequence of yet another isoform has been recently deduced from complementary cDNA in rat brain (126). The matter of pump isoforms is developing very rapidly, and while the significance is not clear at the moment, the possibility of differences in regulatory properties, possibly reflecting tissue specificity, appears attractive.

ACKNOWLEDGMENTS

The original work described has been aided by the financial contribution of the Swiss National Science Foundation (Grants 3.634.080, 3.189.082, 3.658.084, and 85.159.084). The financial support of the National Institutes of Health is also gratefully acknowledged (Grant 28835).

Literature Cited

1. Agre, P., Gardner, K., Bennett, V. 1983. Association between human erythrocyte calmodulin and the cytoplasmic surface of human erythrocyte membranes. *J. Biol. Chem.* 258:6258–65
2. Ansah, T. A., Molla, A., Katz, S. 1984. Ca^{2+}-ATPase activity in pancreatic acinar plasma membranes. Regulation by calmodulin and acidic phospholipids. *J. Biol. Chem.* 259:13442–50
3. Au, K. S. 1986. Activation of erythrocyte membrane Ca^{2+}-ATPase by calpain. *Biochim. Biophys. Acta* 905:273–78
4. Bachs, O., Famulski, K. S., Mirabelli, F., Carafoli, E. 1985. ATP-dependent Ca^{2+} transport in vesicles isolated from the bile canalicular region of the hepatocyte plasma membrane. *Eur. J. Biochem.* 147:1–7
5. Baker, P. F., Blaustein, M., Hodgkin, Steinhardt, R. 1967. The effect of sodium concentration on calcium movements in giant axons of *Loligo forbesi*. *J. Physiol.* 192:43–44
6. Baltensberger, E., Carafoli, E., Chiesi, M. 1988. The Ca^{2+}-pumping ATPase and the major substrate of the cGMP-dependent protein kinase in smooth muscle sarcolemma are distinct entities. *Eur. J. Biochem.* 172:7–16
7. Bayerdoerfer, E., Streb, H., Eckhardt, L., Hasse, W., Schulz, I. 1984. Characterization of calcium uptake in rough endoplasmic reticulum of rat pancreas. *J. Membr. Biol.* 81:69–82
8. Benaim, G., Zurini, M., Carafoli, E. 1984. Different conformational states of the purified Ca^{2+} ATPase of the erythrocyte plasma membrane revealed by controlled trypsin proteolysis. *J. Biol. Chem.* 259:8471–77
9. Bond, G. H., Hudgins, P. 1979. Kinetic of inhibition of $Na^{+}K^{+}$-ATPase by Mg^{2+},K^{+} and vanadate. *Biochemistry* 18:325–31
10. Borke, J. L., Caride, A., Verma, A. K., Kelly, L. K., Smith, C. H., et al. 1989. Calcium pump epitopes in placental trophoblast membranes. *Am. J. Physiol.* 257:C341–46
11. Borke, J. L., Caride, A. J., Yaksh, T. L., Penniston, J. T., Kumar, R. 1989. Cerebrospinal fluid calcium homeostasis: Evidence for a plasma membrane Ca^{++}-pump in mammalian choroid plexus. *Brain Res.* 489:355–60
12. Borke, J. L., Epstein, F. H., Penniston, J. T., Kumar, R. 1989. Localization of a plasma membrane Ca^{++}-pump in gill chloride cells and kidney distal tubule cells of the American eel, *Anguilla rostrata*. *M. Desert Isl. Biol. Lab. Bull.* 28:48–51
13. Borke, J. L., Eriksen, E. F., Minami, J., Keeting, P., Mann, K. G., et al. 1988. Epitopes to the human erythrocyte Ca^{++}-Mg^{++}ATPase pump in human osteoblast-like cell plasma membranes. *J. Clin. Endocrinol. Metab.* 67:1299–1304
14. Borke, J. L., Minami, J., Verma, A., Penniston, J. T., Kumar, R. 1987. Monoclonal antibodies to human erythrocyte membrane Ca^{++}-Mg^{++} adenosine triphosphatase pump recognize an epitope in the basolateral membrane of human kidney distal tubule cells. *J. Clin. Invest.* 80:1225–31
15. Borke, J. L., Minami, J., Verma, A. K., Penniston, J. T., Kumar, R. 1988. Colocalization of erythrocyte Ca^{++}-Mg^{++} ATPase and vitamin D-dependent 28-kilodalton-calcium binding protein in the cells of human kidney distal tubules. *Kidney Int.* 34:262–67
16. Brandl, C. J., Green, N. M., Korczak, B., MacLennan, D. H. 1986. Two Ca^{2+} ATPase genes: homologies and mechanistic implications of deduced amino acid sequences. *Cell* 44:597–607
17. Brandt, N. R., Caswell, A. H., Brunschwig, J. P. 1980. ATP-energized Ca^{2+} pump in isolated transverse tubules of skeletal muscle. *J. Biol. Chem.* 255: 6290–98
18. Breitbart, H., Darshan, R., Rubinstein, S. 1984. Evidence for the presence of ATP-dependent calcium pump and ATPase activities in bull sperm head membranes. *Biochem. Biophys. Res. Commun.* 122:479–84
19. Carafoli, E., Zurini, M. 1982. The cal-

cium pumping ATPase of plasma membranes. Purification, reconstitution, and properties. *Biochim. Biophys. Acta* 683: 279–301
20. Caroni, P., Carafoli, E. 1980. An ATP-dependent Ca^{2+} transport system in dog heart sarcolemma. *Nature* 283:765–67
21. Caroni, P., Carafoli, E. 1981. The Ca^{2+} pumping ATPase of heart sarcolemma is activated by a phosphorylation-dephosphorylation process. *J. Biol. Chem.* 256: 9371–73
22. Caroni, P., Carafoli, E. 1981. The Ca^{2+} pumping ATPase of heart sarcolemma. Characterization, calmodulin dependence, and partial purification. *J. Biol. Chem.* 256:3263–70
23. Chan, K. M., Junger, K. D. 1983. Calcium transport and phosphorylated intermediate of (Ca^{2+} + Mg^{2+})-ATPase in plasma membranes of rat liver. *J. Biol. Chem.* 253:4404–10
24. Choquette, D., Hakim, G., Filoteo, A. G., Plishker, G. A., Bostwick, G. R., Penniston, J. T. 1984. Regulation of plasma membrane Ca^{2+} ATPases by lipids of the phosphatidylinositol cycle. *Biochem. Biophys. Res. Commun.* 125: 908–15
25. Clarke, D. M., Loo T. W., Inesi, G., MacLennan D. H. 1989. Location of high affinity Ca^{2+}-binding sites within the predicted transmembrane domain of the sarcoplasmic reticulum CA^{2+}-ATPase. *Nature* 239:476–78
26. Condrescu, M., Asses, L., DiPolo, R. 1984. Partial purification and characterization of the (Ca^{2+} + Mg^{2+})ATPase from squid optic nerve plasma membranes. *Biochim. Biophys. Acta* 769: 261–69
27. Conigrave, A. D., Treiman, M., Saermark, T., Thorn, N. A. 1981. Stimulation by calmodulin of Ca^{2+} uptake and (Ca^{2+} + Mg^{2+})-ATPase activity in membrane fractions from ox neurohypophysis. *Cell Calcium* 2:125–36
28. Coty, W. A., McConkey, C. Jr. 1982. A high affinity calcium stimulated ATPase activity in the hen oviduct shell gland. *Arch. Biochem. Biophys.* 219: 444–53
29. DeJonge, H. R., Ghijsen, W. E. J. M., Van Os, C. H. 1981. Phosphorylated intermediates of Ca^{2+} ATPase and alkaline phosphatase in plasma membranes from rat duodenal epithelium. *Biochim. Biophys. Acta,* 647:140–49
30. De Smedt, H., Paris, J. B., Borghgraef, R. 1986. Biochemical characterization of two different high affinity calcium pumps in endoplasmic reticulum and basal lateral membranes from renal cortex. *Renal Physiol.* 9:80–81
31. De Smedt, H., Paris, J. B., Borghgraef, R., Wuytack, F. 1981. Calmodulin stimulation of renal (Ca^{2+} + Mg^{2+}) ATPase. *FEBS Lett.* 131:60–62
32. De Smedt, H., Paris, J. B., Borghgraef, R., Wuytack, F. 1983. Phosphorylated intermediates of (Ca^{2+} + Mg^{2+})-ATPase and alkaline phosphatase in renal plasma membranes. *Biochim. Biophys. Acta* 728:409–18
33. De Smedt, H., Paris, J. B., Wuytack, F., Borghgraef, R. 1984. Calcium-induced phosphorylation and [^{125}] I-calmodulin binding in renal membrane preparations. *Biochim. Biophys. Acta* 776:122–32
34. Dieter, P., Marmé, D. 1981. A calmodulin-dependent microsomal ATPase from corn (*Zea mays* L.). *FEBS Lett.* 125:245–48
35. Di Polo, R. 1979. Ca pump driven by ATP in squid axon. *Nature* 274:390–92
36. Doucet, A., Katz, A. 1982. High-affinity Ca-Mg-ATPase along the rabbit nephron. *Am. J. Physiol.* 242:F346–52
37. Dunham, E. T., Glynn, I. M. 1961. Adenosine-triphosphatase activity and the active movements of alkali metal ions. *J. Physiol.* 156:274–93
38. Enouf, J., Lompre, Z., Bredous, R., Bordeau, N., De La Bastie, D., Levy-Toledano, S. 1988. Different sensitivity to trypsin of human platelet plasma and intracellular membrane Ca^{2+} pumps. *J. Biol. Chem.* 263:13922–29
39. Enyedi, A., Flura, M., Sarkadi, B., Gardos, G., Carafoli, E. 1987. The maximal velocity and the calcium affinity of the red cell calcium pump may be regulated independently. *J. Biol. Chem.* 262:6425–30
40. Enyedi, A., Sarkadi, B., Foldes-Papp, Z., Monostory, S., Gardos, G. 1986. Demonstration of two distinct calcium pumps in human platelet membrane vesicles. *J. Biol. Chem.* 261:9558–63
41. Enyedi, A., Sarkadi, B., Szasz, I., Bot, B., Gardos, G. 1980. Molecular properties of the red cell calcium pump. II Effects of proteolysis, proteolytic digestion and drugs on the calcium-induced phosphorylation by ATP in inside/out red cell membrane vesicles. *Cell Calcium* 1:299–310
42. Ferreira, H. G., Lew, V. L. 1976. Use of inophore A23187 to measure cytoplasmic Ca^{2+} buffering and activation of the Ca pump by internal Ca. *Nature* 259:47–49
43. Garrahan, P. J., Rega, A. F. 1978. Activation of partial reactions of the

Ca^{2+}-ATPase from human red cells by Mg^{2+} and ATP. *Biochim. Biophys. Acta* 513:59–65

44. Ghijsen, W. E. J. M., De Jonge, M. D., Van Os, C. H. 1982. ATP-dependent Ca^{2+} transport and its correlation with Ca^{2+}-ATPase activity in basolateral plasma membrane of rat duodenum. *Biochim. Biophys. Acta* 689:327–36
45. Ghijsen, W., Gmaj, P., Murer, H. 1984. Ca^{2+}-stimulated, Mg^{2+}-independent ATP-hydrolysis of the high affinity Ca^{2+} pumping ATPase. Two different activities in rat kidney basolateral membranes. *Biochim. Biophys. Acta.* 778:481–88
46. Ghijsen, W. E. J. M., Van Os, C. H. 1979. Ca-stimulated ATPase in brush border and basolateral membranes of rat duodenum with high affinity sites for Ca ions. *Nature* 279:802–4
47. Gietzen, K., Tejcka, M., Wolf, H. V. 1980. Calmodulin affinity chromatography yields a functionally purified erythrocyte (Ca^{2+} + Mg^{2+})-dependent adenosine triphosphatase. *Biochem. J.* 189:81–88
48. Gmaj, P., Murer, H., Carafoli, E. 1982. Localization and properties of a high affinity (Ca^{2+} + Mg^{2+}) ATPase in isolated kidney cortex plasma membranes. *FEBS Lett.* 131:60–62
49. Gmaj, P., Murer, H., Kinne, R. 1979. Calcium ion transport across plasma membranes isolated from rat kidney cortex. *Biochem. J.* 178:549–57
50. Gmaj, P., Zurini, M., Murer, H., Carafoli, E. 1983. A high affinity, calmodulin-dependent Ca^{2+} pump in the basal-lateral plasma membranes of kidney cortex. *Biochim. Biophys. Acta* 778:481–88
51. Gopinath, R. M., Vincenzi, F. F. 1977. Phosphodiesterase protein activator mimics red blood cell cytoplasmatic activator of the (Ca^{2+} + Mg^{2+}) ATPase. *Biochem. Biophys. Res. Commun.* 77:1203–9
52. Graf, E., Filoteo, A. G., Penniston, J. T. 1980. Preparation of ^{125}I-calmodulin with retention of full biological activity: its binding to human erythrocyte ghosts. *Arch. Biochem. Biophys.* 203:719–26
53. Green, N. M. 1989. ATP-driven cation pumps, alignment of sequences. *Trans. Biochem. Soc.* 17:970–72
54. Gross, J., Marmé, D. 1978. ATP-dependent Ca^{2+} uptake into plant membrane vesicles. *Proc. Natl. Acad. Sci. USA* 75:1232–36
55. Hakim, G., Itano, T., Verma, A. K., Penniston, J. T. 1982. Purification of the Ca^{2+} and Mg^{2+}-requiring ATPase from rat brain synaptic plasma membrane. *Biochem. J.* 207:225–31
56. Hidalgo, C., Gonzales, M. E., Garcia, A. M. 1986. Calcium transport in transverse tubules isolated from rabbit skeletal muscle. *Biochim. Biophys. Acta* 854:279–86
57. Hildmann, B., Schmidt, A., Murer, H. 1982. Ca^{2+}-transport across basolateral plasma membranes from rat small intestinal epithelial cells. *J. Membr. Biol.* 65:55–62
58. Hinds, T. R., Andreasen, T. J. 1981. Photochemical cross-linking of azidocalmodulin to the (Ca^{2+} Mg^{2+})-ATPase at low Ca^{2+} concentrations. *J. Biol. Chem.* 256:7877–82
59. Imamura, K., Schulz, I. 1985. Phosphorylated intermediate of (Ca^{2+} + K^{+})-stimulated, Mg^{2+}-dependent transport ATPase in endoplasmic reticulum from rat pancreatic acinar cells. *J. Biol. Chem.* 260:11339–47
60. Iwasa, T., Iwasa, Y., Krishnarnaraj, R. 1983. A high-affinity (Ca^{2+} + Mg^{2+})-ATPase in plasma membranes of rat ascites hepatoma AH 109A cells. *Biochim. Biophys. Acta* 731:229–38
61. Iwasa, Y., Iwasa, T., Higashi, K., Matsui, K., Miyamoto, E. 1982. Demonstration of a high affinity Ca^{2+}-ATPase in rat liver plasma membranes. *Biochem. Biophys. Res. Commun.* 105:448–94
62. James, P., Maeda, M., Fischer, R., Verma, A. K., Krebs, J., et al. 1988. Identification and primary structure of a calmodulin binding domain of the CA^{2+} pump of human erythrocytes. *J. Biol. Chem.* 263:2905–10
63. James, P. H., Pruschy, M., Vorherr, T., Penniston, J. T., Carafoli, E. 1989. Primary structure of the cAMP-dependent phosphorylation site of the plasma membrane calcium pump. *Biochemistry* 28: 4253–58
64. James, P., Vorherr, T., Krebs, J., Morelli, A., Castello, G., et al. 1989. Modulation of erythrocyte Ca^{2+} ATPase by selective calpain cleavage of the calmodulin binding domain. *J. Biol. Chem.* 264:8289–96
65. Jarrett, H. W., Penniston, J. T. 1977. Partial purification of the (Ca^{2+} + Mg^{2+}) ATPase activator from human erythrocytes: its similarity to the activator of 3'-5'-cyclic nucleotide phosphodiesterase. *Biochem. Biophys. Res. Commun.* 77:1210–16
66. Kasai, K., Field, J. B. 1982. Ca^{2+}-stimulated, Mg^{2+}-dependent ATPase in bovine thyroid plasma membranes. *Biochim. Biophys. Acta* 685:225–29

67. Katz, S., Blostein, R. 1975. Ca^{2+}-stimulated membrane phosphorylation and ATPase activity of the human erythrocyte. *Biochim. Biophys. Acta* 389:314–24
68. Klaven, N. B., Pershadsingh, H. A., Henius, G. V., Laris, P. C., Long, J. W., McDonald, J. M. 1983. A high affinity calmodulin sensitive (Ca^{2+} + Mg^{2+})-ATPase and associated calcium transport pump in the Ehrlich ascites tumour cell plasma membrane. *Arch. Biochem. Biophys.* 226:618–28
69. Knauf, P. A., Proverbio, F., Hoffmann, J. F. 1974. Electrophoretic separation of different phosphoproteins associated with Ca^{2+}-ATPase and Na^+, K^+-ATPase in human red cell ghosts. *J. Gen. Physiol.* 63:324–36
70. Kosk-Kosicka, D., Bzdega, T. 1988. Activation of the erythrocyte Ca^{2+}-ATPase by either self-association or interaction with calmodulin. *J. Biol. Chem.* 263:18184–89
71. Kotagal, N., Patker, C., Landt, M., McDonald, J. M., Colca, J., et al. 1982. Regulation of pancreatic islet-cell plasma membrane (Ca^{2+} + Mg^{2+})-ATPase by calmodulin. *FEBS Lett.* 137:249–52
72. Kraus-Friedmann, N., Biber, J., Murer, H., Carafoli, E. 1982. Calcium uptake in isolated hepatic plasma membrane vesicles. *Eur. J. Biochem.* 129:7–12
73. Kuwayama, H., Kanazawa, T. 1982. Purification of cardiac sarcolemma vesicles: high sodium pump content and ATP-dependent, calmodulin-activated calcium uptake. *J. Biochem.* 91:1419–26
74. Kyte, J., Doolittle, R. F. 1982. A simple method for displaying the hydrophobic character of a protein. *J. Mol. Biol.* 157:106–32
75. Lamers, J. M. J., Stinis, J. T. 1981. An electrogenic Na^+/Ca^{2+} antiporter in addition to the Ca^{2+} pump in cardiac sarcolemma. *Biochim. Biophys. Acta* 640:521–34
76. Larsen, F. L., Katz, S., Roufogalis, G. D. 1981. Calmodulin regulation of Ca^{2+} transport in human erythrocytes. *Biochem. J.* 200:185–91
77. Lew, P. D., Stossel, T. P. 1980. Calcium transport by macrophage plasma membranes. *J. Biol. Chem.* 255:5841–46
78. Lew, V. L., Tsien, R. Y., Miner, C., Bookchin, R. M. 1982. Physiological (Ca^{2+}) level and pump-leak turnover in intact red cells measured using an incorporated Ca^{2+} chelator. *Nature* 298:478–80
79. Lichtman, A. H., Segal, G. B., Lichtman, M. A. 1981. Calcium transport and calcium-ATPase activity in human lymphocyte plasma membrane vesicles. *J. Biol. Chem.* 256:6148–54
80. Lin, S. H., Fain, J. N. 1984. Purification of (Ca^{2+} + Mg^{2+})-ATPase from rat liver plasma membrane. *J. Biol. Chem.* 259:3016–20
81. Lotersztajn, S., Hanoune, J., Pecker, F. 1981. A high affinity calcium-stimulated, Mg^{2+}-dependent ATPase in rat liver plasma membranes. Dependence on an endogenous protein activator distinct from calmodulin. *J. Biol. Chem.* 257:11209–15
82. Lynch, T. J., Cheung, W. Y. 1979. Human erythrocyte (Ca^{2+} Mg^{2+})-ATPase: mechanism of stimulation by Ca^{2+}. *Arch. Biochem. Biophys.* 194:165–70
83. MacLennan, D. H., Brandl, C. J., Korczak, B., Green, N. M. 1985. Amino-acid sequence of a Ca^{2+} + Mg^{2+}-dependent ATPase from rabbit muscle sarcoplasmic reticulum, deduced from its complementary DNA sequence. *Nature* 316:696–700
84. Marmé, D., Dieter, P. 1983. Role of Ca^{2+} and calmodulin in plants. In *Calcium and Cell Function,* ed. W. Y. Cheung, 4:264–312. New York: Academic
85. Michalak, M., Famulski, R., Carafoli, E. 1984. The calcium pumping ATPase in skeletal muscle sarcolemma. Calmodulin dependence, regulation by cAMP dependent phosphorylation, and purification. *J. Biol. Chem.* 259:15540–47
86. Mickelson, J. R., Beaudry, T. M., Louis, C. F. 1985. Regulation of skeletal muscle sarcolemmal ATP-dependent calcium transport by calmodulin and cAMP-dependent protein kinase. *Arch. Biochem. Biophys.* 242:127–36
87. Moore, L., Fitzpatrick, D. F., Chen, T. S., Landon, E. J. 1974. Calcium pump activity of renal plasma membranes and renal microsomes. *Biochim. Biophys. Acta* 345:405–18
88. Morcos, N. C., Drummond, G. I. 1979. (Ca^{2+} + Mg^{2+}) ATPase in enriched sarcolemma from dog heart. *Biochim. Biophys. Acta* 598:27–39
89. Morel, N., Wibo, N., Godfraind, T. 1981. A calmodulin-stimulated Ca^{2+} pump in rat aorta membranes. *Biochim. Biophys. Acta* 644:82–88
90. Morimoto, S., Birge, S. J., Shen, V., Avioli, L. V. 1985. (Ca^{2+} + Mg^{2+})-ATPase activity in plasma membrane of circulating mononuclear cells. *J. Biol. Chem.* 260:14953–57

91. Muallem, S., Karlish, S. J. D. 1980. Regulatory interaction between calmodulin and ATP in the red cell Ca^{2+} pump. *Biochim. Biophys. Acta* 597:631–36
92. Nellans, H. N., Popovich, J. E. 1981. Calmodulin-regulated, ATP-driven calcium transport by basolateral in membranes of rat small intestine. *J. Biol. Chem.* 256:9932–36
93. Nguyen, T. D., Siegenthaler, P.-A. 1985. Purification and some properties of a Mg^{2+}-Ca^{2+}- and calmodulin stimulated ATPase from spinach chloroplast envelope membranes. *Biochim. Biophys. Acta* 840:99–106
94. Niggli, V., Adunyah, E. S., Carafoli, E. 1981. Acidic phospholipids, unsaturated fatty acids, and limited proteolysis mimic the effect of calmodulin on the purified erythrocyte Ca^{2+}-ATPase. *J. Biol. Chem.* 256:8588–92
95. Niggli, V., Adunyah, E. S., Penniston, J. T., Carafoli, E. 1981. Purified (Ca^{2+} + Mg^{2+}) ATPase of the erythrocyte membrane:reconstitution and effect of calmodulin and phospholipids. *J. Biol. Chem.* 256:395–401
96. Niggli, V., Penniston, J. T., Carafoli, E. 1979. Purification of the (Ca^{2+} + Mg^{2+})-ATPase from human erythrocyte membranes using a calmodulin affinity column. *J. Biol. Chem.* 254:9955–58
97. Niggli, V., Ronner, P., Carafoli, E., Penniston, J. T. 1979. Effect of calmodulin on the (Ca^{2+} Mg^{2+})-ATPase partially purified from erythrocyte membranes. *Arch. Biochem. Biophys.* 198: 124–30
98. Niggli, V., Sigel, E., Carafoli, E. 1982. Inhibition of the purified and reconstituted Ca^{2+} pump of erythrocytes by μM levels of DIDS and NAP-taurine. *FEBS Lett.* 138:164–66
99. Ochs, D. L., Reed, P. W. 1983. ATP-dependent calcium transport in plasma membrane vesicles from neutrophil leucocytes. *J. Biol. Chem.* 258:10116–22
100. Papazian, D., Rahamimoff, H., Goldin, S. M. 1979. Reconstitution and purification by "transport specificity fraction" of an ATP-dependent calcium transport component from synaptosome-derived vesicles. *Proc. Natl. Acad. Sci. USA* 76:3708–12
101. Pedersen, P. L., Carafoli, E. 1987. Ion motive ATPases. *Trends Biochem. Sci.* 12:146–50
102. Pedersen, P. L., Carafoli, E. 1987. Ion motive ATPases. *Trends Biochem. Sci.* 12:186–89
103. Penniston, J. T. 1982. Plasma membrane Ca^{2+}-pumping ATPases. Ann. NY Acad. Sci. 402:296–303
104. Pershadsingh, H. A., McDaniel, M. L., Lamdt, M., Bry, C. G., Lacy, P. E., McDonald, J. M. 1980. Ca^{2+}-activated ATPase and ATP-dependent calmodulin-stimulated Ca^{2+}-transport in islet cell plasma membrane. *Nature* 288:492–94
105. Pershadsingh, H. A., McDonald, J. M. 1979. Direct addition of insulin inhibits a high affinity Ca^{2+} ATPase in isolated adipocyte plasma membranes. *Nature* 281:495–97
106. Pershadsingh, H. A., McDonald, J. M. 1980. A high-affinity, calcium-stimulated, Mg^{2+}-dependent adenosine triphosphatase in rat adipocyte plasma membranes. *J. Biol. Chem.* 255:4087–93
107. Popescu, L. M., Ignat, P. 1983. Calmodulin-dependent Ca^{2+} pump ATPase of human smooth muscle sarcolemma. *Cell Calcium* 4:219–35
108. Deleted in proof
109. Prentki, M., Wollheim, C. B., Lew, P. D. 1984. Ca^{2+} homeostasis in permeabilized human neutrophils. *J. Biol. Chem.* 259:13777–82
110. Quist, E. E., Roufogalis, E. D. 1975. Determination of the stoichiometry of the calcium pump in human erythrocytes using lanthanum as a selective inhibitor. *FEBS Lett.* 50:135–39
111. Resink, T., Tkachuk, V. A., Erne, P., Bühler, F. R. 1986. Platelet membrane calmodulin-stimulated calcium-adenosine triphosphatase. Altered activity in essential hypertension. *Hypertension* 8:159–66
112. Reuter, H., Seitz, N. 1968. The dependence of Ca^{2+} efflux from cardiac muscle on temperature and external ion composition. *J. Physiol.* 195:451–70
113. Richards, D. E., Rega, A. G., Garrahan, D. J. 1978. Two classes of site for ATP in the Ca^{2+}-ATPase from human red cell membranes. *Biochim. Biophys. Acta* 511:194–201
114. Ronner, P., Gazzotti, P., Carafoli, E. 1977. A lipid requirement for the (Ca^{2+} Mg^{2+})-activated ATPase of erythrocyte membranes. *Arch. Biochem. Biophys.* 179:578–83
115. Rossi, J. P. F. C., Schatzmann, H. J. 1982. Is the red cell calcium pump electrogenic? *J. Physiol.* 327:1–15
116. Sarkadi, B., Enyedi, A., Gardos, G. 1980. Molecular properties of the red cell calcium pump. I. Effects of calmodulin, proteolytic digestion, and drugs on the kinetics of active calcium uptake in inside/out red cell membrane vesicles. *Cell Calcium* 1:287–98

117. Sarkadi, B., Szasz, I., Garloczi, A., Gardos, G. 1977. Transport parameters and stoichiometry of active calcium ion extrusion in intact human red cells. *Biochim. Biophys. Acta* 464:93–107
118. Sarmiento, J. G., Janis, R. A., Lincoln, T. M. 1981. Cyclic GMP-dependent protein kinase stimulates calcium uptake by smooth muscle microsomes. *Fed. Proc.* 40:551
119. Schatzmann, H. J. 1966. ATP-dependent Ca^{++} extrusion from human red cells. *Experientia* 22:364–68
120. Schatzmann, H. J. 1973. Dependence on calcium concentration and stoichiometry of the calcium pump in human red cells. *J. Physiol.* 235:551–69
121. Schatzmann, H. J. 1982. The calcium pump of erythrocytes and other animal cells. In *Membrane Transport of Calcium,* ed. E. Carafoli, pp. 41–108. London: Academic
122. Schneider, C., Mottola, C., Romeo, D. 1979. Phosphorylation intermediate in the Ca^{2+}-dependent ATPase reaction of macrophage plasma membrane. *J. Supramol. Struct.* 10:433–441
123. Scully, S. P., Segal, G. B., Lichtmann, M. A. 1982. Plasma membrane vesicles prepared from unadhered monocytes: characterization of calcium transport and the calcium ATPase. *Cell Calcium* 3:515–30
124. Shen, V., Kohler, G., Peck, W. A. 1983. High affinity, calmodulin-responsive (Ca^{2+} + Mg^{2+})-ATPase in isolated bone cells. *Biochim. Biophys. Acta* 727:230–38
125. Shull, G. E., Greeb, J. 1988. Molecular cloning of two isoforms of the plasma membrane Ca^{2+} transporting ATPase from rat brain. Structural and functional domains exhibit similarity to Na^+,K^+- and other cation transport ATPases. *J. Biol. Chem.* 263:8646–57
126. Shull, G. E., Greeb, J. 1989. Molecular cloning of a 3rd isoform of the calmodulin-sensitive plasma membrane Ca^{2+}-transporting ATPase that is expressed predominantly in brain and skeletal muscle. *J. Biol. Chem.* 264:18569–76
127. Smallwood, J. I., Gügi, B., Rasmussen, H. 1988. Modulation of erythrocyte Ca^{2+} pump activity by protein kinase C. *J. Biol. Chem.* 263:2195–2202
128. Sorensen, R. G., Mahler, H. R. 1981. Calcium-stimulated adenosine triphosphatases in synaptic membranes. *J. Neurochem.* 37:1407–18
129. Spitzer, B., Bohmer, F. D., Grosse, R. 1983. Identification of Ca^{2+}-pump related phosphoprotein in plasma membrane vesicles of Ehrlich ascites carcinoma cells. *Biochim. Biophys. Acta* 728: 50–58
130. Steiner, B., Lüscher, E. F. 1985. Evidence that the platelet plasma membrane does not contain a (Ca^{2+} + Mg^{2+})-dependent ATPase. *Biochim. Biophys. Acta* 818:299–309
131. Strehler, E. E., James, P., Fischer, R., Heim, R., Vorherr, T., et al. 1990. Peptide sequence analysis and molecular cloning reveal two calcium pump isoforms in the human erythrocyte membrane. *J. Biol. Chem.* 265:2835–42
132. Strehler, E. E., Strehler-Page, M. A., Vogel, G., Carafoli, E. 1989. mRNAs for plasma membrane calcium pump isoforms differing in their regulatory domain are generated by alternative splicing involving two internal donor sites in a single exon. *Proc. Natl. Acad. Sci. USA* 86:6908–12
133. Sulakhe, P. V., Drummond, G. I., Ng, D. C. 1973. Adenosine triphosphatase activities of muscle sarcolemma. *J. Biol. Chem.* 248:4158–62
134. Szasz, I., Sarkadi, B., Schubert, A., Gardos, G. 1978. Effects of lanthanum on calcium-dependent phenomena in human red cells. *Biochim. Biophys. Acta* 512:331–40
135. Taverna, R. D., Hanahan, D. H. 1980. Modulation of human erythrocyte Ca^{2+}/Mg^{2+} ATPase activity by phospholipase A_2 and proteases. A comparison with calmodulin. *Biochim. Biophys. Res. Commun.* 94:652–59
136. Tuana, B. S., Dzurba, A., Panagia, V., Dhalla, N. S. 1981. Stimulation of heart sarcolemmal calcium pumps by calmodulin. *Biochem. Biophys. Res. Commun.* 100:1245–50
137. Van Corven, E. J. J. M., Roche, C., and Van Os, C. H. 1985. Distribution of Ca^{2+} ATPase, ATP-dependent Ca^{2+} transport calmodulin and vitamin D-dependent Ca^{2+} binding protein along the villus/crypt axis in rat duodenum. *Biochim. Biophys. Acta* 820:274–82
138. Verma, A. K., Filoteo, A. G., Stanford, D. R., Wieben, E. D., Penniston, J. T., et al. 1988. Complete primary structure of a human plasma membrane Ca^{2+} pump. *J. Biol. Chem.* 263:14152–59
139. Volpi, M., Naccache, P. H., Sha'afi, R. I. 1983. Calcium transport in inside-out membrane vesicles prepared from rabbit neutrophils. *J. Biol. Chem.* 258:4153–58
140. Waisman, D. M., Gimble, J. M., Goodman, D. B. P., Rasmussen, H. 1981. Studies on the Ca^{2+} transport mech-

anism of human erythrocyte inside-out plasma membrane vesicle. I. Regulation of the Ca^{2+} pump by calmodulin. *J. Biol. Chem.* 256:409–14
141. Waisman, R., Walters, J. R. F., Weiser, M. M. 1988. Identification and isolation of the phosphorylated intermediate of the calcium pump in rat intestinal basolateral membranes. *Biochem. J.* 256: 593–98
142. Wang, K. K., Villabobo, A., Roufogalis, B. D. 1988. Activation of the Ca^{2+}-ATPase of human erythrocyte membrane by an endogenous Ca^{2+}-dependent neutral protease. *Arch. Biochem. Biophys.* 260:696–704
143. Wuytack, E., DeSchutter, G., Casteels, R. 1980. The affect of calmodulin on active calcium ion transport and (Ca^{2+} + Mg^{2+})-dependent ATPase in microsomal fractions. *Biochem. J.* 190:827–31
144. Wuytack, R., DeSchutter, G., Casteels, R. 1981. Partial purification of (Ca^{2+} + Mg^{2+})-dependent ATPase from pig smooth muscle and reconstitution of an ATP-dependent Ca^{2+} transport system. *Biochem. J.* 198:265–71
145. Zurini, M., Krebs, J., Penniston, J. T., Carafoli, E. 1984. Controlled proteolysis of the Ca^{2+} ATPase of the erythrocyte membrane. A correlation between the structure and the function of the enzyme. *J. Biol. Chem.* 259:618–27
146. Zvaritch, E., James, P., Vorherr, T., Falchetto, R., Modyanov, N., Carafoli, E. 1990. Mapping of functional domains in the plasma membrane Ca^{2+} pump using trypsin proteolysis. *Biochemistry.* 29:8070–76

Annu. Rev. Physiol. 1991. 53:549–64

THE BAND 3-RELATED ANION EXCHANGER (AE) GENE FAMILY

Seth L. Alper

Department of Cellular and Molecular Physiology, Harvard Medical School; Molecular Medicine and Renal Units, Beth Israel Hospital, Boston, Massachusetts 02215

KEY WORDS: chloride/bicarbonate exchange, pH regulation, volume regulation, ion transport, membrane proteins

INTRODUCTION

Plasma membrane anion exchange is a nearly ubiquitous function in vertebrate cells. Anion exchange has been studied in greatest detail in the erythrocyte. There its dominant form is chloride/bicarbonate exchange, which is mediated by the most abundant integral protein of the plasma membrane, band 3 (AE1). Several recent reviews have focused on AE1 in the erythrocyte (33, 39, 56). Others have focused on anion exchange and transport in renal proximal tubule (8), or in white blood cells (31, 65). This review focuses on the attempts of recent years to define nonerythroid polypeptides related in structure to AE1. These efforts arose from observations that anion exchange in many tissues shares (to varying degrees) with erythroid AE1 sensitivity to the disulfonic stilbene class of antagonists, electroneutrality of transport, and ion substrate specificities. After a brief introduction to the general cellular functions of chloride/bicarbonate exchange, the review considers the molecular biology of the AE gene family, structure-function relationships in the AE proteins, and the localization and roles of AE proteins in the kidney and in other nonerythroid cells. It closes with a consideration of those Cl^-/HCO_3^- exchangers that remain uncloned. AE1 will serve throughout as the touchstone for our understanding of nonerythroid anion exchange.

0066–4278/91/0315–0549$02.00

CELLULAR FUNCTIONS OF CHLORIDE/BICARBONATE EXCHANGE

Erythroid AE1 has two principal structural domains, which subserve independent functions. The N-terminal cytoplasmic domain attaches the spectrin-actin cytoskeleton to the plasma membrane via its binding interactions with ankyrin, protein 4.1, and protein 4.2. In some species it also provides membrane-binding sites for glycolytic enzymes and for denatured hemoglobin (51). The C-terminal membrane-embedded domain mediates a chloride/bicarbonate exchange that increases by fivefold the total CO_2 carrying capacity of the blood (79). In nonerythroid cells, Cl^-/HCO_3^- exchangers function in concert with other transport systems to regulate cell pH, cell volume, and cell $[Cl^-]$. Normal ion concentration gradients across nonerythroid cell plasma membranes drive the exchange of intracellular bicarbonate for extracellular chloride, thus producing an intracellular acid load. Also functioning as acid loaders are the HCO_3^- channel and (membrane potential permitting) the electrogenic Na^+/HCO_3^- cotransporter. Together with metabolic acid production and inward diffusion of protonated weak acids, these transport systems account for the total cellular acid load. Countering the acid-loaders are the acid-extruders (base-loaders), which include the Na^+/H^+ exchanger, the Na^+-dependent Cl^-/HCO_3^- exchanger, the vacuolar H^+-ATPase, the H^+/K^+-ATPase, and the H^+/lactate cotransporter. Only in cells with unusually elevated $[Cl^-]$, such as HL-60, does the Cl^-/HCO_3^- exchanger function as an acid extruder (58).

The HCO_3^- transporters appear to be the principal determinants of resting pH_i in many tissue culture cells in which the Na^+/H^+ antiporter is inactive at resting pH_i (12, 16, 72). As depicted in Figure 1, the acid-loading Cl^-/HCO_3^- exchangers are activated by elevated pH_i and inactivated by lowered pH_i. In contrast, the acid extruders are activated by lowered pH_i and inactivated by elevated pH_i. Each cell type displays a characteristic profile of maximal activity, hormone responsiveness, and pH_i set-points at which activity is half-maximal (9, 12, 16, 25, 27, 29, 57, 72, 80). The pH_i set-point is the major locus of rapid regulation by hormones. In mesangial cells, a single hormone, arginine vasopressin (AVP), has been shown to activate in parallel Na^+/H^+ exchange, Na^+-dependent Cl^-/HCO_3^- exchange, and Cl^-/HCO_3^- exchange (27). In an osteoblast cell line, extracellular Ca^{2+} entry can also activate Cl^-/HCO_3^- exchange (29). Cl^-/HCO_3^- exchange was also activated by cholecystokinin (53a) and TPA (72) and was inhibited by isoproterenol (76). In different systems, cAMP has either stimulated (63) or inhibited (76) anion exchange. More recently, serum has been reported to strongly activate Cl^-/Cl^- self-exchange and Cl^-/HCO_3^- exchange, while inhibiting Na^+-dependent Cl^-/HCO_3^- exchange. Both effects appear to be mediated by

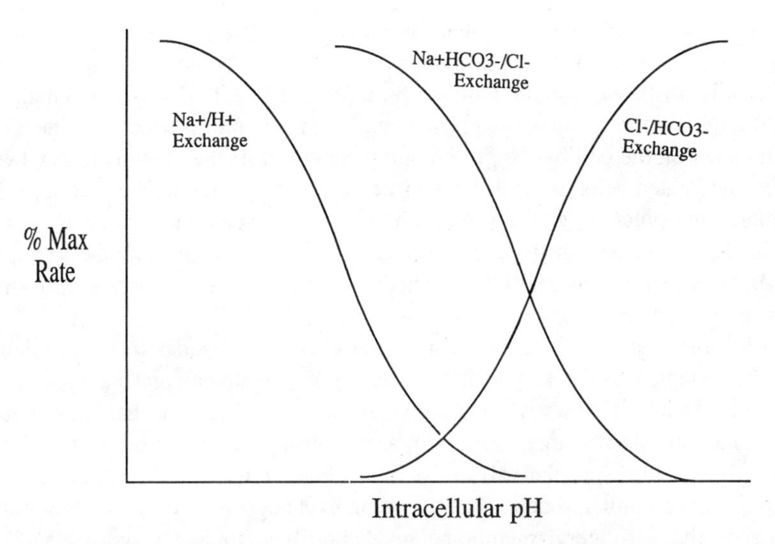

Figure 1. Idealized profiles of dependence of pH-regulatory ion exchange activities on intracellular pH. Activation of Cl^-/HCO_3^- exchange produces a leftward shift in its curve. Activation of Na^+/H^+ exchange and of $Na^+HCO_3^-/Cl^-$ exchange produces rightward shifts in their curves. Slopes and points of half-maximal activity of real curves are cell type-specific.

protein kinase C (72). The overall pattern is that of hormonal activation of multiple pH_i regulatory systems, acid-loading and base-loading, so that the principal response(s) to hormone can proceed with minimal perturbation of pH_i (27).

Cl^-/HCO_3^- exchange also plays an important role in the maintenance of $[Cl^-]_i$ above its electrochemical equilibrium concentration in many cells (30). In some cell types, Cl^-/HCO_3^- exchange appears to be the principal contributor to secondary active inward transport of Cl^-, as in cardiac Purkinje fibers (74) and in ureteral smooth muscle (1). Cell volume regulation is yet another function mediated in certain cell types by Cl^-/HCO_3^- exchange. In lymphocytes (31), in CHO cells (61), and in other cells, a regulatory volume increase (RVI) driven by coupled-Cl^-/HCO_3^- and Na^+/H^+ exchanges can be triggered by hypertonic shrinkage. Cells of the renal medullary thick ascending limb exhibit a similar hypertonic RVI under the control of arginine vasopressin (67).

Renal and other epithelial cells exploit Cl^-/HCO_3^- exchange activities to regulate extracellular compartmental and systemic pH, $[Cl^-]$, and volume, sometimes in the process of regulating their own pH_i, $[Cl^-]_i$, and volume. They do so by restricting the expression of Cl^-/HCO_3^- exchange to either the basolateral or the apical plasma membrane. Acid-secreting cells such as the Type A intercalated cell of the kidney collecting duct (5), the gastric parietal cell (70), and the osteoclast (13), must dispose of the intracellular HCO_3^- left behind by the combined activity of carbonic anhydrase and the apically disposed proton pumps. In these cells, Cl^-/HCO_3^- exchangers function in the basolateral plasma membrane to redress the alkaline load imposed on the cell by the proton pump. In contrast, the base-secreting Type B intercalated cells of the kidney cortical collecting duct display the opposite functional polarity, with a proton pump on the basolateral surface and Cl^-/HCO_3^- exchange on the apical surface (5, 62). Such an arrangement may serve, with a basolateral Cl^- channel, to mediate Cl^- reabsorption by the Type B cell (63).

In renal cortical thick ascending limb (26), gall bladder (60), and ileum (40), coupled anion and cation exchange in the apical plasma membrane is harnessed, in concert with anion and cation efflux mechanisms in the basolateral plasma membrane, to accomplish transepithelial NaCl reabsorption. More speculatively, in parotid gland acinar cells (73) and in choroid plexus epithelial cells (6, 50), anion exchange coupled to sodium entry across the basolateral membrane may contribute to NaCl or to $NaHCO_3$ secretion.

MOLECULAR BIOLOGY OF THE AE GENE FAMILY

Kopito & Lodish published the cDNA sequence and the deduced amino acid sequence of AE1 (band 3) from murine anemic spleen in 1985 (45). Since then, the postulated AE gene family (4) has taken form with two more genes (Figure 2). Following the isolation of the first partial AE1 cDNA clone by antibody screening, all ensuing cDNAs have been isolated by hybridization screening at high or reduced stringency. AE1 cDNA has been cloned from mouse (15, 45), chicken (19a, 38)[1], human (52, 68), and rat (47). The encoded AE1 proteins range from 848 to 929 amino acids in length. AE2 has been cloned from mouse (3), rat (46, 50) and, in partial length, human (20) and rabbit (18). The encoded AE2 proteins are 1237 and 1234 amino acids in length. AE3 cDNAs have been cloned from mouse (44) and rat (46) and encode polypeptides of 1227 amino acids in length.

Genomic clones of murine (43) and chicken (37, 38) AE1 have also been reported. The single-copy murine gene consists of 20 exons and extends across more than 17 kb. Most of the predicted transbilayer alpha helices of the anion exchange domain are each encoded within a single exon. The single-copy chicken gene extends across more than 28 kb. The human AE gene family is, thus far, genetically unlinked. The human AE1 gene resides on

[1]These DNA sequences differ. Those of Reference 38 are confirmed by genomic DNA sequence.

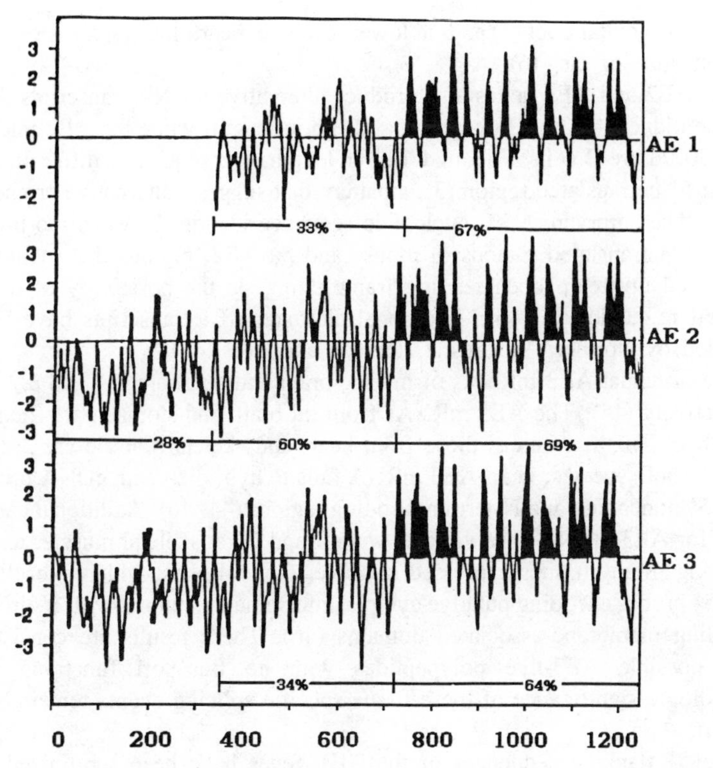

Figure 2. Aligned Kyte-Doolittle hydropathy profiles of the deduced amino acid sequences of AE1, AE2, and AE3. Amino acid residue numbers are plotted on the abscissa. Hydropathy scores are plotted on the ordinate. Modified from (46).

chromosome 17 (52, 64), whereas the AE2 gene resides on chromosome 7 (55).

Each of the AE genes transcribes multiple forms of mRNA, some of which produce variant polypeptide products. Though mammalian erythrocytes synthesize single AE1 polypeptides, chicken erythrocytes synthesize two AE1 polypeptides in equal abundance throughout erythroid development. The shorter form lacks the N-terminal 33 amino acids present in the longer (37, 38). In rodent kidney, two (mouse) or three (rat) alternate AE1 transcripts have been detected. The minor mRNA transcript of mouse kidney initiates some 70 bases 5'-ward of the erythroid transcriptional initiation sites (42) and encodes a translation product identical to erythroid AE1 (15). The major kidney mRNAs of both mouse (15) and rat (47) each encode an AE1 polypeptide predicted to lack the N-terminal 79 amino acids of the erythroid sequence and to begin with Met 80 (murine numbering). Northern blot analysis suggests the expression of additional alternate transcripts of AE1 in the murine genital tract (4) and, at lower levels, in heart, lung, liver, stomach, and intestine of rat (46).

The AE2 and AE3 genes also produce alternative mRNA transcripts. The murine kidney AE2 mRNA is about 4.3 kb in length, while the AE2 mRNA from 70Z/3 pre-B cells is about 4.1 kb in length. The sequences differ only in the far 5' untranslated region (3), a pattern that suggests alternative promoter usage. The surprising 95% nucleotide sequence identity between the proximate 5' untranslated regions of mouse and rat AE2, regions that include a conserved upstream open reading frame, suggests the possibility of translational regulation (3, 46). Additional alternate AE1 transcripts have been detected by Northern blot in rat stomach and liver (46).

The principal AE3 mRNAs of murine brain and heart are 4.1 and 3.4 kb, respectively (44). The AE3 mRNAs from rat brain and stomach are roughly 4.4 kb in length, whereas those from heart and skeletal muscle are 3.8 kb (46). In both species, heart AE3 mRNA fails to hybridize with cDNA probes from 5' noncoding and N-terminal coding regions (44, 46). Additional candidates for AE3 mRNA slice variants were found in rat skeletal muscle, testis, and lung. Many tissues expressed multiple short mRNAs, which hybridized with 5' probes encoding putative cytoplasmic domains, but not with 3' probes encoding membrane-associated domains (46). These results are consistent with possible AE3-like polypeptides with no transport function. The physiologic significance of these tissue-specific splicing events remains unknown.

The 5' flanking sequences of the AE1 genes have been scrutinized for transcriptional regulation sequence motifs. Classical TATA or CAAT boxes are present in each of the chicken erythroid promoters and in the putative promoter for rat kidney AE1 (47). The chicken erythroid promoters are highly unusual in that both are equally active and of equal tissue specificity at each phase of embryonic development (37). Transcription of the AE1 gene in chicken erythroblasts was constitutively repressed by the viral co-oncogene v-*erbA*. The cellular proto-oncogene c-*erbA*, transfected into erythroblasts, also repressed transcription. Transcriptional repression of AE1 by c-*erbA*, but not by the mutant v-*erbA*, was abrogated by thyroid hormone (81, 81). However, no classical thyroid hormone response element has been identified in the chicken AE1 gene. Though erythroid-specific GATA-1 (GF-1) boxes (72a) are located upstream of exon 1 in the AE1 genes, their functional significance remains untested. The sequences that confer kidney-specific expression of N-terminal-foreshortened AE1 may reside within intron 3 in the rat (47), but are undefined in mouse and human.

Though acute regulation of anion exchange activity has been studied by measurement of pH_i and isotopic flux in many cell types, investigations of the physiologic regulation of AE protein and mRNA levels in mammalian cells are just beginning. Preliminary data suggest that levels of AE1 mRNA (69) and numbers of AE1-expressing intercalated cells (D. Brown, S. Alper, unpublished) in rat kidney are increased in conditions of chronic acidosis. Data such as this will direct future studies of promoter function.

STRUCTURE-FUNCTIONAL RELATIONSHIPS IN THE AE GENE FAMILY

The topography of AE1 in the erythrocyte membrane has been under study for more than 15 years. Through the use of impermeant labeling probes and, more recently, monoclonal and polyclonal antibodies against random and synthetic peptide epitopes of AE1, more than 80% of the AE1 linear sequence, extending from the amino terminus, has received a topographic assignment. Both the amino- and carboxy-termini are cytoplasmically disposed (49). The membrane-spanning domain of AE1 traverses the bilayer more than eight times, and probably between 10 and 14 times (4, 33, 34, 35a, 52). The aligned hydropathy profiles of the rat AE proteins (Figure 2) illustrate the principal similarities and differences among their predicted secondary structures (46). There is no biochemical evidence pertaining to secondary structures for AE2 or AE3, but their predicted topography is similar to that of AE1. The corresponding murine sequences and their hydropathy profiles are virtually identical (3, 44).

The hydrophobic, membrane-associated transport domains of the AE proteins display the highest degree of amino acid sequence identity (64–69%). When the comparison is restricted to those stretches of protein sufficiently hydrophobic to reside within the plane of the lipid bilayer, the identity rises to 80%. The ectoplasmically disposed, hydrophilic loops, which connect the hydrophobic putatively transmembrane spans, show a lower degree of amino acid sequence identity. The region of greatest sequence divergence within the membrane-spanning domain is the ectoplasmic loop between hydrophobic peaks four and five, corresponding to putative transmembrane spans five and six (3, 45). Not only does this segment differ in sequence and in length among the AE proteins; it serves as a probable site of (nonidentical) N-linked glycosylations in AE2 and AE3, whereas AE1 is glycosylated on the subsequent ectoplasmic loop between putative spans seven and eight. The function of N-linked glycosylation in AE protein biosynthesis or in AE-mediated ion translocation is unknown.

The arginine(s) of the AE1 C-terminal region labeled by phenylglyoxal in parallel with transport inhibition (33) remain unidentified. A number of individual residues in the membrane domain of AE1, however, have been identified by covalent labeling with inhibitors of anion exchange, followed by isolation of the labeled proteolytic fragment and partial protein sequenc-

Table 1 Conservation of chemically defined residues[a] in the ion transport domains of the AE proteins

	AE1	AE2	AE3	Significance in AE1	Location[b]
449	K	K	K	Eosin maleimide covalent binding site	Ecto 1–2
558	K	K	K	DIDS covalent binding site, mutation does not affect transport	Ecto 5–6
572	Y	S	A	Chymotrypsin cleavage site, no effect on transport	Ecto 5–6
608	K	K	K	Phenyl isothiocyanate covalent binding site	Endo 6–7
648	Q	Q	Q	Papain cleavage site, blocks transport	Ecto 7–8
660	N	A	S	N-linked glycosylation site	Ecto 7–8
699	E	E	E	Woodward's Reagent K binding site, borohydride reduction blocks transport, accessible from both sides of membrane	Endo 8–9
761	K	K	T	Intracellular trypsin cleavage site	Endo 8–9
869	K	M	K	Pyridoxal phosphate covalent binding site, accessible from both sides of membrane	Ecto 11–12 (?)

[a] All residue numbers derive from murine AE1. For references see text.
[b] Location of amino acid residue in externally (ecto) or internally (endo) disposed loop of the membrane-associated domain of AE1, and predicted locations in AE2 and AE3.

ing. As summarized in Table 1 some, but not all, of these residues are conserved in AE2 and/or AE3. The use of these data to implicate specific amino acid residues in the ion transport process is not straightforward. For example, the strict conservation of the lysines that serve as covalent-binding sites for eosin maleimide (19), DIDS (11, 28), and phenyl isothiocyanate (14) may reflect only the covalent-binding function of these drugs, not the transport-inhibitory function. When the DIDS-binding lysine of human (28) or mouse (11) AE1 was altered, reversible DIDS-sensitive ion transport remained unaffected, while only irreversible inhibition was blocked. Perhaps the most interesting of the defined labeled residues are E669 (M. L. Jennings, unpublished) and K869 (10). Both residues can, under proper conditions, be labeled by "impermeant" reagents from either side of the membrane. These data suggest that the residues might reside near or along the ion translocation pathway. It is tempting to interpret the sequence conservation at E669 and variation at K869 in light of the intriguing Cl^-/Cl^- exchange kinetics in AE2-expressing (20) HL-60 cells (59). Unlike the ping-pong mechanism of exchange displayed by AE1, HL-60 anion exchange displays a simultaneous mechanism. Perhaps K869 is crucial for a ping-pong mechanism. Only with more physiologic and biochemical data will AE protein sequence comparisons give rise to structural hypotheses that do not require brute force mutagenesis for their initial testing.

The middle, putatively cytoplasmic portions of AE2 and AE3 display almost as much amino acid identity (60%) as do the neighboring membrane-associated domains (Figure 2). This similarity drops to just over 30%, however, when either is compared to the cytoplasmic domain of AE1. Several short sequences in this region are conserved in all three proteins, including the 30 or so residues immediately adjacent to the presumed entry of the polypeptide chains into the lipid bilayer. Any of these stretches might contribute to AE binding to cytoskeleton. The far N-terminal portions of AE2 and AE3, sharing only 28% amino acid identity, are remarkable for stretches rich in proline, histidine, and charged amino acids, whose functional significance is still unknown.

Analysis of structure-function relationships suggested by deduced amino acid sequence requires expression systems for the cDNAs and derived mutants. AE polypeptides have been expressed as chloride transporters in two transient expression systems. Kidney AE1 (15) and AE2 (2) have been shown to mediate Cl^- influx in *Xenopus* oocytes injected with in vitro-transcribed mRNA. Erythroid AE1 has been shown to mediate both influx and efflux sensitive to stilbene disulfonates at physiologic concentrations (11, 28). As expressed in oocytes, AE1 preserves the sensitivities and rank-order of potency for a range of competitive and noncompetitive inhibitors (28). The signal-to-noise ratio in the oocyte experiments is high enough for the analysis of mutations in AE proteins that inactivate transport or leave it unaffected, but may not be for analysis of mutations that may partially reduce or more subtly alter activity.

AE proteins transiently expressed in COS cells are easily detected by immunoprecipitation (2) or by immunoblot (44, 50). Parallel assessment of AE transport function with isotopic flux studies has not been possible since only 5–15% of the cells are typically transfected, and COS cells have considerable endogenous anion exchange. More successful has been single-cell fluorometric determination of pH_i in the presence of CO_2/HCO_3^-, using the pH-sensitive dye BCECF (44, 50). As assessed by this approach, all AE cDNAs encode polypeptides capable of mediating Cl^-/HCO_3^- exchange. The N-terminal cytoplasmic domains of the AE proteins are not needed to mediate Cl^-/HCO_3^- exchange. Most interestingly, in AE3 (44) (though not in AE2) (50) removal of the N-terminal cytoplasmic domain appeared to alter the sensitivity of Cl^-/HCO_3^- exchange rate to pH_i. A significant shortcoming in this experimental approach, however, has been the absence of a separate determination of the transfection status of each cell, independent of its pH_i response to extracellular removal of Cl^-.

The pharmacological characterization of AE2 and AE3 is just beginning. Ion substrate specificities of AE proteins expressed from cDNA or mRNA in heterologous systems have not been reported. When expressed in COS cells and monitored by fluorometric determination of pH_i, both AE2 and AE3 were orders of magnitude more resistant to inhibition by DIDS than is AE1 in the erythrocyte (44, 50) or in the microinjected oocyte (15, 28). The array of other inhibitors with a range of kinetic mechanisms already tried against AE1 (28, 56) largely remains untested against AE2 and AE3 in heterologous expression systems. Unfortunately, potent inhibitors of anion exchange in nonerythroid tissues are unknown. Perhaps the recent report of inhibition of Cl^-/HCO_3^- exchange by therapeutic concentrations of nonsteroidal anti-inflammatory drugs in wide clinical use (70a) will lead to development of additional inhibitors of greater potency.

Though transient expression systems serve better in functional screens of numerous mutants, development of cell lines that stably overexpress (or underexpress) AE proteins will also be important for the elucidation of the role of AE proteins in cell function. Until recently stable expression of AE cDNAs in heterologous cell lines had not been achieved, probably because of chronic acid-loading and consequent negative growth selection mediated by the heterologous AE proteins (44, 50). By growing retrovirally transduced cells in a relatively alkaline, reduced chloride, elevated bicarbonate medium, H. Beug & colleagues (personal communication) have produced fibroblast lines that overexpress chicken AE1.

LOCALIZATION OF AE GENE FAMILY POLYPEPTIDES

Though AE mRNAs can be found in most tissues and cells, detection of the corresponding polypeptides has proven considerably more difficult. The criteria for definition of an AE protein (a band 3-related protein) should now include either primary sequence data, or specific immunoreactivity with more than one antibody against distinct AE epitopes. AE1 protein expression has been detected with many antibodies on the basolateral surface of Type A intercalated cells of kidney from human (77), rat (5, 23, 32, 75), rabbit (62), mouse (41), and in turtle urinary bladder (22). AE1 functions on the side of the cell opposite that of the vacuolar H^+ ATPase (5). Electron microscopic analysis has demonstrated localization to the basolateral plasma membrane in both human (21) and rat (75). Antipeptide antibodies to AE1 segments N-terminal to Met 80 failed to detect kidney AE1, while antibodies to peptide sequences C-terminal to Met 80 revealed the same staining pattern as did the earlier reported antibodies (D. Drenckhahn, personal communication). These data confirm the structure of the major form of kidney AE1 predicted from cDNA cloning. The still poorly delimited region of erythroid AE1, thought to bind to the cytoskeletal protein ankyrin, is intact in kidney AE1, consistent with immunolocalization data in rat kidney (23). Human renal oncocytoma also expresses AE1 at the basolateral membrane in better differentiated, duct-like portions of tumor, and circumferentially in less well differentiated regions (66).

Although AE2 and AE3 mRNA are transcribed in kidney, and AE2 cDNA had been cloned from kidney, the corresponding polypeptides have escaped immunocytological detection to date. AE2 mRNA is present in MDCK, PK-1, BSC-1, and COS cells (3) and probably mediates Na^+-independent Cl^-/HCO_3^- exchange in most cultured renal cells of tubular origin (17, 25, 35, 48, 50, 71) and perhaps in mesangial cells as well (27). AE2 protein has been convincingly localized to the choroid plexus, the gastric parietal cell, and the osteoclast. In the basolateral plasma membrane of choroid plexus, AE2 has been detected with antibodies directed against four distinct peptide epitopes, three of which show no homology with the aligned sequences of AE1 and AE3 (6, 50). AE2 in this tissue may play a role in the secretion of cerebrospinal fluid. AE2 protein is also expressed in murine and human choroid plexus papillomas (S. L. Alper, unpublished) The same antibodies have demonstrated AE2 in the basolateral plasma membrane of the parietal cell, but not the chief cell, of the gastric antrum (70; S. L. Alper, unpublished). The respective roles of AE2 and AE3 in gastric acid secretion remain to be defined. In the osteoclast, AE2 resides in the contralacunar membrane (R. Baron, unpublished), across the cell from the vacuolar H^+ ATPase, which acidifies the periosteal lacunar space (13), thus suggesting an important role for AE2 in bone remodeling. In situ hybridization studies have demonstrated AE3 transcription in virtually all types of neurons of the brain. Especially interesting with respect to the control of respiration by pCO_2 is the strong hybridization signal in the deep pontine gray matter and the moderate signal in midbrain, medulla, and brain stem reticular formation (44).

The possibility that intracellular organellar anion exchangers comprise part of the AE gene family is raised by AE1-immunoreactive material localized to the Golgi region in rat (36) and human (24) osteosarcoma cells and to mitochondria in thin sections of Type A intercalated cells in rabbit kidney (54). The Golgi stain may correspond to a 115-kd membrane protein detected on immunoblot (36). The mitochondrial antigen may correspond to a 44-kd membrane protein on immunoblot (54). No AE-related cDNAs that encode polypeptides of these descriptions have been cloned in these cells. In contrast, an AE2 cDNA, which encodes protein identical to that of kidney (3, 46) and choroid plexus (50), has been cloned from ROS cells (R. Baron, unpublished).

OTHER ANION EXCHANGERS

The last five years have seen the characterization of three members of the AE gene family. However, the majority of anion exchangers in the kidney has eluded structural definition. The basolateral $C1^-/HCO_3^-$ exchangers of principal cells (78), proximal tubule cells (7), and medullary thick limb (67) may be encoded by or related to the already cloned AE cDNAs. The apical $C1^-/HCO_3^-$ exchanger(s) of the cortical collecting duct Type B intercalated cell (5, 62), the cortical thick limb (26), the gallbladder (60), the ileum (40), and the multiple apical $C1^-$/base antiporters of the proximal tubular brush border (8) are likely new AE gene products or products of unrelated genes, as is the hydroxycinnamate-sensitive $C1^-/HCO_3^-$ exchanger of polymorphonuclear leukocytes (64). The widespread endogenous expression of $C1^-/HCO_3^-$ exchange has posed a problem for transport expression cloning of AE cDNAs, a problem magnified by the comparatively low signal-to-noise ratio of electroneutral compared to electrogenic transport. The absence of $C1^-/HCO_3^-$ exchange antagonists of both high affinity and high specificity has temporarily ruled out ligand-binding expression cloning. The application of polymerase chain reaction to conserved AE sequences may be a fruitful approach to cloning additional AE cDNAs. In the meantime, AE sequence information and first generation AE expression systems promise to accelerate investigation of the mechanisms and regulation of $C1^-/HCO_3^-$ exchange and its multiple roles in cell function.

ACKNOWLEDGMENTS

Original results included in this review were supported by National Institutes of Health grants DK01506, DK39249, and by the Whitaker Foundation. The author thanks Harvey Lodish for his support and the many colleagues who shared their unpublished results.

Literature Cited

1. Aickin, C. C. 1988. Movement of acid equivalents across the mammalian smooth muscle cell membrane. *Ciba Found. Symp.* 139:3–22.
2. Alper, S. L., Brosius, F. C., Garcia, A. M., Gluck, S., Brown, D., Lodish, H. F. 1989. Two band 3-related gene products encode putative anion exchangers of the kidney. In *Anion Transport Protein of the Red Blood Cell Membrane,* ed. N. Hamasaki, M. L. Jennings, pp. 153–164. Amsterdam: Elsevier
3. Alper, S. L., Kopito, R. R., Libresco, S. M., Lodish, H. F. 1988. Cloning and characterization of a murine band 3-related cDNA from kidney and from a lymphoid cell line. *J. Biol. Chem.* 263: 17092–99
4. Alper, S. L., Kopito, R. R., Lodish, H. F. 1987. A molecular biological approach to the study of anion transport. *Kidney Int.* 32:S117–28
5. Alper, S. L., Natale, J., Gluck, S., Lodish, H. F., Brown, D. 1989. Subtypes of intercalated cells in rat kidney collecting duct defined by antibodies against erythroid band 3 and renal vacuolar H^+-ATPase. *Proc. Natl. Acad. Sci. USA* 86:5429–33
6. Alper, S. L., Stuart-Tilley, A., Brown, D. 1990. Tissue distribution of the $C1^-/HCO_3^-$ exchanger AE2: Abundant expression in the choroid plexus. *J. Am. Soc. Nephrol.* 1:711a
7. Alpern, R. J. 1990. Cell mechanisms of proximal tubule acidification. *Physiol. Rev.* 70:79–114
8. Aronson, P. S. 1989. The renal proximal tubule: a model for diversity of anion exchangers and stilbene-sensitive anion transporters. *Annu. Rev. Physiol.* 51:419–441
9. Aronson, P. S., Nee, J., Suhm, M. A. 1982. Modifier role of internal H^+ in

activating the Na^+/H^+ exchanger in renal microvillus membrane vesicles. *Nature* 299:161–63
10. Bar-Noy, S., Cabantchik, Z. I. 1990. Transport domain of the erythrocyte anion exchange protein. *J. Memb. Biol.* 115:217–28
11. Bartel, D., Lepke, S., Layh-Schmitt, G., Legrum, B., Passow, H. 1989. Anion transport in oocytes of *Xenopus laevis* induced by expression of mouse erythroid band 3 protein-encoding cRNA and a cRNA derivative obtained by site-directed mutagenesis at the stilbene disulfonate binding site. *EMBO J.* 8:3601–9
12. Bierman, A. J., Cragoe, E. J. Jr., de-Laat, S. W., Moolenaar, W. H. 1988. Bicarbonate determines cytoplasmic pH and suppresses mitogen-induced alkalinization in fibroblastic cells. *J. Biol. Chem.* 263:15253–56
13. Blair, H. C., Teitelbaum, S. L., Ghiselli, R., Gluck, S. 1989. Osteoclastic bone resorption by a polarized vacuolar proton pump. *Science* 245:855–57
14. Brock, C. J., Tanner, M. J. A., Kempf, C. 1983. The human anion transport protein: partial amino acid sequence, conformation, and a possible molecular mechanism for anion exchange. *Biochem. J.* 213:577–86
15. Brosius, F. C., Alper, S. L., Garcia, A. M., Lodish, H. F. 1989. The major kidney band 3 transcript predicts an amino-terminal truncated band 3 polypeptide. *J. Biol. Chem.* 264:7784–87
16. Cassel, D., Scharf, O., Rotman, M., Cragoe, E. J. Jr., Katz, M. 1988. Characterization of Na^+-linked and Na^+-independent $C1^-/HCO_3^-$ exchange systems in Chinese hamster lung fibroblasts. *J. Biol. Chem.* 263:6122–27
17. Chaillet, J. R., Amsler, K., Boron, W. F. 1986. Optical measurements of intracellular pH in single LLC-PK1 cells: demonstration of $C1^-/HCO_3^-$ exchange. *Proc. Natl. Acad. Sci. USA* 83:522–26
18. Chow, A., Dobbins, J. W., Hildebrandt, F., Aronson, P. S., Igaraski, P. 1989. Cloning of a rabbit ileum cDNA related to erythroid band 3. *Gastroenterology* 96:A87
19. Cobb, C. E., Beth, A. H. 1990. Identification of the eosin-5-maleimide on the human erythrocyte anion-exchange protein reaction site. *Biochemistry* 29: 8283–90
19a. Cox, J. V., Lazarides, E. 1988. Alternative primary structures in the transmembrane domain of the chicken erythroid anion transporter. *Mol. Cell. Biol.* 8: 1327–35
20. Demuth, D. R., Showe, L. C., Ballantine, M., Palumbo, A., Fraser, P. J., et al. 1986. Cloning and structural characterization of a human nonerythroid band 3-like protein. *EMBO J.* 5:1205–14
21. Drenckhahn, D., Merte, C. 1987. Restriction of the human kidney band 3-like anion exchanger to specialized subdomains of the basolateral plasma membrane of intercalated cells. *Eur. J. Cell Biol.* 45:107–15
22. Drenckhahn, D., Oelmann, M., Schaaf, P. Wagner, M., Wagner, S. 1987. Band 3 is the basolateral anion exchanger of the dark epithelial cells of the turtle urinary bladder. *Am. J. Physiol.* 252:C570–74
23. Drenckhahn, D., Schluter, K., Allen, D. P., Bennett, V. 1985. Colocalization of band 3 with ankyrin and spectrin at the basal membrane of intercalated cells in the rat kidney. *Science* 230:1287–89
24. Drenckhahn, D., Wagner, S., Jons, T., Oelmann, M., Koob, R. 1989. Molecular characterization of band 3-related anion exchangers in the vertebrate urinary system and Golgi apparatus. See Ref. 2, pp. 165–75
25. Fineman, I., Hart, D., Nord, E. P. 1990. Intracellular pH regulates Na^+-independent $C1^-$/base exchange in JTC-12 (proximal tubule) cells. *Am. J. Physiol.* 258:F883–92
26. Friedman, P. A., Andreoli, T. E. 1982. CO_2-stimulated NaC1 absorption in the mouse renal cortical thick limb of Henle. *J. Gen. Physiol.* 80:683–711
27. Ganz, M. B., Boyarsky, G., Sterzl, R. B., Boron, W. F. 1989. Arginine vasopressin enhances pH_i regulation in the presence of HCO_3^- by stimulating the three acid-base transport systems. *Nature* 337:648–51
28. Garcia, A.-M. Lodish, H. F. 1989. Lysine 539 of human band 3 is not essential for ion transport or inhibition by stilbene disulfonates. *J. Biol. Chem.* 264:19607–13
29. Green, J., Yamaguchi, D. T., Kleeman, C. R., Muallem, S. 1990. Cytosolic pH regulation in osteoblasts. Regulation of anion exchange by intracellular pH and Ca^{2+} ions. *J. Gen. Physiol.* 95:121–45
30. Grinstein, S. 1987. Intracellular chloride concentration: determinants and consequences. *Prog. Clin. Biol. Res.* 254: 31–43
31. Grinstein, S., Foskett, J. K. 1990. Ionic mechanisms of cell volume regulation in

leukocytes. *Annu. Rev. Physiol.* 52: 399–414

32. Holthofer, H., Schulte, B. A., Pasternak, G. Siegel, G. J., Spicer, S. S. 1987. Three distinct cell populations in rat kidney collecting duct. *Am. J. Physiol.* 253:C323–28
33. Jennings, M. L. 1989. Structure and function of the red blood cell anion transport protein. *Annu. Rev. Biophys. Biophys. Chem.* 18:397–430
34. Jennings, M. L., Anderson, M. P., Monaghan, R. 1986. Monoclonal antibodies against human-erythrocyte band 3 protein: localization of proteolytic cleavage sites and stilbenedisulfonate-binding residues. *J. Biol. Chem.* 261–9002–10
35. Jentsch, T. J., Janicke, I., Sorgenfrei, D., Keller, S. K., Wiederholt, M. 1986. The regulation of intracellular pH in monkey kidney epithelial cells (BSC-1). *J. Biol. Chem.* 261:12120–27

35a. Kay, M. B., Marchalonis, J. J., Watanabe, K., Schluter, S. F. 1990. Definition of a physiologic aging autoantigen by using synthetic peptides of membrane protein band 3: Localization of the active antigenic sites. *Proc. Natl. Acad. Sci. USA* 87:5734–38

36. Kellokumpu, S., Neff, L., Jamsa-Kellokumpu, S., Kopito, R., Baron, R. 1988. A polypeptide immunologically related to erythrocyte band 3 is present in Golgi membranes. *Science* 242:1308–11
37. Kim, H.-R. C., Kennedy, B. S., Engel, J. D. 1989. Two chicken erythrocyte band 3 mRNAs are generated by alternative transcriptional initiation and differential RNA splicing. *Mol. Cell. Biol.* 9:5198–5206
38. Kim, H.-R. C., Yew, N. S., Ansorge, W., Voss, H., Schwager, C., et al. 1988. Two different mRNAs are transcribed from a single genomic locus encoding the chicken erythrocyte anion transport proteins (band 3). *Mol. Cell. Biol.* 8:4416–24
39. Knauf, P. A. 1989. Kinetics of anion transport. In *The Red Cell Membrane,* ed. B. U. Raess, G. Tunnicliff, pp. 171–200. Clifton, NJ: Humana
40. Knickelbein, R. G., Aronson, P. S., Dobbins, J. W. 1988. Membrane distribution of sodium-hydrogen and chloride-bicarbonate exchangers in crypt and villus cell membranes from rabbit ileum. *J. Clin. Invest.* 82:2158–63
41. Kopito, R. R., Andersson, M. A., Herzlinger, D. A., Al-Awqati, A., Lodish, H. F. 1988. Structure and tissue-specific expression of the mouse anion-exchanger gene in erythroid and renal cells. In *Cell Physiology of Blood,* ed., R. B. Gunn, J. C. Parker., pp. 151–161. New York: Rockefeller Univ. Press
42. Kopito, R. R., Andersson, M. A., Lodish, H. F. 1987. Multiple tissue-specific sites of transcriptional initiation of the mouse anion antiport gene in erythroid and renal cells. *Proc. Natl. Acad. Sci. USA* 84:7149–53
43. Kopito, R. R., Andersson, M. A., Lodish, H. F. 1987. Structure and organization of the murine band 3 gene. *J. Biol. Chem.* 262:8035–40
44. Kopito, R. R., Lee, B. S., Simmons, D. M., Lindsey, A. E., Morgans, C. W., Schneider, K. 1989. Regulation of intracellular pH by a neuronal homolog of the erythrocyte anion exchanger. *Cell* 59:927–37
45. Kopito, R. R., Lodish, H. F. 1985. Primary structure and transmembrane orientation of the murine anion exchange protein. *Nature* 316:234–38
46. Kudrycki, K. E., Newman, P. R., Shull, G. E. 1990. cDNA cloning and tissue distribution of mRNAs for two proteins that are related to the band 3 $C1^-HCO_3^-$ exchanger. *J. Biol. Chem.* 265:462–71
47. Kudrycki, K. E., Shull, G. E. 1989. Primary structure of the rat kidney band 3 anion exchange protein deduced from a cDNA. *J. Biol. Chem.* 264:8185–92
48. Kurtz, I., Golchini, K. 1987. Na^+-independent $C1^-/HCO_3^-$ exchange in Madin-Darby canine kidney cells. Role in intracellular pH regulation. *J. Biol. Chem.* 262:4516–20
49. Lieberman, D. M., Reithmeier, R. A. F. 1988. Localization of the carboxyl terminus of band 3 to the cytoplasmic side of the erythrocyte membrane using antibodies raised against a synthetic peptide. *J. Biol. Chem.* 263:10022–28
50. Lindsey, A. E., Schneider, K., Simmons, D. M., Baron, R., Lee, B. S., Kopito, R. R. 1990. Functional expression and subcellular localization of an anion exchanger cloned from choroid plexus. *Proc. Natl. Acad. Sci. USA* 87:5278–82
51. Low, P. S., Willardson, B. M., Thevenin, B., Kannan, R., Mehler, E., et al. 1989. The other functions of erythrocyte membrane band 3. See Ref. 24, pp. 103–18.
52. Lux, S. E., John, K. M., Kopito, R. R., Lodish, H. F. 1989. Cloning and characterization of band 3, the human erythrocyte anion exchange protein

(AE1). *Proc. Natl. Acad. Sci. USA* 86: 9089–93
53. Mason, M. J., Smith, J. D., Garcia-Soto, J. J., Grinstein, S. 1989. Internal pH-sensitive site couples $C1^-/HCO_3^-$ exchange to Na^+/H^+ antiport in lymphocytes. *Am. J. Physiol.* 256:C428–33
53a. Muallem, S., Loessberg, P. A. 1990. Internal pH-regulatory mechanisms in pancreatic acinar cells. *J. Biol. Chem.* 265:12813–19
54. Ostedgaard, L. S., Jennings, M. L., Karniski, L. P., Schuster, V. L. 1990. Mitochondria of collecting duct acid-secreting cells express a protein antigenically similar to the anion transporting (membrane) domain of RBC band 3. *Kidney Int.* 37:227a
55. Palumbo, A. P., Isobe, M., Huebner, K., Shane, S., Rovera, G. et al. 1986. Chromosomal localization of a human band 3-like gene to region 7q35-7q36. *Am. J. Hum. Genet.* 39:307–16
56. Passow, H. 1986. Molecular aspects of the band 3 protein-mediated anion transport across the red blood cell membrane. *Rev. Physiol. Biochem. Pharmacol.* 103:61–203
57. Reinertsen, K. V., Tonnessen, T. I., Jacobsen, J., Sandvig, K. Olsnes, S. 1988. Role of chloride/bicarbonate antiport in the control of cytosolic pH: Cell-line differences in activity and regulation of antiport. *J. Biol. Chem.* 263:1117–25
58. Restrepo, D., Kozody, D. J., Spinelli, L. J., Knauf, P. A. 1988. pH homeostasis in promyelocytic leukemic HL60 cells. *J. Gen. Physiol.* 92:489–507
59. Restrepo, D., Kozody, D. J., Spinelli, L. J., Knauf, P. A. 1989. C1-C1 exchange in promyelocytic HL-60 cells follows simultaneous rather than ping-pong kinetics. *Am. J. Physiol.* 257: C520–27
60. Reuss, L. 1989. Ion transport across gallbladder epithelium. *Physiol. Rev.* 69:503–45
61. Rotin, D., Grinstein, S. 1989. Impaired cell volume regulation in Na^+-H^+ exchange-deficient mutants. *Am. J. Physiol.* 257:C1158–65
62. Schuster, V. L., Bonsib, S. M., Jennings, M. L. 1986. Two types of collecting duct mitochondria-rich (intercalated) cells: lectin and band 3 cytochemistry. *Am. J. Physiol.* 251:C347–55
63. Schuster, V. L.. Stokes, J. B. 1987. Chloride transport by the cortical and outer medullary collecting duct. *Am. J. Physiol.* 253:F203–12
64. Showe, L. C., Ballantine, M., Huebner, K. 1987. Localization of the gene for the erythroid anion exchange protein, band 3, to human chromosome 17. *Genomics* 1:71–76
65. Simchowitz, L., Bibb, J. A. 1990. Functional analysis of the modes of anion transport in neutrophils and HL-60 cells. *Annu. Rev. Physiol.* 52:381–97
66. Storkel, S., Pannen, B., Thoenens, W., Steart, P. V., Wagner, S., Drenckhahn, D. 1988. Intercalated cells as a probable source for the development of renal oncocytoma. *Virchows Archiv. B* 56: 185–89
67. Sun, A., Hebert, S. C. 1989. Rapid hypertonic cell volume regulation in the perfused inner medullary collecting duct. *Kidney Int.* 36:831–42
68. Tanner, M. J. A., Martin, P. G., High, S. 1988. The complete amino acid sequence of the human erythrocyte membrane anion transport protein deduced from the cDNA sequence. *Biochem. J.* 256:703–12
69. Texeira da Silva, J. C. Jr., Perrone, R. D., Johns, C. A., Madias, N. E. 1990. Kidney band 3 mRNA modulation in chronic respiratory acidosis. *Kidney Int.* 37:547a
70. Thomas, H. A., Machen, T. E., Smolka, A., Baron, R., Kopito, R. R. 1989. Identification of a 185 kDa band 3-related polypeptide in oxyntic cells. *Am J. Physiol.* 257:C537–44
70a. Tonnessen, T. I., Aas, A. T., Sandvig, K., Olsnes, S. 1909. Inhibition of chloride/bicarbonate antiports in monkey kidney cells (Vero) by non-steroidal anti-inflammatory drugs. *Biochem. Pharmacol.* 38:3583–91
71. Tonnessen, T. I., Ludt, J., Sandvig, K., Olsnes, S. 1987. Bicarbonate/chloride antiport in Vero cells: I. Evidence for both sodium-linked and sodium-independent exchange. *J. Cell. Physiol.* 132:183–91
72. Tonnessen, T. I., Sandvig, K., Olsnes, S. 1990. Role of Na^+-H^+ and $C1^-HCO_3^-$ antiports in the regulation of cytoplasmic pH near neutrality. *Am. J. Physiol.* 258:C1117–26
72a. Tsai, S.-F., Martin, D. I. K., Zon, L. I., D'Andrea, A. D., Wong, G. G., Orkin, S. H. 1989. Cloning of cDNA for the major DNA-binding protein of the erythroid lineage through expression in mammalian cells. *Nature* 339:446–51
73. Turner, R. J., George, J. N. 1988. $C1^-$-HCO_3^- exchange is present with Na^+-K^+-$C1^-$ cotransport in rabbit parotid acinar basolateral membranes. *Am. J. Physiol.* 254:C391–94
74. Vaughn-Jones, R. D. 1986. Anion ex-

change in sheep Purkinje fibers. *J. Physiol.* 379:377–406
75. Verlander, J. W., Madsen, K. M., Low, P. S., Allen, D. P., Tisher, C. C. 1988. Immunocytochemical localization of band 3 protein in the rat collecting duct. *Am. J. Physiol.* 255:F115–25
76. Vigne, P., Breittmayer, J.-P., Frelin, C., Lazdunski, M. 1988. Dual control of the intracellular pH in aortic smooth muscle cells by a cAMP-sensitive HCO_3^-/Cl^- antiporter and a protein kinase C-sensitive Na^+/H^+ antiporter. *J. Biol. Chem.* 263:18023–29
77. Wagner, S., Vogel, R., Lietzke, R., Koob, R., Drenckhahn, D. 1987. Immunochemical characterization of a band 3-like anion exchanger in collecting duct of human kidney. *Am. J. Physiol.* 253:F213–21
78. Weiner, I. D., Hamm, L. L. 1990. Regulation of intracellular pH in the rabbit cortical collecting tubule. *J. Clin. Invest.* 85:274–81
79. Weith, J. O., Andersen, O. S., Brahm, J., Bjerrum, P. J., Borders, C. L. Jr. 1982. Chloride-bicarbonate exchange in red blood cells: physiology of transport and chemical modification of binding sites. *Phil. Trans. R. Soc. Ser. B* 299: 383–99
80. Wenzl, E., Machen, T. E. 1989. Intracellular pH dependence of buffer capacity and anion exchange in the parietal cell. *Am. J. Physiol.* 257:G741–47
81. Zenke, M., Kahn, P., Disela, C., Vennström, B., Leutz, A., et al. 1988. v-*erbA* specifically suppresses transcription of the avian erythrocyte anion transporter (band 3) gene. *Cell* 52:107–19
82. Zenke, M., Munoz, A., Sap, J., Vennström, B., Beug, H. 1990. v-*erbA* oncogene activation entails the loss of hormone-dependent regulator activity of c-*erbA*. *Cell* 61:1035–49

Annu. Rev. Physiol. 1991. 53:565–84

STRUCTURE-FUNCTION RELATIONSHIP OF Na,K-ATPase

Jean-Daniel Horisberger[1], *Victor Lemas*[2], *Jean-Pierre Kraehenbühl*[3], *and Bernard C. Rossier*[1]

[1]Institut de Pharmacologie, Université de Lausanne, Bugnon 27, CH-1005 Lausanne, Switzerland

[2]Department of Biology, The Johns Hopkins University, Baltimore, Maryland 21218

[3]Institut de Biochimie, Université de Lausanne and Institut Suisse de la Recherche Expérimentale sur le Cancer, CH-1066 Epalinges, Switzerland

KEY WORDS: sodium pump, isoforms, sodium-potassium-adenosinetriphosphatase

INTRODUCTION

In animal cells, the major ionmotive ATPase is the ouabain-inhibitable sodium pump, a membrane-bound enzyme that couples the free energy contained within the ATP molecule to the translocation of Na^+ and K^+ across the plasma membrane. The enzyme consists of a heterodimer of an α and β subunit (Figure 1*a*), which constitutes the minimal functional unit able to hydrolyze ATP and to undergo E_1–E_2 transition (Figure 1*b*), a conformational change characteristic of the P-type ATPase (57). Na^+,K^+-coupled transport has evolved in higher eukaryotes (vertebrate and invertebrate) to accomplish functions specific to these multicellular organisms (64). Ubiquitous distribution of Na,K-ATPase in all cells insures the primary control of cell volume and the maintenance of the gradients of Na^+ and K^+ across the cell membrane. Asymmetric distribution of Na,K-ATPase to the basolateral membrane of epithelial cells allows the vectorial transport of salt and water from one side of the cell layer (as occurs in the kidney and the intestine), thereby controlling the extracellular volume and the osmotic balance between the intra- and extracellular compartments. In excitable cells, the Na^+ and K^+

0066-4278/91/0315-0565$02.00

gradients are essential for the control of membrane potential and thus responsible for the excitability of the tissue. Na,K-ATPase belongs to a multigene family (77, 8, 41). Three α subunit (α_1, α_2, α_3) and two β subunit (β_1, β_2) isoforms have been described so far. Tissue-specific and developmental stage-dependent expression have been recently reviewed (41, 77). Two distinct explanations have been proposed to account for the existence of several Na,K-ATPase isoforms differentially expressed in various tissues (80). One possible explanation for the existence of a multigene family is that it represents a selective advantage in evolution because it simplifies the problem of regulating gene expression to suit the needs of each developmental stage or each cell type of the organism. Alternatively, each isoform could be distinct from each other by specific functional characteristics (80).

The aim of the present review is to examine critically (*a*) the molecular evidence for structural heterogeneity for both α and β subunits; (*b*) the physiological evidence for functional heterogeneity of Na,K-ATPase; and (*c*) the experimental evidence directly testing the structure-function relationship of Na,K-ATPase. Within the framework of this short review, a limited number of specific references will be cited. Extensive and excellent recent reviews covering functional and structural aspects of this field should be consulted for a more complete reference list (77, 41, 8, 32, 13, 73, 56).

STRUCTURAL HETEROGENEITY OF Na,K-ATPase

α *Subunit*

The primary sequence of α subunits (also designated catalytic subunits) has been deduced from cDNAs isolated from invertebrates and vertebrates. Amino acid sequences for human (36), pig (see reference in 8), rat (67), chicken (79), *Xenopus laevis* (83), *Torpedo* (34), *Drosophila* (40), and *Artemia* (4) α subunits have been reported. With the exception of the *Artemia* (brine shrimp) α subunit, which shows ~ 70% identity with the other subunits, the degree of conservation between α_1 subunits is extremely high (90% identity or more) from *Drosophila* to human. Based on hydropathy plot, the predicted topology for membrane insertion is shown in Figure 2*a*. Models with six (34), seven (55), or eight (67) hydrophobic putative transmembrane domains (H_1–H_8) have been proposed. Eight to ten putative transmembrane hydrophobic domains appear to be a well conserved feature for all ionmotive P ATPase (46). Alignment of H_1–H_2 and H_3–H_4 ectodomains (i.e. facing the extracellular space) and FITC-binding sites (i.e. facing the cytoplasm) for all reported α isoforms is depicted in Figure 3*a*. Based on chemical modification of the α subunit followed by amino acid sequencing and site-directed mutagenesis, some functional domains of the α subunit have been identified. The N-terminus domain faces the cytoplasm, and it diverges most among all α

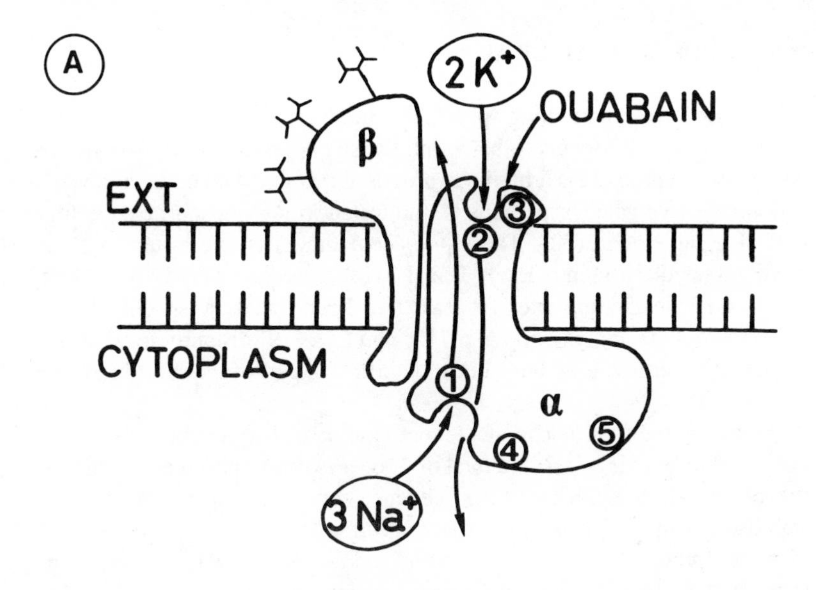

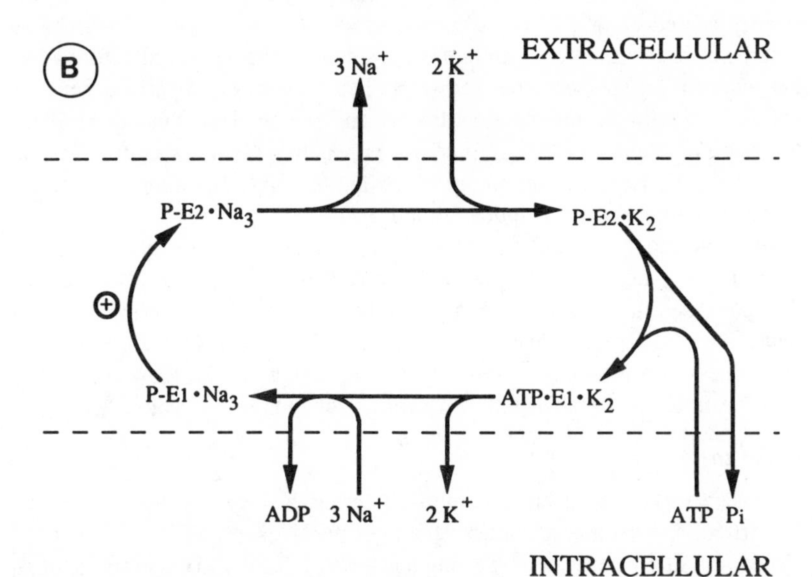

Figure 1 (*A*) General model for Na,K-ATPase: an $\alpha\beta$ heterodimer is schematically represented with binding sites for Na^+ (1), K^+ (2), ouabain (3), phosphorylation (4), and the ATP binding site (5). Most of the β subunit mass is thought to be on the extracellular space while most of the α subunit mass is facing the cytoplasm. (*B*) Simplified Albers-Post scheme of the Na,K-pump cycle. E_1 and E_2 are the conformations of the enzyme with the cation-binding sites facing the cytoplasm and the extracellular space, respectively. Charge translocation occurs between the $P\text{-}E_1.Na_3$ state and the delivery of the Na^+ ions to the extracellular space (2, 47), while the $P\text{-}E_2.K\text{-}E_1$ is probably electroneutral (75, 25, 2). Cardiac glycosides bind only to the E_2 state, and probably more specifically to the $P\text{-}E_2.Na_3$ state.

subunit isoforms and among species (Figure 2*a*, Figure 3*a*). This domain is lysine-rich. Lys 30 seems to be within the site accessible to trypsin in the E_1 Na^+ conformation (32). It has been proposed that this domain is involved as a cation-selective gate, or perhaps is implicated in ion transport by the formation of a salt bridge (32). The H_1–H_2 ectodomain is implicated in ouabain binding (see discussion below). The H_3–H_4 ectodomain (Trp310) is also part of the ouabain-binding site. At least five amino acids [Asp 369, Lys 501 (labeled by FITC), Cys 356, Asp 710, and Lys 719] distantly located on the second cytoplasmic loop have been identified as part of the ATP-binding site (Figure 2*a*).

Following the first biochemical identification of two α subunit isoforms, α and $\alpha(+)$ (see review in 77), a total of three α isoforms have been found in the rat (68) and in the chicken (80). Sequence comparison indicates an extreme stability among isoforms from distant species. Thus, rat α_1 and α_2 were 93% identical (protein level) with chicken α_1 and α_2, respectively. Rat α_3 shared a striking 96% identity with the corresponding α_3 avian isoform. Since the identity shared among isoforms of the same species is lower (80–86%), it would appear that the triplication of the α subunit genes occurred before avian and mammalian species separated (80). The sequence comparison between isoforms of two species, such as the rat and the chicken, thus allowed the definition of sequences that are isoform rather than species specific. Overall 40 out of 77 isoform-specific residues are expected to alter the protein structure markedly (80) (Figure 2*a* and 3*a*).

The ubiquitous α_1 isoform is the predominant, if not exclusive, kidney form. The α_2 and α_3 are the predominant isoforms of the brain, but they are also expressed in other excitable tissues (heart, muscle) and during development, in a stage-specific manner (53, 16, 65, 36, 52, 12). Overall tissue- and cell-specific expression is quite complex (see review in 77). How the various α isoforms are associated with β isoforms remains to be established.

β Subunit

Evidence for β isoforms has accumulated during the last year, in contrast with the earlier proposal that the heterogeneity of mRNA sizes observed in various tissues was solely generated by a single gene (85). The primary structure of β_1 subunit from human (35), sheep (69), dog (9), pig (54), rat (85), chicken (78), *Xenopus laevis* (83), and *Torpedo* (48) cDNAs is shown in Figure 2*b*. Within mammalian species, the β_1 isoform shares over 90% similarity, but this similarity decreases sharply when one compares mammal to fish or amphibia (60% identity), which is in contrast with the more highly conserved α subunits. A human fetal and a rat brain β_2 isoform were isolated (44) and were both virtually identical (3% divergence) to a mouse adhesion molecule on glia (AMOG) (24). The rat β_2 isoform copurifies with Na,K-ATPase

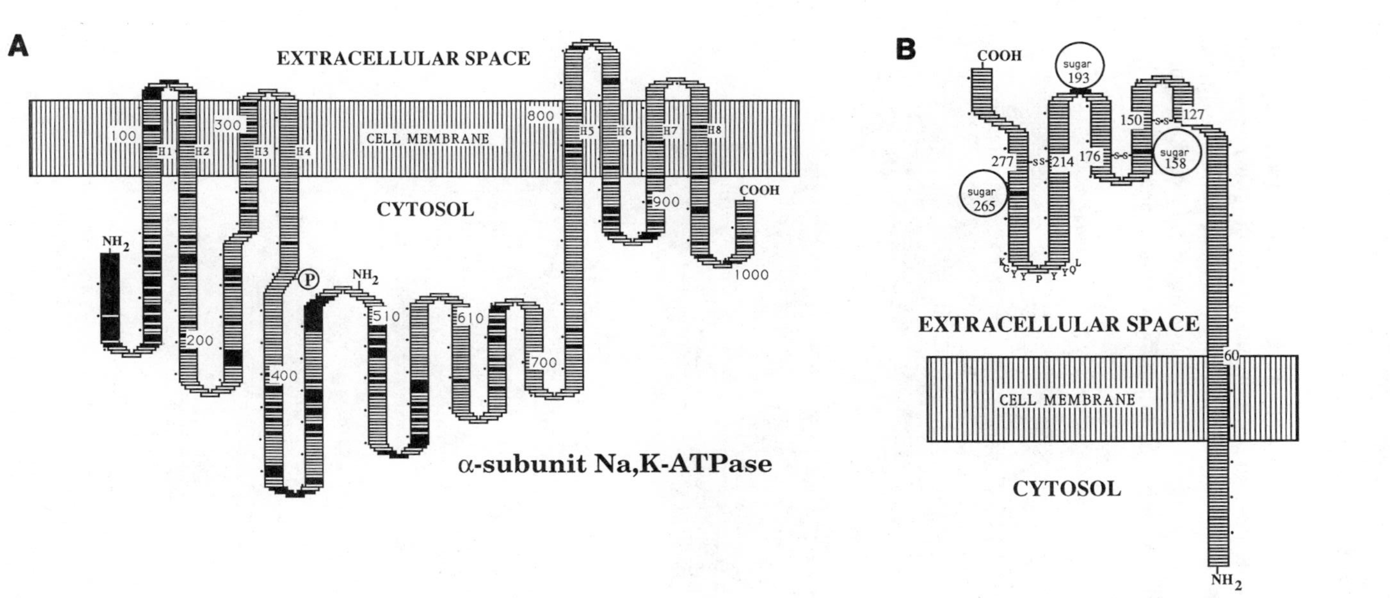

Figure 2 (*A*) Model representing predicted α subunit topology according to hydropathy plot (after reference 67) (adapted, with permission, from reference 80). Each amino acid is represented by a rectangle. For positions at which there is sequence diversity among isoforms (only chicken isoforms are compared), the rectangles are shaded in black. Eight putative transmembrane domains are predicted (H_1–H_8). H_1–H_2, H_3–H_4, H_5–H_6, H_7–H_8 are short ectoplasmic loops. H_2–H_3 and H_4–H_5 cytoplasmic loops are longer. P corresponds to Asp369, site of phosphorylation. NH_2 in the position 501 (Lys) is the FITC-binding site near the ATP-binding site (*B*) Model representing predicted β1-subunit topology according to hydropathy plot. Each amino acid is represented by a rectangle. Amino acid numbering begins with the first methionine at the NH_2 terminus of the human β1 sequence. The subunit is labeled with its three potential glycosylation sites *(black rectangles)* and three disulfide bridges. No regions of homology are indicated in this figure.

activity from the brain (71). This β_2 isoform, predominantly found in glial cells (11, 12), appears to be up- and down-regulated (by drug or hormones) together with the α_2 isoform (12). In addition, a new brain-specific β_3 isoform has been isolated from the *Xenopus laevis* embryo (P. Good, I. Dawid, personal communication). A single hydrophobic domain, predicted by hy

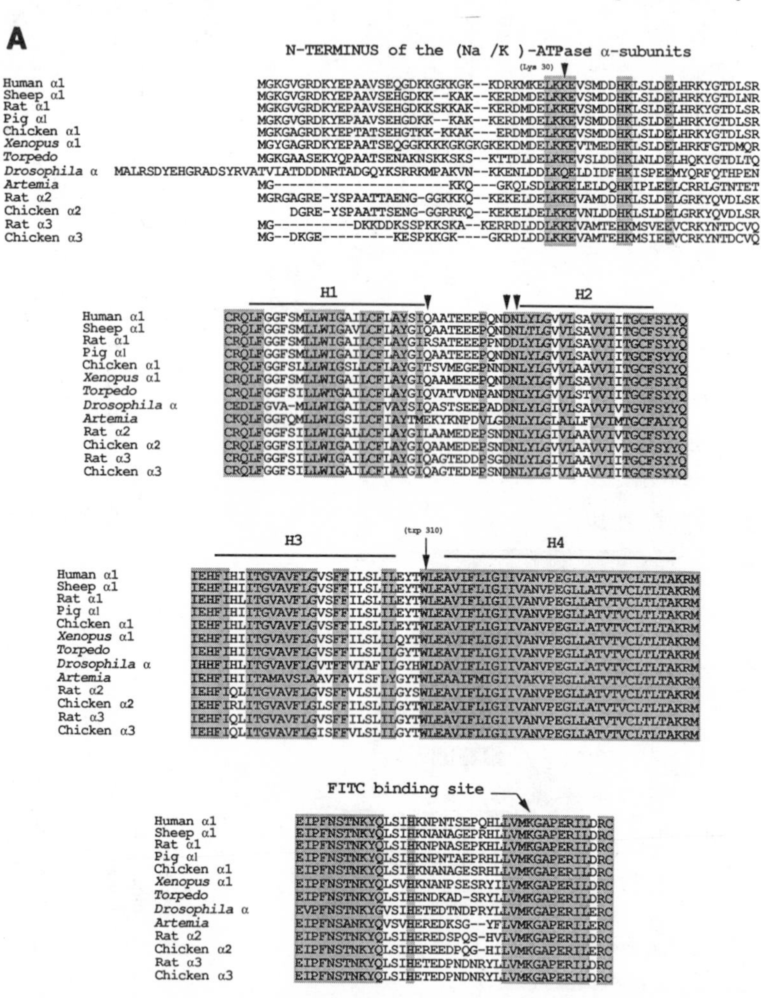

Figure 3 (*A*) Alignment of amino acid sequences within four defined regions of the α1 isoform for human, sheep, pig, rat, chicken, *Xenopus, Torpedo, Drosophila, Artemia;* α2 isoform: rat and chicken; α3 isoform; rat and chicken. NH_2 terminus, H_1–H_2 ectodomain, H_3–H_4 ectodomain, and FITC-binding site comparisons are displayed. Amino acids implicated with function (discussed in text) have been labeled with numbering according to Lingrel (41). *Arrows* over H_1–H_2 ectodomain denote amino acids implicated with ouabain resistance. *Shaded regions* represent sequence homology where only one of the thirteen amino acids aligned may vary.

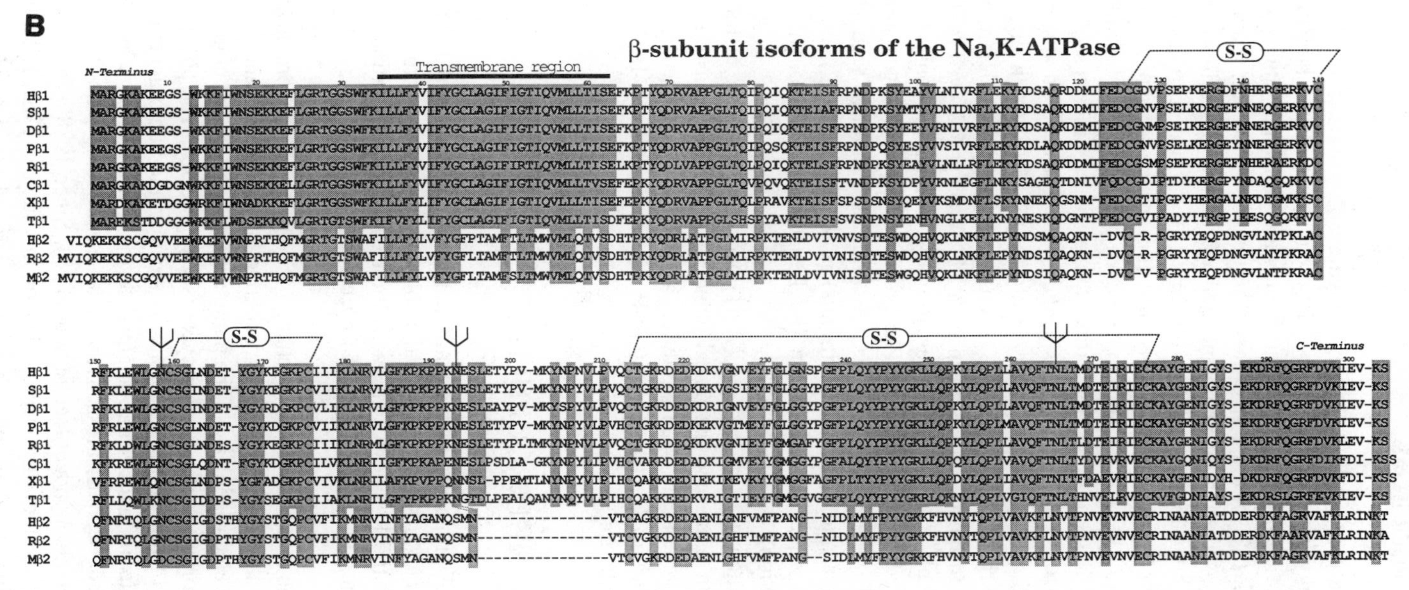

Figure 3 (*B*) Alignment of amino acid sequences of human $\beta 1$, H$\beta 1$; sheep $\beta 1$, S$\beta 1$; dog$\beta 1$, D$\beta 1$; pig$\beta 1$, P$\beta 1$; rat$\beta 1$, R$\beta 1$; chicken $\beta 1$, C$\beta 1$; *Xenopus*$\beta 1$, X$\beta 1$; *Torpedo*$\beta 1$, T$\beta 1$; human $\beta 2$, H$\beta 2$; rat $\beta 2$, R$\beta 2$; mouse $\beta 2$, M$\beta 2$. The putative transmembrane domain (amino acids 34–60 relative to the human 1 sequence) is indicated. Glycosylation sites and disulfide bridges are also shown. *Shaded regions* depict sequence homology where only one amino acid, of either $\beta 1$ alone or of combined $\beta 1$ and $\beta 2$, may be different among the isoforms.

dropathy plot analysis in all β isoforms (Figure 3*b*), mediates membrane insertion, as demonstrated by various deletion mutants of the human β_1 isoform (33). Not surprisingly, the transmembrane domain is highly conserved among all β_1 isoforms. It differs significantly, however, from the corresponding conserved transmembrane domain of the β_2 isoform. The predicted extracellular domain (aa 61 to 302 or 304 for β_1 isoform) has three potential sites of N-linked (Figure 2*b*) glycosylation, which are apparently all used (see review in 21). The β_2 isoform has seven potential sites of N-linked glycosylation, while β_3 has three (according to classical consensus sequence Asn-X-Thr/Ser). Six cysteine residues (Figure 2*b*) involved in disulfide bridges are remarkably conserved in all β isoforms (45, 38), which suggests a conserved pattern of folding. Some specific ectodomains are extremely conserved. For instance, the sequence YYPYY (Tyr242-Tyr-Pro-Tyr-Tyr) is found in all β_1 isoforms, whereas in β_2 isoforms a conservative change is observed YFPYY (Tyr242-Phe-Pro-Tyr-Tyr). A charged amino acid motif (Lys216, Glu219, Asp220) is present in all β isoforms sequenced so far. The cytoplasmic domain (N-terminus) is short (3 kd) (22), and its deletion does not affect $\alpha\beta$ interaction (K. Renaud, D. Fambrough, personal communication).

The β_1 is ubiquitous (for review, see 77, 41), whereas β_2 is more restricted and found in brain tissue and the pineal gland (70, 71). The β_3 isoform is developmentally regulated, brain-specific, and highly expressed during neurulation of *Xenopus laevis* embryo (63; P. Good, K. Richter, I. Dawid, personal communication).

FUNCTIONAL HETEROGENEITY

Four physiological properties of the Na,K-pump will be considered: 1) the stoichiometry of the Na/K exchange; 2) the voltage-dependence of the Na,K-pump activity; 3) the kinetics of the activation by intra- and extracellular cations; and 4) the kinetics of inhibition by cardiac glycosides.

1. The stoichiometry of the Na/K exchange has obviously important consequences for the amount of ion transported by the pump, and it also determines the electrogenicity of the pump activity, i.e. the net number of charges transported during a pump cycle (see Figure 1*b*). The physiological relevance of this point is twofold: an electrogenic pump generates a current and thus influences the potential of the membrane in which the pump is located; second, the activity of an electrogenic pump must be somehow voltage-dependent (see review in 15). Since 1988 a few studies have been published, giving accurate data on this subject. First, Rakowski et al (62), using the dialyzed and voltage-clamped squid axon, simul-

taneously measured the ouabain-sensitive current and Na^+ fluxes. Their results indicated that the Na/K exchange ratio was precisely 3:2 and remained constant over a large range of inside and outside Na^+ and K^+ concentrations and membrane voltages. Second, Goldshleger et al (26) simultaneously measured Na^+ flux and electrogenic activity of Na,K-ATPase isolated from pig kidney and reconstituted in proteoliposomes. Over large ranges of cytosolic Na^+ activity (2–50 mM), pH (6.5–8.5), and ATP (1–1000 μM) concentrations, they found that the classical 3 Na^+:2 K^+ ratio was maintained. Other modes of net Na^+ transport by the pump, such as Na/H exchange or uncoupled Na^+ flux, have been observed in extreme situations, such as in the total absence of K^+ ions, or with a cytosolic Na^+ concentration lower than 1 mM (26, 58). In addition, purified preparations of the kidney (α_1 isoform) and axolemma (α_2, α_3 isoforms) enzyme reconstituted in lipid vesicles had a ratio of ATP-stimulated Na^+ to K^+ transport that was compatible in both cases with a 3:2 stoichiometry (76). It now appears likely that under physiological conditions the 3 Na^+:2 K^+ stoichiometry is a common characteristic of various isoforms of Na,K-pump found in excitable and epithelial cells.

2. The Na,K-pump is electrogenic, implying that the membrane potential affects the rate constant of the charge translocating step(s) of the pump cycle (15) (see Figure 1*b*). The precise relation of Na,K-pump activity to transmembrane voltage depends, however, on a number of yet unknown kinetic parameters of the pump cycle. The experimental evidence showing a voltage-dependence of the pump activity has been reviewed recently (14, 15, 2). Figure 4 shows four examples of the relation between the ouabain-sensitive current and the membrane potential observed in squid axon (62), heart cells (20), frog oocyte (66), and amphibian renal-collecting tubule (30). In squid axon ATPase (62), the current does not saturate over the explored potential range, and in heart cells saturation is observed only at positive membrane potentials. In contrast, in the amphibian tight epithelia (30), a steep voltage-dependence was observed (between −180 and −100 mV), but the current saturated between −60 and 0 mV. Similar results have been observed in A6 cells (J.-D. Horisberger, unpublished results). Using purified Na,K-ATPase isolated from rabbit kidney medulla and reconstituted in proteoliposomes, Apell & Bersch (3) also inferred a steep voltage-dependence at high negative membrane potentials, but a voltage-independent pump rate between −100 and 0 mV.

Although apparent saturation of the pump current activity might have many other causes than intrinsic kinetic properties of the pump, the differences of I–V curves obtained in excitable tissue and epithelial cells suggest the possibility that the various Na,K-ATPase isoforms have different voltage sensitivities. This question needs to be addressed specifically

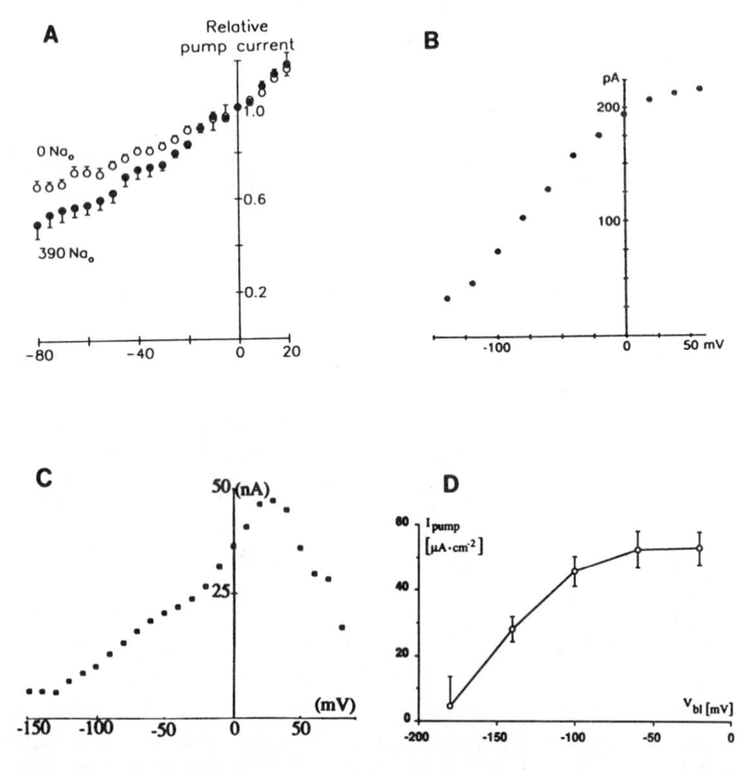

Figure 4 Voltage-current relationship for Na,K-pump expressed in various cells. The four graphs demonstrate the relation between the Na,K-pump-generated current and the membrane potential. The intracellular (Na_i, K_i) and extracellular (Na_o, K_o) cation concentrations are indicated for each case. (*Panel A*) Relative dihydrodigitoxigenin-sensitive current measured in internally dialysed and voltage-clamped squid giant axon (62) [Na_i] 50, [K_i] 0, [K_o] 10, two values of [Na_o] are indicated on the figure. (*Panel B*) Strophanthidin-sensitive current obtained by the whole cell recording technique in cells isolated from guinea pig heart ventricle (20) (Na_i 50, K_i 0, Na_o 150, K_o 5.4). (*Panel C*) Strophanthidin-sensitive current in Na^+-loaded *Xenopus laevis* oocytes, using the two electrode voltage-clamped technique (66) (Na_o 110, K_o 3); Na_i estimated to be 30–50 mM, from reference 39. (*Panel D*) Strophanthidin-sensitive current across the voltage-clamped basolateral membrane of isolated *Amphiuma*-collecting tubules (30) (Na_o 97, K_o 3); Na_i and K_i activities estimated to be 40–50 and 10–20 mM, respectively (from Reference 29) (by copyright permission of the Rockefeller Univ. Press).

in future experiments. A steep voltage-dependence in the physiological range of membrane potentials indicates an appreciable control of the Na,K-ATPase activity by the membrane potential. In cells, such as cardiac myocytes, which spend a considerable time in a strongly depolarized state, the effect of the membrane potential on the pump rate appears physiologically relevant (25), whereas in epithelial cells, the range of physiological membrane potentials is too restricted to allow for a significant effect of the membrane potential on the pump activity (30).

3. Activation kinetics by intracellular Na^+ or external K^+ might also be different in organs where the pumping of Na^+ is linked to such varied functions as bulk water and solute transport across the cells (epithelia), or maintenance of transmembrane ion gradients in spite of fast changes of membrane conductances (excitable cells).

Due to the complexity of the pump cycle and the fact that substrates can bind only to specific states of this cycle, the half-maximal activation constant ($K_{1/2}$) of the different substrates, Na^+, K^+, or ATP, as well as the K_i of cardiac glycosides might differ considerably from their real affinity for the specific state of the pump to which they bind. Thus the apparent affinities might vary by large amounts, depending on the conditions under which they are measured. Ideally, $K_{1/2}$ measurements should be performed under conditions where the membrane potential, the ATP concentration, and Na^+ and K^+ activities on both sides of the membrane are set and stable at all levels of activation or inhibition. Except for internally dialyzed voltage-clamped cells, these requirements have rarely been met. Therefore it is not surprising that some contradictory results have been reported concerning the affinity of Na^+ and K^+ for the Na,K-ATPase in tissues with various isozyme compositions.

In several studies concerning Na^+ affinity, Na,K-ATPase extracted from mammalian kidney (predominantly α_1 isoform) had a significantly higher $K_{1/2}$ (lower affinity) than enzyme extracted from nervous tissue (mostly α_2 and α_3 isoforms) (72, 81, 18). Sweadner (76), however, failed to observe a significantly higher affinity for Na^+ in brain ATPase than kidney enzyme. In contrast, several investigators observed the presence of an ouabain-sensitive component with a very low affinity for Na^+ in rat adipocytes (42), rat brain synaptosomes (7), and brine shrimp intestine (10). Several studies failed to observe differences in the K^+ activation constant (76, 81). In *Artemia salina,* however, Cortas et al (10) found a higher K^+ affinity in the tissue with high ouabain sensitivity. More specifically with the α_3 isoform, Shyjan et al (70) took advantage of the predominance of the α_3 isoform in the pineal gland to compare the functional properties of Na,K-pump isolated from this organ to that of the kidney enzyme; they found that Na^+ had a higher affinity for the pineal gland enzyme, but there was no difference for K^+ affinity.

In two cited studies (42, 7), large differences in Na^+ affinity for Na,K-pump from the same tissue have been observed, depending on which type of preparation was used (isolated cells, synaptosomes, or isolated membranes). This indicates that factors other than the α subunit isoform may have a large influence on the apparent affinity and that one must carefully consider these differing causes before causally relating isoform and cation affinity. Concerning K^+ affinity, more direct evidence has been brought by Guillaume et al (27): Na,K-ATPase from cat or human brain cortex was phosphorylated in the presence of Na^+, Mg^{2+}, and ATP and then electrophoretically separated; the higher molecular weight isoforms (α_2, α_3) were then dephosphorylated by K^+ with a higher affinity than the lower molecular weight isoform (α_1).

In view of these contradictory results, and although some data are suggestive of differences in affinity for Na^+ and K^+ of the various isoforms, no firm conclusions can yet be drawn.

4. Finally, the best characterized difference between Na,K-pump isoforms is certainly the sensitivity to inhibitors of the cardiac glycosides family. A number of recent studies (reviewed in 28) indicate that inhibition through ouabain-like endogenous compounds may have a physiological role in the regulation of the pump activity, although these so-called endo-ouabains and their precise function(s) have yet to be fully characterized. Thus this primarily pharmacological difference may also be an important physiological difference between enzyme isoforms.

The observed differences in ouabain sensitivity between tissues were among the first clues of the existence of functionally different forms of the Na,K-ATPase. After biochemical and genetic evidence for the existence of several isozymes had been obtained, the coincidence of isoform distribution and specific range of cardiac glycoside sensitivity in different tissues or cell types has provided the main argument for the hypothesis of a glycoside sensitivity determined by the α subunit isoform. This subject was extensively reviewed recently by Sweadner (77) and will be only briefly summarized here. Differences in ouabain sensitivity of brain and kidney enzymes have been observed in several species, and these differences are large (three to four orders of magnitude) in a few species such as rats and mice. In these so-called ouabain-insensitive species, the kidney enzyme has a very low affinity ($\sim$10 μM), whereas the brain enzyme has a high affinity ($\sim$10 nM), similar to those observed in the other ouabain-sensitive species. More precisely in rat heart or brain, the dose-inhibition curves appears biphasic, indicating two levels of inhibition, and the binding studies present a nonlinear Scatchard plot, indicating two types of binding sites with different affinities (the lower affinity site being similar to the site present in the kidney). These findings, along with the biochemical and genetic evidence of one specific α subunit isoform in the kidney and two or three isoforms in heart and brain, suggest an ouabain sensitivity determined by the α subunit isoform. An even more convincing argument was provided by the demonstration that while complete neural tissue had both low and high affinity ouabain sensitivity, cultured glial cells, which express only the α_1 isoform, had only the low affinity component, and axolemma membrane preparations, in which only the α_2,α_3 isoforms are biochemically detected, had only the high affinity component (43). Observed differences of a half-inhibition constant must also be interpreted with caution. Cardiac glycosides bind only to the E_2 state of the enzyme (see Figure 1*b*), and thus the apparent affinity may vary according to the part of the enzyme present in the state able to bind the glycoside. Thus any condition known to alter the equilibrium distribution of the enzyme between the two states (such as ATP, Na^+, or K^+ concentrations, membrane potential) would be expected to modify the apparent affinity. For instance, differences as large as a tenfold change have been observed in relation to the intracellular Na^+ concentration (74). The effect of outside K^+ concentration is also well documented (19). Differences of ouabain affinity between rat kidney and brain enzyme are very large, however, and not easily explained by these types of effects. Thus Sweadner (77) determined that there was overwhelming evidence for the presence of an α_1 subunit linked to low ouabain sensitivity, while the higher molecular weight forms (α+) had a high ouabain sensitivity.

The high glycoside sensitivity of both components of the α+ (α_2 and α_3 isoforms) has been supported by several recent papers. First, Urayama & Sweadner (82) used the relative resistance to trypsinolysis of the α_3 isoform to demonstrate that the α_3 preparation had a high affinity, similar to that of the $\alpha_2 + \alpha_3$ mixture present in axolemma membrane. Second, Shyjan et al (70) used the high expression of α_3 isoform in the pineal gland to demonstrate a high glycoside affinity of this isoform. And finally, Berrebi-Bertrand et al (5), using both dose/response curves and binding assays with rat brain membranes, could resolve three components of the ouabain inhibition with K_is of 0.02, 0.5, and 320 μM, which indicated two high affinity and one low affinity sites.

STRUCTURE-FUNCTION RELATIONSHIP: EXPERIMENTAL APPROACHES

The data reviewed in the preceding section strongly suggest that structural heterogeneity of Na,K-ATPase parallels specific functions expressed in different cells or tissues. The correlation between ouabain sensitivity and tissue-specific expression of various isoforms is impressive. To establish a causal relationship will require direct experimentation. Two different and complementary approaches have been followed so far: the chemical modification of the subunit polypeptides, and the expression of genetically engineered subunits in different cell types.

1. Site specific ligands were used to define the ouabain-binding domain, the phosphorylation, and ATP-binding sites on the α subunit. Controlled trypsinolysis of the α subunit allows mapping of important residues involved in the cation-dependent E_1–E_2 transition [56, 32]. One limitation of this approach, however, is the need of a highly purified Na,K-ATPase enzyme preparation.
2. The second strategy involves recombinant molecules expressed in different systems in order to correlate the function of an isoform to its primary structure. Since the three-dimensional structure of Na,K-ATPase subunits has not been established, it is rather difficult to select the sequences that can be mutated in order to alter the enzyme's function without affecting assembly and oligomerization. The choice of the sequences to be mutated is based on the biochemical data gathered from the chemical modification approach outlined above, or by the identification of conserved isoform-specific residues based on sequence alignment of isoforms from various species (80). Generation of chimeric molecules allows one to screen for functional domains, such as the ouabain-binding domain. This type of approach requires homologous polypeptides, such as the various isoforms, which minimize gross perturbation of the polypeptide and, hence, the enzyme architecture. Once functional domains are identified, the fine mapping of the amino acids required for function can be achieved by site-directed mutagenesis. The risk of the site-directed mutation approach is to generate numerous either misfolded or silent mutants. Despite this potential drawback, new information based on recombinant molecules has recently been obtained.

Characterization of α-Subunit Functional Sites

CATALYTIC PHOSPHORYLATION SITE Asp 376 of the α subunit is part of the highly conserved sequence among all E_1–E_2/P-type ATPase (Cys-Ser-Asp376-Lys). Asp 376 has been shown to be phosphorylated during the catalytic cycle (84). Mutation of Asp376 of the *Torpedo* α subunit to Asn, Glu, or Thr and its co-expression with an unmutated β subunit in a *Xenopus laevis* oocyte led to the loss of Na,K-ATPase activity and ouabain-binding capacity (51).

FITC-BINDING SITES FITC reacts with Na,K-ATPase and completely inhibits its activity (review in 56). Phosphorylation from ATP is prevented by FITC labeling, which suggests that the FITC-binding site is close to that of ATP. The consensus sequence around the labeled lysine residue (Lys501) is highly conserved throughout evolution (Figure 3*a*). When the FITC-labeled residue (Lys 501 or 507 in *Torpedo*) is mutated to methionine, both the Na,K-ATPase activity and the ouabain-binding capacity are markedly decreased (51).

OUABAIN-BINDING SITES Chimeric α_1 subunit molecules between species known for their resistance to ouabain (the rat) and α_1 subunits from species known for their sensitivity to ouabain (sheep, *Torpedo*) yielded concordant results (59, 50). Transfection of rat α_1 subunit into an ouabain-sensitive cell line (CVI) conferred resistance to the drug (17). Conversely, transfection of chicken α-$_1$ subunit (ouabain-sensitive species) to mouse fibroblast conferred ouabain sensitivity to the rodent cell line (78, 79). These data clearly indicate that the α subunit carries most of the functional domains conferring ouabain resistance or sensitivity. Chimeric molecule experiments suggested that the N-terminus (first half) of the α subunit was involved. Therefore H_1–H_2 and H_3–H_4 ectodomains (Figure 3*a*) become the most likely domains involved in ouabain binding (review in 41). As shown in Figure 3*a*, the H_1–H_2 ectodomain of the rat α_1 subunit is characterized by the presence of a positively charged amino acid (Arg 111) and a negatively charged residue (Asp 122). These residues are rat isoform α_1 specific, which suggests that they are involved in the lack of ouabain sensitivity. This was directly and elegantly tested by site-directed mutagenesis (59–61). Five different mutants of the sheep α_1 subunit (ouabain-sensitive) were generated, inserted into an expression vector, and screened for their capacity to confer ouabain resistance in stably transfected HeLa cells (a highly ouabain-sensitive cell line). When Arg 111 and Asp 122 were introduced in the sheep sequence, the expression of a highly ouabain-resistant phenotype was observed (59). When only one charged residue (Arg 111 or Asp 122) was introduced, only partial resistance to ouabain was observed. In a second study, Asp 121, a conserved residue for all α isoforms (Figure 3*a*), was mutated in either a conservative or non-conservative manner (Asp 121 Ala, Asp 121 Glu, Asp 121 Asn, Asp 121 Ser, Asp 121 Lys). The data indicated that Asp 121 was also involved in ouabain binding. The results suggested that the carboxyl group of Asp 121 was involved either directly or indirectly in binding activity (60). In the most recent study, it was confirmed that double mutants of charged residues are more resistant than single mutants. It was also found that the resistance to ouabain was increased further by substituting an amino acid of opposite charge at the two borders of H_1–H_2 ectodomains (Arg 111 and Asp 122). The mechanism of resistance is more complex than originally thought and depends on both the charge and the identity of the two residues at the border of the H_1–H_2 ectodomain (61).

Role of β Subunit

Functional expression of Na,K-ATPase in various expression systems such as the *Xenopus* oocyte or stably transfected cell lines requires the coexpression of the β subunit, either endogenously or exogenously (37, 79, 49). Thus, the β subunit appears to play a critical role in the assembly and export to the plasma membrane of a mature Na,K-ATPase. Maturation includes both cation transport capacity and ouabain binding. The *Xenopus* oocyte is especially well suited to study the possible function of the β_1 subunit since its mRNA is not translated at this stage of development (23). The α subunit is apparently synthesized and inserted into the membrane correctly, but is highly trypsin-sensitive, which suggests incomplete folding. When cRNAs encoding β_1 subunits are injected into the oocyte, the endogenous α subunit becomes trypsin-resistant and more functional pumps are expressed at the plasma membrane (23). In addition, α subunits synthesized from injected α_1 cRNA are rapidly degraded, probably in the ER, unless β cRNA is coinjected (1). In this system, it was also possible to test the functional assembly of $\alpha_1\beta_2$ and $\alpha_1\beta_3$ heterodimers. In both cases, the β_2 or β_3 isoforms were found competent to assemble and stabilize α subunits into an $\alpha\beta$ heterodimeric functional complex (K. Geering, personal communication). It remains to be seen whether such $\alpha_1\beta_2$ or $\alpha_1\beta_3$ complexes are expressed in normal cells or tissues and whether they mediate tissue-specific functions.

LIMITATIONS AND FUTURE DIRECTIONS

Site-directed mutagenesis of the cDNAs encoding the two Na,K-ATPase subunits has mainly confirmed observations based on a classical biochemical approach. More information will become available in the near future as more isoforms in various species are sequenced. Alternatively, random mutagenesis might elucidate which amino acid residues are important to the function of the pump. This approach remains a cumbersome task, mainly because the heterodimer consists of large subunit polypeptides in which most mutations could remain functionally silent.

A rational approach to mutagenesis and recombinant technology relies on the elucidation of the three-dimensional structure of a protein. So far, no eukaryotic transport protein has been crystallized. Whereas the task will be particularly difficult for the membrane-embedded α subunit, one can reasonably expect that the three-dimensional structure of the β subunit will be established in the near future. Indeed, other ectoplasmically oriented proteins have been expressed in high yield and crystallized without their membrane anchor (6).

Finally, expression of various Na,K-ATPase isoforms is rendered difficult by the presence of endogenous Na,K-ATPase subunits, which form heterogenous complexes with the exogenous polypeptides. This problem can be overcome by using cell systems such as yeast, which have other ionmotive ATPases for their housekeeping function (31). Alternatively, homologous recombination, with gene substitution combined with expression in transgenic animals, should allow the introduction of interesting mutants in animals, provided the function of the pump is not drastically altered.

ACKNOWLEDGMENTS

We would like to thank Nicole Skarda-Coderey for her excellent assistance in preparing this manuscript. We are also very grateful to Kathi Geering and James Schafer for comments and suggestions. This work was supported by a grant # 31-27798.89 to J.-D. Horisberger, # 31-26404.89 to J.-P. Kraehenbühl and B. C. Rossier, and # 31-26497.89 to B. C. Rossier, from the Swiss National Fund for Scientific Research.

Literature Cited

1. Ackermann, U., Geering, K. 1990. Mutual dependence of Na,K-ATPase α- and β-subunits for correct posttranslational processing and intracellular transport. *FEBS Lett.* 269:105–8
2. Apell, H.-J. 1989. Electrogenic properties of the Na,K pump. *J. Membr. Biol.* 110:103–14
3. Apell, H.-J., Bersch, B. 1988. Na,K-ATPase in artificial lipid vesicles: potential dependent transport rates investigated by a fluorescence method. In *Progress in Clinical and Biological Research,* Vol. 268A: *the Na^+,K^+-Pump, Part A: Molecular Aspects,* ed. J. C. Skou, J. G. Nørby, A. B. Maunsbach, M. Esmann, pp. 469–76. New York: Liss
4. Baxter-Lowe, L. A., Guo, J. Z., Bergstrom, E. E., Hokin, L. E. 1989. Molecular cloning of the Na,K-ATPase α-subunit in developing brine shrimp and sequence comparison with higher organisms. *FEBS Lett.* 257:181–87
5. Berrebi-Bertrand, I., Maixent, J. M., Christe, G., Lelièvre, L. G. 1990. Two active Na^+/K^+-ATPases of high affinity for ouabain in adult rat brain membranes. *Biochim. Biophys. Acta* 1021: 148–56
6. Bjorkman, P. J., Saper, M. A., Samraoui, B., Bennett, W. S., Strominger, J. L., et al. 1987. Structure of the human class I histocompatibility antigen, HLA-A2. *Nature* 329:506–12
7. Brodsky, J. L., Guidotti, G. 1990. Sodium affinity of brain Na^+-K^+-ATPase is dependent on isozyme and environment of the pump. *Am. J. Physiol.* 258:C803–11
8. Broude, N. E., Modyanov, N. N., Monastyrskaya, G. S., Sverdlov, E. D. 1989. Advances in Na^+,K^+-ATPase studies: From protein to gene and back to protein. *FEBS Lett.* 257:1–9
9. Brown, T. A., Horowitz, B., Miller, R. P., McDonough, A. A., Farley, R. A. 1987. Molecular cloning and sequence analysis of the (Na^+ + K^+)-ATPase β subunit from dog kidney. *Biochim. Biophys. Acta* 912:244–53
10. Cortas, N., Arnaout, M., Salon, J., Edelman, I. S. 1989. Isoforms of Na,K-ATPase in *Artemia salina:* II. Tissue distribution and kinetic characterization. *J. Membr. Biol.* 108:187–95
11. Corthésy-Theulaz, I., Mérillat, A. M., Honegger, P., Rossier, B. C. 1990. Na^+-K^+-ATPase gene expression during in vitro development of rat fetal forebrain. *Am. J. Physiol.* 258:C1062–69
12. Corthésy-Theulaz, I., Rossier, B., Honegger, P. 1990. Differential expression and developmental regulation of Na,K-ATPase isoforms in rat fetal telencephalon organotypic cell cultures. In *Progress in Cell Research, Vol. 1: Proc. 13th Int. Meet. Biol. Membr., Crans-Montana, June 1989,* ed. J. M. Ritchie, P. J. Magistretti, L. Bolis, pp. 241–48. Amsterdam: Elsevier
13. De Weer, P. 1985. Cellular sodium-potassium transport. In *The Kidney: Physiology and Pathophysiology,* ed. D. W. Seldin, G., Giebisch, pp. 31–48. New York: Raven
14. De Weer, P., Gadsby, D. C., Rakowski, R. F. 1988. Voltage dependence of the Na-K pump. *Annu. Rev. Physiol.* 50:225–41
15. De Weer, P., Gadsby, D. C., Rakowski, R. F. 1988. Stoichiometry and voltage dependence of the Na/K pump. See Ref. 3, pp. 421–34
16. Emanuel, J. R., Garetz, S., Stone, L., Levenson, R. 1987. Differential expression of Na^+,K^+-ATPase α- and β-subunit mRNAs in rat tissues and cell lines. *Proc. Natl. Acad. Sci. USA* 84: 9030–34
17. Emanuel, J. R., Schulz, J., Zhou, X. M., Kent, R. B., Housman, D., et al. 1988. Expression of an ouabain-resistant Na,K-ATPase in CV-1 cells after

transfection with a cDNA encoding the rat Na,K-ATPase α1 subunit. *J. Biol. Chem.* 263:7726–33

18. Feige, G., Leutert, T., De Pover, A. 1988. Na,K-ATPase isozymes in rat tissues: differential sensitivities to sodium, vanadate and dihydroouabain. See Ref. 3, pp. 377–84
19. Forbush, B. III. 1983. Cardiotonic steroid binding to Na,K-ATPase. *Curr. Top. Membr. Transp.* 19:167–201
20. Gadsby, D. C., Nakao, M. 1989. Steady-state current-voltage relationship of the Na/K pump in guinea pig ventricular myocytes. *J. Gen. Physiol.* 94: 511–37
21. Geering, K. 1990. Subunit assembly and functional maturation of Na,K-ATPase. *J. Membr. Biol.* 115:109–21
22. Geering, K., Meyer, D. I., Paccolat, M. P., Kraehenbühl, J.-P., Rossier, B. C. 1985. Membrane insertion of α- and β-subunits of Na^+,K^+-ATPase. *J. Biol. Chem.* 260:5154–60
23. Geering, K., Theulaz, I., Verrey, F., Häuptle, M. T., Rossier, B. C. 1989. A role for the β-subunit in the expression of functional Na^+-K^+-ATPase in *Xenopus* oocytes. *Am. J. Physiol.* 257:C851–58
24. Gloor, S., Antonicek, H., Sweadner, K. J., Pagliusi, S., Frank, R., et al. 1990. The adhesion molecule on glia (AMOG) is a homologue of the β subunit of the Na,K-ATPase. *J. Cell Biol.* 110:165–74
25. Goldshleger, R., Karlish, S. J. D., Rephaeli, A., Stein, W. D. 1987. The effect of membrane potential on the mammalian sodium-potassium pump reconstituted into phospholipid vesicles. *J. Physiol.* 387:331–55
26. Goldshleger, R., Shahak, Y., Karlish, S. J. D. 1990. Electrogenic and electroneutral transport modes of renal Na/K ATPase reconstituted into proteoliposomes. *J. Membr. Biol.* 113:139–54
27. Guillaume, D., Grisar, T., Delgado-Escueta, A. V., Laschet, J., Bureau-Heeren, M. 1990. Two isoenzymes of Na^+,K^+-ATPase have different kinetics of K^+ dephosphorylation in normal cat and human brain cortex. *J. Neurochem.* 54:130–34
28. Haber, E., Haupert, G. T. Jr. 1987. The search for a hypothalamic Na^+,K^+-ATPase inhibitor. *Hypertension* 9:315–24
29. Horisberger, J.-D., Giebisch, G. 1988. Intracellular Na^+ and K^+ activities and membrane conductances in the collecting tubule of *Amphiuma*. *J. Gen. Physiol.* 92:643–65
30. Horisberger, J.-D., Giebisch, G. 1989. Na-K pump current in the *Amphiuma* collecting tubule. *J. Gen. Physiol.* 94: 493–510
31. Horowitz, B., Eakle, K. A., Scheiner-Bobis, G., Randolph, G. R., Chen, C. Y., et al. 1990. Synthesis and assembly of functional mammalian Na,K-ATPase in yeast. *J. Biol. Chem.* 265:4189–92
32. Jørgensen, P. L., Andersen, J. P. 1988. Structural basis for E_1-E_2 conformational transitions in Na,K-pump and Ca-pump proteins. *J. Membr. Biol.* 103:95–120
33. Kawakami, K., Nagano, K. 1988. The transmembrane segment of the human Na,K-ATPase β-subunit acts as the membrane incorporation signal. *J. Biochem.* 103:54–60
34. Kawakami, K., Noguchi, S., Noda, M., Takahashi, H., Ohta, T., et al. 1985. Primary structure of the α-subunit of *Torpedo californica* (Na^+ + K^+)-ATPase deduced from cDNA sequence. *Nature* 316:733–36
35. Kawakami, K., Nojima, H., Ohta, T., Nagano, K. 1986. Molecular cloning and sequence analysis of human Na,K-ATPase β-subunit. *Nucleic Acids Res.* 14:2833–44
36. Kawakami, K., Ohta, T., Nojima, H., Nagano, K. 1986. Primary structure of the α-subunit of human Na,K-ATPase deduced from cDNA sequence. *J. Biochem.* 100:389–97
37. Kent, R. B., Emanuel, J. R., Ben Neriah, Y., Levenson, R., Housman, D. E. 1987. Ouabain resistance conferred by expression of the cDNA for a murine Na^+,K^+-ATPase α subunit. *Science* 237:901–3
38. Kirley, T. L. 1989. Determination of three disulfide bonds and one free sulfhydryl in the β subunit of (Na,K)-ATPase. *J. Biol. Chem.* 264:7185–92
39. Lafaire, A. V., Schwarz, W. 1986. Voltage dependence of the rheogenic Na^+/K^+ ATPase in the membrane of oocytes of *Xenopus laevis*. *J. Membr. Biol.* 91:43–51
40. Lebovitz, R. M., Takeyasu, K., Fambrough, D. M. 1989. Molecular characterization and expression of the (Na^+ + K^+)-ATPase alpha-subunit in *Drosophila melanogaster*. *EMBO J.* 8:193–202
41. Lingrel, J. B., Orlowski, J., Shull, M. M., Price, E. M. 1990. Molecular genetics of Na, K-ATPase. *Prog. Nucleic Acids Res. Mol. Biol.* 38:37–89
42. Lytton, J. 1985. Insulin affects the sodium affinity of the rat adipocyte (Na^+,K^+)-ATPase. *J. Biol. Chem.* 260: 10075–10080

43. Marks, M. J., Seeds, N. W. 1978. Ouabain-ATPase interaction in brain cells maintained as reaggregates or surface cultures. *Life Sci*. 23:2745–55
44. Martin-Vasallo, P., Dackowski, W., Emanuel, J. R., Levenson, R. 1989. Identification of a putative isoform of the Na,K-ATPase β subunit. Primary structure and tissue-specific expression. *J. Biol. Chem*. 264:4613–18
45. Miller, R. P., Farley, R. A. 1990. The beta subunit of ($Na^+ + K^+$)-ATPase contains three disulfide bonds. *Biochemistry* 29:1524–32
46. Nakamoto, R. K., Rao, R., Slayman, C. W. 1989. Transmembrane segment of the P-type cation-transporting ATPases. A comparative study. *Ann. NY Acad. Sci*. 574:165–79
47. Nakao, M., Gadsby, D. C. 1986. Voltage dependence of Na translocation by the Na/K pump. *Nature* 323:628–30
48. Noguchi, S., Noda, M., Takahashi, H., Kawakami, K., Ohta, T., et al. 1986. Primary structure of the β-subunit of *Torpedo californica* (Na^+ + K^+)-ATPase deduced from the cDNA sequence. *FEBS Lett*. 320:315–20
49. Noguchi, S., Mishina, M., Kawamura, M., Numa, S. 1987. Expression of functional (Na^+ + K^+)-ATPase from cloned cDNAs. *FEBS Lett*. 225:27–32
50. Noguchi, S., Ohta, T., Takeda, K., Ohtsubo, M., Kawamura, M. 1988. Ouabain sensitivity of a chimeric α subunit (*Torpedo*/rat) of the (Na,K)-ATPase expressed in *Xenopus* oocyte. *Biochem. Biophys. Res. Commun*. 155: 1237–43
51. Ohtsubo, M., Noguchi, S., Takeda, K., Morohashi, M., Kawamura, M. 1990. Site-directed mutagenesis of Asp-376, the catalytic phosphorylation site, and Lys-507, the putative ATP-binding site, of the α-subunit of *Torpedo californica* Na^+/K^+-ATPase. *Biochim. Biophys. Acta* 1021:157–60
52. Orlowski, J., Lingrel, J. B. 1988. Differential expression of the Na, K-ATPase α1 and α2 subunit genes in a murine myogenic cell line. Induction of the α2 isozyme during myocyte differentiation. *J. Biol. Chem*. 263:17817–21
53. Orlowski, J., Lingrel, J. B. 1988. Tissue-specific and developmental regulation of rat Na, K-ATPase catalytic α isoform and β subunit mRNAs. *J. Biol. Chem*. 263:10436–42
54. Ovchinnikov, Y. A., Modyanov, N. N., Broude, N. E., Petrukhin, K. E., Grishin, A. V., et al. 1986. Pig kidney Na^+,K^+-ATPase. Primary structure and spatial organization. *FEBS Lett*. 201: 237–45
55. Ovchinnikov, Y. A., Arzamazova, N. M., Arystarkhova, E. A., Gevondyan, N. M., Aldanova, N. A., et al. 1987. Detailed structural analysis of exposed domains of membrane-bound Na^+,K^+-ATPase. A model of transmembrane arrangement. *FEBS Lett*. 217:269–74
56. Pedemonte, C. H., Kaplan, J. H. 1990. Chemical modification as an approach to elucidation of sodium pump structure-function relations. *Am. J. Physiol*. 258: C1–C23
57. Pedersen, P. L., Carafoli, E. 1987. Ion motive ATPases. I. Ubiquity, properties, and significance to cell function. *Trends Biochem. Sci*. 12:146–50
58. Polvani, C., Blostein, R. 1989. Effects of cytoplasmic sodium concentration on the electrogenicity of the sodium pump. *J. Biol. Chem*. 264:15182–85
59. Price, E. M., Lingrel, J. B. 1988. Structure-function relationships in the Na,K-ATPase α subunit: site-directed mutagenesis of glutamine-111 to arginine and asparagine-122 to aspartic acid generates a ouabain-resistant enzyme. *Biochemistry* 27:8400–8
60. Price, E. M., Rice, D. A., Lingrel, J. B. 1989. Site-directed mutagenesis of a conserved, extracellular aspartic acid residue affects the ouabain sensitivity of sheep Na,K-ATPase. *J. Biol. Chem*. 264:21902–6
61. Price, E. M., Rice, D. A., Lingrel, J. B. 1990. Structure-function studies of Na,K-ATPase. Site-directed mutagenesis of the border residues from the H1-H2 extracellular domain of the α subunit. *J. Biol. Chem*. 265:6638–41
62. Rakowski, R. F., Gadsby, D. C., De Weer, P. 1989. Stoichiometry and voltage dependence of the sodium pump in voltage-clamped, internally dialyzed squid giant axon. *J. Gen. Physiol*. 93: 903–41
63. Richter, K., Grunz, H., Dawid, I. B. 1988. Gene expression in the embryonic nervous system of *Xenopus laevis*. *Proc. Natl. Acad. Sci. USA* 85:8086–90
64. Rossier, B. C., Geering, K., Kraehenbühl, J.-P. 1987. Regulation of the sodium pump: how and why?. *Trends Biochem. Sci*. 12:483–87
65. Schneider, J. W., Mercer, R. W., Gilmore-Hebert, M., Utset, M. F., Lai, C., et al. 1988. Tissue specificity, localization in brain, and cell-free translation of mRNA encoding the A3 isoform of Na^+,K^+-ATPase. *Proc. Natl. Acad. Sci. USA* 85:284–88
66. Schweigert, B., Lafaire, A. V.,

Schwarz, W. 1988. Voltage dependence of the Na-K ATPase: measurements of ouabain-dependent membrane current and ouabain binding in oocytes of *Xenopus laevis*. *Pflügers Arch.* 412:579–88

67. Shull, G. E., Schwartz, A., Lingrel, J. B. 1985. Amino-acid sequence of the catalytic subunit of the (Na^+ + K^+)-ATPase deduced from a complementary DNA. *Nature* 316:691–95
68. Shull, G. E., Greeb, J., Lingrel, J. B. 1986. Molecular cloning of three distinct forms of the Na^+,K^+-ATPase α-subunit from rat brain. *Biochemistry* 25:8125–32
69. Shull, G. E., Lane, L. K., Lingrel, J. B. 1986. Amino-acid sequence of the β-subunit of the (Na^+ + K^+)ATPase deduced from a cDNA. *Nature* 321:429–31
70. Shyjan, A. E., Ceña, V., Klein, D. C., Levenson, R. 1990. Differential expression and enzymatic properties of the Na^+,K^+-ATPase $\alpha 3$ isoenzyme in rat pineal glands. *Proc. Natl. Acad. Sci. USA* 87:1178–82
71. Shyjan, A. W., Gottardi, C., Levenson, R. 1990. The Na,K-ATPase $\beta 2$ subunit is expressed in rat brain and copurifies with Na,K-ATPase activity. *J. Biol. Chem.* 265:5166–69
72. Skou, J. C. 1962. Preparation from mammalian brain and kidney of the enzyme system involved in active transport of Na^+ and K^+. *Biochim. Biophys. Acta* 58:314–25
73. Skou, J. C. 1988. The Na, K-pump. *Methods Enzymol.* 156:1–25
74. Stimers, J. R., Lobaugh, L. A., Liu, S., Shigeto, N., Lieberman, M. 1990. Intracellular sodium effects ouabain interaction with the Na/K pump in cultured chick cardiac myocytes. *J. Gen. Physiol.* 95:77–95
75. Stürmer, W., Apell, H.-J., Wuddel, I., Läuger, P. 1989. Conformational transitions and charge translocation by the Na,K pump: Comparison of optical and electrical transients elicited by ATP-concentration jumps. *J. Membr. Biol.* 110:67–86
76. Sweadner, K. J. 1985. Enzymatic properties of separated isozymes of the Na,K-ATPase. Substrate affinities, kinetic cooperativity, and ion transport stoichiometry. *J. Biol. Chem.* 260:11508–13
77. Sweadner, K. J. 1989. Isozymes of the Na^+/K^+-ATPase. *Biochim. Biophys. Acta* 988:185–220
78. Takeyasu, K., Tamkun, M. M., Siegel, N. R., Fambrough, D. M. 1987. Expression of hybrid (Na^+ + K^+)ATPase molecules after transfection of mouse LtK^- cells with DNA encoding the β-subunit of an avian brain sodium pump. *J. Biol. Chem.* 262:10733–40
79. Takeyasu, K., Tamkun, M. M., Renaud, K. J., Fambrough, D. M. 1988. Ouabain-sensitive (Na^+ + K^+)-ATPase activity expressed in mouse L cells by transfection with DNA encoding the α-subunit of an avian sodium pump. *J. Biol. Chem.* 263:4347–54
80. Takeyasu, K., Lemas, V., Fambrough, D. M. 1990. Stability of (Na^++K^+)-ATPase α-subunit isoforms in evolution. *Am. J. Physiol.* 259:C619–30
81. Urayama, O., Nakao, M. 1979. Organ specificity of rat sodium- and potassium-activated adenosine triphosphatase. *J. Biochem.* 86:1371–81
82. Urayama, O., Sweadner, K. J. 1988. Ouabain sensitivity of the alpha 3 isozyme of rat Na,K-ATPase. *Biochem. Biophys. Res. Commun.* 156:796–800
83. Verrey, F., Kairouz, P., Schaerer, E., Fuentes, P., Geering, K., et al. 1989. Primary sequence of *Xenopus laevis* Na^+-K^+-ATPase and its localization in A6 kidney cells. *Am. J. Physiol.* 256:F1034–43
84. Walderhaug, M. O., Post, R. L., Saccomani, G., Leonard, R. T., Briskin, D. P. 1985. Structural relatedness of three ion-transport adenosine triphosphatases around their active sites of phosphorylation. *J. Biol. Chem.* 260:3852–59
85. Young, R. M., Shull, G. E., Lingrel, J. B. 1987. Multiple mRNAs from rat kidney and brain encode a single Na^+,K^+-ATPase β subunit protein. *J. Biol. Chem.* 262:4905–10

Annu. Rev. Physiol. 1991. 53:585–605

THE ROLE OF ACTIN POLYMERIZATION IN CELL MOTILITY

John A. Cooper

Department of Cell Biology and Physiology, Washington University Medical School, St. Louis, Missouri 63110

KEY WORDS: cytoskeleton, actin-binding proteins, assembly

INTRODUCTION AND SCOPE

The general question considered in this review is what is the role of actin polymerization in cell motility? Two specific questions are (*a*) do individual actin filaments undergo net assembly or disassembly as part of a process in cell motility, and (*b*) does the energy of assembly or disassembly drive processes in cell motility? Actin filaments have anisotropic distributions in cells, which often have asymmetric shapes. During development, structures with high concentrations of actin filaments appear, and during normal physiologic activity of many non-muscle cells, the actin distribution changes. Does this anisotropy occur because filaments move about the cytoplasm, or because subunits move, with net filament assembly at certain places, and with net disassembly at other places? Changes in intracellular actin distribution often accompany cell movement or changes in cell shape. Does the energy available from actin polymerization drive the motions of the cell? Interest in this question has increased because mutant cells lacking myosin are normal in some aspects of cell motility. These mutants and other investigations into myosin funtion have been reviewed recently (59, 60, 95) (see Pollard, Doberstein, Zot this volume). This review is not complete in its description of the literature and concentrates on a few systems and experimental approaches. Recent reviews on related topics include references 71, 77, 82, and 96.

0066-4278/91/0315-0585$02.00

STATUS OF ACTIN POLYMERIZATION IN CELLS

Much has been learned about the polymerization of actin in vitro, including its regulation by small molecules and actin-binding proteins (16, 82, 84, 97), which presents the opportunity to determine how actin polymerization occurs in cells. Under depolymerizing condition in vitro, actin is a monomer with a single polypeptide of 42 kd. Under polymerizing conditions, actin forms long helical filaments, which undergo dynamic exchange with small subunits. Although the physical state of the subunits has been assumed to be monomeric, a variety of physical techniques detect dimers and other small oligomers in solutions with filaments (44, 67, 76). What fraction of the small subunits are oligomers and whether these oligomers are the species that exchange with filaments is still controversial because of conflicting data. The exchange of subunits occurs at both ends of the filament by addition or loss of the terminal subunit, which is the mechanism by which filaments grow or shrink in vitro. Filaments can also break or anneal (join end-to-end) to change length (75).

In vivo, actin filaments with similar helical structure are observed; however, they are much shorter than ones in vitro (about 0.1 vs 10 μm) (49), which suggests that the ends are blocked by another molecule, perhaps an actin-binding protein like capping protein or gelsolin. About half of the actin is in the form of filaments, with local concentrations as high as 300–400 μM in lamellae, the peripheral motile regions of cells (49).

The other half of the actin is in a state with certain properties that resemble monomers in vitro, although the exact physical characteristics of that pool of actin have not been determined. In vitro, in the presence of filaments, the monomer concentration is 0.1–1 μM (8, 83) at steady-state[1], whereas in cytoplasm the apparent monomer concentration is about 100 μM (7, 10), which indicates that actin monomers in cells are sequestered in a non-polymerizing state by modification, or by binding to another molecule, such as profilin.

To test whether monomers in cells are sequestered, fluorescein-labeled actin filaments were microinjected into the cytoplasm of cells (87). No polymerization of cellular actin onto the microinjected filaments was observed. On the other hand, when rhodamine-labeled actin monomers were injected 20 min after the fluorescein filaments, the rhodamine monomers did polymerize onto the fluorescein filaments. This result indicates that both ends of the microinjected fluorescein filaments are not rapidly capped by free actin-binding proteins. Therefore, the absence of polymerization of cellular actin onto the microinjected filaments suggests that cells do not contain a large pool of monomers capable of polymerization; instead, the monomers are

[1]This monomer concentration is also called the critical concentration because actin filaments are only present if the total actin concentration exceeds this concentration.

sequestered. A number of actin-binding proteins that sequester actin monomers in vitro have been described, and are discussed below. The only posttranslational modification of actin that inhibits its polymerization is phosphorylation, described in *Amoeba proteus* (92).

ACTIN-BINDING PROTEINS

Experiments with actin-binding proteins may be useful to understand the role of actin polymerization in cell motility. Many actin-binding proteins have been purified and shown to affect actin polymerization in vitro. If an actin-binding protein also affects actin polymerization in vivo, then one may be able to selectively inhibit or enhance that function and correlate altered actin polymerization with a cell phenotype.

Muscle

Striated muscle is an important paradigm because all the actin filaments have the same length and polarity in the half-sarcomere, which implies that the position of their ends is specified, most likely by an actin-binding protein that binds to the end and caps it. The barbed end[2] of the actin filaments are probably capped by CapZ, a member of the capping protein family, which caps barbed ends in vitro and is located at the Z line, the location of barbed ends, in situ (14, 18–20). CapZ also nucleates actin polymerization in vitro (13), which suggests that during myofibril assembly, CapZ might bind to a nascent Z line and then nucleate the polymerization of actin filaments, which would specify their polarity and the location of their barbed ends.

The pointed ends of skeletal, but not cardiac, muscle are all at equivalent longitudinal positions (86), although they do not terminate at a recognized structure like the Z line. β-actinin, once a potential pointed end capping protein, has been shown to not cap pointed ends in vitro and to not be located at the pointed ends in situ (66). These improved preparations of β-actinin contain protein that is functionally and structurally similar to CapZ, a barbed end capper (66). Tropomyosin from skeletal muscle profoundly inhibits polymerization and depolymerization at the pointed end, (11, 111a), which helps explain the stability of the filaments, but does not seem to explain the uniform location of the pointed ends.

Although myofibrillar actin turns over (113), and microinjected fluorescent derivatives of actin incorporate into myofibrils by light microscopy (69), no evidence exists as to where and how the subunit-filament exchange occurs in cells. Despite the strong evidence from in vitro studies that subunits only

[2]The barbed and pointed ends of the actin filament are defined by the arrowheads formed by the binding of heavy meromyosin.

exchange at filament ends, this point has not been documented at the ultrastructural level in vivo. If exchange does occur at ends, it is not clear whether it occurs at one or another end, and how or whether the capping protein at that end releases.

Non-muscle

ATTACHMENT Non-muscle cells also contain actin-binding proteins that may attach filaments to structures via nucleation or capping. Actin filaments are concentrated in the distal cytoplasm, which suggests that the plasma membrane nucleates polymerization and/or caps filament ends. Radixin is a barbed-end capping protein associated with the membrane at cell-cell junctions (107). Ponticulin, a plasma membrane protein of *Dictyostelium,* binds filaments via their sides (89) and also binds subunits to nucleate polymerization in vitro (90).

REGULATION OF THE BARBED END Whether the ends of actin filaments in non-muscle cells are capped is an open question. The results of Sanders & Wang (87), discussed above, indicate that microinjected filaments are not rapidly capped on both ends. Actin-binding proteins of both the capping protein and gelsolin families, which bind to the barbed ends of filaments and stop subunit addition and loss (i.e. cap) in vitro, are present in all eukaryotic cells examined (3, 84, 97).

The gene for the β subunit of capping protein has been deleted in yeast (3). Features of the mutant phenotype include the loss of actin cables and appearance of actin spots in the mother cell, increased size, slow growth rate, and delocalized pattern of chitin deposition. The cell motility of yeast is limited, and the ultrastructure and function of actin in yeast are not well understood so the significance of these phenotypic features is currently unknown. However, conditional-lethal actin mutants and mutants in actin suppressing genes have similar phenotypes (reviewed in 30), which suggests that capping protein does act through actin. *Dictyostelium* null mutants of severin, an actin-binding protein of the gelsolin family, are normal in all of the many aspects of motility that were examined (4). Two possible conclusions from these negative results are that (*a*) other proteins perform the same function as severin, and (*b*) that severin does not interact with actin in vivo. The conclusion that actin polymerization and organization are altered in the mutant, but not important for cell motility, seems unlikely.

One limitation of non-lethal null mutants is that the cells lack the deleted protein for a long time; therefore, secondary effects may occur, which could include negative consequences of the lack of the protein and positive compensatory metabolic changes that the cell makes in response to the lack of the protein. A better approach is to halt actin polymerization during a process and determine whether the process is affected. One possibility is the creation of temperature-sensitive mutants in which the protein loses function rapidly as the temperature is changed. Alternatively, antibodies that inhibit function could be microinjected during a process; however, this approach has been limited by a lack of antibodies that inhibit function.

In another experimental approach, actin-binding proteins and fragments of acting-binding proteins have been microinjected into cells. For example, the microinjection of capping protein (39) leads to the loss of stress fibers, and the microinjection of an active fragment of gelsolin can lead to the loss of stress fibers and to cell rounding (23, 56a). These effects are similar to those of cytochalasin, which makes sense because these proteins have an in vitro mechanism of action similar to that of cytochalasin. The fact that the proteins and cytochalasin have the same effect indicates that the effects of cytochalasin are through actin and not via some other unidentified mechanism. Of course, this merely confirms the conclusion of experiments with cytochalasin (discussed below) that a certain supramolecular arrangement of actin filaments is necessary for cell motility, and it does not indicate what role, if any, actin polymerization plays.

REGULATION OF THE POINTED END The existence of pointed-end capping proteins is controversial. Experiments describing the activity of pointed-end capping proteins are difficult and have not been definitive. The actin polymerization assays used to detect and purify barbed-end capping proteins would probably not have detected pointed-end capping activity, so pointed-end capping proteins may exist. As mentioned above, muscle tropomyosin inhibits depolymerization at the pointed end, and non-muscle tropomyosins have similar effects (12). The single gene for tropomyosin in yeast has been deleted, which results in loss of actin cables and slow growth (65). Tropomyosin could obviously control the interaction of myosin and other proteins with actin, so these phenotypic features cannot be attributed to abnormal actin polymerization. A monoclonal antibody specific for certain non-muscle isoforms of tropomyosin inhibits the movement of intracellular granules in chick embryo fibroblasts (50). This antibody does not inhibit the binding of tropomyosin to actin, which makes it likely that it inhibits actin-myosin interactions instead of actin polymerization.

MONOMER SEQUESTRATION Several proteins that bind actin monomers in vitro are candidates to explain the high apparent monomer concentration (~100 μM) in cytoplasm. Profilin, the best-studied, is present at high concentration (100 μM) in *Acanthamoeba* (106); however, the amount in platelets (64) and neutrophils (93) is clearly not sufficient to sequester monomeric actin. Also, the affinity of actin for profilin is so low ($K_d = 5\ \mu M$ (61)) that even at 100 μM (106), only 2 μM of actin-profilin complex is calculated to form, given an actin monomer concentration of 0.1 μM, the barbed-end critical concentration in vitro. If all barbed ends are capped, and the critical concentration is 0.6 μM, the complex concentration is calculated to be 10 μM. An interesting possibility is that because both ends of all filaments are capped, the monomer concentration is elevated to supersaturated levels, and spontaneous nucleation is specifically suppressed by a protein-like actobindin (62). Profilin does participate in another 1:1 complex with actin, which is of high affinity and which allows purification of the complex (63, 93). This complex can be formed in vitro with spleen profilin and actin under some conditions (62a); however, it dissociates under physiologic ionic conditions in some experiments (63).

The gene for profilin has been deleted in yeast, and the mutants have altered actin distributions, grow very slowly, and are large (46). Actin cables are lost, as in the tropomyosin and capping protein mutants, and an abnormal bar of actin appears in most cells. This bar is also occasionally seen in the tropomyosin mutants (65), but not in the capping protein mutants (3). The significance of these differences is unclear.

Other small monomeric actin-binding proteins, such as actobindin (62) and the family that includes actin-depolymerizing factor (42), cofilin (68), depactin (98), a 5-kd platelet peptide (86a), and actophorin (22) are additional candidates that have not been as well-studied.

OTHER YEAST PROTEINS Despite certain drawbacks, the yeast system has been extremely valuable because of the speed and certainty associated with a wide range of genetic and biochemical procedures. Conditional-lethal actin mutants have been developed and used to isolate actin suppressors (30). One of the actin suppressors, SAC6, encodes a 67-kd protein that binds actin in vitro (1). Another protein, termed ABP1, was isolated by actin affinity chromatography and interacts with actin in vitro and in vivo (31, 32). The effects of SAC6 and ABP1 on actin polymerization have not yet been described. Other actin suppressors and actin-binding proteins remain to be characterized and sequenced.

INHIBITOR STUDIES

Many experiments have been performed in which cell motility is inhibited by cytochalasin. Since cytochalasin binds to the barbed end of actin filaments and inhibits subunit addition (9), these results are often offered as evidence that actin polymerization drives the motility process. While this conclusion may turn out to be correct, it seems premature for two reasons. First, while the actin filaments may be a necessary structural component for motility powered by a motor protein, their polymerization may not provide the energy for movement. Alternatively, actin polymerization may simply fill in space cleared by another component and then provide the support and stability for the final structure. The newly-polymerized filaments would be necessary for the end result, but their formation would not provide the energy for the movement. Second, the mechanism of action of cytochalasin is unclear (21). Of particular concern is that instead of inhibiting new growth from pre-existing filaments, cytochalasin may disrupt the architecture of pre-existing filaments (88) by sequestering monomers or nucleating new filament growth (43), or by competing for the binding of filament ends to structures with attached capping proteins. If cytochalasin can sever actin filaments, a point that remains controversial (9, 108), then the effects of cytochalasin on cell motility are even more difficult to interpret in molecular terms.

Other toxins that affect actin polymerization also affect cell motility, thus confirming the conclusion that actin filaments are necessary for cell motility. Microinjection of phalloidin, which binds selectively to actin filaments and thereby shifts the polymerization equilibrium toward filaments (33), inhibits the translocation of cultured cells (111). Botulinum toxin ADP ribosylates a fraction of cell actin, which causes it to cap the barbed end of actin filaments (2) and lead to cell rounding and loss of motility. Latrunculin, a toxin that binds to and sequesters actin monomers in vitro (26), also causes cell rounding and loss of motility (94).

DOES ASSEMBLY PROVIDE ENERGY FOR CELL MOVEMENT?

Theoretical Plausibility

First consider whether the thermodynamics and kinetics of actin polymerization, as determined in vitro, are in the correct range to explain the force and rate of cell movements.

One can distinguish between net assembly and treadmilling. In treadmilling, the filaments are at steady-state with the monomers. The monomer concentration lies between the critical concentration for the barbed and pointed ends, and there is net addition (ON $-$ OFF $>$ 0) at the barbed end and net loss (ON $-$ OFF $<$ 0) at the pointed end. The amount of net addition at the barbed end is quantitatively identical to the amount of net loss at the pointed end. On the other hand, net assembly occurs when monomers are added to a system at steady-state. The net addition at the barbed end will be greater than the net loss at the pointed end, and there may even be net addition at the pointed end if the monomer concentration is great enough.

Theoretical considerations show that both treadmilling and net assembly can provide the energy to push or pull an object along the axis of the filament (51, 52). Treadmilling of actin requires ATP hydrolysis and some of this energy can be converted to movement. If an actin filament is held fixed at one point along its length, then treadmilling would cause both ends of the filament to move in the barbed direction, with the potential to push an object in front. In net assembly, the energy is derived from the fact that the addition of monomer has taken the system away from steady-state and it is returning to steady-state. This energy is theoretically available for conversion to movement. If a filament is held fixed at one point along its length, then the barbed end will move in the barbed direction and the pointed end will move in either the barbed or pointed direction depending on the monomer concentration.

Based on in vitro determinations of the equilibrium and rate constants for actin polymerization, one can calculate the maximal force and velocity, respectively, that might be produced by actin polymerization in cells. For treadmilling, the calculated velocity, based on elongation rate constants measured in vitro (83), is 0.1 μm/min. This value is low compared to the rate of extension of fibroblast filopodia and lamellipodia [2–5 μm/min (35)], the translocation of neutrophils [12 μm/min (55)], *Dictyostelium* [12 μm/min (4)], and fish keratocytes [10–30 μm/min (24)], and the rate of centripetal movement of a photobleached actin spot in the lamellipodium of a stationary fibroblast [0.8 μm/min (110)] or the cytoplasmic material, presumably including actin, in the growth cone of a neuron [3–6 μm/min (36)]. To achieve polymerization rates as high as 30 μm/min with net assembly at the barbed end, as opposed to treadmilling, the monomer concentration would have to be 16 μM.[3] If the buffered actin monomer pool is 100 μM, then the release of 16 μM is possible.

If the actin is polymerizing in one place at such a high rate, it must be depolymerizing in another place at the same rate. The dissociation rate constants are only 0.04 μm/min and 0.13 μm/min at the pointed end for ADP-actin and ATP-actin, respectively (83). These values are well below the rates of centripetal movement of cytoplasm and cell translocation seen above. The values at the barbed end are higher—1.2 μm/min and 0.23 μm/min for ADP-actin and ATP-actin, respectively (83)—but still not as high as the rates of movement. This incongruity suggests that cells actively depolymerize filaments, perhaps by severing them to create new ends.

The force potentially available from actin polymerization to drive the extension of a typical microvillar process is calculated to be 30 pN, assuming release of 1 μM of monomer and polymerization onto the barbed ends of a

[3] 30 μm/min = 180 s^{-1} = (11.6 $\mu M^{-1}s^{-1}$ * 16 μM) − 1.4 s^{-1} [Rate constants from (83)].

bundle of 10 actin filaments.[4] If the bundle is about 100 nm wide (the width of a typical microvillus), the pressure is 30 pN/8000nm^2 = 40,000 dyn/cm^2 Measurements of the forces produced in extending filopodia or lamellae are not yet available, but may be forthcoming. As a rough comparison, the force required to indent an activated neutrophil 1 μm with a 2-μm diameter probe is 200 pN (112), and the pressure required to aspirate a 2-μm diameter section of membrane is 400 dyn/cm^2 (34) or 120 pN over that area.

One unknown feature of models in which actin polymerization pushes objects, such as membranes, is how subunits can add if the filament end is closely apposed to the membrane. Even if one hypothesizes the existence of a strut of fixed length that connects the side of the end of the filament to the membrane and keeps the end of the filament away from the membrane, one still has to understand how the strut moves along the filament in the distal direction. One possibility is to invoke a motor in the strut. In this case, actin polymerization might contribute only part or none of the energy to push the membrane forward. Another possibility is that the membrane and the filament are not connected, and thermal energy causes the position of the membrane to fluctuate back and forth. When the membrane moves away (centrifugally), the filament polymerizes out to meet it, and then the membrane cannot move back in. Measurements of membrane surface undulations have been made in erythrocytes with flicker spectroscopy, and show root mean square excursions of 0.1 μm (38), with a half-height frequency of 5 s^{-1} (37). These values indicate that motions of 0.1 μm/0.2 s = 0.5 μm/s are possible. Similar measurements have not been made in other cells, where one expects that links between the cytoplasmic cytoskeleton and the membrane would dampen the membrane movements.

Experiments with in vitro Systems

Two sets of experiments with in vitro systems show that actin polymerization is sufficient to change the shape of membranes.

When actin monomers in spherical lipid vesicles are induced to polymerize, the vesicles assume asymmetric, irregular shapes (25). The shape changes are modified by actin-binding proteins that control filament length (gelsolin) and filament-filament crosslinking (filamin). Two ways in which this system differs from cell systems are that the polymerization and shape changes occur over tens of minutes in vitro, and the membranes are not bound to a cytoskeleton.

[4] The calculation uses the equation $\Delta G = RT \ln (c_1/c_c)$; where R, the gas constant, is 8.3 J/°K/mol; T, absolute temperature, is 300 °K; c_1, monomer concentration, is 1 μM; c_c, barbed end critical concentration, is 0.1 μM; ΔG is 5700 J/mol; 10 filaments are 1.7×10^{-23} mol; and the distance moved per subunit added is 3 nm.

When monomeric actin is added to isolated brush borders and then polymerized, new actin growth is observed at the distal ends of filaments in microvilli (74). The membrane, which is closely apposed to the filament ends, is pushed outwards. The new growth of 0.2–0.4 μm was measured at five min with an initial actin monomer concentration of 48 μM. Therefore, the rate is at least 0.06 μm/min and is probably much higher since earlier time points were not examined, and the actin monomer concentration probably fell rapidly.

Experiments with Living Cells

The most instructive set of in vivo experiments are those of Tilney & co-workers, who examined the acrosomal reaction of *Thyone* sperm (99, 101, 104). In this cell, actin is complexed with profilin and aggregated in one place near the front of cell. Upon activation, the aggregate becomes lucent and disappears while actin filaments polymerize from a structure, the actomere. The filaments polymerize with their barbed ends distal, facing the membrane. The filaments are organized into a bundle, and the growth of the bundle corresponds to the growth of the membrane-bound acrosomal process.

The initial theory that actin polymerization drives the extension of the acrosomal process is supported by the observation that cytochalasin rapidly inhibits process extension and that the length of the process over time can be predicted by a model in which the diffusion of actin from the center of the cell up to the growing tip of the bundle is the rate-limiting process (102). One observation not consistent with the theory is that the tip of process is rounded and swollen, an appearance that does not suggest that it is being pushed forward by the growing filament bundle. Additional experiments also show that the osmolarity of the medium can regulate the rate of the process extension, which suggests that water influx drives process extension (103). A model for water influx also predicts the time course of the length of the process (78). Therefore, based on inhibitor studies, both actin polymerization and water influx are necessary for process extension, and the source of the energy is unknown.

Other examples in which actin filaments appear while a microvillar structure forms during development include the fertilization tubule of *Chlamydomonas,* microvilli of intestinal epithelial cells and sea urchin eggs, and stereocilia of cochlear hair cells. The filaments in the fertilization tubule of *Chlamydomonas* appear quickly and are associated at their pointed ends with a cytoplasmic structure, the doublet zone (28). Their barbed ends are distal and apposed to the membrane, and growth is inhibited by cytochalasin, which is consistent with the hypothesis that the filaments are nucleated from the doublet zone and grow at their barbed ends, pushing the membrane in front of them. In cochlear hair cells, the time course of formation of the staircase pattern of stereocilia (microvilli) length suggests that the bundled filaments are growing by addition of subunits (105). The microvilli of intestinal epithelial cells (73) and sea urchin eggs (5) contain bundles of actin filaments with their barbed ends at the membrane. These processes elongate, but there is little morphologic evidence to indicate that the actin filaments are nucleated and growing from a sub-cellular structure. In these cases, the cytoplasm contains a few disorganized actin filaments at the early stage, and many organized actin filaments appear at the later stage.

MICROSCOPY OF ACTIN POLYMERIZATION IN LIVING CELLS

The best evidence for filament assembly and disassembly during the normal function of non-developing cells comes from fluorescence photobleaching experiments in which a segment of filaments is marked and followed over time. The lamellipodium of a stationary fibroblast includes a dense meshwork of actin filaments. A photobleached spot in the lamellipodium moves centripetally and disappears at the proximal edge of the band of actin, which suggests that actin filaments are undergoing net assembly at their distal, membrane-associated barbed ends and net disassembly at their proximal pointed ends (110). Centripetal movement of cytoplasmic material has also been observed in fibroblasts (35) and neuronal growth cones (36).

The effect of cytochalasin on cytoplasmic movement in growth cones (36) argues for the exclusion of certain models to explain the movement. When cytochalasin is added, the cytoplasmic material continues to move centripetally and the cytoplasmic material separates from the plasma membrane at the distal edge of the cell. The distal border of the cytoplasmic material moves centripetally at the same rate as the material, and the plasma membrane at the edge of the cell does not move. This result indicates that actin filaments do not slide centripetally because subunits are inserted at the barbed ends distally. This raises the possibility that another factor, such as a motor protein, actively moves the filaments (91). When cytochalasin is washed out of these cells, the cytoplasmic material, presumably including newly polymerized actin filaments, appears at the plasma membrane and moves centripetally. The proximal margin of the cytoplasmic material moves at the same rate as the components visualized in the material (36). The molecular basis for this apparent nucleation from the membrane is not known, but one might speculate that a barbed-end nucleating/capping protein is active at the membrane. Nucleation of actin polymerization by this protein would lead to filaments with barbed ends distal. This protein might at some later time have to dissociate from the barbed end to allow for centripetal sliding and/or barbed-end growth. The actin of cytochalasin might be explained by competition for barbed-end binding with this protein and monomer sequestration, as mentioned above.

An important challenge for the future will be to determine whether and how this centripetal movement contributes to forward (centrifugal) movement—the extension of cell processes. If a motor protein, such as myosin-I, which is found at the leading edge of *Dictyostelium* (40), does power this movement, one can construct hypotheses in which actin filaments near the basal surface are anchored (perhaps membrane-bound myosin-I is in rigor), while other actin filaments slide forward on top of the basal ones, using the two actin-binding sites of myosin-I. Obviously, the spatial and temporal regulation of myosin-I in this scheme is complex. Alternatively, forward extension might be generated by anchoring all the actin filaments to the basal surface and then having actin polymerization or osmotic forces push the distal membrane away from the ends of the filament [Figure 1 and (71)], as presumably occurs in *Thyone* sperm activation. These hypotheses might be tested by a photobleaching experiment on an extending cell process.

On the other hand, in certain cases actin filaments can move without assembly/disassembly. This obviously occurs in muscle contraction, but can also happen in non-muscle cells. The work of Tilney & co-workers (100, 27) on invertebrate sperm provides illustrative examples. Sperm of the mussel *Mytilus* undergo an acrosomal reaction in which a bundle of actin filaments is projected anteriorly, forming the acrosomal process (100). The filaments do not change length, and their polarity indicates that myosin cannot power the movement. Sperm of the horseshoe crab *Limulus* have a coiled bundle of actin filaments that uncoils into a straight bundle, forming the acrosomal process (27).

These cases involve the movement of filament bundles. The movement of single actin filaments seems unlikely because the cytoplasm is a dense, cross-linked meshwork of filaments that impede movements. The possibility still exists, however, that single actin filaments could reptate (move longitudinally) through the meshwork, or that small aggregates of filaments could move together. During cytokinesis, actin and myosin are localized to the contractile ring, and the myosin-driven contraction may pull the actin filaments to the ring. In a test of this hypothesis, fluorescent phalloidin was microinjected into mitotic cells (15). Phalloidin binds tightly to actin filaments with a low dissociation rate constant, so it should remain with one filament for a long period of time. Metaphase cells were injectd with trace amounts of rhodamine-phalloidin to label existing actin filaments. During cytokinesis, the cells were fixed and stained with fluorescein-phalloidin to localize all the actin filaments. The rhodamine-phalloidin was relatively concentrated in the contractile ring, which suggests that pre-existing filaments move into the contractile ring.

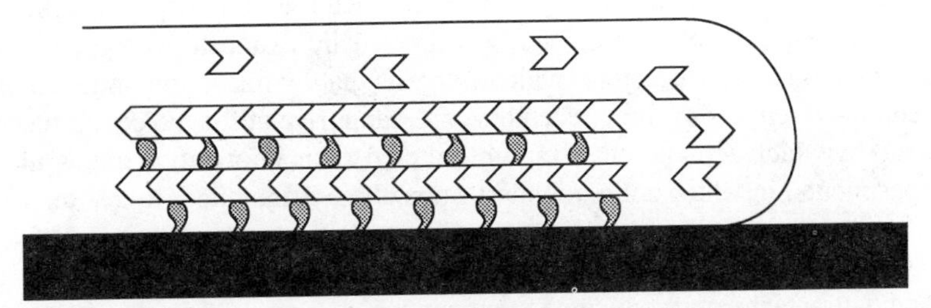

Figure 1 Hypothetical drawing of the leading edge of a cell, viewed from the side. Actin subunits *(single chevron-shaped units)* add to the barbed ends of actin filaments, near the distal margin of the cell. Myosin-I connects the filaments to each other and to the ventral membrane, where it is fixed to the substrate. When myosin-I is active, the actin filaments move centripetally *(leftward)*, and new polymerization fills the space between filament ends and the membrane. When myosin-I is in a rigor or latched state, actin polymerization pushes the membrane centrifugally *(rightward)*.

CHANGES IN NET POLYMERIZATION IN CELLS

One of the best lines of evidence for the importance of actin polymerization in cell motility is that cells stimulated to undergo motility show changes in their ratios of monomeric to filamentous actin. The interpretation of these experiments is guarded because the two assays used to measure actin levels in cells, DNase I inhibition and fluorescent-phalloidin binding, have limitations.

DNase I binds to actin monomers, and its hydrolytic activity is thereby inhibited (7). Several investigations however, indicate that DNase I also binds to actin filaments and is inhibited, although there is disagreement about whether DNAse I binds to one or another end or along the side of the filament (53, 80, 81). Also, complexes of actin monomers, with as yet undescribed actin-binding proteins, might be incapable of binding DNase I. Phalloidin binds selectively to actin filaments as opposed to monomers in vitro (21, 33), so the binding of fluorescent-phalloidin to fixed, permeabilized cells has been used as an assay for actin filaments (56). The binding of phalloidin to actin filaments may be modified by actin-binding proteins, because fluorescent-phalloidin stains myofibrils in variable conflicting patterns, which reflect subsets of actin filaments (41, 69, 72; Cooper & Elson, 1988 unpublished observations). This issue is of particular concern when the assay employs less than a 1:1 molar ratio of phalloidin to actin, in which case the extent of phalloidin binding could be particularly sensitive to effects of actin-binding proteins.

Despite these potential complications, these assays do agree on the direction of the change (e.g. 70) and have been used to detect changes in the monomeric and filamentous actin pools (G-actin and F-actin, respectively) in many cells undergoing changes in shape and motility. This correlation leads to the hypothesis that actin polymerization is required for shape changes. In many systems these changes can be triggered by extracellular ligands that bind to cell surface receptors, which suggests that by tracing the intracellular second messengers of these receptors, one can arrive at the molecular mechanism by which actin polymerization is altered. This information might allow experiments, in which actin polymerization alone is inhibited, to test the role of actin polymerization in the motile response.

The response of neutrophils and *Dictyostelium discoideum* amoebae to chemoattractants are promising systems in which a mechanism may be elucidated. This topic was recently reviewed (29). The two systems are remarkably similar, which indicates that the mechanism may exist in other cells as well. In both systems, chemoattractants bind to receptors that transmit signals through GTP-binding proteins. The cells become polarized and move in the direction of the chemotactic gradient with actin filaments concentrated in lamellipodia at the leading edge. In neutrophils, the F-actin level increases and remains high (109) in association with a pool of labile F-actin in the newly formed lamellipodia (20a). In *Dictyostelium,* the F-actin level shows a rapid increase and decrease, followed by a slower sustained increase (47). Investigations into the mechanism by which the F-actin level increases show that the number of nucleation sites for actin polymerization is increased transiently (17, 47, 54). The nucleation sites are largely cytochalasin-sensitive, which indicates that they are or quickly become barbed ends of actin filaments and that they sediment in a low speed spin following detergent extraction, which indicates that they are part of the detergent-insoluble cytoskeleton. The amount of actin associated with the detergent-insoluble cytoskeleton also increases (54). Together these results suggest that existing filaments are uncapped at their barbed ends or severed to create free barbed ends. The nucleation activity is insensitive to Ca^{2+} and decays over time after cell lysis. In *Dictyostelium,* after the nucleation activity is pelleted, it is stable over time, and the supernatant contains an inhibitor of actin polymerization that presumably is responsible for the decay of nucleation activity over time (47). In addition, the level of the inhibitor changes after chemoattractant stimulation with a time course that roughly mirrors that of the nucleation activity.

Phosphoinositides have been proposed to mediate signal transduction between cell surface receptors and actin assembly (96). The actin-binding proteins, profilin (163), gelsolin (58), cofilin (112a), destrin (112a), DNase I (112a), and Cap Z (S. Heiss, J. Cooper, unpublished results), bind the phosphoinositides, PIP and PIP_2, which inhibit their ability to bind to actin. If the phosphoinositides are added to actin-gelsolin complexes, the actin is released (58), which is especially important because conditions that dissociate gelsolin-actin complexes, short of denaturation, had not been found previously. In neutrophils, the chemoattractant causes hydrolysis of phosphoinositides to inositol phosphates and diacylglycerol (6). This action leads to the hypothesis that fluctuations in phosphoinositide concentration control the activity of profilin and gelsolin. Specifically, increased amounts of phosphoinositides might lead to release of actin monomers from profilin-actin complexes and release of free barbed ends of filaments from gelsolin-actin filament complexes. This mechanism would explain the increase in nucleation sites, which are barbed ends, and the net conversion of G to F actin. The level of profilin-actin complexes does decrease after stimulation; however, the amount of the change is not sufficient to account for the G to F change (93). The level of gelsolin-actin complexes decreases after chemoattractant stimulation concomitant with an increase in barbed-end nucleating activity (54). Phosphoinositide levels have been measured in one system and found not to correlate with levels of gelsolin-actin and profilin-actin complexes (26a).

Another piece of evidence against this mechanism is that null mutants of *Dictyostelium* lacking severin, the member of the gelsolin family in these cells, show normal motility and chemotaxis (4). Although G/F actin ratios in mutants treated with chemoattractants have not been reported, this striking observation casts doubt on a role for gelsolin in the actin polymerization associated with chemotaxis.

Another finding, which complicates the hypothesis, is that phosphoinositide bound to profilin is unavailable as a substrate for phospholipase C (45). In platelets, profilin could bind a large fraction of the phosphoinositide, based on the stoichiometry and affinity of binding and the concentrations of the reactants. Perhaps profilin's primary physiologic role is regulation of phosphoinositide metabolism, and its interaction with actin has less physiologic importance.

The response of macrophages to signals has some differences that may indicate the existence of another mechanism. Phorbol ester, which induces changes in cell shape and motility, transiently increases the level of nucleation sites, which are free barbed ends as indicated by their cytochalasin sensitivity (48). In constrast to neutrophils and *Dictyostelium,* the nucleation activity is soluble, not associated with the detergent-insoluble cytoskeleton, and the amount of actin associated with the detergent-insoluble cytoskeleton does not change. These observations indicate that the increased nucleation activity is most likely not caused by uncapping of barbed ends of filaments in the cytoskeleton. The nucleation activity requires Ca^{2+}, another difference compared to neutrophils and *Dictyostelium*.

One notable exception to the association of G/F changes with cell motility is the capping of cell surface receptors. No changes in G-actin level (by DNase I inhibition), F-actin level (by fluorescent-phalloidin binding), or actin nucleation sites were detected in lymphocytes undergoing capping of surface immunoglobulin or concanavalin A receptors (57). Null mutants of *Dic-*

tyostelium lacking myosin II (conventional myosin) do not cap or become stiff in response to concanavalin A, which indicates that an actomyosin contraction in the cell cortex powers capping (79). Capping is inhibited by cytochalasin, which indicates that cytochalasin may have effects other than blocking addition to barbed ends of actin filaments. In this case cytochalasin may compete to disrupt the binding of barbed ends of filaments to other structures or perhaps nucleate the formation of new filaments in inappropriate locations, which disrupt the actomyosin contraction.

SUMMARY AND COMMENTS

A tremendous amount of work and insight, coupled with important advances in the technology of biochemistry, molecular biology, and optical microscopy, have generated a great deal of new information about how cells move and how actin polymerizes. The status of current research makes one optimistic that answers to the difficult and interesting questions of whether actin polymerization causes cell movement and why actin filaments or polymerization are necessary for cell movement will be realized in the future.

In *Thyone* sperm, actin polymerization is necessary for protrusion of a cell process, and the morphology of the growing filament and the biochemistry of the components suggest that actin polymerization provides the energy as well. The ambiguity that persists in this simple system illustrates how difficult elucidating cause and effect will be in more complex systems.

Centripetal movement of filaments, observed by photobleaching and optical microscopy, is strong evidence that actin polymerization occurs extensively in cells at rest. The reason for this centripetal movement and whether a variation of this mechanism is employed to generate protrusive movement is an important problem.

Progress in understanding signal transduction makes it likely that the connection between extracellular signals, actin polymerization, and cell motility will be understood.

The existence of actin-binding proteins that regulate actin polymerization in nearly every conceivable manner offers a wide variety of hypotheses for mechanisms to be tested in vivo. Our ability to inhibit or alter the activity of these proteins with molecular genetics and antibodies provides many experiments with which to test these hypotheses.

ACKNOWLEDGMENTS

I am grateful to Kay Broschat, Tom Howard, Kei Maruyama, Patrick Moore, Mike Sheetz, Fred Southwick, Lans Taylor, and Yu-Li Wang for preprints and discussions of their work, to Jim Amatruda, Elliot Elson, and Kathy Miller for reading the manuscript, and to the members of the cytoskeleton journal club and the graduate student seminar course for discussions. Elliot Elson was especially helpful with the section on feasibility. The writing of this article was supported by grants from the National Institutes of Health and the Lucille P. Markey Charitable Trust. The author is a Lucille P. Markey Scholar.

Literature Cited

1. Adams, A., E., Bostein, D., Drubin, D. 1989. A yeast actin-binding protein is encoded by SAC6, a gene found by suppression of an actin mutation. *Science* 243:231–33
2. Aktories, K., Wegner, A. 1989. ADP-ribosylation of actin by clostridial toxins. *J. Cell Biol.* 109:1385–87
3. Amatruda, J. F., Cannon, J. F., Tatchell, K., Hug, C., Cooper, J. A. 1990. Disruption of the actin cytoskeleton in yeast capping protein mutants. *Nature* 344:352–54
4. Andre, E., Brink, M., Gerisch, G., Isenberg, G., Noegel, A., Schleicher, M., et al. 1989. A *Dictyostelium* mutant deficient in severin, an F-actin fragmenting protein, shows normal motility and chemotaxis. *J. Cell Biol.* 108:985–95
5. Begg, D. A., Rebhun, L. I. 1979. pH regulates the polymerization of actin in the sea urchin egg cortex. *J. Cell Biol.* 83:241–48
6. Bengtsson, T., Rundquist, I., Stendahl, O., Wymann, M. P., Andersson, T. 1988. Increased breakdown of phosphatidylinositol 4,5-bisphosphate is not an initiating factor for actin assembly in human neutrophils. *J. Biol. Chem.* 263: 17385–89
7. Blikstad, I., Markey, F., Carlsson, L., Persson, T., Lindberg, U. 1978. Selective assay of monomeric and filamentous actin in cell extracts, using inhibition of deoxyribonuclease I. *Cell* 15:935–43
8. Bonder, E. M., D., Fishkind, J., Mooseker, M. S. 1983. Direct measurement of critical concentrations and assembly rate constants at the two ends of an actin filament. *Cell* 34:491–501
9. Bonder, E. M., Mooseker, M. S. 1986. Cytochalasin-B slows but does not prevent monomer addition at the barbed end of the actin filament. *J. Cell Biol.* 102:282–88
10. Bray, D., Thomas, C. 1976. Unpolymerized actin in fibroblasts and brain. *J. Mol. Biol.* 105:527–44
11. Broschat, K. O. 1990. Tropomyosin prevents depolymerization of actin filaments from the pointed end. *J. Biol. Chem.* 265:21323–29
12. Broschat, K. O., Weber, A., Burgess, D. R. 1989. Tropomyosin stabilizes the pointed end of actin filaments by slowing depolymerization. *Biochemistry* 28: 8501–6
13. Caldwell, J. E., Heiss, S. G., Mermall, V., Cooper, J. A. 1989. Effects of CapZ, an actin capping protein of muscle, on the polymerization of actin. *Biochemistry* 28:8506–14
14. Caldwell, J. E., Waddle, J. A., Cooper, J. A., Hollands, J. A., Casella, S. J., Casella, J. F. 1989. cDNAs encoding the β subunit of CapZ, the actin-capping protein of the Z line of muscle. *J. Biol. Chem.* 264:12648–52
15. Cao, L.-G., Wang, Y.-L. 1990. Mechanism of the formation of the contractile ring in dividing cultured animal cells. I. Recruitment of pre-existing actin filaments into the cleavage furrow. *J. Cell Biol.* 110:1089–95
16. Carlier, M.-F. 1989. Role of nucleotide hydrolysis in the dynamics of actin filaments and microtubules. *Int. Rev. Cytol.* 115:139–70
17. Carson, M., Weber, A., Zigmond, S. 1986. An actin-nucleating activity in polymorphonuclear leukocytes is modulated by chemotactic peptides. *J. Cell Biol.* 103:2707–14
18. Casella, J. F., Casella, S. J., Hollands, J. A., Caldwell, J. E., Cooper, J. A. 1989. Isolation and characterization of cDNA encoding the alpha subunit of CapZ, an actin-capping protein from the Z-line of skeletal muscle. *Proc. Natl. Acad. Sci. USA* 86:5800–4
19. Casella, J. F., Craig, S. W., Maack, D. J., Brown, A. E. 1987. CapZ(36/32), a barbed end actin-capping protein, is a component of the Z-line of skeletal muscle. *J. Cell Biol.* 105:371–79
20. Casella, J. F., Maack, D. J., Lin, S. 1986. Purification and initial characterization of a protein from skeletal muscle that caps the barbed ends of actin filaments. *J. Biol. Chem.* 261: 10915–21

20a. Cassimeris, L., McNeill, H., Zigmond, S. 1990. Chemoattractant-stimulated polymorphonuclear leukocytes contain two populations of actin filaments that differ in their spatial distributions and relative stabilities. *J. Cell Biol.* 110:1067–75

21. Cooper, J. A., 1987. Effects of cytochalasin and phalloidin on actin. *J. Cell Biol.* 105:1473–78
22. Cooper, J. A., Blum, J. D., Pollard, T. D. 1986. Purification and characterization of actophorin, a new 15,000 dalton actin binding protein from *Acanthamoeba castellanii*. *J. Biol. Chem.* 261: 477–85
23. Cooper, J. A., Bryan, J., Schwab, B. III, Frieden, C., Loftus, D. J., Elson, E. L. 1987. Microinjection of gelsolin into living cells. *J. Cell Biol.* 104:491–501
24. Cooper, M. S., Schliwa, M. 1986. Motility of cultured fish epidermal cells in the presence and absence of direct current electrical fields. *J. Cell Biol.* 102:1384–99
25. Cortese, J. D., Schwab, B., Frieden, C., Elson, E. L. 1989. Actin polymerization induces a shape change in actin-containing vesicles. *Proc. Natl. Acad. Sci. USA* 86:5773–77
26. Coue, M., Brenner, S. L., Spector, I., Korn, E. D. 1987. Inhibition of actin polymerization by latrunculin A. *FEBS Lett.* 213:316–18

26a. Dadabay, C., Patton, E., Cooper, J. A., Pike, L. J. 1991. Lack of correlation between changes in polyphosphoinositide levels and actin/gelosin complexes in A431 cells treated with EGF. *J. Cell Biol.* In press

27. DeRosier, D. J., Tilney, L. G., Bonder, E. M., Frankel, P. 1982. A change in twist of actin provides the force for the extension of the acrosomal process in *Limulus* sperm. *J. Cell Biol.* 93:324–37
28. Detmers, P. A., Goodenough, U. W., Condeelis, J. 1983. Elongation of the fertilization tubule in *Chlamydomonas:* New observations on the core microfilaments and the effect of transient intracellular signals on their structural integrity. *J. Cell Biol.* 97:522–32
29. Devreotes, P. N., Zigmond, S. H. 1988. Chemotaxis in eukaryotic cells: A focus on leukocytes and *Dictyostelium*. *Annu. Rev. Cell Biol.* 4:649–86
30. Drubin, D. G. 1990. Actin and actin-binding proteins in yeast. *Cell Motil. Cytoskelet.* 15:7–11
31. Drubin, D. G., Miller, K. G., Botstein, D. 1988. Yeast actin-binding proteins: evidence for a role in morphogenesis. *J. Cell Biol.* 107:2552–62
32. Drubin, D. G., Mulholland, J., Zhu, Z., Botstein, D. 1990. Homology of a yeast actin-binding protein to signal transduction proteins and myosin-I. *Nature* 343:288–90
33. Estes, J. E., Selden, L. A., Gershman, L. C. 1981. Mechanism of action of phalloidin on the polymerization of muscle actin. *Biochemistry* 20:708–12
34. Evans, E., Yeung, A. 1989. Apparent viscosity and cortical tension of blood granulocytes determined by micropipet aspiration. *Biophys. J.* 56:151–60
35. Fisher, G. W., Conrad, P. A., DeBiasio, R. L., Taylor, D. L. 1988. Centripetal transport of cytoplasm, actin, and the cell surface in lamellipodia of fibroblasts. *Cell Motil. Cytoskelet.* 11:235–47
36. Forscher, P., Smith, S. J. 1988. Actions of cytochalasins on the organization of actin filaments and microtubules in a neuronal growth cone. *J. Cell Biol.* 107:1505–16
37. Fricke, K., Sackmann, E. 1984. Variation of frequency spectrum of the erythrocyte flickering caused by aging, osmolarity, temperature and pathological changes. *Biochim. Biophys. Acta* 803:145–52
38. Fricke, K., Wirthensohn, K., Laxhuber, R., Sackmann, E. 1986. Flicker spectroscopy of erythrocytes. A sensitive method to study subtle changes of membrane bending stiffness. *Eur. Biophys. J.* 14:67–81
39. Fuchtbauer, A., Jockusch, B. M., Maruta, H., Kilimann, M. W., Isenberg, G. 1983. Disruption of microfilament organization after injection of F-actin capping proteins into living tissue culture cells. *Nature* 304:361–64
40. Fukui, Y, Lynch, T. J., Brzeska, H., Korn, E. D. 1989. Myosin I is located at the leading edges of locomoting *Dictyostelium* amoebae. *Nature* 341:328–31
41. Funatsu, T., Higuchi, H., Ishiwata, S. 1990. Elastic filaments in skeletal muscle revealed by selective removal of thin filaments with plasma gelsolin. *J. Cell Biol.* 110:53–62
42. Giuliano, K. A., Khatib, F. A., Hayden, S. M., Daoud, E. W. R., Adams, M. E., et al. 1988. Properties of purified actin depolymerizing factor from chick brain. *Biochemistry* 27:8931–38
43. Goddette, D. W., Frieden, C. 1986. Actin polymerization. The mechanism of action of cytochalasin D. *J. Biol. Chem.* 261:15974–80
44. Goddette, D. W., Uberbacher, E. C., Bunick, G. J., Frieden, C. 1986. Formation of actin dimers as studied by small

angle neutron scattering. *J. Biol. Chem.* 261:2605–9

45. Goldschmidt-Clermont, P. J., Machesky, L. M., Baldassare, J. J., Pollard, T. D. 1990. The actin-binding protein profilin binds to PIP_2 and inhibits its hydrolysis by phospholipase C. *Science* 247:1575–78
46. Haarer, B. K., Lillie, S. H., Adams, A. E. M., Magdolen, V., Bandlow, W., Brown, S. S. 1990. Purification of profilin from *Saccharomyces cerevisiae* and analysis of profilin-deficient cells. *J. Cell Biol.* 110:105–14
47. Hall, A. L., Warren, V., Dharmawardhane, S., Condeelis, J. 1989. Identification of actin nucleation activity and polymerization inhibitor in ameboid cells: Their regulation by chemotactic stimulation. *J. Cell Biol.* 109:2207–13
48. Hartwig, J. H., Janmey, P. A. 1989. Stimulation of a calcium-dependent actin nucleation activity by phorbol 12-myristate 13-acetate in rabbit macrophage cytoskeletons. *Biochim. Biophys. Acta* 1010:64–71
49. Hartwig, J. H., Shevlin, P. 1986. The architecture of actin filaments and the ultrastructural location of actin-binding protein in the periphery of lung macrophages. *J. Cell Biol.* 103:1007–1020
50. Hegmann, T. E., Lin, J. L.-C., Lin, J. J.-C. 1989. Probing the role of nonmuscle tropomyosin isoforms in intracellular granule movement by microinjection of monoclonal antibodies. *J. Cell Biol.* 109:1141–52
51. Hill, T. L. 1981. Microfilament or microtubule assembly or disassembly against a force. *Proc. Natl. Acad. Sci. USA* 78:5613–17
52. Hill, T. L., Kirschner, M. W. 1982. Subunit treadmilling of microtubules or actin in the presence of cellular barriers: Possible conversion of chemical free energy into mechanical work. *Proc. Natl. Acad. Sci. USA* 79:490–94
53. Hitchcock, S. E., Carlsson, L., Lindberg, U. 1976. Depolymerization of F-actin by deoxyribonuclease I. *Cell* 7: 531–42
54. Howard, T., Chaponnier, C., Yin, H., Stossel, T. 1990. Gelsolin-actin interaction and actin polymerization in human neutrophils. *J. Cell Biol.* 110:1983–91
55. Howard, T. H., Meyer, W. H. 1984. Chemotactic peptide modulation of actin assembly and locomotion in neutrophils. *J. Cell Biol.* 98:1265–71
56. Howard, T. H., Oresajo, C. O. 1985. The kinetics of chemotactic peptide-induced change in F-actin content, F-actin distribution and the shape of neutrophils. *J. Cell Biol.* 101:1078–85

56a. Huckriede, A., Fuchtbauer, A., Hinssen, H., Chaponnier, C., Weeds, A., Jockusch, B.-M. 1990. Differential effects of gelsolins on tissue-culture cells. *Cell Motil. Cytoskelet.* 16:229–38

57. Jackman, W. T., Burridge, K. 1989. Polymerization of additional actin is not required for capping of surface antigen in B-lymphocytes. *Cell Motil. Cytoskelet.* 12:23–32
58. Janmey, P., Iida, K., Yin, H. L., Stossel, T. P. 1987. Polyphosphoinositide micelles and polyphosphoinositide-containing vesicles dissociate endogenous gelsolin-actin complexes and promote actin assembly from the fast-growing end of actin filaments blocked by gelsolin. *J. Biol. Chem.* 262:12228–36
59. Kiehart, D. P. 1990. Molecular genetic dissection of myosin heavy chain function. *Cell* 60:347–50
60. Korn, E. D., Hammer, J. A. III. 1988. Myosins of nonmuscle cells. *Annu. Rev. Biophys. Biophys. Chem.* 17:23–45
61. Lal, A. A., Korn, E. D. 1985. Reinvestigation of the inhibition of actin polymerization by profilin. *J. Biol. Chem.* 260:10132–38
62. Lambooy, P. K., Korn, E. D. 1988. Inhibition of an early stage of actin polymerization by actobindin. *J. Biol. Chem.* 263:12836–43

62a. Larsson, H., Lindberg, U. 1988. The effect of divalent cations on the interaction between calf spleen profilin and different actins. *Biochim. Biophys. Acta* 953:95–105

63. Lassing, I., Lindberg, U. 1985. Specific interaction between phosphatidylinositol 4,5-bisphosphate and profilactin. *Nature* 314:472–74
64. Lind, S. E., Janmey, P. A., Chaponnier, C., Herbert, T.-J., Stossel, T. P. 1987. Reversible binding of actin to gelsolin and profilin in human platelets. *J. Cell Biol.* 105:833–42
65. Liu, H., Bretscher, A. 1989. Disruption of the single tropomyosin gene in yeast results in the disappearance of actin cables from the cytoskeleton. *Cell* 57: 233–42
66. Maruyama, K., Kurokawa, H., Oosawa, M., Shimaoka, S., Yamamoto, H., et al. 1990. β-actinin is equivalent to Cap Z protein. *J. Biol. Chem.* 265: 8712–15
67. Matsudaira, P., Bordas, J., Koch, M. 1987. Synchrotron x-ray diffraction studies of actin structure during polymerization. *Proc. Natl. Acad. Sci. USA* 84:3151–55

68. Matsuzaki, F., Matsumoto, S., Yahara, I., Yonezawa, N., Nishida, E., Sakai, H. 1988. Cloning and characterization of porcine brain cofilin cDNA. Cofilin contains the nuclear transport signal sequence. *J. Biol. Chem.* 263:11564–68
69. McKenna, N., Meigs, J. B., Wang, Y.-L. 1985. Identical distribution of fluorescently labeled brain and muscle actins in living cardiac fibroblasts and myocytes. *J. Cell Biol.* 100:292–96
70. Meyer, W. H., Howard, T. H. 1987. Actin polymerization and its relationship to locomotion and chemokinetic response in maturing human promyelocytic leukemia cells. *Blood* 70:363–67
71. Mitchison,T., Kirschner, M. 1988. Cytoskeletal dynamics and nerve growth. *Neuron* 1:761–72
72. Moore, P. L., Haugland, R. P. 1989. Fluorescent probes for simultaneous, multi-color fluorescence studies of actin and myosin. *J. Cell Biol.* 109:270a. (see Fig. 6 of the cover of the catalog from Molecular Probes, Eugene, OR)
73. Mooseker, M. S. 1985. Organization, chemistry, and assembly of the cytoskeletal apparatus of the intestinal brush border. *Annu. Rev. Cell Biol.* 1:209–42
74. Mooseker, M. S., Pollard, T. D., Wharton, K. A. 1982. Nucleated polymerization of actin from the membrane-associated ends of microvillar filaments in the intestinal brush border. *J. Cell Biol.* 95:223–33
75. Murphy, D. B., Gray, R. O., Grasser, W. A., Pollard, T. D. 1988. Direct demonstration of actin filament annealing in vitro. *J. Cell Biol.* 106:1947–54
76. Newman, J., Estes, J. E., Selden, L. A., Gershman, L. C. 1985. Presence of oligomers at subcritical actin concentrations. *Biochemistry* 24:1538–44
77. Oster, G. 1988. Biophysics of the leading lamella. *Cell Motil. Cytoskelet.* 10:164–71
78. Oster, G. F., Perelson, A. S., Tilney, L. G. 1982. A mechanical model for elongation of the acrosomal process in *Thyone* sperm. *J. Math. Biol.* 15:259–65
79. Pasternak, C., Spudich, J. A., Elson, E. L. 1989. Capping of surface receptors and concomitant cortical tension are generated by conventional myosin. *Nature* 341:549–51
80. Pinder, J. C., Gratzer, W. B. 1982. Investigation of the actin deoxyribonuclease-I interaction using a pyrene-conjugated actin derivative. *Biochemistry* 21:4886–90
81. Podolski, J. L., Steck, T. L. 1988. Association of deoxyribonuclease I with the pointed ends of actin filaments in human red blood cell membrane skeletons. *J. Biol. Chem.* 263:638–45
82. Pollard, T. D. 1990. Actin. *Curr. Opin. Cell Biol.* 2:30–40
83. Pollard, T. D. 1986. Rate constants for the reactions of ATP- and ADP-actin with the ends of actin filaments. *J. Cell Biol.* 103:2747–54
84. Pollard, T. D., Cooper, J. A. 1986. Actin and actin-binding proteins. A critical evaluation of mechanisms and functions. *Annu. Rev. Biochem.* 55:987–1035
85. Deleted in proof
86. Robinson, T. F., Winegrad, S. 1979. The measurement and dynamic implications of thin filament lengths in heart muscle. *J. Physiol.* 286:607–19
86a. Safer, D., Golla, R., Nachimias, V. T. 1990. Isolation of a 5-kilodalton actin-sequestering peptide from human blood platelets. *Proc. Natl. Acad. Sci. USA* 87:2536–40
87. Sanders, M. C., Wang, Y.-L. 1990. Exogenous nucleation sites fail to induce detectable polymerization of actin in living cells. *J. Cell Biol.* 110:359–65
88. Schliwa, M. 1982. Action of cytochalasin-D on cytoskeletal networks. *J. Cell Biol.* 92:79–91
89. Schwartz, M. A., Luna, E. J. 1988. How actin binds and assembles onto plasma membranes from *Dictyostelium discoideum*. *J. Cell Biol.* 107:201–9
90. Sharif, A., Luna, E. J. 1990. *Dictyostelium discoideum* plasma membranes contain an actin-nucleating activity that requires ponticulin, an integral membrane glycoprotein. *J. Cell Biol.* 110:681–92
91. Smith, S. J. 1988. Neuronal cytomechanics: the actin-based motility of growth cones. *Science* 242:708–15
92. Sonobe, S., Takahashi, S., Hatano, S., Kuroda, K. 1986. Phosphorylation of amoeba G-actin and its effect on actin polymerization. *J. Biol. Chem.* 261: 14837–43
93. Southwick, F. S., Young, C. L. 1990. The actin released from profilin-actin complexes is insuffient to account for the increase in F-actin in chemoattractant-stimulated polymorphonuclear leukocytes. *J. Cell Biol.* 110:1965–73
94. Spector, I., Shochet, N. R., Blasberger, D., Kashman, Y. 1989. Latrunculins—novel marine macrolides that disrupt microfilament organization and affect cell growth: I. Comparison with cytochalasin D. *Cell Motil. Cytoskelet.* 13:127–44
95. Spudich, J. A. 1989. In pursuit of myosin function. *Cell Regul.* 1:1–11

96. Stossel, T. P. 1989. From signal to pseudopod. How cells control cytoplasmic actin assembly. *J. Biol. Chem.* 264:18261–64
97. Stossel, T. P., Chaponnier, C., Ezzell, R. M., Hartwig, J. H., Janmey, P. A., et al. 1985. Nonmuscle actin-binding proteins. *Annu. Rev. Cell Biol.* 1:353–402
98. Takagi, T., Konishi, K., Mabuchi, I. 1988. Amino acid sequence of starfish oocyte depactin. *J. Biol. Chem.* 263: 3097–3102
99. Tilney, L. G. 1978. Polymerization of actin. V. A new organelle, the actomere, that initiates the assembly of actin filaments in *Thyone* sperm. *J. Cell Biol.* 77:551–64
100. Tilney, L. G., Fukui, Y., DeRosier, D. J. 1987. Movement of the actin filament bundle in *Mytilus* sperm: A new mechanism is proposed. *J. Cell Biol.* 104: 981–93
101. Tilney, L. G., Inoue, S. 1982. Acrosomal reaction of *Thyone* sperm. I. Changes in the sperm head visualized by high resolution video microscopy. *J. Cell Biol.* 93:812–19
102. Tilney, L. G., Inoue, S. 1982. Acrosomal reaction of *Thyone* sperm. II. The kinetics and possible mechanism of acrosomal process elongation. *J. Cell Biol.* 93:820–27
103. Tilney, L. G., Inoue, S. 1985. Acrosomal reaction of *Thyone* sperm. III. The relationship between actin assembly and water influx during the extension of the acrosomal process. *J. Cell Biol.* 100:1273–83
104. Tilney, L. G., Kallenbach, N. 1979. Polymerization of actin. VI. The polarity of the actin filaments in the acrosomal process and how it might be determined. *J. Cell Biol.* 81:608–23
105. Tilney, L. G., Tilney, M.S., Cotanche, D. A. 1988. Actin filaments, stereocilia, and hair cells of the bird cochlea. V. How the staircase pattern of stereociliary lengths is generated. *J. Cell Biol.* 106:355–65
106. Tseng, P. C., Runge, M. S., Cooper, J. A., Williams, R. C. Jr., Pollard, T. D. 1984. Physical, immunochemical, and functional properties of *Acanthamoeba* profilin. *J. Cell Biol.* 98:214–21
107. Tsukita, S., Hieda, Y., Tsukita, S. 1989. A new 82-kd barbed end-capping protein (radixin) localized in the cell-to-cell adherens junction: purification and characterization. *J. Cell Biol.* 108:2369–82
108. Urbanik, E., Ware, B. R. 1989. Actin filament capping and cleaving activity of cytochalasins B, D, E, and H. *Arch. Biochem. Biophys.* 269:181–87
109. Wang, D., Berry, K., Howard, T. H. 1990. Kinetic analysis of chemotactic peptide induced actin polymerization in neutrophils. *Cell Motil. Cytoskelet.* 16: 80–87
110. Wang, Y.-L. 1985. Exchange of actin subunits at the leading edge of living fibroblasts: Possible role of treadmilling. *J. Cell Biol.* 101:597–602
111. Wehland, J., Osborn, M., Weber, K. 1977. Phalloidin-induced actin polymerization in the cytoplasm of cultured cells interferes with cell locomotion and growth. *Proc. Natl. Acad. Sci. USA* 74:5613–17
111a. Weight, C., Schoepper, B., Wegner, A. 1990. Tropomyosin-troponin complex stabilizes the pointed ends of actin filaments against polymerization and depolymerization. *FEBS Lett.* 260:266–68
112. Worthen, G. S., Schwab, B. III, Elson, E. L., Downey, G. P. 1989. Mechanics of stimulated neutrophils: Cell stiffening induces retention in capillaries. *Science* 245:183–86
112a. Yonezawa, N., Nishida, E., Iida, K., Yahara, I., Sakai, H. 1990. Inhibition of the interactions of cofilin, destrin, and deoxy ribonuclease I with actin by phosphoinositides. *J. Biol. Chem.* 265:8382–86
113. Zak, R., Martin, A. F., Prior, G., Rabinowitz, M. 1977. Comparison of turnover of several myofibrillar proteins and critical evaluations of double isotope method. *J. Biol. Chem.* 252:3430–35

Annu. Rev. Physiol. 1991. 53:607–28

GENETIC ALTERATION OF PROTEINS IN ACTIN-BASED MOTILITY SYSTEMS

G. Gerisch, A. A. Noegel, and M. Schleicher

Department of Cell Biology, Max-Planck-Institute of Biochemistry, D-8033 Martinsried, Germany

KEY WORDS: muscle fiber development, myosin and actin filament assembly, thick filament-associated proteins, microfilament cross-linking, severing and capping proteins, cytoskeleton

---

INTRODUCTION

Skeletal muscle fibers are endpoints of extreme structural and functional specialization, but the basic components of their thin and thick filaments, actin and myosin, are similar to the constituents of motor systems in non-muscle cells. The same is true for various regulatory and anchoring proteins of the actomyosin system. Sequence information of cytoskeletal proteins from lower eukaryotes indicates that proteins related to those in muscles have emerged during evolution. Together these proteins constitute the actin-based motors in non-muscle cells of a great variety of organisms. Often these proteins are built of domains: units of defined structure and function that can be used as modules to generate families of related proteins.

Three principal questions are posed by molecular geneticists: (*a*) what is the role of domains in cytoskeletal proteins, (*b*) what is the relationship between primary sequence and function, and (*c*) what are the in vivo activities of these proteins? In this review we cover actin, myosin, and proteins that regulate the activity or assembly state of these two proteins, but we do not discuss the system of proteins like vinculin and spectrin that anchor the cytoskeleton to the plasma membrane. We summarize genetic approaches

0066-4278/91/0315-0607$02.00

focused on organisms in which molecular techniques are highly advanced. The yeast *Saccharomyces* is notable in the broad spectrum of techniques in molecular and classical genetics that can be combined to analyze functions of proteins in vivo. *Dictyostelium* is distinguished by the amoeboid motility of its cells, which can be rapidly reoriented by chemoattractants. Gene disruption and replacement is applicable to this microorganism as it is to yeast. The nematode *Caenorhabditis* consists of a fixed number of strictly determined cells, among them various types of muscle cells that differ in the isoforms of myosin and other proteins they express. *Drosophila* provides the possibility of introducing defined numbers of gene copies using mobile elements (P-elements), and has the advantage that specific isoforms of proteins are expressed in flight muscles. These muscles are specialized to contract at a frequency higher than nerve impulses, but are not necessary for keeping the animal alive and fertile. The most widely-investigated mammals are mice, in which transgenic progeny can be generated by introducing foreign genes into the germ line. Transformation of myogenic cell lines is also possible, but interpretation of the results might be limited by the extent to which the characteristics of fully differentiated muscle fibers are manifested in cell culture. Finally, genetic diseases of man, for instance muscular dystrophies (47) and hemolytic anemias (14), provide additional information on structure-function relationships in proteins related to the actin cytoskeleton.

MYOSIN HEAVY CHAIN (MHC) MUTATIONS IN NON-MUSCLE AND MUSCLE CELLS

Myosin Defects Primarily Impair Cytokinesis in Non-Muscle Cells

Amoebae of *Dictyostelium discoideum* are free-living, non-muscle cells, which in motility and chemotactic behavior closely resemble polymorphonuclear granulocytes. The amoebae have a transient polarity with a front portion of pseudopods and a posterior portion where pseudopod formation is largely suppressed. Movement is oriented by the chemoattractant cAMP, which is capable of eliciting new fronts from any part of the cell periphery. Thus the motor system is designed in a way that facilitates rapid reorganization in response to external signals (68).

Thus far, two types of actin-based motor proteins have been identified in *D. discoideum:* (*a*) conventional double-headed myosin, designated as myosin II, which forms filaments concentrated close to the membrane in the posterior part of the cells, and (*b*) short-tailed single-headed myosin I accumulated at the leading edge (23) (see review by T. Pollard in this volume). The heavy chains of myosin II are encoded by a single gene. Several genes encoding heavy chains of the myosin I type have been identified in *D. discoideum,* which indicates expression of a family of proteins with probably overlapping functions (36, 70). One member of this family has been eliminated by gene disruption. One change attributable to the absence of this protein is an impairment of phagocytosis (35).

The role of myosin II in *D. discoideum* cells has been investigated by manipulating MHC expression by transformation. Anti-sense constructs have been used to efficiently suppress MHC synthesis (42). As a result of homologous recombination, MHC null mutants have been generated by gene disruption in transfected cells (48), as well as cell lines that produce only heavy meromyosin fragments of myosin II (15). These fragments are unable to assemble into filaments. In all of these transformants the amoebae retain motility and chemotactic responsiveness, although speed and precision of orientation in a cAMP gradient is reduced (74). Development is arrested in MHC-deficient transformants at the tipped aggregate stage, which demarcates transition to the slug stage. In the wild-type, morphogenesis at the multicellular level would proceed beyond this stage.

The most remarkable functional defect in MHC-depleted cells is paralysis of cytokinesis (15, 42). Normal cells of *D. discoideum* divide when attached to a substratum, and they also divide as free-floating cells in suspension. The MHC-defective cells do not divide in suspension. Instead they develop by synchronous nuclear divisions into plasmodia containing more than 50 nuclei and finally die. When spread on a substratum, these cells undergo a process called traction-mediated cytofission: they create multiple fronts pointing into pseudopods, which draw regions of the cells apart. These regions often include multiple nuclei and are finally disconnected from each other in a fission process not synchronized with karyokinesis (22). MHC null mutants can be complemented in *D. discoideum* by MHC DNA cloned into a vector that integrates into the genome. Complementation with wild-type DNA restores cytokinesis, and MHC-expressing cells can be selected on the basis of their capacity to grow in suspension (19).

Another clearly defined functional consequence of MHC gene disruption is the inability of cells to cap cell-surface glycoproteins that are cross-linked by fluorescent concanavalin A (58). Even in the absence of capping, the labeled lectin is efficiently endocytosed by these cells. Again, transformants producing heavy meromyosin behave like MHC null strains. Cytochemical studies have shown that the meromyosin fragments are distributed throughout the cytoplasm with no accumulation close to the membrane where normal myosin would be concentrated. Of interest is the normal location of F-actin in the cortex of MHC-defective cells. As in wild-type cells, the F-actin is enriched at the fronts where pseudopods are formed (22). During nuclear cleavage, the actin even accumulates in pseudo-cleavage furrows (42), but without colocalization of myosin II, the actin does not produce the mechanical force required for efficient constriction. Interaction between microfilament-associated myosin and the microtubular system is indicated by the finding that in cells expressing only heavy meromyosin, microtubules penetrate into dense actin networks as they fill the front of pseudopods, whereas microtubules are excluded from these areas in wild-type cells (22).

Complementation with mutated MHC DNA can be employed in dissecting myosin functions and in analyzing the mechanisms of their regulation. In vivo, myosin II is phosphorylated at threonine and serine residues of its heavy chains and also at serine residues of its light chains. Three phosphorylatable threonine residues are located in the carboxy-terminal portion of the MHC tail distal to the heads (45). In myosin null mutants complemented by a truncated MHC that lacks this portion (56), cytokinesis is restored although the myosin is not correctly localized within the cells (18). Constructs in which specific sets of phosphorylation sites are eliminated will help in analyzing the regulatory role of myosin II heavy chain phosphorylation.

Results comparable to those obtained in *Dictyostelium* have been reported for *Saccharomyces cerevisiae* (72). Disruption of a gene that encodes a MHC-like protein of the yeast results in disturbances of cell division. Multiple buds are formed, cells remain together in chains because of incomplete division, and nuclei do not separate correctly.

Myosin Mutations in Caenorhabditis elegans

In the nematode *C. elegans,* four genes encode myosin heavy chains (MHC) of muscle cells (16). Two of these heavy chains, MHC A and B, are primarily produced in muscles of the body wall and are required for motility of the animals. The two other heavy chains, MHC C and D, are specifically expressed in the pharynx and are essential for nutrition. MHC A and B are incorporated into thick filaments of the same muscle cells, but occupy different positions in these filaments. MHC A is located in the central region where thick filament assembly is initiated and appears to have a unique role in initiation (71), whereas MHC B assembles into the peripheral portions of the filaments.

The most extensively investigated MHC gene in *C. elegans* is the *unc-54* gene, which encodes MHC B. Null alleles of *unc-54* produce muscle defects responsible for uncoordinated movement. These mutations designated *unc-54 (0)* are recessive (5). Mutations designated *unc-54(d)* produce altered MHC B heavy chains that not only fail to assemble into thick filaments, but also interfere with the assembly of wild-type MHC B and MHC A. These mutations are of particular interest as tools for the analysis of myofilament assembly in *Caenorhabditis*. In *unc-54 (d)*/+ heterozygotes the myofilament lattice is disorganized, although number and orientation of thin filaments are normal, which indicates that actin can polymerize into filaments with the right polarity, independent of a stringent interaction with thick filaments. As little as 2% of the wild-type level is sufficient for the mutated product to prevent myosin molecules with normal A or B chains from assembling into thick filaments.

Most *unc-54 (d)* mutants produce a MHC B polypeptide of a size similar to wild-type. Thus small defects, often only single amino acid substitutions, are responsible for the mutant phenotype. In analyzing a series of independent mutations, amino acid substitutions are found to cluster in the MHC head region, most of them in a highly conserved glycine-rich loop near to the ATP-binding site, others within an actin-binding site (6). These results indicate that the myosin heads are important for thick filament assembly and suggest a role for ATPase in this process.

Myosin Mutations in Drosophila melanogaster

REDUCTION OF THICK FILAMENT NUMBER AFFECTS FUNCTION MOST SEVERELY IN INDIRECT FLIGHT MUSCLES In contrast to *C. elegans* and all vertebrates investigated, *Drosophila melanogaster* has, in addition to a cytoplasmic-MHC gene (41), only a single skeletal-muscle MHC gene. Nevertheless, the highly specialized indirect flight muscles of adults contain another isoform of MHC than the larval body-wall muscles. The two isoforms are generated by differential RNA splicing and differ in their carboxy-terminal regions (8, 64, 12). One isoform is specifically expressed in the thorax of the flies, most likely as a tissue-specific protein of indirect flight muscles. These muscles, specialized to contract at high frequency, have a regular myofilament organization characterized by a lattice of six thin filaments surrounding one thick filament, whereby the ratio of thin to thick filaments is 3 to 1. Other muscles of *D. melanogaster* have ratios of 9 to 12 thin filaments per thick filament. Reduction of the amount of MHC protein severely affects the indirect flight muscles and also the jump muscles in the legs, while muscles that are essential for viability are still functioning (55). This is shown by analyzing heterozygotes that carry the mutation *Mhc*^{1} in which a 101 bp deletion eliminates the ATP-binding site and causes a shift of reading frame in both splice products of the MHC RNA. Apparently because the carboxy-terminally truncated MHC proteins are unstable, *Mhc*^{1} is a null mutation, which is lethal in the homozygous state because the entire MHC is absent from all muscles. The mutation is dominant flightless; in the heterozygotes only the non-essential muscles with highly organized myofilament arrays, i.e. the indirect flight muscles and the jump muscles of adults, are paralyzed by reduction in the ratio of thick to thin filaments by nearly one half (55).

MYOSIN IS IMPORTANT FOR STABILITY OF THICK FILAMENT PROTEINS BUT NOT FOR ASSEMBLY OF THIN FILAMENTS *Ifm(2)2* is a mutant allele of the MHC gene that abolishes expression of the protein only in the indirect flight muscles (11). Since no MHC mRNA is detectable in these muscles, elimination of tissue-specific transcription or a defect in alternative splicing are the most likely reasons for absence of the myosin. Although the primary effect of the mutation is to eliminate MHC synthesis, several other components of thick filaments such as myosin light chains do not accumulate in the indirect flight muscles. Pulse-labeling shows that these proteins are synthesized at a rate similar to the wild-type proteins. The conclusion is that absence of myosin assembly results in rapid degradation of thick filament-associated proteins. In contrast, the thin filament proteins, actin and tropomyosin, accumulate normally and can even assemble along the longitudinal axis of the muscle fiber into thin filaments that are connected to Z-discs. The organization into sarcomeres is, however, lacking in the MHC-defective cells because of an improper alignment of Z-discs perpendicular to the long axis of the myofiber (11).

Mutations in Caenorhabditis *Affecting Two Thick Filament-Associated Proteins: Paramyosin and Twitchin*

Paramyosin, a protein that resembles the rod region of myosin, is a component of thick filaments in invertebrate muscle cells. The importance of paramyosin for normal filament assembly in *Caenorhabditis* is demonstrated by mutations at two loci, *unc-15I* and *unc-82IV,* which specify paramyosin and a gene product that interacts with paramyosin. These mutations are responsible for the formation of paracrystalline arrays of paramyosin, which atypically extend at both ends into branched structures of multiple thick filaments (20).

In mutants lacking the product of another gene *(unc-22),* body-wall muscles are unable to contract normally. They show frequent twitching caused by transient contraction of small regions within the myofilament lattice, independent of the contraction of adjacent regions. The *unc-22* gene product, called twitchin, is located within the thick filaments (51). It is an unusually large protein with a calculated molecular mass of 669 kd, and it has a peculiar domain structure (7). The major part of the twitchin molecule consists of two repeated motifs, each containing about 100 amino acids. Both motifs I and II have sequence similarities to the immunoglobulin superfamily, particularly to the neural cell adhesion molecule N-CAM. The carboxy-terminal portion of the twitchin sequence is similar to that of the catalytic domains of threonine/serine-specific protein kinases, especially to light chain kinases from chicken smooth muscle and rabbit skeletal muscle.

Since missense mutations of the *unc-54* gene, which encodes MHC B, act as suppressors in *unc-22* mutants, the *unc-22* gene product appears to interact directly with myosin in regulating contraction. Benian et al (7) hypothesize that twitchin acts as a myosin light chain kinase. The array of motifs in twitchin might be in line with the staggering of myosin rods in the thick filaments, thus optimizing interaction between the kinase and its substrate.

Phosphorylation of the myosin light chains, which is important for initiating contraction in vertebrate smooth muscle and non-muscle cells, is thought to be required for coordinated contraction of body muscles in *C. elegans*. The twitching of *C. elegans* muscles in the absence of light chain phosphorylation is due to incomplete activation thought to be based on thin filament regulation of contraction.

MUTATIONS IN ACTIN

Consequences of Substituting Conserved Amino Acids

Actin is a highly conserved protein. There is usually no problem with exchanging actins from different organisms in cell-free assays of actin-binding proteins, or in studies on actomyosin-based motility. On the other hand, various actin isoforms may be co-expressed in one cell, or may be expressed during development of an organism in a stage or tissue-specific pattern (64a). Genetic studies have centered on two questions: what are the features in the conserved portions of actin that are essential for its basic functions, and what are the functional consequences, if any, of subtle differences between the isoforms? A solid basis for the design of directed mutations and the interpretation of their consequences is the recently established atomic model of rabbit skeletal-muscle actin, as derived from X-ray crystallography (37, 33).

Conversion of an actin precursor into mature actin involves the removal of amino acids from its amino-terminus and requires the tagging of the precursor for recognition by a processing enzyme. Post-translational methylation of histidine-73 has been found in all but one actin species analyzed and might serve as a tag. This modification was tested by replacing the normal 3-methylhistidine with arginine. No discernible changes were observed in the polymerization of actin, in its DNase-binding activity, or in the processing of the precursor.

Substitution of another strictly conserved residue, Asp-11, results in two different fractions of mutated actin, one of which is not processed and is inhibited in DNase binding. The substitution of Asp-11 appears to cause a fraction of the actin to fold in a pathway different from the usual one. False folding is then the mechanism by which an effect is transmitted from the position of the altered amino acid to a DNase-binding site about 50 residues apart. The discussion of these findings by Rubenstein et al (65) is noteworthy as a caveat against any unsophisticated interpretation of the consequences of single amino acid substitutions.

Role of Actin Isoform Polymorphism

In vivo studies on actin functions are complicated by the presence of multiple actin genes in most eukaryotic systems. One exception of experimental interest is the yeast *Saccharomyces cerevisiae,* whose immobile cells contain only one actin gene. Another exception is the system of indirect flight muscle fibers in *Drosophila melanogaster*. A recurring theme of this review is that highly ordered filament assembly of these muscles and their specialized functions are based on a specific set of isoforms of thick and thin filament proteins. The *Act88F* gene, which is active in the flight muscles, encodes actin III of *Drosophila,* the only isoform of actin present in these muscles. Flies, in which one or both copies of the gene are silenced, are flightless, but they are fertile because other muscles are not paralyzed. One promising means of investigating the relevance of isoform polymorphism is to replace single amino acids, or groups of them, in one isoform of actin by those of another isoform. In order to analyze the structural and functional consequences of these natural replacements, the mutated actin genes are introduced into the region of *Act88F* null embryos, where germ cells are being formed. Offspring that have the gene integrated into a chromosome by P-element-mediated transformation are then investigated. Some of the amino acid replacements have parallels in the function and structure of the indirect flight muscle fibers, often in form of Z-disc abnormalities (24). These results show that the isoform-specific structure of actin III is critical for some interactions in vivo. It is conceivable that only this isoform fits optimally to the co-expressed isoforms of actin-binding proteins and that this fit is necessary for efficient cooperation of proteins in the flight muscles. Correlation of MHC isoform expression with speed and strength of muscle contraction (12), as well as allele-specific intergenic complementation, also indicates that protein-protein interactions are highly specific in *Drosophila* flight muscle fibers (34).

Importance of Actin-Myosin Ratios in Sarcomere Construction and Muscle Function

The role of actin filaments in sarcomere formation and the importance of proper stoichiometry between actin and myosin for the regular packing of thin and thick filaments has been demonstrated in *Drosophila* by combining null mutations in the *Act88F* gene with the *Ifm(2)2* mutation. As reported by Beall et al (4), the *Ifm(2)2* mutation prevents MHC production in the indirect flight muscles of *Drosophila* where actin III, the product of the *Act88F* gene, is also expressed. In *Act88F* null homozygotes thick filaments are formed, although no thin filaments or Z-discs are present in flight muscles. The thick filaments even associate laterally and give rise to clearly visible M lines and bare zones in their center.

Analysis of actin/MHC double heterozygotes shows that the balance between actin and myosin is more important for structure and function of indirect flight muscles than the absolute amounts of these proteins. The myofibrils are thinner than in wild-type, but mainly consist of perfectly packed lattices of thick and thin filaments. This contrasts with actin(0)/+ and MHC(0)/+ heterozygotes where the areas of well-packed filaments are smaller than in the double heterozygotes. When cross sections of actin (0)/+ heterozygotes are examined, these ordered arrays are found in the central portion of the myofibrils. The periphery of the myofibrils is filled with thick filaments that are not integrated into lattices. In MHC(0)/+ heterozygotes, small, well-organized arrays of thick and thin filaments are embedded into areas filled with surplus thin filaments. In line with the highly organized myofilament structure found in actin/myosin heterozygotes, these double heterozygotes are better flyers than animals that are heterozygous for only the actin or the MHC mutation.

The actin-to-myosin ratio also influences the length of sarcomeres. While in actin/MHC double heterozygotes the sarcomeres are about as long as in wild-type muscle, they are longer in actin(0)/+ heterozygotes and shorter in MHC(0)/+ heterozygotes (4).

Taken together, pathways for thick and thin filament assembly appear to be independent of each other. Also Z-bodies may assemble by an independent pathway as suggested by Chun & Falkenthal (11). Despite these independent assembly processes, perfect alignment into well-organized sarcomeres requires interaction between thick and thin filaments, and the length of sarcomeres critically depends on the stoichiometry of the major thick and thin filament proteins.

Crossbridges Formed by Actin Filaments of Inverse Polarity

Substitution of Gly-Ala in positions six and seven of *Act88F* actin III by Ala-Thr renders *D. melanogaster* flightless (62). The flight muscles of homozygotes are distinguished by interrupted Z-lines, portions of which are located on multiple levels in the central region of muscle fibers. At the periphery of these fibers, thick and thin filaments are variably located and not associated with a Z-line. At the border between the central and peripheral regions, thick filaments are often flanked by thin filaments having opposite polarity. Here single thick filaments can be seen to form rigor crossbridges with thin filaments of both orientations. This finding indicates that crossbridges in the muscle fibers retain a high degree of flexibility around the head-tail junction. This is in agreement with in vitro data showing that tethered heavy meromyosin fragments are capable of moving actin filaments in either direction.

Alterations in Actin that Induce Stress Responses

Two single-base substitutions in the 3' region of the *Act88F* coding sequence induce heat-shock responses. In one of them, the codon for Trp-356 is turned into a stop codon, in the other Gly-366 is replaced by Ser (57). These mutations are antimorphic, which means they interfere with myofibril development and render adult animals flightless even in the presence of a diploid set of the normal actin gene. Enlargement of nuclei is found exclusively in the flight muscles where the mutated actin gene is expressed. This observation has led to the hypothesis that the nuclear actin framework is disrupted through the antimorphic impairment of actin polymerization and that this disruption acts like other stresses known to induce a heat-shock response (57).

Identification of Actin-Binding Proteins in Yeast by Second-Site Suppressor Mutations

Inactivation of the actin gene in *Saccharomyces cerevisiae* is lethal, as is introduction of an extra copy of this gene (65). Replacement of the actin gene by mutated sequences makes it possible to study the structural requirements of actin functions within the context of the living cell and to identify proteins that interact with the actin. Conditional actin mutants show that actin is involved in vesicle transport, secretion, and polarized deposition of chitin during budding (53).

After a conditional actin mutation is established, actin-binding proteins can be identified by the help of second-site suppressor mutations. The rational behind this approach is that *SAC* (*S*uppressor of *AC*tin) mutations restore defective actin functions by causing complementary changes in an actin-binding protein. It is consistent with this premise that, in the absence of the corresponding actin mutation, *SAC* mutations cause phenotypes similar to those of actin mutations. This finding implies that actin and *SAC* mutations mutually suppress each other (1, 54). The power of this genetic approach is demonstrated by identification of the *SAC6* gene product as a 67-kd protein that has been isolated on an actin affinity column (1). In yeast cells, this protein colocalizes with actin cables and membrane-associated actin patches as they are concentrated in buds (17).

MUTATIONS IN THIN FILAMENT-ASSOCIATED PROTEINS

Troponin C (TnC)

TnC is a 17-kd Ca^{2+}-binding protein that confers Ca^{2+} sensitivity to the contractile system by undergoing a conformational change that is communicated to tropomyosin. As a consequence, binding of myosin to actin is no longer inhibited, and the actomyosin Mg^{2+}-ATPase can be activated. Independent of this action, Ca^{2+} is required for TnC to form a complex with troponin I and T. TnC is a dumbbell-shaped molecule with a central nine-turn α-helix and two pairs of Ca^{2+}-binding EF-hand motifs (30a). A low-affinity

Ca^{2+}-specific pair of EF-hands is located at the amino-terminus, and a Ca^{2+}/Mg^{2+}-binding pair with at least one high-affinity Ca^{2+}-binding site is found at the carboxy-terminus. Site-directed mutagenesis has been employed (*a*) to study whether the central helix modifies Ca^{2+}-binding and participates in the conformational changes of TnC that eventually activate actomyosin Mg^{2+}-ATPase, and (*b*) to dissect the function of the amino- and carboxy-terminal pairs of Ca^{2+}-binding sites.

The central helix has been lengthened or shortened, and its helical tendency has been increased or decreased by single amino acid substitutions. None of these changes substantially alters the Ca^{2+}-binding properties of the high- and low-affinity domains of TnC (63, 77, 31). Some of these changes in the central helix alter the interaction of TnC with troponin I and the effectiveness of actomyosin Mg^{2+}-ATPase activation by the complex (63, 77, 31). These results parallel those obtained with the ubiquitous TnC analogue calmodulin. Changes in the central helix of calmodulin alter the ability of the protein to activate certain target enzymes rather than affecting Ca^{2+}-binding (13, 59, 60).

Functions of the helix-loop-helix motifs of the four EF-hands in TnC have been investigated by testing Ca^{2+}-binding and force generation with the use of bacterially expressed, wild-type and mutated chicken TnC (61). The TnC used in these studies has been cardiac TnC, an isoform found in heart and slow skeletal muscle. In cardiac TnC, the first amino-terminal EF-hand is imperfect and not functional, in contrast to TnC from fast skeletal muscle where the four EF-hands are perfect. Force generation has been assayed with skinned muscle fibers. Most of the endogenous TnC can be removed from these fibers with EDTA and EGTA, and the fibers can be reconstituted with the TnC forms under investigation. Cardiac TnC fully reactivates cardiac and slow skeletal muscle fibers.

Conversion of a single amino acid, Asp-65 into Ala, in cardiac TnC inactivates EF-hand II, thus leaving only the carboxy-terminal pair of EF-hands intact. The mutated TnC associates with troponin I and T and also integrates into TnC-depleted skinned muscle fibers, but is incapable of generating any force in these fibers. Two conclusions are drawn from these results: the carboxy-terminal pair of EF-hands is sufficient for TnC to form a troponin complex, and EF-hand II is essential for Ca^{2+}-elicited contractibility.

By deleting one amino acid and substituting four others with the corresponding amino acids of the fast muscle isoform, the inactive EF-hand in cardiac TnC is converted into a Ca^{2+}-binding structure (61). The effect of this mutation on slow-muscle fibers is an increase in cooperativity of Ca^{2+}-dependent force generation, which indicates that EF-hand I can modify the basic function of EF-hand II in activating muscle contraction.

Tropomyosin (TM)

MUTATIONS FOR STUDYING STRUCTURE-FUNCTION RELATIONSHIPS Tropomyosin is a filamentous dimer composed of 33-kd subunits that are oriented in parallel. With the exception of nine amino acids at each end, the polypeptide chains are α-helical and are organized into 14 repeats. Each repeat contains a zone of charged residues followed by a zone rich in non-polar amino acids. The repetitive regions of the two TM subunits are associated in register as a coiled-coil. The amino-terminal regions of muscle and non-muscle TMs are highly conserved and, at least in muscle TM, the terminal methionine is acetylated. These amino-terminal regions interact with the carboxy-terminal portions in head-to-tail polymerization, each TM molecule spanning seven actin monomers along a thin filament (78).

In vitro studies with genetically altered TM forms have focused on three topics: (*a*) the role of amino- and carboxy-terminal regions in polymerization, (*b*) the importance of head-to-tail polymerization for the binding to actin filaments, and (*c*) the requirement of the 14 negatively charged repeats for the cooperative binding to actin. With respect to topic (*a*), two results are pertinent. First, TM with a truncated carboxy-terminal end is unable to polymerize (46, 70a). Second, a protein expressed in *E. coli* that contains the full-length polypeptide chain of chicken α-TM does not polymerize, presumably because its amino-terminal methionine is not acetylated. Polymerization is also blocked in a fusion protein where 80 amino acids of an influenza viral protein are added to the amino-terminus of the TM sequence (30–32). The same approach is relevant to topic (*b*) since the fusion protein does bind to F-actin in a cooperative manner with an affinity similar to muscle TM. This result indicates that polymerization of TM is not essential for appropriate association with actin and also shows that the actin-binding site in the amino-terminal region of TM is not hindered by the addition of a foreign polypeptide. The finding that the non-acetylated TM obtained from *E. coli* shows much weaker binding suggests that the amino-terminus is involved in the interaction with actin and must be modified to be fully active (31). Involvement of the carboxy-terminal region in the interaction with actin is inferred from the observation that the truncated TM shows reduced binding to actin filaments (46, 70a).

The importance of the regularly spaced repeats in the cooperative interaction of TM with F-actin, topic (*c*), has been addressed by Hitchcock-DeGregori & colleagues (31). These authors have investigated the binding of genetically altered TM in which about one half or two thirds of a putative binding site or an entire site has been deleted, assuming that two of the 14 repeats correspond to one binding site. The lengths of the deleted sections of the sequence have been multiples of seven amino acids in order to retain the

α-helical coiled-coil structure. If proper alignment of multiple binding sites is important for the interaction of TM with actin filaments, then removal of an entire binding site should have less severe consequences than elimination of a fraction of it. This has been found to be true for the fusion-TM carrying a viral polypeptide at its amino-terminus: eliminating roughly a single repeat has a dramatic effect on binding to actin, which supports the view that each of the periodic actin binding sites in TM is composed of two repeats. These data, however, are also consistent with the hypothesis that a set of seven sites, each represented by one repeat, is involved in attaching TM to actin in the relaxed state of the muscle and, upon a conformational change, seven alternating sites become attached to actin in the activated state (50). Removal of one repeat from the sequence would disturb alignment of the binding sites to the actin subunits in both frames. A point relevant to interpretation of these deletion experiments is the role that adequate spacing of the TM head and tail groups plays in the overall binding of the TM molecule to the actin filament. Elimination of two repeats may have little effect on binding because it brings the end groups in phase with the regularly spaced actin subunits similar to the way they align in wild-type TM.

Results obtained with mutated, bacterially expressed non-fusion TM modify the conclusions drawn from the fusion-TM data (32a). Upon addition of troponin, the non-fusion TM efficiently binds to actin and also confers Ca^{2+}-sensitivity to actomyosin Mg^{2+}-ATPase. Elimination of one of the 14 repeats, which means one half of a putative binding site, from non-fusion TM has little effect on binding to actin, whereas elimination of two thirds of a proposed site strongly reduces the binding. These mutations indicate the importance of a 14-fold periodicity for the binding of non-fusion TM to actin in the presence of troponin (32a).

In Vivo Role of Tropomyosins

The in vivo functions of proteins of the TM family have been studied by gene disruption in the yeast *Saccharomyces cerevisiae* and in the indirect flight muscles of *Drosophila melanogaster*. The TM-related protein from *S. cerevisiae* is encoded by a single gene. Cells in which this gene is inactivated are viable, but suffer from a reduced growth rate. A structural consequence of the null mutation is the disappearance of actin cables. Suppression of a conditional mutation *(act 1–2)* in the yeast actin gene also indicates that the TM-related protein has F-actin bundling activity. Under permissive temperature the mutant cells lack actin cables. Overexpression of the TM-related protein restores actin bundling in these cells (44).

In *Drosophila* two isoforms of TM are produced from one of its two genes by tissue-specific alternate splicing. The first of these isoforms is expressed in body muscles of the larvae and flies and is required for viability, the second isoform is specifically expressed in the indirect flight muscles and in small amounts in the leg muscles, which are responsible for jumping (39, 40, 69). In a flightless mutant, *Ifm(3)3*, a mobile element has been found in the TM gene in a position that interrupts an intron in the first splicing mode and an exon in the second mode. The integration of the mobile element into the TM gene does not interfere with synthesis of the first isoform, but dramatically reduces production of the other isoform, the one specifically expressed in flight and leg muscles. In the flight muscles of homozygous mutants the hexagonal pattern of thick and thin filaments is replaced at the periphery of myofibrils by an irregular arrangement of these filaments. Variations observed in the length of sarcomeres are related to the ease with which the myofibrils can be stretched, torn, and broken (39).

By inserting the entire TM gene into chromosomes of the germ line, *Ifm(3)3* mutants can be rescued (25). As it is the case with several other proteins of thin or thick filaments, jumping of the flies is already restored when a single intact gene per diploid genome is present in the leg muscles, while flight requires two genes to be active in the indirect flight muscles (69).

MUTATIONS IN PROTEINS THAT REGULATE ACTIN POLYMERIZATION

Monomeric F-actin Severing and Capping Proteins

All members of this family of proteins sever actin filaments in a strictly Ca^{2+}-dependent manner and cap their fast growing ends (49). They also bind to actin monomers and facilitate nucleation during the initial phase of actin polymerization, and several members are regulated by polyphosphoinositide. No sequence motif resembling EF-hands has been found in any of these proteins, which indicates that the Ca^{2+}-binding sites in monomeric severing proteins differ fundamentally from those in the calmodulin-troponin C family of Ca^{2+}-regulated proteins.

Severin from *Dictyostelium discoideum* and fragmin from the slime mold *Physarum polycephalum* have a molecular mass of 40 kd, and gelsolin and villin from vertebrates have molecular masses of 82 and 95 kd, respectively. In principle, the latter proteins can be considered as tandemly arranged duplications of proteins of the 40-kd class. They can be cleaved by proteolysis or genetic engineering into roughly two halves, an amino-terminal half, which retains F-actin severing and capping activity, and a carboxy-terminal half, which binds only to monomeric actin and is required in the intact molecule for nucleation (73).

Fragments of gelsolin truncated at the carboxy-terminal end have been expressed in Cos cells in order to attribute specific activities to small portions of the sequence (43). The Cos strain of monkey kidney cells efficiently expresses foreign proteins. Transfected DNA is replicated in these cells to a high copy number under the control of an SV40 origin. The advantage of this eukaryotic expression system is that the synthesized proteins are correctly folded and processed and, if secreted, they can be harvested from the medium. The results obtained with the carboxy-terminally truncated gelsolin fragments seem to reflect the functional divergence of two originally separate and equivalent halves of the molecule. Functional sites may have been lost in one half or have become cryptic in the intact molecule during evolution. As a consequence, interaction between the two halves may be favored. For instance, removal of only 3% of the gelsolin sequence from the carboxy-terminus results in the loss of Ca^{2+} requirement for the severing activity of a site located within the first 160 amino acids of the amino-terminal region. Removal of about 70% of the sequence restores Ca^{2+} sensitivity, which indicates the presence of a cryptic Ca^{2+}-binding site in the amino-terminal half of the molecule.

Villin is an integral constituent of the microvilli in the brush border of intestinal epithelia and kidney tubules. It is distinguished from other severing and capping proteins by an extra actin-binding site located in a 8.5-kd carboxy-terminal domain, the head-piece, which is responsible for Ca^{2+}-independent bundling of actin filaments. A modulating effect of villin on actin-cytoskeleton and cell-surface organization has been demonstrated by transiently expressing villin in monkey kidney fibroblasts (21). Normally these cells do not produce villin, nor are they related to cells having a brush border. After transfection with villin cDNA, numerous microvilli of about 2.4 μm length are formed on the dorsal surface of cells that strongly express villin. Part of the villin is associated in these cells with bundles of densely packed microfilaments making up the core of the induced cell-surface extensions. The villin also causes actin redistribution: stress fibers typical of the control fibroblasts are disintegrated in the transfected cells. Only the intact villin molecule strongly induces microvilli, whereas expression of the head piece alone is sufficient for the disintegration of stress fibers.

Severin has been eliminated by mutation in *Dictyostelium* cells (3). The mutant cells expressing no severin are viable. They move and chemotax, grow and divide, and develop without obvious difficulties under laboratory conditions. The presence or absence of severin thus has no impact on the shape or behavior of *Dictyostelium* cells that would be comparable to the striking effect of villin in fibroblasts. This result is surprising because of the high abundance and in vitro activity of severin and because no other severing protein of comparable activity has been found in fractions of cell lysates from the severin-deficient mutant.

Yeast Mutants Lacking Profilin

Profilins are 12–15-kd proteins of eukaryotic cells that bind to actin monomers. They also cap, but do not sever, actin filaments. Anionic phospholipids dissociate profilin-actin complexes, thus giving rise to free actin that is capable of polymerizing under appropriate conditions. Profilin also inhibits hydrolysis of PIP_2 by phospholipase C (27). From these in vitro effects, it is likely that profilins play a double role within cells. Depending on the conditions, they may preferentially inhibit actin polymerization or prevent signaling through the phosphoinositide pathway.

The in vivo function of profilin has been investigated in *Saccharomyces cerevisiae*. The single profilin gene in this yeast has been disrupted in order to produce mutants that lack any functional profilin. The profilin null mutants obtained are conditionally lethal: they are more temperature-sensitive than wild-type, grow more slowly, and sporulate only under special conditions (28). The profilin null phenotype resembles that of actin-defective mutants: the polarized budding pattern is disturbed together with the loss of the cell's ellipsoidal shape, the cells become multinucleate, and they increase in size. Actin assembles in thick bars within the cells rather than into oriented filaments. F-actin is only detected in cortical patches, which are more or less randomly distributed in the rounded cells of the mutants, in contrast to their accumulation in the budding region of wild-type cells.

Mutations in a Heterodimeric Capping Protein

Heterodimeric capping proteins bind to the fast growing end of actin filaments without a requirement for Ca^{2+}; they inhibit the addition of monomers to this barbed end but do not sever. In skeletal muscle, they are located in the Z-lines. Subunits of the capping proteins have molecular masses of 32-36 kd for the larger subunit and 28-32 kd for the smaller subunit. They constitute a family of highly conserved proteins with no obvious relationship to other known polypeptides (29).

In *Saccharomyces cerevisiae* a gene coding for the small subunit of a putative capping protein has been disrupted. The mutant cells exhibit deficiencies quite similar to the phenotypes of profilin null mutants as described above, or of conditional actin mutants (2). These findings suggest that although they may originate from mutations in different proteins, imbalances in the actin cytoskeleton of yeast result in a general breakdown of actin functions with about the same consequences.

MUTATIONS IN F-ACTIN CROSS-LINKING PROTEINS

α-Actinin Mutations in Dictyostelium *Raise the Question of Redundancy of Actin Cross-linking Proteins*

α-Actinin and a series of related proteins contain a highly conserved F-actin binding site in their amino-terminal domain, as shown for ABP-120, an actin cross-linking protein of *Dictyostelium* (9), and β-spectrin (38). The amino-terminal domain of α-actinin is followed by a fourfold repeat with high

α-helical probability. A third domain comprising the carboxy-terminal region includes two EF-hand motifs. These Ca^{2+}-binding structures are perfect in the sequence of α-actinin from *Dictyostelium,* whose actin-binding activity is strongly inhibited by Ca^{2+}, and are degenerated in vertebrate muscle α-actinin. By anti-parallel orientation of the two α-actinin subunits, the Ca^{2+}-binding domain of one subunit is thought to become juxtaposed to the actin-binding site of the other (52). Insertion of a foreign sequence of 13 amino acids into the second EF-hand of *Dictyostelium* α-actinin greatly reduces not only Ca^{2+}-binding, but also actin-cross-linking activity, probably because the modified Ca^{2+}-binding site directly inhibits the actin-binding site (66).

In *Dictyostelium,* mutants defective in α-actinin production have been isolated in two ways: (*a*) by chemical mutagenesis followed by screening of clones for the absence of monoclonal-antibody binding, and (*b*) by gene disruption via homologous recombination. A mutant isolated by the first method produces not more than trace amounts of α-actinin polypeptide (67). The primary defect has been identified as a G to A substitution in the consensus sequence of the second 5'-splice site of the α-actinin gene (76), so that two RNA species, one uncleaved at this side and one cleaved but not religated, are produced. These RNAs are released into the cytoplasm, but are not efficiently incorporated into polysomes. Phenotypically, the mutant does not exhibit a significant alteration in any of the cellular activities tested, including motility, chemotaxis, and capping of membrane proteins, apart from a 5% decrease in the growth rate (67). Mutants independently obtained by gene disruption do not produce any detectable α-actinin polypeptide (75). Again, the phenotype of these mutants is not substantially altered, which indicates that α-actinin is not vital for *Dictyostelium* under the laboratory conditions employed. The conservation of pertinent details of the α-actinin sequence among eukaryotes does suggest a general role for this protein not only in muscle, but also non-muscle cells. Possibly the slightly higher growth rate of α-actinin-containing cells is sufficient for selection during evolution. Alternatively, the lack of α-actinin might have more dramatic consequences for survival under special conditions in nature.

Another F-actin cross-linking protein in *Dictyostelium* amoebae, thought to control organization of the actin cytoskeleton during pseudopod formation, is the 120-kd gelation factor, renamed ABP-120 (9). Like α-actinin, this protein has been eliminated both by chemical mutagenesis (10) and by gene disruption (52) without dramatic alterations in cellular activities. This result indicates that the 120-kd protein is not important for these activities, but it might have subtle effects on motility or chemotactic responses. Indeed, a modifying effect of the 120-kd protein on chemoattractant-elicited changes in the cytoskeleton has been observed. The quantity of pelletable actin increases in cell lysates after stimulation of cells by cAMP, and in wild-type and mutant shows a sharp peak at 6 to 7 sec. The mutant differs from wild-type by a significantly higher peak (10).

Although only α-actinin is regulated by Ca^{2+}, the functions of α-actinin and the 120-kd protein may sufficiently overlap to allow replacement of one protein by the other. Therefore, the next step in analyzing the in vivo function of these and other F-actin cross-linking proteins will be to eliminate more than a single protein in one cell. By progressively introducing multiple defects, one should obtain minimal redundancy mutants. At this point, elimination of one more protein would severely alter motility or other cytoskeletal functions.

Role of α-Actinin in the Z-Lines of Drosophila *Flight Muscles*

As in other skeletal muscles, α-actinin is located in the Z-disks in the indirect flight muscles of *Drosophila*. Two classes of mutations in the α-actinin gene have been analyzed: null mutations caused by disruption of the gene as the result of chromosomal inversions, and mutations not associated with major DNA rearrangements, which probably represent point mutations (26). Mutations of the first category are homozygous lethal. But embryos are able to hatch and to develop into second-instar larvae, which indicates that for completing embryonic development the product of the disrupted α-actinin gene is not necessary. Mutations of the second category are not lethal, but have impaired flight muscle function. The organization of Z-discs and alignment of myofilaments is disturbed to varying degrees, most strongly in the basal sarcomeres where muscle fibers are connected to tendon cells that link these fibers to the cuticle of the thorax. The epithelial tendon cells show almost no alteration resulting from the mutations, again suggesting that α-actinin is essential only for the function of muscle fibers. Although in low-stringency Southern blots only a single α-actinin gene has been detected, expression of a second, distantly related gene in non-muscle cells is not completely ruled out (26).

CONCLUDING REMARKS

Our principal attempt in this review has been to exemplify the increasing range of applications that molecular genetics has in studies on the actomyosin system. The advantages of combining in vitro and in vivo studies have been emphasized. The wide variety of activities of a particular protein, for instance myosin, has become apparent by comparing its role in motility systems with different levels of organization from unicellular amoebae to highly specialized muscle fibers.

A noteworthy aspect is the variability in the consequences that quantitative or qualitative changes in proteins of the actomyosin system have in different cell types. In yeast, actin and associated proteins are required for a limited number of cellular activities without a need for adapting motility to changing environmental conditions. In these immobile cells, the quantity of actin is critical; presence of even two actin genes per haploid genome results in cell death. Similarly, the elimination of single actin-binding proteins causes severe deficiencies in yeast, thus indicating that all these proteins are needed for appropriate function of the entire system. At the other extreme, amoebae of *Dictyostelium* appear to be particularly adept in keeping their motility system flexible. This system is buffered against changes in the activities of a number of actin-binding proteins. Eliminating these proteins by mutation does not have the dramatic effects that one would expect if the fine-tuned cooperation of all the interacting proteins were important for motility and its control. Some muscles tolerate substantial changes in the absolute amounts of proteins constituting their contractile system without a dramatic impairment of function. Changes in the relative amounts of proteins are less easily tolerated. Other muscles, represented by the indirect flight muscles of insects, probably owe their extremely high power of performance to an optimization of every detail of their construction. This is indicated by the expression of specific isoforms of thick and thin filament proteins and is visualized by the invariant ratio and regular array of their myofilaments.

A promising line of future research will be based on the expression of proteins normally not synthesized in a particular cell. There the morphological and functional consequences of expressing a protein can be analyzed, as pioneered by the reported work on villin. Another challenging goal is to combine domains from different cytoskeletal proteins, as modules for the creation of artificial proteins, and to integrate such proteins into in vitro systems designed to display novel properties that are not found in the natural systems operating in organisms.

ACKNOWLEDGMENT

We thank Drs. Eugenio de Hostos, Annette Müller-Taubenberger, and Murray Stewart for comments, and Maria Birkhofer for organizing the manuscript. Our work was supported by grants of the Deutsche Forschungsgemeinschaft.

Literature Cited

1. Adams, A. E. M., Botstein, D., Drubin, D. G. 1989. A yeast actin-binding protein is encoded by *SAC6,* a gene found by suppression of an actin mutation. *Science* 243:231–33
2. Amatruda, J. F., Cannon, J. F., Tatchell, K., Hug, C., Cooper, J. A. 1990. Disruption of the actin cytoskeleton in yeast capping protein mutants. *Nature* 344:352–54
3. André, E., Brink, M., Gerisch, G., Isenberg, G., Noegel, A., et al. 1989. A *Dictyostelium* mutant deficient in severin, an F-actin fragmenting protein, shows normal motility and chemotaxis. *J. Cell Biol.* 108:985–95
4. Beall, C. J., Sepanski, M. A., Fyrberg, E. A. 1989. Genetic dissection of *Drosophila* myofibril formation: effects of actin and myosin heavy chain null alleles. *Genes Dev.* 3:131–40
5. Bejsovec, A., Anderson, P. 1988. Myosin heavy-chain mutations that disrupt *Caenorhabditis elegans* thick filament assembly. *Genes Dev.* 2:1307–17
6. Bejsovec, A., Anderson, P. 1990. Func-

tions of the myosin ATP and actin binding sites are required for *C. elegans* thick filament assembly. *Cell* 60:133–40

7. Benian, G. M., Kiff, J. E., Neckelmann, N., Moerman, D. G., Waterston, R. H. 1989. Sequence of an unusually large protein implicated in regulation of myosin activity in *C. elegans*. *Nature* 342:45–50
8. Bernstein, S. I., Hansen, C. J., Becker, K. D., Wassenberg, D. R. II, Roche, E. S., et al. 1986. Alternative RNA splicing generates transcripts encoding a thorax-specific isoform of *Drosophila melanogaster* myosin heavy chain. *Mol. Cell. Biol.* 6:2511–19
9. Bresnick, A. R., Warren, V., Condeelis, J. 1990. Identification of a short sequence essential for actin binding by *Dictyostelium* ABP-120. *J. Biol. Chem.* 265:9236–40
10. Brink, M., Gerisch, G., Isenberg, G., Noegel, A. A., Segall, J. E., et al. 1990. A *Dictyostelium* mutant lacking an F-actin cross-linking protein, the 120-kD gelation factor. *J. Cell Biol.* 111:1477–89
11. Chun, M., Falkenthal, S. 1988. *Ifm(2)2* is a myosin heavy chain allele that disrupts myofibrillar assembly only in the indirect flight muscle of *Drosophila melanogaster*. *J. Cell Biol.* 107:2613–21
12. Collier, V. L., Kronert, W. A., O'Donnell, P. T., Edwards, K. A., Bernstein, S. I. 1990. Alternative myosin hinge regions are utilized in a tissue-specific fashion that correlates with muscle contraction speed. *Genes Dev.* 4:885–95
13. Craig, T. A., Watterson, D. M., Prendergast, F. G., Haiech, J., Roberts, D. M. 1987. Site-specific mutagenesis of the α-helices of calmodulin. Effects of altering a charge cluster in the helix that links the two halves of calmodulin. *J. Biol. Chem.* 262:3278–84
14. Davies, K. A., Lux, S. E. 1989. Hereditary disorders of the red cell membrane skeleton. *Trends Genet.* 5:222–27
15. De Lozanne, A., Spudich, J. A. 1987. Disruption of the *Dictyostelium* myosin heavy chain gene by homologous recombination. *Science* 236:1086–91
16. Dibb, N. J., Maruyama, I. N., Krause, M., Karn, J. 1989. Sequence analysis of the complete *Caenorhabditis elegans* myosin heavy chain gene family. *J. Mol. Biol.* 205:603–13
17. Drubin, D. G., Miller, K. G., Botstein, D. 1988. Yeast actin-binding proteins: Evidence for a role in morphogenesis. *J. Cell Biol.* 107:2551–61
18. Egelhoff, T. T., Brown, S. B., Spudich, J. A. 1991. A carboxy-terminal truncation of *Dictyostelium* myosin eliminates control of disassembly in vivo. *J. Cell Biol.* In press
19. Egelhoff, T. T., Manstein, D. J., Spudich, J. A. 1990. Complementation of myosin null mutants in *Dictyostelium discoideum* by direct functional selection. *Dev. Biol.* 137:359–67
20. Epstein, H. F., Ortiz, I., Berliner, G. C. 1987. Assemblages of multiple thick filaments in nematode mutants. *J. Muscle Res. Cell Motil.* 8:527–36
21. Friederich, E., Huet, C., Arpin, M., Louvard, D. 1989. Villin induces microvilli growth and actin redistribution in transfected fibroblasts. *Cell* 59:461–75
22. Fukui, Y., De Lozanne, A., Spudich, J. A. 1990. Structure and function of the cytoskeleton of a *Dictyostelium* myosin-defective mutant. *J. Cell Biol.* 110:367–78
23. Fukui, Y., Lynch, T. J., Brzeska, H., Korn, E. D. 1989. Myosin I is located at the leading edges of locomoting *Dictyostelium* amoebae. *Nature* 341:328–31
24. Fyrberg, E. A. 1989. Study of contractile and cytoskeletal proteins using *Drosophila* genetics. *Cell Motil. Cytoskel.* 14:118–27
25. Fyrberg, E. A., Karlik, C. C. 1987. Genetic rescue of muscle defects associated with a mutant *Drosophila melanogaster* tropomyosin allele. *Mol. Cell. Biol.* 7:2977–80
26. Fyrberg, E., Kelly, M., Ball, E., Fyrberg, C., Reedy, M. C. 1990. Molecular genetics of *Drosophila* alpha-actinin:mutant alleles disrupt Z disc integrity and muscle insertions. *J. Cell Biol.* 110:1999–2011
27. Goldschmidt-Clermont, P. J., Machesky, L. M., Baldassare, J. J., Pollard, T. D. 1990. The actin-binding protein profilin binds to PIP_2 and inhibits its hydrolysis by phospholipase C. *Science* 247:1575–78
28. Haarer, B. K., Lillie, S. H., Adams, A. E. M., Magdolen, V., Bandlow, W., Brown, S. S. 1990. Purification of profilin from *Saccharomyces cerevisiae* and analysis of profilin-deficient cells. *J. Cell Biol.* 110:105–14
29. Hartmann, H., Schleicher, M., Noegel, A. A. 1990. Heterodimeric capping proteins constitute a highly conserved group of actin-binding proteins. *Dev. Genet.* 11:369–76
30. Heald, R. W., Hitchcock-DeGregori, S. E. 1988. The structure of the amino terminus of tropomyosin is critical for binding to actin in the absence and presence of troponin. *J. Biol. Chem.* 263:5254–59

30a. Heizmann, C. W., Hunziker, W. 1990.

Intracellular calcium-binding molecules. In *Intracellular Calcium Regulation,* pp. 211–48. New York: Liss
31. Hitchcock-DeGregori, S. E. 1989. Structure-function analysis of thin filament proteins expressed in *Escherichia coli. Cell Motil. Cytoskel.* 14:12–20
32. Hitchcock-DeGregori, S. E., Heald, R. W. 1987. Altered actin and troponin binding of amino-terminal variants of chicken striated muscle α-tropomyosin expressed in *Escherichia coli. J. Biol. Chem.* 262:9730–35
32a. Hitchcock-DeGregori, S. E., Varnell, T. A. 1990. Tropomyosin has discrete actin-binding sites with sevenfold and fourteenfold periodicities. *J. Mol. Biol.* 214:885–96
33. Holmes, K. C., Popp, D., Gebhard, W., Kabsch, W. 1990. Atomic model of the actin filament. *Nature* 347:44–49
34. Homyk, T. Jr., Emerson, C. P. Jr. 1990. Functional interactions between unlinked muscle genes within haploid-sufficient regions of the *Drosophila* genome. *Genetics* 119:105–21
35. Jung, G., Hammer, J. A. III. 1990. Generation and characterization of *Dictyostelium* cells deficient in a myosin I heavy chain isoform. *J. Cell Biol.* 110:1955–64
36. Jung, G., Saxe, C. L. III, Kimmel, A. R., Hammer, J. A. III. 1989. *Dictyostelium discoideum* contains a gene encoding a myosin I heavy chain. *Proc. Natl. Acad. Sci. USA* 86:6186–90
37. Kabsch, W., Mannherz, H. G., Suck, D., Pai, E. F., Holmes, K. C. 1990. Atomic structure of the actin: DNase I complex. *Nature*. 347:37–44
38. Karinch, A. M., Zimmer, W. E., Goodman, S. R. 1990. The identification and sequence of the actin-binding domain of human red blood cell β-spectrin. *J. Biol. Chem.* 265:11833–40
39. Karlik, C. C., Fyrberg, E. A. 1985. An insertion within a variably spliced *Drosophila* tropomyosin gene blocks accumulation of only one encoded isoform. *Cell* 41:57–66
40. Karlik, C. C., Fyrberg, E. A. 1986. Two *Drosophila melanogaster* tropomyosin genes: structural and functional aspects. *Mol. Cell. Biol.* 6:1965–73
41. Kiehart, D. P., Lutz, M. S., Chan, D., Ketchum, A. S., Laymon, R. A., et al. 1989. Identification of the gene for fly non-muscle myosin heavy chain: *Drosophila* myosin heavy chains are encoded by a gene family. *EMBO J.* 8:913–22
42. Knecht, D. A., Loomis, W. F. 1987. Antisense RNA inactivation of myosin heavy chain gene expression in *Dictyostelium discoideum. Science* 236: 1081–86
43. Kwiatkowski, D. J., Janmey, P. A., Yin, H. L. 1989. Identification of critical functional and regulatory domains in gelsolin. *J. Cell Biol.* 108:1717–26
44. Liu, H., Bretscher, A. 1989. Disruption of the single tropomyosin gene in yeast results in the disappearance of actin cables from the cytoskeleton. *Cell* 57: 233–42
45. Lück-Vielmetter, D., Schleicher, M., Grabatin, B., Wippler, J., Gerisch, G. 1990. Replacement of threonine residues by serine and alanine in a phosphorylatable heavy chain fragment of *Dictyostelium* myosin II. *FEBS Lett.* 269:239–43
46. Mak, A. S., Golosinska, K., Smillie, L. B. 1983. Induction of nonpolymerizable tropomyosin binding to F-actin by troponin and its components. *J. Biol. Chem.* 258:14330–34
47. Mandel, J. L. 1989. Dystrophin—The gene and its product. *Nature* 339:584–86
48. Manstein, D. J., Titus, M. A., De Lozanne, A., Spudich, J. A. 1989. Gene replacement in *Dictyostelium:* generation of myosin null mutants. *EMBO J.* 8:923–32
49. Matsudaira, P., Janmey, P. 1988. Pieces in the actin-severing protein puzzle. *Cell* 54:139–40
50. McLachlan, A. D., Stewart, M. 1976. The 14-fold periodicity in α-tropomyosin and the interaction with actin. *J. Mol. Biol.* 103:271–98
51. Moerman, D. G., Benian, G. M., Barstead, R. J., Schriefer, L. A., Waterston, R. H. 1988. Identification and intracellular localization of the *unc-22* gene product of *Caenorhabditis elegans. Genes Dev.* 2:93–105
52. Noegel, A. A., Leiting, B., Witke, W., Gurniak, C., Harloff, C., et al. 1989. Biological roles of actin-binding proteins in *Dictyostelium discoideum* examined using genetic techniques. *Cell Motil. Cytoskel.* 14:69–74
53. Novick, P., Botstein, D. 1985. Phenotypic analysis of temperature-sensitive yeast actin mutants. *Cell* 40:405–16
54. Novick, P., Osmond, B. C., Botstein, D. 1989. Suppressors of yeast actin mutations. *Genetics* 121:659–74
55. O'Donnell, P. T., Bernstein, S. I. 1988. Molecular and ultrastructural defects in a *Drosophila* myosin heavy chain mutant: differential effects on muscle function produced by similar thick filament abnormalities. *J. Cell Biol.* 107:2601–12

56. O'Halloran, T. J., Ravid, S., Spudich, J. A. 1990. Expression of *Dictyostelium* myosin tail segments in *Escherichia coli:* Domains required for assembly and phosphorylation. *J. Cell. Biol.* 110:63–70
57. Okamoto, H., Hiromi, Y., Ishikawa, E., Yamada, T., Isoda, K., et al. 1986. Molecular characterization of mutant actin genes which induce heat-shock proteins in *Drosophila* flight muscles. *EMBO J.* 5:589–96
58. Pasternak, C., Spudich, J. A., Elson, E. L. 1989. Capping of surface receptors and concomitant cortical tension are generated by conventional myosin. *Nature* 341:549–51
59. Persechini, A., Blumenthal, D. K., Jarrett, H. W., Klee, C. B., Hardy, D. O., Kretsinger, R. H. 1989. The effects of deletions in the central helix of calmodulin on enzyme activation and peptide binding. *J. Biol. Chem.* 264:8052–58
60. Putkey, J. A., Ono, T., VanBerkum, M. F. A., Means, A. R. 1988. Functional significance of the central helix in calmodulin. *J. Biol. Chem.* 263:11242–49
61. Putkey, J. A., Sweeney, H. L., Campbell, S. T. 1989. Site-directed mutation of the trigger calcium-binding sites in cardiac troponin C. *J. Biol. Chem.* 264:12370–78
62. Reedy, M. C., Beall, C., Fyrberg, E. 1989. Formation of reverse rigor chevrons by myosin heads. *Nature* 339:481–83
63. Reinach, F. C., Karlsson, R. 1988. Cloning, expression, and site-directed mutagenesis of chicken skeletal muscle troponin C. *J. Biol. Chem.* 263:2371–76
64. Rozek, C. E., Davidson, N. 1986. Differential processing of RNA transcribed from the single-copy *Drosophila* myosin heavy chain gene produces four mRNAs that encode two polypeptides. *Proc. Natl. Acad. Sci. USA* 83:2128–32
64a. Rubenstein, P. A. 1990. The functional importance of multiple actin isoforms. *BioEssays* 12:309–15
65. Rubenstein, P. A., Solomon, L. R., Solomon, T., Gay, L. 1989. Actin structure-function relationships in vitro using oligodeoxynucleotide-directed site-specific mutagenesis. *Cell Motil. Cytoskel.* 14:35–39
66. Schleicher, M., Eichinger, L., Witke, W., Noegel, A. A. 1990. Ca^{2+}-binding proteins as components of the cytoskeleton. *Adv. Exp. Med. Biol.* 269:99–102
67. Schleicher, M., Noegel, A., Schwarz, T., Wallraff, E., Brink, M., et al. 1988. A *Dictyostelium* mutant with severe defects in α-actinin: its characterization using cDNA probes and monoclonal antibodies. *J. Cell Sci.* 90:59–71
68. Segall, J. E., Gerisch, G. 1989. Genetic approaches to cytoskeleton function and the control of cell motility. *Curr. Opin. Cell Biol.* 1:44–50
69. Tansey, T., Mikus, M. D., Dumoulin, M., Storti, R. V. 1987. Transformation and rescue of a flightless *Drosophila* tropomyosin mutant. *EMBO J.* 6:1375–85
70. Titus, M. A., Warrick, H. M., Spudich, J. A. 1989. Multiple actin-based motor genes in *Dictyostelium*. *Cell Regul.* 1:55–63
70a. Walsh, T. P., Trueblood, C. E., Evans, R., Weber, A. 1984. Removal of tropomyosin overlap and the co-operative response to increasing calcium concentrations of the acto-subfragment-1 ATPase. *J. Mol. Biol.* 182:265–69
71. Waterston, R. H. 1989. The minor myosin heavy chain, mhcA, of *Caenorhabditis elegans* is necessary for the initiation of thick filament assembly. *EMBO J.* 8:3429–36
72. Watts, F. Z., Shiels, G., Orr, E. 1987. The yeast *MYO1* gene encoding a myosin-like protein required for cell division. *EMBO J.* 6:3499–3505
73. Way, M., Gooch, J., Pope, B., Weeds, A. G. 1989. Expression of human plasma gelsolin in *Escherichia coli* and dissection of actin binding sites by segmental deletion mutagenesis. *J. Cell Biol.* 109:593–605
74. Wessels, D., Soll, D. R., Knecht, D., Loomis, W. F., De Lozanne, A., Spudich, J. 1988. Cell motility and chemotaxis in *Dictyostelium* amoebae lacking mysoin heavy chain. *Dev. Biol.* 128: 164–77
75. Witke, W., Nellen W., Noegel, A. 1987. Homologous recombination in the *Dictyostelium* α-actinin gene leads to an altered mRNA and lack of the protein. *EMBO J.* 6:4143–48
76. Witke, W., Noegel, A. A. 1990. A single base exchange in an intron of the *Dictyostelium discoideum* α-actinin gene inhibits correct splicing of the RNA but allows transport to the cytoplasm and translation. *J. Biol. Chem.* 265:34–39
77. Xu, G.-Q., Hitchcock-DeGregori, S. E. 1988. Synthesis of a troponin C cDNA and expression of wild-type and mutant proteins in *Escherichia coli*. *J. Biol. Chem.* 263:13962–69
78. Zot, A. S., Potter, J. D. 1987. Structural aspects of troponin-tropomyosin regulation of skeletal muscle contraction. *Annu. Rev. Biophys. Biophys. Chem.* 16:535–59

Annu. Rev. Physiol. 1991. 53:629–52

FUNCTIONS OF MICROTUBULE-BASED MOTORS

Trina A. Schroer[1]

Michael P. Sheetz[2]

Department of Cell Biology and Physiology, Washington University Medical School, St. Louis, Missouri 63110

KEY WORDS: kinesin, cytoplasmic dynein, vesicle transport, motility

---

INTRODUCTION

Energy-dependent transport of macromolecules along microtubules is the basis for a variety of intracellular processes including vesicle transport, mitosis, and the motility of cilia and flagella. This review focuses primarily on microtubule-based transport of membrane vesicles. It is becoming apparent that microtubule-based transport is important in the pathways of membrane biogenesis and recycling, and in some cases specific roles for the microtubule-dependent mechano-enzymes, kinesin and cytoplasmic dynein, have been proposed. In this article we review recent work in the field and summarize what is known about the role of microtubule-based motility in vesicle transport.

MICROTUBULE-BASED TRANSPORT

Functions

A fundamental teleological question is why a cell would utilize energy (ATP) to deliver materials to their intracellular destinations rather than relying on

[1]Department of Biology, The Johns Hopkins University, Baltimore, Maryland 21218

[2]Department of Cell Biology, Duke University Medical Center, Durham, North Carolina 27710

0066–4278/91/0315–0629$02.00

diffusion. When we consider the movement of chromosomes that occurs in mitosis, the answer seems clear. Chromosomes are large objects (1–20 μm long) that would be expected to have a low diffusion coefficient in cytoplasm ($D = 10^{-10}$-10^{-12} cm^2/sec). During cell division, daughter chromosomes are separated from one another and a complete set of chromosomes is delivered to each daughter cell. The microtubules of the mitotic spindle provide the structural support for this process and are absolutely required for chromosome alignment, segregation, and subsequent delivery to the two daughter cells, all steps that require ATP hydrolysis. Thus mitosis requires that chromosomes be moved in an energy-dependent, directed process. This is the essential role played by all varieties of microtubule-based intracellular transport.

The transport of membrane vesicles within neuronal axons and dendrites requires energy for the simple reason that diffusion does not allow rapid transport over long distances (i.e. hundreds of mm). Moreover, neuronal viability requires the highly directional anterograde transport of material to the synapse, as well as the retrograde transport of material to the cell body. In smaller, less highly elongated cells, the functions served by microtubule-based vesicle transport are less well understood. Most intracellular vesicles need only travel short distances (< 20 μm) at rates (10 μm in five min) that could result from diffusion through an aqueous medium. Cytoplasm is a viscoelastic liquid, however, that does not allow free diffusion of large molecules ($>$ 20–40 nm in diameter). The intracellular cytoskeleton allows diffusion at rates inversely proportional to particle size (71). These studies predict that a vesicle larger than 50 nm in diameter (M_r 1×10^8) would diffuse at an extremely slow rate and might not even have access to certain regions of the cytoplasm. An active transport mechanism would greatly facilitate the movement of these vesicles through the cytoplasm. We will discuss the possible functions for microtubule-based motility in intracellular membrane traffic. For example, the behavior of early endocytic and late exocytic vesicles is not affected if cells are treated with microtubule inhibitors (see below). In contrast, microtubules seem to facilitate membrane export (1, 29; G. van Meer, K. Simons, personal communication), perhaps by directing membrane vesicles to their destinations (95). Likewise, microtubules may facilitate membrane traffic through the endocytic pathway. The positioning of the Golgi apparatus and lysosomes within cells also depends on an intact microtubule cytoskeleton (19, 45, 75). What is less clear is the extent to which these processes continue in the absence of microtubules and whether there are membrane transport processes that absolutely depend on microtubules.

In summary, the functions of energy-dependent transport are (*a*) to provide the force to move large intracellular components, (*b*) to deliver and concentrate these components at specific locations, and (*c*) to transport these

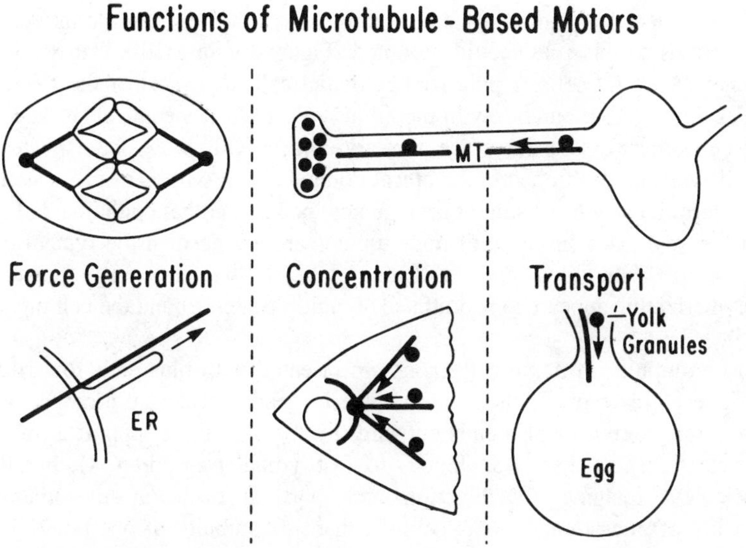

Figure 1 This diagram illustrates the three major functions of the microtubule-based motility in cells: force generation, concentration, and transport. Examples of force generation are the separation of chromosomes during mitosis and the extension of the endoplasmic reticulum (ER) network. Membranes become concentrated in the synapse by microtubule-based transport from the cell body through the axon over long distances. Similarly, the Golgi apparatus remains concentrated in the centrosomal region by transport along microtubules that have their minus ends anchored at the MTOC (45). In the insect ovariole, yolk granules are transported along microtubules to the egg (110).

components faster and over longer distances than allowed by diffusion (Figure 1).

Microtubule Organization

A microtubule is a head-to-tail polymer of asymmetric subunits, hence each microtubule filament has an intrinsic polarity. The two ends of the filament are termed the plus and minus ends based on relative rates of tubulin polymerization (the plus end supports rapid polymerization, whereas the minus end polymerizes at a slower rate). This polarity also directs the mechanochemical motors that have specific polarity preferences (either plus end or minus end directed; see below). The arrangement of microtubules within a cell will therefore determine the direction of motor-based transport. Microtubule polymerization is nucleated at intracellular sites aptly named microtubule organizing centers (MTOCs); most cells contain a single MTOC, which provides a unique site for polymerization. Microtubules polymerize from the MTOC with their plus ends distal; in fibroblasts, for example, microtubules radiate from a site near the nucleus toward the periphery. The MTOC is usually coincident with the centrosome; however, some interesting exceptions to this rule should be noted (Figure 2). In Madin-Darby canine kidney (MDCK) cells, a polarized epithelial cell line, most of the microtubules are found in bundles with the minus ends nearest the apical surface and plus ends near the basal surface; therefore the MTOCs would be expected to be diffuse and positioned in the apical domain (9). It will be of great interest to determine whether a similar arrangement occurs in other epithelial cells. In cardiac myocytes (in culture) microtubules are arranged in the typical configuration with plus ends radiating toward the periphery; however, polymerization appears to be initiated at multiple sites around the cell nucleus (65).

Microtubules in nerve cell axons are oriented with plus ends toward the periphery. In contrast, the microtubules in dendrites can be arranged with either minus ends or plus ends outward (8, 20). Dendrites support a form of vesicle transport that is analogous to fast axonal transport (34), but it is difficult to imagine how directional transport can occur on an antiparallel mixture of microtubules. It is possible that microtubules of one polarity are somehow modified so that they are not recognized by the microtubule motors (108). This modification might be mediated by a microtubule-binding protein that inhibits motility, for example, by microtubule-associated protein 2 (MAP 2) (89).

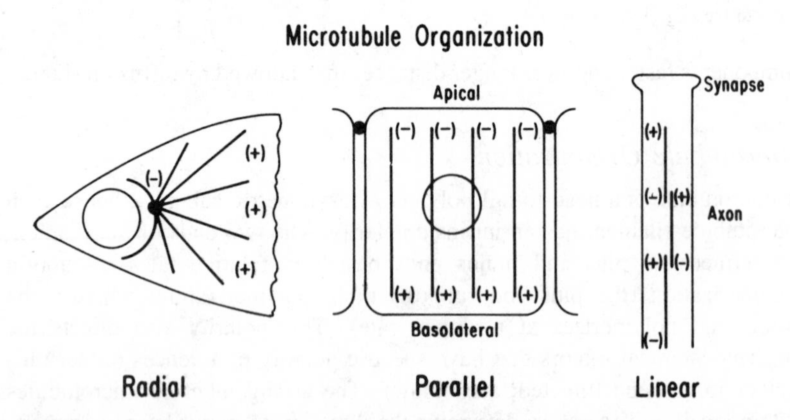

Figure 2 Three basic types of microtubule organization are illustrated in this diagram. In fibroblasts, the microtubules are typically arrayed radially from a single MTOC, which colocalizes with the centrosome. In epithelial cells (specifically in MDCK) there are multiple MTOCs in the apical region of the cell that produce a parallel array of microtubules stretching from the apical to the basolateral surface (9). A third pattern is found in the axon where microtubules are aligned in an overlapping linear array with a single polarity (21).

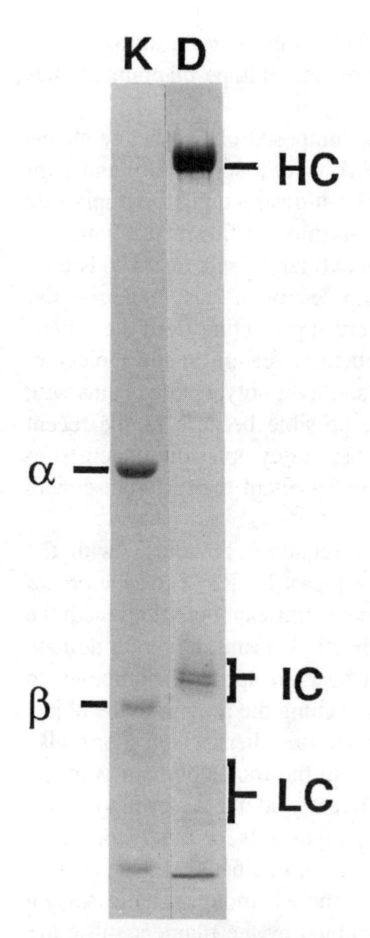

Figure 3 This polyacrylamide gel shows the polypeptide compositions of the two purified motors, kinesin (K) and cytoplasmic dynein (D). The kinesin alpha subunit is 116 kd and the beta subunit is about 60 kd. For cytoplasmic dynein the subunit molecular weights are 440 (HC), 70 (IC), and 50 (LC) kd.

Microtubule-Based Motors

The microtubule-based mechano-enzymes (motors), kinesin and cytoplasmic dynein, are discussed at length elsewhere (80, 120, 121). Both are ubiquitous and are present in high concentrations intracellularly. The motors are microtubule-activated ATPases that can drive the gliding movements of microtubules on glass coverslips; kinesin causing movement toward the plus ends of microtubules, and cytoplasmic dynein causing movement toward the minus ends of microtubules. Kinesin is a heterotetramer, $M_r \approx 350{,}000$, composed of two α chains ($M_r \approx 116{,}000$) and two β chains ($M_r \approx 62{,}000$; Figure 3). The amino acid sequence of the α chain has been determined (63, 133). This polypeptide appears to contain three structural domains; an N-terminal head, which contains the microtubule- and ATP-binding sites (this has been termed the motor domain; 121); a filamentous rod domain; and a tail domain that is believed to be the site for the binding to membrane vesicles or other structures. The predicted structure corresponds well to the kinesin ultrastructure defined by rotary shadow electron microscopy and epitope mapping studies (6, 43, 44, 102).

Cytoplasmic dynein ($M_r \approx$ 1,200,000) is composed of two heavy chains ($M_r \approx$ 440,000) and multiple intermediate ($M_r \approx$ 68,000–72,000) and light chains ($M_r \approx$ 50,000–55,000; Figure 3). The ultrastructure of cytoplasmic dynein is well characterized; the molecule resembles a flower pot with two blooms (111, 124). Cytoplasmic dynein has two large, spherical heads connected to a compact base; the base is composed of at least four globular subdomains. Filaments are occasionally observed projecting from the spherical heads, but they are not a consistent structural feature of the molecule. Studies correlating the heavy, intermediate, and light polypeptide chains with specific structural domains should soon be possible because of the recent development of monoclonal antibodies against the cytoplasmic dynein subunits (112). Determination of the primary sequences of the different dynein subunits is no doubt forthcoming.

A family of proteins that share primary sequence homology with the kinesin α chain has recently been discovered [yeast KAR3 (81); *Drosophila ncd* (30, 79)]. These kinesin-like proteins have significant homology with the kinesin motor domain, but in contrast to authentic kinesin, the motor domain is found at the C-terminus. The N-termini bear no apparent homology to kinesin and are presumed to be involved in attaching the protein to the object it moves (vesicle, chromosome, microtubule, or other). *Aspergillus* also contains a kinesin-like protein, but in this case the motor domain is at the N-terminus and the protein diverges significantly at the C-terminus. The kinesin-like proteins are reminiscent of the myosin Is, a family of actin-binding motors that are encoded by at least five distinct genes in *Dictyostelium* (117). The actin- and microtubule-based motors share several features; the direction of movement is determined by the filament substrate, and both classes of motors have similar ATPase cycles (39, 54). What distinguishes the motors from one another are the filament substrates, the direction of movement, the objects moved by each, and the mechanisms for regulation of movement.

The Organelle Motor Complex

Kinesin and cytoplasmic dynein by themselves can convert the energy derived from ATP hydrolysis into movement, as evidenced by the fact that they cause microtubule gliding. One might expect that the enzymes would be competent to drive organelle motility as well. It is now apparent that kinesin and dynein alone cannot drive the movement of membrane vesicles and that other soluble proteins play a key role (104, 105). It is also clear that membrane proteins are required (103, 123). It has been proposed that the motors interact with the organelle surface as part of a larger protein complex that has been called the organelle motor complex. This includes the motor, a membrane-associated motor receptor, and the other soluble components required for motility (108). We have identified two distinct soluble accessory factors that stimulate vesicle movement (T. Schroer, M. Sheetz, manuscript in preparation), and a potential candidate for the membrane protein that binds kinesin (the kinesin receptor) has been found in brain microsomes (I. Toyoshima, M. Sheetz, manuscript in preparation). Further work is required to define how the components of the organelle motor complex interact to regulate vesicle transport.

EXPERIMENTAL APPROACHES

Pharmacological Studies

Pharmacological agents that affect microtubule polymerization are commonly used to determine the role(s) played by microtubules in different intracellular processes. These studies utilize the microtubule-depolymerizing drugs, colchicine, colcemide, and nocodazole, or the microtubule-polymerizing drug, taxol. As is often the case with pharmacological studies, the results of these experiments must be interpreted with caution. Non-specific effects of the drugs on processes that do not involve microtubules are common and must be determined before strong conclusions can be drawn. For example, a microtubule poison may bind to and inhibit a non-microtubule protein; this has occurred in the case of colchicine (60). Fortunately, lumicolchicine (a photoinactivated form of colchicine) can be used to determine colchicine's nonspecific effects. It is useful to determine whether a process is inhibited by more than one anti-microtubule drug. Recent studies have found inhibitory effects whose magnitudes correlate well with the ability of each drug to induce microtubule depolymerization (87). Microtubule-depolymerizing agents act by binding to depolymerized tubulin and blocking its assembly into tubulin polymer, consequently, only microtubules that are dynamic (i.e. those undergoing continual polymerization and depolymerization) are affected; stabilized microtubules are not induced to depolymerize. Microtubule poisons commonly leave intact a subset of cytoplasmic microtubules that may be competent to support vesicle transport. A final complication to the pharmacological approach arises because microtubules contribute significantly to cytoplasmic viscosity which, as described above, profoundly affects the rate of intracellular diffusion. Despite these caveats, pharmacological studies have contributed significantly to our understanding of the role played by microtubules in intracellular motility.

In general, most agents that inhibit kinesin (i.e. NEM, AMP-PNP, and vanadate) inhibit cytoplasmic dynein and vice versa; moreover these agents affect a myriad of other cellular proteins and functions. One pharmacological treatment exists that is selective for dyneins, vanadate-mediated ultraviolet cleavage (32, 72, 90, 92). UV-photocleavage of dynein selectively inhibits minus-end directed vesicle movement in vitro (100, 105). This treatment has not been used in studies of motility in vivo because vanadate does not readily permeate intact cell membranes.

Genetics

The combined use of classical and modern molecular genetic techniques makes the genetic approach a particularly powerful means for studying protein function in vivo. Genetic analyses of kinesin and cytoplasmic dynein function are currently being performed in several organisms including the budding yeast (*Saccharomyces cerevesiae*), *Aspergillus, Dictyostelium, Drosophila,* and *C. elegans*. A common approach is to clone and sequence a motor gene, then use the deduced protein sequence to design and create mutations in the gene of interest. The mutant gene is then reintroduced into the organism, and the phenotype is determined. For example, if the gene encoding the heavy chain of kinesin is deleted from *Drosophila,* the resulting flies do not survive to adulthood; the phenotype of early embryos and larvae suggests defects in nerve cell function (98). This finding is consistent with the hypothesis that kinesin plays an essential role in fast axonal transport. Kinesin and cytoplasmic dynein were recently isolated from *Dictyostelium* (61, 78), an organism that has been used extensively in analogous genetic studies of myosin function (116). Once the genes for the *Dictyostelium* microtubule motors are cloned, it will be possible to perform gene disruption experiments to determine the roles they play in vesicle motility, mitosis, and other microtubule-based motile behaviors. This line of investigation is likely to yield a wealth of information in the near future.

Another type of genetic analysis of motor function relies heavily on serendipity. The starting point is a previously described mutation. When the mutant gene is cloned and sequenced, it is discovered to have primary sequence homology with a motor. This approach was the basis for the discovery of the aforementioned kinesin-like proteins *ncd* in *Drosophila,* KAR3 in yeast, and *bimC* in *Aspergillus*. Mutations in the *Drosophila ncd* gene result in defective meioses and early embryonic mitoses (30, 79). KAR3 mutants (81) demonstrate incomplete karyogamy, the process by which parent haploid nuclei migrate toward each other and fuse to form a diploid nucleus. *Aspergillus bimC* mutants cannot complete mitosis (31).

In summary, genetic studies suggest that kinesin and its homologues drive a variety of intracellular transport events. It is highly likely that cytoplasmic dynein-like proteins exist to fulfill a complementary set of transport functions. Discovery of dynein homologues will have to wait until the primary sequence of the motor domain of cytoplasmic dynein is known.

In Vitro Assays

VESICLE TRANSPORT The development of an in vitro assay for microtubule-based transport was a major breakthrough that led to the discovery and characterization of the motor activities of kinesin and cytoplasmic dynein. The movement of vesicles on microtubules has also been reconstituted from isolated components, thus making it possible to define the soluble factors required for transport. As described above, kinesin and cytoplasmic dynein provide the force for plus-end and minus-end vesicle transport, but both require additional accessory factors to move vesicles (104, 105). Multiple soluble factors that activate motor-driven vesicle transport have been identified (T. Schroer, M. Sheetz, manuscript in preparation). The reconstituted assay for vesicle transport should facilitate the identification and purification of membrane receptors for kinesin and cytoplasmic dynein and will be useful in future studies of the regulation of vesicle motility.

MITOSIS It has not been possible to reconstitute the entire process of mitosis in vitro because of the complexity of the mitotic apparatus. The presently available in vitro systems mimic individual mitotic phases. Mitchison & Kirschner (82) bound isolated chromosomes to centrosome microtubules; under certain experimental conditions the chromosomes moved toward plus and minus ends of microtubules in a manner reminiscent of prometaphase (52). A similar assay reconstituted the movement of chromosomes toward the centrosome (analogous to poleward movement in anaphase A; 62). Others have isolated metaphase-arrested mitotic spindles from diatoms and fission yeast (*Schizosaccharomyces pombe*); the spindles can be reactivated in vitro to enter into and complete anaphase (74). Further effort should lead to the identification of components of the chromosome and the spindle microtubules that contribute to mitotic motility.

Antibody Inhibition Studies

Antibody probes are commonly used as a means for determining the function of a protein. The antibody is introduced into the experimental system, then various experimental parameters are measured to determine if the antibody has an effect on the process of interest. This approach was used to determine the effects of anti-motor antibodies on vesicle transport in squid axoplasm. Antibodies against either dynein or kinesin inhibited motility in both the anterograde and retrograde directions [anti-dynein antibody (33); anti-kinesin antibody (17)]. These studies must be interpreted with caution because intact antibody molecules (not Fab fragments) were used at high concentrations. The antibodies may have cross-linked vesicles and microtubules to produce a physical block to movement.

MICROTUBULE-BASED VESICLE TRANSPORT

General Features

Early light microscopic observations of living cells revealed that cytoplasm contains a significant number of moving particles; however, these studies were limited by the fact that only particles larger than 200 nm in diameter were visible (reviewed in 93). This population of large membrane-bound organelles includes mitochondria, lysosomes, and secretory granules, but not the smaller vesicles that mediate anterograde axonal transport and many other membrane traffic events. The technique of video-enhanced light microscopy (3, 53, 99) made it possible to study the movements of extremely small vesicles (50–80 nm) and allowed fast axonal transport in the anterograde direction to be observed for the first time (4, 16). In recent years the video microscope has been turned on a wide variety of cells to demonstrate that, in general, cytoplasm is teeming with moving particles (vesicles). In the majority of cells vesicle motility is microtubule-based; vesicles move along linear paths that suggest microtubules and motility can be blocked by microtubule depolymerization. Moving vesicles display a spectrum of behaviors. Some undergo bidirectional saltatory movements, while others move unidirectionally over great distances (> 10 μm). In extremely flat regions of cells it is possible to observe vesicle movements on single microtubules (119) and the motility of a tubulovesicular membrane system (S. Dabora, M. Sheetz, unpublished) that behaves like the endoplasmic reticulum (ER) (67). Differential interference contrast microscopy does not indicate the identities of membranes, but certain intracellular membranes can be specifically labeled with fluorescent probes. The ER can be stained with $DiOC_6$ (3) (115), Golgi membranes become labeled with NBD-ceramide (70), mitochondria stain with rhodamine 123 (55), and lysosomes and other low pH compartments accumulate acridine orange (10). It is also possible to tag intracellular membranes with fluorescently labeled antibodies introduced by microinjection (7). These studies have revealed that the ER, Golgi membranes, secretory granules, and endocytic vesicles undergo extensive transport (23, 28, 45, 64). Additional probes that are specific for different intracellular compartments will be useful in future studies of vesicle motility.

Fast Axonal Transport

Fast axonal transport is the archetype of microtubule-based vesicle transport (5, 101), and much of our understanding of its molecular basis has come from axonal systems (57, 108). Nerve cell axons are highly elongated processes that must support the transport of membranous organelles at rates and over distances far greater than can occur by diffusion. Fast transport is unequivocally an energy-dependent (2), microtubule-based process (5, 101).

Since axonal microtubules are uniformly aligned with their plus ends distal to the cell body, anterograde fast transport would be expected to be driven by kinesin and retrograde fast transport by cytoplasmic dynein. This has been demonstrated by reconstituted studies of axonal transport in squid axoplasm (100, 104).

Although the motors for fast transport are now identified, a number of questions regarding the mechanism of fast transport remain unanswered. Some progress has been made toward identifying the accessory factors required by kinesin and dynein (T. Schroer, M. Sheetz, manuscript in preparation), but it is not known how the factors regulate motor activity. A significant problem arises from the fact that protein synthesis occurs only in the nerve cell body (soma) so all proteins required at the synapse must be delivered there by anterograde transport. Specifically, how does cytoplasmic dynein reach the synapse? It has been proposed that dynein is transported on vesicles, presumably in association with its normal receptor (108). After arrival at the synapse, the anterogradely transported membrane returns to the cell body in the form of a retrograde transport vesicle. The switch from anterograde to retrograde must occur at the synapse.

The problem of directionality switching is not limited to neurons. As a bit of membrane moves through the biosynthetic and recycling compartments, it is subject to both plus-end and minus-end directed motility. An example of this is the behavior of the poly-Ig receptor (pIgR) in polarized epithelia. The pIgR is synthesized and processed in the ER and Golgi apparatus and is then delivered to the basolateral plasma membrane. After binding ligand (poly-Ig) at the cell surface, the receptor is endocytosed and transported across the cell to the apical surface. This process is known as transcytosis (66, 84), and it has been demonstrated to rely on intact microtubules (see below). During the course of its life cycle, the pIgR first appears in vesicles that move by diffusion and later in vesicles that are competent to be transported on microtubules. Clearly the cell must be able to distinguish naked pIgR from ligand-bound pIgR to transport the receptor appropriately. A completely novel mechanism for directionality control was recently postulated by Heuser (42), who observed that the direction of movement of endosomes would change in response to changes in cytoplasmic pH. A more complete understanding of the organelle motor complex is needed before the molecular events that control vesicle directionality can be defined.

It is also unclear why the microtubule-based motors should be present in such high concentration in axons. Both kinesin and cytoplasmic dynein are abundant soluble proteins (46, 112), yet only one or a few motor molecules per vesicle are required to drive transport (48). This translates into a 1,000–5,000-fold excess of motors over vesicles in the axoplasm (104). Motor activity must be tightly regulated, most likely by the components of the organelle motor complex. It is possible that the interaction of motors with their membrane receptors is highly dynamic (105). This might explain the variable amounts of vesicle staining observed in kinesin immunolocalization studies (46, 85, 91). No matter how dynamic the kinesin-vesicle interaction, kinesin is transported rapidly in axons, which suggests that it is associated with membranes (83).

A newly synthesized vesicle in a neuron can be transported through the axon or the dendrites. Since different proteins are targeted in the two directions, a sorting mechanism must exist to ensure that materials reach the proper destination. The microtubules within dendrites are arranged with $\approx$ 50% plus end distal and $\approx$ 50% minus end distal, which may influence motility (8, 20). Vesicle transport may also be affected by MAPs that have different distributions in axons and dendrites (reviewed in 77). Because the direction of transport is determined by the polarity of microtubules, and because moving vesicles can switch between adjacent microtubules, it is difficult to imagine a mechanism for unidirectional vesicle transport on a mixed microtubule substrate. One subset of microtubules might be coated with a MAP to activate or inhibit vesicle motility; this would create a microtubule array that was effectively unidirectional. Vesicle transport in dendrites raises several important questions that can only be answered by further study.

Tubular Membrane Systems

Certain intracellular membranes adopt an extended tubular conformation. These include the ER (67, 68, 114), the ER-Golgi intermediate compartment (69), the *trans*-Golgi network (TGN) (35), endosomes (42, 73) and, in some cases, lysosomes (113). In some cases, the distribution of membrane correlates with the distribution of microtubules. Our understanding of the mechanisms that drive tubule extension, motility, and fusion is based largely on in vitro studies. Large membrane aggregates were observed to spread out into interconnected networks in an ATP-, motor- and microtubule-dependent manner (24; V. Mermall et al, manuscript in preparation). Initially, small membrane buds emerged from the aggregates and became elongated as they were pulled along microtubules. Intersecting tubules fused and branched into polygonal shapes. The motility process has been called microtubule-dependent tethering to emphasize its similarity to the biophysically characterized process of tether formation (129). Similar membrane tubules are also formed as a result of the movement of microtubules along the substratum (122), by the movement of a myosin-like motor on actin filaments (56), or simply by focal application of force to a membrane bilayer (128). The behavior of membrane networks in vitro bears a striking resemblance to behavior of the ER in live cells where motility occurs on stationary microtubules (67, 68).

The dynamic morphology of the ER is dependent on the microtubule-based motors (V. Mermall et al, manuscript in preparation). In contrast, other tubular membranes (such as lysosomes) may be formed from the fusion of small vesicles. Microinjection of inhibitory anti-kinesin antibodies causes tubular lysosomes to collapse into the cell center, which suggests that kinesin is involved in tubule extension (47). Similar studies should elucidate the role of microtubule-based motility in the function and motility of other membrane tubule systems.

MEMBRANE TRAFFIC AND MICROTUBULES

Pathways of Membrane Traffic

Membrane vesicles mediate the transport of proteins and lipids between the biochemically distinct compartments that comprise the pathways of membrane biogenesis and recycling. Several steps have been proposed to involve microtubule-based motility. Although microtubules are clearly required for vesicle transport over long distances (i.e. in neurons) the small size of most cells (10–50 μm diameter) makes the need for a microtubule-dependent transport mechanism less obvious. Still, cytoplasmic vesicles may be immobilized by their interactions with the cytoskeleton or other membranes so that microtubule-based transport is required for movement. Alternatively, kinesin and cytoplasmic dynein may facilitate vesicle movements that would otherwise occur by diffusion, albeit at a reduced rate. In the first case, inhibition of microtubule-based transport should block the process altogether. In the second case, inhibition of transport would be expected to reduce the rate of membrane traffic, but not its overall extent. In order to distinguish between these possibilities, it is necessary to assay the process both immediately after inhibition and at much later times. Most studies evaluating the role of microtubules in membrane traffic utilize microtubule inhibitors; not surprisingly the findings are controversial, and conflicting results are often obtained. Better, more specific, inhibitors are needed, but despite the problems associated with working with microtubule poisons, a consensus picture is slowly emerging.

It is generally agreed that endocytosis (membrane invagination and vesicle budding) and exocytosis (the fusion of vesicles with the plasma membrane), the first and last events in membrane recycling and biogenesis, continue normally in the presence of microtubule poisons. Transport of materials between the *cis,* medial, and *trans* compartments of the Golgi apparatus is also microtubule-independent (95). Similarly, transfer of material between early endosomal vesicles (before reaching the common sorting compartment where these materials diverge) does not require microtubules (26, 36). None of these events involves vesicle movements farther than a few microns.

Microtubule-based transport seems to play at least one major role in the secretory and endocytic pathways common to all cells (reviewed in 58). The events that are consistently inhibited by microtubule depolymerization are (*a*) the recycling of membrane from the *cis*-Golgi region to the ER, and (*b*) the movement of vesicles between early and late endosomes (see below). Translocation of material from the basolateral to the apical surface of polarized epithelia (transcytosis) also appears to depend upon microtubule-based transport. As we will discuss below, treatment of most cells with anti-microtubule agents does not significantly inhibit movement of membrane and secretory proteins from the site of synthesis (the ER) to the plasma membrane.

Early Events in Membrane Biogenesis: ER Through Golgi

Our understanding of the mechanism of synthesis and export of membrane and secreted proteins ever increases, yet it remains a mystery how the process occurs efficiently, considering the complex three-dimensional structures of the organelles involved. The ER and Golgi apparatus are highly structured organelles whose unique morphologies depend on intact cytoplasmic microtubules (19, 45, 114) (see Figure 4). In cells in culture, the ER is a highly extended network of membrane tubules that undergoes continuous microtubule-based rearrangements (67, 68). The amount of membrane traffic from the ER to the Golgi apparatus is so great that the entire fluid volume of the ER can be transferred to the Golgi in less than 15 min (130). Obviously the ER would become rapidly depleted of membrane without a highly efficient recycling system. A recycling mechanism has been proposed to mediate the retention of proteins that are normally resident in the ER (127; reviewed in 59). Recycled membrane passes through a compartment lying between the ER and *cis*-Golgi (the "salvage" compartment) that is enriched in two markers, a 53-kd protein (106) and the receptor for the peptide signal (KDEL) that governs protein retention in the ER (125). Under certain conditions the salvage compartment accumulates and can be observed to extend tubular processes (125) in a microtubule-dependent manner (69) (Figure 4). This suggests that membrane recycling from the transition compartment to the ER is mediated by microtubule-based motility.

Since the Golgi apparatus and transition compartment lie in the center of the cell and the ER is highly spread, movement toward the ER is expected to be driven by kinesin, the plus-end motor. Membranes of the *trans*-Golgi network have also been observed to extend tubular processes that undergo microtubule-based movements (23), thus indicating that these membranes are also competent to move on microtubules. Depolymerization of microtubules, either pharmacologically or during mitosis, causes the Golgi apparatus to vesiculate and disperse (19). When the microtubules are allowed to repolymerize, Golgi vesicles are observed to move in a saltatory fashion toward the MTOC, i.e. toward the minus ends of microtubules. The motility

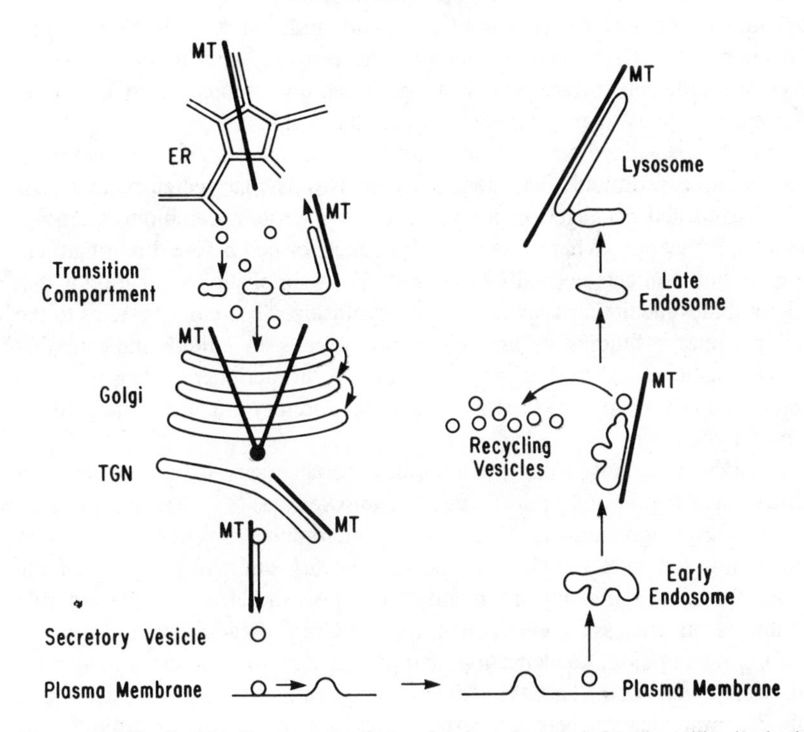

Figure 4 This diagram illustrates the basic roles for microtubule-based motility in the intracellular traffic of membranes. The ER network is formed by the movement of membrane strands on microtubules (68), and recycling of membranes from the transition compartment back to the ER is also microtubule-dependent (69). Golgi assembly at the microtubule organizing center (MTOC) appears to depend on cytoplasmic dynein (45), and elements of the *trans*-Golgi network move along microtubules (23). In some cases, secretory vesicle movements may depend upon microtubules (118). In the endocytic pathway the transition from the early to late endosome is microtubule-dependent (36) and, in some cases, recycling vesicles move toward the MTOC before returning to the plasma membrane. Finally, lysosomes can align along microtubules (113).

of Golgi-derived membranes is obviously complicated and mechanisms for its control are not yet understood.

Late Events in Membrane Biogenesis: TGN to the Plasma Membrane

As described above, the process of fast axonal transport allows the export of newly synthesized membranes and their contents from the cell body toward the periphery. By analogy, membrane secretion in all cells probably relies on microtubule-based motility. In the majority of cells, treatment with microtubule depolymerizing agents does not inhibit the delivery of material to the plasma membrane. For example, the amount of a viral glycoprotein (VSV G) arriving at the surface of fibroblasts is not reduced after treatment with colchicine (95). Disruption of microtubules seems to alter the distribution of VSV G on the cell surface, which suggests that microtubules normally target secretory vesicles to particular regions of the cell.

In cells specialized for secretion, the effect of microtubule depolymerization is more profound. The general consensus is that secretory materials synthesized and packaged in the presence of microtubule inhibitors are not secreted efficiently, whereas secretory granules formed before drug treatment release their contents normally (15, 22, 131). A simplistic explanation is that microtubules mediate transport of newly synthesized secretory vesicles to the cell periphery. Studies of anterior pituitary cells in culture indicate that ACTH-containing secretory granules move to the periphery along microtubules (64, 118) (Figure 4). The movement of secretory granules is most likely driven by kinesin.

It has been proposed that microtubules are necessary for the correct and efficient packaging of secretory materials into vesicles (41). The morphology of the Golgi apparatus is disrupted by microtubule poisons, but protein processing and transport through the *cis, medial,* and *trans* regions of the Golgi are not significantly inhibited. In contrast, the effects of microtubule inhibitors on processing events in the *trans*-Golgi network such as protein sorting, aggregation, condensation, and packaging into secretory granules are not well understood. The TGN extends tubules and buds off vesicles that allow communication between different regions of the network; motility is believed to be microtubule-dependent (23) (Figure 4). Membrane dynamics may facilitate any of the processes known to occur in the TGN. Future studies should help clarify the role of microtubules in TGN function.

Delivery to Apical and Basolateral Plasma Membrane in Polarized Epithelia

Polarized epithelia have two plasma membrane domains of distinct protein and lipid compositions (see reviews 50, 109). The mechanisms for sorting of materials to the two membranes and for maintenance of their distinct compositions are currently of great interest. Membrane polarity is commonly studied in three epithelia: kidney (the model system used is the Madin-Darby canine kidney cell line, MDCK), intestine (either intestinal epithelium or the cell line Caco-2), and hepatocytes. Two different mechanisms for delivery of material to the apical membrane have been described: direct transfer from the *trans*-Golgi network to the plasma membrane, and indirect transport wherein materials are first delivered to the basal surface and are then taken up and transported to the apical domain by transcytosis (reviewed in 50). Newly synthesized materials destined for the basolateral membrane are transported exclusively by a direct pathway. A central question is the role of microtubules in delivery of membrane and secreted proteins to the apical and basolateral domains. All studies to date indicate that microtubules are not required for delivery to the basolateral surface, whereas transport to the apical domain by both direct and indirect routes seems to involve microtubule-based motility.

In MDCK cells, proteins destined to the different domains are sorted into distinct vesicles as they leave the *trans*-Golgi network; basolaterally and apically directed materials are transported directly to the appropriate plasma membrane domain (109). In MDCK cells, the role of microtubules in apical delivery remains controversial. In one model the microtubules facilitate the movement of vesicles to the apical membrane. When microtubules are depolymerized, the delivery of membrane proteins, glycolipids, and secreted proteins to the apical surface occurs at a significantly reduced rate, but is not completely inhibited (glycolipids, G. van Meer, K. Simons, personal communication; membrane proteins, 94). Some reports indicate that inhibition of apical delivery results in mistargeting to the basolateral surface (94), while other reports do not observe mistargeting (in rat kidney; 38). Recent studies by Matlin & co-workers suggest that, in the presence of colchicine, apically directed membrane proteins are degraded at an increased rate (M. van Zeijl, K. Matlin, unpublished results). Others have observed an increase in the intracellular degradation rate of glycoproteins in the presence of colchicine, which suggests that vesicles prevented from reaching the cell surface have an increased probability of being mis-sorted to the lysosomal pathway (13, 96). Since most microtubules in MDCK cells are oriented in longitudinal bundles with minus ends nearest the apical surface (see Figure 2; 9) microtubule-based transport toward the apical membrane would be expected to be driven by cytoplasmic dynein.

In other epithelia, components travel indirectly to the apical surface. Hepatocytes use the indirect route exclusively (11). Caco-2 cells have both direct and indirect pathways for transport to the apical domain (76). Microtubule inhibitors profoundly inhibit apical delivery in both systems (29, 49). The microtubule-dependent step appears to be transport from the basolateral to apical surface (transcytosis), a process that is predicted to utilize a cytoplasmic dynein-based (minus-end-directed) transport mechanism.

Endocytic Pathway

The endocytic pathway, like the secretory pathway, involves the movement of vesicular carriers between different membrane compartments; from plasma membrane to endosome to lysosome. For many years investigators have utilized the light microscope to observe the movements of vesicles loaded with endocytic tracers. The vesicles move in a saltatory manner and are ultimately translocated into the central region of the cell where lysosomes are found (25, 28, 40, 132, 134). Studies with microtubule inhibitors indicate that uptake of endocytic markers is not microtubule-dependent. However, centripetal, saltatory vesicle movements are abolished (12, 25, 40, 126), and degradation of endocytic materials is inhibited (18, 86). This work clearly indicates that endocytic vesicles move centripetally in a microtubule-dependent manner in order to deliver their contents to lysosomes. Endosome motility would therefore be directed toward the minus ends of microtubules and should occur via cytoplasmic dynein. In keeping with this prediction, isolated endosomes can be observed to move toward the minus ends of microtubules in vitro (V. Mermall et al, manuscript in preparation).

While the observational approach has allowed the motility of endosomes to be studied in great detail, cell fractionation and immunochemical studies have provided the most information on the biochemical compartments that comprise the endocytic pathway (37). It has recently become possible to correlate the microtubule-dependent events with movement of materials between biochemically defined compartments. In vitro assays that measure the intermixing and processing of endocytic markers have allowed the role of microtubules and microtubule-based motors to be tested directly. The first events in the pathway, namely endocytosis, delivery of markers from the endocytic vesicle into the early endosome, and transfer of markers between early endosomes have been clearly demonstrated to be microtubule-independent (26, 27, 37). These assays utilize a crude cell homogenate that contains late endosomes and lysosomes, yet in some cases (26, 27) the endocytic markers were not processed further, which suggested that transfer to later compartments did not occur in vitro. It was suggested that the endosomes age and are not competent to be processed further in vitro. It was also possible that the subsequent steps of movement toward and fusion with late endosomes required microtubules. The elegant study of Gruenberg & co-workers (36) has defined a microtubule-dependent step in the pathway. Endocytic materials move from the early endosome into transport vesicles that mediate delivery to late endosomes and lysosomes. Transfer of materials from the transport vesicles into the late endosome is blocked by microtubule inhibitors, thus suggesting that the process is microtubule-based.

Endocytic tracers taken up at the apical and basolateral faces of polarized epithelia are delivered to a common sorting compartment that is effectively a late endosome (14, 51, 88). An in vitro assay that measures the intermixing of material taken up from the two domains was developed in MDCK cells and was used to determine the role of microtubules and the microtubule-based motors (kinesin and cytoplasmic dynein) in this process (13a). Both in vivo and in vitro, the key microtubule-dependent step was found to be transfer of material from the early endosome to the common sorting compartment (late endosome). Removal of either kinesin or dynein led to partial inhibition of transfer. This is consistent with the hypothesis that endocytic vesicles move centripetally along the longitudinal microtubule bundles present in these cells (9). According to this model, apically-derived endocytic vesicles should be subject to kinesin-based motility and basolaterally-derived endocytic vesicles would be expected to be transported by cytoplasmic dynein.

SUMMARY

Microtubule-dependent transport is necessary for the intracellular functions of mitosis and axonal transport. In addition, a variety of microtubule-based vesicle movements occur in all cells. Recent studies indicate that the depolymerization of microtubules results in significant inhibition of the recycling of the ER membrane from the ER-Golgi transition compartment and inhibition of the maturation of endosomes. Other membrane traffic events are inhibited by microtubule depolymerization, but in most cases alternate pathways can accomplish the function in question. With a more in-depth understanding of these alternate pathways and improved tools for inhibiting motor function without affecting cytoplasmic viscosity, we should be able to determine more precisely the roles of motor-dependent vesicle transport.

ACKNOWLEDGMENTS

We would like to thank those investigators who shared their recent studies with us, and we also thank members of the Sheetz laboratory for their helpful comments.

Literature Cited

1. Achler, C., Filmer, D., Merte, C., Drenckham, D. 1989. Role of microtubules in polarized delivery of apical membrane proteins to the brush border of the intestinal epithelium. *J. Cell Biol.* 109:179–89
2. Adams, R. J. Organelle movement in axons depends on ATP. 1982. *Nature* 297:327–29
3. Allen, R. D., Allen, N. S., Travis, J. L. Video-enhanced contrast, differential interference contrast (AVEC-DIC) microscopy: a new method capable of analyzing microtubule related motility in the reticulopodial network of *Allogromia laticollans*. 1981. *Cell Motil.* 1:291–302
4. Allen, R. D., Metuzals, J., Tasaki, I., Brady, S. T., Gilbert, S. P. Fast axonal transport in squid giant axon. 1982. *Science* 218:1127–29
5. Allen, R. D., Weiss, D. G., Hayden, J. H., Brown, D. T., Fujiwake, H., Simpson, M. Gliding movement of and bidirectional transport along single native microtubules from squid axoplasm: evidence for an active role of microtubules in cytoplasmic transport. 1985. *J. Cell Biol.* 100:1736–52
6. Amos, L. A. Kinesin from pig brain studied by electron microscopy. 1987. *J. Cell Sci.* 87:105–11
7. Arnheiter, H., Dubois-Dalcq, M., Lazzarini, R. A. Direct visualization of protein transport and processing in the living cell by microinjection of specific antibodies. 1984. *Cell* 39:99–109
8. Baas, P. W., Deitch, J. S., Black, M. M., Banker, G. A. 1988. Polarity orientation of microtubules in hippocampal neurons: uniformity in the axon

and nonuniformity in the dendrite. *Proc. Natl. Acad. Sci. USA* 85:8335–39

9. Bacallao, R., Antony, C., Dotti, C., Karsenti, E., Stelzer, E. H. K., Simons, K. 1989. The subcellular organization of Madin-Darby canine kidney cells during the formation of a polarized epithelium. *J. Cell Biol.* 109:2817–32
10. Barasch, J., Gershon, M. D., Nunez, E. A., Tamir, H., Al-Awqati, Q. 1988. Thyrotropin induces the acidification of the secretory granules of parafollicular cells by increasing the chloride conductance of the granular membrane. *J. Cell Biol.* 107:2137–47
11. Bartles, J. R., Feracci, H. M., Stieger, B., Hubbard, A. L. 1987. Biogenesis of the rat hepatocyte plasma membrane *in vivo:* comparison of the pathways taken by apical and basolateral proteins using subcellular fractionation. *J. Cell Biol.* 105:1241–51
12. Bhisey, A. D., Freed, J. J. 1971. Altered movement of endosomes in colchicine-treated cultured macrophages. *Exp. Cell Res.* 64:430–38
13. Bienkowski, R. S., Cowan, M. J., McDonald, J. A., Crystal, R. G. 1978. Degradation of newly synthesized collagen. *J. Biol. Chem.* 253:4356–63

13a. Bomsel, M., Parton, R., Kuznetsov, S. A., Schroer, T. A., Gruenberg, J. 1990. Microtubule- and motor-dependent fusion in vitro between apical and basolateral endocytic vesicles from MDCK cells. *Cell* 62:719–31

14. Bomsel, M., Prydz, K., Parton, R. G., Gruenberg, J., Simons, K. 1989. Endocytosis in filter-grown Madin-Darby canine kidney cells. *J. Cell Biol.* 109: 3243–58
15. Boyd, A. E., Bolton, W. E., Brinkley, B. R. 1982. Microtubules and beta cell function: effect of colchicine on microtubules and insulin secretion in vitro by mouse beta cells. *J. Cell Biol.* 92:425–34
16. Brady, S. T., Lasek, R. J., Allen, R. D. 1982. Fast axonal transport in extruded axoplasm from squid giant axon. *Science* 218:1129–31
17. Brady, S. T., Pfister, K. K., Bloom, G. S. 1990. A monoclonal antibody to the heavy chain of kinesin inhibits both anterograde and retrograde axonal transport in squid axoplasm. *Proc. Natl. Acad. Sci. USA* 87:1061–65
18. Brown, K. D., Friedkin, M., Rozengurt, E. 1980. Colchicine inhibits epidermal growth factor degradation in 3T3 cells. *Proc. Natl. Acad. Sci. USA* 77:480–84
19. Burke, B., Griffiths, G., Reggio, H., Louvard, D., Warren, G. 1982. A monoclonal antibody against a 135-K Golgi membrane protein. *EMBO J.* 1:1621–28
20. Burton, P. R. 1988. Microtubule polarity in dendrites. *Brain Res.* 473:107–15
21. Burton, P. R., Paige, J. L. 1981. Polarity of axoplasmic microtubules in the olfactory nerve of the frog. *Proc. Natl. Acad. Sci. USA* 78:3269–73
22. Busson-Mabillot, S., Chambaut-Guerin, A.-M., Ovtracht, L., Muller, P., Rossignol, B. 1982. Microtubules and protein secretion in rat lacrimal glands: localization of short-term effects of colchicine on the secretory process. *J. Cell Biol.* 95:105–17
23. Cooper, M. S., Cornell-Bell, A. H., Chernjavsky, A., Dani, J. W., Smith, S. J. 1990. Tubulovesicular processes emerge from *trans*-Golgi cisternae, extend along microtubules, and interlink adjacent *trans*-Golgi elements into a reticulum. *Cell* 61:135–45
24. Dabora, S. L., Sheetz, M. P. 1988. The microtubule-dependent formation of a tubulovesicular network with characteristics of the ER from cultured cell extracts. *Cell* 54:27–35
25. DeBrabander, M., Nuydens, R., Geerts, H., Hopkins, C. R. 1988. Dynamic behavior of the transferrin receptor followed in living epidermoid carcinoma (A431) cells with nanovid microscopy. *Cell Motil. Cytoskel.* 9:30–47
26. Diaz, R., Mayorga, L., Mayorga, L. E., Stahl, P. 1989. In vitro clustering and multiple fusion among macrophage endosomes. *J. Biol. Chem.* 264: 13171–80
27. Diaz, R., Mayorga, L., Stahl, P. 1988. In vitro fusion of endosomes following receptor-mediated endocytosis. *J. Biol. Chem.* 263:6093–6100
28. Dunn, K. W., McGraw, T. E., Maxfield, F. R. 1989. Iterative fractionation of recycling receptors from lysosomally destined ligands in an early sorting endosome. *J. Cell Biol.* 109:3303–14
29. Eilers, U., Klumperman, J., Hauri, H.-P. 1989. Nocodazole, a microtubule-active drug, interferes with apical protein delivery in cultured intestinal epithelial cells (Caco-2). *J. Cell Biol.* 108:13–22
30. Endow, S. A., Henikoff, S., Niedziela, L. S. 1990. Mediation of meiotic and early mitotic chromosome segregation in *Drosophila* by a protein related to kinesin. *Nature* 345:81–83
31. Enos, A. P., Morris, N. R. 1990. Mutation of a gene that encodes a kinesin-like protein blocks nuclear division in *A. nidulans*. *Cell* 60:1019–27
32. Gibbons, I. R., Lee-Eiford, A., Mocz,

G., Phillipson, C. A., Tang, W.-J. Y., Gibbons, B. H. 1987. Photosensitized cleavage of dynein heavy chains. *J. Biol. Chem.* 262:2780–86
33. Gilbert, S. P., Sloboda, R. D. 1989. A squid dynein isoform promotes axoplasmic vesicle translocation. *J. Cell Biol.* 109:2379–94
34. Grafstein, B., Forman, D. S. 1980. Intracellular transport in neurons. *Physiol. Rev.* 60:1167–1283
35. Griffiths, G., Simons, K. 1986. The *trans*-Golgi network: sorting at the exit site of the Golgi complex. *Science* 234:438–42
36. Gruenberg, J., Griffiths, G., Howell, K. E. 1989. Characterization of the early endosome and putative endocytic carrier vesicles *in vivo* and *in vitro* with an assay of vesicle fusion. *J. Cell Biol.* 108:1301–16
37. Gruenberg, J., Howell, K. 1989. Membrane traffic in endocytosis: Insights from cell-free assays. *Annu. Rev. Cell Biol.* 5:453–81
38. Gutmann, E. J., Niles, J. L., McCluskey, R. T., Brown, D. 1989. Colchicine-induced redistribution of an apical membrane glycoprotein (gp330) in proximal tubules. *Am. J. Physiol.* 257(2):397–407
39. Hackney, D. D. 1988. Kinesin ATPase: rate-limiting ADP release. *Proc. Natl. Acad. Sci. USA* 85:6314–18
40. Herman, B., Albertini, D. F. 1984. A time-lapse video image intensification analysis of cytoplasmic organelle movements during endosome translocation. *J. Cell Biol.* 98:565–76
41. Herman, G., Busson, S., Gorbunoff, M. J., Mauduit, P., Timasheff, S. N., Rossignol, B. 1989. Colchicine analogues that bind reversibly to tubulin define microtubular requirements for newly synthesized protein secretion in rat lacrimal gland. *Proc. Natl. Acad. Sci. USA* 86:4515–19
42. Heuser, J. 1989. Changes in lysosome shape and distribution correlated with changes in cytoplasmic pH. *J. Cell Biol.* 108:855–64
43. Heuser, J. E., Schroer, T. A., Steuer, E., Gelles, J., Sheetz, M. Kinesin structure in the electron microscope. 1988. *Cell Motil. Cytoskel.* 11:202
44. Hirokawa, N., Pfister, K. K., Yorifuji, H., Wagner, M. C., Brady, S. T., Bloom, G. S. 1989. Submolecular domains of bovine brain kinesin identified by electron microscopy and monoclonal antibody decoration. *Cell* 56:867–78
45. Ho, W. C., Allan, V. J., van Meer, G., Berger, E. G., Kreis, T. E. 1989. Reclustering of scattered Golgi elements occurs along microtubules. *Eur. J. Cell Biol.* 48:250–63
46. Hollenbeck, P. J. 1989. The distribution, abundance and subcellular localization of kinesin. *J. Cell Biol.* 108:2335–42
47. Hollenbeck, P. J., Swanson, J. A. 1990. Radial extension of macrophage tubular lysosomes supported by kinesin. *Nature* 346:864–66
48. Howard, J., Hudspeth, A. J., Vale, R. D. 1989. Movement of microtubules by single kinesin molecules. *Nature* 342: 154–58
49. Hubbard, A. L., Steiger, B. 1988. Involvement of microtubules in the transport of bile canalicular proteins from the basolateral to the apical plasma membrane domain in rat hepatocytes. *J. Cell Biol.* 107:447a
50. Hubbard, A. L., Stieger, B., Bartles, J. R. 1989. Biogenesis of endogenous plasma membrane proteins in epithelial cells. *Annu. Rev. Physiol.* 51:755–70
51. Hughson, E. J., Hopkins, C. R. 1990. Endocytotic pathways in polarized Caco-2 cells: identification of an endosomal compartment accessible from both apical and basolateral surfaces. *J. Cell Biol.* 110:337–48
52. Hyman, A. A., Mitchison, T. J. 1990. Modulation of microtubule stability by kinetochores in vitro. *J. Cell Biol.* 111:1607–16
53. Inoue, S. 1981. Video image processing greatly enhances contrast, quality, and speed in polarization-based microscopy. *J. Cell Biol.* 89:346–56
54. Johnson, K. A. 1985. Pathway of the microtubule-dynein ATPase and the structure of dynein: a comparison with actomysoin. *Annu. Rev. Biophys. Biophys. Chem.* 14:161–88
55. Johnson, L. V., Walsh, M. L., Chen, L. B. 1980. Localization of mitochondria in living cells with rhodamine 123. *Proc. Natl. Acad. Sci. USA* 77:990–94
56. Kachar, B., Reese, T. S. 1988. The mechanism of cytoplasmic streaming in characaen algal cells: sliding of endoplasmic reticulum along actin filaments. *J. Cell Biol.* 106:1545–52
57. Kelly, R. B. 1990. Associations between microtubules and intracellular organelles. *Curr. Opin. Cell Biol.* 2: 105–8
58. Kelly, R. B. 1990. Microtubules, membrane traffic and cell organization. *Cell* 61:5–7
59. Kelly, R. B. 1990. Tracking an elusive receptor. *Nature* 345:480–81
60. Kocha, T., Fekudo, T., Isobe, T., Okuyama, T. 1989. Specific purification

of glyceraldehyde-3-phosphate dehydrogenase by hydrophobic chromotography on immobilized colchicine, *Biochim. Biophys. Acta.* 991(1):56–61
61. Koonce, M. P., McIntosh, J. R., 1990. Identification and immunolocalization of a cytoplasmic dynein in *Dictyostelium. Cell Motil. Cytoskel.* 15:51–62
62. Koshland, D. E., Mitchison, T. J., Kirschner, M. W., 1988. Polewards chromosome movement driven by microtubule depolymerization in vitro. *Nature* 331:499–504
63. Kosik, K. S., Orecchio, L. D., Schnapp, B., Inouye, H., Neve, R. L. 1990. The primary structure and analysis of the squid kinesin heavy chain. *J. Biol. Chem.* 265:3278–83
64. Kreis, T. E., Matteoni, R., Hollinshead, M., Tooze, J. 1989. Secretory granules and endosomes show saltatory movement biased to the anterograde and retrograde directions, respectively along microtubules in At T20 cells. *Eur. J. Cell Biol.* 49:128–39
65. Kronenbusch, P. J., Singer, S. J. 1987. The microtubule-organizing complex and the Golgi apparatus are co-localized around the entire nuclear envelope of interphase cardiac myocytes. *J. Cell Sci.* 88:25–34
66. Kuhn, L. C., Kraehenbuhl, J. P. 1982. The sacrificial receptor translocation of polymeric IgA across epithelia. *Trends Biochem. Sci.* 7:299–302
67. Lee, C., Chen, L. B. 1988. Dynamic behavior of endoplasmic reticulum in living cells. *Cell* 54:37–46
68. Lee, C., Ferguson, M., Chen, L. B. 1989. Construction of the endoplasmic reticulum. *J. Cell Biol.* 109:2045–55
69. Lippincott-Schwartz, J., Donaldson, J. G., Schweizer, A., Berger, E. G., Hauri, H., et al. 1990. Microtubule-dependent retrograde transport of proteins into the ER in the presence of brefeldin A suggests an ER recycling pathway. *Cell* 60:821–36
70. Lipsky, N. G., Pagano, R. E. 1985. A vital stain for the Golgi apparatus. *Science* 228:745–47
71. Luby-Phelps, K., Taylor, D. L. 1986. Subcellular compartmentalization by local differentiation of cytoplasmic structure. *Cell Motil. Cytoskel.* 10:28–37
72. Lye, R. J., Porter, M. E., Scholey, J. M., McIntosh, J. R. 1987. Identification of a microtubule-based cytoplasmic motor in the nematode *C. elegans. Cell* 51:309–18
73. Marsh, M., Griffiths, G., Dean, G. E., Mellman, I., Helenius, A. 1986. Three-dimensional structure of endosomes in BHK-21 cells. *Proc. Natl. Acad. Sci. USA* 83:2899–2903
74. Masuda, H., Hirano, T., Yanagida, M., Cande, W. Z. 1990. In vitro reactivation of spindle elongation in fission yeast nuc2 mutant cells. *J. Cell Biol.* 110: 417–26
75. Matteoni, R., Kreis, T. E. 1987. Translocation and clustering of endosomes and lysosomes depends on microtubules. *J. Cell Biol.* 105:1253–65
76. Matter, K., Brauchbar, M., Bucher, K., Hauri, H.-P. 1990. Sorting of endogenous plasma membrane proteins occurs from two sites in cultured human intestinal epithelial cells (Caco-2). *Cell* 60:429–37
77. Matus, A. 1990. Microtubule-associated proteins. *Curr. Opin. Cell Biol.* 2:10–14
78. McCaffrey, G. M., Vale, R. D. 1989. Identification of a kinesin-like molecule from *Dictyostelium discoideum. EMBO J.* 8:3229–3284
79. McDonald, H. B., Goldstein, L. S. B. 1990. Identification and characterization of a gene encoding a kinesin-like protein in *Drosophila*. Cell 61:991–1000
80. McIntosh, J. R., Porter, M. E. 1989. Microtubule-dependent motors. *J. Biol. Chem.* 264:6001–4
81. Meluh, P. B., Rose, M. D. 1990. KAR3, a kinesin-related gene required for yeast nuclear fusion. *Cell* 60:1029–41
82. Mitchison, T. J., Kirschner, M. W. 1985. Properties of the kinetochore in vitro. II. microtubule capture and ATP-dependent translocation. *J. Cell Biol.* 101:766–77
83. Morin, P. J., Fine, R. E. 1988. Kinesin is rapidly transported in association with constitutive and regulated exocytic vesicles. *J. Cell Biol.* 107:672a
84. Mostov, K. E., Simister, N. E. 1985. Transcytosis. *Cell* 43:389–90
85. Neighbors, B. W., Williams, R. C. J., McIntosh, J. R. 1988. Localization of kinesin in cultured cells. *J. Cell Biol.* 106:1193–1204
86. Oka, J. A., Weigel, P. H. 1983. Microtubule-depolymerizing agents inhibit asialo-orosomucoid delivery to lysosomes but not its endocytosis or degradation in isolated rat hepatocytes. *Biochim. Biophys. Acta* 763:368–76
87. Ouyang, Y., Wang, W., Bhuta, S., Chang, Y.-H. 1989. Mechanism of action of colchicine VI: effect of colchicine of generation of leukotriene B4 by human polymorphonuclear leukocytes. *Clin. Exp. Rheum.* 7:397–402

88. Parton, R. G., Prydz, K., Bomsel, M., Simons, K., Griffiths, G. 1989. Meeting of the apical and basolateral endocytic pathways of the Madin-Darby canine kidney cell in late endosomes. *J. Cell Biol.* 109:3259–72
89. Paschal, B. M., Obar, R. A., Vallee, R. B. 1989. Interaction of brain cytoplasmic dynein and MAP2 with a common sequence at the C terminus of tubulin. *Nature* 342:569–72
90. Paschal, B. M., Shpetner, H. S., Vallee, R. B. 1987. MAP 1C is a microtubule-activated ATPase which translocates microtubules in vitro and has dynein-like properties. *J. Cell Biol.* 105: 1273–82
91. Pfister, K. K., Wagner, M. C., Stenoien, D. L., Brady, S. T. ,Bloom, G. S. 1989. Monoclonal antibodies to kinesin heavy and light chains stain vesicle-like structures, but not microtubules, in cultured cells. *J. Cell Biol.* 108:1453–64
92. Porter, M. E., Grissom, P. M., Pfarr, C. M., McIntosh, J. R. 1987. Vanadate-sensitized UV cleavage as a probe for dynein-like polypeptides. *J. Cell Biol.* 105:33a
93. Rebhun, L. I. 1972. Polarized intracellular particle transport: saltatory movements and cytoplasmic streaming. *Int. Rev. Cytol.* 32:93–137
94. Rindler, M. J., Ivanov, I. E., Sabatini, D. D. 1987. Microtubule-acting drugs lead to the nonpolarized delivery of the influenza hemagglutinin to the cell surface of polarized Madin-Darby Canine Kidney cells. *J. Cell Biol.* 104:231–41
95. Rogalski, A. A., Bermann, J. E., Singer, S. J. 1984. Effect of microtubule assembly status on the intracellular processing and surface expression of an integral membrane protein of the plasma membrane. *J. Cell Biol.* 99:1101–16
96. Rojkind, M., Mourelle, M., Kershenobich, D. 1984. Anti-inflammatory and antifibrogenic activities of colchicine: treatment of liver cirrhosis. *Prog. Clin. Biol. Res.* 154:475–89
97. Salas, P. J. I., Misek, D. E., Vega-Salas, D. E., Gundersen, D., Cereijido, M. et al. 1986. Microtubules and actin filaments are not critically involved in the biogenesis of epithelial cell surface polarity. *J. Cell Biol.* 102:1853–67
98. Saxton, W. M., Raff, E. C. 1988. *Drosophila* kinesin: looking for a function. *J. Cell Biol.* 107:673a
99. Schnapp, B. J. 1986. Viewing single microtubules by video light microscopy. *Methods Enzymol.* 134:561–73
100. Schnapp, B. J., Reese, T. S. 1989. Dynein is the motor for retrograde axonal transport of organelles. *Proc. Natl. Acad. Sci. USA* 86:1548–52
101. Schnapp, B. J., Vale, R. D., Sheetz, M. P., Reese, T. S. 1985. Single microtubules from squid axoplasm support bidirectional movement of organelles. *Cell* 40:455–62
102. Scholey, J. M., Heuser, J., Yang, J. T., Goldstein, L. S. B. 1989. Identification of globular mechanochemical beads of kinesin. *Nature* 338:355–57
103. Schroer, T. A., Brady, S. T., Kelly, R. B. 1985. Fast axonal transport of foreign synaptic vesicles in squid axoplasm. *J. Cell Biol.* 101:568–72
104. Schroer, T. A., Schnapp, B. J., Reese, T. S., Sheetz, M. P. 1988. The role of kinesin and other soluble factors in organelle movement along microtubules. *J. Cell Biol.* 107:1785–92
105. Schroer, T. A., Steuer, E. R., Sheetz, M. P. 1989. Cytoplasmic dynein is a minus-end directed motor for membranous organelles. *Cell* 56:937–46
106. Schweizer, A., Fransen, J., Bachi, T., Ginsel, L., Hauri, H. 1988. Identification, by a monoclonal antibody, of a 53 kD protein associated with a tubulo-vesicular compartment at the *cis*-side of the Golgi apparatus. *J. Cell Biol.* 107: 1643–53
107. Deleted in proof
108. Sheetz, M. P., Steuer, E. R., Schroer, T. A. 1989. The mechanism and regulation of fast axonal transport. *Trends Neurosci.* 12:474–78
109. Simons, K., Fuller, S. D., 1985. Cell surface polarity in epithelia. *Annu. Rev. Cell Biol.* 1:243–88
110. Stebbings, H., Hunt, C. 1983. Microtubule polarity in the nutrient tubes of insect ovarioles. *Cell Tissue Res.* 233: 133–41
111. Steuer, E. R., Heuser, J. E., Sheetz, M. P. 1988. Cytoplasmic dynein and ciliary outer arm dynein: a structural comparison. *Cell Motil. Cytoskel.* 11:200
112. Steuer, E. R., Schroer, T. A., Wordeman, L., Sheetz, M. P. 1990. Cytoplasmic dynein localizes to mitotic spindles and kinetochores. *Nature* 345:266–68
113. Swanson, J., Bushnell, A., Silverstein, S. C. 1987. Tubular lysosome morphology and distribution within macrophages depend on the integrity of cytoplasmic microtubules. *Proc. Natl. Acad. Sci. USA* 84:1921–25
114. Terasaki, M., Chen, L. B., Fujiwara, K. 1986. Microtubules and the endoplasmic reticulum are highly interdependent structures. *J. Cell Biol.* 103:1557–68
115. Terasaki, M., Song, J., Wong, J. R.,

Weiss, M. J., Chen, L. B. 1984. Localization of endoplasmic reticulum in living and glutaraldehyde-fixed cells with fluorescent dyes. *Cell* 38:101–8
116. Titus, M., Egelhoff, T., Spudich, J. A. 1990. Genetic manipulation of motility. *Curr. Opin. Cell Biol.* 2:125–32
117. Titus, M. A., Warrick, H. M., Spudich, J. A. 1989. Multiple actin-based motor genes in *Dictyostelium*. *Cell Reg.* 1:55–63
118. Tooze, J., Burke, B. 1987. Accumulation of adrenocorticotropin secretory granules in the midbody of telophase AtT-20 cells: Evidence that secretory granules move anterogradely along microtubules. *J. Cell Biol.* 104:1047–57
119. Travis, J. L., Kenealy, J. F. X., Allen, R. D. 1983. Studies on the motility of the foraminifera. II. The dynamic microtubular cytoskeleton of the reticulopodial network of *Allogromia laticollaris*. *J. Cell Biol.* 97:1668–76
120. Vale, R. D. 1990. Microtubule-based motor proteins. *Curr. Opin. Cell Biol.* 2:15–22
121. Vale, R. D., Goldstein, L. S. B. 1990. One motor, many tails: an expanding repertoire of force-generating enzymes. *Cell* 60:883–85
122. Vale, R. D., Hotani, H. 1988. Formation of membrane networks *in vitro* by kinesin-driven microtubule movement. *J. Cell Biol.* 107:2233–42
123. Vale, R. D., Schnapp, B. J., Reese, T. S., Sheetz, M. P. 1985. Organelle, bead, and mirotubule translocations promoted by soluble factors from the squid giant axon. *Cell* 40:559
124. Vallee, R. B. Shpetner, H. S., Paschal, B. M. 1989. The role of dynein in retrograde axonal transport. *Trends Neuro. Sci.* 12:66–70
125. Vaux, D., Tooze, J., Fuller, S. 1990. Identification by anti-idiotype antibodies of an intracellular membrane protein that recognizes a mammalian endoplasmic reticulum retention signal. *Nature* 345: 495–502
126. Wang, E., Goldman, R. D. 1978. Functions of cytoplasmic fibers in intracellular movements in BHK-21 cells. *J. Cell Biol.* 79:708–26
127. Warren, G. 1987. Protein transport: Signals and salvage sequences. *Nature* 327:17–18
128. Waugh, R. E. 1982. Surface viscosity measurements from large bilayer vesicle tether formation: II. Experiments. *Biophys. J.* 38:29–37
129. Waugh, R. E., Hochmuth, R. M. 1987. Mechanical equilibrium of thick, hollow, liquid membrane cylinders. *Biophys. J.* 52:391–402
130. Wieland, F. T., Gleason, M. L., Serafini, T. A., Rothman, J. E. 1987. The rate of bulk flow from the endoplasmic reticulum to the cell surface. *Cell* 50:289–300
131. Williams, J. A. 1981. Effects of antimitotic agents on ultrastructure and intracellular transport of proteins in pancreatic acini. *Methods Cell Biol.* 23: 247–58
132. Willingham, N. C., Pastan, I. 1978. The visualization of fluorescent proteins in living cells by video intensification microscopy (VIM). *Cell* 14:501–7
133. Yang, J. T., Laymon, R. A., Goldstein, L. S. B. 1989. A three-domain structure of kinesin heavy chain revealed by DNA sequence and microtubule binding analyses. *Cell* 56:879–89
134. Young, M. R., D'Arcy Hart, P. 1986. Movements and other distinguishing features of small vesicles identified by Darkfield microscopy in living macrophages. *Exp. Cell Res.* 164:199–210

Annu. Rev. Physiol. 1991. 53:653–81

MYOSIN-I

Thomas D. Pollard, Stephen K. Doberstein, and Henry G. Zot

Department of Cell Biology and Anatomy, The Johns Hopkins University School of Medicine, 725 N. Wolfe Street Baltimore, Maryland, 21205

KEY WORDS: myosin, membrane, motility

OVERVIEW AND PERSPECTIVES

Myosin-I is the name given to a diverse collection of single-headed myosin molecules. This name distinguishes them from double-headed myosins called myosin-II (Figure 1), which were discovered earlier and have been subject to extensive investigation in muscle and non-muscle cells [reviewed by Warrick & Spudich, (119); Korn & Hammer, (64)]. All myosins have at least one head domain with mechanochemical activity capable of transducing energy stored in ATP into motion along actin filaments.

All myosin-Is have one head composed of a single heavy chain. Additional polypeptide domains may be present at the C- and/or N-termini of the head domain. The existence and the properties of these domains flanking the myosin-I head are variable even among the myosin-I isoforms from a single cell type. At least one light chain is associated with the myosin-I heavy chain. To date, all myosin-Is that have been investigated have a C-terminal extension of the heavy chain with lipid-binding properties. Some myosin-Is have, in addition, C-terminal extensions of the heavy chain that bind actin filaments or calmodulin. In one class of myosin-I there is an N-terminal extension with a primary sequence suggestive of kinase activity.

Evidence is rapidly accumulating that myosin-I is associated with membranes in cells, and it is widely speculated that myosin-I is the motor for movement of membranes along actin filaments. There is not yet any direct evidence in live cells that this is true, but this hypothesis is supported by the biochemical properties of isolated myosin-Is and their localization in cells. This proposal is also supported by evidence that many actin-based movements occur in cells that have been depleted of active myosin-II. The movements of membranes powered by myosin-I may include pseudopod extension, membrane ruffles, and organelle movements.

0066-4278/91/0315-0653$02.00

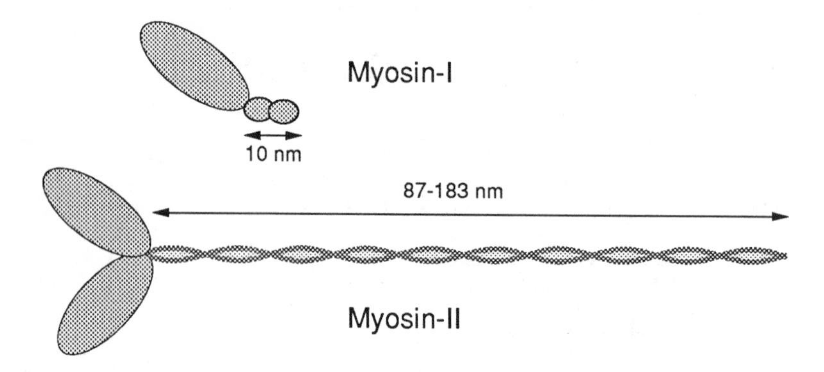

Figure 1 Schematic of myosin-I and myosin-II. The myosins share a common head structure and differ markedly in the structure of the tail. The length of the myosin-II tail is species and tissue specific. The structure of the tail of myosin-I has not been fully elucidated and a consensus structure may not exist. For illustrative purposes, two globular regions are shown, which correspond to possible functional domains.

The existence of single-headed myosin molecules may provide a clue about the evolution of the whole myosin protein family. We argue that the primitive form of myosin consisted of a small head similar to contemporary myosin-Is. This primitive form of myosin then acquired extra domains by gene fusions that led eventually to myosin-II molecules with two heads and a long alpha-helical tail. Myosin-II now dominates the actomyosin systems of higher organisms, especially those that evolved muscle cells to contract with massive force at high velocities. Myosin-I today may provide us with a glimpse of how the actomyosin system functioned early in the evolution of eukaryotic cells.

We have attempted a comprehensive review of the literature on myosin-I up to mid-1990. Earlier commentaries on myosin-I have been written by Korn & Hammer (64, 65), Korn et al (62), Adams & Pollard (3, 4), Spudich (110), and Kiehart (59).

IDENTIFICATION OF MYOSIN-I

The Discoveries of Myosin-I

Myosin-I has been discovered independently at least four times. The original myosin-I was discovered by Pollard & Korn (94, 96–99) using a K^+-EDTA ATPase assay to look for myosin in *Acanthamoeba*. A highly purified protein was obtained with actin-activated ATPase activity dependent on the presence of a second protein called a cofactor. This ATPase also bound to actin filaments in an ATP-sensitive fashion. On the other hand, it differed from any known myosin in that it had a single, small heavy chain and did not form filaments. In spite of these differences in physical properties from conventional myosin-II, Pollard & Korn named this molecule *Acanthamoeba* myosin. Subsequent findings have established that this protein is a true myosin, and the first representative of the new class is now called myosin-I.

Myosin-I was discovered a second time by investigators studying the interaction of the plasma membrane with the bundle of actin filaments in microvilli of intestinal epithelial cells. Early electron microscopic studies by Mooseker & Tilney (89) showed that there are radial links between actin filament bundle and the surrounding plasma membrane. Subsequently, Matsudaira & Burgess (81) found that this linking protein has a molecular weight of 110,000 and can be dissociated from the actin filaments by ATP, a characteristic of myosin. Collins & Borysenko (20) then showed that this 110-kd protein has ATPase activity like myosin. Confirmation that this 110-kd protein is myosin-I has been obtained from the primary structure (39, 51), in vitro motility assays (87, 88), and its lipid-binding properties (48).

Myosin-I was discovered for the third time in *Drosophila* during an analysis of mutations affecting photoreceptor cells in the eye. One mutant called *ninaC* has defective photoreceptor microvilli (82). The sequence of the protein encoded by the *ninaC* gene revealed that it is a myosin-I with a unique kinase-like domain at its N-terminus (86).

More recently, a myosin-I-like sequence was obtained during the analysis of a temperature-sensitive mutation, *cdc-66-1,* which arrests the cell cycle in a budding yeast (100; G. C. Johnston, personal communication). This mutation in the *MYO2* gene causes cells to arrest with an unbudded morphology and to accumulate large numbers of small vesicles in the cytoplasm.

Criteria for Identifying Myosin-I

The only certain way to identify a myosin-I is to purify the protein in order to verify that it is an actin-activated ATPase and to demonstrate by physical-chemical criteria that it has a single heavy chain and a single head. Tentative identification of a myosin-I is possible from sequence information alone, using the presence of a myosin head domain and the absence of the heptad repeat characteristic of coiled-coils in the C-terminal tail of myosin-II. We have designated several molecules as myosin-Is based on sequence information alone, but it should be noted that these are merely putative assignments in the absence of biochemical characterization. It is possible, of course, that some of these will represent new classes of myosin distinct from either myosin-I or myosin-II. There is an emerging consensus of sequence criteria unique for the myosin-I head (see below), but the available tail sequences are so variable in size and sequence that they are not diagnostic of myosin-I.

Nomenclature

We recommend, in agreement with Korn & Hammer (64), that myosins fulfilling the above criteria should be called myosin-I and that double-headed

```
                                                                          -63                          -40
AcanthHMW                                                                 MHFLFFFANRQFLSLKCPQAEFVW IPHPVHGYITGKFIQEDYGGTSYCQTEEGESLSVACAPSC
SacchroMI                                                                   MSFEVGTRCWYPHKELGW IGAEVIKNEFNDGKYHLELQLEDDEIVSVDTKDLNNDKDC
           0                                        40                                       80
  BovBBMI     MTLLEGSVGVEDLVLLEPLEQESLIRNLQLRYEKKE IYTYIGNVLVSVNPYQQLPI.YDLEFVAKYRDYTFYELKP HIYALANMAYQSLRDRDRDQCILITGESGAGKTEASKLVM
AvianBBMI                                                QVVISVNPYKPLPI.YTPEKVEEYHNCNFFAVKP HIYAIADDAYRSLRDRDRDQCILITGESGAGKTEASKLVM
DictyoMIA  MAEFKRDLTKNVGVEDLIMLEV.SESSLHENLKIRYKEGL IYTSIGPVLVSMNPYKQLGI.YGNDQINLYKGKHEFEIPP HIYSIADKAYRALRSEGENQCIIISGESGAGKTEASKYIM
DictyoMIB     MSKKVQAKQGTDDLVMLPKVSEDEICENLKKRYMNDF IYTNIGPVLISVNPFRNLNN.SGPDFIEAYRGKHAQEVPP HVYQLAESAYRAMKNDQENQCVIISGESGAGKTEAAKLIM
DictyoMIC                                                                                            EKENQCVIISGESGAGKTEAAKKIM
AcanthMIB     MGKAAVEQRGVDDLVLMPKITEQDICANLEKRYFNDL IYTNIGPVLISVNPFRRIDALLTDECLHCYRGRYQHEQPP HVYALAEAAYRGVKSENINQCVIISGESGAGKTEASKLVM
AcanthMIC       MAYTSKHGVDDMVMLTSISNDAINDNLKKRFAADL IYTYIGHVLISVNPYKQINNLYTERTLKDYRGKYRYELPP HVYALADDMYRTMLSESEDQCVIISGESGAGKTEASKKIM
AcanthHMW  .LAKVAKSVLDKSVDDLVQMDDINEAMIVHNLRKRFKNDQ IYTNIGTILISVNPFKRL.PLYTPTVMDQYMHKVPKEMPP HTYNIADDAYRAMIDNRMNQSILISGESGAGKTECTKQCL
SacchroMI  SLPLLRNPPILEATEDLTSLSYLNEPAVLHAIKQRYSQLN IYTYSGIVLIATNPFDRVDQLYTQDMIQAYAGKRRGELEP HLFAIAEEAYRLMKNDKQNQTIVVSGESGAGKTVSAKYIM
DrosninaC          PEKMYPEDLAALENPVDENIIESLRHRILMGE SYSFIGDILLSLNS.NEIKQEFPQEFHAKYRFKSRSENQP HIFSVADIAYQDMLHHKEPQHIVLSGESYSGKSTNARLLI

 Myosin I  .........k.gv-DLvmL..Δse-.i.eNLkkRy..dl IYT.IGpVLISVNPy+.Δ..LY..-.Δ..Y+gK...E.pP HΔYaΔA--AYR.m+.-.enQCΔΔISGESGAGKTEAsKlΔM
 MyosinII  ..v..mNPpkfdk.EdMsmlthlnepaVLyNLkkRYaadl iyTYSGLFcV.ΔNPYK.lp.vYt.e.Δ..yrGk+R.EΔpP HΔFaisD.AYr.mL.d+enQSΔLITGESGAGKTeNTK+ΔΔ

           120                                     160                                      200
  BovBBMI  SYVAAVCGKGEQ..........VNSV....KEQLLQSNP VLEA...FGNAKTIRNNNSSRFGKYMDIEFDFKGFPLGGV ITNYLLEKSRVVKQLEGERNFHIFYQLLAG..ADAQLLKA
AvianBBMI  SYVAAVSSKGEE..........VDKV....KEQLIQSNP VLEA...FGNAKTIRNDNSSRFGKYMDVEFDFKGDPLGGV ISNYLLEKSRIVRHVKGERNFHIFYQLLAG..GSAQLLQQ
DictyoMIA  QYIASITGSSTE..........VERV....KKTILESNP LLEA...FGNGKTLRNNNSSRFGKYMEIQFNLGGDPEGGK ITNYLLEKSRVINQTQGERNFHIFYQLLKG..HQGKKTYN
DictyoMIB  GYVSAISGSTEK..........VEYV....KHVILESNP LLEA...FGNAKTLRNNNSSRFGKYFEIQFDKAGDPVGGK IYNYLLEKSRVVYQNPGERNFHIFYQLLRGASAQEKRDYV
DictyoMIC  QYIADVSGERGSSSNQK......VEHV....KSIILETNP LLEA...FGNAKTLRNNNSSRFGKYFEIQF
AcanthMIB  QYVAAVSGNSGG..........VDFV........KHSNP LLEA...FGNAKTLRNNNSSRFGKYFEIHFNRLGEPCGGR ITNYLLEKSRVTFQTRGERSFHIFYQLLAGASDAEAQEMQ
AcanthMIC  QYIAAVSGATGD..........VMRV....KDVI..... .LEA...FGNAKTIRNNNSSRFGKYMEIQFDLKGDPVGGR ISNYLLEKSRVVYQTNGERNFHIFYQLLAARARRPEAKFG
AcanthHMW  TYFAELAGSTNG..........VEQN.......ILLANP ILES...FGNAKTLRNN.SSRFGKWVEIHFDQKGSICGAS TINHLLEKSRVVYQIKGERNFRIVATELVKAPPRSRGGGG
SacchroMI  RYFASVEEENSATVQHQ......VEMSETEQK..ILATNP IMEA...FGNAKTTRNDNSSRFGKYLEILFDKDTSIIGAR IRTYLLERSRLVYQPPIERNYHIFYQLMAGLPAQTKDYFY
DrosninaC  KHLCYLGDGNRGATGRV...................ES SIKAILMLVNAGTPVNNDCTRCVLQYCLTFGKTGKMSGAV FNMYMLEKLRVATTDGTQHNFHIFYYFYDFINQQNQLKEY

 Myosin I  qYΔAaΔsG..............V-.V....K+.ILeSNP ΔLEA...FGN AKTΔRNNNSSRFGKYmEIqFD..G-P.GG+ I.NYLLEKSRVV.Q..GERNFHIFYQLLaGa........
 MyosinII  QYfA.Δa.tgd..k.............gtLEdQIΔ.aNP ΔLEA...FGN AKTvRNnNSSRFGKFIrIhF...G.Δasad Ie.YLLEKSRVtfQ...ER.yHIFyQΔls.....pe.Δk.

           240                                     280                                     320
  BovBBMI  LKLERDTGGYAYLNPDT........SRVDGMDDD.ANFK V....LQSAMTVIGFSDEEIRQVLEVAALVLKLGNVELINE FQANGVP.....ASGIRDGRGVQEIGELVGLNSVELER
AvianBBMI  LKLRPDCSHYGYLNHEK........SVLPGMDDA.ANFR A....MQDAMAIIGFAPAEVTALLEVTAVVLKLGNVKLSSS FQASGME.....ASSIAEPRELQEISQLIGLDPSTLEQ
DictyoMIA  LLSPDQYHYLTRNASNGWF.......SLPDGIDDQ.IGFK Q....TKNAMKVVGIDEPLQKKSFATLSAILLLGNLSFNKS ..ASGN......GSVISDKKLANTIASLMGVDAIVLES
DictyoMIB  LSSPESYYYLNQSQ..........CYTVDGINDV.SDYA E....VRQAMDTIGLTAQEQSDIIRIVACVLHIGNIYFIED ..DKGN......AAIYPDNAL.ELAASMLCIDSATLQN
AcanthMIB  LYAPENFNYLNQSA..........CYTVDGIDDI.KEFA D....TRNAINVMGMTAEEQRQVFHLVAGILHLGNVAFHDG ..GKGT......AAVHDRTPF.............ALKN
AcanthMIC  LQTPDYYFYLQGK...........TYTVDGMDNQ..EFQ D....TWNAMKVIGFTAEEQHEIFRLVTAILYLGNVQFVDD ..GKGG.......STIADSRPV...........AVET
AcanthHMW  SSPARPESFKFLSQSG........CIDVEGVDDV.KEFE ERVLCHGQARVRVQFSEDDINNCMELISAILHLGNFEFVSG .QGKNV.....ETSTVANREEV...........KIVA
SacchroMI  MNQGGDTKIN..................GIDDA.KEYK I....TVDALTLVGITKETQHQIFKILAALLHIGNIEIKKT .RNDAS......LSADEPNLKLACELLGIDAYNFAKWV
DrosninaC  NLKADRNYRYLRVPPEVPPSKLKYRRDDPEGNVERCREFE NILRDIDFNH.......KQLETVRKVLAAILNIGNIRFRQN ..GKYAEVENTDIVSRIAELLRV...........DEKK

 Myosin I  L..p-...yl.....t........c...dG.dd....f. ....-t.nAm.viGf..e.q+.ΔΔ+ΔΔaΔΔL+ΔGNΔ.f... ...kg.......a.sΔΔ.-.r...............l..
 MyosinII  l..t.pydy..q....................dDEE..f. .....tdsA.dIlgF..-Ek..iy+l..aΔlh.GNΔkFkq+ ....rEe.....q.aepdgteΔ....a-ka..l....s.


           360                                     400                                      440
  BovBBMI  ALCSRTMET....AK.....EKVVTTLNVI....QAQYAR DALAKNIYSRLFNWLVNRINESIKV..GTGEKR.KVMGVL DI...YGFEILEDNSFEQFVINYCNEKLQQVFIEMTLKEEQ
AvianBBMI  ALCSRTVKV....RD.....ESVLTALSVS....QGYYGR DALAKNIYSRLFDWLVNRINTSIQV..KPGKQR.KVMGVL DI...YGFEIFQDNGFEQFIINYCNEKLQQIFILMTLKEEQ
DictyoMIA  SLVSRQIST....GQ.....GARISTYSVPQTVEQAMYAR DAFAKATYSKLFDFIVRKINQSIEV..KTIG...KVIGVL DI...YGFEIFENNSFEQFCINYVNETLQQIFIDLTLKTEQ
DictyoMIB  AILFRVINTGGAGGAGN.....RRSTYNVPQNVEQANGTR DALARTIYDRMFSWLVEKVNQSLSYYKSPVQ...NVIGIL DI...FGFEIFEKNGFEQFCINFVNEKLQQFFIELTLKAEQ
DictyoMIC          EFRQMETRHGNQRGTQYNVPLNKTQAIAGR DALAKIY
DictyoMID                 GTQGRSARVSTYACTF.PEGAYYSR DALAKALYSRLFDWIVGRVNSLA
AcanthMIA                        AGTTYALNLNKMQAIGSR DALAKAMYSRIFD
AcanthMIB  ALLFRVLNTGGAG.......AKKMSTYNVPQNVEQAASAR DALAKTIYSRMFDWIVSKVNEALQKQGGSGDHNNNMIGVL DI...FGFEIFEQNGFEQFCINYVNEKLQQYFIELTLKAEQ
AcanthMIC  ALLYRTITTGEQG.......RGRSSVYSCPQDPLGAIYSR DALSKALYSRMFDYIIQRVNDAMYIDDP...EALTT.GIL DI...YGFEIFGKNGFEQLCINFVNEKLQQIFIQLTLKAEQ
AcanthHMW  TLLKVDPATLEQNVTSKLMEIKGCDPTRIPLTPVQATDAT NALAKAIYSKLFDWLVKKINESME...PQKGAKTTTIGVL DI...FGFEIFDKNSFEQLCINFTNEKLQQHFNQYTFKLEE
SacchroMI  TKKQIITRSEKIVS...............NLNYSQALVAK DSVAKFIYSALFDWLVENINTVLC.NPAVNDQISSFIGVL DI...YGFEHFEKNSFEQFCINYANEKLQQEFNQHVFKLEQ
DrosninaC  FMWSLTNFIMVKG.........GIAERRQYTTEEARDAR DAVASTLYSRLVDFIINRINMNMS....FPRAVFGDTNAI IIHYMFGFKCFNRNGLEQLMINTLNEQMQYHYNQRIFISEM
                          * Acanthamoeba Phosphorylation Site
 Myosin I  allsrtΔ.t.............+.sty.vpqnveQA.yaR DALAK.ΔYSRlFDWΔV.+ΔN.sΔ.v..........v.GvL DI...yGFEIFe.NgFEQfcINyvNEKLQQΔFI-lTLK.EQ
 MyosinII  -llk......al..P.....kvGn-.Vtkgqnv.qv...v .Al.k.ly.r.Fl.wV..iN.ld.kr.... ...yfIGVL DI...aGFEIF..NSfEQLcINftNEKLQQFFNHHMFvLE

           480                                     520                                      560
  BovBBMI  EEYKREGIPWVKVEYFDNGIICNLI.EHNQRGILAMLDEE CLR...PGVVSDSTFLAKLNQLFSKHSHYESKVTQNAQRQ YDHSMGLSCFRICHYAGKVTYNVNSFIDKNNDLLFRDLSQA
AvianBBMI  EEYVREAIQWTPVEFFDNSIICDLI.ENSKVGILAMLDEE CLR...PGTVNEDTFITKLNQIFASHKRYESKETLNAKHV TDVSLPLRCFRIHHYAGKVTYNVTGFIEKNNDLLFRDLSQA
DictyoMIA  EEYVQEGITWIPVQYINNKACVDLI.EKKPIGILSLLDEE CLF...PEGNDQTMIDKLNKHFSNHTHYSKVERQKNSQ.. .........FIINHYAGKVFYNIDGFLDKNRDTLFNDLVTL
DictyoMIB  EEYVREGIKWEPIKYFNNQIVCDLIEGKSPPGIFSLLDDI CSTLHAQSTGTDQKFLEKMAGIYDGHLHW.....RGMTGA .........FAIKHYAGEVTYEAEGFSDKNKDTLFFDLIEA
AcanthMIB  EEYVNEGIQWTPIKYFNNKVVCELIEGKRPPGIFSLLDDI CFTMHAQSDGMDGKFLQKCQGGFPSHLHF.....RGMNNA .........FSIKHYAGEVTYEAEGFCEKNKDTLFDDLIAV
AcanthMIC  EEYGAEGIQWENIDYFNNKICCDLIEEKRPPGLMTILDDV CNF...PKGT.DDKFREKLLGAFPTHAHL.....AATSQP DE.......FVIKHYAGDVVYNVDGFCDKNKDLLFKDLIGL
AcanthHMW  KLYQSEEVKYEHITFIDNQPVLDLIEKKQPQGLMLVLDEQ ISI...PKSS.DATFFIKANQTQAARSTQ....LRGGEDS RTD......FIIKHYAGDVIYDSTGMLEKNKDTLQKDLLVL
SacchroMI  EEYVKEEIEWSFIEFNDNQPCIDLIENK..LGILSLLDEE SRL...PAGS.DESWTQKLYQTLDKSPTNKVFSKPRFGQT K........FIVSHYALDVAYDVEGFIEKNRDTVSDGHLEV
Drosninac  LEMEAEDIDTINLNFYDNKTALDNLLTK.PDGLFYIIDDA SRSCQDQNVIMDRVSE.KHSQFVKKHTAT........EIS VA.......HYTGRIIYDTRAFTDINRDFVPPEMIETFRSS

 Myosin I  EEyv.EgI.W.pΔ.yfdNkΔ.cDLIEek+p.Gi..ΔLD-. C.....p.g..D.kfΔe K.......h.h.........n.. .........F.I+HYAG-VtYnΔ-GF.-KN+D.LF.DLΔ..
 MyosinII  eEY.kEgI.W.fidfG.DlacIeLI.Ek.Pmgi.sΔl-Ee c.f....PkatDtsf.. KL..qhlgk.nnf.....kpk. ...kgkEahFsl.hYAGtV.y....wleKnkDPLn.tv..l

           600                                     640                                      680
  BovBBMI  MWKARHPLLRSLFPEGDPK..................... ........QASLKRPPTAGAQFKSS.............. ..............VTTLMKNLYSKNPNYIRCIKPNEHQQ
AvianBBMI  MWAARHTLLRSLFPEGDPQ..................... ........RPSLKLPPTTGSQFKAS.............. ..............VATLMKNLYSKNPNYIRCIKPNDTKT
DictyoMIA  ATSSSCSLLVEIFKYVPPLEVDPEQEKKNRDKFSKNGFAN NAAKTFI.PTDKKSPITAGFQFKNQ.............. ..............VTSLLKSLYSCSPHYVRCIKPNSNMR
DictyoMIB  IQCSKMPFLASLFNE......................... ....DTG.SLQKKRPTTAGFKIKTS.............. ..............AGELMKALSQCTPHYIRCIKPNETKK
AcanthMIB  IQESENRLLVSWFPE......................... ....DTK.QLQKKRPTTAGFKLKTS.............. ..............CDALMEALSRCSPHYIRCIKPNDNKA
AcanthMIC  AECTSSTFFAGLFPE......................... ....AKEVATSKKKPTTAGFKIKES.............. ..............INILVATLSKCTPHYIRCIKPNEKKA
AcanthHMW  SESSKQKLMKLLFPP......................... ....SEGDQKTSK..VTLGGQFRKQ.............. ..............LDSLMTALNATEPHYIRCIKPNSEKC
SacchroMI  LKASTNETLINILEG....LEKAAKKLEEAKKLELEQAG SKKPGPI.RTVNRKP.TLGSMFKQS.............. ..............LIELMNTINSTNVHYIRCIKPNADKE
Drosninac  LDESIMLMFTNQLTK......................... ....AGNLTMPFEAVQHKDESERKSYALNTLSAGCISQVNN LRTLAANFRFTCLTLLKMLSQNANLGVHFVRCIRADLEYK

 Myosin I  Δ..s...ll.slFpe......................... ..........kK+P.TaGf..K.S.............. ..............Δ..Lmk.L..c.PHYIRCIKPN-.k.
 MyosinII  ....s......lf............................ ....g..k...kkgsfTvsal.re.............. ..............lnkLm..LrsThPHFvRCiIPNe.k.

           720                                     760                                      800
  BovBBMI  RGHFSFELVSVQAQYLGLLENVRVRRAGYAYRQAYGSFLE RYRLLSRSTWPRWNGGDQEGVEKVLGELSMS........SE ELAFGKTKIFIR..SPKTLFYLEEQRRLRLQQ
AvianBBMI  AMLFTPDLVLAQVRYLGLMENVRVRRAGYAFRQLYQPFLE RYKMLSRKTWPRWTGGDREGAEVLLAELKFP........PE ELAYGHTKIFIR..SPRTLFDLEKRRQQRVAE
DictyoMIA  ALEWDQSKCAEQVAYLGSFENLLVRRAGYCYRQTFSKFMR RYYMIGKSTWPKWSGDAEKGVNLLMGELTQEINI.....KE EVQYGKTKIFIR..NPQPLFLLEDKRNKRLND
DictyoMIB  AKDWENSRVKHQVQYLGLLENVRVRRAGFAYRNTFDKVLK RYKKLSSKTWGIWGEWKGDAIEGCKTIFQDMNLE.....AG QWQLGKTKVFIR..HPETVFLLEEALDKKDFD
AcanthMIB  YHDWDATRTKHQVQYLGLLENVRVRRAGFAYRAEFDRFLR RYKKLSPKTWGIWGEWSGAPKDGCQTLLNDLGLD.....TS QWQLGKSKVFIR..YPETLFHLEECLDRKDYD
AcanthMIC  ANAFNNSLVLHQVKYLGLLENVRIRRAGYAYRQSYDKFFY RYRVVCPKTW..WSGWNGDMVSGAEAILNHVGMS....LGK EYQKGKTKIFIR..QPESVFSLEELRDRTVFS
AcanthHMW  ADLFHGFMSLQQLRYAGVFEAVRIRQTGYPFRYSHENFLK RYGFLVKD.....HKRYGPNLKQNCDLLLKSMKG....DWS KVQVGKTRVLYR..APEQR.GLELQRNIAVER
SacchroMI  AWQFDNLMVLSQLRACGVLETIRISCAGFPSRWTFEEFVL RYYILIPHEQWDLIFKKKETTEEDIISVVKMILDATVKDKS KYQIGNTKIFFK..AGMLA.YLEKLRSNKMHN
Drosninac  PRSFHSDVVQQQMKALGVLDTVIARQKGFSSRLPFDEFLR RYQFLA.......FDFDEPVEMTKDNCRLLFLRL....KME GWALGKTKVFLHYYNDEFLARLYELQVKKVIK

 Myosin I  A.df....v..Qv.YLGllENVRvRRAGyayRq.fd+Fl+ RY+.ls+kTWp+W.g......-.....l...........e e.q.GKTKΔFIR...PetΔF.LE-.r.++Δ.-
 MyosinII  pg..e..lvL.qLrCNGVLEGIRIcRkGfPnRily.-f.q RY..L.a.a.p........skK.A..kll........id.. .y+fG.TKΔFFk..aG..L..lEe.Rd..a.
```

myosins with tails that polymerize into bipolar filaments be called myosin-II. This practice has been accepted for more than a decade by those working on *Acanthamoeba,* the first cell shown to have both classes of cytoplasmic myosin. We realize that by historic accident some myosin-I genes will inevitably receive other types of names. Since all well-characterized muscle myosins are two-headed (but see reference 69), and since they traditionally are called myosin, we feel that it is superfluous to call them muscle myosin-II. Muscle myosin should suffice for now.

Distribution of Myosin-I in Nature

The available evidence strongly suggests that myosin-I is present in all eukaryotic species. Myosin-I has been identified unequivocally by biochemical studies of purified proteins, or by determination of primary structure from cloned DNA from vertebrate and invertebrate animals, a protozoan, a myxomycete, and a fungus (Table 1). Less definitive but highly suggestive evidence exists for myosin-I in humans (19), algae (102), and higher plants (117). This inventory is incomplete and provides ample opportunities for future research.

Since the first preliminary report on myosin-I (94), there have been indications of multiple myosin-I isoforms. The initial support for this concept came from peptide maps (38), immunochemistry (36, 43), biochemical separation (26, 77), and mRNA analysis (45, 46). Isolation and sequencing of myosin-I DNAs (Figure 2) have firmly established that multiple isoforms are

←

Figure 2 Comparison of the deduced primary sequences of myosin-I heads. Sequences are aligned by the method of Needleman & Wunsch (91) allowing limited gaps (gap weight = 6.0, length weight = 0.1) and are ordered by relative evolutionary distance as determined by the method of Feng & Doolittle (33). The numbering of the consensus sequence differs from all of the individual sequences. The consensus sequences are defined as follows: uppercase letters indicate amino acids conserved among more than six sequences. Lowercase letters indicate more than 50% of sequences contain the consensus amino acid, and a period indicates no clear consensus. A plus sign (+) indicates basic residues (R,K, and H) are conserved, a minus sign (−) indicates acidic residues (D and E) are conserved, and a delta (Δ) indicates hydrophobic residues (A,V,L, and I) are conserved. The myosin-II consensus is modified from the alignment of Warrick & Spudich (119). Conserved residues are boldface in the individual sequences. The *Acanthamoeba* myosin-I phosphorylation site is marked by an asterisk and the phosphorylated amino acids are underlined. BovBBM1, bovine intestinal brush border myosin-I (51); AvianBBMI, avian brush border myosin-I (39); DictyoMIA, *Dictyostelium* myosin-IA (115); DictyoMIB, *Dictyostelium* myosin-IB (55); DictyoMIC, *Dictyostelium* myosin-IC (115); DictyoMID, Dictyostelium myosin-ID (M. A. Titus, personal communication); AcanthMIA, *Acanthamoeba* myosin-IA (17); AcanthMIB, *Acanthamoeba* myosin-IB (56); AcanthMIC, *Acanthamoeba* myosin-IC (54); AcanthHMW, *Acanthamoeba* high molecular weight myosin-I (49); SaccharoM1, *Saccharomyces cerevisae* myosin-I (G. C. Johnston, personal communication); DrosninaC, *Drosophila ninaC* (86).

Table 1 Identification of myosin-I

Organism	Catalytic activity	Primary sequence	Motility
Acanthamoeba	63, 73, 78, 94	49, 54, 56	2, 6
Dictyostelium	26	55, 115	—
Chicken	20, 69, 112	12, 39	21, 87
Cow	—	51	—
Yeast	—	100	—
Drosophila	—	86	—
Plants	117	—	—
Algae	—	—	61, 102

the rule rather than the exception, even in species like *Dictyostelium* (53, 115) and *Saccharomyces* (42, G. C. Johnston, personal communication) with single myosin-II genes. The full extent of isoform diversity and its biological significance has yet to be established. References are indicated by number.

Contemporary Methods to Identify Myosin-I

At the present time more myosin-Is are being found using a combination of techniques. In some cases these new myosin-Is are first identified by biochemical purification and characterization. In other cases DNA probes for myosin head sequences have successfully identified new genes coding for myosin-I. In addition some myosin-I-like proteins were identified by their ability to bind calmodulin (41). Together these newer studies have established that there are multiple isoforms of myosin-I in different organisms and that the expression of these isoforms is tissue-specific.

Two features of the myosin-I primary structures limit the power of both DNA and antibody probes for myosin-I. The heads of all myosins are so similar that these probes for heads usually fail to discriminate between myosin-I and myosin-II (18). On the other hand, there is enough diversity in the myosin-I tails between species and among isoforms that both DNA and antibody probes to tails have extremely limited cross-reactivity between myosin-Is (18, 55). Antibodies have also revealed cross-reactivities with non-myosin proteins such as a nuclear actin-binding protein (43, 101).

STRUCTURE OF MYOSIN-I

Primary Structure

The complete primary structures of ten myosin-I heavy chains (Figure 2) reveal that all consist of two major structural domains: a well-conserved myosin head and a variable N-terminal tail. None of these tails has the heptad repeat characteristic of the alpha-helical coiled-coil tails of myosin-II and muscle myosins. This accounts for the inability of myosin-Is to polymerize like myosin-II. Although the myosin-I tails are diverse and quite dissimilar, they have some common structural elements.

THE MYOSIN-I HEAD The primary structures of myosin-I heads are well-conserved (Figure 3). Nearly all of the well-conserved residues are also found in myosin-II and muscle myosins. These homologous features were reviewed previously by Warrick & Spudich (119). The smallest myosin-Is have substantially fewer residues at the N-terminus of the head than myosin-IIs. This small number defines the minimum myosin head required for mechanochemical activity and probably reflects the primitive origins of these myosins.

A sequence of well-conserved residues around consensus position 400 distinguishes most known myosin-Is from myosin-IIs (Figure 2). This is just C-terminal to the phosphorylation site near residues 311–315 of *Acanthamoeba* myosin-Is (17). It is not yet established whether other myosin-Is are phosphorylated at this site, but phosphorylation of myosin-II heads has not been observed probably because of the absence of the hydroxyl amino acid and the divergence of the sequence in this region. This region presents a possible marker for myosin-I that should prove valuable for the production of

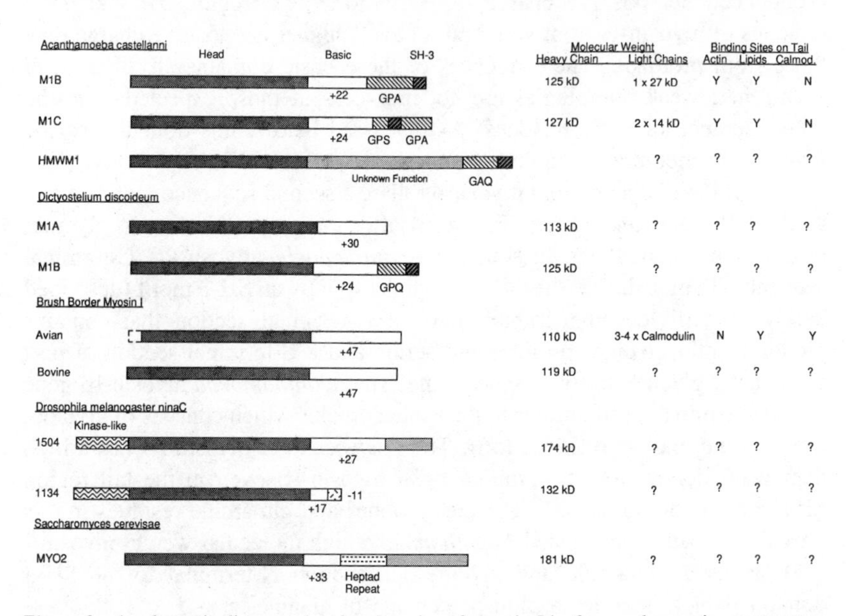

Figure 3 A schematic diagram showing domains of myosin-I isoforms whose primary structure has been determined. The avian brush border sequence is presumed to be incomplete. References are identical to Figure 2. *Dictyostelium* M1A is the product of the *abmA* gene (115). The *Dictyostelium* myosin-IB gene was described by Jung et al (55).

myosin-I specific antibodies and DNA probes, as well as for cloning of further myosin-I genes by the polymerase chain reaction even in the presence of myosin-II genes.

MYOSIN-I TAILS The sequences of myosin-I tails are divergent, but have some common features that have been related to function. The tail of *Acanthamoeba* myosin-IA has been most extensively characterized from a biochemical standpoint, but unfortunately the primary sequence is not yet available for this isoform. The other *Acanthamoeba* isoforms and the avian brush border myosin-I have been less well-characterized, but some conclusions can be drawn from the sequence and biochemical data.

The high molecular weight presumptive myosin-I from *Acanthamoeba* (49) is a special case since its classification will remain in question until the biochemical studies of the protein are completed. Biochemical studies are also needed to confirm that the *Saccharomyces, Drosophila,* and several of the *Dictyostelium* presumptive myosin-Is have a single head, especially since the putative yeast myosin-I encoded by the *MYO2* gene has a short heptad repeat in the tail.

Most myosin-I tails have a region of 180 to 250 amino acids with a pronounced net positive charge of + 19 to + 42 (Figure 3). The basic domains of myosin-Is from vertebrates have a higher net positive charge than those from protozoa. The sequences of these basic domains all differ from each other; weak homologies are not in excess of those expected from the preponderance of basic residues. As discussed below, this domain may be involved in membrane binding (28).

Four of the five amoeboid myosin-Is share a second sequence motif known as the GPA domain (54; see Figure 3) after the preponderance of glycine, proline, and alanine residues in the *Acanthamoeba* myosin-IC C-terminal sequence. In myosin-IC, the GPA domain is split by an SH-3 motif (described below) that divides the domain into an N-terminal section that contains predominantly glycine, proline, and serine and a C-terminal section of predominantly glycine, proline, and alanine. The *Acanthamoeba* myosin-IB gene has a C-terminal motif similar to the basic domain, which consists of glycine, proline, and alanine residues (56). The *Dictyostelium* myosin-IB has a high degree of identity to the *Acanthamoeba* myosin-IB even in the tail region (55), but has predominantly glycine, proline, and glutamine residues in this area. The recently sequenced *Acanthamoeba* high molecular weight myosin-I (49) shares a glutamine and glycine-rich section N-terminal to the SH-3 domain, which also has a high percentage of alanines.

Most amoeboid myosin-Is have an SH-3 domain (Figure 4). This motif was first identified as a 50-residue sequence shared by some proto-oncogenes and phospholipase-C (83, 111). Later observers (30, 103) noted the existence of this domain in spectrin (68, 120), myosin-I (55, 103), a yeast cell division cycle mutant (103), and the yeast actin-binding protein, ABP1 (30). Since some of the other proteins bearing the SH-3 motif are associated with membranes, this motif has been suggested as a candidate for the membrane-binding site. This is plausible, but all of the metazoan myosin-Is (including the avian brush border myosin-I, which binds membranes) lack this domain. Another possibility is that SH-3 domains form a structure that participates in actin binding, since many of these proteins either bind actin, or are peripherally associated with the plasma membrane through short membrane-bound actin filaments similar to those found in the mature erythrocyte (myosin-I, ABP1, spectrin).

The avian and bovine intestinal brush border myosin-Is have three sequences just C-terminal to the head, which are highly suggestive of calmodulin-binding sites (48, 50). One of these putative calmodulin-binding domains shares convincing homology with the calmodulin-binding domain of erythroid calcium ATPase over a stretch of about 30 residues (48). The other two sites share a calmodulin-binding consensus sequence that is less well-conserved (50). The amoeboid myosin-Is, which do not bind calmodulin, do not share these sites.

Both of the myosin-Is encoded by the *Drosophila ninaC* gene have a heavy

```
AcanthMIB    ALYDYDAQTGDELTFKEGD...TIIVHQK.DPAGWWEGELN..GKRGWVPANYV
AcanthMIC    ALYDFAAENPDELTFNEGA...VVTVINK.SNPDWWEGELN..GQRGVFPASYV
DictyoMIB    ALYDYDASSTDELSFKEGD...IIFIVQK.DNGGWTQGELK.SGQKGWAPTNYL
AcanthHMW    VVYDYDGGGDAQRLVLVKGA..IITVI.K.EYEGWAYGSTD.DGQVGLYPINYT

MI Consen    ALYDYDA...DELtFkEGd...ΔItVΔqK.dn.GWweGELn..GQrGwΔPanYΔ
Consensus    ALYDy-a..---LsF+kG-+..ΔΔ...e....g-WW.a..Δ.tg..G.ΔPsNYV

Sacc ABP1    AEYDYDAAEDNELTFVENDK..IINIEFV..DDDWWLGELEKDGSKGLFPSNYV
PLC gamma    ALFDYKAQREDELTFTK...SAIIQNVEKQEGGGWWRGDYHHKKQL.WFPSNYV
v-yes        ALYDYEARTTDDLSFKKGERFQIIMNTE....GDWWEARSIATGKTGYIPSNYV
syn          ALYDYEARTEDDLSFHKGEKFQILNSSE....GDWWEARSLTTGETGYIPSNYV
hck          ALYDYEAIHHEDLSFQKGDQMVVLEES.....GEWWKARSLATRKEGYIPSNYV
v-src        ALYDYESRTETDLSFKKGERLQIVNNTE....GDWWLAHSLTTGQTGYIPSNYV
lyn          ALYPYDGIHPDDLSFKKGEKMKVLEEH.....GEWWKAKSLLTKKEGFIPSNYV
c-src        SLYDYKSRDESDLSFMKGDRMEVIDDTE....SDWWRVVNLTTRQEGLIPLNFV
Spectrin     ALYDYQEKSPREVTMKKGDILTLLNSTN....KDWWKVEVN..DRQGFVPAAYV
Human abl    ALYDFVASGDNTLSITKGEKLRVLGYNHNK..GEWCEAQTKNG..QGWVPSNYI
Drosopabl    ALYDFQAGGENQLSLKKGEQVRILSYNKS...GEWCEAHSDSGNV.GWVPSNYV
ASV v-crk    ALFDFKGNDDGDLPFKKGDILKIRDKPE....EQWWNAEDMD.GKRGMIPVPYV
lsk          ALHSYEPSHDGDLGFEKGEQLRILEQS.....GEWWKAQSLTTGQEGFIPFNFV
c-yes        ALYDYEARTTEDLSFKKGERFQIINNTE....GDWWEARSIATGKNGYIPSNYV
c-fgr        ALYDYEARTEDDLTFTKGEKFHILNNTE....GDWWEARSLSSGKTGCIPSNYV
```

Figure 4 Sequence comparison of the SH3 domains of myosin-I and other SH3-containing molecules. Consensus sequences are determined as before except that an uppercase, boldface letter indicates residues conserved in at least 80% of sequences for the overall consensus and residues conserved in 75% of sequences for the myosin-I consensus. AcanthMIB, *Acanthamoeba* myosin-IB (56); AcanthMIC, *Acanthamoeba* myosin-IC (54); AcanthHMW, *Acanthamoeba* high molecular weight myosin-I (49); DictyoMIB, *Dictyostelium* myosin-IB (55). Other sequence references can be found in (103) and Drubin et al (30).

chain sequence strikingly reminiscent of protein kinases on the N-terminal side of the head (86). The activation of *Acanthamoeba* and *Dictyostelium* myosin-Is by phosphorylation suggests that these unique myosin-Is may be autophosphorylated. The tail of the longer *ninaC* protein has the basic domain and a stretch of sequence containing several proline residues, while the shorter product produced by alternative splicing has a truncated basic domain merged with a short acidic domain.

Light Chains

All known myosin-Is have a light chain associated with the heads (Figure 3). Calmodulin appears to serve as the light chain of brush border myosin-I. Up to 3.3 calmodulins have been isolated with the 110-kd heavy chain (22); an integer number has yet to be established. Nothing is known about the sequence of other myosin-I light chains. The light chain of *Acanthamoeba* myosin-I is not essential for its activity in vitro, since it can be removed without compromising the actin-activated ATPase or phosphorylation of the heavy chain (76).

Molecular Structure

The hydrodynamic properties of purified myosin-Is first revealed that they have a single head (98). This has been confirmed by analytical ultracentrifugation (5) for *Acanthamoeba* myosin-IA and -IB and by electron microscopy for brush border (25) and *Acanthamoeba* myosin-Is (J. Heuser, personal communication).

Myosin-Is are elongated molecules that look essentially like a muscle myosin head with a short, slightly asymmetric tail (25). Myosin-I has an extension 10 nm long at one end of the 20 × 10 nm head.

ENZYME ACTIVITY AND ACTIN FILAMENT INTERACTION

Enzyme Activity of Myosin-I

All myosins catalyze the hydrolysis of ATP and, like many other myosins, most myosin-Is have highest enzyme activity under two characteristic conditions (Table 2). First, actin filaments activate the ATPase at physiologic concentrations of Mg^{2+} and salts. Second, in the presence of EDTA (where most ATPases are inactive) the ATPase activity of myosin-I alone is stimulated by K^+ or NH_4^+ but not by Na^+. Activity under these unusual conditions has no known physiologic significance, but has proven useful as a marker for the purification of myosin-Is from *Acanthamoeba* (73) and *Dictyostelium* (26). Furthermore, the V_{max} (maximum enzyme rate) of K^+-EDTA ATPase of *Acanthamoeba* and *Dictyostelium* myosin-Is is similar to rabbit fast

Table 2 ATPase rate constants

Myosin	Actin-activated V_{max} s^{-1}	Actin-activated K_{ATPase} μM	K+-EDTA s^{-1}	Reference
Acanthamoeba myosin-IA			22	73
phase 1	18	0.25		9
phase 2	14	44		8
Acanthamoeba myosin-IB			21	73
phase 1	10	0.30		9
phase 2	17	34		8
Acanthamoeba myosin-IC			15	73
phase 1		0.20[a]		73
phase 2	20	52		73
Dictyostelium myosin-I			12[b]	26
Brush border myosin-I	0.9	40		21
			0.6[b]	20, 25, 66
Fast skeletal muscle S-1[c]	19	11	11	75
Phosphorylated	1.9	38		104
smooth muscle HMM[d]			3.5	92

[a] This is the K_d for binding of actin which is generally equal to K_{ATPase} of phase 1;
[b] based on M_r = 150k;
[c] subfragment-1;
[d] heavy meromyosin.

skeletal muscle myosin (Table 2). In contrast, brush border myosin-I has a much lower K^+-EDTA ATPase activity (Table 2).

The K^+-EDTA ATPase is also a useful measure of myosin-I function. For example, photo-affinity labeling of the catalytic site correlates with the loss of K^+-EDTA ATPase activity of *Acanthamoeba* myosin-I (79). K^+-EDTA ATPase was also used to demonstrate that *Acanthamoeba* myosin IB retained its ATPase activity after removal of the light chains (76).

Actin-Binding Sites

All myosins have a similar, ATP-sensitive actin-binding site in the head domain. In the absence of ATP (the rigor state in muscle), all myosin heads bind to actin filaments with high affinity with K_ds in the subnanomolar range. In the presence of ATP, myosin heads still bind to actin filaments, but the affinity is lower by more than four orders of magnitude so that there is a rapid equilibrium between bound and free myosin (118). This interaction with actin filaments stimulates the Mg^{2+}-ATPase of myosins by promoting the dissociation of the products of ATP hydrolysis (70).

Acanthamoeba myosin-Is have a second actin filament-binding site located near the C-terminus of the heavy chain (71). This site is unique among actin-binding sites of myosin molecules because it is not sensitive to the presence of ATP. Similar sites have yet to be identified on other myosin-Is. Proteolytic digestion of native myosin-IA with chymotrypsin releases a 30-kd fragment from the C-terminus, which has a second actin binding site (71).

The existence of two actin-binding sites allows a single myosin-I molecule to cross-link two actin filaments. Cross-linking by myosin-I has been visualized directly by electron microscopy (71, 97, 99) and inferred from increases in low shear viscosity (34). This cross-linking activity allows myosin-I to cause an ATP-dependent contraction of an actomyosin gel, an in vitro assay for the mechanochemical activity referred to as superprecipitation (34).

Actin-Activated ATPase

All well-characterized myosin-Is are actin-activated Mg^{2+}-ATPases (Table 2). Both *Dictyostelium* myosin-I (26) and brush border myosin-I (21, 25) behave like isolated heads of a muscle myosin with a hyperbolic dependence of the ATPase rate on the concentration of actin filaments (31). This behavior arises from the independent cyclic interactions of freely diffusing myosin heads with actin filaments. Both of these myosin-Is lack the SH-3 domain in the tail (Figure 3) as well as the ATP-insensitive actin-binding site. The ATPase activity of brush border myosin-I is approximately tenfold lower than rabbit fast skeletal muscle myosin and *Acanthamoeba* myosin-I, but similar to smooth muscle myosin (Table 2).

The activation of the Mg^{2+}-ATPase of *Acanthamoeba* myosin-I by actin filaments differs markedly from all other myosins and has three distinct phases of activation (Figure 5) at low, intermediate, and high actin concentrations (99). At a low concentration of actin, or more precisely, low ratios of actin:myosin-I (Figure 5 points *A* and *B*), the reaction has three important characteristics (9). First, the actin concentrations required for half-maximal ATPase (K_{ATPase}) and half-maximal myosin-I binding (K_d) are the same. Second, the values of the K_{ATPase}s, 0.1 μM for myosin-IA and 0.2 μM for myosin-IB, are the lowest reported for any myosin. Third, phosphorylation of the myosin-I heavy chain activates the ATPase rate more than 20-fold without altering the binding of myosin to actin. At intermediate actin concentrations (Figure 5 point *C*), the ATPase reaches a minimum in spite of the fact that the myosin-I is tightly bound to the filaments. At high actin concentrations (Figure 5 point *D*), the ATPase rate is high. The actin concentration dependence gives a K_{ATPase} of 44 μM for myosin-IA and 34 μM for myosin-IB. These values are approximately 200-fold greater than at low ratios of actin to myosin-I, but the V_{max}s for the two phases are about the same (Table 2; 8). These values for K_{ATPase} and V_{max} are quite close to those measured for rabbit fast skeletal muscle myosin (Table 2). In contrast, in the presence of ATP, direct binding studies showed that the 100-kd N-terminal fragment of myosin-IA has a much higher affinity for actin filaments (71).

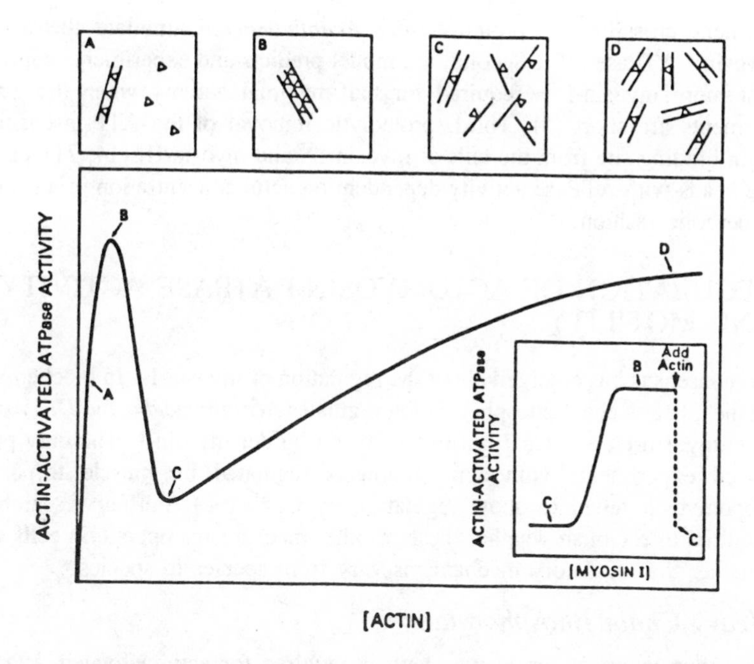

Figure 5 A schematic drawing showing the triphasic activation of *Acanthamoeba* myosin-I by actin. Phase 1 is an activation, A, that occurs at a low ratio of actin:myosin-I and peaks at B. Phase 2 is a decline in activity that occurs at intermediate actin concentrations and reaches a minimum, C. Phase 3 is a reactivation, D, at high ratios of actin:myosin-I in which the activity again reaches a maximum. The small figures A,B,C,D illustrate, schematically, the proposed relationship of myosin-I (triangles) and actin filaments at corresponding points of the graph. The apex and base of the triangle represent the high affinity site and low affinity sites of myosin-I respectively. [taken from (8) with permission.]

The complex triphasic dependence of the Mg^{2+}-ATPase on actin concentration can be explained by the participation of the two different actin-binding sites of these myosin-Is (8, 93). The high affinity site with a K_d of 0.1 μM is insensitive to ATP. The low affinity site has a K_{ATPase} of 30 μM and is linked to hydrolysis of ATP. At all actin concentrations, the ATP-insensitive site dominates binding measurements. The hypothesis explains the high activity at low ratios of actin:myosin-I as a consequence of the high local concentration of actin in bundles of filaments cross-linked between the two actin-binding sites (8, 62, 93). At high actin concentrations, the myosin-I is distributed over many widely separated actin filaments so that the effective concentration of actin in the vicinity of the ATP-sensitive binding sites depends on the bulk concentration of actin alone.

Three independent tests support this cooperative model. First, the model predicts that activation depends on the degree of cross-linking, and three actin filament cross-linking proteins from *Acanthamoeba* stimulate the actin-myosin-I ATPase (10). Second, the model predicts and experiments confirm that more myosin-I is required for half-maximal activity when the actin filaments are short (5). Third, proteolytic removal of the ATP-insensitive actin-binding site from the tails of myosin-IA and myosin-IB (14, 71) leaves the heads with ATPase activity dependent on actin concentration in a simple hyperbolic fashion.

REGULATION OF ACTOMYOSIN-I ATPASE ACTIVITY AND MOTILITY

No consensus has emerged about the regulation of myosin-Is. In biochemical studies, heavy chain phosphorylation regulates *Acanthamoeba* and *Dictyostelium* myosin-Is, and Ca^{2+} influences brush border myosin-I. The only published experiments with actin filaments regulated by muscle troponin-tropomyosin failed to show regulation by Ca^{2+} (95). Further research is required to establish whether these or other mechanisms operate in cells and whether the regulatory mechanisms vary from species to species.

Heavy Chain Phosphorylation

Phosphorylation of the heavy chain is required for actin-activated ATPase activity of myosin-Is from *Acanthamoeba* (44, 78) and *Dictyostelium* (26) as well as for motility of *Acanthamoeba* myosin-I in vitro (6). The *Acanthamoeba* phosphorylation sites are Ser-315 of myosin-IB, Ser-311 of myosin-IC, and a corresponding Thr in the incomplete sequence of myosin-IA (17). A basic residue precedes the phosphorylated residue in both of the complete sequences (17).

Phosphorylation of myosin-I stimulates the actin-activated Mg^{2+}ATPase approximately 20-fold without a significant change in its affinity for actin filaments (9). Since the phosphorylation site lies between the heavy chain residues that interact with ATP and actin (14, 15), phosphorylation may induce conformational changes in adjacent domains (7, 15, 72, 80) that make myosin-I behave more like the fast skeletal muscle myosin, which is active without heavy chain phosphorylation. Further elucidation of the regulatory mechanism will probably require more information about the structure of the head at atomic resolution.

Myosin Heavy Chain Kinase

The cofactor protein required for activation of Mg^{2+}-ATPase of *Acanthamoeba* myosin-I by actin (96) is the heavy chain kinase (78). The purified kinase has an apparent mass of 107 kd in the phosphorylated form (44) and 97 kd in the dephosphorylated form (16). Typically, 0.2–0.5 mg of kinase can be purified from 1 kg of packed cells (44).

The *Acanthamoeba* heavy chain kinase phosphorylates a number of proteins, but has the highest affinity for myosin-Is (44). Myosin-IA and -IB are phosphorylated rapidly at concentrations of 1–2 μM. The heavy chain of *Dictyostelium* myosin-I (26), the regulatory light chain of smooth muscle myosin (47), and a synthetic peptide corresponding to the phosphorylation site of myosin-IC are also good substrates for the kinase (16). Optimal synthetic peptide substrates have two basic residues within five residues preceding the phosphorylation site and a tyrosine exactly two residues after the phosphorylation site (16a). The heavy chain kinase phosphorylates Thr-18 on the smooth muscle myosin light chain, the same site phosphorylated by myosin light chain kinase, but not Ser-1, Ser-2, or Thr-9, which are phosphorylated by protein kinase C (116). The significance of this reaction is unclear, since smooth muscle myosin light chain kinase does not phosphorylate the heavy chain of myosin-I (47), and the myosin-I heavy chain kinase does not phosphorylate the light chains or heavy chain of *Acanthamoeba* myosin-II (44). Histone 2A is a moderately good substrate and casein a poor one for the heavy chain kinase (44).

Phosphorylation and lipid binding are potential regulatory mechanisms for myosin-I heavy chain kinase. Kinase activity appears to be strongly stimulated by phosphorylation (16), but not by Ca^{2+} (16, 78). The enzyme that phosphorylates the kinase has not yet been separated from the kinase, so the kinase may autophosphorylate (16). The rate of kinase phosphorylation is enhanced approximately 20-fold by phosphatidylserine (16). Since myosin-I also binds to membrane lipids including phosphatidylserine (see below), it may form a regulatory complex with the heavy chain kinase and membrane lipids. Additional work will establish whether these interactions occur in cells and will elucidate mechanisms for activating and deactivating this novel regulatory mechanism.

Regulation of Brush Border Myosin-I by Calcium

Because of the association of calmodulin with brush border myosin-I and the well-established role of calmodulin in Ca^{2+}-regulated processes, an intense effort has been made to implicate Ca^{2+} in the regulation of this myosin-I. In spite of these efforts, the role of physiologic concentrations of Ca^{2+} remains uncertain. In the physiologic range of 10^{-6} and 10^{-5} M, Ca^{2+} stimulates the actin-activated ATPase about fourfold (21, 25), but the effects on actin binding (22, 52) and motility have been inconsistent. Two preparations of brush border myosin-I were motile in low Ca^{2+} and non-motile at high Ca^{2+} (21, 87), but one was non-motile in low Ca^{2+} and motile at high Ca^{2+} (88). Millimolar concentrations of Ca^{2+} dissociate some of the calmodulin and inhibit both ATPase and motility (21, 22). On the other hand, calmodulin is not required for actin binding or ATP hydrolysis, since a proteolytic fragment of the heavy chain that is devoid of calmodulin, retains both of these functions (23). Activity may be regulated differently over two ranges of Ca^{2+}, with activation below 10^{-5} M and an inactivation above 10^{-4} M. This biphasic effect of Ca^{2+} differs from its effect on other systems where high Ca^{2+} promotes the high affinity association of calmodulin with target proteins and might be related to the role that the brush border plays in calcium absorption.

ASSOCIATION OF MYOSIN-I WITH MEMBRANES

Intracellular Localization

Morphological and biochemical studies of both motile cells and vertebrate epithelial cells have established the association of myosin-I with the plasma membrane, especially differentiated domains like microvilli and extending pseudopodia, but questions remain about the association of myosin-I with the membranes of cytoplasmic organelles. The identity of these intracellular membranes, the mechanism of binding, and the extent of binding all need to be established. The existence of multiple myosin-I isoforms begs the question of specialized localization and function, so key questions are whether and how the various isoforms are targeted to specific membranes, or other sites in cells. Finally, the localization of myosin-I has been investigated in only a limited number of cells, and much additional work is needed to establish the generality of the conclusions made to date.

MORPHOLOGICAL LOCALIZATION IN MOTILE CELLS Numerous studies with a variety of antibodies have established that myosin-I isoforms are associated with membranes, particularly the plasma membrane, in *Acanthamoeba* and *Dictyostelium*. In whole mounts of *Acanthamoeba* (2, 13, 37, 43, 85, 123), sections of *Acanthamoeba* (37, 43), and flattened whole mounts of *Dictyostelium* (35), antibodies to myosin-I stain the region of the plasma membrane more intensely than other parts of the cell. Antibodies to all isoforms tested, including myosin-IA, -IB, and -IC stain the plasma membrane in *Acanthamoeba*. Gadasi & Korn (37) reported no reaction of the antibodies with intact cells, but Baines & Korn (13) observed by electron microscopy some reaction of antibodies with the outer surface of the plasma membrane after permeabilization with saponin.

Myosin-I is concentrated within differentiated zones of the plasma membrane, most strikingly at the leading edge of advancing pseudopodia of *Dictyostelium* (35) and *Acanthamoeba* (123) and in the phagocytic cups of *Dictyostelium* (35) and *Acanthamoeba* (13). The antibodies used by Miyata et al (85) did not stain microspikes strongly, but one monoclonal antibody stained the tips of such microspikes intensely (123), possibly indicating the preferential localization of a specific isoform.

All observers report that antibodies to myosin-I isoforms stain cytoplasmic components, but the details are still unclear. All of the observations suggest some association of myosin-I with membrane-bounded organelles, but it is not clear how much of the myosin-I is soluble and diffusely distributed in the cytosol free of the membranes. The problem is that small vesicles are not well preserved and not resolved by the methods employed. A second problem is that the staining patterns vary from diffuse to punctate. A possible explanation for the variability is that the several isoforms are associated with different membranes and that the available antibodies react with different subsets of these isoforms. This is consistent with the observations on *Acanthamoeba* contractile vacuoles. Antibodies to myosin-IB never stained contractile vacuoles (85), while a polyclonal antibody to myosin-IC (13) and two of four monoclonal antibodies to myosin-Is (123) stain contractile vacuoles strongly, at least during some stages in their physiologic cycle.

BIOCHEMICAL LOCALIZATION IN MOTILE CELLS All of the cell fractionation studies on *Acanthamoeba* (1, 37, 85) agree that a substantial portion of the myosin-I is associated with membranes, particularly the plasma membrane. By sedimentation equilibrium, 20% of the myosin-I is associated with dense organelles and another 20% is associated with organelles of intermediate density (1). Careful quantitative fractionation is consistent with about 25% of the total myosin-I being bound to plasma membrane (85). Even more intriguing, up to 75% of the total myosin-I seems to be associated with smaller vesicles or membrane fragments after homogenization in sucrose (85). This myosin-I might be bound to membranes directly, but the participation of actin filaments in the pelleting of the myosin-I with the small vesicle fraction needs further study.

MORPHOLOGICAL AND BIOCHEMICAL LOCALIZATION OF MYOSIN-I IN VERTEBRATE EPITHELIAL CELLS The myosin-I isozyme found in the brush border of intestinal epithelial cells was identified as the radial connection between the microvillar actin filament bundle and the surrounding plasma membrane (40, 81, 89, 90) even before the molecule was recognized to be myosin-I (20). The relationship of the morphological structure and the brush border myosin-I is now established unequivocally by cell fractionation and differential extraction (81), immunolocalization (29, 50), and by reconstitution from purified components (24). The radial links are arranged along the microvillar actin filament bundle in a helix with a pitch of 33 nm (81, 81a, 90). Although there are many intramembranous particles in the surrounding membrane, they do not seem to be positioned correctly to be anchors for the myosin-I (114).

Not all of the myosin-I in intestinal epithelial cells is located in the microvilli; small vesicles with myosin-I are present in the terminal web (29).

The myosin-I may first transport these vesicles along the microvillar rootlets to the point where they fuse with the plasma membrane and then anchor the newly expanded plasma membrane to the actin bundle (32).

LOCALIZATION OF MYOSIN-I IN INSECT PHOTORECEPTORS The two products of the *ninaC* gene of *Drosophilia* are localized to the rhabdomeral microvilli in the eye (82, 86). These microvilli have only two actin filaments (11), but they bear the same relationship to the surrounding plasma membrane as the larger bundle of actin filaments in intestinal microvilli. As in the brush border, these rhabdomeral actin filaments are connected to the plasma membrane by radial links, widely speculated (but unproven) to be myosin-I.

Biochemical Analysis of Membrane Binding

Myosin-Is from both *Acanthamoeba* (2, 85) and the chicken intestinal brush border (48) bind phospholipid membranes with a K_d of 30 to 500 nM. This binding has been reconstituted with purified myosin-I and membranes stripped of peripheral proteins to eliminate indirect association via actin. Electrostatic interactions play an important role in the binding of myosin-I to membranes. High salt inhibits the binding of purified myosin-I to membranes (2) and promotes its dissociation from purified plasma membranes (85).

Membrane-binding sites are located on the C-terminal tails of both *Acanthamoeba* and brush border myosin-I (2, 28, 48). A 100-kd chymotryptic fragment of *Acanthamoeba* myosin-IA consisting of the head and 30 kd of the tail binds to membranes, but the C-terminal 30 kd of the tail does not. Since the heads of other myosins do not bind to membranes, this suggests that the membrane-binding site is located in the basic N-terminal part of the tail. This has been confirmed by showing that a fusion protein consisting of residues 626–888 from the *Acanthamoeba* myosin-IC tail and *E. coli* β-galactosidase binds to purified *Acanthamoeba* membranes with a K_d of 300 nM and competes for binding sites with myosin-IA (28). This fusion protein contains the entire basic domain of myosin-IC.

Membrane-associated proteins are not required for binding of myosin-I to acidic phospholipids. *Acanthamoeba* and brush border myosin-Is bind to micelles and vesicles composed of acidic phospholipids or mixed vesicles of acidic and neutral phospholipids (2, 47). Since both *Acanthamoeba* and brush border myosin-Is bind to either phosphatidylserine or phosphatidylinositol bisphosphate, the nature of the acidic head group does not appear to be important. Neither of these myosin-Is binds to basic phospholipids.

Although an electrostatic interaction between the basic domain of myosin-I tails and acidic phospholipid head groups is sufficient for their high affinity association, we suspect that protein-lipid interactions are only half of the story because they do not account for the emerging evidence that isoforms of myosin-I are bound to specific membranes, like the microvillar plasma membrane of the brush border. We speculate that such specific localization is accomplished by a combination of nonspecific concentration of myosin-I on the surface of membranes via lipid interactions and relatively weak associations with membrane proteins. The high affinity binding to the phospholipids may keep most of the myosin-I associated with membranes. The increased concentration and reduced dimensionality on the surface of the membrane might allow relatively low affinity interactions with membrane proteins to target isoforms to specific membranes. Such bifunctional binding might also explain the weak phenotype of a *Dictyostelium* mutant with a disrupted myosin-IB gene (53). Although myosin-IB may be necessary for full function of the cell, the other myosin-I proteins may bind at some level to the IB-specific membranes. The different isoforms might then be capable of complementing, at some level, a mutation in one myosin-I gene simply by virtue of their shared affinity for membrane lipids.

It has been suggested that the affinity of myosin-I for PIP_2 might somehow link the membrane association of myosin-I to the phospholipase-C signal transduction system. Given the equal affinity of myosin-I for phosphatidylserine (48) and the great excess of this lipid over PIP_2, the metabolism of this lipid may have little effect on myosin-I binding to membranes.

FUNCTIONS OF MYOSIN-I

In Vitro Assays for Motility

Two assays have been used to demonstrate the mechanical function of myosin-I. In the first assay, a myosin moves a particle (large enough to image by light microscopy) unidirectionally along actin cables provided by *Nitella* (106). In the second assay, fluorescent actin filaments move relative to myosin immobilized on a substrate (67, 122). Both assays theoretically reveal the maximum velocity for a particular myosin, which is comparable to the speed of shortening of an unloaded muscle.

Brush border myosin-I moves plastic beads at 0.008 μm/s (87) and membrane fragments at 0.03 μm/s (88) in the *Nitella* assay, and it moves fluorescent actin filaments at 0.08–0.1 μm/s (21) in the sliding filament assay. These low velocities correlate well with a low rate of actin-activated ATP hydrolysis, both of which are similar to smooth muscle myosin (115).

Acanthamoeba myosin-I has moved at a wide range of rates in the *Nitella* assay. Purified *Acanthamoeba* myosin-I moved plastic beads approximately 0.03 μm/s (6). Crude organelles moved at 0.2 μm/s and were inhibited by an antibody to myosin-I (1). These rates are far lower than expected from the actin-activated ATPase rates for *Acanthamoeba* myosin-I. Part of the

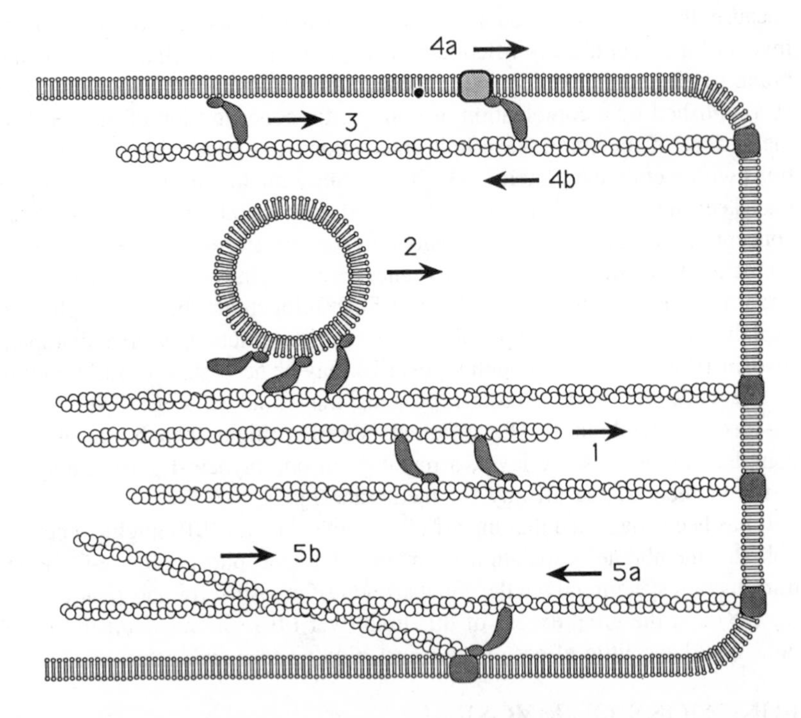

Figure 6 The drawing illustrates possible myosin-I based movements in a highly schematic cell. (*1*) An actin filament is bound to the tail and the actomyosin complex moves along a second actin filament, which produces a sliding of one filament passed the other. (*2*) A membrane vesicle bound to the tail is translocated along an actin filament by myosin-I. (*3*) Myosin-I with its tail associated with the plasma membrane slides along the plane of the membranes as it moves along an actin filament. (*4*) Similar to *3*, but with the tail of myosin-I bound to an intrinsic membrane protein. (*5*) Myosin-I is bound to the membrane and to a membrane associated actin filament, which allows the myosin-I to pull a second actin filament toward the rear. [Adapted from (3) with permission of the authors.]

problem may be that the ATP-insensitive actin-binding site on the tail of *Acanthamoeba* myosin-I can, under some conditions, impede its own translocation.

Functions of Myosin-I in Cells

The biochemical properties, the ability to produce movements in vitro, and the cellular localization of myosin-I all suggest that myosin-I produces force on membranes relative to actin filaments. There are many possibilities (Figure 6), but we do not know with certainty which of these potential movements are used by cells. This is the area where the greatest advances are likely to be made in the future. We will not be surprised if all of the movements postulated in the figure (and more) are eventually shown to be produced by myosin-I in one cell or another.

The movement most likely to be produced by myosin-I is the transport of membrane-bounded organelles along actin filaments (Figure 6 item *2*). Plants and algae appear to make the most obvious use of this mechanism. For example, in *Nitella,* high velocity cytoplasmic streaming is thought to be generated by the transport of endoplasmic reticulum along actin filament bundles in the cortex of the cell (58). This drags the rest of the cytoplasm along for the ride. Velocities of 50 μm/s are achieved in vivo (61) and have been reconstituted with isolated vesicles in vitro (57, 107). Since the tracks are actin filaments and the movement is toward their barbed ends, a myosin is the most likely motor. Early efforts to isolate this motor (102) are consistent with its identity as myosin-I. If this proves to be true, *Nitella* myosin-I holds the world record for speed among all known myosins by nearly an order of magnitude.

The remaining potential myosin-I-based movements are all more difficult to sort out because they are more complex, and none has been reconstituted in vitro. On the other hand, the persistence of these apparently actin-based movements in cells depleted of myosin-II (27, 60, 121) has encouraged speculation that myosin-I is responsible.

The persistence of pseudopod extension in cells without myosin-II and the concentration of myosin-I (but not myosin-II) in spreading pseudopods (35, 123) argue for a role of myosin-I in pseudopod extension. While such a motor might facilitate the process, the assembly of actin alone could conceivably push the front of the cell ahead as in the growth of the acrosomal process of echinoderm sperm (113). There are several ways that myosin-I could promote pseudopod extension. One would be for the myosin-I to gain traction on the substrate by attachment to the basal plasma membrane and then to pull actin filaments attached directly or indirectly to the plasma membrane at the upper surface of the cell. An equally plausible speculation is that myosin-I anchored to the upper surface of the cell would pull it forward by moving along actin filaments attached directly or indirectly to the basal surface, perhaps through a cytoplasmic actin filament gel. None of these speculations has been addressed experimentally, but we have detailed them here to illustrate the possible mechanics and potential complexity of such a system.

Myosin-I has been postulated as the motor that carries plasma membrane precursors, in the form of small vesicles, to the expanding surface of a cell (32). The inhibition of budding and the accumulation of small vesicles at restrictive temperatures in yeast cells with mutations in the gene for a presumed myosin-I (100; G. C. Johnston, personal communication) provides the first experimental evidence for this process. Such a transport mechanism could provide membrane at the tip of advancing pseudopods including growth cones of neurons (84, 109).

A related class of movements involves the attachment of myosin-I to membrane proteins, providing them with a motor to move actively in the plane of the membrane along underlying actin filaments (Figure 6 item *4*). The movements of membrane proteins are well-documented (105). Cytochalasin inhibits these movements, but there is no evidence regarding the mechanism of force production. One difficulty with the myosin-I hypothesis for explaining these movements is that the cortical actin filaments are usually oriented randomly and would not appear to be aligned in a fashion that would favor long translations in the plane of the membrane. It will be important to document the architecture of the actin filaments in the cortex underlying these movements.

The retraction of thin veils of plasma membrane called ruffles at the leading edge of tissue culture cells appears to be an ideal candidate for a myosin-I-powered membrane movement. The close apposition of the dorsal and ventral plasma membrane should facilitate the production of shearing force between the membranes generated by myosin-I anchored on one surface pulling on an actin filament attached to the other surface. Such a shearing force could easily account for the elevation of these veils of membrane and their bending back toward the rear of the cell. As attractive as this is, there is not yet any evidence for myosin-I in such ruffles (or in any cultured vertebrate cell). Myosin-I anchored to the substrate through the plasma membrane (Figure 6 item *5*) could also participate in the continuous rearward movement of actin filaments in growth cones (109).

The concentration of myosin-I in the cortical cytoplasm surrounding particles that are being ingested (35) and the partial inhibition of phagocytosis in $DMIB^-$ cells argue that myosin-I has a role in phagocytosis. No mechanism has been proposed for this interesting process.

The association of specific myosin-I isoforms with the contractile vacuole of a protozoa (13, 123), raised the possibility that this organelle contracts actively and that myosin-I contributes to the production of this force. This has not been tested experimentally.

The ability of some myosin-Is to cross-link actin filaments and to cause superprecipitation in the presence of ATP (34) established the potential for these single-headed myosins to participate in a wide range of contractile processes (Figure 6 item *1*) generally thought to be the province of myosin-II. Such movements would employ a sliding filament mechanism (8, 71, 98) like bipolar filaments of myosin-II. No cellular movement is known to be powered in this way by myosin-I, and the failure of cytokinesis in cells depleted of myosin-II (27, 60, 74) shows that such a mechanism is inadequate to produce cytokinesis. This does not rule out the participation of myosin-I-based sliding filament mechanisms for other types of cytoplasmic contraction or streaming.

EVOLUTION OF MYOSINS

We speculate that all contemporary myosins evolved from a primitive myosin consisting of a small myosin-I-like head and a short tail capable of membrane binding. This original myosin then acquired extra domains by duplication of the sequence coding the head and its fusion with the sequence of a tropomyosin-like molecule, which led eventually to myosin-II molecules with two heads and a long alpha-helical tail. With the rise of multicellular metazoan organisms, a specialized form of myosin-II evolved that is capable of forming sarcomeres.

If this speculation is true, primitive eukaryotic cells may have behaved much like modern cells depleted of active myosin-II by molecular genetics (27, 60) or antibody injection (74, 108). Such myosin-I cells locomote relatively inefficiently, but still can divide and carry out the other processes required for survival. Nonetheless, cytokinesis is inefficient and unreliable. Instead of a contractile ring, cytokinesis is achieved by "traction-mediated cytofission" in which two halves of a binucleate cell crawl away from each other (110). The addition of myosin-II to the cellular repertoire allowed primitive protozoans to chemotact more directly and to divide much more efficiently and reproducibly, thus leading to a tremendous selective advantage.

One way to test our hypothesis would be to identify a primitive eukaryote whose lineage branched off from the main evolutionary stem prior to the development of myosin-II. Such an organism would presumably have one or more myosin-I genes, but no myosin-II genes. No such organism has been found and may never be because the development of myosin-II led to such a selective advantage for the original myosin-II organism that its progeny have dominated eukaryotic evolution ever since.

PROSPECTS

Much work needs to be done on the diversity, distribution, structure, and biochemistry of myosin-Is, but the current speculations regarding the functions of myosin-I emphasize the importance of future efforts to develop experimental tests for these processes. The initial experiments on yeast with mutations of myosin-I are promising (G. C. Johnston, personal communication, H. V. Goodson, personal communication). This organism is well suited for the study of organelle and vesicle movements. *Dictyostelium* has a wider range of cellular movements, but the existence of multiple myosin-I genes and a limited number of selectable markers will complicate the analysis. Disruption of individual myosin-I genes is likely to give subtle phenotypes as already observed (53). Perhaps expression of an antisense RNA selective for all myosin-Is will deplete all of the isoforms simultaneously and provide a tentative answer regarding their collective functions in cells.

ACKNOWLEDGMENTS

We thank our colleagues in the myosin-I field for providing us with preprints and advice on the manuscript. Our own experimental work is supported by National Institutes of Health Research Grant GM-26132.

Literature Cited

1. Adams, R. J., Pollard, T. D. 1986. Propulsion of organelles isolated from *Acanthamoeba* along actin filaments by myosin-I. *Nature* 322:754–56
2. Adams, R. J., Pollard, T. D. 1989. Binding of myosin-I to membrane lipids. *Nature* 340:565–88
3. Adams, R. J., Pollard, T. D. 1989. Membrane-bound myosin-I provides new mechanisms in cell motility. *Cell Motil. Cytoskel.* 14:178–82
4. Adams, R. J., Pollard, T. D. 1989. Prediction of common properties of particle translocation motors through comparison of myosin-I, cytoplasmic dynein and kinesin. In *Cell Movement,* ed. F. D. Warner, J. R. McIntosh, 2:3–12. New York: Liss
5. Albanesi, J. P., Coue, M., Fujisaki, H., Korn, E. D. 1985. Effect of actin filament length and filament number concentration on the actin-activated ATPase activity of *Acanthamoeba* myosin-I. *J. Biol. Chem.* 260:13276–80
6. Albanesi, J. P., Fujisaki, H., Hammer, J. A., Korn, E. D., Jones, R., Sheetz, M. P. 1985. Monomeric *Acanthamoeba* myosins-I support movement in vitro. *J. Biol. Chem.* 260:8649–52
7. Albanesi, J. P., Fujisaki, H., Korn, E. D. 1984. Localization of the active site and phosphorylation site of *Acanthamoeba* myosin-IA and myosin-IB. *J. Biol. Chem.* 259:4184–89
8. Albanesi, J. P., Fujisaki, H., Korn, E. D. 1985. A kinetic model for the molecular basis of the contractile activity of *Acanthamoeba* myosin-IA and myosin-IB. *J. Biol. Chem.* 260:11174–79
9. Albanesi, J. P., Hammer, J. A., Korn, E. D. 1983. The interaction of F-actin with phosphorylated and unphosphorylated myosin-IA and myosin-IB from *Acanthamoeba castellani. J. Biol. Chem.* 258:176–81
10. Albanesi, J. P., Lynch, T., Fujisaki, H., Korn, E. D. 1986. Regulation of the actin-activated ATPase activity of *Acanthamoeba* myosin-I by cross-linking actin filaments. *J. Biol. Chem.* 261: 10445–49
11. Arikawa, K., Hicks, J., Williams, D. 1990. Identification of actin filaments in the rhabdomeral microvilli of *Drosophila* photoreceptors. *J. Cell Biol.* In press
12. Atkinson, M. A., Collins, J. H. 1989. Sequence similarities between chicken intestinal 110kD-ATPase and myosin-I-like enzymes. *J. Protein C* 8:495–98
13. Baines, I. C., Korn, E. D. 1989. Immunofluorescence microscopy and immunogold electron microscopy of myosin I, myosin II and actin distribution in *Acanthamoeba. J. Cell Biol.* 109:174a
14. Brzeska, H., Lynch, T. J., Korn, E. D. 1988. Localization of the actin-binding sites of *Acanthamoeba* myosin-1B and effect of limited proteolysis on its actin-activated Mg^{-2+}ATPase activity. *J. Biol. Chem.* 263:427–35
15. Brzeska, H., Lynch, T. J., Korn, E. D. 1989. The effect of actin and phosphorylation on the tryptic cleavage pattern of *Acanthamoeba* myosin-IA. *J. Biol. Chem.* 264:243–50
16. Brzeska, H., Lynch, T. J., Korn, E. D. 1990. *Acanthamoeba* myosin I heavy chain kinase is activated by phosphatidylserine-enhanced phosphorylation. *J. Biol. Chem.* 265:3591–94

16a. Brzeska, H., Lynch, T. J., Martin, B., Corigliano-Murphy, A., Korn, E. D. 1990. Substrate specificity of *Acanthamoeba* myosin-I heavy chain kinase as determined with synthetic peptides. *J. Biol. Chem.* 256:16138–44

17. Brzeska, H., Lynch, T. J., Martin, B., Korn, E. D. 1989. The localization and sequences of the phosphorylation sites of *Acanthamoeba* myosins I. An improved method for locating the phosphorylated amino acid. *J. Biol. Chem.* 264:19340–48
18. Carboni, J. M., Conzelman, K. A., Adams, R. A., Kaiser, D. A., Pollard, T. D., Mooseker, M. S. 1988. Structural and immunological characterization of the myosin-like 110-kD subunit of the intestinal microvillar 110k-calmodulin complex—evidence for discrete myosin head and calmodulin-binding domains. *J. Cell Biol.* 107:1749–57
19. Carboni, J. M., Howe, C. L., West, A. B., Borwick, K. W., Mooseker, M. S., Morrow, J. S. 1987. Characterization of intestinal brush border cytoskeletal proteins of normal and neoplastic human epithelial cells. *Am. J. Pathol.* 129:589–600
20. Collins, J. H., Borysenko, C. W. 1984. The 110,000-dalton actin-binding and calmodulin-binding protein from intestinal brush-border is a myosin-like ATPase. *J. Biol. Chem.* 259:4128–35
21. Collins, K., Sellers, J. R., Matsudaira, P. T. 1990. Calmodulin dissociation regulates brush border myosin-I (110K-calmodulin) activity in vitro. *J. Cell Biol.* 110:1137–47
22. Coluccio, L. M., Bretscher, A. 1987. Calcium-regulated cooperative binding of the microvillar 110K-calmodulin complex to F-actin—formation of decorated filaments. *J. Cell Biol.* 105:325–33
23. Coluccio, L. M., Bretscher, A. 1988. Mapping of the microvillar 110K-calmodulin complex—calmodulin-associated or calmodulin-free fragment of the 110-KD polypeptide bind F-actin and retain ATPase activity. *J. Cell Biol.* 106:367–73
24. Coluccio, L. M., Bretscher, A. 1989. Reassociation of microvillar core proteins: making a microvillar core in vitro. *J. Cell Biol.* 108:495–502
25. Conzelman, K. A., Mooseker, M. S. 1987. The 110-KD protein calmodulin complex of the intestinal microvillus is an actin-activated Mg ATPase. *J. Cell Biol.* 105:313–24
26. Côté, G. P., Albanesi, J. P., Uelo, T., Hammer, J. A., Korn, E. D. 1985. Purification from *Dictyostelium discoideum* of a low-molecular-weight myosin that resembles myosin-I from *Acanthamoeba castellanii*. *J. Biol. Chem.* 260:4543–46
27. DeLozanne, A., Spudich, J. A. 1987. Disruption of the *Dictyostelium* myosin heavy chain gene by homologous recombination. *Science* 236:1086–1091
28. Doberstein, S. K., Pollard, T. D. 1989. Recombinant myosin-I fusion proteins bind isolated membranes. *J. Cell Biol.* 109:86a
29. Drenckhahn, D., Dermietzel, R. 1988. Organization of the actin filament cytoskeleton in the intestinal brush border: a quantitative and qualitative immunoelectron microscope study. *J. Cell Biol.* 207:1037–1048
30. Drubin, D. G., Mulholland, J., Zhu, Z., Botstein, D. 1990. Homology of a yeast actin-binding protein to signal transduction proteins and myosin-I. *Nature* 343:288–90
31. Eisenberg, E., Moos, C. 1968. The adenosine triphosphatase activity of acto-heavy meromyosin: a kinetic analysis of actin activation. *Biochemistry* 7:1486
32. Fath, K. R., Obernauf, S. D., Burgess, D. R. 1990. Cytoskeletal protein and mRNA accumulation during brush border formation in adult chicken enterocytes. *Development* 109:449–59
33. Feng, D.-F., Doolittle, R. F. 1987. Progressive sequence alignments as a prerequisite to correct phylogenetic trees. *J. Mol. Evol.* 25:351–60
34. Fujisaki, H., Albanesi, J. P., Korn, E. D. 1985. Experimental evidence for the contractile activities of *Acanthamoeba* myosin-IA and myosin-IB. *J. Biol. Chem.* 260:1183–89
35. Fukui, Y., Lynch, T. J., Brzeska, H., Korn, E. D. 1989. Myosin I is located at the leading edges of locomoting *Dictyostelium* amoebae. *Nature* 341:328–31
36. Gadasi, H., Korn, E. D. 1979. Immunochemical analysis of *Acanthamoeba* myosin-IA, myosin-IB, and myosin-II. *J. Biol. Chem.* 242:8095–98
37. Gadasi, H., Korn, E. D. 1989. Evidence for differential intracellular localization of the *Acanthamoeba* myosin isoenzymes. *Nature* 286:452–56
38. Gadasi, H., Maruta, H., Collins, J. H., Korn, E. D. 1979. Peptide maps of the myosin isoenzymes of *Acanthamoeba castellanii*. *J. Biol. Chem.* 254:3631–36
39. Garcia, A. E., Coudrier, E., Carboni, J., Anderson, J., Vandekerckhove, M. S., et al. 1989. Partial deduced sequence of the 110-kD-calmodulin complex of the avian intestinal microvillus shows that this mechanoenzyme is a member of the myosin-I family. *J. Cell Biol.* 109:2895–2903
40. Glenney, J. R., Osborn, M., Weber, K.

1982. The intracellular localization of the microvillus 110K protein, a component considered to be involved in side-on membrane attachment of F-actin. *Exp. Cell Res.* 138:199–205

41. Glenney, J. R., Weber, K. 1980. Calmodulin-binding proteins of the microfilaments present in isolated brush-borders and microvilli of intestinal epithelial cells. *J. Biol. Chem.* 255:551–54
42. Goodson, H. V., Titus, M. A., Brown, S. S., Spudich, J. A. 1989. Identification of a myosin-related gene from yeast distinct from conventional myosin. *J. Cell Biol.* 109:84a
43. Hagen, S. J., Kiehart, D. P., Kaiser, D. A., Pollard, T. P. 1986. Characterization of monoclonal antibodies to *Acanthamoeba* myosin-I that cross-react with both myosin-II and low molecular weight nuclear proteins. *J. Cell Biol.* 103:2121–28
44. Hammer, J. A., Albanesi, J. P., Korn, E. D. 1983. Purification and characterization of a myosin-I heavy-chain kinase from *Acanthamoeba castellanii*. *J. Biol. Chem.* 258:168–75
45. Hammer, J. A., Jung, G., Korn, E. D. 1986. Genetic evidence that *Acanthamoeba* myosin-I is a true myosin. *Proc. Natl. Acad. Sci. USA* 83;4655–59
46. Hammer, J. A., Korn, E. D., Paterson, B. M. 1984. *Acanthamoeba* myosin-IA, myosin-IB, and myosin-II heavy-chains are synthesized in vitro from *Acanthamoeba* messenger RNA. *J. Biol. Chem.* 259:1157–59
47. Hammer, J. A., Sellers, J. R., Korn, E. D. 1984. Phosphorylation and activation of smooth muscle myosin by *Acanthamoeba* myosin-I heavy chain kinase. *J. Biol. Chem.* 259:3224–29
48. Hayden, S. M., Wolenski, J. S., Mooseker, M. S. 1990. Binding of brush border myosin I to phospholipid vesicles. *J. Cell Biol.* 111:443–51
49. Horowitz, J. A., Hammer, J. A. 1990. Identification of a new myosin heavy chain in *Acanthamoeba*. *Biophys. J.* 57:330a
50. Hoshimaru, M., Fujio, Y., Sobue, K., Sugimoto, T., Nakanishi, S. 1989. Immunochemical evidence that myosin-I heavy chain-like protein is identical to the 110-kilodalton brush-border protein. *J. Biochem.* 206:455–59
51. Hoshimaru, M., Nakanishi, S., 1987. Identification of a new type of mammalian myosin heavy chain by molecular cloning: overlap of its mRNA with preprotachykinin-B mRNA. *J. Biol. Chem.* 262:14625–32
52. Howe, C. L., Mooseker, M. S. 1983. Characterization of the 110-kDalton actin, calmodulin- and membrane-binding protein from microvilli of intestinal epithelial cells. *J. Cell Biol.* 97:974–85
53. Jung, G., Hammer, J. A. 1990. Generation and characterization of *Dictyostelium* cells deficient in a myosin-I heavy chain isoform. *J. Cell Biol.* 110:1955–64
54. Jung, G., Korn, E. D., Hammer, J. A. 1987. The heavy-chain of *Acanthamoeba* myosin-IB is a fusion of myosin-like and non-myosin-like sequences. *Proc. Natl. Acad. Sci. USA* 84:6720–24
55. Jung, G., Saxe, C. L., Kimmel, A. R., Hammer, J. A. 1989. *Dictyostelium discoideum* contains a gene encoding a myosin-I heavy chain. *Proc. Natl. Acad. Sci. USA* 86:6186–90
56. Jung, G., Schmidt, C. J., Hammer, J. A. III 1989. Myosin-I heavy-chain genes of *Acanthamoeba castellanii:* cloning of a second gene and evidence for the existence of a third isoform. *Gene* 82:269–80
57. Kachar, B. 1985. Direct visualization of organelle movement along actin filaments dissociated from characean algae. *Science* 227:1355–57
58. Kachar, B., Reese, T. S. 1988. The mechanism of cytoplasmic streaming in characean algal cells: sliding of endoplasmic reticulum along actin filaments. *J. Cell Biol.* 106:1545–52
59. Kiehart, D. P. 1990. Molecular genetic dissection of myosin heavy chain function. *Cell* 60:347–50
60. Knecht, D. A., Loomis, W. F. 1987. Antisense RNA inactivation of myosin heavy chain gene expression in *Dictyostelium discoideum*. *Science* 236:1081–1086
61. Kohno, T., Shimmen, T. 1988. Accelerated sliding of pollen tube organelles along characeae actin bundles regulated by Ca^{2+}. *J. Cell Biol.* 106:1539–43
62. Korn, E. D., Atkinson, M. A., Brzeska, H., Hammer, J. A., Jung, G., Lynch, T. J. 1988. Structure-function studies on *Acanthamoeba* myosin-IA, myosin-IB, and myosin-II. *J. Cell Biochem.* 36:37–50
63. Korn, E. D., Collins, J. H., Maruta, H. 1982. Myosins from *Acanthamoeba castellanii*. *Methods Enzymol.* 85:357–63
64. Korn, E. D., Hammer, J. A. III. 1988. Myosins of nonmuscle cells. *Annu. Rev. Biophys. Biophys. Chem.* 17:23–45
65. Korn, E. D., Hammer, J. A. 1990. Myosin, I. *Curr. Opin. Cell Biol.* 2:57
66. Krizek, J., Coluccio, L. M., Bretscher, A. 1987. ATPase activity of the micro-

villar 110kDA polypeptide-calmodulin complex is activated in MG^{+2}, and inhibited in K-EDTA by F-actin. *FEBS Lett.* 225:289–72

67. Kron, S. J., Spudich, J. A. 1986. Fluorescent actin filaments move on myosin fixed to a glass surface. *Proc. Natl. Acad. Sci. USA* 83:6272–76
68. Lehto, V.-P., Wasenius, V.-M., Salven, P., Saraste, M. 1988. Transforming and membrane proteins. *Nature* 334:388
69. Lin, Y., Takaroohasi, H., Kohoma, K. 1989. Myosin I-like protein in gizzard smooth muscle. *J. Jpn. Acad. (Biol.)* 65:203–6
70. Lymm, R. W., Taylor, E. W. 1971. Mechanism of adenosine triphosphate hydrolysis by acto-myosin. *Biochemistry* 10:4617–24
71. Lynch, T. J., Albanesi, J. P., Korn, E. D., Robinson, E. A., Bowers, B., Fujisaki, H. 1986. ATPase activities and actin-binding properties of subfragments of *Acanthamoeba* myosin IA. *J. Biol. Chem.* 261:17156–62
72. Lynch, T. J., Brzeska, H., Korn, E. D. 1987. Limited tryptic digestion of *Acanthamoeba* myosin-IA abolishes regulation of actin-activated ATPase activity by heavy-chain phosphorylation. *J. Biol. Chem.* 262:3842–49
73. Lynch, T. J., Brzeska, H., Miyata, H., Korn, E. D. 1989. Purification and characterization of a third isoform of myosin I from *Acanthamoeba castellanii*. *J. Biol. Chem.* 264:19333–39
74. Mabuchi, M., Okuno, M. 1977. The effect of myosin antibody on the division of starfish blastomeres. *J. Cell Biol.* 74:251–63
75. Margossian, S. S., Lowey, S. 1982. Preparation of myosin and its subfragments from rabbit fast skeletal muscle. *Methods Enzymol.* 85:55–71
76. Maruta, H., Gadasi, H., Collins, J. H., Korn, E. D. 1978. Isolated heavy-chain of an *Acanthamoeba* myosin contains full enzymatic-activity. *J. Biol. Chem.* 253:6297–6300
77. Maruta, H., Gadasi, H., Collins, J. H., Korn, E. D. 1979. Multiple forms of *Acanthamoeba* myosin-I. *J. Biol. Chem.* 254:3624–30
78. Maruta, H., Korn, E. D. 1977. *Acanthamoeba* cofactor protein is a heavy-chain kinase required for actin activation of Mg^{2+}-ATPase activity of *Acanthamoeba* myosin-I. *J. Biol. Chem.* 252: 8329–32
79. Maruta, H., Korn, E. D. 1981. Direct photoaffinity labeling by nucleotides of the apparent catalytic site on the heavy-chains of smooth muscle and *Acanthamoeba* myosins. *J. Biol. Chem.* 256: 499–502
80. Maruta, H., Korn, E. D. 1981. Proteolytic separation of the actin-activatable ATPase site from the phosphorylation site on the heavy-chain of *Acanthamoeba* myosin IA. *J. Biol. Chem.* 256:503–6
81. Matsudaira, P. T., Burgess, D. R. 1979. Identification and organization of the components in the isolated microvillus cytoskeleton. *J. Cell Biol.* 83:667–73

81a. Matsudaira, P. T., Burgess, D. R. 1982. Organization of the cross-filaments in intestinal microvilli. *J. Cell Biol.* 92:657–64

82. Matsumoto, H., Isono, K., Pye, Q., Pak, W. L. 1987. Gene encoding cytoskeletal proteins in *Drosophila* rhabdomeres. *Proc. Natl. Acad. Sci. USA* 84: 985–89
83. Mayer, B. J., Hamaguchi, M., Hanafusa, H. 1988. A novel viral oncogene with structural similarity to phospholipase-C. *Nature* 332:272–75
84. Mitchison, T., Kirschner, M. 1988. Cytoskeletal dynamics and nerve growth. *Neuron* 1:761–72
85. Miyata, H., Bowers, B., Korn, E. D. 1989. Plasma membrane association of *Acanthamoeba* myosin-I. *J. Cell Biol.* 109:1519–28
86. Montell, C., Rubin, G. 1988. The *Drosophila ninaC* locus encodes two photoreceptor cell specific proteins with domains homologous to protein kinases and the myosin heavy chain head. *Cell* 52:757–72
87. Mooseker, M. S., Coleman, T. R. 1989. The 110-kD protein-calmodulin complex of the intestinal microvillus (brush-border myosin-I) is a mechanoenzyme. *J. Cell Biol.* 108:2395–2400
88. Mooseker, M. S., Conzelman, K. A., Coleman, T. R., Heuser, J. E., Sheetz, M. P. 1989. Characterization of intestinal microvillar membrane disks: detergent-resistant membrane sheets enriched in associated brush border myosin-I (110K-calmodulin). *J. Cell Biol.* 109:1153–61
89. Mooseker, M. S., Tilney, L. G. 1975. Actin filament-membrane attachment: are membrane particles involved? *J. Cell Biol.* 71:402–16
90. Mooseker, M. S., Tilney, L. G. 1975. Organization of an actin filament-membrane complex. Filament polarity and membrane attachment in microvilli of intestinal epithelial cells. *J. Cell Biol.* 67:725–43
91. Needleman, S. B., Wunsch, C. D.

1970. A general method applicable to the search for similarities in the amino acid sequence of two proteins. *J. Mol. Biol.* 48:443–53
92. Nishikawa, M., Sellers, J. R., Adelstein, R. S., Hidaka, H. 1984. Protein kinase C modulates in vitro phosphorylation of the smooth muscle heavy meromyosin by myosin light chain kinase. *J. Biol. Chem.* 259:8808–14
93. Pantaloni, D. 1985. Thermodynamic model of the kinetics of the actin-activated ATPase activity of *Acanthamoeba* myosin-I—appendix. *J. Biol. Chem.* 260:1180–82
94. Pollard, T. D. 1971. An EDTA/Ca-ATPase from *Acanthamoeba. Fed. Proc.* 30:1309
95. Pollard, T. D., Eisenberg, E., Korn, E. D., Kielley, W. W. 1973. Inhibition of Mg-ATPase activity of actin-activated *Acanthamoeba* myosin by muscle troponin-tropomyosin: implications for the mechanism of control of amoeba motility and muscle contraction. *Biochem. Biophys. Res. Commun.* 51:693
96. Pollard, T. D., Korn, E. D. 1972. A protein cofactor required for the actin activation of a myosin-like ATPase of *Acanthamoeba castellanii. Fed. Proc.* 31:502
97. Pollard, T. D., Korn, E. D. 1973. The "contractile" proteins of *Acanthamoeba castellanii. Cold Spring Harbor Symp. Quant. Biol.* 37:573–83
98. Pollard, T. D., Korn, E. D. 1973. *Acanthamoeba* myosin. I. Isolation from *Acanthamoeba castellanii* of an enzyme similar to muscle myosin. *J. Biol. Chem.* 248:4682–90
99. Pollard, T. D., Korn, E. D. 1973. *Acanthamoeba* myosin. II. Interaction with actin and with a new cofactor protein required for actin activation of Mg-ATPase activity. *J. Biol. Chem.* 248: 4691–97
100. Prendergast, J. A., Murray, L. E., Rowley, A., Carruthers, D.R., Singer, R. A., Johnston, G. C. 1990. Size selection identifies new genes that regulate *Saccharomyces cerevisae* cell proliferation. *Genetics* 124:81–90
101. Rimm, D. L., Pollard, T. D. 1989. Purification and characterization of an *Acanthamoeba* nuclear actin-binding protein. *J. Cell Biol.* 109:585–91
102. Rivolta, M. N., Urrutia, R., Sellers, J., Kachar, B. 1990. Preliminary characterization of an actin based organelle motor from *Nitella. Biophys. J.* 57:535a
103. Rodaway, A. R. F., Sternberg, M. J. E., Bentley, D. L. 1989. Similarity in membrane proteins. *Nature* 342:624
104. Sellers, J. R., Eisenberg, E., Adelstein, R. S. 1982. The binding of smooth muscle heavy meromyosin to actin in the presence of ATP. *J. Biol. Chem.* 257: 13880–83
105. Sheetz, M. P., Baumrind, N. L., Wayne, D. B., Pearlman, A. L. 1990. Concentration of membrane antigens by forward transport and trapping in neuronal growth cones. *Cell* 61:231–41
106. Sheetz, M. P., Spudich, J. A. 1983. Movement of myosin-coated fluorescent beads on actin cables in vitro. *Nature* 303:31–35
107. Shimmen, T., Tazawa, M. 1982. Reconstitution of cytoplasmic streaming in *Characeae. Protoplasma* 113:127–31
108. Sinard, J. H., Pollard, T. D. 1989. Microinjection into *Acanthamoeba castellanii* of monoclonal antibodies to myosin-II slows but does not stop cell locomotion. *Cell Motil. Cytoskelet.* 12: 42–53
109. Smith, S. J. 1988. Neuronal cytomechanics—the actin-based motility of growth cones. *Science* 242:708–15
110. Spudich, J. A. 1989. In pursuit of myosin function. *Cell Regul.* 1:1–11
111. Stahl, M. L., Ferenz, C. R., Kelleher, K. L., Kriz, R. W., Knopf, J. L. 1988. Sequence similarity of phospholipase-C with a non-catalytic region of *src. Nature* 332:269–72
112. Swanljung-Collins, H., Montibeller, J., Collins, J. H. 1987. Purification and characterization of the 110-kDa actin- and calmodulin-binding protein from intestinal brush border: a myosin-like ATPase. *Methods Enzymol.* 139:137–48
113. Tilney, L. G., Hatano, S., Ishikawa, H., Mooseker, M. S. 1973. The polymerization of actin: its role in the generation of the acrosomal process of certain echinoderm sperm. *J. Cell Biol.* 59:109–26
114. Tilney, L. G., Mooseker, M. S. 1976. Actin filament-membrane attachment. Are membrane particles involved? *J. Cell Biol.* 71:402–16
115. Titus, M. A., Warrick, H. M., Spudich, J. A. 1989. Multiple actin-based motor genes in *Dictyostelium. Cell Regul.* 1:55–63
116. Umemoto, S., Benger, A. R., Sellers, J. R. 1989. Effect of multiple phosphorylations of smooth muscle and cytoplasmic myosins on movement in an in vitro motility assay. *J. Biol. Chem.* 264: 1431–36
117. Vahey, M., Titus, M., Trautwein, R., Scordilis, S. 1982. Tomato actin and

myosin: contractile proteins from a higher land plant. *Cell Motil.* 2:131–48

118. Wagner, P. D., Weeds, A. G. 1979. Determination of the association of myosin subfragment-1 with actin in the presence of ATP. *Biochemistry* 18: 2260–66
119. Warrick, H. M., Spudich, J. A. 1987. Myosin structure and function in cell motility. *Annu. Rev. Cell Biol.* 3:379–421
120. Wasenius, V.-M., Saraste, M., Salven, P., Eramaa, M., Holm, L., Lehto, V.-P. 1988. Primary structure of the brain alpha-spectrin. *J. Cell Biol.* 108:79–93
121. Wessells, D., Soll, D. R., Knecht, D., Loomis, W. F., DeLozanne, J., Spudich, J. 1988. Cell motility and chemotaxis in *Dictyostelium* amoeba lacking myosin heavy chain. *Dev. Biol.* 128: 164–77
122. Yanagida, T., Nakase, M., Nishiyama, K., Oosawa, F. 1984. Direct observation of motion of a single actin filament in the presence of myosin. *Nature* 307:58–60
123. Yonemura, S., Pollard, T. D. 1990. Localization of myosin-I and myosin-II in *Acanthamoeba*. *J. Cell Sci.* Submitted

SUBJECT INDEX

D

H

I

N

Y

Z

CUMULATIVE INDEXES

CONTRIBUTING AUTHORS, VOLUMES 49–53

CHAPTER TITLES, VOLUMES 49–53

ANNUAL REVIEWS INC.

A NONPROFIT SCIENTIFIC PUBLISHER

4139 El Camino Way
P.O. Box 10139
Palo Alto, CA 94303-0897 • USA

ORDER FORM

ORDER TOLL FREE
1-800-523-8635
(except California)

FAX: 415-855-9815

Annual Reviews Inc. publications may be ordered directly from our office; through booksellers and subscription agents, worldwide; and through participating professional societies. Prices subject to change without notice. ARI Federal I.D. #94-1156476

- **Individuals:** Prepayment required on new accounts by check or money order (in U.S. dollars, check drawn on U.S. bank) or charge to credit card — American Express, VISA, MasterCard.
- **Institutional buyers:** Please include purchase order.
- **Students:** $10.00 discount from retail price, per volume. Prepayment required. Proof of student status must be provided (photocopy of student I.D. or signature of department secretary is acceptable). Students must send orders direct to Annual Reviews. Orders received through bookstores and institutions requesting student rates will be returned. You may order at the Student Rate for a maximum of 3 years.
- **Professional Society Members:** Members of professional societies that have a contractual arrangement with Annual Reviews may order books through their society at a reduced rate. Check with your society for information.
- **Toll Free Telephone orders:** Call 1-800-523-8635 (except from California) for orders paid by credit card or purchase order and customer service calls only. California customers and all other business calls use 415-493-4400 (not toll free). Hours: 8:00 AM to 4:00 PM, Monday-Friday, Pacific Time. **Written confirmation** is required on purchase orders from universities before shipment.
- **FAX: 415-855-9815 Telex: 910-290-0275**
- **We do not ship on approval.**

Regular orders: Please list below the volumes you wish to order by volume number.
Standing orders: New volume in the series will be sent to you automatically each year upon publication. Cancellation may be made at any time. Please indicate volume number to begin standing order.
Prepublication orders: Volumes not yet published will be shipped in month and year indicated.
California orders: Add applicable sales tax. **Canada:** Add GST tax.
Postage paid (4th class bookrate/surface mail) **by Annual Reviews Inc.** UPS domestic ground service available (except Alaska and Hawaii) at $2.00 extra per book. Airmail postage or UPS air service also available at prevailing costs. UPS must have street address. P.O. Box, APO or FPO not acceptable.

ANNUAL REVIEWS SERIES		Prices postpaid, per volume USA & Canada / elsewhere Until 12-31-90	After 1-1-91	Regular Order Please Send Vol. Number:	Standing Order Begin With Vol. Number:
Annual Review of **ANTHROPOLOGY**					
Vols. 1-16	(1972-1987)	**$31.00/$35.00**	**$33.00/$38.00**		
Vols. 17-18	(1988-1989)	**$35.00/$39.00**	**$37.00/$42.00**		
Vol. 19	(1990)	**$39.00/$43.00**	**$41.00/$46.00**		
Vol. 20	(avail. Oct. 1991)	**$41.00/$46.00**	**$41.00/$46.00**	Vol(s). ______	Vol. ______
Annual Review of **ASTRONOMY AND ASTROPHYSICS**					
Vols. 1, 5-14	(1963, 1967-1976)				
16-20	(1978-1982)	**$31.00/$35.00**	**$33.00/$38.00**		
Vols. 21-27	(1983-1989)	**$47.00/$51.00**	**$49.00/$54.00**		
Vol. 28	(1990)	**$51.00/$55.00**	**$53.00/$58.00**		
Vol. 29	(avail. Sept. 1991)	**$53.00/$58.00**	**$53.00/$58.00**	Vol(s). ______	Vol. ______
Annual Review of **BIOCHEMISTRY**					
Vols. 30-34, 36-56	(1961-1965, 1967-1987)	**$33.00/$37.00**	**$35.00/$40.00**		
Vols. 57-58	(1988-1989)	**$35.00/$39.00**	**$37.00/$42.00**		
Vol. 59	(1990)	**$39.00/$44.00**	**$41.00/$47.00**		
Vol. 60	(avail. July 1991)	**$41.00/$47.00**	**$41.00/$47.00**	Vol(s). ______	Vol. ______
Annual Review of **BIOPHYSICS AND BIOPHYSICAL CHEMISTRY**					
Vols. 1-11	(1972-1982)	**$31.00/$35.00**	**$33.00/$38.00**		
Vols. 12-18	(1983-1989)	**$49.00/$53.00**	**$51.00/$56.00**		
Vol. 19	(1990)	**$53.00/$57.00**	**$55.00/$60.00**		
Vol. 20	(avail. June 1991)	**$55.00/$60.00**	**$55.00/$60.00**	Vol(s). ______	Vol. ______

ANNUAL REVIEWS SERIES		Prices postpaid, per volume USA & Canada / elsewhere Until 12-31-90	After 1-1-91	Regular Order Please Send Vol. Number:	Standing Order Begin With Vol. Number:
Annual Review of **CELL BIOLOGY**					
Vols. 1-3	(1985-1987)	**$31.00/$35.00**	**$33.00/$38.00**		
Vols. 4-5	(1988-1989)	**$35.00/$39.00**	**$37.00/$42.00**		
Vol. 6	(1990)	**$39.00/$43.00**	**$41.00/$46.00**		
Vol. 7	(avail. Nov. 1991)	**$41.00/$46.00**	**$41.00/$46.00**	Vol(s). ________	Vol. ________
Annual Review of **COMPUTER SCIENCE**					
Vols. 1-2	(1986-1987)	**$39.00/$43.00**	**$41.00/$46.00**		
Vols. 3-4	(1988, 1989-1990)	**$45.00/$49.00**	**$47.00/$52.00**	Vol(s). ________	Vol. ________
Series suspended until further notice. SPECIAL OFFER: Volumes 1-4 are available at the special promotional price of $100.00 USA & Canada / $115.00 elsewhere, when all 4 volumes are purchased at one time. Orders at the special price must be prepaid.					
Annual Review of **EARTH AND PLANETARY SCIENCES**					
Vols. 1-10	(1973-1982)	**$31.00/$35.00**	**$33.00/$38.00**		
Vols. 11-17	(1983-1989)	**$49.00/$53.00**	**$51.00/$56.00**		
Vol. 18	(1990)	**$53.00/$57.00**	**$55.00/$60.00**		
Vol. 19	(avail. May 1991)	**$55.00/$60.00**	**$55.00/$60.00**	Vol(s). ________	Vol. ________
Annual Review of **ECOLOGY AND SYSTEMATICS**					
Vols. 2-18	(1971-1987)	**$31.00/$35.00**	**$33.00/$38.00**		
Vols. 19-20	(1988-1989)	**$34.00/$38.00**	**$36.00/$41.00**		
Vol. 21	(1990)	**$38.00/$42.00**	**$40.00/$45.00**		
Vol. 22	(avail. Nov. 1991)	**$40.00/$45.00**	**$40.00/$45.00**	Vol(s). ________	Vol. ________
Annual Review of **ENERGY**					
Vols. 1-7	(1976-1982)	**$31.00/$35.00**	**$33.00/$38.00**		
Vols. 8-14	(1983-1989)	**$58.00/$62.00**	**$60.00/$65.00**		
Vol. 15	(1990)	**$62.00/$66.00**	**$64.00/$69.00**		
Vol. 16	(avail. Oct. 1991)	**$64.00/$69.00**	**$64.00/$69.00**	Vol(s). ________	Vol. ________
Annual Review of **ENTOMOLOGY**					
Vols. 10-16, 18 20-32	(1965-1971, 1973) (1975-1987)	**$31.00/$35.00**	**$33.00/$38.00**		
Vols. 33-34	(1988-1989)	**$34.00/$38.00**	**$36.00/$41.00**		
Vol. 35	(1990)	**$38.00/$42.00**	**$40.00/$45.00**		
Vol. 36	(avail. Jan. 1991)	**$40.00/$45.00**	**$40.00/$45.00**	Vol(s). ________	Vol. ________
Annual Review of **FLUID MECHANICS**					
Vols. 2-4, 7 9-19	(1970-1972, 1975) (1977-1987)	**$32.00/$36.00**	**$34.00/$39.00**		
Vols. 20-21	(1988-1989)	**$34.00/$38.00**	**$36.00/$41.00**		
Vol. 22	(1990)	**$38.00/$42.00**	**$40.00/$45.00**		
Vol. 23	(avail. Jan. 1991)	**$40.00/$45.00**	**$40.00/$45.00**	Vol(s). ________	Vol. ________
Annual Review of **GENETICS**					
Vols. 1-21	(1967-1987)	**$31.00/$35.00**	**$33.00/$38.00**		
Vols. 22-23	(1988-1989)	**$34.00/$38.00**	**$36.00/$41.00**		
Vol. 24	(1990)	**$38.00/$42.00**	**$40.00/$45.00**		
Vol. 25	(avail. Dec. 1991)	**$40.00/$45.00**	**$40.00/$45.00**	Vol(s). ________	Vol. ________
Annual Review of **IMMUNOLOGY**					
Vols. 1-5	(1983-1987)	**$31.00/$35.00**	**$33.00/$38.00**		
Vols. 6-7	(1988-1989)	**$34.00/$38.00**	**$36.00/$41.00**		
Vol. 8	(1990)	**$38.00/$42.00**	**$40.00/$45.00**		
Vol. 9	(avail. April 1991)	**$41.00/$46.00**	**$41.00/$46.00**	Vol(s). ________	Vol. ________
Annual Review of **MATERIALS SCIENCE**					
Vols. 1, 3-12	(1971, 1973-1982)	**$31.00/$35.00**	**$33.00/$38.00**		
Vols. 13-19	(1983-1989)	**$66.00/$70.00**	**$68.00/$73.00**		
Vol. 20	(1990)	**$70.00/$74.00**	**$72.00/$77.00**		
Vol. 21	(avail. Aug. 1991)	**$72.00/$77.00**	**$72.00/$77.00**	Vol(s). ________	Vol. ________